Science Fundamentals
Second Edition

A Pearson Custom Publication

Science Fundamentals
Second Edition

Compiled from:

Statistical and Data Handling Skills in Biology
by Roland Ennos

Physics
Third Edition
by James S. Walker

Chemistry: The Central Science
Tenth Edition
by Theodore L. Brown, H. Eugene LeMay, Jr. and
Bruce E. Bursten

Chemistry
Fourth Edition
by John McMurry and Robert C. Fay

PEARSON
Custom
Publishing

Pearson Education Limited
Edinburgh Gate
Harlow
Essex CM20 2JE

And associated companies throughout the world

Visit us on the World Wide Web at:
www.pearsoned.co.uk

First published 2006
This Custom Book Edition © 2007 Published by Pearson Education Limited

Taken from:

Statistical and Data Handling Skills in Biology
by Roland Ennos
ISBN 0 582 31278 7
Copyright © Pearson Education Limited 2000

Physics
Third Edition
by James S. Walker
ISBN 0 13 153631 1
Copyright © 2007, 2004, 2002 by Pearson Education, Inc.
Pearson Prentice Hall,
Pearson Education, Inc.
Upper Saddle River, New Jersey 07458

Chemistry: The Central Science
Tenth Edition
by Theodore L. Brown, H. Eugene LeMay, Jr. and Bruce E. Bursten
ISBN 0 13 109686 9
Copyright © 2006, 2003, 2000, 1997, 1994, 1991, 1988, 1985, 1981, 1977 by Pearson
Education, Inc., Upper Saddle River, New Jersey 07458

Chemistry
Fourth Edition
by John McMurry and Robert C. Fay
ISBN 0 13 140208 0
Copyright © 2004, 2001, 1998, 1995 by Pearson Education, Inc.,
Upper Saddle River, New Jersey 07458

ISBN-10   1 84658 475 2
ISBN-13   978 1 84658 475 6

Printed and bound in Great Britain

Contents

Preface   1

Statistics   3

Chapters from
Statistical and Data Handling Skills in Biology
by Roland Ennos

Chapter 2 'Dealing with Measurements'   4

Chapter 3 'Dealing with Variation'   21

Chapter 4 'Testing for Differences'   34

Chapter 5 'Finding Associations'   57

Chapter 6 'Dealing with Categorical Data'   75

Physics   85

Excerpts from
Physics
Third Edition
by James S. Walker

Introduction to Physics   87

Newton's Laws of Motion   101

Applications of Newton's Laws   113

Work and Kinetic Energy: Power 131

Potential Energy and Conservative Forces 134

Waves and Sound 158

Fluids 176

Temperature and Heat 202

Electric Current 221

Electromagnetic Waves 227

Quantum Physics 239

Atomic Physics 250

Nuclear Physics and Nuclear Radiation 253

Chemistry

273

Chapters from

Chemistry: The Central Science
Tenth Edition
by Theodore L. Brown, H. Eugene LeMay, Jr. and
Bruce E. Bursten

Chapter 1 'Introduction: Matter and Measurement' 274

Chapter 2 'Atoms, Molecules, and Ions' 310

Chapter 3 'Stoichiometry: Calculations with Chemical Formulas
and Equations' 352

Chapter 4 'Aqueous Reactions and Solution Stoichiometry' 394

Chapter 6 'Electronic Structure of Atoms' 440

Chapter 7 'Periodic Properties of the Elements' 484

Chapter 8 'Basic Concepts of Chemical Bonding' 524

Chapter 14 'Chemical Kinetics' 568

Chapter 16 'Acid-Base Equilibria' 622

Chapter 17 'Additional Aspects of Aqueous Equilibria' 674

Chapters from
Chemistry
Fourth Edition
by John McMurry and Robert C. Fay

Chapter 23 'Organic Chemistry' 723

Chapter 24 'Biochemistry' 769

PREFACE

Science Fundamental-1X and 1Y are level-1 courses at Glasgow University that have been developed to assist students wishing to take biological degrees. The courses are also suitable for students wishing to take degree subjects other than biology but have, for whatever reason, limited knowledge in the areas of mathematics, physics and chemistry.

Science Fundamentals covers basic mathematical and statistical skills to a level which should be a suitable introduction for a biology degree. The concepts of physics and chemistry often seem daunting to those who have not covered these subjects at school. These courses aim to introduce concepts that are essential to understanding aspects of biological science whether studied at the molecular or whole organism level.

By necessity this text has been put together by extracting sections from various books on chemistry, physics and statistics which are considered relevant by the course lecturers. This should enable students to have support material for the Science Fundamentals courses at a reasonable cost, without the need to purchase several books that contain large amounts of nonessential material. Any comments on the omission or inclusion of material should be passed onto the course coordinator (or any of the lecturers) so that the text can be refined in future years.

Dr A.J. Lapthorn

Statistics

CHAPTER TWO

Dealing with measurements

$6.3452 \times 10^4, 6.3453 \times 10^4$..........

2.1 Introduction

It is surprising, considering that most students of biology have studied mathematics for many years, how often they make errors in the ways they deal with and present numerical information. In fact there are many ways of getting things wrong. Primary data can be measured wrongly, or given too high or low a degree of precision. The data can be taken and presented in non-SI units, or mistakes can be made while attempting to convert to SI units. Calculations based on primary data can be carried out incorrectly. Finally, the answers can be given to the wrong degree of precision, in the wrong units, or with no units at all!

Many of the errors are made not only through ignorance but also because of haste, lack of care, or even panic. This chapter shows how you can avoid such mistakes by carrying out the following logical sequence of steps carefully and in the right order: measuring, converting data into SI units, combining data together, and expressing the answer in SI units to the correct degree of precision.

2.2 Measuring

Measurements should always be taken to the highest possible degree of precision. This is straightforward with modern digital devices, but it is more difficult in the more old-fashioned devices, which have a graduated analogue scale. The highest degree of precision of analogue instruments is usually to the smallest graduation of the scale. Using a 30 cm ruler, lengths can only be measured to the nearest millimetre. However, if the graduations are far enough apart, as they are on some thermometers, it is usually possible to judge the measurements to the next decimal place. This is made even easier by devices, like calipers or microscope stages, which have a vernier scale.

2.3 Converting to SI units

2.3.1 SI units

Before carrying out any further manipulation of data or expressing it, it should be converted into the correct SI units. The *Système International d'Unités* (SI) is the accepted scientific convention for measuring physical quantities, under which the most basic units of length, mass and time are kilograms, metres and seconds respectively. The complete list of the basic SI units is given in Table 2.1.

All other units are derived from these basic units. For instance, volume should be expressed in cubic metres or m^3. Similarly density, mass per unit volume, should be expressed in kilograms per cubic metre or $kg\,m^{-3}$. Some important derived units have their own names; the unit of force ($kg\,m\,s^{-2}$) is called a newton (N), and the unit of pressure ($N\,m^{-2}$) is called a pascal (Pa). A list of important derived SI units is given in Table 2.2.

Table 2.1 The base and supplementary SI units.

Measured quantity	SI unit	Symbol
Base		
Length	metre	m
Mass	kilogram	kg
Time	second	s
Amount of substance	mole	mol
Temperature	kelvin	K
Electric current	ampere	A
Luminous intensity	candela	cd
Supplementary		
Plane angle	radian	rad
Solid angle	steradian	sr

Table 2.2 Important derived SI units.

Measured quantity	Name of unit	Symbol	Definitions
Mechanics			
Force	newton	N	$kg\ m\ s^{-2}$
Energy	joule	J	$N\ m$
Power	watt	W	$J\ s^{-1}$
Pressure	pascal	Pa	$N\ m^{-2}$
Electricity			
Charge	coulomb	C	$A\ s$
Potential difference	volt	V	$J\ C^{-1}$
Resistance	ohm	Ω	$V\ A^{-1}$
Conductance	siemens	S	Ω^{-1}
Capacitance	farad	F	$C\ V^{-1}$
Light			
Luminous flux	lumen	lm	$cd\ sr^{-1}$
Illumination	lux	lx	$lm\ m^{-2}$
Others			
Frequency	hertz	Hz	s^{-1}
Radioactivity	becquerel	Bq	s^{-1}
Enzyme activity	katal	kat	$mol\ substrate\ s^{-1}$

2.3.2 Dealing with large and small numbers

The problem with using a standard system, like the SI system, is that the units may not always be convenient. The mass of organisms ranges from 0.000 000 000 1 kg for algae to 100 000 kg for whales. For convenience, therefore, two different systems can be used to present large and small measurements. Both these systems also have the added advantage that large numbers can be written without using a large number of zeros, which would imply an unrealistic degree of precision. It would be difficult to weigh a whale to the nearest kilogram (and pointless, since the weight will fluctuate wildly at this degree of precision), which is what the weight of 100 000 kg implies.

Use of prefixes

Using prefixes, each of which stands for a multiplication factor of 1000 (Table 2.3), is the simplest way to present large or small measurements. Any quantity can be simply presented as a number between 0.1 and 1000 multiplied by a suitable prefix. For instance, 123 000 J is better presented as 123 kJ or 0.123 MJ. Similarly, 0.000 012 m is better presented as 12 µm (not 0.012 mm).

Use of scientific notation

The problem with using prefixes is that they are rather tricky to combine mathematically when carrying out calculations. For this reason, when

Table 2.3 Prefixes used in SI.

Small numbers

Multiple	10^{-3}	10^{-6}	10^{-9}	10^{-12}	10^{-15}	10^{-18}
Prefix	milli	micro	nano	pico	femto	atto
Symbol	m	μ	n	p	f	a

Large numbers

Multiple	10^{3}	10^{6}	10^{9}	10^{12}	10^{15}	10^{18}
Prefix	kilo	mega	giga	tera	peta	exa
Symbol	k	M	G	T	P	E

performing a calculation it is usually better to express your data using **scientific notation**. As we shall see, this makes calculations much easier.

Any quantity can be expressed as a number between 1 and 10 multiplied by a power of 10 (also called an exponent). For instance, 123 is equal to 1.23 multiplied by 10 squared or 10^2. Here the exponent is 2, so it can be written as 1.23×10^2. Similarly, 0.001 23 is equal to 1.23 multiplied by the inverse of 10 cubed, or 10^{-3}. Therefore it is best written as 1.23×10^{-3}. And 1.23 itself is equal to 1.23 multiplied by 10 to the power 0, so it does not need an exponent.

A simple way of determining the value of the exponent is to count the number of digits from the decimal point to the right of the first significant figure. For instance, in 18 000 there are four figures to the right of the 1, which is the first significant figure, so $18\,000 = 1.8 \times 10^4$. Similarly, in 0.000 000 18 there are seven figures between the point and the right of the 1, so $0.000\,000\,18 = 1.8 \times 10^{-7}$.

Prefixes can readily be converted to exponents, since each prefix differs by a factor of 1000 or 10^3 (Table 2.3). The pressure 4.6 MPa equals 4.6×10^6 Pa, and 46 MPa equals $4.6 \times 10^1 \times 10^6 = 4.63 \times 10^7$ Pa.

2.3.3 Converting from non-SI units

Very often textbooks and papers, especially old ones, present quantities in non-SI units, and old apparatus may also be calibrated in non-SI units. Before carrying out calculations, you will need to convert them to SI units. Fortunately, this is very straightforward.

Non-SI metric units
The most common non-SI units are those which are metric but based on obsolete systems. The most useful biological examples are given in Table 2.4, along with a conversion factor. These units are very easy to convert into the SI system. Simply multiply your measurement by the conversion factor.

Science Fundamentals Second Edition

Table 2.4 Conversion factors from obsolete units to SI.[a]

Quantity	Old unit/Symbol	SI unit/Symbol	Conversion factor
Length	angstrom/Å	metre/m	1×10^{-10}
	yard	metre/m	0.9144
	foot	metre/m	0.3048
	inch	metre/m	2.54×10^{-2}
Area	hectare/ha	square metre/m^2	1×10^4
	acre	square metre/m^2	4.047×10^3
	square foot/ft^2	square metre/m^2	9.290×10^{-2}
	square inch/in^2	square metre/m^2	6.452×10^{-4}
Volume	litre/l	cubic metre/m^3	1×10^{-3}
	cubic foot/ft^3	cubic metre/m^3	2.832×10^{-2}
	cubic inch/in^3	cubic metre/m^3	1.639×10^{-5}
	UK pint/pt	cubic metre/m^3	5.683×10^{-4}
	US pint/liq pt	cubic metre/m^3	4.732×10^{-4}
	UK gallon/gal	cubic metre/m^3	4.546×10^{-3}
	US gallon/gal	cubic metre/m^3	3.785×10^{-3}
Angle	degree/°	radian/rad	1.745×10^{-2}
Mass	tonne	kilogram/kg	1×10^3
	ton (UK)	kilogram/kg	1.016×10^3
	hundredweight/cwt	kilogram/kg	5.080×10^1
	stone	kilogram/kg	6.350
	pound/lb	kilogram/kg	0.454
	ounce/oz	kilogram/kg	2.835×10^{-2}
Energy	erg	joule/J	1×10^{-7}
	kilowatt hour/kWh	joule/J	3.6×10^6
Pressure	bar/b	pascal/Pa	1×10^5
	mm Hg	pascal/Pa	1.332×10^2
Radioactivity	curie/Ci	becquerel/Bq	3.7×10^{10}
Temperature	centigrade/°C	kelvin/K	$C + 273.15$
	Fahrenheit/°F	kelvin/K	$\frac{5}{9}(F + 459.7)$

[a] Metric units are given in italics. To get from a measurement in the old unit to a measurement in the SI unit, multiply by the conversion factor.

Example 2.1

Give the following in SI units:

(a) 24 ha

(b) 25 cm

Solution

(a) 24 ha equals 24×10^4 m^2 = 2.4×10^5 m^2

(b) 25 cm equals 25×10^{-2} m = 2.5×10^{-1} m

Litres and concentrations

The most important example of a unit which is still widely used even though it does not fit into the SI system is the litre (1 dm^3 or 10^{-3} m^3), which is used in the derivation of the concentration of solutions. For instance, if 1 litre contains 2 moles of a substance then its concentration is given as $2\,M$ or molar.

The mole is now a bona fide SI unit, but it too was derived before the SI system was developed, since it was originally the amount of a substance which contains the same number of particles as 1 g (rather than the SI kilogram) of hydrogen atoms. In other words, the mass of 1 mole of a substance is its molecular mass in grams.

When working out concentrations of solutions it is probably best to stick to these units, since most glassware is still calibrated in litres and small balances in grams.

The molarity M of a solution is obtained as follows:

$$M = \frac{\text{Number of moles}}{\text{Solution volume (l)}}$$

$$= \frac{\text{Mass (g)}}{\text{Molecular mass} \times \text{Solution volume (l)}}$$

Example 2.2

A solution contains 23 g of copper sulphate ($CuSO_4$) in 2.5 litres of water. What is its concentration?

Solution

$$\text{Concentration} = 23/((63.5 + 32 + 64) \times 2.5)$$

$$= 5.768 \times 10^{-2}\ M$$

$$= 5.8 \times 10^{-2}\ M \quad \text{(2 significant figures)}$$

Non-metric units

Non-metric units, such as those based on the old Imperial scale, are also given in Table 2.4. Again you must simply multiply your measurement by the conversion factor. However, they are more difficult to convert to SI, since they must be multiplied by factors which are not just powers of 10. For instance,

$$6\,\text{ft} = 6 \times 3.048 \times 10^{-1}\,\text{m} = 1.83\,\text{m}$$

Note that the answer was given as 1.83 m, not the calculated figure of 1.8288 m. This is because a measure of 6 ft implies that the length was measured to the nearest inch. The answer we produced is accurate to the nearest centimetre, which is the closest SI unit.

If you have to convert square or cubic measures into metric, simply multiply by the conversion factor to the power of 2 or 3. So 12 cubic feet $= 12 \times (3.038 \times 10^{-1})^3\,\text{m}^3 = 3.4 \times 10^{-1}\,\text{m}^3$ to 2 significant figures.

2.4 Combining values

Once measurements have been converted into SI units with exponents, they are extremely straightforward to combine using either pencil and paper or calculator (most calculators use exponents nowadays). When multiplying two measurements, for instance, you simply multiply the initial numbers, add the exponents and multiply the units together. If the multiple of the two initial numbers is greater than 10 or less than 1, you simply add or subtract 1 from the exponent. For instance,

$$2.3 \times 10^2\,\text{m} \times 1.6 \times 10^3\,\text{m} = (2.3 \times 1.6) \times 10^{(2+3)}\,\text{m}^2$$

$$= 3.7 \times 10^5\,\text{m}^2$$

Notice that the area is given to 2 significant figures because that was the degree of precision with which the lengths were measured. Similarly,

$$2.3 \times 10^2\,\text{m} \times 6.3 \times 10^{-4}\,\text{m} = (2.3 \times 6.3) \times 10^{(2-4)}\,\text{m}^2$$

$$= 1.4 \times 10^1 \times 10^{-2}\,\text{m}^2$$

$$= 1.4 \times 10^{-1}\,\text{m}^2$$

In the same way, when dividing one measurement by another you divide the first initial number by the second, subtract the second exponent from the first, and divide the first unit by the second.

$$\text{Therefore} \quad (4.8 \times 10^3\,\text{m}) / (1.5 \times 10^2\,\text{s}) = (4.8/1.5) \times 10^{(3-2)}\,\text{m s}^{-1}$$

$$= 3.2 \times 10^1\,\text{m s}^{-1}$$

2.5 Expressing the answer

When you have completed all calculations, you must be careful how you express your answer. First, it should be given to the same level of precision as the *least* accurate of the measurements from which it was calculated. This book and many statistical packages use the following convention: the digits 1 to 4 go down, 6 to 9 go up and 5 goes to the nearest even digit. Here are some examples:

0.343   becomes   0.34   to   2   significant figures

0.2251   becomes   0.22   to   2   significant figures

0.6354   becomes   0.64   to   2   significant figures

Second, it is sometimes a good idea to express it using a prefix. So if we work out from figures given to two significant figures that a pressure is 2.678×10^6 Pa, it should be expressed as 2.7 MPa. Always adjust the degree of precision *at the end* of the calculation.

2.6 Doing all three steps

The various steps can now be carried out to manipulate data to reliably derive further information. It is important to carry out each step in its turn, producing an answer before going on to the next step in the calculation. Doing all the calculations at once can cause confusion and lead to silly mistakes.

Example 2.3

A sample of heartwood taken from an oak tree was 12.1 mm long by 8.2 mm wide by 9.5 mm deep and had a wet mass of 0.653 g. What was its density?

Solution

Density has units of mass (in kg) per unit volume (in m^3). Therefore the first thing to do is to convert the units into kg and m. The next thing to do is to calculate the volume in m^3. Only then can the final calculation be performed. This slow building up of the calculation is ponderous but is the best way to avoid making mistakes.

$$\text{Mass} = 6.53 \times 10^{-4} \text{ kg}$$

$$\text{Volume} = 1.21 \times 10^{-2} \times 8.2 \times 10^{-3} \times 9.5 \times 10^{-3}$$

$$= 9.4259 \times 10^{-7} \text{ m}^3$$

$$\text{Density} = \frac{\text{mass}}{\text{volume}} = \frac{6.53 \times 10^{-4}}{9.4259 \times 10^{-7}}$$

$$= 0.6928 \times 10^3 \text{ kg m}^{-3}$$

$$= 6.9 \times 10^2 \text{ kg m}^{-3}$$

Notice that the answer is given to two significant figures, like the dimensions of the sample.

Table 2.5 Some useful constants and formulae.

Physical constants

Density of water	$= 1000$ kg m^{-3}
Density of air	$= 1.2$ kg m^{-3}
Specific heat of water	$= 4.2 \times 10^3$ J K^{-1} kg^{-1}

Chemical constants

1 mol	$= 6 \times 10^{23}$ particles
Mass of 1 mol	$=$ molecular mass (g) $= 10^{-3} \times$ molecular mass (kg)
Volume of 1 mol of Gas	$= 24$ l $= 2.4 \times 10^{-2}$ m^3
	(at room temperature and pressure)
1 molar solution (1 M)	$= 1$ mol l$^{-1} = 1000$ mol m^{-3}
1 normal Solution (1 N)	$= 1$ mol l$^{-1} = 1000$ mol m^{-3} of ions
pH $= -\log_{10}[H^+]$	
Composition of air	$= 78.1\%$ nitrogen, 20.9% oxygen, 0.93% argon and 0.03% carbon dioxide, plus traces of others, by volume

Mathematical formulae

Area of a circle of radius R	$= \pi R^2$
Volume of a sphere of radius R	$= \frac{4}{3}\pi R^3$
Area of a sphere of radius R	$= 4\pi R^2$
Volume of a cylinder of radius R and height H	$= \pi R^2 H$
Volume of a cone of radius R and height H	$= \frac{1}{3}\pi R^2 H$

Mathematical constants

$\pi = 3.1416$

$\log_e x = 2.30 \log_{10} x$

2.7 Constants and formulae

Frequently, raw data on their own are not enough to work out other import-ant quantities. You may need to include physical or chemical constants in your calculations, or insert your data into basic mathematical formulae. Table 2.5 is a list of some useful constants and formulae. Many of them are worth memorising.

Example 2.4

A total of 25 micropropagated plants were grown in a 10 cm diameter Petri dish. At what density were they growing?

Solution

The first thing to calculate is the area of the Petri dish. Since its diameter is 10 cm, its radius R will be 5 cm (or 5×10^{-2} m). A circle's area A is given by the formula $A = \pi R^2$. Therefore

$$\text{Area} = 3.1416 \times (5 \times 10^{-2})^2$$

$$= 7.854 \times 10^{-3} \text{ m}^2$$

The density is the number per unit area, so

$$\text{Density} = 25/(7.854 \times 10^{-3})$$

$$= 3.183 \times 10^3 \text{ m}^{-2}$$

$$= 3.2 \times 10^3 \text{ m}^{-2} \quad \text{(2 significant figures)}$$

2.8 Using calculations

Once you can reliably perform calculations, you can use them for far more than just working out the results of your experiments from your raw data. You can use them to put your results into perspective or extrapolate from your results into a wider context. You can also use calculations to help design your experiments: to work out how much of each ingredient you need, or how much the experiment will cost. But even more usefully, they can help you to work out whether a particular experiment is worth attempting in the first place. Calculations are thus an invaluable tool for the research biologist to help save time, money and effort. They don't even have to be very exact calculations. Often, all that is required is to work out a rough or ball-park figure.

Example 2.5

Elephants are the most practical form of transport through the Indian rainforest because of the rough terrain; the only disadvantage is their great weight. A scientific expedition needs to cross a bridge with a weight limit of 10 tonnes, in order to enter a nature reserve. Will their elephants be able to cross this bridge safely?

Solution

You are unlikely, in the rainforest, to be able to look up or measure the weight of an elephant, but most people have some idea of just how big they are. Since the mass of an object is equal to volume × density, the first thing to calculate is the volume. What is the volume of an elephant? Well, elephants are around 2–3 m long and have a (very roughly) cylindrical body of diameter, say, 1.5 m (so the radius = 0.75 m). The volume of a cylinder is given by $V = \pi R^2 L$, so with these figures the volume of the elephant is approximately

$$V = \pi \times 0.75^2 \times 2 \quad \text{up to} \quad \pi \times 0.75^2 \times 3$$

$$V = 3.53\text{--}5.30 \text{ m}^3$$

The volume of the legs, trunk, etc., is very much less and can be ignored in this rough calculation. So what is the density of an elephant? Well, elephants (like us) can just about float in water and certainly swim, so they must have about the same density as water, 1000 kg m^{-3}. The approximate mass of the elephant is therefore

$$\text{Mass} = 1000 \times (3.5 \text{ to } 5.3)$$

$$= 3530\text{--}5300 \text{ kg}$$

Note, however, that the length of the beast was estimated to only one significant figure, so the weight should also be estimated to this low degree of accuracy. The weight of the elephant will be $(4\text{--}5) \times 10^3$ kg or 4–5 tonnes. (Textbook figures for weights of elephants range from 3 to 7 tonnes.) The bridge should easily be able to withstand the weight of an elephant.

This calculation would not have been accurate enough to determine whether our elephant could cross a bridge with weight limit 4.5 tonnes. It would have been necessary to devise a method of weighing it.

2.9 Logarithms, graphs and pH

2.9.1 Logarithms to base 10

Though scientific notation (such as 2.3×10^4) is a good way of expressing large and small numbers (such as 23 000), it is a bit clumsy since the numbers consist of two parts, the initial number and the exponent. Nor does it help very large and very small numbers to be conveniently represented on the same graph. For instance, if you plot the relationship between the numbers of bird species in woods of areas 100, 1000, 10 000, 100 000 and 1 000 000 m^2 (Figure 2.1a), most of the points will be congested at the left.

These problems can be overcome by the use of **logarithms**. Any number can be expressed as a single **exponent**, as 10 to the power of a second number, e.g. $23\,000 = 10^{4.362}$ The 'second number' (here 4.362) is called the logarithm to base 10 ($\log_{10}$) of the first, so that

$$4.362 = \log_{10} 23\,000$$

Numbers above 1 have a positive logarithm, whereas numbers below 1 have a negative logarithm, e.g.

$$0.0045 = 10^{-2.347} \quad \text{so} \quad -2.347 = \log_{10} 0.0045$$

Logarithms to the base 10 of any number can be found simply by pressing the log button on your calculator, and can be converted back to real numbers by pressing the 10^x button on your calculator.

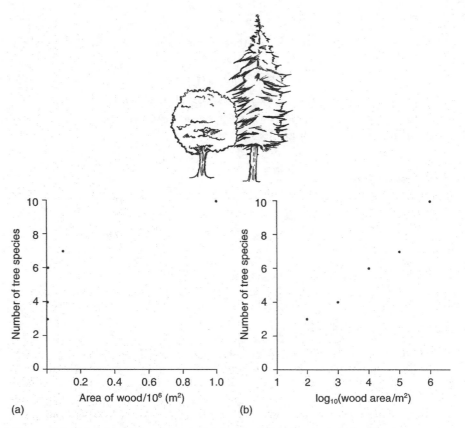

Figure 2.1 Using logarithms. (a) A simple graph showing the relationship between the size of woods and the number of tree species they contain; the points are hopelessly congested at the left of the plot. (b) Plotting number of species against $\log_{10}$ (area) spreads the data out more evenly.

Properties and uses of logarithms

The most important property of logarithms is that if numbers have a constant ratio between them, their logarithms will differ by a constant amount. Hence the numbers 1, 10 and 100, which differ by ratios of 10, have logarithms of 0, 1 and 2, which differ by 1 each time. This gives them some useful mathematical properties, which can help us work out relationships between variables, as we shall see in Chapter 5. However, it also gives them two immediate uses.

Use of logarithms for graphs

Logarithms allow very different quantities to be compared and plotted on the same graph. For instance, you can show the relationship between wood area and number of tree species (Figure 2.1a) more clearly by plotting species number against $\log_{10}$ (area) (Figure 2.1b).

pH

The single most important use of logarithms in biology is in the units for acidity. The unit pH is given by the formula

$$pH = -\log_{10}[H^+] \tag{2.1}$$

where $[H^+]$ is the hydrogen ion concentration in moles per litre (M). Therefore, a solution containing 2×10^{-5} mole (mol) of hydrogen ions per litre will have a pH of $-\log_{10}(2 \times 10^{-5}) = 4.7$.

Example 2.6

A solution has a pH of 3.2. What is the hydrogen ion concentration?

Solution

The hydrogen ion concentration is $10^{-3.2} = 6.3 \times 10^{-4}$ M.

2.9.2 Natural logarithms

Logarithms can be calculated for other bases as well as 10. Other important types of logarithms are **natural logarithms** ($\log_e$ or ln) in which numbers that differ by the ratio 2.718 (which is given the letter e) have logs that differ by 1. Thus ln 2.718 = 1. As we shall see in Chapter 5, natural logarithms are particularly useful when describing and investigating exponential increases in populations or exponential decay in radioactivity.

To convert from a number to its natural logarithm, you should press the ln button on your calculator. To convert back, you should press the e^x button.

2.10 Self-assessment problems

Problem 2.1

What are the SI units for the following measurements?

(a) Area
(b) The rate of height growth for a plant
(c) The concentration of red cells in blood
(d) The ratio of the concentrations of white and red cells in blood

Problem 2.2

How would you express the following quantities using appropriate prefixes?

(a) 192 000 000 N
(b) 0.000 000 102 kg

(c) 0.000 12 s
(d) 21.3 cm

Problem 2.3

How would you express the following quantities in scientific notation using appropriate exponents?

(a) 0.000 046 1 J
(b) 461 000 000 s

Problem 2.4

How would you express the following quantities in scientific notation using the appropriate exponents?

(a) 3.81 GPa
(b) 4.53 mW
(c) 364 mJ
(d) 4.8 mg
(e) 0.21 pg

Problem 2.5

Convert the following to SI units expressed in scientific notation.

(a) 250 tonnes
(b) 0.3 bar
(c) 24 angstroms

Problem 2.6

Convert the following into SI units.

(a) 35 yards
(b) 3 feet 3 inches
(c) 9.5 square yards

Problem 2.7

Perform the following calculations.

(a) $1.23 \times 10^3 \, \text{m} \times 2.456 \times 10^5 \, \text{m}$
(b) $(2.1 \times 10^{-2} \, \text{J}) \, / \, (4.5 \times 10^{-4} \, \text{kg})$

Problem 2.8

Give the following expressions in prefix form and to the correct degree of precision.

(a) 1.28×10^{-3} mol to 2 significant figures
(b) 3.649×10^{8} J to 3 significant figures
(c) 2.423×10^{-7} m to 2 significant figures

Problem 2.9

A blood cell count was performed. Within the box on the slide, which had sides of length 1 mm and depth of 100 µm, there were 652 red blood cells. What was the concentration of cells (in m^{-3}) in the blood?

Problem 2.10

An old-fashioned rain gauge showed that 0.6 inches of rain had fallen on an experimental plot of area of 2.6 ha. What volume of water had fallen on the area?

Problem 2.11

What is the concentration of a solution of 25 g of glucose (formula $C_6H_{12}O_6$) in a volume of 2000 ml of water?

Problem 2.12

An experiment to investigate the basal metabolic rate of human beings showed that in 5 minutes the subject breathed out 45 litres of air into a Douglas bag. The oxygen concentration in this air had fallen from 19.6% by volume to 16.0%, so it contained 3.6% CO_2 by volume. What was the mass of this CO_2 and at what rate had it been produced?

Problem 2.13

A chemical reaction heated 0.53 litre of water by 2.4 K. How much energy had it produced?

Problem 2.14

An experiment which must be repeated around 8 times requires 80 ml of a 3×10^{-3} M solution of the substance X. Given that X has a molecular mass of 258 and costs £56 per gram, and given that your budget for the year is £2000, do you think you will be able to afford to do the experiment?

Problem 2.15

It has been postulated that raised bogs may be major producers of methane and, because methane is a greenhouse gas, therefore an important cause of the greenhouse effect. A small microcosm experiment was carried out to investigate the rate at which methane is produced by a raised bog in North Wales. This showed that the rate of production was 21 ml m^{-2} per day. Given that (1) world production of CO_2 by burning fossil fuels is 25 Gt per year, (2) weight for weight methane is said to be 3 times more efficient a greenhouse gas than CO_2 and (3) there is 3.4×10^6 km^2 of blanket bog in the world, what do you think of this idea?

Problem 2.16

Calculate $\log_{10}$ of

(a) 45
(b) 450
(c) 0.000 45
(d) 1 000 000
(e) 1

Problem 2.17

Reconvert the following logarithms to base 10 back to numbers.

(a) 1.4
(b) 2.4
(c) −3.4
(d) 4
(e) 0

Problem 2.18

Calculate the pH of the following solutions.

(a) 3×10^{-4} M HCl
(b) 4×10^{-6} M H_2SO_4

Problem 2.19

Calculate the mass of sulphuric acid (H_2SO_4) in 160 ml of a solution which has a pH of 2.1.

Problem 2.20

Calculate the natural logarithm of

(a) 30
(b) 0.024
(c) 1

Problem 2.21

Convert the following natural logarithms back to numbers.

(a) 3
(b) −3
(c) 0

CHAPTER THREE

Dealing with variation

So men aren't all the same!

3.1 Introduction

We saw in the last chapter that you have to be extremely careful in the way you take measurements, manipulate them and express them to produce reliable results. However, on its own that is not enough. One of the main problems biologists encounter when they carry out research is that because all organisms are unique no useful information can be gleaned from just a single measurement. For instance, if you have reliable scales and want to measure exactly how much bull elephants weigh, it is no use just weighing one animal. Because of the great deal of variation seen in nature, we would not know how characteristic it was of elephants as a whole.

It is because of the problem of variation that we need to do so much work in biology carrying out **replicated** surveys and experiments. In turn, we need to analyse the results using complex statistical tests to tease out the variation.

This chapter outlines how and why biological measurements vary, describes how variation is quantified, and finally shows how, by combining results from several measurements, you can obtain useful quantitative information despite the variation.

3.2 Variability: causes and effects

There are three main reasons why the measurements we take of biological phenomena vary. The first is that organisms differ because their genetic make-up varies. Most of the continuous characters, like height, weight, metabolic rate or blood [Na$^+$], are influenced by a large number of genes, each of which has a small effect; they act to either increase or decrease the value of the character by a small amount. Second, organisms also vary because they are influenced by a large number of environmental factors, each of which has similarly small effects. Third, we may make a number of small errors in our actual measurements.

So how will these factors influence the **distribution** of the measurements we take? Let's look first at the simplest possible system; imagine a population of rats whose length is influenced by a single factor found in two forms. Half the time it is found in the form which increases length by 20% and half the time in the form which decreases it by 20%. The distribution of heights will be that shown in Figure 3.1a. Half the rats will be 80% of the average length and half 120% of the average length.

What about the slightly more complex case in which length is influenced by two factors, each of which is found half the time in a form which increases length by 10% and half the time in a form which decreases it by 10%. Of the four possible combinations of factors, there is one in which both factors increase length (and hence length will be 120% of average), and one in which they both reduce length (making length 80% of average). The chances of being either long or short are $\frac{1}{2} \times \frac{1}{2} = \frac{1}{4}$. However, there are two possible cases in which overall length is average: if the first factor increases length and the second decreases it; and if the first factor decreases length and the second increases it. Therefore one-half of the rats will have average length (Figure 3.1b).

Figure 3.1c gives the results for the even more complex case when length is influenced by four factors, each of which is found half the time in the form which increases length by 5% and half the time in the form which decreases it by 5%. In this case, of 16 possible combinations of factors, there is only one combination in which all four factors are in the long form and one combination in which all are in the short form. The chances of each are therefore $\frac{1}{2} \times \frac{1}{2} \times \frac{1}{2} \times \frac{1}{2} = \frac{1}{16}$. The rats are much more likely to be intermediate in size, because there are four possible combinations in which three long and one short factor (or three short and one long) can be arranged, and six possible combinations in which two long and two short factors can be arranged. It can be seen that the central peak is higher than those further out. The process is even more apparent, and the shape of the distribution becomes more obviously humped if there are eight factors, each of which increases or decreases length by 2.5% (Figure 3.1d). The resulting distributions are known as **binomial distributions**.

If length were affected by more and more factors, this process would continue; the curve would become smoother and smoother until, if length were affected by an infinite number of factors, we would get a bowler-hat-

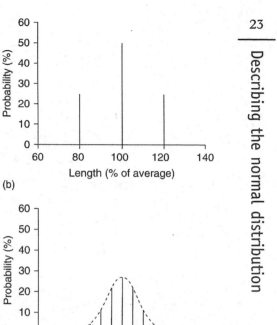

Figure 3.1 Length distributions for a randomly breeding population of rats. Length is controlled by a number of factors, each of which is found 50% of the time in the form which reduces length and 50% in the form which increases length. The graphs show length control by (a) 1 factor, (b) 2 factors, (c) 4 factors and (d) 8 factors. The greater the number of influencing factors, the greater the number of peaks and the more nearly they approximate a smooth curve (dashed outline).

shaped distribution curve (Figure 3.2). This is the so-called **normal distribution** (also known as the Z distribution). If we measured an infinite number of rats, most would have length somewhere near the average, and the numbers would tail off on each side.

3.3 Describing the normal distribution

Once we know (or assume) that a measurement follows the normal distribution, we can describe the distribution of the measurements using just two numbers. The position of the centre of the distribution is described by the **population mean** μ, which on the graph is located at the central peak of the distribution. The mean is the average value of the measurement and is found mathematically by dividing the sum of the lengths of all the rats by the number of rats:

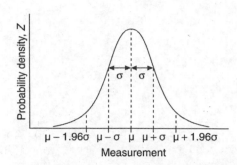

Figure 3.2 A normal distribution. Here 68% of measurements are found within one standard deviation σ from the mean μ; 95% are found within 1.96 times the standard deviation from the mean.

$$\mu = \frac{\Sigma x_i}{N} \tag{3.1}$$

where x_i is the values of length and N is the number of rats.

The width of the distribution is described by the **population standard deviation** σ, which is the distance from the central peak to the point of inflexion of the curve (where it changes from being convex to concave). This standard deviation is a measure of about how much, on average, points differ from the mean. It is actually calculated by a two-stage process. The first stage is to calculate the **population variance** V, which is the average amount of the square of the distance of each point from the mean. The variance is therefore equal to the 'sum of squares' divided by the number of points:

$$V = \frac{\Sigma(x_i - \mu)^2}{N} \tag{3.2}$$

To calculate the **standard deviation** it is necessary to take the square root of this value, which gets us back to the same units as the mean. Mathematically, standard deviation σ is given by

$$\sigma = \sqrt{\frac{\Sigma(x_i - \mu)^2}{N}} \tag{3.3}$$

It turns out that 68.2% of measurements will be within one standard deviation of the mean, 95% of all measurements will be within 1.96 times the standard deviation from the mean, 99% within 2.58 times the standard deviation from the mean and 99.9% within 3.29 times the standard deviation from the mean.

Example 3.1

Suppose adult cats have a mean mass of 3.52 kg with a standard deviation of 0.65 kg. What are the upper and lower limits of mass between which 95% of the cats are found?

Solution

We know that 95% of cats will be within $(1.96 \times 0.65) = 1.27$ kg of 3.52 kg. Therefore 95% will have mass between 2.25 kg and 4.79 kg.

3.4 Estimating the mean and standard deviation

It is all very well being able to say things about populations whose means and standard deviations we know with certainty. However, in real life it is virtually impossible to find the exact mean and standard deviation of any population. To calculate them we would have to take an infinite number of measurements!

The only practical thing to do is to take a **sample** of a manageable size and use the results from the measurements we have taken to **estimate** the population mean and standard deviation. It is very easy to calculate an **estimate of the population mean**. It is simply the average of the sample, or the sample mean $\bar{x}$. This is calculated just like the population mean; it is simply the sum of all the lengths divided by the number of rats measured. In mathematical terms this is given by the expression

$$\bar{x} = \frac{\Sigma x_i}{N} \tag{3.4}$$

where x_i is the values of length and N is the number of rats.

The **estimate of the population standard deviation**, written s or σ_{n-1}, is given by a different expression from equation (3.3). Rather than dividing the sum of squares by N, we divide by $(N-1)$ to give the formula

$$s = \sigma_{n-1} = \sqrt{\frac{\Sigma(x_i - \bar{x})^2}{N-1}} \tag{3.5}$$

We use $(N-1)$ because this expression will give an unbiased estimate of the population standard deviation, whereas using N would tend to underestimate it. To see why this is so, it is perhaps best to consider the case when we have only taken one measurement. Since the estimated mean $\bar{x}$ necessarily equals the single measurement, the standard deviation we calculate when we use N will be zero. Similarly, if there are two points, the estimated mean will be constrained to be exactly halfway between them, whereas the real mean is probably not. Thus the variance (calculated from the square of the distance of each point to the mean) and hence standard deviation will probably be underestimated.

The quantity $(N-1)$ is known as the number of **degrees of freedom** of the sample. Since the concept of degrees of freedom is repeated throughout the rest of this book, it is important to describe what it means. In a sample of N observations each is free to have any value. However, if we have used the measurements to calculate the sample mean, this restricts the value the last point can have. Take a sample of two measurements, for instance. If the mean is 17 and the first measurement is $17 + 3 = 20$, the other measurement *must* have the value $17 - 3 = 14$. Thus, knowing the first measurement fixes the second, and there will only be one degree of freedom. In the same way, if you calculate the mean of any sample of size N, you restrict the value of the last measurement, so there will be only $(N - 1)$ degrees of freedom.

It can take time calculating the standard deviation by hand, but fortunately few people have to bother nowadays; estimates for the mean and standard deviation of the population can readily be found using computer statistics packages or even scientific calculators. All you need do is type in the data values and press the $\bar{x}$ button for the mean and the s or σ_{n-1} button for the population standard deviation. Do not use the σ_n button, since this is for equation (3.3) not equation (3.5).

Example 3.2

The masses (in tonnes) of a sample of 16 bull elephants from a single reserve in Africa were as follows.

4.5	5.2	4.9	4.3	4.6	4.8	4.6	4.9
4.5	5.0	4.8	4.6	4.6	4.7	4.5	4.7

Using a calculator, estimate the population mean and standard deviation.

Solution

The estimate for the population mean is 4.70 tonnes and the population standard deviation is 0.2251 tonne, rounded to 0.22 tonne to 2 decimal places. Note that both figures are given to one more degree of precision than the original data points because so many figures have been combined.

3.5 The variability of samples

It is relatively easy to calculate estimates of a population mean and standard deviation from a sample. Unfortunately, though, the estimate we calculated of the population mean $\bar{x}$ is unlikely to exactly equal the real mean of the population μ. In our elephant survey we might by chance have included more light elephants in our sample than one might expect, or more heavy ones. The estimate itself will be variable, just like the population. However, we can estimate how much it should vary and work out limits between which the mean is likely to be found.

3.5.1 The variability of samples from a known population

If we took an infinite number of samples from a population whose mean μ and standard deviation σ we knew, their means $\bar{x}$ would be normally

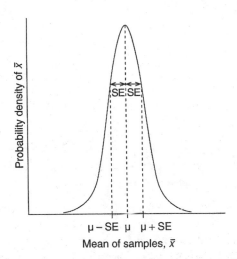

Figure 3.3 Distribution of sample means. The sample means $\bar{x}$ have a normal distribution with mean µ and standard error SE. The distribution is narrower than for single points (Figure 3.2) because, in a sample, high and low values tend to cancel each other out.

distributed just like the original measurements (Figure 3.3). However, the amount of spread of the means would be much narrower because high and low measurements would tend to cancel each other out in each sample, particularly in large samples. The **standard error** (SE) of the mean is a measure of how much the sample means would on average differ from the population mean. Just like standard deviation, standard error is the distance from the centre of the distribution to the inflexion point of the curve (Figure 3.3). It is given by the formula

$$SE = \sigma/\sqrt{N} \tag{3.6}$$

where σ is the standard deviation and N is the number of observations in the sample. Note that the bigger the sample size, the smaller the standard error. Just as we saw for standard deviation, 95% of the samples would have a mean within 1.96 times the standard error of the population, 99% within 2.58 times the standard error and 99.9% within 3.29 times the standard error. These limits are called 95%, 99% and 99.9% **confidence intervals**.

3.5.2 The variability of estimates of population means

There is a problem with calculating the variability of $\bar{x}$, like the value we calculated for the mass of elephants in Example 3.2. We do not know σ precisely, we only have our **estimate** s. However, we can still make an **estimate of the standard error**:

$$\overline{SE} = s/\sqrt{N} \tag{3.7}$$

Note that the larger the sample size, the smaller the value of $\overline{SE}$.

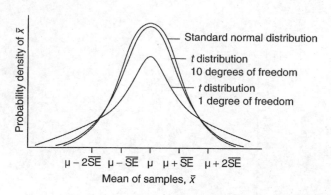

Figure 3.4 Normal distribution and *t* distribution. The distribution of sample means $\bar{x}$ relative to the estimate of the standard error $\overline{SE}$ calculated from samples with 1, 10 and infinite degrees of freedom. With infinite degrees of freedom the distribution equals the normal distribution. However, it becomes more spread out as the sample size decreases (fewer degrees of freedom) because the estimate of standard error becomes less reliable.

3.6 Confidence limits for the population mean

Because standard error is only estimated, $\bar{x}$ will have a wider distribution relative to it than the normal distribution shown in Figure 3.3. In fact it will follow what is known as the ***t* distribution** (Figure 3.4). The exact shape of the *t* distribution depends on the number of degrees of freedom; it becomes progressively more similar to the normal distribution as the number of degrees of freedom increases (and hence as the estimate of standard deviation becomes more exact).

Knowing all this, it is fairly straightforward to calculate **confidence limits** for the population mean μ using the tabulated **critical values** of the *t* statistic given at the end of the book. The critical *t* value $t_{(N-1)}(5\%)$ is the number of standard errors $\overline{SE}$ away from the estimate of population mean $\bar{x}$ within which the real population mean μ will be found 95 times out of 100. The 95% confidence limits define the 95% confidence interval, or 95% CI; this is expressed as follows:

$$95\% \ \text{CI(mean)} = \bar{x} \pm (t_{(N-1)}(5\%) \times \overline{SE}) \tag{3.8}$$

where $(N-1)$ is the number of degrees of freedom. It is most common to use a 95% confidence interval but it is also possible to calculate 99% and 99.9% confidence intervals for the mean by substituting the critical *t* values for 1% and 0.1% respectively into equation (3.8).

Note that the larger the sample size *N*, the narrower the confidence interval. This is because as *N* increases, not only will the standard error $\overline{SE}$ be lower but so will the critical *t* values. Quadrupling the sample size reduces the distance between the upper and lower limits of the confidence interval by more than one-half.

Example 3.2

Our survey of bull elephants gave an estimate of mean mass of 4.70 tonnes and an estimate of standard deviation of 0.2251 tonne. We want to calculate 95% and 99% confidence limits for the mean mass.

Solution

The estimate of standard error is $\overline{SE} = 0.2251/\sqrt{16} = 0.0563$ tonne, which is rounded to 0.056 tonne to 3 decimal places. Notice that standard errors are usually given to one more decimal place than the mean or standard deviation.

To calculate the 95% confidence limits we must look in Table S1 (at the end of the book) for the critical value of t for $16 - 1 = 15$ degrees of freedom. In fact $t_{15}(5\%) = 2.131$. Therefore 95% confidence limits of the population mean are $4.70 \pm (2.131 \times 0.0563) = 4.70 \pm 0.12 = 4.58$ and 4.82 tonnes. So 95 times out of 100 the real population mean would be between 4.58 and 4.82 tonnes.

Similarly, $t_{15}(1\%) = 2.947$. Therefore 99% confidence limits of the population mean are $4.70 \pm (2.947 \times 0.0563) = 4.70 \pm 0.16 = 4.54$ and 4.86 tonnes. So 99 times out of 100 the real population mean would be between 4.54 and 4.86 tonnes.

3.7 The importance of descriptive statistics

We have seen that it is straightforward to calculate the mean, standard deviation, standard error of the mean and 95% confidence limits of a sample using a hand calculator. Together these sum up what you know about your sample and they are called **descriptive statistics**. Calculating them is the first and most important step in looking at the results of your surveys or experiments. You should work them out as soon as possible and try to see what they tell you.

3.8 Using computer packages

Nowadays you don't usually have to perform statistical calculations yourself. You can use one of the many computer-based statistical packages which are available, such as MINITAB, SPSS or EXCEL. You simply enter all your results straight into a spreadsheet in the computer package and let the computer take the strain. Using a package has two advantages: (1) the computer carries out the calculations more quickly; and (2) you can save the results for future analysis.

Most packages work in much the same way. You enter the results from different samples into their own separate columns. You can then run tests on the different columns from the command screen of the package.

Example 3.3

In order to calculate descriptive statistics for the data given in Example 3.2, the 16 values should be placed in rows 1 to 16 of the first column as follows:

		c1	c2	c3	c4	c5	c6	...
Rows	1	4.5						
	2	5.2						
	3	4.9						
	4	4.3						
	5	4.6						
	6	4.8						
	7	4.6						
	8	etc.						
	9	etc.						
	10	:						
	11							
	:							

It is then straightforward to investigate or to perform statistical tests on the data by running through menus or typing in commands. In MINITAB you can examine descriptive statistics by going to the Statistics menu, then choosing Basic Statistics and then Descriptives. Finally, select the column you want to examine. MINITAB will produce the following output:

	N	MEAN	MEDIAN	TRMEAN	STDEV	SE MEAN
bull	16	4.7000	4.6500	4.6929	0.2251	0.0563

	MIN	MAX	Q1	Q3
bull	4.3000	5.2000	4.5250	4.8750

It gives you the number, and estimates for the mean, standard deviation and standard error. Unfortunately, it also gives you some information you may not want, and it does not calculate the 95% confidence limits. The median is halfway between the eighth and ninth highest points; Q1 and Q3 are the points one-quarter and three-quarters of the way up the distribution. Their importance is explained in Chapter 7.

Note that the package gives some items with too much precision. Don't copy things from computer screens without thinking!

3.9 Presenting descriptive statistics

3.9.1 In text or tables

Once you have obtained your descriptive statistics, you need to express them in the correct way in your write-ups. There are two main ways of doing this.

The simplest is just to write them in your text or in tables as the mean followed by the standard deviation or the standard error in parentheses, e.g. $\bar{x}$ (s) or $\bar{x}$ ($\overline{SE}$). You must say whether you are giving the standard deviation or standard error and you must give the number of observations in your sample; this is so that the reader can calculate the other statistic. A 95% confidence interval can be given as $\bar{x} \pm (t_{(N-1)}(5\%) \times \overline{SE})$. For example, in our elephants example:

Mean and standard deviation = 4.70 (0.22) t ($n = 16$)

Mean and standard error = 4.70 (0.056) t ($n = 16$)

95% confidence interval = 4.70 ± 0.12 t ($n = 16$)

3.9.2 Graphically

The other way to present data is on a point graph or a bar chart (Figure 3.5). The mean is the central point of the graph or the top of the bar.

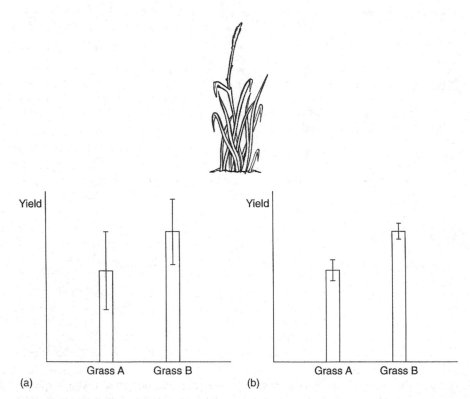

Figure 3.5 Graphing data with error bars. (a) The mean yield of two species of grass with error bars showing their standard deviation; this emphasises the high degree of variability in each grass, and the fact that the distributions overlap a good deal. (b) Standard error bars emphasise whether or not the two means are different; here the error bars do not overlap, suggesting that the means *might* be significantly different.

Error bars are then added. From the mean, bars are drawn both up and down a length equal to either the standard deviation or standard error. Finally, lines are drawn across the ends of the bars. Again you must say in the captions or legends which measure of error you are using.

The choice of standard deviation or standard error bars depends on what you want to emphasise about your results. If you want to show how much **variation** there is, you should choose standard deviation (Figure 3.5a). On the other hand, if you want to show how confident you can be of the mean, you should choose standard error (Figure 3.5b). In general, if two samples have overlapping standard error bars, they are unlikely to be statistically different (Chapter 4).

3.10 Self-assessment problems

Problem 3.1

In a population of women, heart rate is normally distributed with a mean of 75 and a standard deviation of 11. Between which limits will 95% of the women have their heart rates?

Problem 3.2

The masses (in grams) for a sample of 10 adult mice from a large laboratory population were measured. The following results were obtained:

5.6 5.2 6.1 5.4 6.3 5.7 5.6 6.0 5.5 5.7

Calculate estimates of the mean and standard deviation of the mass of the mice.

Problem 3.3

Nine measurements were taken of the pH of nine leaf cells. The results were as follows:

6.5 5.9 5.4 6.0 6.1 5.8 5.8 5.6 5.9

(a) Use the data to calculate estimates of the mean, standard deviation, and standard error of the mean. Use these estimates to calculate the 95% confidence interval for cell pH.
(b) Repeat the calculation assuming that you had only taken the first four measurements. How much wider is the 95% confidence interval?

Problem 3.4

The masses (in kilograms) of 25 newborn babies were as follows.

| 3.5 | 2.9 | 3.4 | 1.8 | 4.2 | 2.6 | 2.2 | 2.8 | 2.9 | 3.2 | 2.7 | 3.4 | 3.0 |
| 3.2 | 2.8 | 3.2 | 3.0 | 3.5 | 2.9 | 2.8 | 2.5 | 2.9 | 3.1 | 3.3 | 3.1 | |

Calculate the mean, standard deviation and standard error of the mean and present your results (a) in figures and (b) in the form of a bar chart with error bars showing standard deviation.

CHAPTER FOUR

Testing for differences

But 2-1 isn't a significant difference

4.1 Introduction

Even though any biological measurement is bound to be variable, by taking samples from a population, we can estimate the average value of the measurement, estimate its variability, and estimate the limits between which the average is likely to lie. This is very useful, but if we are going to carry out biological research, we might also want to answer specific questions about the things we are measuring. There are several questions we could ask:

- We might want to know if, and by how much, the average value of a measurement taken on a single population is different from an expected value. Is the birthweight of babies from a small town different from the national average?
- We might want to know if, on average, two measurements made on a single population are different from each other. Do patients have a different heart rate after taking beta blockers? Or is the pH of ponds different at dawn and dusk?
- We might want to know if experimentally treated organisms or cells are, on average, different from controls. Does shaking sunflowers alter their height compared with unshaken controls?
- We might want to know if two or more groups of organisms or cells are, on average, different from each other. Do different strains of bacteria have different growth rates?

This chapter describes how you can use statistical tests to help determine whether there are differences and how to work out their size.

4.2 Why we need statistical tests

4.2.1 The problem

You might imagine it would be easy to find out whether there are differences. You would just need to take measurements on your samples and compare the average values to see if they were different. However, there is a problem. Because of variation we can never be certain that the differences between our **sample means** reflect real differences in the **population means**. We might have got different means just by chance.

Suppose μ is the mean length of a population of rats. If we take measurements on a sample of rats, it is quite likely we could get a mean value $\bar{x}$ that is one standard error $\overline{SE}$ greater or smaller than μ. In fact the chances of getting a mean that different *or more* from μ is equal to the shaded area in Figure 4.1a. In contrast it is much less likely that we could get a value which is different by more than three standard errors from μ (Figure 4.1b). The probability is given by the tiny (though still real) area in the two tails of the distribution.

Therefore, if we take a sample and find that its mean is very different from an expected value, we can say that the mean of the population is very likely to be different from the expected value. However, we cannot be sure. Variation means we can never be sure that differences are real; and because

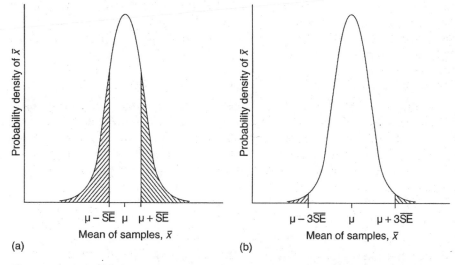

(a)   (b)

Figure 4.1 Sample means different from an expected value. (a) There is a high probability (shaded areas) of obtaining a mean at least one standard error $\overline{SE}$ away from the expected mean μ. (b) There is a very low probability (shaded areas) of getting a mean at least three standard errors $3\overline{SE}$ away from the expected mean μ.

we can never be sure, we have to use statistical tests. These tests calculate just how likely it is that the differences are real, and how large any differences are likely to be.

4.2.2 The logic of statistics

All statistical tests use the same sort of counterintuitive logic, a logic which may seem difficult to follow. They all involve testing a hypothesis. This is done in four steps; a fifth step is also possible.

Step 1: Formulate a null hypothesis
The first stage is to assume the opposite of what you are testing. Here we are testing whether there is a difference, so we assume there is no difference. This is called the **null hypothesis**.

Step 2: Calculate the test statistic
The next stage is to examine the data values and calculate a test statistic from them. When testing for differences, the test statistic is usually a measure of how different the means are relative to the variability. The greater the difference in the means and the smaller the scatter in the data, the bigger the absolute value of the test statistic (i.e. the further away from zero it will be). The smaller the difference in the means and the greater the scatter, the smaller the absolute value of the test statistic.

Step 3: Calculate the significance probability
Next you must examine the test statistic and assess the probability of getting an absolute value that high or greater if the null hypothesis were true. The larger the absolute value of the test statistic (i.e. the further away from zero it is), hence the greater the distance between the means, the smaller the probability. The smaller the absolute value of the test statistic, the larger the probability.

Step 4: Decide whether to reject the null hypothesis

- If the significance probability is below a **critical value**, you must reject the null hypothesis and conclude that there is a **significant difference**. Usually in biology one rejects the null hypothesis if the significance probability is less than 1 in 20. This probability is often written as the decimal 0.05, or as 5%. This criterion for rejecting the null hypothesis is therefore known as the 5% significance level.
- If the significance probability is greater than 5%, you have no evidence to reject the null hypothesis. But this does not mean you have evidence to support it.

Statisticians have taken a lot of the hard work out of calculating the significance probability and deciding whether to reject the null hypothesis by preparing tables of critical values for test statistics. Three of these tables are given at the end of the book. All you need do is consult the appropriate table for the critical value. Statistical tables often come in two different

Table 4.1 Four conventional ways to present the results of significance tests.[a]

Probability is less than 1 in 20	Probability is less than 1 in 100	Probability is less than 1 in 1000
5% level	1% level	0.1% level
$P < 0.05$	$P < 0.01$	$P < 0.001$
$0.01 < P < 0.05$	$0.001 < P < 0.01$	$P < 0.001$
*	**	***

[a] The second is the most commonly used.

versions: one-tailed and two-tailed. In this book we use the **two-tailed tests**, by far the more common in biology; they test whether there are differences from expected values but not which sign they are. With our rats, therefore, we would be testing whether they had a different length but not whether they were longer or shorter than expected. The criterion for rejecting the null hypothesis in the two-tailed test is when the total area in the two tails of the distribution (Figure 4.1) is less than 5%, so each tail must have an area of less than 2.5%.

Sometimes you may find the probability P falls below critical levels of 1 in 100 or 1 in 1000. If this is true, you can reject the null hypothesis at the 1% or 0.1% levels respectively. There are several ways in which significance levels may be presented in scientific papers and reports. Four of the commonest ways are shown in Table 4.1. The second way is the most common.

Step 5: Calculate confidence limits

Whether or not there is a **significant difference**, you can calculate **confidence limits** to give a set of plausible values for the differences of the means. Calculating 95% confidence limits for the difference of means is just as straightforward as calculating 95% confidence limits for the means themselves (Section 3.6).

This may sound rather abstract, so let's look at some examples. We begin with the simplest of all tests for differences, the one-sample t test.

4.3 The one-sample t test

4.3.1 Purpose

To test whether the sample mean of one measurement taken on a single population is different from an expected value E.

4.3.2 Rationale

You work out how many standard errors the sample mean is away from the expected value. The further away it is, the less probable it is that the real mean is the expected value.

4.3.3 Carrying out the test

Step 1: Formulate the null hypothesis
The null hypothesis is that the mean of the population *is not* different from the expected value.

Step 2: Calculate the test statistic
The test statistic t is the number of standard errors the sample mean is away from the expected value. It can be found using a calculator or using MINITAB.

Using a calculator

$$t = \frac{\text{Sample mean} - \text{Expected value}}{\text{Standard error of mean}} = \frac{\bar{x} - E}{\text{SE}} \tag{4.1}$$

Note that t could be positive or negative. It is the difference from zero which matters.

Using MINITAB
Statistical packages such as MINITAB can readily work out t as well as other important elements in the test. Simply put the data into a column, go into the Statistics menu, then into Basic Statistics and choose 1-Sample t. Finally, select the column you want to test and the test value you want to compare it with.

Step 3: Calculate the significance probability
You must calculate the probability P that the absolute value of t, written $|t|$, would be this high or greater if the null hypothesis were true.

Using a calculator
You must compare your value of $|t|$ with the critical value of the t statistic for $(N-1)$ degrees of freedom and at the 5% level $(t_{(N-1)}(5\%))$. This is given in Table S1 (at the end of the book).

Using MINITAB
MINITAB will directly work out the probability P. (Note that the bigger the value of $|t|$, the smaller the value of P.)

Step 4: Decide whether to reject the null hypothesis

Using a calculator

- If $|t|$ is greater than the critical value, you must reject the null hypothesis. Therefore you can say that the mean is significantly different from the expected value.
- If $|t|$ is less than the critical value, you have no evidence to reject the null hypothesis. Therefore you can say that the mean is not significantly different from the expected value.

- If $P < 0.05$ you must reject the null hypothesis. Therefore you can say that the mean is significantly different from the expected value.
- If $P > 0.05$ you have no evidence to reject the null hypothesis. Therefore you can say that the mean is not significantly different from the expected value.

Step 5: Calculate confidence limits
The 95% confidence limits for the difference are given by the equation

$$95\% \text{ CI(difference)} = \bar{x} - E \pm (t_{(N-1)}(5\%) \times \overline{SE}) \qquad (4.2)$$

Example 4.1

Do the bull elephants we first met in Example 3.2 have a different mean mass from the mean value for the entire population of African elephants of 4.50 tonnes?

Solution

Formulate the null hypothesis
The null hypothesis is that the mean weight of bull elephants *is* 4.50 tonnes.

Calculate the test statistic

Using a calculator
The mean weight $\bar{x}$ of the sample of bull elephants is 4.70 tonnes with an estimate of the standard error $\overline{SE}$ of 0.0563 tonnes. Therefore $t = (4.70 - 4.50)/0.0563 = 3.55$. The mean is 3.55 standard errors away from the expected value.

Using MINITAB
MINITAB produces the following output:

```
TEST OF MU = 4.5000 VS MU N.E. 4.5000
          N      MEAN     STDEV    SE MEAN       T    P VALUE
bull     16    4.7000    0.2251    0.0563    3.55     0.0029
```

Calculate the significance probability

Using a calculator
Looking up in the t distribution for $16 - 1 = 15$ degrees of freedom, the critical value that $|t|$ must exceed for the probability to drop below the 5% level is 2.131.

Using MINITAB
The MINITAB printout shows that the probability P of $|t|$ being this high or greater is $P = 0.0029$.

Decide whether to reject the null hypothesis

Using a calculator

$$|t| = 3.55 > 2.131$$

Using MINITAB

$$P = 0.0029 < 0.05$$

Therefore we must reject the null hypothesis. We can say that bull elephants have a weight significantly different from 4.50 tonnes; in fact they are heavier.

Calculate confidence limits

The difference between the actual and expected mean = 4.70 − 4.50 = 0.20, the standard error is 0.0563, and the critical t value for 15 degrees of freedom is 2.131. Therefore

$$95\% \text{ CI(difference)} = 0.20 \pm (2.131 \times 0.0563) = 0.08 \text{ to } 0.32$$

Bull elephants are 95% likely to be between 0.08 and 0.32 tonnes heavier than 4.5 tonnes.

4.4 The paired t test

4.4.1 Purpose

To test whether the means of **two** measurements made on a **single** identifiable population are different from each other.

4.4.2 Rationale

This test has two stages. You first calculate the difference d between the two measurements you have made on each item. You then use a one-sample t test to determine whether the mean difference $\bar{d}$ is different from zero.

4.4.3 Carrying out the test

Step 1: Formulate the null hypothesis
The null hypothesis is that the mean difference $\bar{d}$ *is not* different from zero.

Step 2: Calculate the test statistic
The test statistic t is the number of standard errors the difference is away from zero. It can be calculated using a calculator or using MINITAB.

Using a calculator

$$t = \frac{\text{Mean difference}}{\text{Standard error of difference}} = \frac{\bar{d}}{\overline{\text{SE}}_d} \tag{4.3}$$

Using *MINITAB*

Statistical packages such as MINITAB can readily work out *t* as well as other important elements in the test. Simply put the data side by side into two columns and subtract one from the other to form a 'difference' column. Finally, from the Statistics menu choose Basic Statistics and then 1-Sample t. This test is used to determine whether the mean of this column is different from zero.

Step 3: Calculate the significance probability

You must calculate the probability *P* that the absolute value of the test statistic would be equal to or greater than *t* if the null hypothesis were true.

Using a calculator

You must compare your value of $|t|$ with the critical value of the *t* statistic for $(N-1)$ degrees of freedom and at the 5% level ($t_{(N-1)}(5\%)$). This is given in Table S1 (at the end of the book).

Using *MINITAB*

MINITAB will directly work out the probability *P*. (Note that the bigger the value of $|t|$, the smaller the value of *P*.)

Step 4: Decide whether to reject the null hypothesis

Using a calculator

- If $|t|$ is greater than the critical value, you must reject the null hypothesis. Therefore you can say that the mean difference is significantly different from zero.
- If $|t|$ is less than the critical value, you have no evidence to reject the null hypothesis. Therefore you can say that the mean difference is not significantly different from zero.

Using *MINITAB*

- If $P < 0.05$ you must reject the null hypothesis. Therefore you can say that the mean difference is significantly different from zero.
- If $P > 0.05$ you have no evidence to reject the null hypothesis. Therefore you can say that the mean is not significantly different from zero.

Step 5: Calculate confidence limits

The 95% confidence limits for the mean difference are given by the equation

$$95\% \text{ CI(difference)} = \bar{d} \pm (t_{(N-1)}(5\%) \times \overline{SE}_d) \tag{4.4}$$

Example 4.2

Two series of measurements were made of the pH of nine ponds: at dawn and at dusk. The results are shown below. Do the ponds have a different pH at these times?

Pond	Dawn pH	Dusk pH	Difference
1	4.84	4.91	0.07
2	5.26	5.62	0.36
3	5.03	5.19	0.16
4	5.67	5.89	0.22
5	5.15	5.44	0.29
6	5.54	5.49	−0.05
7	6.01	6.12	0.11
8	5.32	5.61	0.29
9	5.44	5.70	0.26
$\bar{x}$	5.362	5.552	0.190
s	0.352	0.358	0.129
$\overline{SE}$	0.1174	0.1194	0.0431

Carrying out descriptive statistics shows that the mean difference $\bar{d} = 0.19$ and the standard error of the difference $\overline{SE}_d = 0.043$.

Solution

Formulate the null hypothesis

The null hypothesis is that the mean of the differences in the pH *is* 0, i.e. the ponds have the same pH at dawn and dusk.

Calculate the test statistic

Using a calculator
We have $t = 0.190/0.0431 = 4.40$. The difference is 4.40 standard errors away from zero.

Using MINITAB
MINITAB produces the following output:

```
TEST OF MU = 0.0000 VS MU N.E.  0.0000
             N     MEAN      STDEV     SE MEAN      T     P VALUE
dusk-dawn    9    0.1900    0.1294    0.0431      4.40    0.0023
```

Calculate the significance probability

Using a calculator
Looking up in the t distribution for $9 - 1 = 8$ degrees of freedom, the critical value of t for the 5% level is 2.306.

Using MINITAB
MINITAB shows that the probability P of $|t|$ being this high or greater is $P = 0.0023$.

Decide whether to reject the null hypothesis

Using a calculator

$$|t| = 4.40 > 2.306$$

Using MINITAB

$$P = 0.0023 < 0.05$$

Therefore we must reject the null hypothesis. We can say that the mean difference between dawn and dusk is significantly different from 0. In other words, the pH of ponds is significantly different at dusk from at dawn; in fact it's higher.

Calculate confidence limits

The 95% confidence interval is $0.19 \pm (2.306 \times 0.043) = 0.09$ to 0.29. It is 95% likely that the pH at dusk will be between 0.09 and 0.29 higher than the pH at dawn.

4.5 The two-sample *t* test

4.5.1 Purpose

To test whether the means of a single measurement made on two populations are different from each other.

4.5.2 Rationale

This test is rather more complex than the previous two because you have to decide the probability of overlap between the distributions of *two* sample means (Figure 4.2). To do this you have to calculate t by comparing the difference in the means of the two populations with an estimate of the **standard error of the difference** between the two populations. The test makes the assumption that the variances of the two populations are the same.

The two-sample t test also makes an important assumption about the measurements: it assumes the two sets of measurements are **independent** of each other. This would not be true of the data on the ponds we examined in Example 4.2, because each measurement has a pair, a measurement from the same pond at a different time of day. Therefore it is not valid to carry out a two-sample t test on this data.

4.5.3 Carrying out the test

Step 1: Formulate the null hypothesis

The null hypothesis is that the mean of the differences *is not* different from zero. In other words, the two groups have the same mean.

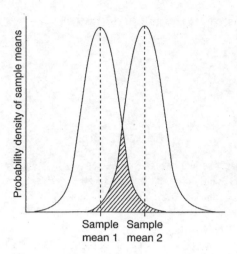

Figure 4.2 Overlapping populations. The estimated probability distributions of two overlapping populations worked out from the results of samples.

Step 2: Calculate the test statistic

The test statistic t is given by the formula

$$t = \frac{\text{Mean difference}}{\text{Standard error of difference}} = \frac{\bar{x}_A - \bar{x}_B}{\overline{SE}_d} \qquad (4.5)$$

In this case it is much more complex to calculate the standard error of the difference $\overline{SE}_d$ because this would involve comparing each member of the first population with each member of the second. But $\overline{SE}_d$ can be estimated if we assume that the variance of the two populations is the same. It is given by the equation

$$\overline{SE}_d = \sqrt{(\overline{SE}_A)^2 + (\overline{SE}_B)^2} \qquad (4.6)$$

where $\overline{SE}_A$ and $\overline{SE}_B$ are the standard errors of the two populations. If the populations are of similar size, $\overline{SE}_d$ will be about $1\frac{1}{2}$ times as big as either population standard error.

Fortunately, computer statistics packages can perform all the calculations almost instantaneously. To perform a test in MINITAB, put the data into two columns, go into the Statistics menu, then Basic Statistics and choose 2-Sample t. Finally select the columns you want to test. You can perform the test with or without making the assumption that the variances are the same.

Step 3: Calculate the significance probability

You must calculate the probability P that the absolute value of the test statistic would be equal to or greater than t if the null hypothesis were true. MINITAB will directly work this out. There are $N_A + N_B - 2$ degrees of freedom, where N_A and N_B are the sample sizes of groups A and B.

Step 4: Decide whether to reject the null hypothesis

- If $P < 0.05$ you must reject the null hypothesis. Therefore you can say that the sample means are significantly different from each other.
- If $P > 0.05$ you have no evidence to reject the null hypothesis. Therefore you can say that the two sample means are not significantly different from each other.

Step 5: Calculate confidence limits
The 95% confidence intervals for the mean difference are given by the equation

$$95\%\ \text{CI(difference)} = \bar{x}_A - \bar{x}_B \pm (t_{N_A+N_B-2}(5\%) \times \overline{\text{SE}}_d) \tag{4.7}$$

But MINITAB also calculates these limits directly.

Example 4.3

The following data were obtained by weighing 16 cow elephants as well as the 16 bull elephants we have already weighed. We will test whether bull elephants have a different mean mass from cow elephants.

Masses of bull elephants (tonnes)

4.5	5.2	4.9	4.3	4.6	4.8	4.6	4.9
4.5	5.0	4.8	4.6	4.6	4.7	4.5	4.7

Masses of cow elephants (tonnes)

4.3	4.6	4.5	4.4	4.7	4.1	4.5	4.4
4.2	4.3	4.5	4.4	4.5	4.4	4.3	4.3

Solution

Carrying out descriptive statistics yields the following results:

Bull elephants: mean = 4.70, $s = 0.22$, $\overline{\text{SE}} = 0.056$

Cow elephants: mean = 4.40, $s = 0.15$, $\overline{\text{SE}} = 0.038$

It looks like bulls are heavier, but are they significantly heavier?

Formulate the null hypothesis
The null hypothesis is that the mean of the differences in weight is 0, i.e. bull and cows have the same mean weight.

Calculate the test statistic

MINITAB comes up with the following output:

```
TWOSAMPLE T FOR bulls VS cows
                N           MEAN          STDEV          SE MEAN
bulls          16          4.700         0.225          0.056
cows           16          4.400         0.151          0.038

95 PCT CI FOR MU bulls - MU cows: (0.161, 0.439)

TTEST  MU  bulls = MU  cows  (Pooled  St  Dev = 0.191):  T = 4.43
P = 0.0001 DF = 30
```

MINITAB has calculated that $t = 4.43$. The means are 4.43 standard errors of the difference away from each other.

Calculate the significance probability

MINITAB has calculated the probability P directly as $P = 0.0001$.

Decide whether to reject the null hypothesis

We have $P = 0.0001 < 0.05$. Therefore we must reject the null hypothesis. We can say that bull elephants have a significantly different mean weight from cow elephants; in fact they are heavier.

Calculate confidence limits

MINITAB has also calculated that the 95% confidence interval for the difference is 0.161 to 0.439. The weight difference between bull and cow elephants has a 95% probability of being between 0.161 and 0.439 tonnes.

4.6 ANOVA: comparing many groups

4.6.1 Why *t* tests are unsuitable

If you want to compare the means of more that two groups, you might think that you could simply compare each group with all the others using two-sample *t* tests. However, there are two good reasons why you should not do this. First, there is the problem of convenience. As the number of groups you are comparing goes up, the number of tests you must carry out rises rapidly, from 3 tests when comparing 3 groups to 45 tests for 10 groups.

Number of groups	3	4	5	6	7	8	9	10
Number of *t* tests	3	6	10	15	21	28	36	45

But there is a second, more important problem. We reject a null hypothesis with 95% confidence, not 100% confidence. This means that in 1 in 20 tests we will falsely assume there is a significant difference between groups when none really exists. If we carry out a lot of tests, the chances of making such an error go up rapidly, so if we carry out 45 tests there is about a 90% chance we will find significant effects even if none exist.

For these reasons you must use a more complex statistical test to determine whether there is a difference between many groups; it is called analysis of variance, usually shortened to **ANOVA**.

4.6.2 The rationale behind one-way ANOVA

One-way ANOVA works in a different manner from t tests. Rather than examine the difference between the means directly, ANOVA looks at the **variability** of the data. Let's examine a simple example in which the means of the weights of just two small samples of fish are compared (Figure 4.3a). The overall variability is the sum of the squares of the distances from each point to the overall mean (Figure 4.3b); here it's $3^2 + 2^2 + 1^2 + 3^2 + 2^2 + 1^2 = 28$. But this can be split into two parts. First, there is the between-group variability, which is due to the differences between the group means. This is the sum of the squares of the distances of each point's group mean from the overall mean (Figure 4.3c); here it's $(6 \times 2^2) = 24$. Second, there is the within-group variability, which is due to the scatter within each group. This is the sum of the squares of the distance from each point to its group mean (Figure 4.3d); here it's $(4 \times 1^2) + (2 \times 0^2) = 4$.

ANOVA compares the between-group variability and the within-group variability. To show how this helps, let's look at two contrasting situations. In Figure 4.4a the two means are far apart and there is little scatter within each group; the between-group variability will clearly be much larger than the within-group variability. In Figure 4.4b the means are close together and there is much scatter within each group; the between-group variability will be lower than the within-group variability.

4.6.3 Carrying out one-way ANOVA

The actual workings of ANOVA tests are actually a little more complex, but they involve the same four basic steps as the t tests we have already carried out.

Step 1: Formulate the null hypothesis
The null hypothesis is that the groups have the same mean. In this case the hypothesis is that the two groups of fish have the same mean weight.

Step 2: Calculate the test statistic
The test statistic in ANOVA tests is the F statistic. Calculating F is quite a complex process; it involves producing a table like the one shown in Example 4.4.

(a) The first stage is to calculate the variabilities due to each factor to produce the so-called sums of squares (SS).
(b) We cannot compare sums of squares, because they are the result of adding up different numbers of points. The next stage is therefore to calculate

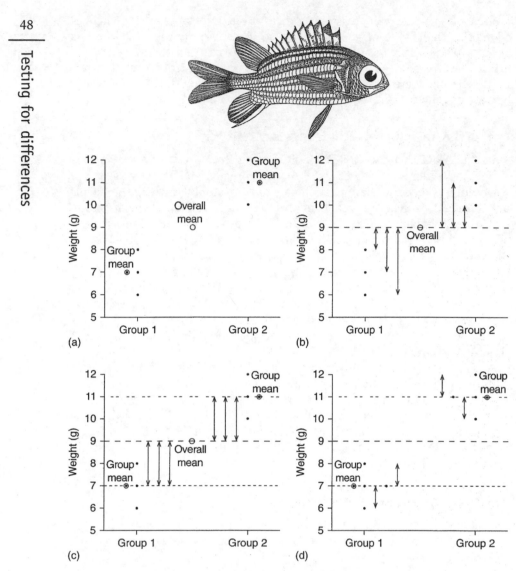

Figure 4.3 The rationale behind ANOVA: hypothetical weights for two samples of fish. (a) Calculate the overall mean and the group means. (b) The total variability is the sum of the squares of the distances of each point from the overall mean; this can be broken down into between-group variability and within-group variability. (c) The between-group variability is the sum of the squares of the distances from each point's group mean to the overall mean. (d) The within-group variability is the sum of the squares of the distances from each point to its group mean.

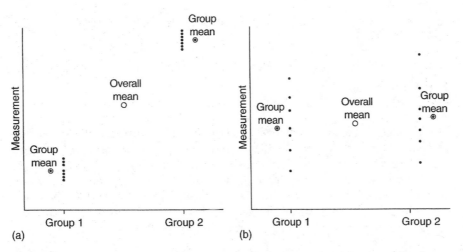

(a)   (b)

Figure 4.4 Two contrasting situations. (a) Most of the variability is caused by the group means being far apart. (b) Most of the variability is caused by differences within the groups.

the actual **variance** or **mean squares** (MS) due to each factor. This is calculated by dividing each sum of squares by the correct number of **degrees of freedom**.

(i)   If there are n groups, the between-group degrees of freedom $DF_B = n - 1$.

(ii) If there are N items in total and r items in each group, there will be $r - 1$ degrees of freedom in each group, hence $n(r - 1)$ in total. The within-group degrees of freedom, $DF_W = N - n$.

(iii) If there are N items in total, the total number of degrees of freedom $DF_T = N - 1$.

(c) The last stage is to calculate the test statistic F. This is the ratio of the between-group mean square MS_B to the within-group mean square MS_W.

$$F = MS_B/MS_W \qquad\qquad (4.9)$$

The larger the value of F, the more likely it is that the means are significantly different.

These calculations tend to be extremely lengthy. Therefore it is best to carry out ANOVA tests on statistical packages such as MINITAB. Simply enter the data from each sample into different columns, go into the Statistics menu, then ANOVA and choose Oneway (separate columns). Finally, select the columns you want to test.

Step 3: Calculate the significance probability
Tables do exist to determine how large F values have to be for different degrees of freedom, but I recommend that you only carry out ANOVA tests using

computer statistics packages. They will automatically calculate the significance probability P.

Step 4: Decide whether to reject the null hypothesis
- If $P < 0.05$ you must reject the null hypothesis.
- If $P > 0.05$ you have no evidence to reject the null hypothesis.

Step 5: Calculate confidence limits and test which groups are different
The problem with the ANOVA test is that though it tells us whether there are differences between groups, it doesn't tell us how big the differences are or even which groups are different. If your ANOVA test is significant, however, you can carry out one of several **post hoc tests**, such as the **Tukey test** or the **least significant difference test**, to answer these questions. Unfortunately, there is not enough space to describe them here.

Example 4.4: Fish data in Figure 4.3

Formulate the null hypothesis
The null hypothesis is that the two groups of fish have the same mean weight.

Calculate the test statistic
MINITAB will come up with the following results:

```
ANALYSIS OF VARIANCE
SOURCE    DF    SS      MS      F       P
BETWEEN   1     24.00   24.00   24.00   0.008
WITHIN    4     4.00    1.00
TOTAL     5     28.00
                                INDIVIDUAL 95 PCT CI'S FOR MEAN
                                BASED ON POOLED STDEV
LEVEL     N     MEAN    STDEV   ---------+---------+---------+-------
Group 1   3     2.000   1.000   (-------*-------)
Group 2   3     6.000   1.000                        (-------*-------)
                                ---------+---------+---------+-------
POOLED STDEV = 1.000                     2.0       4.0       6.0
```

Hence we can see that $F = 24$.

Calculate the significance probability
Here $P = 0.008$. Note that the error bars are not overlapping; this suggests there is likely to be a significant difference.

Decide whether to reject the null hypothesis
In our example $P = 0.008 < 0.05$, so we must reject the null hypothesis. We can say that the two groups of fish have significantly different mean weights.

4.6.4 Problems with names

ANOVA is hard enough to understand anyway. Unfortunately, things are made more difficult because, for historical reasons, there are two synonyms for *between* and *within*:

between = treatment = factor

within = error = residual

You must be able to recognise all of them. Then you can cope with any statistics book or any lecturer!

4.7 Further uses of ANOVA

ANOVA is so counterintuitive and complex that many students are inclined to forget all about it. However, this would be a mistake because it can be used for many other things than just comparing the means of a number of groups. It allows you to carry out and analyse a whole new range of experiments in which you can look at the effect of two or more factors at once:

- You might want to examine the effect on corn yield of adding different amounts of nitrogen and phosphorus.
- You might want to examine the effect on yield of adding different amounts of nitrogen to more than one wheat variety.

In the first case, let's say you grow wheat at two different levels of nitrogen and at two different levels of phosphorus. As long as you grow at all possible combinations of nitrogen and phosphorus levels (so there are $2 \times 2 = 4$ combinations in total), and you have the same number of replicates for each combination, you can analyse such an experiment using what is called **two-way ANOVA**. The yields (t ha^{-1}) from just such an experiment are tabulated here.

No nitrate or phosphate Mean = 1.88, $s = 0.32$, $\overline{SE} = 0.105$	1.4	1.8	2.1	2.4	1.7	1.9	1.5	2.0	2.1
Added nitrate only Mean = 2.80, $s = 0.24$, $\overline{SE} = 0.082$	2.4	2.7	3.1	2.9	2.8	3.0	2.6	3.1	2.6
Added phosphate only Mean = 3.44, $s = 0.40$, $\overline{SE} = 0.132$	3.5	3.2	3.7	2.8	4.0	3.2	3.9	3.6	3.1
Added nitrate and phosphate Mean = 6.88, $s = 0.61$, $\overline{SE} = 0.203$	7.5	6.4	8.1	6.3	7.2	6.8	6.4	6.7	6.5

You can carry out two-way ANOVA using statistical packages such as MINITAB and get results in a table like the ones we have already seen. The results for our yield data are as follows.

```
ANALYSIS OF VARIANCE FOR YIELD
Source          DF        SS        MS        F          P
Nitrogen        1      42.684    42.684    248.65      0.000
Phosphorus      1      71.684    71.684    417.58      0.000
Interaction     1      14.188    14.188     82.65      0.000
Error          32       5.493     0.172
Total          35     134.050
```

Just like the one-way ANOVA we have already looked at, two-way ANOVA partitions the variability and variance. However, there will be not two possible causes of variability but four: the effect of nitrogen; the effect of phosphorus; the **interaction** between the effects of nitrogen and phosphorus; and finally, variation within the groups (here called error).

These possibilities can be used to produce three F ratios, which can answer three questions in just one experiment:

1. Does nitrogen significantly affect yield?
2. Does phosphorus significantly affect yield?
3. Do nitrogen and phosphorus interact?

Here the F ratios are all high and the significance probabilities are low. In this case all three terms are clearly significant. So what does this mean?

1. It is clear from looking at the descriptive statistics that adding nitrogen increases yield (by 0.92 t ha^{-1}).
2. Looking at the descriptive statistics, it is also clear that adding phosphorus increases yield (by 1.56 t ha^{-1}).
3. Looking at the descriptive statistics, you can also tell that adding both nitrogen and phosphorus together increases yield much more than just the sum of the effects of nitrogen and phosphorus alone (by 5.0 t ha^{-1} rather than by just $0.92 + 1.56 = 2.48$ t ha^{-1}). In this case, the significant interaction term shows that the two fertilisers potentiate each other's effects and so act synergistically.

The interaction term would also have been significant if the two fertilisers inhibited each other's effect, causing a reduced yield when added together.

4.8 Self-assessment problems

Problem 4.1

The scores (in percent) of 25 students in a statistics test were as follows.

| 58 | 65 | 62 | 73 | 70 | 42 | 56 | 53 | 59 | 56 | 60 | 64 | 63 |
| 78 | 90 | 31 | 65 | 58 | 59 | 21 | 49 | 51 | 58 | 62 | 56 | |

Calculate the mean, standard deviation and standard error of the mean for these scores. The mean mark of students in finals exams is supposed to be 58%. Perform a one-sample t test to determine whether these students did significantly differently from expected.

Problem 4.2

The masses (in grams) of 16 randomly chosen tomatoes grown in a commercial glasshouse were as follows.

32	56	43	48	39	61	29	45
53	38	42	47	52	44	36	41

Other growers have found that the mean mass of this sort of tomato is 50 g. Perform a one-sample t test to determine whether the mean mass of tomatoes from this glasshouse is different from the expected mass. Give the 95% confidence intervals for the mean mass.

Problem 4.3

Students were tested on their ability to predict how moving bodies behave, both before and after attending a course on Newtonian physics. Their marks are tabulated here. Did attending the course have a significant effect on their test scores, and if so by how much?.

	Before	After
Martha	45	42
Denise	56	50
Betty	32	19
Amanda	76	78
Eunice	65	63
Ivy	52	43
Pamela	60	62
Ethel	87	90
Letitia	49	38
Patricia	59	53

Problem 4.4

The pH of cactus cells was measured at dawn and at dusk using microprobes. The following results were obtained.

Dawn	5.3	5.6	5.2	7.1	4.2	4.9	5.4	5.7	6.3	5.5	5.7	5.6
Dusk	6.7	6.4	7.3	6.2	5.2	5.9	6.2	6.5	7.6	6.4	6.5	

(a) Using a statistical package such as MINITAB, carry out a two-sample *t* test to determine if there is any significant difference in pH between the cells at these times.

(b) The cactus was identifiable and two sets of measurements were carried out on it. So why can't you analyse this experiment using the paired *t* test?

Problem 4.5

An experiment was carried out to investigate the effect of mechanical support on the yield of wheat plants. The masses of seed (in grams) produced by 20 control plants and 20 plants whose stems had been supported throughout their life were as follows.

Control	9.6	10.8	7.6	12.0	14.1	9.5	10.1	11.4	9.1	8.8
	9.2	10.3	10.8	8.3	12.6	11.1	10.4	9.4	11.9	8.6
Supported	10.3	13.2	9.9	10.3	8.1	12.1	7.9	12.4	10.8	9.7
	9.1	8.8	10.7	8.5	7.2	9.7	10.1	11.6	9.9	11.0

Using a statistical package such as MINITAB, carry out a two-sample *t* test to determine whether support has a significant effect on yield.

Problem 4.6

The effect of three different antibiotics on the growth of a bacterium was examined by adding them to Petri dishes, which were then inoculated with the bacteria. The diameter of the colonies (in millimetres) was then measured after three days. A control where no antibiotics were added was also included. The following results were obtained.

Control	4.7	5.3	5.9	4.6	4.9	5.0	5.3	4.2
	5.7	5.3	4.6	5.8	4.7	4.9		
Antibiotic A	4.5	5.6	5.4	4.9	4.8	4.6	5.1	5.3
	5.3	5.8	5.1	6.0	4.4	5.3		
Antibiotic B	4.7	5.2	5.4	4.4	6.1	4.8	5.3	5.5
	4.7	5.2						
Antibiotic C	4.3	5.7	5.3	5.6	4.5	4.9	5.1	5.3
	4.7	6.3	4.8	4.9	5.2	5.4	4.8	5.0

Carry out a one-way ANOVA test on a statistical package to determine whether there is any evidence that the antibiotic treatments affected the growth of the bacteria.

Problem 4.7

Interpret the following ANOVA table. How many groups were being compared? What was the total number of observations? And was there a significant difference between the groups?

	DF	SS	MS	F	P
Factor	4	654	164	1.71	0.35
Residual	25	2386	95		
Total	29	3040			

Problem 4.8

In a second experiment, two different varieties of wheat, Widgeon and Hereward, were grown at three different levels of nitrogen. The following results were obtained.

Widgeon	Nitrates added (kg m^{-2})		
	0	1	2
Yield (t ha^{-1})	4.7	6.4	7.8
	5.3	7.5	7.4
	5.1	6.9	8.3
	6.0	8.1	6.9
	6.5	5.9	6.5
	4.8	7.6	7.2
	5.6	7.1	6.3
	5.8	6.4	7.9
	5.4	8.6	7.7

Hereward	Nitrates added (kg m^{-2})		
	0	1	2
Yield (t ha^{-1})	1.3	6.1	10.8
	2.2	7.2	9.8
	2.1	7.4	11.4
	3.3	8.6	10.6
	1.8	5.7	12.2
	2.4	7.2	9.6
	2.6	6.7	11.1
	2.7	6.9	10.4
	3.1	8.4	10.9

Carrying out two-way ANOVA in MINITAB yielded the following results:

```
ANALYSIS OF VARIANCE FOR YIELD
Source            DF       SS        MS        F        P
nitrogen           2   240.911   120.456   208.65   0.000
variety            1     0.145     0.145     0.25   0.618
nitrogen*variety   2    95.189    47.595    82.44   0.000
Error             48    27.711     0.577
Total             53   363.957
```

(a) Examine the results of the experiment and the ANOVA table. Which of the three possible effects, variety, nitrogen and interaction, are significant?

(b) Examine the original data to work out what these results mean in real terms.

CHAPTER FIVE

Finding associations

An experiment to test whether the more really is the merrier

5.1 Introduction

We saw in the last chapter that one can use a paired *t* test to determine whether two measurements taken on a single group of organisms are different. For instance, one can test whether students have a different heart rate after drinking coffee compared with before. But we may instead want to know if and how the two measurements are **associated**. Do the students who have a higher heart rate before drinking coffee have a higher heart rate afterwards as well? Or we might ask other questions. How are the lengths of snakes related to their age? How is the wing area of birds related to their weight? Or how is the blood pressure of stroke patients related to their heart rate?

This chapter has three sections. First, it shows how to examine data to see whether variables are associated. Second, it describes some of the ways in which biological variables can be related. Finally, despite the inevitable variability, it shows how you can use statistical tests to work out whether there is a real association between the variables, and how to determine what it is.

5.2 Examining data for associations

The first thing you should do if you feel that two variables might be associated is to draw a **scatter plot** of one against the other. This will allow you to see at a glance what is going on. For instance, it is clear from Figure 5.1 that as the age of eggs increases, their mass decreases. But it is important

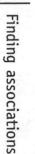

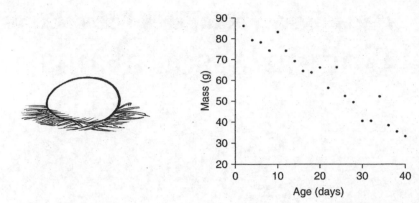

Figure 5.1 The relationship between the age of eggs and their mass. Note that the dependent variable, mass, is plotted along the vertical axis.

to make sure you plot the graph the correct way round. This depends on how the variables affect each other. One of the variables is called the independent variable; the other variable is called the dependent variable. The independent variable affects, or may affect, the dependent variable but is not itself affected. Plot the **independent variable** along the horizontal axis, often called the x-axis. Plot the **dependent variable** along the vertical axis, often called the y-axis. You would then say you were plotting the dependent variable against the independent variable. In Figure 5.1, age is the independent variable and mass is the dependent variable. This is because age can affect an egg's mass, but mass can't affect an egg's age.

Things are not always so clear-cut. It is virtually impossible to tell whether blood pressure would affect heart rate or vice versa. They are probably both affected by a third variable – artery stiffness. In this case, it does not really matter which way round you plot the data.

5.3 Examining graphs

Once you have plotted your graph, you should examine it for associations. There are several main ways in which variables can be related:

- There may be no relationship: points are scattered all over the graph paper (Figure 5.2a).
- There may be a positive association (Figure 5.2b): the dependent variable increases as the independent variable increases.
- There may be a negative association (Figure 5.2c): the dependent variable decreases as the independent variable increases.
- There may be a more complex relationship: Figure 5.2d shows a relationship in which the dependent variable rises and falls as the independent variable increases.

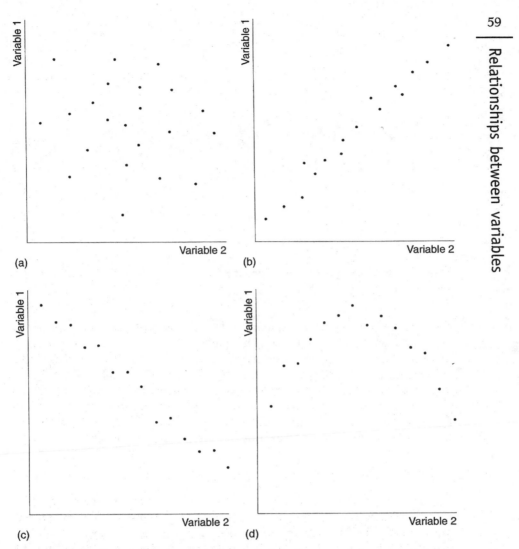

Figure 5.2 Ways in which variables can be related. (a) No association. (b) Positive association. (c) Negative association. (d) A complex curvilinear association.

5.4 Relationships between variables

There are an infinite number of ways in which two variables can be related. However, most are complex. Perhaps the simplest relationships to describe are linear relationships such as the one shown in Figure 5.3. In these cases, the dependent variable y is related to the independent variable x by the general equation

$$y = a + bx \tag{5.1}$$

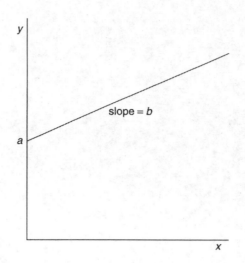

Figure 5.3 A straight line relationship. The straight line $y = a + bx$ has y-intercept a and slope b.

where b is the **slope** of the line and a is the **intercept**. The intercept is the value of y where the line crosses the y-axis.

Linear relationships are important because they are by far the easiest to analyse statistically. When biologists test whether two variables are related, they are usually testing whether they are linearly related. Fortunately, linear relationships between variables are surprisingly common in biology. Many other common relationships between variables can also be converted into linear relationships by **transforming** the data using logarithms.

5.4.1 Scaling and power relationships

If you examine organisms of different size, many of their characteristics scale according to **power relationships**. If an organism changes in size by a given ratio, some characteristic will increase or decrease by, the square, cube or some other power of that ratio. For instance, the mass of unicellular algae would be expected to rise with the cube of their diameter; and the metabolic rate of mammals rises with mass to the power of around 0.75. Other physical processes are also related in this way. The lift produced by a bird's wings should rise with the square of the flight speed.

In these sorts of relationships, the dependent variable y is related to the independent variable x by the general equation

$$y = ax^b \tag{5.2}$$

Looking at the curves produced by this sort of relationship (Figure 5.4a), it is very difficult to determine the values of a and b. However, it is possible, by using some clever mathematical tricks, to produce a straight line graph from which a and b can be easily calculated. The first thing to do is to take logarithms of both sides of the equation. We have $y = ax^b$, so

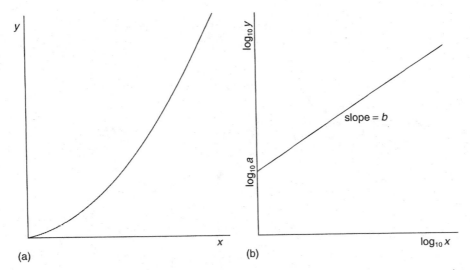
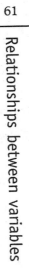

(a)   (b)

Figure 5.4 How to describe a power relationship. The curvilinear relationship $y = ax^b$ (a) can be converted to a straight line (b) by taking logarithms ($\log_{10}$) of both x and y. The graph has y-intercept $\log_{10} a$ and slope b.

$$\log_{10} y = \log_{10}(ax^b) \tag{5.3}$$

Now logarithms have two important properties:

$$\log_{10}(c \times d) = \log_{10} c + \log_{10} d \tag{5.4}$$

$$\log_{10}(c^d) = d \times \log_{10} c \tag{5.5}$$

Using these properties we can rearrange the equation to show that

$$\log_{10} y = \log_{10} a + b \log_{10} x \tag{5.6}$$

Therefore plotting $\log_{10} y$ against $\log_{10} x$ (Figure 5.4b) will produce a straight line with slope b and intercept $\log_{10} a$.

5.4.2 Exponential growth and decay

Other biological phenomena have an **exponential relationship** with time. In these cases, when a given period of time elapses, some characteristic increases or decreases by a certain ratio. For instance, bacterial colonies demonstrate exponential growth, doubling in number every few hours. In contrast, radio-activity shows exponential decay, halving over a given period. Other physical processes are also related in this way. Rates of reaction, indeed the metabolic rates of whole organisms, increase exponentially with temperature.

In these sorts of relationship the dependent variable y can be related to the independent variable x by the general equation

$$y = ae^{bx} \tag{5.7}$$

where e is the base of natural logarithms ($e = 2.718$), which we met in Section 2.9.2. Looking at the curve produced by this sort of relationship (Figure 5.5a),

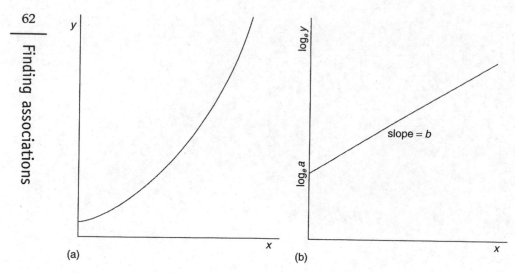

Figure 5.5 How to describe an exponential relationship. The curvilinear relationship $y = ae^{bx}$ (a) can be converted to a straight line (b) by taking natural logarithms ($\log_e$) of y. The graph has y-intercept $\log_e a$ and slope b.

it is very difficult to determine the values of a and b, just as it was with power relationships. However, we can again use some clever mathematical tricks to produce a straight line graph. As before, the first thing to do is to take logarithms of both sides of the equation. Therefore

$$\log_e y = \log_e(ae^{bx}) \tag{5.8}$$

and rearranging

$$\log_e y = \log_e a + bx \tag{5.9}$$

Therefore plotting $\log_e y$ against x (Figure 5.5b) will produce a straight line with slope b and y-intercept $\log_e a$.

5.5 Statistical tests for associations

The points on your plots will never exactly follow a straight line, or indeed any exact mathematical function, because of the variability which is inherent in biology. There will always be some scatter away from a line. The difficulty in determining whether two measurements are really associated is that when you were taking a sample you might have chosen points which followed a straight line even if there was no association in the population. If there appears only to be a slight association and if there are only a few points, this is quite likely. In contrast it is very unlikely that you would choose large numbers of points all along a straight line just by chance if there was no real relationship. Therefore you have to carry out statistical tests to work out the probability you could get your apparent association by chance. If there is an association, you can then work out what it is. This involves testing hypotheses and finding confidence limits. Testing for associations uses the same counterintuitive statistical logic we met in the last chapter. There are two main tests for association: correlation and regression.

5.6 Correlation

5.6.1 Purpose

To test whether two sets of measurements taken on a single population are linearly associated.

5.6.2 The rationale behind correlation

Correlation analysis examines the extent to which two sets of measurements show positive or negative association. The basic idea is that if there is positive association, all points will either be above and to the right or below and to the left of the distribution's centre (Figure 5.6a). If there is negative

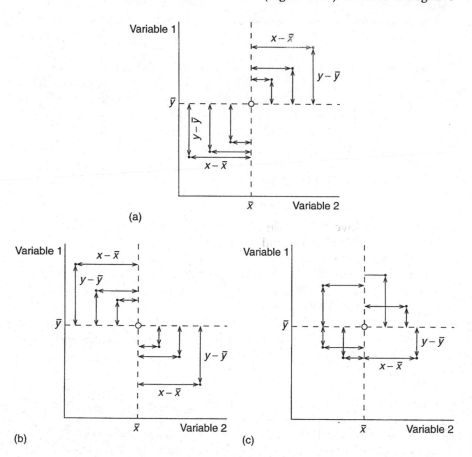

Figure 5.6 Correlation. (a) Positive correlation: $\Sigma(x - \bar{x})(y - \bar{y})$ is large and positive. (b) Negative correlation: $\Sigma(x - \bar{x})(y - \bar{y})$ is large and negative. (c) No correlation: $\Sigma(x - \bar{x})(y - \bar{y})$ is small.

association, all points will be above and to the left or below and to the right of the distribution's centre (Figure 5.6b). If there is no association, the points will be scattered on all sides (Figure 5.6c).

5.6.3 Carrying out the test

Correlation analysis follows all four of the usual steps of statistical tests.

Step 1: Formulate the null hypothesis
In correlation, the null hypothesis is that there is no association between the two measurements, i.e. they show random scatter.

Step 2: Calculate the test statistic
The test statistic for correlation is the correlation coefficient r. It is calculated in three stages.

Stage 1
Calculate the means of the two sets of measurements, $\bar{x}$ and $\bar{y}$.

Stage 2
For each point, calculate the product of its x and y distances from the mean $(x - \bar{x})(y - \bar{y})$. Note that if both x and y are greater than the mean, this figure will be positive because both $(x - \bar{x})$ and $(y - \bar{y})$ will be positive. It will also be positive if both x and y are smaller than the mean, because both $(x - \bar{x})$ and $(y - \bar{y})$ will be negative and their product will be positive. However, if one is larger than the mean and the other smaller, the product will be negative.

These points are added together to give

$$\text{Sum} = \Sigma(x - \bar{x})(y - \bar{y})$$

- If there is positive association (Figure 5.6a), with points all either above and to the right or below and to the left of the overall mean, the sum will be large and positive.
- If there is negative association (Figure 5.6b), with points all either above and to the left or below and to the right of the overall mean, the sum will be large and negative.
- If there is no association (Figure 5.6c), points will be on all sides of the overall mean, and the positive and negative numbers will cancel each other out. The sum will therefore be small.

Stage 3
Scale the sum obtained in stage 2 by dividing it by the product of the variation within each of the measurements. The correlation coefficient r is therefore given by the formula

$$r = \frac{\Sigma(x - \bar{x})(y - \bar{y})}{[\Sigma(x - \bar{x})^2 \Sigma(y - \bar{y})^2]^{1/2}} \tag{5.10}$$

The correlation coefficient can vary from −1 (perfect negative correlation) through 0 (no correlation) up to a value of 1 (perfect positive correlation). The calculation is somewhat involved, so it is recommended that you carry out correlation analysis on a computer package such as MINITAB. Simply put your data into two columns; from the Statistics menu choose Basic Statistics and then Correlation. Finally, select the two columns and run the test.

Step 3: Calculate the significance probability

You must calculate the probability P that the absolute value of the correlation coefficient $|r|$ would be equal to or greater than a critical value if the null hypothesis were true. The larger the value of $|r|$ and the larger the sample, the less likely this will be. Critical values of $|r|$ required for P to fall below 0.05, and hence for the association to be significant, are given for a range of degrees of freedom in Table S2.

Since MINITAB does not calculate P, you must look up in Table S2 (at the end of the book) the critical value of r for $(N-2)$ degrees of freedom, where N is the number of pairs of observations.

Step 4: Decide whether to reject the null hypothesis

- If $|r|$ is greater than the critical value, you must reject the null hypothesis. You can say that the two variables show significant correlation.
- If $|r|$ is less than the critical value, you cannot reject the null hypothesis. There is no evidence of a linear association between the two variables.

Example 5.1

In an investigation of the cardiovascular health of elderly patients, the heart rate and blood pressure of 30 patients were taken. The following results were obtained. Is there any association between the variables?

Patient	Heart rate (min⁻¹)	Blood pressure (mm Hg)
1	67	179
2	75	197
3	63	175
4	89	209
5	53	164
6	76	180
7	98	212
8	75	187
9	71	189
10	65	176
11	69	167
12	74	186
13	80	198

Patient	Heart rate (min⁻¹)	Blood pressure (mm Hg)
14	58	170
15	76	187
16	68	175
17	64	169
18	76	190
19	79	176
20	72	168
21	60	158
22	67	160
23	63	167
24	90	221
25	50	149
26	73	180
27	64	168
28	68	162
29	65	168
30	70	157

Solution

Formulate the null hypothesis
The null hypothesis is that blood pressure and heart rate are not associated.

Calculate the test statistic
MINITAB comes up with the following output:

```
Correlation of Heart Rate and Blood Pressure = 0.866
```

Calculate the significance probability
Looking up r in Table S2 (at the end of the book), the critical value that r must exceed at $30 - 2 = 28$ degrees of freedom is about 0.381.

Decide whether to reject the null hypothesis
We have $|r| = 0.866 > 0.381$. Therefore we must reject the null hypothesis. We can say that heart rate and blood pressure show a significant positive association.

5.6.4 Uses of the correlation coefficient

Correlation is a useful technique since it tells you whether two measurements are associated, and it can be used even if neither of the variables is independent of the other. However, the results of correlation analysis need to be treated with caution for three reasons:

- Correlation only finds linear associations between measurements, so a non-significant correlation does not prove there is no association between the variables.
- A significant correlation does not imply a **causal relationship** between the two measurements.
- The size of the correlation coefficient does not reflect the slope of the relationship between the two measurements, it just reflects how close the association is. If you want to determine the nature of the linear relationship between two sets of measurements, you need to carry out regression analysis. However, this is only valid if one of the variables is obviously independent of the other and so is plotted along the x-axis of your graph.

5.7 Regression

5.7.1 Purpose

To quantify the linear relationship between two sets of measurements taken on a single population.

5.7.2 Rationale

Regression analysis finds an estimate of the line of best fit $y = \bar{a} + \bar{b}x$ through the scattered points on your graph. If you measure the vertical distance of each point from the regression line (Figure 5.7a), the line of best fit is the one which minimises the sum of the squares of the distances.

The estimate of the slope $\bar{b}$ is actually worked out in a similar way to the correlation coefficient, using the formula

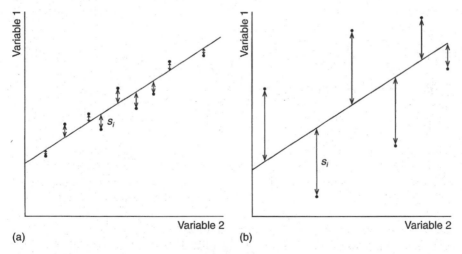

(a) (b)

Figure 5.7 Regression. The line of best fit minimises the variability Σs_i^2 from the line. (a) Significant regression: Σs_i^2 is low. (b) Non-significant regression: Σs_i^2 is high.

$$\bar{b} = \frac{\Sigma(x - \bar{x})(y - \bar{y})}{\Sigma(x - \bar{x})^2} \qquad (5.11)$$

Since the line of best fit always passes through the means of x and y, $\bar{x}$ and $\bar{y}$, the estimate of the constant $\bar{a}$ can then be found by substituting them into the equation to give

$$\bar{a} = \bar{y} - \bar{b}\bar{x} \qquad (5.12)$$

This is all very well, but data with very different degrees of scatter, such as those shown in Figure 5.7, can have identical regression lines. In Figure 5.7a there is clearly a linear relationship. However, in Figure 5.7b there may actually be no relationship between the variables; you might have chosen a sample that suggests there is a relationship just by chance.

In order to test whether there is really a relationship, therefore, you would have to carry out one or more statistical tests. You could do this yourself, but the calculations needed are a bit long and complex, so it is much better now to use a computer package. MINITAB not only calculates the regression equation but also performs two statistical tests and gives you the information you need to carry out a whole range of other tests:

- It works out the **standard deviation** of $\bar{a}$ and $\bar{b}$ and uses them to carry out two separate **t tests** to determine whether they are significantly different from zero. The data can also be used to calculate 95% confidence intervals for a and b.
- It carries out an **ANOVA** test, which essentially compares the amount of variation explained by the regression line with that due to the scatter of the points away from the regression line. This tells you whether there is a significant slope, e.g. if $\bar{b}$ is significantly different from zero.
- It also tells you the percentage of the total variation which the regression line explains. This r^2 value is equal to the square of the correlation coefficient.

5.7.3 Carrying out the test

Step 1: Formulate the null hypotheses
The null hypotheses MINITAB tests are (i) y does not depend on x, so the true slope of the line is zero ($b = 0$); and (ii) the intercept is zero ($a = 0$).

Step 2: Calculate the test statistics
In MINITAB first enter your data into two columns. Then choose Regression from the Statistics menu. Put the dependent variable into the response box and the independent variable into the predictor box. Run the test.

Step 3: Calculate the significance probability
The next thing to read off is the probability P that absolute values of the test statistics would be equal to or greater than t and F respectively if the null hypotheses were true.

Step 4: Decide whether to reject the null hypothesis

- If $P < 0.05$ you should reject the null hypothesis. Therefore you can say that the slope (or intercept) is significantly different from zero.
- If $P > 0.05$ you have no evidence to reject the null hypothesis. Therefore you can say that the slope (or intercept) is not significantly different from zero.

Step 5: Calculate confidence limits

To work out how different the slope is from zero, we must work out 95% confidence limits for the slope b. These are calculated in just the same way as we calculated 95% confidence limits for means in Chapter 4:

$$95\% \ \text{CI(slope)} = \bar{b} \pm (t_{(N-2)}(5\%) \times \overline{\text{SD}} \ \text{of slope}) \qquad (5.13)$$

Here $t_{(N-2)}$ is the critical t value for $(N-2)$ degrees of freedom, where N is the number of data points. Confidence limits can also be calculated for the intercept.

Example 5.2

In a survey to investigate the way in which chicken eggs lose weight after they are laid, one egg was collected newly laid every 2 days. Each egg was put into an incubator, and after 40 days all 20 eggs were weighed. The results are tabulated here and plotted in Figure 5.1. Carry out a regression analysis to determine whether age significantly affects egg weight. If there is a relationship, determine what it is.

Age (days)	2	4	6	8	10	12	14	16	18	20	22
Mass (g)	87	80	79	75	84	75	70	65	64	67	57

Age (days)	24	26	28	30	32	34	36	38	40
Mass (g)	67	53	50	41	41	53	39	36	34

Solution

Formulate the null hypothesis

The null hypothesis is that age has no effect on egg weight. In other words, the slope of the regression line is zero.

Calculate the test statistic

Carrying out the test in MINITAB yields the following output:

```
THE REGRESSION EQUATION IS
Mass = 89.4 - 1.36 Age
Predictor        Coef         Stdev         t ratio          P
Constant        89.437        2.279          39.24       0.000
Age            -1.36128       0.09514       -14.31       0.000
s = 4.907            R-sq = 91.9%         R-sq(adj) = 91.5%
```

ANALYSIS OF VARIANCE

SOURCE	DF	SS	MS	F	P
Regression	1	4929.2	4929.2	204.74	0.000
Error	18	433.4	24.1		
Total	19	5362.6			

The slope of the regression equation is −1.36, which appears to be well below zero. But is this difference significant? Looking at the probabilities that the slope is zero, we have to look at the t ratio for age and the F value for the analysis of variance table. Here $t = -14.31$ and $F = 204.74$ (note that $F = t^2$).

Calculate the significance probability

Looking at the t and F probabilities, both equal 0.000.

Decide whether to accept or reject the null hypothesis

We have $P = 0.000 < 0.05$. Therefore we must reject the null hypothesis. We can say that age has a significant effect on egg weight; in fact older eggs are lighter.

Calculate confidence limits

We need to look up the critical values for t for $20 - 2 = 18$ degrees of freedom in Table S1. Using equation (5.13)

$$95\% \text{ CI(slope)} = -1.36 \pm (t_{18}(5\%) \times 0.09514)$$

$$95\% \text{ CI(slope)} = -1.36 \pm (2.101 \times 0.09514)$$

$$= -1.56 \text{ to } -1.16$$

5.7.4 Other tests on regression data

The t tests worked out by the computer investigate whether the slope and constant are different from zero. The value of t is simply given by the expression

$$t = \frac{\text{Observed value} - 0}{\text{Standard deviation}} \qquad (5.14)$$

However, it is also possible from MINITAB output to carry out a whole range of t tests to determine whether the slope or constant are different from any expected value. Then t is simply given by the expression

$$t = \frac{\text{Observed value} - \text{Expected value}}{\text{Standard deviation}} \qquad (5.15)$$

and you can carry out the t test for $N - 2$ degrees of freedom just as the computer did to determine whether the slope or constant were different from zero.

Example 5.3

From the egg weight data in Example 5.2, we want to determine whether the initial egg weight was significantly different from 90 g, which is the mean figure for the general population. In other words, we must test whether the intercept (or constant as MINITAB calls it) is different from 90.

Solution

Formulate the null hypothesis
The null hypothesis is that the constant is equal to 90.

Calculate the test statistic
The necessary data can be extracted from the MINITAB output in Example 5.2 (see p. 69). This shows that the estimate of the intercept = 89.437 and its standard deviation = 2.279. Therefore if the expected value = 90, the test statistic is

$$t = \frac{89.437 - 90}{2.279}$$

$$= -0.247$$

Calculate the significance probability
Here $|t|$ must be compared with the critical value for $20 - 2 = 18$ degrees of freedom. This is 2.101.

Decide whether to reject the null hypothesis
We have $|t| = 0.247 < 2.101$. Hence there is no evidence to reject the null hypothesis. We can say that initial egg mass is not significantly different from 90 g.

5.7.4 Validity

You must be careful to use regression appropriately; there are many cases where it is not valid:

- Regression is not valid for data in which there is no independent variable. For example, you should not regress heart rate against blood pressure, because each factor could affect the other.
- All your measurements must be independent. Therefore you should not use regression to analyse repeated measures, such as the height of a single plant at different times.

5.8 Self-assessment problems

Problem 5.1

Which way round would you plot the following data?

(a) Cell number of an embryo and time since fertilisation
(b) Pecking order of hens and of their chicks
(c) Height and body weight of women
(d) Length and breadth of limpets

Problem 5.2

(a) The logarithms of the wing area A of birds and their body length L are found to be related by the straight line relationship $\log_{10} A = 0.3 + 2.36 \log_{10} L$. What is the relationship between A and L?
(b) The natural logarithm of the numbers of cells N in a bacterial colony is related to time T by the equation $\log_e N = 2.3 + 0.1T$. What is the relationship between N and T?

Problem 5.3

A study of the density of stomata in vine leaves of different areas came up with the following results. Calculate the correlation coefficient r between these two variables and determine whether this is a significant correlation. What can you say about the relationship between leaf area and stomatal density?

Leaf area (mm²)	45	56	69	32	18	38	48	26	60	51
Stomatal density (mm⁻²)	36	28	27	39	56	37	32	45	24	31

Problem 5.4

In a survey to investigate why bones become more brittle in older women, the density of bone material was measured in 24 post-menopausal women of contrasting ages. Bone density is given as a percentage of the average density in young women.

Age (years)	43	49	56	58	61	63	64	66	68	70	72	73
Relative bone density	108	85	92	90	84	83	73	79	80	76	69	71

Age (years)	74	74	76	78	80	83	85	87	89	92	95	98
Relative bone density	65	64	67	58	50	61	59	53	43	52	49	42

(a) Plot the data.
(b) Using a statistics package, carry out a regression analysis to determine the relationship between age and bone density. Does bone density change significantly with age?
(c) Calculate the expected bone density of women of age 70.

Problem 5.5

In an experiment to examine the ability of the polychaete worm *Nereis diversicolor* to withstand zinc pollution, worms were grown in solutions containing different concentrations of zinc and their internal zinc concentration was measured. The following results were obtained.

$\log_{10}[Zn]_{water}$	1.96	2.27	2.46	2.65	2.86	2.92	3.01	3.24	3.37	3.49
$\log_{10}[Zn]_{worm}$	2.18	2.23	2.22	2.27	2.25	2.30	2.31	2.34	2.36	2.35

(a) Plot the data.
(b) Using a statistics package, carry out a regression analysis to determine how zinc in the solution affects the concentration within the worm. If *Nereis* did not actively control its level of zinc, the concentrations inside and outside would be equal and the slope of the regression line would be 1. Work out the *t* value which compares a slope of 1 with the slope of the line you obtained, hence determine whether *Nereis* actively controls its zinc level.

Problem 5.6

A study of the effect of seeding rate on the yield of wheat gave the following results.

Seeding rate (m^{-2})	50	80	100	150	200	300	400	500	600	800
Yield (tonnes)	2.5	3.9	4.7	5.3	5.6	5.9	5.4	5.2	4.6	3.2

(a) Plot a graph of yield against seeding rate.
(b) Using a statistics package, carry out regression analysis to determine whether there is a linear relationship between seeding rate and yield.
(c) What can you say about the relationship between seeding rate and yield?

Problem 5.7

An investigation was carried out into the scaling of heads in worker army ants. Body length and jaw width were measured in 20 workers of contrasting size. The following results were obtained.

Length (mm)	3.2	3.6	4.2	4.3	4.6	5.0	5.2	5.3	5.5	5.5
Jaw width (mm)	0.23	0.29	0.32	0.38	0.45	0.44	0.55	0.43	0.60	0.58

Length (mm)	5.7	6.2	6.6	6.9	7.4	7.6	8.5	9.2	9.7	9.9
Jaw width (mm)	0.62	0.73	0.74	0.88	0.83	0.93	1.03	1.15	1.09	1.25

(a) Convert the data to logarithms ($\log_{10}$) and plot them.
(b) Using a statistics package, carry out regression analysis to investigate the relationship between $\log_{10}$(length) and $\log_{10}$(jaw width). Convert this equation back to real numbers.
(c) Perform a t test on the slope of the regression line to determine whether it is different from 1. Do the jaws of the ants remain the same relative size, or do they get significantly smaller or larger in bigger ants?

CHAPTER SIX

Dealing with categorical data

Among professors there are significantly more goats than expected

6.1 Introduction

Often in biology you do not take **measurements** on organisms or other items, but classify them into different **categories**. For instance, birds belong to different species and have different colours; habitats (and Petri dishes) can have particular species present or absent; and people can be healthy or diseased. You cannot sensibly assign numbers to such arbitrarily defined classes; green is not larger in any real sense than yellow! For this reason you cannot use any of the statistical tests we examined in Chapters 4 and 5, which look for differences or associations between measurements.

Instead, this categorical data is best quantified by counting the numbers of observations in the different categories. This will allow you to estimate the **frequency** with which each character state turns up. This data can then be used to answer one of two questions:

- We might want to know whether the character frequencies in a single group are different from expected values. Do rats in a maze turn to the right rather than left at a different frequency from the expected 1 : 1? Or is the frequency of rickets different in a small mining town from that in the general population?
- We might want to know whether the character frequencies in two or more groups are different from each other. In other words, are certain characteristics associated with each other? For example, is smoking more common in men than women? Or do different insect species preferentially visit different species of flower?

6.2 The problem of variation

At first glance it might seem easy to tell whether character frequencies are different. When looking at a sample of sheep, if we found that eight were black and six white, we might conclude that black ones were commoner than white. Unfortunately, there might easily have been the same number of black and white sheep in the population and we might just have picked more black ones by chance.

A character state is, in fact, unlikely to appear at exactly the same frequency in a small sample as in the whole population. Let's examine what happens when we take samples of a population of animals, 50% of which are white and 50% black. In a sample of 2 there is only a 50% chance of getting a 1 : 1 ratio; the other times both animals would be either black or white. With 4 animals there will be a 1 : 1 ratio only 6 times out of 16; there will be a 3 : 1 or 1 : 3 ratio 4 times out of 16 and a 4 : 0 or 0 : 4 ratio once every 16 times.

As the number of animals in the sample increases, the most likely frequencies are those closer and closer to 1 : 1, but the frequency will hardly ever equal 1 : 1 exactly. In fact the probability distribution will follow an increasingly tight **binomial distribution** (Figure 6.1) with **mean** $\bar{x}$ equal to

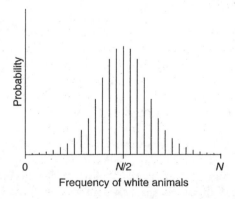

Figure 6.1 Binomial distribution. Probabilities of choosing different numbers of white animals in a sample of size N from a population with 50% white animals.

$N/2$, where N is the sample size and **standard deviation** s equal to $\sqrt{x}$. The probability that the ratio is near $1:1$ increases, and the chances of it being further away decreases. However, there is always a finite, if increasingly tiny, chance of getting all white animals.

Things get more complex if the expected frequencies are different from $1:1$ and if there are a larger number of categories, but essentially the same pattern will occur: as the sample size increases, the frequencies will tend to approach, but seldom equal, the frequencies in the population. The probability of obtaining frequencies similar to that of the population rises, but there is still a finite probability of the frequencies being very different.

So if the results from a sample are different from the expected frequency, you cannot be sure this is because the population you are sampling is really different. Even if you sampled 100 animals and all were white, the population still might have contained a ratio of $1:1$; you might just have been very unlucky. However, the greater the difference and the larger the sample, the less likely this becomes. To determine whether differences from an expected frequency are likely to be real, you must use the final statistical test we will introduce, the **chi-squared test**. There are two main types of chi-squared (χ^2) test:

- The χ^2 test for differences
- The χ^2 test for association

6.3 The χ^2 test for differences

6.3.1 Purpose

To test whether character frequencies are different from expected values. It is best used when you expect numbers in different groups to be in particular ratios. Here are some examples:

- Experiments in Mendelian genetics
- Maze or choice chamber experiments
- Examining sex ratios
- Comparing your results with figures from the literature

6.3.2 Rationale

The test calculates the chi-squared statistic (χ^2); this is a measure of the difference between the observed frequencies and the expected frequencies. The larger χ^2, the less likely the results could have been obtained by chance if the population frequency was the expected one.

6.3.3 Carrying out the test

Steep 1: Formulate the null hypothesis
The null hypothesis is that the frequencies of the different categories in the population are equal to the expected frequencies.

Step 2: Calculate the test statistic

The χ^2 statistic is a measure of how far your observed frequencies are from the expected frequencies. It is given by the simple expression

$$\chi^2 = \sum \frac{(O-E)^2}{E} \tag{6.1}$$

where O is the observed frequency and E is the expected frequency for each character state. The larger the difference between the frequencies, the larger the value of χ^2 and the less likely it is that observed and expected frequencies are different just by chance. Similarly, the bigger the sample, the larger O and E, hence the larger the value of χ^2; this is because of the squared term in the top half of the fraction. So the bigger the sample you take, the more likely you will be to detect any differences.

The greater the number of possible categories, the greater the degrees of freedom; this also tends to increase χ^2. The distribution of χ^2 has been worked out for a range of degrees of freedom, and Table S3 (at the end of the book) gives the critical values of χ^2 above which there is less than a 5%, 1% or 0.1% probability of getting the observed values by chance. You cannot carry out this test in MINITAB.

Step 3: Calculate the significance probability

You must calculate the probability P of obtaining χ^2 values equal to or greater than the observed values if the null hypothesis were true. To do this you look up in Table S3 (at the end of the book) the critical value that χ^2 must exceed at $(N-1)$ degrees of freedom, where N is the number of groups, for the probability to be less than 5%.

Step 4: Decide whether to reject the null hypothesis

- If χ^2 is greater than the critical value, you must reject the null hypothesis. You can say that the distribution is significantly different from expected.
- If χ^2 is less than the critical value, you cannot reject the null hypothesis. You have found no significant difference from the expected distribution.

Example 6.1

We will examine an example from Mendelian genetics in which F1 hybrids of smooth and wrinkled peas are crossed together. The following results were obtained:

Number of smooth peas = 69

Number of wrinkled peas = 31

We will test whether the ratio of smooth to wrinkled peas in the 100 progeny is different from the 3 : 1 ratio predicted by Mendelian genetics.

Formulate the null hypothesis

The null hypothesis is that the ratio smooth : wrinkled is 3 : 1.

Calculate the test statistic

The first thing to do is to calculate the expected values. Here 3/4 should be smooth and 1/4 wrinkled. Since there are 100 progeny,

$$\text{Expected number of smooth} = (3 \times 100)/4 = 75$$

$$\text{Expected number of wrinkled} = (1 \times 100)/4 = 25$$

So we have

$$\chi^2 = \sum \frac{(O - E)^2}{E}$$

$$\chi^2 = \frac{(69 - 75)^2}{75} + \frac{(31 - 25)^2}{25}$$

$$\chi^2 = 36/75 + 36/25 = 0.48 + 1.44 = 1.92$$

Calculate the significance probability

Looking up in Table S3 (at the end of the book) the value of χ^2 for $2 - 1 = 1$ degree of freedom, we find that χ^2 must be greater than 3.84.

Decide whether to reject the null hypothesis

We have $\chi^2 = 1.92 < 3.84$, so we have no evidence to reject the null hypothesis. The relative frequencies of smooth and wrinkled peas are not significantly different from the expected 3 : 1 ratio.

6.4 The χ^2 test for association

6.4.1 Purpose

To test whether the character frequencies of two or more groups are different from each other. In other words, to test whether character states are associated in some way. It is used when there is no expected frequency. Here are some examples:

- Ecological surveys: are different species found in different habitats?
- Medical surveys: are infection rates different for people in different blood groups?
- Sociological surveys: do men and women have a different probability of smoking?

6.4.2 Rationale

The test investigates whether the distribution is different from what it would be if the character states were distributed randomly among the population.

6.4.3 Carrying out the test

Just like the test for differences, this test follows all four of the usual steps of statistical tests.

We will examine an example from a sociological study which found that out of 30 men, 18 were smokers and 12 non-smokers, while of the 60 women surveyed, 12 were smokers and 48 were non-smokers. We will test whether the rates of smoking are significantly different between the sexes.

Step 1: Formulate the null hypothesis

The null hypothesis is that there is no difference between the frequencies of the groups, hence no association between the character states.

Step 2: Calculate the test statistic

Using a calculator

This is a complex process because before we can calculate χ^2 we must first calculate the expected values for each character state if there had been no association. The first stage is to arrange the data in a **contingency table**.

	Smoking	Non-smoking	Total
Men	18	12	30
Women	12	48	60
Total	30	60	90

It is now straightforward to calculate the frequencies if there had been no association between smoking and gender. Of the total number of people examined, one-third (30) were men, and one-third (30) of all people smoked. Therefore if the same proportion of men smoked as in the general population, you would expect one-third of all men (10) to be smokers. Hence 20 men should be non-smokers. Similarly, of the 60 women only one-third (20) should be smokers and 40 should be non-smokers.

A general expression for the expected number E in each cell of the contingency table is given by

$$E = \frac{\text{Column total} \times \text{Row total}}{\text{Grand total}} \qquad (6.2)$$

where the grand total is the total number of observations (here 90). Therefore, the expected value for male smokers is found by multiplying its row total (30) by the column total (30) and dividing by 90, to give 10. These expected values are then put into the contingency table, written in parentheses. It is now straightforward to calculate χ^2 using equation (6.1).

	Smoking	Non-smoking	Total
Men	18 (10)	12 (20)	30
Women	12 (20)	48 (40)	60
Total	30	60	90

MINITAB can perform this whole process in an instant. Simply enter the observed frequencies into columns. From the Statistics menu choose Tables and then Chisquare Test. Enter the columns to be tested and run the test.

Step 3: Calculate the significance probability

To do this you look up the value that χ^2 must exceed at $(R-1) \times (C-1)$ degrees of freedom, where R is the number of rows in the table and C is the number of columns, for the probability to be less than 5%.

Step 4: Decide whether to reject the null hypothesis

- If χ^2 is greater than the critical value, you must reject the null hypothesis. You can say that the distribution is significantly different from expected, hence there is a significant association between the characters.
- If χ^2 is less than the critical value, you cannot reject the null hypothesis. You have found no significant difference from the expected distribution, hence no evidence of an association between the characters.

Example 6.2: Smoking data of Section 6.4.3

Formulate the null hypothesis

The null hypothesis is that men and women smoke with equal frequency. Therefore smoking is not associated with a particular sex.

Calculate the test statistic

MINITAB will produce the following output. Expected counts are printed below observed counts. Some versions of MINITAB also calculate P.

```
                Men              Women            Total
    1           18               12               30
                10.00            20.00
    2           12               48               60
                20.00            40.00
Total           30               60               90
ChiSq = 6.400 + 3.200 + 3.200 + 1.600 = 14.400
df = 1
```

Calculate the significance probability

Looking up in Table S3 (at the end of the book) the value of χ^2 for $(2-1) \times (2-1) = 1$ degree of freedom, we find that χ^2 must be greater than 3.84.

Decide whether to reject the null hypothesis

We have $\chi^2 = 14.4 > 3.84$, so we have strong evidence to reject the null hypothesis. We can say there is a significant association between sex and smoking. In other words, the two sexes are different in the frequency with which they smoke. In fact men smoke more than women.

You can tell even more about your results by looking at the χ^2 values for each of the cells. The larger the value, the more the results for the cell differ from the expected results. In this example χ^2 for male smokers is by far the largest at 6.4. Therefore we can say that in particular more men smoke than one would expect.

6.5 Validity of χ^2 tests

We have seen that the bigger the number of observations, the more likely you are to be able to detect differences or associations with the χ^2 test. In fact χ^2 tests are only valid if all expected values are larger than 5. If any expected values are lower than 5, there are two possibilities:

- You could combine data from two or more groups, but only if this makes biological sense. For instance, different species of fly could be combined in Problem 6.4 because flies have more in common with each other than with the other insects studied.
- If there is no sensible reason for combining data, small groups should be left out of the analysis.

6.6 Self-assessment problems

Problem 6.1

In an experiment to test the reactions of mice to a potential pheromone, they were run down a T-junction maze; the pheromone was released in one of the arms of the T. After the first 10 trials, 3 mice had turned towards the scent and 7 had turned away. After 100 trials, 34 had turned towards the scent and 66 had turned away. Is there any evidence of a reaction to the scent?

(a) After 10 trials
(b) After 100 trials

Problem 6.2

A cross was carried out between peas which were heterozygous in the two characters: height (tall H or short h) and pea colour (green G or yellow g). The following offspring were obtained.

	Number
Tall plants, green peas	87
Tall plants, yellow peas	34
Short plants, green peas	28
Short plants, yellow peas	11

For unlinked genes the expected ratios of each sort of plant are 9 : 3 : 3 : 1. Carry out a chi-squared test to determine whether there is any evidence of gene linkage between these characters.

Problem 6.3

A study of the incidence of a childhood illness in a small mining town showed that out of a population of 165 children, 9 had developed the disease. This compares with a rate of 3.5% in the country as a whole. Is there any evidence of a different rate in the town?

Problem 6.4

In a study of insect pollination, the numbers of insect visitors belonging to different taxonomic groups were investigated at flowers of different colours. The following results were obtained.

Insect visitors	Flower colour			Total
	White	Yellow	Blue	
Beetles	56	34	12	102
Flies	31	74	22	127
Bees and wasps	57	103	175	335
Total	144	211	209	564

(a) Carry out a χ^2 test to determine whether there is any association between the types of insects and the colour of the flowers they visit.
(b) Which cells have the three highest χ^2 values? What do these results tell you about the preferences of different insects?

Problem 6.5

A study was carried out to determine whether there is a link between the incidence of skin cancer and the possession of freckles. Of the 6045 people examined, 978 had freckles, of whom 33 had developed skin cancer. Of the remaining people without freckles, 95 had developed skin cancer. Is there any evidence that people with freckles have an increased risk of developing skin cancer?

Problem 6.6

A field study on the distribution of two species of newt found that of 745 ponds studied, 180 contained just smooth newts, 56 just palmate newts, 236 had both species present and the remainder had neither. Is there any association between the two species and, if so, what is it?

Physics

Introduction
to Physics

1-1	Physics and the Laws of Nature	2
1-2	Units of Length, Mass, and Time	2
1-3	Dimensional Analysis	4
1-4	Significant Figures	5
1-5	Converting Units	8
1-6	Order-of-Magnitude Calculations	10
1-7	Scalars and Vectors	11
1-8	Problem Solving in Physics	11

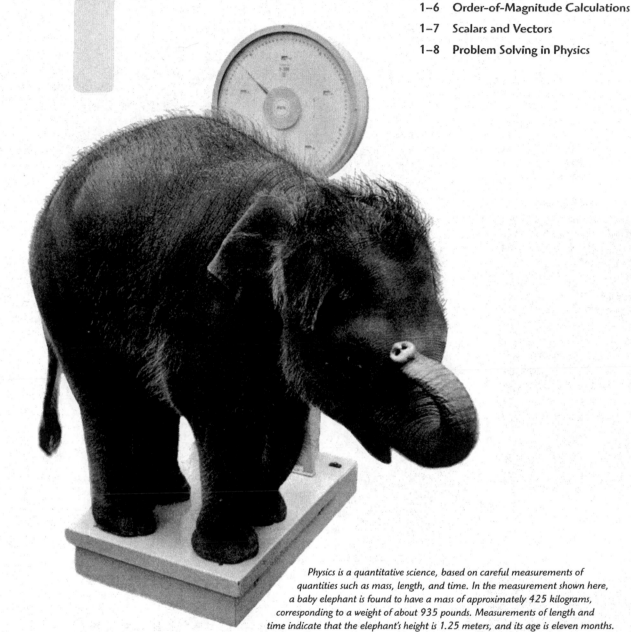

Physics is a quantitative science, based on careful measurements of quantities such as mass, length, and time. In the measurement shown here, a baby elephant is found to have a mass of approximately 425 kilograms, corresponding to a weight of about 935 pounds. Measurements of length and time indicate that the elephant's height is 1.25 meters, and its age is eleven months.

The goal of physics is to gain a deeper understanding of the world in which we live. For example, the laws of physics allow us to predict the behavior of everything from rockets sent to the Moon, to integrated chips in computers, to lasers used to perform eye surgery. In short, everything in nature—from atoms and subatomic particles to solar systems and galaxies—obeys the laws of physics.

As we begin our study of physics, it is useful to consider a range of issues that underlies everything to follow.

One of the most fundamental of these is the system of units we use when we measure such things as the mass of an object, its length, and the time between two events. Other equally important issues include methods for handling numerical calculations and basic conventions of mathematical notation. By the end of the chapter we will have developed a common "language" of physics that will be used throughout this book and probably in any science that you study.

1

Science Fundamentals Second Edition

1-1 Physics and the Laws of Nature

Physics is the study of the fundamental laws of nature, which, simply put, are the laws that underlie all physical phenomena in the universe. Remarkably, we have found that these laws can be expressed in terms of mathematical equations. As a result, it is possible to make precise, quantitative comparisons between the predictions of theory—derived from the mathematical form of the laws—and the observations of experiments. Physics, then, is a science rooted equally firmly in theory and experiment, and, as physicists make new observations, they constantly test and—if necessary—refine the present theories.

What makes physics particularly fascinating is the fact that it relates to everything in the universe. There is a great beauty in the vision that physics brings to our view of the universe; namely, that all the complexity and variety that we see in the world around us, and in the universe as a whole, are manifestations of a few fundamental laws and principles. That we can discover and apply these basic laws of nature is both astounding and exhilarating.

For those not familiar with the subject, physics may seem to be little more than a confusing mass of formulas. Sometimes, in fact, these formulas can be the trees that block the view of the forest. For a physicist, however, the many formulas of physics are simply different ways of expressing a few fundamental ideas. It is the forest—the basic laws and principles of physical phenomena in nature—that is the focus of this text.

1-2 Units of Length, Mass, and Time

To make quantitative comparisons between the laws of physics and our experience of the natural world, certain basic physical quantities must be measured. The most common of these quantities are **length** (L), **mass** (M), and **time** (T). In fact, in the next several chapters these are the only quantities that arise. Later in the text, additional quantities, such as temperature and electric current, will be introduced as needed.

We begin by defining the units in which each of these quantities is measured. Once the units are defined, the values obtained in specific measurements can be expressed as multiples of them. For example, our unit of length is the **meter** (m). It follows, then, that a person who is 1.94 m tall has a height 1.94 times this unit of length. Similar comments apply to the unit of mass, the **kilogram,** and the unit of time, the **second.**

The detailed system of units used in this book was established in 1960 at the Eleventh General Conference of Weights and Measures in Paris, France, and goes by the name Système International d'Unités, or SI for short. Thus, when we refer to **SI units,** we mean units of meters (m), kilograms (kg), and seconds (s). Taking the first letter from each of these units leads to an alternate name that is often used—the **mks system.**

In the remainder of this section we define each of the SI units.

Length

Early units of length were often associated with the human body. For example, the Egyptians defined the cubit to be the distance from the elbow to the tip of the middle finger. Similarly, the foot was at one time defined to be the length of the royal foot of King Louis XIV. As colorful as these units may be, they are not particularly reproducible—at least not to great precision.

In 1793 the French Academy of Sciences, seeking a more objective and reproducible standard, decided to define a unit of length equal to one ten-millionth the distance from the North Pole to the equator. This new unit was named the metre (from the Greek *metron* for "measure"). The preferred spelling in the United States is *meter*. This definition was widely accepted, and in 1799 a "standard" meter was produced. It consisted of a platinum-iridium alloy rod with two marks on it one meter apart.

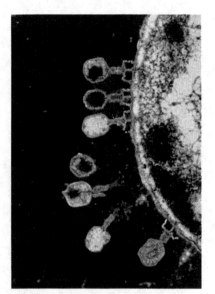

▲ The size of these viruses, seen here attacking a bacterial cell, is about 10^{-7} m.

▲ The diameter of this typical galaxy is about 10^{21} m. (How many viruses would it take to span the galaxy?)

TABLE 1–1 Typical Distances	
Distance from Earth to the nearest large galaxy (the Andromeda galaxy, M31)	2×10^{22} m
Diameter of our galaxy (the Milky Way)	8×10^{20} m
Distance from Earth to the nearest star (other than the sun)	4×10^{16} m
One light year	9.46×10^{15} m
Average radius of Pluto's orbit	6×10^{12} m
Distance from Earth to the Sun	1.5×10^{11} m
Radius of Earth	6.37×10^{6} m
Length of a football field	10^{2} m
Height of a person	2 m
Diameter of a CD	0.12 m
Diameter of the aorta	0.018 m
Diameter of a period in a sentence	5×10^{-4} m
Diameter of a red blood cell	8×10^{-6} m
Diameter of the hydrogen atom	10^{-10} m
Diameter of a proton	2×10^{-15} m

Since 1983 we have used an even more precise definition of the meter, based on the speed of light in a vacuum. In particular:

One meter is defined to be the distance traveled by light in a vacuum in 1/299,792,458 of a second.

No matter how its definition is refined, however, a meter is still about 3.28 feet, which is roughly 10 percent longer than a yard. A list of typical lengths is given in Table 1–1.

Mass

In SI units, mass is measured in kilograms. Unlike the meter, the kilogram is not based on any natural physical quantity. By convention, the kilogram has been defined as follows:

The kilogram, by definition, is the mass of a particular platinum-iridium alloy cylinder at the International Bureau of Weights and Standards in Sèvres, France.

To put the kilogram in everyday terms, a quart of milk has a mass slightly less than 1 kilogram. Additional masses, in kilograms, are given in Table 1–2.

Note that we do not define the kilogram to be the *weight* of the platinum-iridium cylinder. In fact, weight and mass are quite different quantities, even though they are often confused in everyday language. Mass is an intrinsic, unchanging property of an object. Weight, in contrast, is a measure of the gravitational force acting on an object, which can vary depending on the object's location. For example, if you are fortunate enough to travel to Mars someday, you will find that your weight is less than on Earth, though your mass is unchanged. The force of gravity will be discussed in detail in Chapter 12.

Time

Nature has provided us with a fairly accurate timepiece in the revolving Earth. In fact, prior to 1956 the mean solar day was defined to consist of 24 hours, with 60 minutes per hour, and 60 seconds per minute, for a total of $(24)(60)(60) = 84,400$ seconds. Even the rotation of the Earth is not completely regular, however.

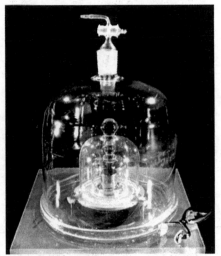

▲ The standard kilogram, a cylinder of platinum and iridium 0.039 m in height and diameter, is kept under carefully controlled conditions in Sèvres, France. Exact replicas are maintained in other laboratories around the world.

TABLE 1–2 Typical Masses	
Galaxy (Milky Way)	4×10^{41} kg
Sun	2×10^{30} kg
Earth	5.97×10^{24} kg
Space shuttle	2×10^{6} kg
Elephant	5400 kg
Automobile	1200 kg
Human	70 kg
Baseball	0.15 kg
Honeybee	1.5×10^{-4} kg
Red blood cell	10^{-13} kg
Bacterium	10^{-15} kg
Hydrogen atom	1.67×10^{-27} kg
Electron	9.11×10^{-31} kg

▲ This atomic clock, which keeps time on the basis of radiation from cesium atoms, is accurate to about three millionths of a second per year. (How long would it take for it to gain or lose an hour?)

"MY GOODNESS, IT'S 12:15:0936420175! TIME FOR LUNCH."

© 2000 Sidney Harris

TABLE 1–3 Typical Times	
Age of the universe	5×10^{17} s
Age of the Earth	1.3×10^{17} s
Existence of human species	6×10^{13} s
Human lifetime	2×10^9 s
One year	3×10^7 s
One day	8.6×10^4 s
Time between heartbeats	0.8 s
Human reaction time	0.1 s
One cycle of a high-pitched sound wave	5×10^{-5} s
One cycle of an AM radio wave	10^{-6} s
One cycle of a visible light wave	2×10^{-15} s

Today, the most accurate timekeepers known are "atomic clocks," which are based on characteristic frequencies of radiation emitted by certain atoms. These clocks have typical accuracies of about 1 second in 300,000 years. The atomic clock used for defining the second operates with cesium-133 atoms. In particular, the second is defined as follows:

> One second is defined to be the time it takes for radiation from a cesium-133 atom to complete 9,192,631,770 cycles of oscillation.

A range of characteristic time intervals is given in Table 1–3.

The nation's time and frequency standard is determined by a *cesium fountain atomic clock* developed at the National Institute of Standards and Technology (NIST) in Boulder, Colorado. The fountain atomic clock, designated NIST-F1, produces a "fountain" of cesium atoms that are projected upward in a vacuum to a height of about a meter. It takes roughly a second for the atoms to rise and fall through this height (as we shall see in the next chapter), and during this relatively long period of time the frequency of their oscillation can be measured with great precision. In fact, the NIST-F1 will gain or lose no more than one second in every 20 million years of operation.

Atomic clocks are almost commonplace these days. For example, the satellites that participate in the Global Positioning System (GPS) actually carry atomic clocks with them in orbit. This allows them to make the precision time measurements that are needed for an equally precise determination of position and speed. Similarly, the "atomic clocks" that are advertised for use in the home, while not atomic in their operation, nonetheless get their time from radio signals sent out from the atomic clocks at NIST in Boulder. You can access the official U. S. time on your computer by going to http://time.gov on the Web.

Other Systems of Units and Standard Prefixes

Although SI units are used throughout most of this book and are used almost exclusively in scientific research and in industry, we will occasionally refer to other systems that you may encounter from time to time.

For example, a system of units similar to the mks system, though comprised of smaller units, is the **cgs system,** which stands for centimeter (cm), gram (g), and second (s). In addition, the British engineering system is often encountered in everyday usage in the United States. Its basic units are the slug for mass, the foot (ft) for length, and the second (s) for time.

Finally, multiples of the basic units are common no matter which system is used. Standard prefixes are used to designate common multiples in powers of ten. For example, the prefix *kilo* means one thousand, or, equivalently, 10^3. Thus, 1 kilogram is 10^3 grams, and 1 kilometer is 10^3 meters. Similarly, *milli* is the prefix for one thousandth, or 10^{-3}. Thus, a millimeter is 10^{-3} meter, and so on. The most common prefixes are listed in Table 1–4.

EXERCISE 1–1

a. A minivan sells for 33,200 dollars. Express the price of the minivan in kilodollars and megadollars.

b. A typical *E. coli* bacterium is about 5 micrometers (or microns) in length. Give this length in millimeters and kilometers.

Solution

a. 33.2 kilodollars, 0.0332 megadollars.

b. 0.005 mm, 0.000000005 km.

1–3 Dimensional Analysis

In physics, when we speak of the **dimension** of a physical quantity, we refer to the *type* of quantity in question, regardless of the units used in the measurement. For example, a distance measured in cubits and another distance measured in light-years both have the same dimension—length. The same is true of compound units such as velocity, which has the dimensions of length per unit time (length/time). A velocity measured in miles per hour has the same dimensions— length/time—as one measured in inches per century.

Now, any valid formula in physics must be **dimensionally consistent;** that is, each term in the equation must have the same dimensions. It simply doesn't make sense to add a distance to a time, for example, any more than it makes sense to add apples and oranges. They are different things.

To check the dimensional consistency of an equation, it is convenient to introduce a special notation for the dimension of a quantity. We will use square brackets, [ ], for this purpose. Thus, if x represents a distance, which has dimensions of length [L], we write this as $x = [L]$. Similarly, a velocity, v, has dimensions of length per time [T]; thus we write $v = [L]/[T]$ to indicate its dimensions. Acceleration, a, which is the change in velocity per time, has the dimensions $a = ([L]/[T])/[T] = [L]/[T^2]$. The dimensions of some common physical quantities are summarized in Table 1–5.

Let's use this notation to check the dimensional consistency of a simple equation. Consider the following formula:

$$x = x_0 + vt$$

In this equation, x and x_0 represent distances, v is a velocity, and t is time. Writing out the dimensions of each term, we have

$$[L] = [L] + \frac{[L]}{[T]}[T]$$

It might seem at first that the last term has different dimensions than the other two. However, dimensions obey the same rules of algebra as other quantities. Thus the dimensions of time cancel in the last term:

$$[L] = [L] + \frac{[L]}{[\cancel{T}]}[\cancel{T}] = [L] + [L]$$

As a result, we see that each term in this formula has the same dimensions. This type of calculation with dimensions is referred to as **dimensional analysis.**

TABLE 1–4 Common Prefixes		
Power	Prefix	Abbreviation
10^{15}	peta	P
10^{12}	tera	T
10^{9}	giga	G
10^{6}	mega	M
10^{3}	kilo	k
10^{2}	hecto	h
10^{1}	deka	da
10^{-1}	deci	d
10^{-2}	centi	c
10^{-3}	milli	m
10^{-6}	micro	μ
10^{-9}	nano	n
10^{-12}	pico	p
10^{-15}	femto	f

TABLE 1–5 Dimensions of Some Common Physical Quantities	
Quantity	Dimension
Distance	[L]
Area	$[L^2]$
Volume	$[L^3]$
Velocity	[L]/[T]
Acceleration	$[L]/[T^2]$
Energy	$[M][L^2]/[T^2]$

EXERCISE 1–2

Show that $x = x_0 + v_0 t + \frac{1}{2}at^2$ is dimensionally consistent. The quantities x and x_0 are distances, v_0 is a velocity, and a is an acceleration.

Solution

Using the dimensions given in Table 1–5, we have

$$[L] = [L] + \frac{[L]}{[\cancel{T}]}[\cancel{T}] + \frac{[L]}{[\cancel{T^2}]}[\cancel{T^2}] = [L] + [L] + [L]$$

Note that $\frac{1}{2}$ is ignored in this analysis because it has no dimensions.

Later in this text you will derive your own formulas from time to time. As you do so, it is helpful to check dimensional consistency at each step of the derivation. If at any time the dimensions don't agree, you will know that a mistake has been made, and you can go back and look for it. If the dimensions check, however, it's not a guarantee the formula is correct—after all, dimensionless factors, like 1/2 or 2, don't show up in a dimensional check.

1–4 Significant Figures

When a mass, a length, or a time is measured in a scientific experiment, the result is known only to within a certain accuracy. The inaccuracy or uncertainty can be caused by a number of factors, ranging from limitations of the measuring device itself to limitations associated with the senses and the skill of the person

Science Fundamentals Second Edition

performing the experiment. In any case, the fact that observed values of experimental quantities have inherent uncertainties should always be kept in mind when performing calculations with those values.

Suppose, for example, that you want to determine the walking speed of your pet tortoise. To do so, you measure the time, t, it takes for the tortoise to walk a distance, d, and then you calculate the quotient, d/t. When you measure the distance with a ruler, which has one tick mark per millimeter, you find that $d = 21.2$ cm, with the precise value of the digit in the second decimal place uncertain. Defining the number of **significant figures** in a physical quantity to be equal to the number of digits in it that are known with certainty, we say that d is known to *three* significant figures.

Similarly, you measure the time with an old pocket watch, and as best you can determine it, $t = 8.5$ s, with the second decimal place uncertain. Note that t is known to only *two* significant figures. If we were to make this measurement with a digital watch, with a readout giving the time to $1/100$ of a second, the accuracy of the result would still be limited by the finite reaction time of the experimenter. The reaction time would have to be predetermined in a separate experiment. (See Problem 71 in Chapter 2 for a simple way to determine your reaction time.)

Returning to the problem at hand, we would now like to calculate the speed of the tortoise. Using the above values for d and t and a calculator with eight digits in its display, we find $(21.2 \text{ cm})/(8.5 \text{ s}) = 2.4941176$ cm/s. Clearly, such an accurate value for the speed is unjustified, considering the limitations of our measurements. After all, we can't expect to measure quantities to two and three significant figures and from them obtain results with eight significant figures. In general, the number of significant figures that result when we multiply or divide physical quantities is given by the following rule of thumb:

> The number of significant figures after multiplication or division is equal to the number of significant figures in the *least* accurately known quantity.

In our speed calculation, for example, we know the distance to three significant figures, but the time to only two significant figures. As a result, the speed should be given with just two significant figures, $d/t = (21.2 \text{ cm})/(8.5 \text{ s}) = 2.5$ cm/s. Note that we didn't just keep the first two digits in 2.4941176 cm/s and drop the rest. Instead, we "rounded up"; that is, because the first digit to be dropped (9 in this case) is greater than or equal to 5, we increase the previous digit (4 in this case) by 1. Thus, 2.5 cm/s is our best estimate for the tortoise's speed.

▲ Every measurement has some degree of uncertainty associated with it. How precise would you expect this measurement to be?

EXAMPLE 1–1 It's the Tortoise by a Hare

A tortoise races a rabbit by walking with a constant speed of 2.51 cm/s for 12.23 s. How much distance does the tortoise cover?

Picture the Problem
The race between the rabbit and the tortoise is shown in our sketch. The rabbit pauses to eat a carrot while the tortoise walks with a constant speed.

Strategy
The distance covered by the tortoise is the speed of the tortoise multiplied by the time during which it walks.

Solution

1. Multiply the speed by the time to find the distance d:

$$d = (\text{speed})(\text{time})$$
$$= (2.51 \text{ cm/s})(12.23 \text{ s}) = 30.7 \text{ cm}$$

Insight
Notice that if we simply multiply 2.51 cm/s by 12.23 s, we obtain 30.6973 cm. We don't give all of these digits in our answer, however. In particular, because the quantity that is known with the least accuracy (the speed) has only three significant

figures, we give a result with three significant figures. Note, in addition, that the third digit in our answer has been rounded up from 6 to 7.

Practice Problem

How long does it take for the tortoise to walk 17 cm?   [**Answer:** $t = (17 \text{ cm})/(2.51 \text{ cm/s}) = 6.8 \text{ s}$]

Some related homework problems: Problem 11, Problem 15

Note that the distance of 17 cm in the Practice Problem has only two significant figures because we don't know the digits to the right of the decimal place. If the distance were given as 17.0 cm, on the other hand, it would have three significant figures.

When physical quantities are added or subtracted, we use a slightly different rule of thumb. In this case, the rule involves the number of decimal places in each of the terms:

> The number of decimal places after addition or subtraction is equal to the smallest number of decimal places in any of the individual terms.

Thus, if you make a time measurement of 16.74 s, and then a subsequent time measurement of 5.1 s, the total time of the two measurements should be given as 21.8 s, rather than 21.84 s.

▲ The finish of the 100-meter race at the 1996 Atlanta Olympics. This official timing photo shows Donovan Bailey setting a new world record of 9.84 s. (If the timing had been accurate to only tenths of a second—as would probably have been the case before electronic devices came into use—how many runners would have shared the winning time? How many would have shared the second-place and third-place times?)

EXERCISE 1–3

You and a friend pick some raspberries. Your flat weighs 12.7 lb, and your friend's weighs 7.25 lb. What is the combined weight of the raspberries?

Solution

Just adding the two numbers gives 19.95 lb. According to our rule of thumb, however, the final result must have only a single decimal place (corresponding to the term with the smallest number of decimal places). Rounding off to one place, then, gives 20.0 lb as the acceptable result.

Scientific Notation

The number of significant figures in a given quantity may be ambiguous due to the presence of zeros at the beginning or end of the number. For example, if a distance is stated to be 2500 m, the two zeros could be significant figures, or they could be zeros that simply show where the decimal point is located. If the two zeros are significant figures, the uncertainty in the distance is roughly a meter; if they are not significant figures, however, the uncertainty is about 100 m.

To remove this type of ambiguity, we can write the distance in **scientific notation**—that is, as a number of order unity times an appropriate power of ten. Thus, in this example, we would express the distance as 2.5×10^3 m if there are only two significant figures, or as 2.500×10^3 m to indicate four significant figures. Likewise, a time given as 0.000036 s has only two significant figures—the preceding zeros only serve to fix the decimal point. If this quantity were known to three significant figures, we would write it as 3.60×10^{-5} s to remove any ambiguity. See Appendix A for a more detailed discussion of scientific notation.

EXERCISE 1–4

How many significant figures are there in (a) 21.00, (b) 21, (c) 2.1×10^{-2}, (d) 2.10×10^{-3}?

Solution

(a) 4, (b) 2, (c) 2, (d) 3

Science Fundamentals Second Edition

Round–Off Error

Finally, even if you perform all your calculations to the same number of significant figures as in the text, you may occasionally obtain an answer that differs in its last digit from that given in the book. In most cases this is not an issue as far as understanding the physics is concerned—usually it is due to **round-off error.**

Round-off error occurs when numerical results are rounded off at different times during a calculation. To see how this works, let's consider a simple example. Suppose you are shopping for knickknacks, and you buy one item for $2.21, plus 8 percent sales tax. The total price is $2.3868, or, rounded off to the nearest penny, $2.39. Later, you buy another item for $1.35. With tax this becomes $1.458 or, again to the nearest penny, $1.46. The total expenditure for these two items is $2.39 + $1.46 = $3.85.

Now, let's do the rounding off in a different way. Suppose you buy both items at the same time for a total before-tax price of $2.21 + $1.35 = $3.56. Adding in the 8 percent tax gives $3.8448, which rounds off to $3.84, one penny different from the previous amount. This same type of discrepancy can occur in physics problems. In general, it's a good idea to keep one extra digit throughout your calculations whenever possible, rounding off only the final result. But while this practice can help to reduce the likelihood of round-off error, there is no way to avoid it in every situation.

1–5 Converting Units

It is often convenient to convert from one set of units to another. For example, suppose you would like to convert 316 ft to its equivalent in meters. Looking at the conversion factors on the inside front cover of the text, we see that

$$1 \text{ m} = 3.281 \text{ ft} \qquad\qquad \text{1–1}$$

Equivalently,

$$\frac{1 \text{ m}}{3.281 \text{ ft}} = 1 \qquad\qquad \text{1–2}$$

Now, to make the conversion, we simply multiply 316 ft by this expression, which is equivalent to multiplying by 1:

$$(316 \text{ ft})\left(\frac{1 \text{ m}}{3.281 \text{ ft}}\right) = 96.3 \text{ m}$$

Note that the conversion factor is written in this particular way, as 1 m divided by 3.281 ft, so that the units of feet cancel out, leaving the final result in the desired units of meters.

Of course, we can just as easily convert from meters to feet if we use the reciprocal of this conversion factor—which is also equal to 1:

$$1 = \frac{3.281 \text{ ft}}{1 \text{ m}}$$

For example, a distance of 26.4 m is converted to feet by canceling out the units of meters, as follows:

$$(26.4 \text{ m})\left(\frac{3.281 \text{ ft}}{1 \text{ m}}\right) = 86.6 \text{ ft}$$

Thus, we see that converting units is as easy as multiplying by 1—because that's really what you're doing.

▲ From this sign, you can calculate factors for converting miles to kilometers and vice versa. (Why do you think the conversion factors seem to vary for different destinations?)

EXAMPLE 1–2 A High-Volume Warehouse

A warehouse is 20.0 yards long, 10.0 yards wide, and 15.0 ft high. What is its volume in SI units?

Picture the Problem
In our sketch we picture the warehouse, and indicate the relevant lengths for each of its dimensions.

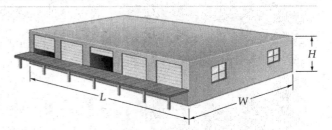

Strategy
We begin by converting the length, width, and height of the warehouse to meters. Once this is done, the volume in SI units is simply the product of the three dimensions.

Solution

1. Convert the length of the warehouse to meters:

$$L = (20.0 \text{ yard})\left(\frac{3 \text{ ft}}{1 \text{ yard}}\right)\left(\frac{1 \text{ m}}{3.281 \text{ ft}}\right) = 18.3 \text{ m}$$

2. Convert the width to meters:

$$W = (10.0 \text{ yard})\left(\frac{3 \text{ ft}}{1 \text{ yard}}\right)\left(\frac{1 \text{ m}}{3.281 \text{ ft}}\right) = 9.14 \text{ m}$$

3. Convert the height to meters:

$$H = (15.0 \text{ ft})\left(\frac{1 \text{ m}}{3.281 \text{ ft}}\right) = 4.57 \text{ m}$$

4. Calculate the volume of the warehouse:

$$V = L \times W \times H = (18.3 \text{ m})(9.14 \text{ m})(4.57 \text{ m}) = 764 \text{ m}^3$$

Insight
We would say, then, that the warehouse has a volume of 764 cubic meters—the same as 764 cubical boxes that are 1 m on a side.

Practice Problem
What is the volume of the warehouse if its length is one-hundredth of a mile, and the other dimensions are unchanged? [**Answer:** $V = 672 \text{ m}^3$]

Some related homework problems: Problem 17, Problem 18

Finally, the same procedure can be applied to conversions involving any number of units. For instance, if you walk at 3.00 mi/h, how fast is that in m/s? In this case we need the following additional conversion factors:

$$1 \text{ mi} = 5,280 \text{ ft} \qquad 1 \text{ h} = 3,600 \text{ s}$$

With these factors at hand, we carry out the conversion as follows:

$$(3.00 \text{ mi/h})\left(\frac{5,280 \text{ ft}}{1 \text{ mi}}\right)\left(\frac{1 \text{ m}}{3.281 \text{ ft}}\right)\left(\frac{1 \text{ h}}{3,600 \text{ s}}\right) = 1.34 \text{ m/s}$$

Note that in each conversion factor the numerator is equal to the denominator. In addition, each conversion factor is written in such a way that the unwanted units cancel, leaving just meters per second in our final result.

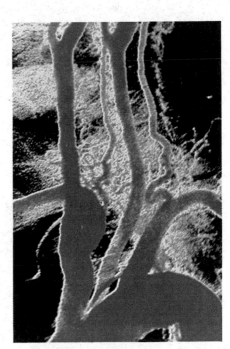

ACTIVE EXAMPLE 1–1 Find the Speed of Blood

Blood in the human aorta can attain speeds of 35.0 cm/s. How fast is this in **(a)** ft/s and **(b)** mi/h?

Solution *(Test your understanding by performing the calculations indicated in each step.)*

Part (a)

1. Convert centimeters to meters and then to feet: 1.15 ft/s

Part (b)

2. First, convert centimeters to miles: 2.17×10^{-4} mi/s

3. Next, convert seconds to hours: 0.783 mi/h

continued on next page

▲ Major blood vessels branch from the aorta (bottom), the artery that receives blood directly from the heart.

Science Fundamentals Second Edition

▲ Enrico Fermi (1901–1954) was renowned for his ability to pose and solve interesting order-of-magnitude problems. A winner of the 1938 Nobel Prize in physics, Fermi would ask his classes to obtain order-of-magnitude estimates for questions such as "How many piano tuners are there in Chicago?" or "How much is a tire worn down during one revolution?" Estimation questions like these are known to physicists today as "Fermi Problems."

continued from previous page

Insight
Of course, the conversions in part (b) can be carried out in a single calculation if desired.

Your Turn
Find the speed of blood in units of km/h.

*(Answers to **Your Turn** problems are given in the back of the book.)*

1–6 Order-of-Magnitude Calculations

An **order-of-magnitude** calculation is a rough "ballpark" estimate designed to be accurate to within a factor of about 10. One purpose of such a calculation is to give a quick idea of what order of magnitude should be expected from a complete, detailed calculation. If an order-of-magnitude calculation indicates that a distance should be on the order of 10^4 m, for example, and your calculator gives an answer on the order of 10^7 m, then there is an error somewhere that needs to be resolved.

For example, suppose you would like to estimate the speed of a cliff diver on entering the water. First, the cliff may be 20 or 30 feet high; thus in SI units we would say that the order of magnitude of the cliff's height is 10 m—certainly not 1 m or 10^2 m. Next, the diver hits the water something like a second later—certainly not 0.1 s later nor 10 s later. Thus, a reasonable order-of-magnitude estimate of the diver's speed is 10 m/1 s = 10 m/s, or roughly 20 mi/h. If you do a detailed calculation and your answer is on the order of 10^4 m/s, you probably entered one of your numbers incorrectly.

Another reason for doing an order-of-magnitude calculation is to get a feeling for what size numbers we are talking about in situations where a precise count is not possible. This is illustrated in the following Example.

EXAMPLE 1–3 Estimation: How Many Raindrops in a Storm

A thunderstorm drops half an inch (~0.01 m) of rain on Washington D.C., which covers an area of about 70 square miles (~10^8 m^2). Estimate the number of raindrops that fell during the storm.

Picture the Problem
Our sketch shows an area $A = 10^8$ m^2 covered to a depth $d = 0.01$ m by rainwater from the storm. Each drop of rain is approximated by a small sphere with a diameter of 4 mm.

Strategy
To find the number of raindrops, we first calculate the volume of water required to cover 10^8 m^2 to a depth of 0.01 m. Next, we calculate the volume of an individual drop of rain, recalling that the volume of a sphere of radius r is $4\pi r^3/3$. We estimate the diameter a raindrop to be about 4 mm. Finally, dividing the volume of a drop into the volume of water that fell during the storm gives the number of drops.

Solution

1. Calculate the order of magnitude of the volume of water, V_{water}, that fell during the storm:

$$V_{water} = Ad = (10^8 \text{ m}^2)(0.01 \text{ m}) \approx 10^6 \text{ m}^3$$

2. Calculate the order of magnitude of the volume of a drop of rain, V_{drop}. Note that if the diameter of a drop is 4 mm, its radius is $r = 2$ mm $= 0.002$ m:

$$V_{drop} = \frac{4}{3}\pi r^3 \approx \frac{4}{3}\pi(0.002 \text{ m})^3 \approx 10^{-8} \text{ m}^3$$

3. Divide V_{drop} into V_{water} to find the order of magnitude of the number of drops that fell during the storm:

$$number\ of\ raindrops \approx \frac{V_{water}}{V_{drop}} \approx \frac{10^6 \text{ m}^3}{10^{-8} \text{ m}^3} = 10^{14}$$

Insight
Thus the number of raindrops in this one small storm is roughly 100,000 times greater than the current population of the Earth.

Practice Problem
If a storm pelts Washington D.C. with 10^{15} raindrops, how many inches of rain fall on the city? [**Answer:** About 5 inches.]

Some related homework problems: Problem 33, Problem 35

Science Fundamentals Second Edition

Appendix B provides a number of interesting "typical values" for length, mass, speed, acceleration, and many other quantities. You may find these to be of use in making your own order-of-magnitude estimates.

1–7 Scalars and Vectors

Physical quantities are sometimes defined solely in terms of a number and the corresponding unit, like the volume of a room or the temperature of the air it contains. Other quantities require both a numerical value *and* a direction. For example, suppose a car is traveling at a rate of 25 m/s in a direction that is due north. Both pieces of information—the rate of travel (25 m/s) and the direction (north)—are required to fully specify the motion of the car. The rate of travel is given the name **speed**; the rate of travel combined with the direction is referred to as the **velocity**.

In general, quantities that are specified by a numerical value only are referred to as **scalars**; quantities that require both a numerical value and a direction are called **vectors**:

- A scalar is a numerical value, expressed in terms of appropriate units. An example would be the temperature of a room or the speed of a car.
- A vector is a mathematical quantity with both a numerical value and a direction. An example would be the velocity of a car.

All the physical quantities discussed in this text are either vectors or scalars. The properties of numbers (scalars) are well known, but the properties of vectors are sometimes less well known—though no less important. For this reason, you will find that Chapter 3 is devoted entirely to a discussion of vectors in two and three dimensions and, more specifically, to how they are used in physics.

The rather straightforward special case of vectors in one dimension is discussed in Chapter 2. There, we see that the direction of a velocity vector, for example, can only be to the left or to the right, up or down, and so on. That is, only two choices are available for the direction of a vector in one dimension. This is illustrated in **Figure 1-1**, where we see two cars, each traveling with a speed of 25 m/s. We also see that the cars are traveling in opposite directions, with car 1 moving to the right and car 2 moving to the left. We indicate the direction of travel with a plus sign for motion to the right, and a negative sign for motion to the left. Thus, the velocity of car 1 is written, $v_1 = +25$ m/s, and the velocity of car 2 is $v_2 = -25$ m/s. The speed of each car is the absolute value, or **magnitude**, of the velocity; that is, speed $= |v_1| = |v_2| = 25$ m/s.

Whenever we deal with one-dimensional vectors, we shall indicate their direction with the appropriate sign. Many examples are found in Chapter 2 and, again, in later chapters where the simplicity of one dimension can again be applied.

$$v_2 = -25 \text{ m/s} \qquad v_1 = +25 \text{ m/s}$$

Positive direction

▲ **FIGURE 1–1 Velocity vectors in one dimension**
The two cars shown in this figure have equal speeds of 25 m/s, but are traveling in opposite directions. To indicate the direction of travel, we first choose a positive direction (to the right in this case), and then give appropriate signs to the velocity of each car. Notice that car 1 moves to the right, and hence its velocity is positive, $v_1 = +25$ m/s; car 2 has a negative velocity, $v_2 = -25$ m/s, because it moves to the left.

1–8 Problem Solving in Physics

Physics is a lot like swimming—you have to learn by doing. You could read a book on swimming and memorize every word in it, but when you jump into a pool the first time you are going to have problems. Similarly, you could read this book carefully, memorizing every formula in it, but when you finish, you still haven't learned physics. To learn physics, you have to go beyond passive reading; you have to interact with physics and experience it by doing problems.

In this section we present a general overview of problem solving in physics. The suggestions given below, which apply to problems in all areas of physics, should help to develop a systematic approach.

We should emphasize at the outset that there is no recipe for solving problems in physics—it is a creative activity. In fact, the opportunity to be creative is one of the attractions of physics. The following suggestions, then, are not intended as a rigid set of steps that must be followed like the steps in a computer program.

Science Fundamentals Second Edition

Rather, they provide a general guideline that experienced problem solvers find to be effective.

- **Read the problem carefully** Before you can solve a problem, you need to know exactly what information it gives and what it asks you to determine. Some information is given explicitly, as when a problem states that a person has a mass of 70 kg. Other information is implicit; for example, saying that a ball is dropped from rest means that its initial speed is zero. Clearly, a *careful* reading is the essential first step in problem solving.

- **Sketch the system** This may seem like a step you can skip—but don't. A sketch helps you to acquire a physical feeling for the system. It also provides an opportunity to label those quantities that are known and those that are to be determined. All Examples in this text begin with a sketch of the system, accompanied by a brief description in a section labeled "Picture the Problem."

- **Visualize the physical process** Try to visualize what is happening in the system as if you were watching it in a movie. Your sketch should help. This step ties in closely with the next step.

- **Strategize** This may be the most difficult, but at the same time the most creative, part of the problem-solving process. From your sketch and visualization, try to identify the physical processes at work in the system. Ask yourself what concepts or principles are involved in this situation. Then, develop a strategy—a game plan—for solving the problem. All Examples in this book have a "Strategy" spelled out before the solution begins.

- **Identify appropriate equations** Once a strategy has been developed, find the specific equations that are needed to carry it out.

- **Solve the equations** Use basic algebra to solve the equations identified in the previous step. Work with symbols such as x or y for the most part, substituting numerical values near the end of the calculations. Working with symbols will make it easier to go back over a problem to locate and identify mistakes, if there are any, and to explore limits and special cases.

- **Check your answer** Once you have an answer, check to see if it makes sense: (i) Does it have the correct dimensions? (ii) Is the numerical value reasonable?

- **Explore limits/special cases** Getting the correct answer is nice, but it's not all there is to physics. You can learn a great deal about physics and about the connection between physics and mathematics by checking various limits of your answer. For example, if you have two masses in your system, m_1 and m_2, what happens in the special case that $m_1 = 0$ or $m_1 = m_2$? Check to see whether your answer and your physical intuition agree.

The **Examples** in this text are designed to deepen your understanding of physics and at the same time develop your problem-solving skills. They all have the same basic structure: Problem Statement; Picture the Problem; Strategy; Solution, presenting the flow of ideas and the mathematics side-by-side in a two-column format; Insight; and a Practice Problem related to the one just solved. As you work through the Examples in the chapters to come, notice how the basic problem-solving guidelines outlined above are implemented in a consistent way.

In addition to the Examples, this text contains a new and innovative type of worked-out problem called the **Active Example,** the first one of which appears on page 9. The purpose of Active Examples is to encourage active participation in the solution of a problem and, in so doing, to act as a "bridge" between Examples—where each and every detail is worked out—and homework problems—where you are completely on your own. An analogy would be to think of Examples as like a tricycle, with no balancing required; homework problems as like a bicycle, where balancing is initially difficult to master; and Active Examples as like a bicycle with training wheels that give just enough help to prevent a fall. When you work through an Active Example, keep in mind that the work you are doing as you progress step-by-step through the problem is just the kind of work you'll be doing later in your homework assignments.

Finally, it is tempting to look for shortcuts when doing a problem—to look for a formula that seems to fit and some numbers to plug into it. It may seem harder to think ahead, to be systematic as you solve the problem, and then to think back over what you have done at the end of the problem. The extra effort is worth it, however, because by doing these things you will develop powerful problem-solving skills that can be applied to unexpected problems you may encounter on exams—and in life in general.

Newton's Laws of Motion

5–1 Force and Mass 108
5–2 Newton's First Law of Motion 108
5–3 Newton's Second Law of Motion 110

Bobsledders know that a force is required to accelerate an object. In fact, the greater the force, the greater the acceleration. What they may not realize, however, is that forces always come in pairs that are equal in magnitude but opposite in direction. For example, when these athletes push on the bobsled, it pushes back on them with equal strength. All of these observations follow directly from Newton's three laws of motion, the subject of this chapter.

We are all subject to Newton's laws of motion, whether we know it or not. You can't move your body, drive a car, or toss a ball in a way that violates his rules. In short, our very existence is constrained and regulated by these three fundamental statements concerning matter and its motion.

Yet Newton's laws are surprisingly simple, especially when you consider that they apply equally well to galaxies, planets, comets, and yes, even apples falling from trees. In this chapter we present the three laws of Newton, and we show how they can be applied to everyday situations. Using them, we go beyond a simple description of motion, as in kinematics, to a study of the *causes* of motion, referred to as **dynamics.**

With the advent of Newtonian dynamics in 1687, science finally became quantitative and predictive. Edmund Halley, inspired by Newton's laws, used them to predict the return of the comet that today bears his name. In all of recorded history, no one had ever before predicted the appearance of a comet; in fact, they were generally regarded as supernatural apparitions. Though Halley didn't live to see his comet's return, his correct prediction illustrated the power of Newton's laws in a most dramatic and memorable way.

Today, we still recognize Newton's laws as the indispensable foundation for all of physics. It would be nice to say that these laws are the complete story when it comes to analyzing motion, but that is not the case. In the early part of the last century, physicists discovered that Newton's laws must be modified for objects moving at speeds near that of light and for objects comparable in size to atoms. In the world of everyday experience, however, Newton's laws still reign supreme.

107

5–1 Force and Mass

A **force**, simply put, is a push or a pull. When you push on a box to slide it across the floor, for example, or pull on the handle of a wagon to give a child a ride, you are exerting a force. Similarly, when you hold this book in your hand, you exert an upward force to oppose the downward pull of gravity. If you set the book on a table, the table exerts the same upward force you exerted a moment before. Forces are truly all around us.

Now, when you push or pull on something, there are two quantities that characterize the force you are exerting. The first is the strength or **magnitude** of your force; the second is the **direction** in which you are pushing or pulling. Because a force is determined by both a magnitude and a direction, it is a vector. We consider the vector properties of forces in more detail in Section 5–5.

In general, an object has several forces acting on it at any given time. In the previous example, a book at rest on a table experiences a downward force due to gravity and an upward force due to the table. If you push the book across the table, it also experiences a horizontal force due to your push. The total, or net, force exerted on the book is the vector sum of the individual forces acting on it.

After the net force acting on an object, the second key ingredient in Newton's laws is the **mass** of an object, which is a measure of how difficult it is to change its velocity—to start an object moving if it is at rest, to bring it to rest if it is moving, or to change its direction of motion. For example, if you throw a baseball or catch one thrown to you, the force required is not too great. But if you want to start a car moving or to stop one that is coming at you, the force involved is much greater. It follows that the mass of a car is greater than the mass of a baseball.

In agreement with everyday usage, mass can also be thought of as a measure of the quantity of matter in an object. Thus, it is clear that the mass of an automobile, for example, is much greater than the mass of a baseball, but much less than the mass of the Earth. We measure mass in units of kilograms (kg), where one kilogram is defined as the mass of a standard cylinder of platinum-iridium, as discussed in Chapter 1. A list of typical masses is given in Table 5–1.

These properties of force and mass are developed in detail in the next three sections.

TABLE 5–1
Typical Masses in Kilograms (kg)

Earth	5.97×10^{24}
Space Shuttle	2,000,000
Blue whale (largest animal on Earth)	178,000
Whale shark (largest fish)	18,000
Elephant (largest land animal)	5400
Automobile	1200
Human (adult)	70
Gallon of milk	3.6
Quart of milk	0.9
Baseball	0.145
Honeybee	0.00015
Bacterium	10^{-15}

5–2 Newton's First Law of Motion

If you've ever stood in line at an airport, pushing your bags forward a few feet at a time, you know that as soon as you stop pushing the bags, they stop moving. Observations such as this often lead to the erroneous conclusion that a force is required for an object to move. In fact, according to Newton's first law of motion, a force is required only to *change* an object's motion.

What is missing in this analysis is the force of friction between the bags and the floor. When you stop pushing the bags, it is not true that they stop moving because they no longer have a force acting on them. On the contrary, there is a rather large *frictional force* between the bags and the floor. It is this force that causes the bags to come to rest.

To see how motion is affected by reducing friction, imagine that you slide on dirt into second base during a baseball game. You won't slide very far before stopping. On the other hand, if you slide with the same initial speed on a sheet of ice—where the friction is much less than on a ball field—you slide considerably farther. If you could reduce the friction more, you would slide even farther.

In the classroom, air tracks allow us to observe motion with practically no friction. An example of such a device is shown in **Figure 5–1**. Note that air is blown through small holes in the track, creating a cushion of air for a small "cart" to ride on. A cart placed at rest on a level track remains at rest—unless you push on it to get it started.

Once set in motion, the cart glides along with constant velocity—constant speed in a straight line—until it hits a bumper at the end of the track. The bumper

Side view

Bumpers   Cart

Air track

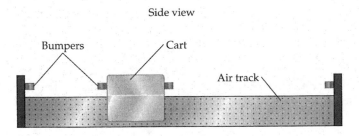

End view

Cart

Pressurized
Air

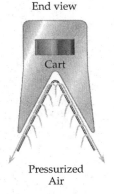

◀ **FIGURE 5-1 The air track**
An air track provides a cushion of air on which a cart can ride with virtually no friction.

exerts a force on the cart, causing it to change its direction of motion. After bouncing off the bumper, the cart again moves with constant velocity. If the track could be extended to infinite length, and could be made perfectly frictionless, the cart would simply keep moving with constant velocity forever.

Newton's first law of motion summarizes these observations in the following statements:

Newton's First Law

An object at rest remains at rest as long as no net force acts on it.

An object moving with constant velocity continues to move with the same speed and in the same direction as long as no net force acts on it.

Notice the recurring phrase, "no net force," in these statements. It is important to realize that this can mean one of two things: (i) no force acts on the object; or (ii) forces act on the object, but they sum to zero. We shall see examples of the second possibility later in this chapter and again in the next chapter.

Newton's first law, which was first enunciated by Galileo, is also known as the **law of inertia**, which is appropriate since the literal meaning of the word inertia is "laziness." Speaking loosely, we can say that matter is "lazy," in that it won't change its motion unless forced to do so. For example, if an object is at rest, it won't start moving on its own. If an object is already moving with constant velocity, it won't alter its speed *or* direction, unless a force causes the change. We call this property of matter its inertia

According to Newton's first law, being at rest and moving with constant velocity are actually equivalent. To see this, imagine two observers: one is in a train moving with constant velocity; the second is standing next to the tracks, at rest on the ground. The observer in the train places an ice cube on a dinner tray. From that person's point of view—that is, in that person's **frame of reference**—the ice cube has no net force acting on it and it is at rest on the tray. It obeys the first law. In the frame of reference of the observer on the ground, the ice cube has no net force on it and it moves with constant velocity. This also agrees with the first law. Thus Newton's first law holds for both observers: They both see an ice cube with zero net force moving with constant velocity—it's just that for the first observer the constant velocity happens to be zero.

In this example, we say that each observer is in an **inertial frame of reference;** that is, a frame of reference in which the law of inertia holds. In general, if one frame is an inertial frame of reference, then any frame of reference that moves with constant velocity relative to that frame is also an inertial frame of reference. Thus, if an object moves with constant velocity in one inertial frame, it is always possible to find another inertial frame in which the object is at rest. It is in this sense that there really isn't any difference between being at rest and moving with constant velocity. It's all relative—relative to the frame of reference the object is viewed from.

This gives us a more compact statement of the first law:

If the net force on an object is zero, its velocity is constant.

▲ An air track provides a nearly frictionless environment for experiments involving linear motion.

Science Fundamentals Second Edition

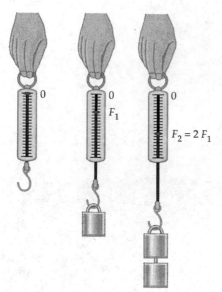

▲ FIGURE 5–2 Calibrating a "force meter"

With two weights, the force exerted by the scale is twice the force exerted when only a single weight is attached.

▶ FIGURE 5–3 Acceleration is proportional to force

The spring calibrated in Figure 5–2 is used to accelerate a mass on a "friction-less" air track. If the force is doubled, the acceleration is also doubled.

As an example of a frame of reference that is not inertial, imagine that the train carrying the first observer suddenly comes to a halt. From the point of view of that observer, there is still no net force on the ice cube. However, because of the rapid braking, the ice cube flies off the tray. In fact, the ice cube simply continues to move forward with the same constant velocity while the *train* comes to rest. To the observer on the train, it appears that the ice cube has accelerated forward, even though no force acts on it, which is in violation of Newton's first law.

In general, any frame that accelerates relative to an inertial frame is a noninertial frame. The surface of the Earth accelerates slightly, due to its rotational and orbital motions, but since the acceleration is so small, it may be considered an excellent approximation to an inertial frame of reference. Unless specifically stated otherwise, we will always consider the surface of the Earth to be an inertial frame.

5–3 Newton's Second Law of Motion

To hold an object in your hand, you have to exert an upward force to oppose, or "balance," the force of gravity. If you suddenly remove your hand so that the only force acting on the object is gravity, it accelerates downward, as discussed in Chapter 2. This is one example of Newton's second law, which states, basically, that unbalanced forces cause accelerations.

To explore this in more detail, consider a spring scale of the type used to weigh fish. The scale gives a reading of the force, F, exerted by the spring contained within it. If we hang one weight from the scale, it gives a reading that we will call F_1. If two identical weights are attached, the scale reads $F_2 = 2F_1$, as indicated in **Figure 5–2**. With these two forces marked on the scale, we are ready to perform some force experiments.

First, attach the scale to an air-track cart, as in **Figure 5–3**. If we pull with a force F_1, we observe that the cart accelerates at the rate a_1. If we now pull with a force $F_2 = 2F_1$, the acceleration we observe is $a_2 = 2a_1$. Thus, the acceleration is proportional to the force—the greater the force, the greater the acceleration.

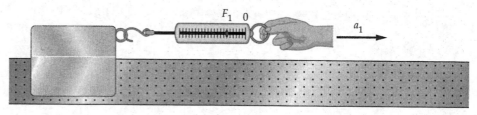

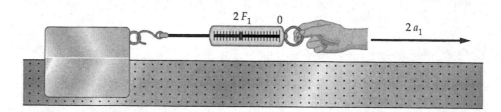

Second, instead of doubling the force, let's double the mass of the cart by connecting two together, as in **Figure 5–4**. In this case, if we pull with a force F_1 we find an acceleration equal to $\frac{1}{2}a_1$. Thus, the acceleration is inversely proportional to mass—the greater the mass, the less the acceleration.

Combining these results, we find that in this simple case—with just one force in just one direction—the acceleration is given by

$$a = \frac{F}{m}$$

Rearranging the equation yields the form of Newton's law that is perhaps best known, $F = ma$.

Science Fundamentals Second Edition

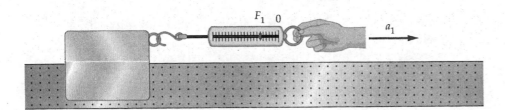

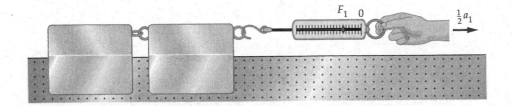

◀ **FIGURE 5–4 Acceleration** *is inversely* **proportional to mass**
If the mass of an object is doubled but the force remains the same, the acceleration is halved.

In general, there may be several forces acting on a given mass, and these forces may be in different directions. Thus, we replace F with the sum of the force vectors acting on a mass:

$$\text{sum of force vectors} = \vec{F}_{net} = \sum \vec{F}$$

The notation, $\sum \vec{F}$, which uses the Greek letter sigma (Σ), is read "sum $\vec{F}$." Recalling that acceleration is also a vector, we arrive at the formal statement of Newton's second law of motion:

Newton's Second Law

$$\vec{a} = \frac{\sum \vec{F}}{m} \quad \text{or} \quad \sum \vec{F} = m\vec{a} \qquad \text{5–1}$$

In words:

If an object of mass m is acted on by a net force $\sum \vec{F}$, it will experience an acceleration $\vec{a}$ that is equal to the net force divided by the mass. Because the net force is a vector, the acceleration is also a vector. In fact, the direction of an object's acceleration is the *same* as the direction of the net force acting on it.

One should note that Newton's laws cannot be derived from anything more basic. In fact, this is what we mean by a law of nature. The validity of Newton's laws, and all other laws of nature, comes directly from comparisons with experiment.

In terms of vector components, an equivalent statement of the second law is:

$$\sum F_x = ma_x \qquad \sum F_y = ma_y \qquad \sum F_z = ma_z \qquad \text{5–2}$$

Note that Newton's second law holds independently for each coordinate direction. This component form of the second law is particularly useful when solving problems.

Let's pause for a moment to consider an important special case of the second law. Suppose an object has zero net force acting upon it. This may be because no forces act on it at all, or that it is acted on by forces whose vector sum is zero. In either case, we can state this mathematically as:

$$\sum \vec{F} = 0$$

Now, according to Newton's second law, we conclude that the acceleration of this object must be zero:

$$\vec{a} = \frac{\sum \vec{F}}{m} = \frac{0}{m} = 0$$

But if an object's acceleration is zero, its velocity must be constant. In other words, if the net force on an object is zero, the object moves with constant velocity. This is

▲ Even though the tugboat exerts a large force on this ship, the ship's acceleration is small. This is because the acceleration of an object is inversely proportional to its mass, and the mass of the ship is enormous. The force exerted on the unfortunate hockey player is much smaller. The resulting acceleration is much larger, however, due to the relatively small mass of the player compared to that of the ship.

Science Fundamentals Second Edition

Newton's first law. Thus we see that Newton's first and second laws are consistent with one another.

Forces are measured in units called, appropriately enough, the **newton (N)**. In particular, one newton is defined as the force required to give one kilogram of mass an acceleration of 1 m/s². Thus,

$$1\,\text{N} = (1\,\text{kg})(1\,\text{m/s}^2) = 1\,\text{kg}\cdot\text{m/s}^2 \qquad \text{5–3}$$

In everyday terms, a newton is roughly a quarter of a pound. Note that a force in newtons divided by a mass in kilograms has the units of acceleration:

$$\frac{1\,\text{N}}{1\,\text{kg}} = \frac{1\,\text{kg}\cdot\text{m/s}^2}{1\,\text{kg}} = 1\,\text{m/s}^2 \qquad \text{5–4}$$

Other common units for force are presented in Table 5–2. Typical forces and their magnitudes in newtons are listed in Table 5–3.

TABLE 5–2 Units of Mass, Acceleration, and Force			
System of units	Mass	Acceleration	Force
SI	kilogram (kg)	m/s²	newton (N)
cgs	gram (g)	cm/s²	dyne (dyn)
British	slug	ft/s²	pound (lb)

(*Note:* $1\,\text{N} = 10^5$ dyne = 0.225 lb.)

TABLE 5–3 Typical Forces in Newtons (N)	
Main engines of space shuttle	31,000,000
Pulling force of locomotive	250,000
Thrust of jet engine	75,000
Force to accelerate a car	7000
Weight of adult human	700
Weight of an apple	1
Weight of a rose	0.1
Weight of an ant	0.001

EXERCISE 5–1

The net force acting on a Jaguar XK8 has a magnitude of 6800 N. If the car's acceleration is 3.8 m/s², what is its mass?

Solution

Since the net force and the acceleration are always in the same direction, we can replace the vectors in Equation 5–1 with magnitudes. Solving $\Sigma F = ma$ for the mass yields

$$m = \frac{\Sigma F}{a} = \frac{6800\,\text{N}}{3.8\,\text{m/s}^2} = 1800\,\text{kg}$$

The following Conceptual Checkpoint presents a situation in which both Newton's first and second laws play an important role.

CONCEPTUAL CHECKPOINT 5–1   Tightening a Hammer

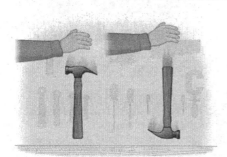

The metal head of a hammer is loose. To tighten it, you drop the hammer down onto a table. Should you (a) drop the hammer with the handle end down, (b) drop the hammer with the head end down, or (c) do you get the same result either way?

Reasoning and Discussion

It might seem that since the same hammer hits against the same table in either case, there shouldn't be a difference. Actually, there is.

In case (a), the handle of the hammer comes to rest when it hits the table, but the head continues downward until a force acts on it to bring it to rest. The force that acts on it is supplied by the handle, which results in the head being wedged more tightly onto the handle. Since the metal head is heavy, the force wedging it onto the handle is great. In case (b) the head of the hammer comes to rest, but the handle continues to move until a force brings it to rest. The handle is lighter than the head, however; thus the force acting on it is less, resulting in less tightening.

Answer:
(a) Drop the hammer with the handle end down.

A similar effect occurs when you walk—with each step you take you tamp your head down onto your spine, as when dropping a hammer handle end down.

This causes you to grow shorter during the day! Try it. Measure your height first thing in the morning, then again before going to bed. If you're like many people, you'll find that you have shrunk by an inch or so during the day.

REAL-WORLD PHYSICS: BIO

How walking affects your height

Free-Body Diagrams

When solving problems involving forces and Newton's laws, it is essential to begin by making a sketch that indicates *each and every external force* acting on a given object. This type of sketch is referred to as a **free-body diagram.** If we are concerned only with nonrotational motion, as is the case in this and the next chapter, we treat the object of interest as a point particle and apply each of the forces acting on the object to that point, as **Figure 5–5** shows. Once the forces are drawn, we choose a coordinate system and resolve each force into components. At this point, Newton's second law can be applied to each coordinate direction separately.

PROBLEM-SOLVING NOTE

External Forces

External forces acting on an object fall into two main classes: (i) Forces at the point of contact with another object, and (ii) forces exerted by an external agent, such as gravity.

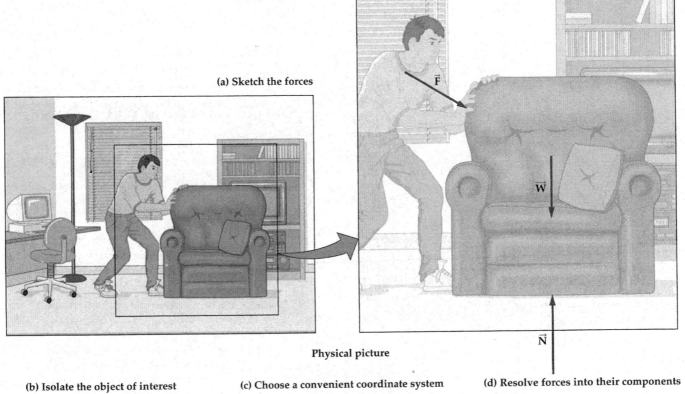

(a) Sketch the forces

Physical picture

(b) Isolate the object of interest

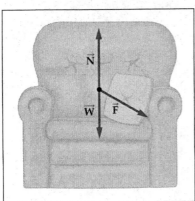

(c) Choose a convenient coordinate system

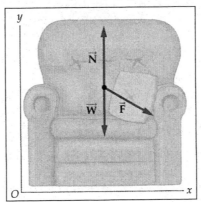

(d) Resolve forces into their components

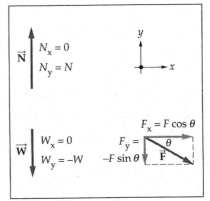

$N_x = 0$
$N_y = N$

$W_x = 0$
$W_y = -W$

$F_x = F \cos \theta$
$F_y = -F \sin \theta$

Free-body diagram

▲ **FIGURE 5–5 Constructing and using a free-body diagram**
The four basic steps in constructing and using a free-body diagram are illustrated in these sketches. **(a)** Sketch all of the external forces acting on an object of interest. Note that only forces acting *on* the object are shown; none of the forces exerted *by* the object are included. **(b)** Isolate the object and treat it as a point particle. **(c)** Choose a convenient coordinate system. This will often mean aligning a coordinate axis to coincide with the direction of one or more forces in the system. **(d)** Resolve each of the forces into components using the coordinate system of part (c).

Science Fundamentals Second Edition

For example, in Figure 5–5 there are three external forces acting on the chair. One is the force $\vec{F}$ exerted by the person. In addition, gravity exerts a downward force, $\vec{W}$, which is simply the weight of the chair. Finally, the floor exerts an upward force on the chair that prevents it from falling toward the center of the Earth. This force is referred to as the *normal force*, $\vec{N}$, because it is perpendicular (that is, normal) to the surface of the floor. We will consider the weight and the normal force in greater detail in Sections 5–6 and 5–7, respectively.

We can summarize the steps involved in constructing a free-body diagram as follows:

Sketch the Forces
Identify and sketch all of the external forces acting on an object. Sketching the forces roughly to scale will help in estimating the direction and magnitude of the net force.

Isolate the Object of Interest
Replace the object with a point particle of the same mass. Apply each of the forces acting on the object to that point.

Choose a Convenient Coordinate System
Any coordinate system will work; however, if the object moves in a known direction, it is often convenient to pick that direction for one of the coordinate axes. Otherwise, it is reasonable to choose a coordinate system that aligns with one or more of the forces acting on the object.

Resolve the Forces into Components
Determine the components of each force in the free-body diagram.

Apply Newton's Second Law to Each Coordinate Direction
Analyze motion in each coordinate direction using the component form of Newton's second law, as given in Equation 5–2.

These basic steps are illustrated in Figure 5–5. Note that the figures in this chapter use the labels "Physical picture" to indicate a sketch of the physical situation and "Free-body diagram" to indicate a free-body sketch.

We start by applying this procedure to a simple one-dimensional example, saving two-dimensional systems for Section 5–5. Suppose, for instance, that you hold a book at rest in your hand. What is the magnitude of the upward force that your hand must exert to keep the book at rest? From everyday experience, we expect that the upward force must be equal in magnitude to the weight of the book, but let's see how this result can be obtained directly from Newton's second law.

We begin with a sketch of the physical situation, as shown in **Figure 5–6 (a)**. The corresponding free-body diagram, in **Figure 5–6 (b)**, shows just the book, represented by a point, and the forces acting on it. Note that two forces act on the book: (i) the downward force of gravity, $\vec{W}$, and (ii) the upward force, $\vec{F}$, exerted by your hand. Only the forces acting *on* the book are included in the free-body diagram.

Now that the free-body diagram is drawn, we indicate a coordinate system so that the forces can be resolved into components. In this case all the forces are vertical. Thus we draw a y axis in the vertical direction in Figure 5–6 (b). Note that we have chosen upward to be the positive direction. With this choice, the y components of the forces are $F_y = F$ and $W_y = -W$. It follows that

$$\sum F_y = F - W$$

Using the y component of the second law ($\sum F_y = ma_y$) we find

$$F - W = ma_y$$

Since the book remains at rest, its acceleration is zero. Thus, $a_y = 0$, which gives

$$F - W = ma_y = 0 \quad \text{or} \quad F = W$$

as expected.

Next, we consider a situation where the net force acting on an object is nonzero, meaning that its acceleration is also nonzero.

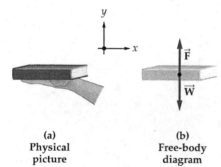

PROBLEM-SOLVING NOTE

Picture the Problem

In problems involving Newton's laws, it is important to begin with a free-body diagram and to identify all the external forces that act on an object. Once these forces are identified and resolved into their components, Newton's laws can be applied in a straightforward way. It is crucial, however, that only external forces acting on the object be included, and that none of the external forces be omitted.

(a)
Physical
picture

(b)
Free-body
diagram

▲ **FIGURE 5–6 A book supported in a person's hand**

(a) The physical situation. (b) The free-body diagram for the book, showing the two external forces acting on it. We also indicate our choice for a coordinate system.

Science Fundamentals Second Edition

EXAMPLE 5–1 Three Forces

Moe, Larry, and Curly push on a 752-kg boat that floats next to a dock. They each exert an 80.5-N force parallel to the dock. **(a)** What is the acceleration of the boat if they all push in the same direction? Give both direction and magnitude. **(b)** What is the magnitude and direction of the boat's acceleration if Larry and Curly push in the opposite direction to Moe's push?

Picture the Problem

In our sketch we indicate the three relevant forces acting on the boat: $\vec{F}_M$, $\vec{F}_L$, and $\vec{F}_C$. Note that we have chosen the positive x direction to the right, in the direction that all three push for part (a). Therefore, all three forces have a positive x component in part (a). In part (b), however, the forces exerted by Larry and Curly have negative x components.

Physical pictures

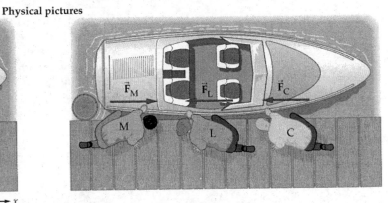

Free-body diagrams

(a)

(b)

Strategy

Since we know the mass of the boat and the forces acting on it, we can find the acceleration using $\Sigma F_x = ma_x$. Even though this problem is one-dimensional, it is important to think of it in terms of vector components. For example, when we sum the x components of the forces, we are careful to use the appropriate signs—just as we always do when dealing with vectors.

Solution

Part (a)

1. Write out the x component for each of the three forces:

$$F_{M,x} = F_{L,x} = F_{C,x} = 80.5\,\text{N}$$

2. Sum the x components of force and set equal to ma_x:

$$\Sigma F_x = F_{M,x} + F_{L,x} + F_{C,x} = 241.5\,\text{N} = ma_x$$

3. Divide by the mass to find a_x. Since a_x is positive, the acceleration is to the right, as expected:

$$a_x = \frac{\Sigma F_x}{m} = \frac{241.5\,\text{N}}{752\,\text{kg}} = 0.321\,\text{m/s}^2$$

Part (b)

4. Again, start by writing the x component for each force:

$$F_{M,x} = 80.5\,\text{N}$$
$$F_{L,x} = F_{C,x} = -80.5\,\text{N}$$

5. Sum the x components of force and set equal to ma_x:

$$\Sigma F_x = F_{M,x} + F_{L,x} + F_{C,x}$$
$$= 80.5\,\text{N} - 80.5\,\text{N} - 80.5\,\text{N} = -80.5\,\text{N} = ma_x$$

6. Solve for a_x. In this case a_x is negative, indicating an acceleration to the left:

$$a_x = \frac{\Sigma F_x}{m} = \frac{-80.5\,\text{N}}{752\,\text{kg}} = -0.107\,\text{m/s}^2$$

Insight

The results of this Example are in agreement with everyday experience: three forces in the same direction cause more acceleration than three forces in opposing directions. The method of using vector components and being careful about their signs gives the expected results in a simple situation like this, and also works in more complicated situations where everyday experience may be of little help.

Practice Problem

If Moe, Larry, and Curly all push to the right with 85.0-N forces, and the boat accelerates at 0.530 m/s², what is its mass? **[Answer: 481 kg]**

Some related homework problems: Problem 1, Problem 3

Science Fundamentals Second Edition

In some problems, we are given information that allows us to calculate an object's acceleration using the kinematic equations of Chapters 2 and 4. Once the acceleration is known, the second law can be used to find the net force that caused the acceleration.

For example, suppose that an astronaut uses a jet pack to push a satellite toward the space shuttle. These jet packs, which are known to NASA as Manned Maneuvering Units, or MMUs, are basically small "one-person rockets" strapped to the back of an astronaut's spacesuit. An MMU contains pressurized nitrogen gas that can be released through varying combinations of 24 nozzles spaced around the unit, producing a force of about 10 pounds. The MMUs contain enough propellant for a six-hour EVA (extra-vehicular activity).

We show the physical situation in **Figure 5–7 (a)**, where an astronaut pushes on a 655-kg satellite. The corresponding free-body diagram for the satellite is shown in **Figure 5–7 (b)**. Note that we have chosen the x axis to point in the direction of the push. Now, if the satellite starts at rest and moves 0.675 m after 5.00 seconds of pushing, what is the force, F, exerted on it by the astronaut?

▶ FIGURE 5–7 **An astronaut using a jet pack to push a satellite**

(a) The physical situation. (b) The free-body diagram for the satellite. Only one force acts on the satellite, and it is in the positive x direction.

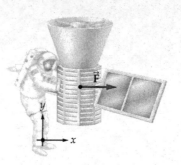

(a) Physical picture   **(b) Free-body diagram**

Clearly, we would like to use Newton's second law (basically, $\vec{F} = m\vec{a}$) to find the force, but we know only the mass of the satellite, not its acceleration. We can find the acceleration, however, by assuming constant acceleration (after all, the force is constant) and using the kinematic equation relating position to time $x = x_0 + v_{0x}t + \frac{1}{2}a_xt^2$. We can choose the initial position of the satellite to be $x_0 = 0$, and we are given that it starts at rest, thus $v_{0x} = 0$. Hence,

$$x = \frac{1}{2}a_xt^2$$

Since we know the distance covered in a given time, we can solve for the acceleration:

$$a_x = \frac{2x}{t^2} = \frac{2(0.675 \text{ m})}{(5.00 \text{ s})^2} = 0.0540 \text{ m/s}^2$$

Now that kinematics has provided the acceleration, we use the x component of the second law to find the force. Only one force acts on the satellite, and its x component is F; thus,

$$\sum F_x = F = ma_x$$
$$F = ma_x = (655 \text{ kg})(0.0540 \text{ m/s}^2) = 35.4 \text{ N}$$

This force corresponds to a push of about 8 lb.

Another problem in which we use kinematics to find the acceleration is presented in the following Active Example.

▲ A technician inspects the landing gear of an airliner in a test of Foamcrete, a solid paving material that is just soft enough to collapse under the weight of an airliner. A plane that has run off the runway will slow safely to a stop as its wheels plow through the crumbling Foamcrete.

ACTIVE EXAMPLE 5–1 The Force Exerted by Foamcrete

Foamcrete is a substance designed to stop an airplane that has run off the end of a runway, without causing injury to passengers. It is solid enough to support a car, but crumbles under the weight of a large airplane. By crumbling, it slows the plane to a safe stop. For example, suppose a 747 jetliner with a mass of 1.75×10^5 kg and an initial speed of 26.8 m/s is slowed to a stop in 122 m. What is the magnitude of the average retarding force $\vec{F}$ exerted by the Foamcrete on the plane?

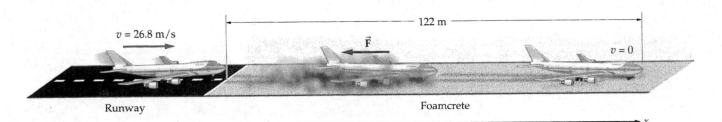

$v = 26.8$ m/s

$\vec{F}$

122 m

$v = 0$

Runway   Foamcrete

x

Solution *(Test your understanding by performing the calculations indicated in each step.)*

1. Use $v^2 = v_0^2 + 2a_x \Delta x$ to find the plane's average acceleration:
   $a_x = -2.94$ m/s^2

2. Sum the forces in the x direction. Let F represent the magnitude of the force $\vec{F}$:
   $\sum F_x = -F$

3. Set the sum of forces equal to mass times acceleration:
   $-F = ma_x$

4. Solve for the magnitude of the average force, F:
   $F = -ma_x = 5.15 \times 10^5$ N

Insight
Though the plane moves in the positive direction, its acceleration, and the net force exerted on it, are in the negative direction. As a result, the plane's speed decreases with time.

Your Turn
Find the plane's stopping distance if the magnitude of the average force exerted by the Foamcrete is doubled.
*(Answers to **Your Turn** problems are given in the back of the book.)*

Note again the care we take with the signs. The plane's acceleration is negative, hence the net force acting on it, $\vec{F}$, is in the negative x direction. On the other hand, the magnitude of the force, F, is positive, as is always the case for magnitudes.
Finally, we end this section with an estimation problem.

EXAMPLE 5-2 Pitch Man: Estimate the Force on the Ball

A pitcher throws a 0.15-kg baseball, accelerating it from rest to a speed of about 90 mi/h. Estimate the force exerted by the pitcher on the ball.

Picture the Problem
We choose the x axis to point in the direction of the pitch. Also indicated in the sketch is the distance over which the pitcher accelerates the ball, Δx. Since we are interested only in the pitch, and not in the subsequent motion of the ball, we ignore the effects of gravity.

Δx

0

x

Strategy
We know the mass, so we can find the force with $F_x = ma_x$ if we can estimate the acceleration. To find the acceleration, we start with the fact that $v_0 = 0$ and $v \approx 90$ mi/h. In addition, we can see from the sketch that a reasonable estimate for Δx is about 2.0 m. Combining these results with the kinematic equation $v^2 = v_0^2 + 2a_x \Delta x$ yields the acceleration, which we then use to find the force.

Solution

1. Starting with the fact that 60 mi/h = 1 mi/min, perform a rough back-of-the-envelope conversion of 90 mi/h to meters per second:
   $$v \approx 90 \text{ mi/h} = \frac{1.5 \text{ mi}}{\text{min}} \approx \frac{2400 \text{ m}}{60 \text{ s}} = 40 \text{ m/s}$$

2. Solve $v^2 = v_0^2 + 2a_x \Delta x$ for the acceleration, a_x. Use the estimates $\Delta x \approx 2.0$ m and $v \approx 40$ m/s:
   $$a_x = \frac{v^2 - v_0^2}{2 \Delta x} \approx \frac{(40 \text{ m/s})^2 - 0}{2(2.0 \text{ m})} = 400 \text{ m/s}^2$$

3. Find the corresponding force with $F_x = ma_x$:
   $$F_x = ma_x \approx (0.15 \text{ kg})(400 \text{ m/s}^2) = 60 \text{ N} \approx 10 \text{ lb}$$

Insight
On the one hand, this is a sizable force, especially when you consider that the ball itself weighs only about 1/3 lb. Thus, the pitcher exerts a force on the ball that is about 30 times greater than the force exerted by Earth's gravity. It follows that ignoring gravity during the pitch is a reasonable approximation.

continued on next page

Science Fundamentals Second Edition

continued from previous page

On the other hand, you might say that 10 lb isn't that much force for a person to exert. That's true, but this force is being exerted with an average speed of about 20 m/s, which means that the pitcher is actually generating about 1.5 horsepower—a sizeable power output for a person. We will cover power in detail in Chapter 7, and relate it to human capabilities.

Practice Problem

What is the approximate speed of the pitch if the force exerted by the pitcher is $\frac{1}{2}(60\,\text{N}) = 30\,\text{N}$?   [**Answer:** 30 m/s or 60 mi/h.]

Some related homework problems: Problem 4, Problem 6

Another way to find the acceleration is to estimate the amount of time it takes to make the pitch. However, since the pitch is delivered so quickly—about 1/10 s—estimating the time would be more difficult than estimating the distance Δx.

Applications of Newton's Laws

6–1   Frictional Forces   142
6–2   Strings and Springs   150
6–3   Translational Equilibrium   154

The climber in this photograph may not be thinking about Newton's laws, but they are involved in every aspect of his endeavor. He relies on the forces transmitted through the ropes to support his weight, and on the pulleys through which the ropes are threaded to give those forces the desired directions. His forward progress is made possible by the substantial frictional force between his hands and the rope. These are but a few of the many real-world applications of Newton's laws that are explored in this chapter.

Newton's laws of motion can be applied to an immense variety of systems, a sampling of which was discussed in Chapter 5. In this chapter we extend our discussion of Newton's laws by introducing new types of forces and by considering new classes of systems.

For example, we begin by considering the forces due to friction between two surfaces. As we shall see, the force of friction is different depending on whether the surfaces are in static contact, or are moving relative to one another—an important consideration in antilock braking systems. And though friction may seem like something that should be eliminated, we show that it is actually essential to life as we know it.

Next, we investigate the forces exerted by strings and springs, and show how these forces can safely suspend a mountain climber over a chasm, or cushion the ride of a locomotive. Finally, we consider the key role that force plays in making circular motion possible.

141

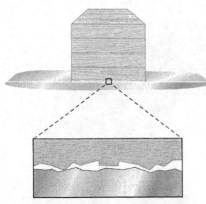

▲ **FIGURE 6–1 The origin of friction**
Even "smooth" surfaces have irregularities when viewed at the microscopic level. This type of roughness contributes to friction.

6–1 Frictional Forces

In Chapter 5 we always assumed that surfaces were smooth and that objects could slide without resistance to their motion. No surface is perfectly smooth, however. When viewed on the atomic level, even the "smoothest" surface is actually rough and jagged, as indicated in **Figure 6–1**. To slide one such surface across another requires a force large enough to overcome the resistance of microscopic hills and valleys bumping together. This is the origin of the force we call **friction.**

We often think of friction as something that should be reduced, or even eliminated if possible. For example, roughly 20 percent of the gasoline you buy does nothing but overcome friction within your car's engine. Clearly, reducing that friction would be most desirable.

On the other hand, friction can be helpful—even indispensable—in other situations. Suppose, for example, that you are standing still and then decide to begin walking forward. The force that accelerates you is the force of friction between your shoes and the ground. We simply couldn't walk or run without friction—it's hard enough when friction is merely reduced, as on an icy sidewalk. Similarly, starting or stopping a car, or even turning a corner, all require friction. Friction is an important and common feature of everyday life.

Since friction is caused by the random, microscopic irregularities of a surface, and since it is greatly affected by other factors such as the presence of lubricants, there is no simple "law of nature" for friction. There are, however, some very useful rules of thumb that give us rather accurate, approximate results for calculating frictional forces. In what follows, we describe these rules of thumb for the two types of friction most commonly used in this text—kinetic friction and static friction.

Kinetic Friction

As its name implies, kinetic friction is the friction encountered when surfaces slide against one another with a finite relative speed. The force generated by this friction, which will be designated with the symbol f_k, acts to oppose the sliding motion at the point of contact between the surfaces.

A series of simple experiments illustrates the main characteristics of kinetic friction. First, imagine attaching a spring scale to a rough object, like a brick, and pulling it across a table, as shown in **Figure 6–2**. If the brick moves with constant velocity, Newton's second law tells us that the net force on the brick must be zero. Hence, the force read on the scale, F, has the same magnitude as the force of kinetic friction, f_k. Now, if we repeat the experiment, but this time put a second brick on top of the first, we find that the force needed to pull the brick with constant velocity is doubled, to $2F$.

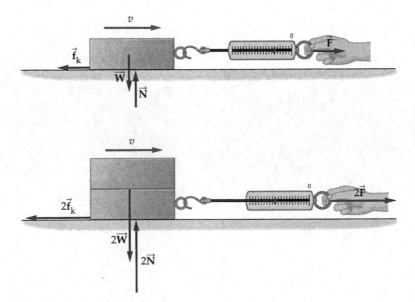

▶ **FIGURE 6–2 Kinetic friction and the normal force**

In the top part of the figure, a force F is required to pull the brick with constant speed v. Thus the force of kinetic friction is $f_k = F$. In the bottom part of the figure, the normal force has been doubled, and so has the force of kinetic friction, to $f_k = 2F$.

Science Fundamentals Second Edition

From this experiment we see that when we double the normal force—by stacking up two bricks, for example—the force of kinetic friction is also doubled. In general, the force of kinetic friction is found to be proportional to the magnitude of the normal force, N. Stated mathematically, this observation can be written as follows:

$$f_k = \mu_k N \qquad \qquad 6\text{--}1$$

The constant of proportionality, μ_k (pronounced "mew sub k"), is referred to as the **coefficient of kinetic friction.** In Figure 6–2 the normal force is equal to the weight of the bricks, but this is a special case. The normal force is greater than the weight if someone pushes down on the bricks, and this would cause more friction, or less than the weight if the bricks are placed on an incline. The former case is considered in several homework problems, and the latter case is considered in Examples 6–2 and 6–3.

Since f_k and N are both forces, and hence have the same units, we see that μ_k is a dimensionless number. The coefficient of kinetic friction is always positive, and typical values range between 0 and 1, as indicated in Table 6–1. The interpretation of μ_k is simple: If $\mu_k = 0.1$, for example, the force of kinetic friction is one-tenth of the normal force. Simply put, the greater μ_k the greater the friction; the smaller μ_k the smaller the friction.

TABLE 6–1 Typical Coefficients of Friction		
Materials	Kinetic, μ_k	Static, μ_s
Rubber on concrete (dry)	0.80	1–4
Steel on steel	0.57	0.74
Glass on glass	0.40	0.94
Wood on leather	0.40	0.50
Copper on steel	0.36	0.53
Rubber on concrete (wet)	0.25	0.30
Steel on ice	0.06	0.10
Waxed ski on snow	0.05	0.10
Teflon on Teflon	0.04	0.04
Synovial joints in humans	0.003	0.01

As we know from everyday experience, the force of kinetic friction tends to oppose motion, as shown in Figure 6–2. Thus, $f_k = \mu_k N$ is not a vector equation, because N is perpendicular to the direction of motion. When doing calculations with the force of kinetic friction, we use $f_k = \mu_k N$ to find its magnitude, and we draw its direction so that it is opposite to the direction of motion.

There are two more friction experiments of particular interest. First, suppose that when we pull a brick, we initially pull it at the speed v, then later at the speed $2v$. What forces do we measure? It turns out that the force of kinetic friction is approximately the same in each case—it certainly does not double when we double the speed. Second, let's try standing the brick on end, so that it has a smaller area in contact with the table. If this smaller area is half the previous area, is the force halved? No, the force remains essentially the same, regardless of the area of contact.

We summarize these observations with the following three rules of thumb for kinetic friction:

Rules of Thumb for Kinetic Friction
The force of kinetic friction between two surfaces is:

1. Proportional to the magnitude of the normal force, N, between the surfaces,

$$f_k = \mu_k N$$

2. Independent of the relative speed of the surfaces.

3. Independent of the area of contact between the surfaces.

▲ Friction plays an important role in almost everything we do. Sometimes it is desirable to reduce friction; in other cases we want as much friction as possible. For example, it is more fun to ride on a water slide (upper) if the friction is low. Similarly, an engine operates more efficiently when it is oiled. When running, however, we need friction to help us speed up, slow down, and make turns. The sole of this running shoe (lower), like a car tire, is designed to maximize friction.

Science Fundamentals Second Edition

Again, these rules are useful and fairly accurate, though they are still only approximate. For simplicity, when we do calculations involving kinetic friction in this text, we will use these rules as if they were exact.

Before we show how to use f_k in calculations, we should make a comment regarding rule 3. This rule often seems rather surprising and counterintuitive. How is it that a larger area of contact doesn't produce a larger force? One way to think about this is to consider that when the area of contact is large, the normal force is spread out over a large area, giving a small force per area, F/A. As a result, the microscopic hills and valleys are not pressed too deeply against one another. On the other hand, if the area is small the normal force is concentrated in a small region, which presses the surfaces together more firmly, due to the large force per area. The net effect is roughly the same in either case.

Now, let's consider a commonly encountered situation in which kinetic friction plays a decisive role.

EXAMPLE 6-1 Pass the Salt—Please

Someone at the other end of the table asks you to pass the salt. Feeling quite dashing, you slide the 50.0-g salt shaker in their direction, giving it an initial speed of 1.15 m/s. If the shaker comes to rest with constant acceleration in 0.840 m, what is the coefficient of kinetic friction between the shaker and the table?

Picture the Problem
We choose the positive x direction to be the direction of motion, and the positive y direction to be upward. Two forces act in the y direction; the shaker's weight, $\vec{W} = -W\hat{y} = -mg\hat{y}$, and the normal force, $\vec{N} = N\hat{y}$. Only one force acts in the x direction; the force of kinetic friction, $\vec{f}_k = -\mu_k N\hat{x}$. Note that the shaker moves through a distance of 0.840 m with an initial speed $v_{0x} = 1.15$ m/s.

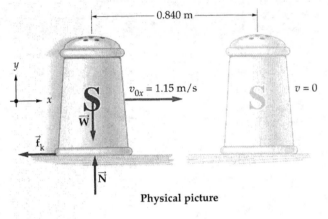

Physical picture

Strategy
Since the frictional force has a magnitude of $f_k = \mu_k N$, it follows that $\mu_k = f_k/N$. Therefore, we need to find the magnitudes of the frictional force, f_k, and the normal force, N.

To find f_k we set $\Sigma F_x = ma_x$, and find a_x with the kinematic equation $v_x^2 = v_{0x}^2 + 2a_x\Delta x$.

To find N we set $a_y = 0$ (since there is no motion in the y direction) and solve for N using $\Sigma F_y = ma_y = 0$.

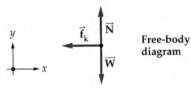

Free-body diagram

Solution

1. Set $\Sigma F_x = ma_x$ to find f_k in terms of a_x:

$$\sum F_x = -f_k = ma_x \quad \text{or} \quad f_k = -ma_x$$

2. Determine a_x by using the kinematic equation relating velocity to position, $v_x^2 = v_{0x}^2 + 2a_x\Delta x$:

$$v_x^2 = v_{0x}^2 + 2a_x\Delta x$$
$$a_x = \frac{v_x^2 - v_{0x}^2}{2\Delta x} = \frac{0 - (1.15 \text{ m/s})^2}{2(0.840 \text{ m})} = -0.787 \text{ m/s}^2$$

3. Set $\Sigma F_y = ma_y = 0$ to find the normal force, N:

$$\sum F_y = N + (-W) = ma_y = 0 \quad \text{or} \quad N = W = mg$$

4. Substitute $N = mg$ and $f_k = -ma_x$ (with $a_x = -0.787$ m/s^2) into $\mu_k = f_k/N$ to find μ_k:

$$\mu_k = \frac{f_k}{N} = \frac{-ma_x}{mg} = \frac{-a_x}{g} = \frac{-(-0.787 \text{ m/s}^2)}{9.81 \text{ m/s}^2} = 0.0802$$

Insight
Note that m canceled in line 4, so our final result is independent of the shaker's mass. For example, if we were to slide a shaker with twice the mass, but with the same initial speed, it would slide the same distance. It is unlikely this independence would have been apparent if we had worked the problem numerically rather than symbolically.

Practice Problem
Given the same initial speed and a coefficient of kinetic friction equal to 0.120, what is **(a)** the acceleration of the shaker, and **(b)** the distance it slides? **[Answer: (a)** $a_x = -1.18$ m/s^2, **(b)** 0.560 m]

Some related homework problems: Problem 1, Problem 14

In the next Example we consider a system that is inclined at an angle θ relative to the horizontal. As a result, the normal force responsible for the kinetic friction is less than the weight of the object. To be very clear about how we handle the force vectors in such a case, we begin by resolving each vector into its x and y components.

PROBLEM-SOLVING NOTE

Choice of Coordinate System: Incline

On an incline, align one axis (x) parallel to the surface, and the other axis (y) perpendicular to the surface. That way the motion is in the x direction. Since no motion occurs in the y direction, we know that $a_y = 0$.

EXAMPLE 6–2 Making a Big Splash

A trained sea lion slides from rest with constant acceleration down a 3.0-m-long ramp into a pool of water. If the ramp is inclined at an angle of 23° above the horizontal and the coefficient of kinetic friction between the sea lion and the ramp is 0.26, how long does it take for the sea lion to make a splash in the pool?

Picture the Problem

As is usual with inclined surfaces, we choose one axis to be parallel to the surface and the other to be perpendicular to it. In our sketch, the sea lion accelerates in the positive x direction ($a_x > 0$), having started from rest, $v_{0x} = 0$. We are free to choose the initial position of the sea lion to be $x_0 = 0$. There is no motion in the y direction, and therefore $a_y = 0$. Finally, we note from the free-body diagram that $\vec{N} = N\hat{y}$, $\vec{f}_k = -\mu_k N\hat{x}$, and $\vec{W} = (mg \sin \theta)\hat{x} + (-mg \cos \theta)\hat{y}$.

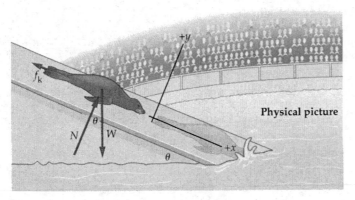

Physical picture

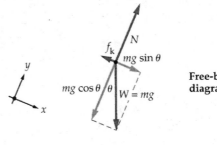

Free-body diagram

Strategy

We can use the kinematic equation relating position to time, $x = x_0 + v_{0x}t + \frac{1}{2}a_x t^2$, to find the time of the sea lion's slide. It will be necessary, however, to first determine the acceleration of the sea lion in the x direction, a_x.

To find a_x we apply Newton's second law to the sea lion. First, we can find N by setting $\Sigma F_y = ma_y$ equal to zero (since $a_y = 0$). It is important to start by finding N because we need it to find the force of kinetic friction, $f_k = \mu_k N$. Using f_k in the sum of forces in the x direction, $\Sigma F_x = ma_x$, allows us to solve for a_x and, finally, for the time.

Solution

1. We begin by resolving each of the three force vectors into x and y components:

$$N_x = 0 \qquad\qquad N_y = N$$
$$f_{k,x} = -f_k = -\mu_k N \qquad f_{k,y} = 0$$
$$W_x = mg \sin \theta \qquad W_y = -mg \cos \theta$$

2. Set $\Sigma F_y = ma_y = 0$ to find N:
We see that N is less than the weight, mg:

$$\sum F_y = N - mg \cos \theta = ma_y = 0$$
$$N = mg \cos \theta$$

3. Next, set $\Sigma F_x = ma_x$:
Note that the mass cancels in this equation:

$$\sum F_x = mg \sin \theta - \mu_k N$$
$$= mg \sin \theta - \mu_k mg \cos \theta = ma_x$$

4. Solve for the acceleration in the x direction, a_x:

$$a_x = g(\sin \theta - \mu_k \cos \theta)$$
$$= (9.81 \text{ m/s}^2)[\sin 23° - (0.26) \cos 23°] = 1.5 \text{ m/s}^2$$

5. Use $x = x_0 + v_{0x}t + \frac{1}{2}a_x t^2$ to find the time when the sea lion reaches the bottom. We choose $x_0 = 0$, and we are given that $v_{0x} = 0$, hence we set $x = \frac{1}{2}a_x t^2 = 3.0$ m and solve for t:

$$x = \frac{1}{2}a_x t^2$$
$$t = \sqrt{\frac{2x}{a_x}} = \sqrt{\frac{2(3.0 \text{ m})}{1.5 \text{ m/s}^2}} = 2.0 \text{ s}$$

continued on next page

continued from previous page

Insight
Note that we don't need the sea lion's mass to find the time. On the other hand, if we wanted the magnitude of the force of kinetic friction, $f_k = \mu_k N = \mu_k mg \cos \theta$, the mass would be needed.

It is useful to compare the sliding salt shaker in Example 6–1 with the sliding sea lion in this Example. In the case of the salt shaker, friction is the only force acting along the direction of motion (opposite to the direction of motion, in fact), and it brings the object to rest. Because of the slope on which the sea lion slides, however, it experiences both a component of its weight in the forward direction and the friction force opposite to the motion. Since the component of the weight is the larger of the two forces, the sea lion accelerates down the slope—friction only acts to slow its progress.

Practice Problem
How long would it take the sea lion to reach the water if there were no friction in this system?   [**Answer:** 1.3 s]

Some related homework problems: Problem 8, Problem 56

Static Friction

Static friction tends to keep two surfaces from moving relative to one another. It, like kinetic friction, is due to the microscopic irregularities of surfaces that are in contact. In fact, static friction is typically stronger than kinetic friction because when surfaces are in static contact, their microscopic hills and valleys can nestle down deeply into one another, thus forming a strong connection between the surfaces that may even include molecular bonding. In kinetic friction, the surfaces bounce along relative to one another and don't become as firmly enmeshed.

As we did with kinetic friction, let's use the results of some simple experiments to determine the rules of thumb for static friction. We start with a brick at rest on a table, with no horizontal force pulling on it, as in **Figure 6–3**. Of course, in this case the force of static friction is zero; no force is needed to keep the brick from sliding.

▶ **FIGURE 6–3 Static friction**
As the force applied to an object increases, so does the force of static friction—up to a certain point. Beyond this maximum value, static friction can no longer hold the object, and it begins to slide. Now kinetic friction takes over.

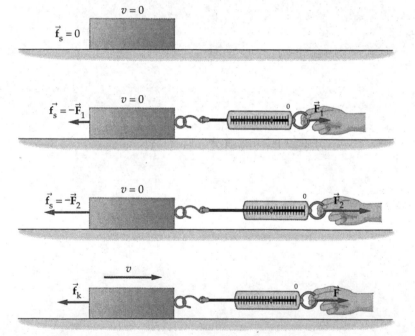

Next, attach a spring scale to the brick and pull with a small force of magnitude F_1, a force small enough that the brick doesn't move. Since the brick is still at rest, it follows that the force of static friction, f_s, is equal in magnitude to the applied force; that is, $f_s = F_1$. Now, increase the applied force to a new value, F_2, which is still small enough that the brick stays at rest. In this case, the force of static friction has also increased so that $f_s = F_2$. If we continue increasing the applied force, we eventually reach a value beyond which the brick starts to move and kinetic friction takes over, as shown in the figure. Thus, there is an upper limit to the force that can be exerted by static friction, and we call this upper limit $f_{s,max}$.

To summarize, the force of static friction, f_s, can have any value between zero and $f_{s,max}$. This can be written mathematically as follows:

$$0 \leq f_s \leq f_{s,max} \qquad 6\text{--}2$$

Imagine repeating the experiment, only now with a second brick on top of the first. This doubles the normal force and it also doubles the maximum force of static friction. Thus, the maximum force is proportional to the magnitude of the normal force, or

$$f_{s,max} = \mu_s N \qquad 6\text{--}3$$

The constant of proportionality is called μ_s (pronounced "mew sub s"), the **coefficient of static friction.** Note that μ_s, like μ_k, is dimensionless. Typical values are given in Table 6–1. In most cases, μ_s is greater than μ_k, indicating that the force of static friction is greater than the force of kinetic friction, as mentioned. In fact, it is not uncommon for μ_s to be greater than 1, as in the case of rubber in contact with dry concrete.

Finally, two additional comments regarding the nature of static friction: (i) Experiments show that static friction, like kinetic friction, is independent of the area of contact. (ii) The force of static friction is not in the direction of the normal force, thus $f_{s,max} = \mu_s N$ is not a vector relation. The direction of f_s is parallel to the surface of contact, and opposite to the direction the object would move if there were no friction.

These observations are summarized in the following rules of thumb:

Rules of Thumb for Static Friction

The force of static friction between two surfaces has the following properties:

1. It takes on any value between zero and the maximum possible force of static friction, $f_{s,max} = \mu_s N$:

$$0 \leq f_s \leq \mu_s N$$

2. It is independent of the area of contact between the surfaces.

3. It is parallel to the surface of contact, and in the direction that opposes relative motion.

Next, we consider a practical method of determining the coefficient of static friction. As with the last Example, we begin by resolving all relevant force vectors into their x and y components.

▲ The coefficient of static friction between two surfaces depends on many factors, including whether the surfaces are dry or wet. On the desert floor of Death Valley, California, occasional rains can reduce the friction between rocks and the sandy ground to such an extent that strong winds can move the rocks over considerable distances. This results in linear "rock trails," which record the direction of the winds at different times.

EXAMPLE 6–3 Slightly Tilted

A flatbed truck slowly tilts its bed upward to dispose of a 95.0-kg crate. For small angles of tilt the crate stays put, but when the tilt angle exceeds 23.2°, the crate begins to slide. What is the coefficient of static friction between the bed of the truck and the crate?

Picture the Problem

We align our coordinate system with the incline, and choose the positive x direction to point down the slope. Note that three forces act on the crate: the normal force, $\vec{N} = N\hat{y}$, the force of static friction, $\vec{f}_s = -\mu_s N\hat{x}$, and the weight, $\vec{W} = (mg \sin \theta)\hat{x} + (-mg \cos \theta)\hat{y}$.

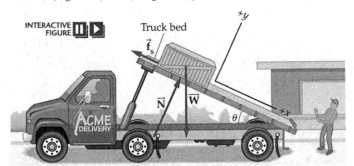

Physical picture

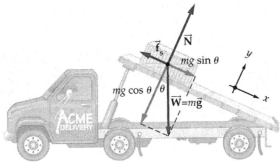

Free-body diagram

continued on next page

continued from previous page

Strategy

When the crate is on the verge of slipping, but has not yet slipped, its acceleration is zero in both the x and y directions. In addition, "verge of slipping" means that the magnitude of the static friction is at its maximum value, $f_s = f_{s,max} = \mu_s N$. Thus, we set $\Sigma F_y = ma_y = 0$ to find N, then use $\Sigma F_x = ma_x = 0$ to find μ_s.

Solution

1. Resolve the three force vectors acting on the crate into x and y components:

$$N_x = 0 \qquad\qquad N_y = N$$
$$f_{s,x} = -f_{s,max} = -\mu_s N \qquad\qquad f_{s,y} = 0$$
$$W_x = mg \sin\theta \qquad\qquad W_y = -mg \cos\theta$$

2. Set $\Sigma F_y = ma_y = 0$, since $a_y = 0$:
   Solve for the normal force, N:

$$\sum F_y = N_y + f_{s,y} + W_y = N + 0 - mg\cos\theta = ma_y = 0$$
$$N = mg\cos\theta$$

3. Set $\Sigma F_x = ma_x = 0$, since the crate is at rest, and use the result for N obtained in step 2:

$$\sum F_x = N_x + f_{s,x} + W_x = ma_x = 0$$
$$= 0 - \mu_s N + mg\sin\theta$$
$$= 0 - \mu_s mg\cos\theta + mg\sin\theta$$

4. Solve the expression for the coefficient of static friction, μ_s:

$$\mu_s mg\cos\theta = mg\sin\theta$$
$$\mu_s = \frac{mg\sin\theta}{mg\cos\theta} = \tan\theta = \tan 23.2° = 0.429$$

Insight

In general, if an object is on the verge of slipping when the surface on which it rests is tilted at an angle θ_c, the coefficient of static friction between the object and the surface is $\mu_s = \tan\theta_c$. Note that this result is independent of the mass of the object. In particular, the critical angle for this crate is precisely the same whether it is filled with feathers or lead bricks.

Practice Problem

Find the magnitude of the force of static friction acting on the crate. [**Answer:** $f_{s,max} = \mu_s N = 367$ N]

Some related homework problems: Problem 9, Problem 68

Recall that static friction can have magnitudes less than its maximum possible value. This point is emphasized in the following Active Example.

ACTIVE EXAMPLE 6–1 The Force of Static Friction

In the previous Example, what is the magnitude of the force of static friction acting on the crate when the truck bed is tilted at an angle of 20.0°?

Solution *(Test your understanding by performing the calculations indicated in each step.)*

1. Sum the x components of force acting on the crate: $\sum F_x = 0 - f_s + mg\sin\theta$

2. Set this sum equal to zero (since $a_x = 0$) and solve for the magnitude of the static friction force, f_s: $f_s = mg\sin\theta$

3. Substitute numerical values, including $\theta = 20.0°$: $f_s = 319$ N

Insight

Notice that the force of static friction in this case has a magnitude (319 N) that is less than the value of 367 N found in the Practice Problem of Example 6–3, even though the coefficient of static friction is precisely the same.

Your Turn

At what tilt angle will the force of static friction have a magnitude of 225 N?

*(Answers to **Your Turn** problems are given in the back of the book.)*

Finally, friction often enters into problems dealing with vehicles with rolling wheels. In Conceptual Checkpoint 6–1, we consider which type of friction is appropriate in such cases.

CONCEPTUAL CHECKPOINT 6-1   Friction for Rolling Tires

A car drives with its tires rolling freely. Is the friction between the tires and the road (**a**) kinetic or (**b**) static?

Reasoning and Discussion
A reasonable-sounding answer is that because the car is moving, the friction between its tires and the road must be kinetic friction—but this is not the case.

Actually, the friction is static because the bottom of the tire is in static contact with the road. To understand this, watch your feet as you walk. Even though you are moving, each foot is in static contact with the ground once you step down on it. Your foot doesn't move again until you lift it up and move it forward for the next step. A tire can be thought of as a succession of feet arranged in a circle, each of which is momentarily in static contact with the ground.

Answer:
(**b**) The friction between the tires and the road is static friction.

To summarize, if a car skids, the friction acting on it is kinetic; if its wheels are rolling, the friction is static. Since static friction is generally greater than kinetic friction, it follows that a car can be stopped in less distance if its wheels are rolling (static friction) than if its wheels are locked up (kinetic friction). This is the idea behind the antilock braking systems (ABS) that are available on many cars. When the brakes are applied in a car with ABS, an electronic rotation sensor at each wheel detects whether the wheel is about to start skidding. To prevent skidding, a small computer automatically begins to modulate the hydraulic pressure in the brake lines in short bursts, causing the brakes to release and then reapply in rapid succession. This allows the wheels to continue rotating, even in an emergency stop, and for static friction to determine the stopping distance. **Figure 6-4** shows a comparison of braking distances for cars with and without ABS. An added benefit of ABS is that a driver is better able to steer and control a braking car if its wheels are rotating.

REAL-WORLD PHYSICS
Antilock braking systems

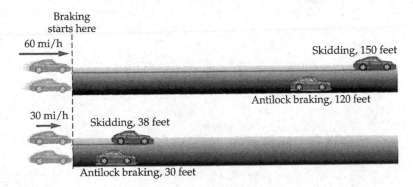

◀ **FIGURE 6-4 Stopping distance with and without ABS**

Antilock braking systems (ABS) allow a car to stop with static friction rather than kinetic friction—even in a case where a person slams on the brakes. As a result, the braking distance is reduced, due to the fact that μ_s is typically greater than μ_k. Professional drivers can beat the performance of ABS by carefully adjusting the force they apply to the brake pedal during a stop, but ABS provides essentially the same performance—within a few percent—for a person who simply pushes the brake pedal to the floor and holds it there.

▲ The angle that the sloping sides of a sand pile (left) make with the horizontal is determined by the coefficient of static friction between grains of sand, in much the same way that static friction determines the angle at which the crate in Example 6-3 begins to slide. The same basic mechanism determines the angle of the cone-shaped mass of rock debris at the base of a cliff, known as a talus slope (right).

Science Fundamentals Second Edition

6–2 Strings and Springs

A common way to exert a force on an object is to pull on it with a string, a rope, a cable, or a wire. Similarly, you can push or pull on an object if you attach it to a spring. In this section we discuss the basic features of strings and springs and how they transmit forces.

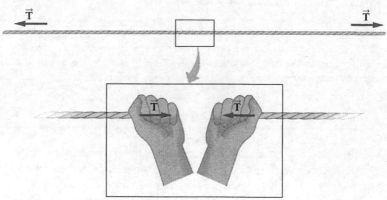

▲ **FIGURE 6–5 Tension in a string**
A string, pulled from either end, has a tension, T. If the string were to be cut at any point, the force required to hold the ends together is T.

Strings and Tension

Imagine picking up a light string and holding it with one end in each hand. If you pull to the right with your right hand with a force T and to the left with your left hand with a force T, the string becomes taut. In such a case, we say that there is a **tension** T in the string. To be more specific, if your friend were to cut the string at some point, the tension T is the force pulling the ends apart, as illustrated in **Figure 6–5**—that is, T is the force your friend would have to exert with each hand to hold the cut ends together. Note that at any given point, the tension pulls equally to the right and to the left.

As an example, consider a rope that is attached to the ceiling at one end, and to a box with a weight of 105 N at the other end, as shown in **Figure 6–6**. In addition, suppose the rope is uniform, and that it has a total weight of 2.00 N. What is the tension in the rope (i) where it attaches to the box, (ii) at its midpoint, and (iii) where it attaches to the ceiling?

First, the rope holds the box at rest; thus, the tension where the rope attaches to the box is simply the weight of the box, $T_1 = 105$ N. At the midpoint of the rope, the tension supports the weight of the box, plus the weight of half the rope. Thus, $T_2 = 105 \, \text{N} + \frac{1}{2}(2.00 \, \text{N}) = 106$ N. Similarly, at the ceiling the tension supports the box plus all of the rope, giving a tension of $T_3 = 107$ N. Note that the tension pulls down on the ceiling but pulls up on the box.

From this discussion, we can see that the tension in the rope changes slightly from top to bottom because of the mass of the rope. If the rope had less mass, the difference in tension between its two ends would also be less. In particular, if the rope's mass were to be vanishingly small, the difference in tension would vanish as well. In this text, we will assume that all ropes, strings, wires, and so on are practically massless—unless specifically stated otherwise—and, hence, that the tension is the same throughout their length.

Pulleys are often used to redirect a force exerted by a string, as indicated in **Figure 6–7**. In the ideal case, a pulley has no mass, and no friction in its bearings. Thus, *an ideal pulley simply changes the direction of the tension in a string, without changing its magnitude.* If a system contains more than one pulley, however, it is possible to arrange them in such a way as to "magnify a force," even if each pulley itself merely redirects the tension in a string. The traction device considered in the next Example shows one way this can be accomplished in a system that uses three ideal pulleys.

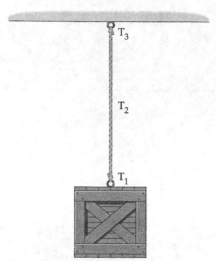

▲ **FIGURE 6–6 Tension in a heavy rope**
Because of the weight of the rope, the tension is noticeably different at points 1, 2, and 3. As the rope becomes lighter, however, the difference in tension decreases. In the limit of a rope of zero mass, the tension is the same throughout the rope.

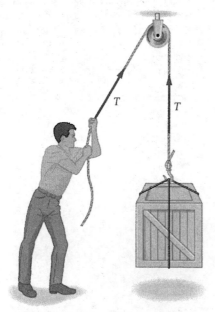

▲ **FIGURE 6–7 A pulley changes the direction of a tension**
In an ideal string, the tension has the same magnitude, T, throughout its length. A pulley can serve to redirect the string, however, so that the tension acts in a different direction.

EXAMPLE 6–4 A Bad Break: Setting a Broken Leg with Traction

A traction device employing three pulleys is applied to a broken leg, as shown in the sketch. The middle pulley is attached to the sole of the foot, and a mass m supplies the tension in the ropes. Find the value of the mass m if the force exerted on the sole of the foot by the middle pulley is to be 165 N.

Picture the Problem

Our sketch shows the physical picture as well as the tension forces acting on the middle pulley. Notice that on the upper portion of the rope the tension is $\vec{T}_1 = (T \cos 40.0°)\hat{x} + (T \sin 40.0°)\hat{y}$; on the lower portion it is $\vec{T}_2 = (T \cos 40.0°)\hat{x} + (-T \sin 40.0°)\hat{y}$.

Strategy

We begin by noting that the rope supports the hanging mass m. As a result, the tension in the rope, T, must be equal in magnitude to the weight of the mass; $T = mg$.

Next, the pulleys simply change the direction of the tension without changing its magnitude. Therefore, the net force exerted on the sole of the foot is the sum of the tension T at 40.0° above the horizontal plus the tension T at 40.0° below the horizontal. We will calculate the net force component by component.

Once we calculate the net force acting on the foot, we set it equal to 165 N and solve for the tension T. Finally, we find the mass using the relation $T = mg$.

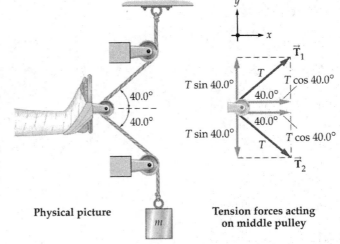

Physical picture

Tension forces acting
on middle pulley

Solution

1. First, consider the tension that acts upward and to the right on the middle pulley. Resolve this tension into x and y components:

$$T_{1,x} = T \cos 40.0° \qquad T_{1,y} = T \sin 40.0°$$

2. Next, consider the tension that acts downward and to the right on the middle pulley. Resolve this tension into x and y components. Note the minus sign in the y component:

$$T_{2,x} = T \cos 40.0° \qquad T_{2,y} = -T \sin 40.0°$$

3. Sum the x and y components of force acting on the middle pulley. We see that the net force acts only in the x direction, as one might expect from symmetry:

$$\sum F_x = T \cos 40.0° + T \cos 40.0° = 2T \cos 40.0°$$
$$\sum F_y = T \sin 40.0° - T \sin 40.0° = 0$$

4. Step 3 shows that the net force acting on the middle pulley is $2T \cos 40.0°$. Set this force equal to 165 N and solve for T:

$$2T \cos 40.0° = 165 \text{ N}$$
$$T = \frac{165 \text{ N}}{2 \cos 40.0°} = 108 \text{ N}$$

5. Solve for the mass, m, using $T = mg$:

$$T = mg$$
$$m = \frac{T}{g} = \frac{108 \text{ N}}{9.81 \text{ m/s}^2} = 11.0 \text{ kg}$$

Insight

As pointed out earlier, this pulley arrangement "magnifies the force" in the sense that a 108-N weight attached to the rope produces a 165-N force exerted on the foot by the middle pulley. Note that the tension in the rope always has the same value—$T = 108$ N—as expected with ideal pulleys, but because of the arrangement of the pulleys the force applied to the foot by the rope is $2T \cos 40.0° > T$.

In addition, notice that the force exerted on the foot by the middle pulley produces an opposing force in the leg that acts in the direction of the head (a cephalad force), as desired to set a broken leg and keep it straight as it heals.

Practice Problem

(a) Would the required mass m increase or decrease if the angles in this device were changed from 40.0° to 30.0°? **(b)** Find the mass m for an angle of 30.0°. [**Answer: (a)** The required mass m will decrease. **(b)** 9.71 kg]

Some related homework problems: Problem 18, Problem 21, Problem 31

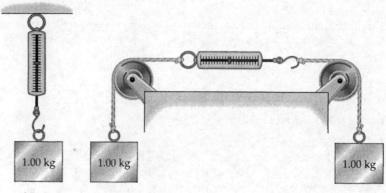

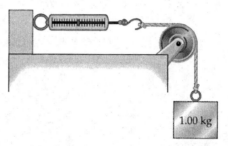

CONCEPTUAL CHECKPOINT 6–2   Compare the Readings on the Scales

The scale at left reads 9.81 N. Is the reading of the scale at right (a) greater than 9.81 N, (b) equal to 9.81 N, or (c) less than 9.81 N?

Reasoning and Discussion

Since a pulley simply changes the direction of the tension in a string without changing its magnitude, it is clear that the scale attached to the ceiling reads the same as the scale shown in the figure below.

There is no difference, however, between attaching the top end of the scale to something rigid and attaching it to another 1.00-kg hanging mass. In either case, the fact that the scale is at rest means that a force of 9.81 N must be exerted to the left on the top of the scale to balance the 9.81-N force exerted on the lower end of the scale. As a result, the two scales read the same.

Answer:
(b) The reading of the scale at right is equal to 9.81 N.

Springs and Hooke's Law

Suppose you take a spring of length L, as shown in **Figure 6–8 (a)**, and attach it to a block. If you pull on the spring, causing it to stretch to a length $L + x$, the spring pulls on the block with a force of magnitude F. If you increase the length of the spring to $L + 2x$, the force exerted by the spring increases to $2F$. Similarly, if you compress the spring to a length $L - x$, the spring pushes on the block with a force of magnitude F, where F is the same force given previously. As you might expect, compression to a length $L - 2x$ results in a push of magnitude $2F$.

As a result of these experiments, we can say that a spring exerts a force that is proportional to the amount, x, by which it is stretched or compressed. Thus, if F is the magnitude of the spring force, we can say that

$$F = kx$$

In this expression, k is a constant of proportionality, referred to as the **force constant,** or, equivalently, as the **spring constant.** Since F has units of newtons and x has units of meters, it follows that k has units of newtons per meter, or N/m. The larger the value of k, the stiffer the spring.

To be more precise, consider the spring shown in **Figure 6–8 (b)**. Note that we have placed the origin of the x axis at the equilibrium length of the spring—that is, at the position of the spring when no force acts on it. Now, if we stretch the spring so that the end of the spring is at a positive value of $x(x > 0)$, we find that

▲ FIGURE 6–8 Spring Forces
When dealing with a spring, it is convenient to choose the origin at the equilibrium (zero force) position. In the cases shown above, the force is strictly in the x direction, and is given by $F_x = -kx$. Note that the minus sign means that the force is opposite to the displacement; that is, the force is restoring.

the spring exerts a force of magnitude kx in the negative x direction. Thus, the spring force (which has only an x component) can be written as

$$F_x = -kx$$

Similarly, consider compressing the spring so that its end is at a negative value of $x (x < 0)$. In this case, the force exerted by the spring is of magnitude kx, and points in the positive x direction, as is shown in Figure 6–8 (b). Again, we can write the spring force as

$$F_x = -kx$$

To see that this is correct—that is, that F_x is positive in this case—recall that x is negative, which means that $(-x)$ is positive.

This result for the force of a spring is known as Hooke's law, after Robert Hooke (1635–1703). It is really just a good rule of thumb rather than a law of nature. Clearly, it can't work for any amount of stretching. For example, we know that if we stretch a spring far enough it will be permanently deformed, and will never return to its original length. Still, for small stretches or compressions, Hooke's law is quite accurate.

Rules of Thumb for Springs (Hooke's Law)

A spring stretched or compressed by the amount x from its equilibrium length exerts a force whose x component is given by

$$F_x = -kx \quad \textit{(gives magnitude and direction)} \qquad 6\text{–}4$$

If we are interested only in the magnitude of the force associated with a given stretch or compression, we use the somewhat simpler form of Hooke's law:

$$F = kx \quad \textit{(gives magnitude only)} \qquad 6\text{–}5$$

In this text, we consider only **ideal springs**—that is, springs that are massless, and that are assumed to obey Hooke's law exactly.

Since the stretch of a spring and the force it exerts are proportional, we can now see how a spring scale operates. In particular, pulling on the two ends of a scale stretches the spring inside it by an amount proportional to the applied force. Once the scale is calibrated—by stretching the spring with a known, or reference, force—we can use it to measure other unknown forces.

Finally, it is useful to note that Hooke's law, which we've introduced in the context of ideal springs, is particularly important in physics because it applies to so much more than just springs. For example, the forces that hold atoms together are often modeled by Hooke's law—that is, as "interatomic springs"—and these are the forces that are ultimately responsible for the normal force (Chapter 5), vibrations and oscillations (Chapter 13), wave motion (Chapter 14), and even the thermal expansion of solids (Chapter 16). And this just scratches the surface—Hooke's law comes up in one form or another in virtually every field of physics. In the following Active Example, we present a biomedical application of Hooke's law.

▲ Springs come in a variety of sizes and shapes. The large springs on a railroad car (top) are so stiff and heavy that you can't compress or stretch them by hand. Still, three of them are needed to smooth the ride of this car. In contrast, the delicate spiral spring inside a watch (bottom) flexes with even the slightest touch. It exerts enough force, however, to power the equally delicate mechanism of the watch.

ACTIVE EXAMPLE 6–2 Nasal Strips

REAL-WORLD PHYSICS: BIO

An increasingly popular device for improving air flow through nasal passages is the nasal strip, which consists of two flat, polyester springs enclosed by an adhesive tape covering. Measurements show that a nasal strip can exert an outward force of 0.22 N on the nose, causing it to expand by 3.5 mm. **(a)** Treating the nose as an ideal spring, find its force constant in newtons per meter. **(b)** How much force would be required to expand the nose by 4.0 mm?

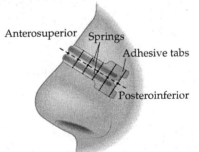

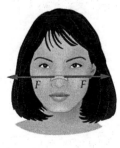

continued on next page

Science Fundamentals Second Edition

continued from previous page

Solution *(Test your understanding by performing the calculations indicated in each step.)*

Part (a)

1. Solve the magnitude form of Hooke's law, $F = kx$, for the force constant, k: $\qquad$ $k = F/x$

2. Substitute numerical values for F and x: $\qquad$ $k = 62\,\text{N/m}$

Part (b)

3. Use $F = kx$ to find the required force: $\qquad$ $F = 0.25\,\text{N}$

Insight

Even though the human nose is certainly not an ideal spring, Hooke's law is still a useful way to model its behavior when dealing with forces and the stretches they cause.

Your Turn

Suppose a new nasal strip comes on the market that exerts an outward force of 0.32 N. What expansion of the nose will be caused by this strip?

(Answers to **Your Turn** *problems are given in the back of the book.)*

6–3 Translational Equilibrium

When we say that an object is in **translational equilibrium,** we mean that the net force acting on it is zero:

$$\sum \vec{F} = 0 \qquad\qquad 6\text{–}6$$

From Newton's second law, this is equivalent to saying that the object's acceleration is zero. In two-dimensional systems, translational equilibrium implies two independent conditions: $\Sigma F_x = 0$ and $\Sigma F_y = 0$. In one dimension, only one of these conditions will apply.

Later, in Chapters 10 and 11, we will study objects that have both rotational and linear motions. In such cases, rotational equilibrium will be as important as translation equilibrium. For now, however, when we say equilibrium, we simply mean translational equilibrium.

As a first example, consider the one-dimensional situation illustrated in **Figure 6–9**. Here we see a person lifting a bucket of water from a well by pulling down on a rope that passes over a pulley. If the bucket's mass is m, and it is rising with constant speed v, what is the tension T_1 in the rope attached to the bucket? In addition, what is the tension T_2 in the chain that supports the pulley?

To answer these questions, we first note that both the bucket and the pulley are in equilibrium; that is, they both have zero acceleration. As a result, the net force on each of them must be zero.

Let's start with the bucket. In Figure 6–9, we see that just two forces act on the bucket: (i) its weight $W = mg$ downward, and (ii) the tension in the rope, T_1 upward. If we take upward to be the positive direction, we can write $\Sigma F_y = 0$ for the bucket as follows:

$$T_1 - mg = 0$$

Therefore, the tension in the rope is $T_1 = mg$. Note that this is also the force the person must exert downward on the rope, as expected.

Next, we consider the pulley. In Figure 6–9, we see that three forces act on it: (i) the tension in the chain, T_2 upward, (ii) the tension in the part of the rope leading to the bucket, T_1 downward, and (iii) the tension in the part of the rope leading to the person, T_1 downward. Note that we don't include the weight of the pulley since we consider it to be ideal; that is, massless and frictionless. If we

Physical picture

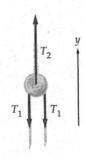

Forces acting
on the pulley

Forces acting
on the bucket

◀ **FIGURE 6–9 Raising a bucket**
A person lifts a bucket of water from the
bottom of a well with a constant speed, v.
Because the speed is constant, the net
force acting on the bucket must be zero.

again take upward to be positive, the statement that the net force acting on the
pulley is zero ($\Sigma F_y = 0$) can be written

$$T_2 - T_1 - T_1 = 0$$

It follows that the tension in the chain is $T_2 = 2T_1 = 2mg$, twice the weight of the
bucket of water!

In the next Conceptual Checkpoint we consider a slight variation of this
situation.

CONCEPTUAL CHECKPOINT 6–3   Comparing Tensions

A person hoists a bucket of water from a well and holds the rope, keeping the bucket at rest, as at
left. A short time later, the person ties the rope to the bucket so that the rope holds the bucket in
place, as at right. In this case, is the tension in the rope (a) greater than, (b) less than, or (c) equal
to the tension in the first case?

continued on next page

Science Fundamentals Second Edition

continued from previous page

Reasoning and Discussion

In the first case (left), the only upward force exerted on the bucket is the tension in the rope. Since the bucket is at rest, the tension must be equal in magnitude to the weight of the bucket. In the second case (right), the two ends of the rope exert equal upward forces on the bucket, hence the tension in the rope is only half the weight of the bucket. To see this more clearly, imagine cutting the bucket in half so that each end of the rope supports half the weight, as indicated in the accompanying diagram.

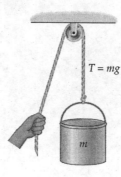 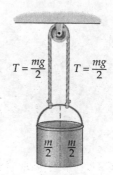

Answer:

(b) The tension in the second case is less than in the first.

In the next two Examples, we consider two-dimensional systems in which forces act at various angles with respect to one another. Hence, our first step is to resolve the relevant vectors into their x and y components. Following that, we apply the conditions for translational equilibrium, $\Sigma F_x = 0$ and $\Sigma F_y = 0$.

EXAMPLE 6–5 Suspended Vegetation

To hang a 6.20-kg pot of flowers, a gardener uses two wires—one attached horizontally to a wall, the other sloping upward at an angle of $\theta = 40.0°$ and attached to the ceiling. Find the tension in each wire.

Picture the Problem

We choose a typical coordinate system, with the positive x direction to the right and the positive y direction upward. With this choice, tension 1 is in the positive x direction, $\vec{T}_1 = T_1\hat{x}$, the weight is in the negative y direction, $\vec{W} = -mg\hat{y}$, and tension 2 has a negative x component and a positive y component, $\vec{T}_2 = (-T_2 \cos \theta)\hat{x} + (T_2 \sin \theta)\hat{y}$.

Strategy

The pot is at rest, and therefore the net force acting on it is zero. As a result, we can say that (i) $\Sigma F_x = 0$ and (ii) $\Sigma F_y = 0$. These two conditions allow us to determine the magnitude of the two tensions, T_1 and T_2.

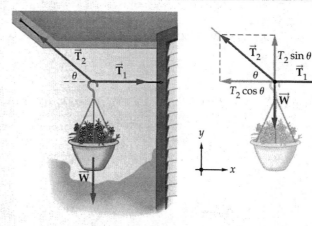

Physical picture   Free-body diagram

Solution

1. First, resolve each of the forces acting on the pot into x and y components:

$$T_{1,x} = T_1 \qquad\qquad T_{1,y} = 0$$
$$T_{2,x} = -T_2 \cos \theta \qquad T_{2,y} = T_2 \sin \theta$$
$$W_x = 0 \qquad\qquad W_y = -mg$$

2. Now, set $\Sigma F_x = 0$. Note that this condition gives a relation between T_1 and T_2:

$$\Sigma F_x = T_{1,x} + T_{2,x} + W_x = T_1 + (-T_2 \cos \theta) + 0 = 0$$
$$T_1 = T_2 \cos \theta$$

3. Next, set $\Sigma F_y = 0$. This time, the resulting condition determines T_2 in terms of the weight, mg:

$$\Sigma F_y = T_{1,y} + T_{2,y} + W_y = 0 + T_2 \sin \theta + (-mg) = 0$$
$$T_2 \sin \theta = mg$$

4. Use the relation obtained in step 3 to find T_2:

$$T_2 = \frac{mg}{\sin \theta} = \frac{(6.20 \text{ kg})(9.81 \text{ m/s}^2)}{\sin 40.0°} = 94.6 \text{ N}$$

5. Finally, use the connection between the two tensions (obtained from $\Sigma F_x = 0$) to find T_1:

$$T_1 = T_2 \cos \theta = (94.6 \text{ N}) \cos 40.0° = 72.5 \text{ N}$$

Insight

Notice that even though two wires suspend the pot, they both have tensions *greater* than the pot's weight, $mg = 60.8$ N. This is an important point for architects and engineers to consider when designing structures.

Practice Problem

Find T_1 and T_2 if the second wire slopes upward at the angle **(a)** $\theta = 20°$, **(b)** $\theta = 60.0°$, or **(c)** $\theta = 90.0°$.
[**Answer: (a)** $T_1 = 167$ N, $T_2 = 178$ N **(b)** $T_1 = 35.1$ N, $T_2 = 70.2$ N **(c)** $T_1 = 0$, $T_2 = mg = 60.8$ N]

Some related homework problems: Problem 29, Problem 32

ACTIVE EXAMPLE 6–3 The Forces in a Low-Tech Laundry

A 1.84-kg bag of clothespins hangs in the middle of a clothesline, causing it to sag by an angle $\theta = 3.50°$. Find the tension, T, in the clothesline.

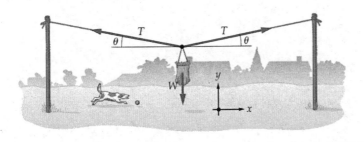

Solution *(Test your understanding by performing the calculations indicated in each step.)*

1. Find the y component for each tension: $T_y = T \sin \theta$

2. Find the y component of the weight: $W_y = -mg$

3. Set $\Sigma F_y = 0$: $T \sin \theta + T \sin \theta - mg = 0$

4. Solve for T: $T = mg/(2 \sin \theta) = 148$ N

▲ Like the bag of clothespins in Active Example 6–3, this mountain climber is in static equilibrium. Since the ropes suspending the climber are nearly horizontal, the tension in them is significantly greater than the climber's weight.

Insight

Note that we only considered the y components of force in our calculation. This is because forces in the x direction automatically balance, due to the symmetry of the system.

Your Turn

At what sag angle, θ, will the tension in the clothesline have a magnitude of 175 N?

(Answers to **Your Turn** *problems are given in the back of the book.)*

At 148 N, the tension in the clothesline is quite large, especially when you consider that the weight of the clothespin bag itself is only 18.1 N. The reason for such a large value is that the vertical component of the two tensions is $2T \sin \theta$, which, for $\theta = 3.50°$, is $(0.122)T$. If $(0.122)T$ is to equal the weight of the bag, it is clear that T must be roughly eight times the bag's weight.

If you and a friend were to pull on the two ends of the clothesline, in an attempt to straighten it out, you would find that no matter how hard you pulled, the line would still sag. You may be able to reduce θ to quite a small value, but as you do so the corresponding tension increases rapidly. In principle, it would take an infinite force to completely straighten the line and reduce θ to zero.

Science Fundamentals Second Edition

On the other hand, if θ were 90°, so that the two halves of the clothesline were vertical, the tension would be $T = mg/(2 \sin 90°) = mg/2$. In this case, each side of the line supports half the weight of the bag, as expected.

7–4 Power

Power is a measure of how *quickly* work is done. To be precise, suppose the work W is performed in the time t. The average power delivered during this time is defined as follows:

Definition of Average Power, *P*

$$P = \frac{W}{t}$$

7–10

SI unit: J/s = watt, W

For simplicity of notation we drop the usual subscript av for an average quantity and simply understand that the power P refers to an average power unless stated otherwise.

Note that the dimensions of power are joules (work) per second (time). We define one joule per second to be a watt (W), after James Watt (1736–1819), the Scottish engineer and inventor who played a key role in the development of practical steam engines:

$$1 \text{ watt} = 1 \text{ W} = 1 \text{ J/s}$$

7–11

Of course, the watt is the unit of power used to rate the output of lightbulbs. Another common unit of power is the horsepower (hp), which is used to rate the output of car engines. It is defined as follows:

$$1 \text{ horsepower} = 1 \text{ hp} = 746 \text{ W}$$

7–12

Though it sounds like a horse should be able to produce one horsepower, in fact, a horse can generate only about 2/3 hp for sustained periods. The reason for the discrepancy is that when James Watt defined the horsepower—as a way to characterize the output of his steam engines—he purposely chose a unit that was overly generous to the horse, so that potential investors couldn't complain he was overstating the capability of his engines.

To get a feel for the magnitude of the watt and the horsepower, consider the power you might generate when walking up a flight of stairs. Suppose, for example, that an 80.0-kg person walks up a flight of stairs in 20.0 s, and that the altitude gain is 12.0 ft (3.66 m). Referring to Example 7–2 and Conceptual Checkpoint 7–1, we find that the work done by the person is $W = mgh = (80.0 \text{ kg})(9.81 \text{ m/s}^2)(3.66 \text{ m}) = 2870 \text{ J}$. To find the power, we simply divide by the time: $P = W/t = (2870 \text{ J})/(20.0 \text{ s}) = 144 \text{ W} = 0.193 \text{ hp}$. Thus, a leisurely stroll up the stairs requires about 1/5 hp or 150 W. Similarly, the power produced by a sprinter bolting out of the starting blocks is about 1 hp, and the greatest power most people can produce for sustained periods of time is roughly 1/3 to 1/2 hp. Further examples of power are given in Table 7–3.

Human-powered flight is a feat just barely within our capabilities, since the most efficient human-powered airplanes require a steady power output of about 1/3 hp. On August 23, 1977, the *Gossamer Condor*, designed by Paul MacCready and flown by Bryan Allen, became the first human-powered airplane to complete a prescribed one-mile, figure-eight course and claim the Kremer Prize of £ 50,000. Allen, an accomplished bicycle racer, used bicycle-like pedals to spin the propeller. Controlling the slow-moving craft while pedaling at full power was no easy task. Allen also piloted the *Gossamer Albatross*, which, in 1979, became the first (and so far the only) human-powered aircraft to fly across the English Channel. This 22.25-mile flight—from Folkestone, England, to Cap Gris-Nez, France— took 2 hours 49 minutes and required a total energy output roughly equivalent to climbing to the top of the Empire State Building 10 times.

Power output is also an important factor in the performance of a car. For example, suppose it takes a certain amount of work, W, to accelerate a car from 0 to 60 mi/h. If the average power provided by the engine is P, then according to Equation 7–10 the amount of time required to reach 60 mi/h is $t = W/P$. Clearly, the greater the power P, the less the time required to accelerate. Thus, in a loose way of speaking, we can say that the power of a car is a measure of "how fast it can go fast."

TABLE 7–3
Typical Values of Power

Source	Approximate power (W)
Hoover Dam	1.34×10^9
Car moving at 40 mph	7×10^4
Home stove	1.2×10^4
Sunlight falling on one square meter	1380
Refrigerator	615
Television	200
Person walking up stairs	150
Human brain	20

REAL-WORLD PHYSICS: BIO
Human Power Output and Flight

▲ The *Gossamer Albatross* on its record-breaking flight across the English Channel in 1979. On two occasions the aircraft actually touched the surface of the water, but the pilot was able to maintain control and complete the 22.25-mile flight.

Science Fundamentals Second Edition

EXAMPLE 7-8 Passing Fancy

To pass a slow-moving truck, you want your fancy 1.30×10^3-kg car to accelerate from 13.4 m/s (30.0 mph) to 17.9 m/s (40.0 mph) in 3.00 s. What is the minimum power required for this pass?

Picture the Problem
Our sketch shows the car accelerating from an initial speed of $v_i = 13.4$ m/s to a final speed of $v_f = 17.9$ m/s. We assume the road is level, so that no work is done against gravity, and that friction and air resistance may be ignored.

Strategy
Power is work divided by time, and work is equal to the change in kinetic energy as the car accelerates. We can determine the change in kinetic energy from the given mass of the car and its initial and final speeds. With this information at hand, we can determine the power with the relation $P = W/t = \Delta K/t$.

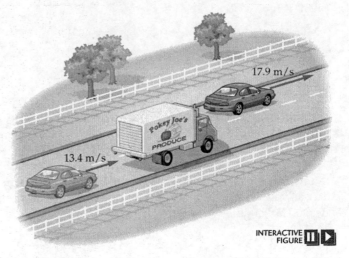

Solution

1. First, calculate the change in kinetic energy:

$$\Delta K = \tfrac{1}{2}mv_f^2 - \tfrac{1}{2}mv_i^2 = \tfrac{1}{2}(1.30 \times 10^3 \text{ kg})(17.9 \text{ m/s})^2$$
$$- \tfrac{1}{2}(1.30 \times 10^3 \text{ kg})(13.4 \text{ m/s})^2$$
$$= 9.16 \times 10^4 \text{ J}$$

2. Divide by time to find the minimum power. (The actual power would have to be greater to overcome frictional losses.):

$$P = \frac{W}{t} = \frac{\Delta K}{t} = \frac{9.16 \times 10^4 \text{ J}}{3.00 \text{ s}} = 3.05 \times 10^4 \text{ W} = 40.9 \text{ hp}$$

Insight
Suppose that your fancy car continues to produce the same 3.05×10^4 W of power as it accelerates from $v = 17.9$ m/s (40.0 mph) to $v = 22.4$ ms (50.0 mph). Is the time required more than, less than, or equal to 3.00 s? *Answer*: It will take more than 3.00 s. The reason is that ΔK is greater for a change in speed from 40.0 mph to 50.0 mph than for a change in speed from 30.0 **mph** to 40.0 mph, since K depends on speed squared. Since ΔK is greater, the time $t = \Delta K/P$ is also greater.

Practice Problem
Find the time required to accelerate from 40.0 mph to 50.0 mph with 3.05×10^4 W of power. [**Answer:** First, $\Delta K = 1.18 \times 10^5$ J. Second, $P = \Delta K/t$ can be solved for time to give $t = \Delta K/P$. Thus, $t = 3.87$ s.]

Some related homework problems: Problem 35, Problem 46

Finally, consider a system in which a car, or some other **object**, is moving with a constant speed v. For example, a car might be traveling uphill on a road inclined at an angle θ above the horizontal. To maintain a constant speed, the engine must exert a constant force F equal to the combined effects of friction, gravity, and air resistance, as indicated in **Figure 7-13**. Now, as the car travels a distance d, the work done by the engine is $W = Fd$, and the power it delivers is

$$P = \frac{W}{t} = \frac{Fd}{t}$$

Since the car has a constant speed, $v = d/t$, it follows that

$$P = \frac{Fd}{t} = F\left(\frac{d}{t}\right) = Fv \qquad 7\text{-}13$$

Note that power is directly proportional to both the force and the speed. For example, suppose you push a heavy shopping cart with a force F. You produce twice as much power when you push at 2 m/s than when you push at 1 m/s, even though you are pushing no harder. It's just that the amount of work you do in a given time period is doubled.

Science Fundamentals Second Edition

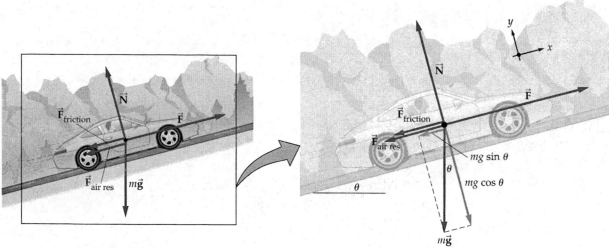

▲ **FIGURE 7–13 Driving up a hill**
A car traveling uphill at constant speed requires a constant force, F, of magnitude $mg \sin \theta + F_{\text{air res}} + F_{\text{friction}}$, applied in the direction of motion.

ACTIVE EXAMPLE 7–2 Find the Maximum Speed

It takes a force of 1280 N to keep a 1500-kg car moving with constant speed up a slope of 5.00°. If the engine delivers 50.0 hp to the drive wheels, what is the maximum speed of the car?

Solution *(Test your understanding by performing the calculations indicated in each step.)*

1. Convert the power of 50.0 hp to watts: $P = 3.73 \times 10^4$ W

2. Solve Equation 7–13 for the speed v: $v = P/F$

3. Substitute numerical values for the power and force: $v = 29.1$ m/s

Insight
Thus, the maximum speed of the car on this slope is approximately 65 mi/h.

Your Turn
How much power is required for a maximum speed of 32.0 m/s?

(Answers to Your Turn problems are given in the back of the book.)

Potential Energy and Conservation of Energy

8–1   Conservative and Nonconservative
      Forces   205

8–2   Potential Energy and the Work Done
      by Conservative Forces   208

8–3   Conservation of Mechanical Energy   214

8–4   Work Done by Nonconservative Forces   222

Probably everyone has seen a high jumper spring into the air, slow, hang motionless in midair for an instant, and then start to descend, picking up speed on the way. At the top of the trajectory, where has the kinetic energy gone? And how does it reappear as the jumper descends? As we answer these questions, we will find that there are other kinds of energy besides those considered in the last chapter.

One of the greatest accomplishments of physics is the concept of energy and its conservation. To realize, for example, that there is an important physical quantity that we can neither see nor touch is an impressive leap of the imagination. Even more astonishing, however, is the discovery that energy comes in a multitude of forms, and that the sum total of all these forms of energy is a constant. The universe, in short, has a certain amount of energy, and that energy simply ebbs and flows from one form to another, with the total amount remaining fixed.

In this chapter we focus on the conservation of energy, the first "conservation law" to be studied in this text. Though only a handful of conservation laws are known, they are all of central importance in physics. Not only do they give deep insight into the workings of nature, they are also practical tools in problem solving. As we shall see in this chapter, many problems that would be difficult to solve using Newton's laws can be solved with ease using the principle of energy conservation.

8–1 Conservative and Nonconservative Forces

In physics, we classify forces according to whether they are *conservative* or *nonconservative*. The key distinction is that when a **conservative force** acts, the work it does is stored in the form of energy that can be released at a later time. In this section, we sharpen this distinction and explore some examples of conservative and nonconservative forces.

Perhaps the simplest case of a conservative force is gravity. Imagine lifting a box of mass m from the floor to a height h, as in **Figure 8–1**. To lift the box with constant speed, the force you must exert against gravity is mg. Since the upward distance is h, the work you do on the box is $W = mgh$. If you now release the box and allow it to drop back to the floor, gravity does the same work, $W = mgh$, and in the process gives the box an equivalent amount of kinetic energy.

Work done by person = mgh Work done by gravity = mgh

◀ **FIGURE 8–1 Work against gravity**
Lifting a box against gravity with constant speed takes a work mgh. When the box is released, gravity does the same work on the box as it falls. Gravity is a conservative force.

Contrast this with the force of kinetic friction, which is nonconservative. To slide a box of mass m across the floor with constant speed, as shown in **Figure 8–2**, you must exert a force of magnitude $\mu_k N = \mu_k mg$. After sliding the box a distance d, the work you have done is $W = \mu_k mgd$. In this case, when you release the box it simply stays put—friction does no work on it after you let go. Thus, the work done by a **nonconservative force** cannot be recovered later as kinetic energy; instead, it is converted to other forms of energy, such as a slight warming of the floor and box in our example.

The differences between conservative and nonconservative forces are even more apparent if we consider moving an object around a closed path. Consider, for example, the path shown in **Figure 8–3**. If we move a box of mass m along this path, the total work done by gravity is the sum of the work done on each segment of the path; that is $W_{\text{total}} = W_{AB} + W_{BC} + W_{CD} + W_{DA}$. The work done by gravity from A to B and from C to D is zero, since the force is at right angles to the displacement on these segments. Thus $W_{AB} = W_{CD} = 0$. On the segment from B to C, gravity does negative work (displacement and force are in opposite directions),

Work = $\mu_k mgd$

◀ **FIGURE 8–2 Work against friction**
Pushing a box with constant speed against friction takes a work $\mu_k mgd$. When the box is released, it quickly comes to rest and friction does no further work. Friction is a nonconservative force.

Science Fundamentals Second Edition

135

▶ **FIGURE 8–3 Work done by gravity on a closed path is zero**

Gravity does no work on the two horizontal segments of the path. On the two vertical segments, the amounts of work done are equal in magnitude but opposite in sign. Therefore, the total work done by gravity on this—or any—closed path is zero.

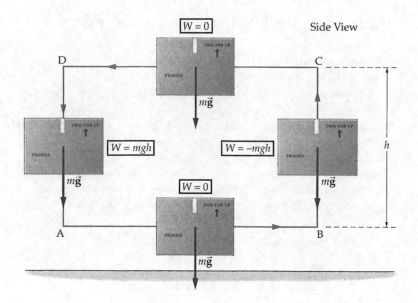

Side View

but it does positive work from D to A (displacement and force are in the same direction). Hence, $W_{BC} = -mgh$ and $W_{DA} = mgh$. As a result, the total work done by gravity is zero:

$$W_{total} = 0 + (-mgh) + 0 + mgh = 0$$

With friction, the results are quite different. If we push the box around the closed horizontal path shown in **Figure 8–4**, the total work done by friction does not vanish. In fact, friction does the negative work $W = -f_k d = -\mu_k mgd$ on each segment. Therefore, the total work done by kinetic friction is

$$W_{total} = (-\mu_k mgd) + (-\mu_k mgd) + (-\mu_k mgd) + (-\mu_k mgd) = -4\,\mu_k mgd$$

These results lead to the following definition of a conservative force:

Conservative Force: Definition 1
A conservative force is a force that does zero total work on any closed path.

▶ **FIGURE 8–4 Work done by friction on a closed path is nonzero**

The work done by friction when an object moves through a distance d is $-\mu_k mgd$. Thus, the total work done by friction on a closed path is nonzero. In this case, it is equal to $-4\,\mu_k mgd$.

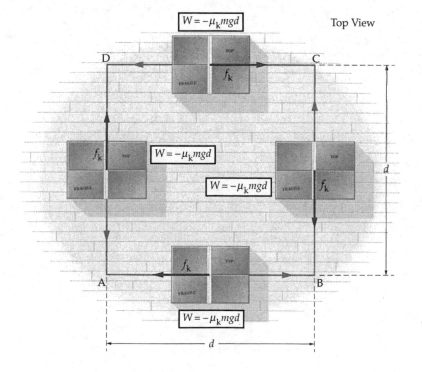

Top View

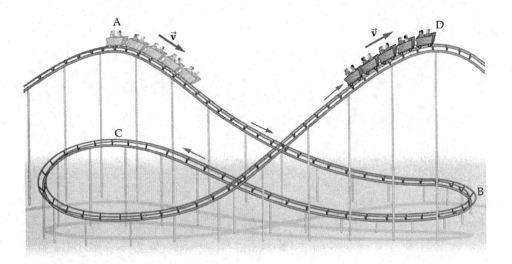

▲ **FIGURE 8–5 Gravity is a conservative force**
If frictional forces can be ignored, a roller coaster car will have the same speed at points A and D, since they are at the same height. Hence, after any complete circuit of the track the speed of the car returns to its initial value. It follows that the change in kinetic energy is zero for a complete circuit, and, therefore, the work done by gravity is also zero.

A roller coaster provides a good illustration of this definition. If a car on a roller coaster has a speed v at point A in **Figure 8–5**, it speeds up as it drops to point B, slows down as it approaches point C, and so on. When the car returns to its original height, at point D, it will again have the speed v, as long as friction and other nonconservative forces can be neglected. Similarly, if the car completes a circuit of the track and returns to point A, it will again have the speed v. Hence, a car's kinetic energy is unchanged ($\Delta K = 0$) after *any* complete circuit of the track. From the work energy theorem, $W_{total} = \Delta K$, it follows that the work done by gravity is zero for the closed path of the car, as expected for a conservative force.

This property of conservative forces has interesting consequences. For instance, consider the closed paths shown in **Figure 8–6**. On each of these paths, we know that the work done by a conservative force is zero. Thus, it follows from paths 1 and 2 that $W_{total} = W_1 + W_2 = 0$, or

$$W_2 = -W_1$$

Similarly, using paths 1 and 3 we have $W_{total} = W_1 + W_3 = 0$, or

$$W_3 = -W_1$$

As a result, we see that the work done on path 3 is the same as the work done on path 2:

$$W_3 = W_2$$

But paths 2 and 3 are arbitrary, as long as they start at point B and end at point A. This leads to an equivalent definition of a conservative force:

Conservative Force: Definition 2
If the work done by a force in going from an arbitrary point A to an arbitrary point B is *independent of the path* from A to B, the force is conservative.

This definition is given an explicit check in Example 8–1.

Table 8–1 summarizes the different kinds of conservative and nonconservative forces we have encountered thus far in this text.

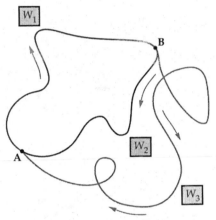

▲ **FIGURE 8–6 The work done by a conservative force is independent of path**
Considering paths 1 and 2, we see that $W_1 + W_2 = 0$, or $W_2 = -W_1$. From paths 1 and 3, however, we see that $W_1 + W_3 = 0$, or $W_3 = -W_1$. It follows, then, that $W_3 = W_2$, since they are both equal to $-W_1$; hence the work done in going from A to B is independent of the path.

TABLE 8–1	
Conservative and Nonconservative Forces	
Force	**Section**
Conservative forces	
Gravity	5–6
Spring force	6–2
Nonconservative forces	
Friction	6–1
Tension in a rope, cable, etc.	6–2
Forces exerted by a motor	7–4
Forces exerted by muscles	5–3

Science Fundamentals Second Edition

EXAMPLE 8–1 Different Paths, Different Forces

(a) A 4.57-kg box is moved with constant speed from A to B along the two paths shown at left below. Calculate the work done by gravity on each of these paths. **(b)** The same box is pushed across a floor from A to B along path 1 and path 2 at right below. If the coefficient of kinetic friction between the box and the surface is $\mu_k = 0.63$, how much work is done by friction along each path?

Picture the Problem

Part **(a)** of our sketch shows two different paths a box might be taken through in going from point A to point B. Path 1 is indicated by two red lines, indicating a vertical displacement of 1.0 m and a horizontal displacement of 3.0 m. Path 2, indicated in green, consists of two horizontal and two vertical displacements. In this case, we are interested in the work done by gravity. Part **(b)** shows the same basic paths—path 1 in orange and path 2 in purple—only this time on a rough floor. Here it is the force of kinetic friction that is of interest.

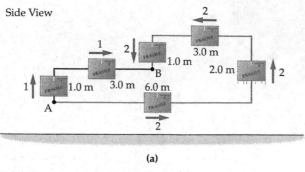

(a)

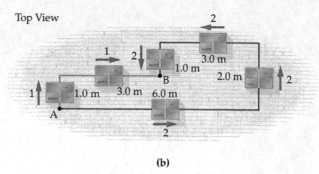

(b)

Strategy

To calculate the work for each path, we break it down into segments. Path 1 is made up of two segments, path 2 has four segments.

a. For gravity, the work is zero on horizontal segments. On vertical segments, the work done by gravity is positive when motion is downward and negative when motion is upward.

b. The work done by kinetic friction is negative on all segments of both paths.

Solution

Part (a)

1. Using $W = Fd = mgy$, calculate the work done by gravity along the two segments of path 1:

$$W_1 = -(4.57 \text{ kg})(9.81 \text{ m/s}^2)(1.0 \text{ m}) + 0 = -45 \text{ J}$$

2. In the same way, calculate the work done by gravity along the four segments of path 2:

$$W_2 = 0 - (4.57 \text{ kg})(9.81 \text{ m/s}^2)(2.0 \text{ m})$$
$$+ 0 + (4.57 \text{ kg})(9.81 \text{ m/s}^2)(1.0 \text{ m}) = -45 \text{ J}$$

Part (b)

3. Using $F = \mu_k N$, calculate the work done by kinetic friction along the two segments of path 1:

$$W_1 = -(0.63)(4.57 \text{ kg})(9.81 \text{ m/s}^2)(1.0 \text{ m})$$
$$- (0.63)(4.57 \text{ kg})(9.81 \text{ m/s}^2)(3.0 \text{ m}) = -110 \text{ J}$$

4. Similarly, calculate the work done by kinetic friction along the four segments of path 2:

$$W_2 = -(0.63)(4.57 \text{ kg})(9.81 \text{ m/s}^2)(6.0 \text{ m})$$
$$- (0.63)(4.57 \text{ kg})(9.81 \text{ m/s}^2)(2.0 \text{ m})$$
$$- (0.63)(4.57 \text{ kg})(9.81 \text{ m/s}^2)(3.0 \text{ m})$$
$$- (0.63)(4.57 \text{ kg})(9.81 \text{ m/s}^2)(1.0 \text{ m}) = -340 \text{ J}$$

Insight

As expected, the conservative force of gravity gives the same work in going from A to B, regardless of the path. The work done by kinetic friction, however, is greater on the path of greater length.

Practice Problem

The work done by gravity when the box is moved from point B to a point C is 140 J. Is point C above or below point B? What is the vertical distance between points B and C?   [**Answer:** Point C is 3.1 m below point B.]

Some related homework problems: Problem 1, Problem 2

8–2 Potential Energy and the Work Done by Conservative Forces

Work must be done to lift a bowling ball from the floor to a shelf. Once on the shelf, the bowling ball has zero kinetic energy, just as it did on the floor. Even so, the work done in lifting the ball has not been lost. If the ball is allowed to fall from

▲ Because gravity is a conservative force, the work done against gravity in lifting these logs (left) can, in principle, all be recovered. If the logs are released, for example, they will acquire an amount of kinetic energy exactly equal to the work done to lift them and to the gravitational potential energy that they gained in being lifted. Friction, by contrast, is a nonconservative force. Some of the work done by this spinning grindstone (right) goes into removing material from the object being ground, while the rest is transformed into sound energy and (especially) heat. Most of this work can never be recovered as kinetic energy.

the shelf, gravity does the same amount of work on it as you did to lift it in the first place. As a result, the work you did is "recovered" in the form of kinetic energy. Thus we say that when the ball is lifted to a new position, there is an increase in **potential energy,** U, and that this potential energy can be converted to kinetic energy when the ball falls.

In a sense, potential energy is a storage system for energy. When we increase the separation between the ball and the ground, the work we do is stored in the form of an increased potential energy. Not only that, but the storage system is perfect, in the sense that the energy is never lost, as long as the separation remains the same. The ball can rest on the shelf for a million years, and still, when it falls, it gains the same amount of kinetic energy.

Work done against friction, however, is not "stored" as potential energy. Instead, it is dissipated into other forms of energy such as heat or sound. The same is true of other nonconservative forces. Only conservative forces have the potential-energy storage system.

Before proceeding, we should point out an interesting difference between kinetic and potential energy. Kinetic energy is given by the expression $K = \frac{1}{2}mv^2$, no matter what force might be involved. On the other hand, each different conservative force has a different expression for its potential energy. To see how this comes about, we turn now to a precise definition of potential energy.

Potential Energy, *U*

When a conservative force does an amount of work W_c (the subscript c stands for conservative), the corresponding potential energy U is changed according to the following definition:

Definition of Potential Energy, *U*

$$W_c = U_i - U_f = -(U_f - U_i) = -\Delta U \qquad \text{8–1}$$

SI unit: joule, J

In words, the work done by a conservative force is equal to the negative of the change in potential energy. For example, when an object falls, gravity does *positive* work on it and its potential energy *decreases*. Similarly, when an object is lifted, gravity does *negative* work and the potential energy *increases*.

Note that since work is a scalar with units of joules, the same is true of potential energy. In addition, our definition determines only the *difference* in potential

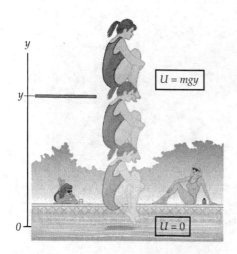

◀ FIGURE 8–7 Gravitational Potential Energy
A person drops from a diving board into a swimming pool. The diving board is at the height y, and the surface of the water is at $y = 0$. We choose the gravitational potential energy to be zero at $y = 0$; hence, the potential energy is mgy at the diving board.

energy between two points, not the actual value of the potential energy. Hence, we are free to choose the place where the potential energy is zero $(U = 0)$ in much the same way we are free to choose the location of the origin in a coordinate system.

Gravity

Let's apply our definition of potential energy to the force of gravity near the Earth's surface. Suppose a person of mass m drops a distance y from a diving board into a pool, as shown in **Figure 8–7**. As the person drops, gravity does the work

$$W_c = mgy$$

Applying the definition given in Equation 8–1, the corresponding change in potential energy is

$$-\Delta U = U_i - U_f = W_c = mgy$$

In this expression, U_i is the potential energy when the diver is on the board, and U_f is the potential energy when the diver enters the water. Rearranging slightly, we have

$$U_i = mgy + U_f \qquad 8\text{--}2$$

Note that U_i is greater than U_f.

As mentioned above, we are free to choose $U = 0$ anywhere we like; *only the difference* in U is important. For example, if you slip and fall to the ground, you hit with the same thud whether you fall in Denver (altitude 1 mile) or in Honolulu (at sea level). It's the difference in height that matters, not the height itself. (The acceleration of gravity does vary slightly with altitude, as we shall see, but the difference is small enough to be unimportant in this case.) The only point to be careful about when choosing a location for $U = 0$ is to be consistent with the choice once it is made.

In general, we choose $U = 0$ in a convenient location. In Figure 8–7, a reasonable place for $U = 0$ is the surface of the water, where $y = 0$; that is, $U_f = 0$. Then, Equation 8–2 becomes $U_i = mgy$. If we omit the subscript on U_i, letting U stand for the potential energy at the arbitrary height y, we have

Gravitational Potential Energy (Near Earth's Surface)

$$U = mgy \qquad 8\text{--}3$$

Note that the gravitational potential energy depends only on the height, y, and is independent of horizontal position.

PROBLEM-SOLVING NOTE

Zero of Potential Energy

When working potential energy problems it is important to make a definite choice for the location where the potential energy is to be set equal to zero. Any location can be chosen, but once the choice is made, it must be used consistently.

▲ The $U = 0$ level for the gravitational potential energy of this system can be assigned to the point where the diver starts his dive, to the water level, or to any other level. Regardless of the choice, however, his kinetic energy when he strikes the water will be exactly equal to the difference in gravitational potential energy between his launch and splash-down points.

EXERCISE 8–1

Find the gravitational potential energy of a system consisting of a 65-kg person on a 3.0-m-high diving board. Let $U = 0$ be at water level.

Solution

Substituting $m = 65$ kg and $y = 3.0$ m in Equation 8–3 yields

$$U = mgy = (65 \text{ kg})(9.81 \text{ m/s}^2)(3.0 \text{ m}) = 1900 \text{ J}$$

The next Example considers the change in gravitational potential energy of a mountain climber, given different choices for the location of $U = 0$.

EXAMPLE 8–2 Pikes Peak or Bust

An 82.0-kg mountain climber is in the final stage of the ascent of 4301-m-high Pikes Peak. What is the change in gravitational potential energy as the climber gains the last 100.0 m of altitude? Let $U = 0$ be **(a)** at sea level or **(b)** at the top of the peak.

Picture the Problem
Our sketch shows the mountain climber and the last 100.0 m of altitude to be climbed. We choose a typical coordinate system, with the positive y axis upward and the positive x axis to the right.

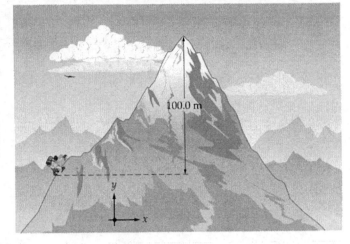

100.0 m

Strategy
The gravitational potential energy of the Earth-climber system depends only on the height y; the path followed in gaining the last 100.0 m of altitude is unimportant. The change in potential energy is $\Delta U = U_f - U_i = mgy_f - mgy_i$, where y_f is the altitude of the peak and y_i is 100.0 m less than y_f.

Solution

Part (a)

1. Calculate ΔU with $y_f = 4301$ m and $y_i = 4201$ m:

$$\Delta U = mgy_f - mgy_i$$
$$= (82.0 \text{ kg})(9.81 \text{ m/s}^2)(4301 \text{ m})$$
$$- (82.0 \text{ kg})(9.81 \text{ m/s}^2)(4201 \text{ m}) = 80{,}400 \text{ J}$$

Part (b)

2. Calculate ΔU with $y_f = 0$ and $y_i = -100.0$ m:

$$\Delta U = mgy_f - mgy_i$$
$$= (82.0 \text{ kg})(9.81 \text{ m/s}^2)(0)$$
$$- (82.0 \text{ kg})(9.81 \text{ m/s}^2)(-100.0 \text{ m}) = 80{,}400 \text{ J}$$

Insight
As expected, the *change* in gravitational potential energy does not depend on where we choose $U = 0$. Nor does it depend on the path taken between the initial and final points.

Practice Problem
Find the altitude of the climber for which the gravitational potential energy of the Earth-climber system is 1.00×10^5 J less than it is when the climber is at the summit.   [**Answer:** 4180 m]

Some related homework problems: Problem 7, Problem 14

A single item of food can be converted into a surprisingly large amount of potential energy. This is shown for the case of a candy bar in Example 8–3.

EXAMPLE 8–3 Converting Food Energy to Mechanical Energy

REAL-WORLD PHYSICS: BIO A candy bar called the Mountain Bar has a calorie content of 212 Cal = 212 kcal, which is equivalent to an energy of 8.87×10^5 J. If an 81.0-kg mountain climber eats a Mountain Bar and magically converts it all to potential energy, what gain of altitude would be possible?

Picture the Problem
We show the mountain climber eating the candy bar at a given level on the mountain, which we can take to be $y = 0$. The altitude gain, then, corresponds to $y = h$.

continued on next page

Science Fundamentals Second Edition

continued from previous page

Strategy

The initial gravitational potential energy of the Earth-climber system is $U = 0$; the final potential energy is $U = mgh$. To find the altitude gain, set $U = mgh$ equal to the energy provided by the candy bar, 8.87×10^5 J, and solve for h.

Solution

1. Solve $U = mgh$ for h:

$$U = mgh$$

$$h = \frac{U}{mg}$$

2. Substitute numerical values, with $U = 8.87 \times 10^5$ J:

$$h = \frac{U}{mg} = \frac{8.87 \times 10^5 \text{ J}}{(81.0 \text{ kg})(9.81 \text{ m/s}^2)} = 1120 \text{ m}$$

Insight

This is more than two-thirds of a mile in elevation. Even if we take into account the fact that metabolic efficiency is only about 25%, the height would still be 280 m, or nearly two-tenths of a mile. It's remarkable just how much our bodies can do with so little.

Practice Problem

If the mass of the mountain climber is increased—by adding more items to the backpack, for example—does the possible elevation gain increase, decrease, or stay the same? Calculate the elevation gain for a climber with a mass of 91.0 kg. [**Answer:** The altitude gain will decrease. For $m = 91.0$ kg we find $h = 994$ m.]

Some related homework problems: Problem 7, Problem 14

We have been careful *not* to say that the potential energy of the mountain climber—or any object—increases when its height increases. The reason is that the potential energy is a property of an entire system, not of its individual parts. The correct statement is that if an object is lifted, the potential energy of the Earth-object system is increased.

Springs

Consider a spring that is stretched from its equilibrium position a distance x. According to Equation 7–8, the work required to cause this stretch is $W = \frac{1}{2}kx^2$. Therefore, if the spring is released—and allowed to move from the stretched position back to the equilibrium position—it will do the same work, $\frac{1}{2}kx^2$. From our definition of potential energy, then, we see that

$$W_c = \tfrac{1}{2}kx^2 = U_i - U_f \qquad \text{8–4}$$

Note that in this case U_f is the potential energy when the spring is at $x = 0$ (equilibrium position), and U_i is the potential energy when the spring is stretched by the amount x.

A convenient choice for $U = 0$ is the equilibrium position of the spring. With this choice we have $U_f = 0$, and Equation 8–4 becomes $U_i = \frac{1}{2}kx^2$. Omitting the subscript i, so that U represents the potential energy of the spring for an arbitrary amount of stretch x, we have

▲ Because springs, and bungee cords, exert conservative forces, they can serve as energy storage devices. In this case, the stretched bungee cord is beginning to give up the energy it has stored, and to convert that potential energy into kinetic energy as the jumper is pulled rapidly skyward.

Potential Energy of a Spring

$$U = \tfrac{1}{2}kx^2 \qquad \text{8–5}$$

Since U depends on x^2, which is positive even if x is negative, the potential energy of a spring is always greater than or equal to zero. Thus, a spring's potential energy increases whenever it is displaced from equilibrium.

EXERCISE 8–2

Find the potential energy of a spring with force constant $k = 680$ N/m if it is **(a)** stretched by 5.00 cm or **(b)** compressed by 7.00 cm.

Solution

Substituting $x = 0.0500$ m and $x = -0.0700$ m in Equation 8–5 yields

  a. $U = \frac{1}{2}(680 \text{ N/m})(0.0500 \text{ m})^2 = 0.850$ J
  b. $U = \frac{1}{2}(680 \text{ N/m})(-0.0700 \text{ m})^2 = 1.67$ J

Finally, comparing Equation 8–3 to Equation 8–5, we see that the potential energies for gravity and for a spring are given by different expressions. As mentioned, each conservative force has its own potential energy.

EXAMPLE 8–4 Compressed Energy and the Jump of a Flea

When a force of 120.0 N is applied to a certain spring, it causes a stretch of 2.25 cm. What is the potential energy of this spring when it is compressed by 3.50 cm?

Picture the Problem

The top sketch shows the spring stretched 2.25 cm by the force $F_1 = 120.0$ N. The lower sketch shows the same spring compressed by a second force, F_2, which causes a compression of 3.50 cm.

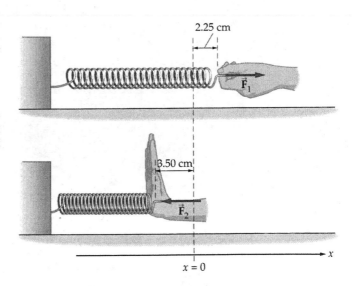

Strategy

From the first piece of information—a certain force causes a certain stretch—we can calculate the force constant using $F = kx$. Once we know k, we find the potential energy with $U = \frac{1}{2}kx^2$.

Solution

1. Solve $F = kx$ for the spring constant, k:

$$F = kx$$
$$k = \frac{F}{x} = \frac{120.0 \text{ N}}{0.0225 \text{ m}} = 5330 \text{ N/m}$$

2. Substitute $k = 5330$ N/m and $x = -0.0350$ m into the potential energy expression, $U = \frac{1}{2}kx^2$:

$$U = \frac{1}{2}kx^2 = \frac{1}{2}(5330 \text{ N/m})(-0.0350 \text{ m})^2 = 3.26 \text{ J}$$

continued on next page

continued from previous page

Insight

Though this example deals with ideal springs, the same basic physics applies to many other real-world situations. A case in point is the jump of a flea, in which a flea can propel itself up to 100 times its body length. The physics behind this feat is the slow accumulation of energy in a "springy" strip of resilin in the coxa of the leg, as shown in the accompanying sketches, and the sudden release of this energy at a later time. Specifically, as the flea's muscles flex the leg, the resilin strip in the coxa is stretched, storing the work done by the muscles in the form of potential energy, $U = \frac{1}{2}kx^2$. Later, when a trigger mechanism unlocks the flexed leg, the energy stored in the resilin is released explosively—rapidly extending the leg and propelling the flea upward. See Problem 77 for a calculation using the force constant of resilin.

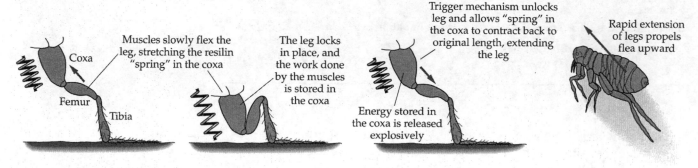

Practice Problem

What stretch is necessary for the spring in this Example to have a potential energy of 5.00 J?   [**Answer:** 4.33 cm]

Some related homework problems: Problem 9, Problem 13

The jump of a flea is similar in many respects to the operation of a bow and arrow. In the latter case, the work done in slowly pulling the string back is stored in the flex of the bow. The string is held in place while aim is taken, and then released to allow the bow to return to its original shape. This propels the arrow forward with great speed—a speed many times faster than could be obtained by simply throwing the arrow with the same arm muscles that pulled back on the string. In fact, if the string returns to its original position in 1/1000th the time it took to pull the string back, the power it delivers to the arrow is magnified by a factor of 1000. Similarly, the spring-loaded jump of the flea gives it a much greater takeoff speed than if it relied solely on muscle power. An analogous process occurs in the flash unit of a camera, as we shall see in Chapter 20.

8–3 Conservation of Mechanical Energy

In this section, we show how potential energy can be used as a powerful tool in solving a variety of problems and in gaining greater insight into the workings of physical systems. To do so, we begin by defining the **mechanical energy,** E, as the sum of the potential and kinetic energies of an object:

$$E = U + K \qquad \text{8–6}$$

The significance of mechanical energy is that it is **conserved** in systems involving only conservative forces. By conserved, we mean that its value never changes; that is, E = constant. (In situations where nonconservative forces are involved, the mechanical energy can change, as when friction causes warming by converting mechanical energy to thermal energy. When *all* possible forms of energy are considered, energy is always found to be conserved.)

To show that E is conserved for conservative forces, we start with the work-energy theorem from Chapter 7:

$$W_{\text{total}} = \Delta K = K_{\text{f}} - K_{\text{i}}$$

Suppose for a moment that the system has only a single force and that the force is conservative. If this is the case, then the total work, W_{total}, is the work done by the conservative force, W_c:

$$W_{total} = W_c$$

From the definition of potential energy, we know that $W_c = -\Delta U = U_i - U_f$. Combining these results, we have

$$W_{total} = W_c$$
$$K_f - K_i = U_i - U_f$$

With a slight rearrangement we find

$$U_f + K_f = U_i + K_i$$

or

$$E_f = E_i$$

Since the initial and final points can be chosen arbitrarily, it follows that E is conserved:

$$E = constant$$

If the system has more than one conservative force, the only change to these results is to replace U with the sum of potential energies of all the forces.

To summarize:

Conservation of Mechanical Energy
In systems with conservative forces only, the mechanical energy E is conserved; that is, $E = U + K = $ constant.

In terms of physical systems, conservation of mechanical energy means that energy can be converted between potential and kinetic forms, but that the sum remains the same. As an example, in the roller coaster shown in Figure 8–5, the gravitational potential energy decreases as the car approaches point B; as it does, the car's kinetic energy increases by the same amount. From a practical point of view, conservation of mechanical energy means that many physics problems can be solved by what amounts to simple bookkeeping.

For example, consider a key chain of mass m that is dropped to the floor from a height h, as illustrated in **Figure 8–8**. The question is, how fast are the keys moving just before they land? We know how to solve this problem using Newton's laws and kinematics, but now let's see how energy conservation can be used instead.

▲ A roller coaster (top) illustrates the conservation of mechanical energy. With every descent, gravitational potential energy is converted into kinetic energy; with every rise, kinetic energy is converted back into gravitational potential energy. If friction is neglected, the total mechanical energy of the car remains constant. The same principle is exploited at a pumped-storage facility, such as this one at the Mormon Flat Dam in Phoenix, Arizona (bottom). When surplus electrical power is available, it is used to pump water uphill into the reservoir. This process, in effect, stores electrical energy as gravitational potential energy. When power demand is high, the stored water is allowed to flow back downhill through the electrical generators in the dam, converting the gravitational energy to kinetic energy and the kinetic energy to electrical energy.

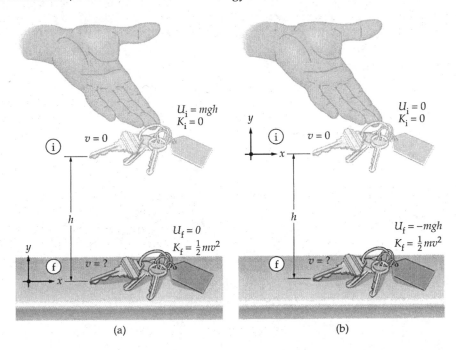

(a)   (b)

◀ FIGURE 8–8 Solving a kinematics problem using conservation of energy
(a) A set of keys falls to the floor. Ignoring frictional forces, we know that the mechanical energy at points i and f must be equal; $E_i = E_f$. Using this condition, we can find the speed of the keys just before they land. (b) The same physical situation as in part (a), except this time we have chosen $y = 0$ to be at the point where the keys are dropped. As before, we set $E_i = E_f$ to find the speed of the keys just before they land. The result is the same.

PROBLEM-SOLVING NOTE

Conservative Systems

A convenient approach to problems involving energy conservation is to first sketch the system, and then label the initial and final points with i and f, respectively. To apply energy conservation, write out the energy at these two points and set $E_i = E_f$.

First, note that the only force acting on the keys is gravity—ignoring air resistance, of course—and that gravity is a conservative force. As a result, we can say that $E = U + K$ is constant during the entire time the keys are falling. To solve the problem, then, we pick two points on the motion of the keys, say i and f in Figure 8–8, and we set the mechanical energy equal at these points:

$$E_i = E_f \qquad\qquad 8-7$$

Writing this out in terms of potential and kinetic energies, we have

$$U_i + K_i = U_f + K_f \qquad\qquad 8-8$$

This one equation—which is nothing but bookkeeping—can be used to solve for the one unknown, the final speed.

To be specific, in Figure 8–8 (a) we choose $y = 0$ at ground level, which means that $U_i = mgh$. In addition, the fact that the keys are released from rest means that $K_i = 0$. Similarly, at point f—just before hitting the ground—the energy is all kinetic, and the potential energy is zero; that is, $U_f = 0$, $K_f = \frac{1}{2}mv^2$. Substituting these values into Equation 8–8, we find

$$mgh + 0 = 0 + \tfrac{1}{2}mv^2$$

Canceling m and solving for v yields the same result we get with kinematics:

$$v = \sqrt{2gh}$$

Suppose, instead, that we had chosen $y = 0$ to be at the **release** point of the keys, as in Figure 8–8 (b), so that the keys land at $y = -h$. Now, when the keys are released, we have $U_i = 0$ and $K_i = 0$, and when they land $U_f = -mgh$ and $K_f = \frac{1}{2}mv^2$. Substituting these results in $U_i + K_i = U_f + K_f$ yields

$$0 + 0 = -mgh + \tfrac{1}{2}mv^2$$

Solving for v gives the same result:

$$v = \sqrt{2gh}$$

Thus, as expected, changing the zero level has no effect on the physical results.

EXAMPLE 8–5 Graduation Fling

At the end of a graduation ceremony, graduates fling their caps into the air. Suppose a 0.120-kg cap is thrown straight upward with an initial speed of 7.85 m/s, and that frictional forces can be ignored. **(a)** Use kinematics to find the speed of the cap when it is 1.18 m above the release point. **(b)** Show that the mechanical energy at the release point is the same as the mechanical energy 1.18 m above the release point.

Picture the Problem

In our sketch we choose $y = 0$ to be at the level where the cap is released with an initial speed of 7.85 m/s. In addition, note that we designate the release point as i (initial) and the point at which $y = 1.18$ m as f (final). It is the speed at point f that we wish to find.

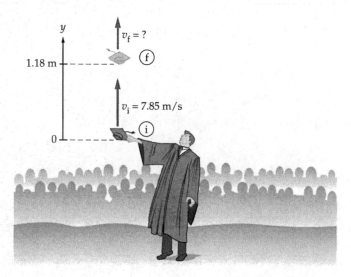

Strategy

a. The cap is in free fall, which justifies the use of constant-acceleration kinematics. Since we want to relate velocity to position, we use $v_y^2 = v_{0y}^2 + 2a_y\Delta y$ (Section 2–5). In this case, $v_{0y} = 7.85$ m/s, $\Delta y = 1.18$ m, and $a_y = -g$. Substituting these values gives v_y.

b. At each point we simply calculate $E = U + K$, with $U = mgy$ and $K = \frac{1}{2}mv^2$.

Solution

Part (a)

1. Use kinematics to solve for v_y:

$$v_y^2 = v_{0y}^2 + 2a_y\,\Delta y$$
$$v_y = \pm\sqrt{v_{0y}^2 + 2a_y\,\Delta y}$$

2. Substitute $v_{0y} = 7.85$ m/s, $\Delta y = 1.18$ m, and $a_y = -g$ to find v_y. Choose the plus sign, since we are interested only in the speed:

$$v_y = \sqrt{v_{0y}^2 + 2a_y\,\Delta y}$$
$$= \sqrt{(7.85\text{ m/s})^2 + 2(-9.81\text{ m/s}^2)(1.18\text{ m})} = 6.20\text{ m/s}$$

Part (b)

3. Calculate E_i. At this point $y_i = 0$ and $v_i = 7.85$ m/s:

$$E_i = U_i + K_i = mgy_i + \tfrac{1}{2}mv_i^2$$
$$= 0 + \tfrac{1}{2}(0.120\text{ kg})(7.85\text{ m/s})^2 = 3.70\text{ J}$$

4. Calculate E_f. At this point $y_f = 1.18$ m and $v_f = 6.20$ m/s:

$$E_f = U_f + K_f = mgy_f + \tfrac{1}{2}mv_f^2$$
$$= (0.120\text{ kg})(9.81\text{ m/s}^2)(1.18\text{ m}) + \tfrac{1}{2}(0.120\text{ kg})(6.20\text{ m/s})^2$$
$$= 1.39\text{ J} + 2.31\text{ J} = 3.70\text{ J}$$

Insight

As expected, E_f is equal to E_i. In the remaining Examples in this section we turn this process around; we start with $E_f = E_i$, and use this relation to find a final speed or a final height. As we shall see, this procedure of using energy conservation is a more powerful approach—it actually makes the calculations simpler.

Practice Problem

Use energy conservation to find the height at which the speed of the cap is 5.00 m/s.   [**Answer:** 1.87 m]

Some related homework problems: Problem 20, Problem 21, and Problem 23.

An interesting extension of this Example is shown in **Figure 8-9**. In this case, we are given that the speed of the cap is v_i at the height y_i, and we would like to know its speed v_f when it is at the height y_f.

To find v_f, we apply energy conservation to the points i and f:

$$U_i + K_i = U_f + K_f$$

Writing out U and K specifically for these two points yields the following:

$$mgy_i + \tfrac{1}{2}mv_i^2 = mgy_f + \tfrac{1}{2}mv_f^2$$

As before, we cancel m and solve for the unknown speed, v_f:

$$v_f = \sqrt{v_i^2 + 2g(y_i - y_f)}$$

This result is in agreement with the kinematic equation, $v_y^2 = v_{0y}^2 + 2a_y\,\Delta y$.

◀ **FIGURE 8-9 Speed is independent of path**

If the speed of the cap is v_i at the height y_i, its speed is v_f at the height y_f, independent of the path between the two heights. This assumes, of course, that frictional forces can be neglected.

Science Fundamentals Second Edition

Note that v_f depends only on y_i and y_f, not on the path connecting them. This is because conservative forces such as gravity do work that is path-independent. What this means physically is that the cap has the same speed v_f at the height y_f, whether it goes straight upward or follows some other trajectory, as in Figure 8–9. All that matters is the height difference.

EXAMPLE 8–6   Catching a Home Run

In the bottom of the ninth inning, a player hits a 0.15-kg baseball over the outfield fence. The ball leaves the bat with a speed of 36 m/s, and a fan in the bleachers catches it 7.2 m above the point where it was hit. Assuming frictional forces can be ignored, find **(a)** the kinetic energy of the ball when it is caught and **(b)** its speed when caught.

Picture the Problem
Our sketch shows the ball's trajectory. We label the hit point i and the catch point f. At point i we choose $y_i = 0$; at point f, then, $y_f = h = 7.2$ m. In addition, we are given that $v_i = 36$ m/s; v_f is to be determined.

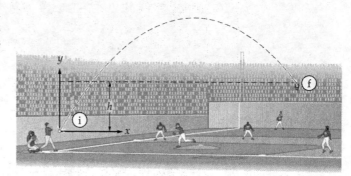

Strategy

a. Because frictional forces can be ignored, it follows that the initial mechanical energy is equal to the final mechanical energy; that is, $U_i + K_i = U_f + K_f$. Use this relation to find K_f.

b. Once K_f is determined, use $K_f = \frac{1}{2}mv_f^2$ to find v_f.

Solution

Part (a)

1. Begin by writing U and K for point i:

$$U_i = 0$$
$$K_i = \tfrac{1}{2}mv_i^2 = \tfrac{1}{2}(0.15 \text{ kg})(36 \text{ m/s})^2 = 97 \text{ J}$$

2. Next, write U and K for point f:

$$U_f = mgh = (0.15 \text{ kg})(9.81 \text{ m/s}^2)(7.2 \text{ m}) = 11 \text{ J}$$
$$K_f = \tfrac{1}{2}mv_f^2$$

3. Set the total mechanical energy at point i, $E_i = U_i + K_i$, equal to the total mechanical energy at point f, $E_f = U_f + K_f$, and solve for K_f:

$$U_i + K_i = U_f + K_f$$
$$0 + 97 \text{ J} = 11 \text{ J} + K_f$$
$$K_f = 97 \text{ J} - 11 \text{ J} = 86 \text{ J}$$

Part (b)

4. Use $K_f = \frac{1}{2}mv_f^2$ to find v_f:

$$K_f = \tfrac{1}{2}mv_f^2$$
$$v_f = \sqrt{\frac{2K_f}{m}} = \sqrt{\frac{2(86 \text{ J})}{0.15 \text{ kg}}} = 34 \text{ m/s}$$

Insight
To find the ball's speed when it was caught, we need to know the height of point f, but we don't need to know any details about the ball's trajectory. For example, it is not necessary to know the angle at which the ball leaves the bat or its maximum height.

The histograms to the right show the values of U and K at the points i and f. Notice that the energy of the system is mostly kinetic at the time the ball is caught.

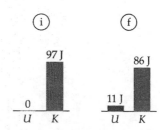

Practice Problem
If the mass of the ball were increased, would the catch speed be greater than, less than, or the same as the value we just found?   [**Answer:** The same. U and K depend on mass in the same way, hence the mass cancels.]

Some related homework problems: Problem 19, Problem 20

The connection between height difference and speeds is explored further in the following Conceptual Checkpoint and Example.

Science Fundamentals Second Edition

CONCEPTUAL CHECKPOINT 8–1   Compare the Final Speeds

Swimmers at a water park can enter a pool using one of two frictionless slides of equal height. Slide 1 approaches the water with a uniform slope; slide 2 dips rapidly at first, then levels out. Is the speed v_2 at the bottom of slide 2 (a) greater than, (b) less than, or (c) the same as the speed v_1 at the bottom of slide 1?

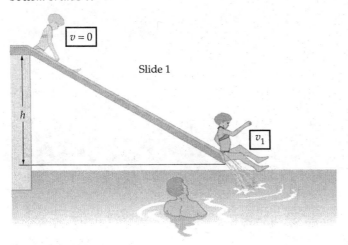

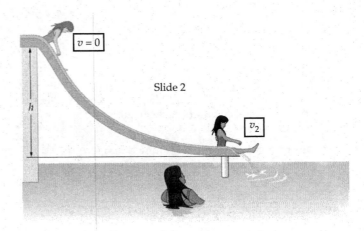

Reasoning and Discussion

In both cases, the same amount of potential energy, mgh, is converted to kinetic energy. Since the conversion of gravitational potential energy to kinetic energy is the *only* energy transaction taking place, it follows that the speed is the same for each slide.

Interestingly, although the final speeds are the same, the time required to reach the water is less for slide 2. The reason is that swimmer 2 reaches a high speed early and maintains it, whereas the speed of swimmer 1 increases slowly and steadily.

Answer:

(c) The speeds are the same.

EXAMPLE 8–7   Skateboard Exit Ramp

A 55-kg skateboarder enters a ramp moving horizontally with a speed of 6.5 m/s and leaves the ramp moving vertically with a speed of 4.1 m/s. Find the height of the ramp, assuming no energy loss to frictional forces.

Picture the Problem

We choose $y = 0$ to be the level of the bottom of the ramp, thus the gravitational potential energy is zero there. Point i indicates the skateboarder entering the ramp with a speed of 6.5 m/s; point f is the top of the ramp, where the speed is 4.1 m/s.

Strategy

To find h, simply set the initial energy, $E_i = U_i + K_i$, equal to the final energy, $E_f = U_f + K_f$.

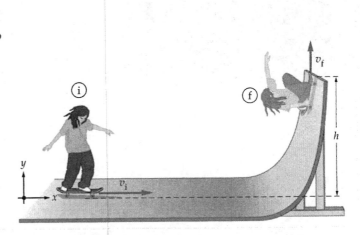

Solution

1. Write expressions for U_i and K_i:

$$U_i = mg \cdot 0 = 0 \qquad K_i = \tfrac{1}{2}mv_i^2$$

2. Write expressions for U_f and K_f:

$$U_f = mgh \qquad K_f = \tfrac{1}{2}mv_f^2$$

3. Set the total mechanical energy at point i, $E_i = U_i + K_i$, equal to the total mechanical energy at point f, $E_f = U_f + K_f$:

$$U_i + K_i = U_f + K_f$$
$$0 + \tfrac{1}{2}mv_i^2 = mgh + \tfrac{1}{2}mv_f^2$$

continued on next page

Science Fundamentals Second Edition

continued from previous page

4. Solve for h. Note that m cancels:

$$mgh = \tfrac{1}{2}mv_i^2 - \tfrac{1}{2}mv_f^2$$

$$h = \frac{v_i^2 - v_f^2}{2g}$$

5. Substitute numerical values:

$$h = \frac{(6.5 \text{ m/s})^2 - (4.1 \text{ m/s})^2}{2(9.81 \text{ m/s}^2)} = 1.3 \text{ m}$$

Insight

Note that our value for h is independent of the shape of the ramp—it is equally valid for one with the shape shown here, or one that simply inclines upward at a constant angle. In addition, the height does not depend on the person's mass, as we see in step 4.

The histograms to the right show U and K to scale at the points i and f, as well as at the maximum height where $K = 0$.

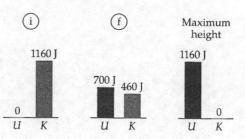

Practice Problem

What is the skateboarder's maximum height above the bottom of the ramp? [**Answer:** 2.2 m]

Some related homework problems: Problem 19, Problem 23

▲ Does the shape of the slide matter? (See Conceptual Checkpoint 8–1.)

It is interesting to express the equation in line 3 from Example 8–7 in words. First, the left side of the equation is the initial kinetic energy of the skateboarder, $\tfrac{1}{2}mv_i^2$. This is the initial energy content of the system. At point f the system still has the same amount of energy, only now part of it, mgh, is in the form of gravitational potential energy. The remainder is the final kinetic energy, $\tfrac{1}{2}mv_f^2$.

Conceptual Checkpoint 8–2 considers the effect of a slight change in the initial speed of an object.

CONCEPTUAL CHECKPOINT 8–2 What is the Final Speed?

A snowboarder coasts on a smooth track that rises from one level to another. If the snowboarder's initial speed is 4 m/s, the snowboarder just makes it to the upper level and comes to rest. With a slightly greater initial speed of 5 m/s, the snowboarder is still moving to the right on the upper level. Is the snowboarder's final speed in this case (a) 1 m/s, (b) 2 m/s, or (c) 3 m/s?

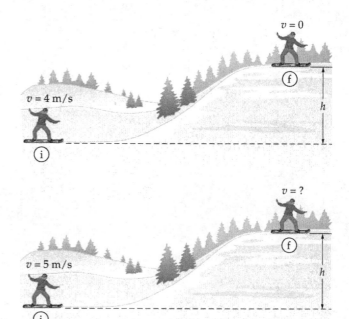

Reasoning and Discussion
A plausible-sounding answer is that since the initial speed is greater by 1 m/s in the second case, the final speed should be greater by 1 m/s as well. Therefore, the answer should be $0 + 1$ m/s $= 1$ m/s. This is incorrect, however.

As surprising as it may seem, an increase in the initial speed from 4 m/s to 5 m/s results in an increase in the final speed from 0 to 3 m/s. This is due to the fact that kinetic energy depends on v^2 rather than v; thus, it is the difference in v^2 that counts. In this case, the initial value of v^2 increases from 16 m²/s² to 25 m²/s², for a total increase of 25 m²/s² $-$ 16 m²/s² $=$ 9 m²/s². The final value of v^2 must increase by the same amount, 9 m²/s² $= (3$ m/s$)^2$. As a result, the final speed is 3 m/s.

Answer:
(c) The final speed of the snowboarder in the second case is 3 m/s.

Let's check the results of the previous Conceptual Checkpoint with a specific numerical example. Suppose the snowboarder has a mass of 74.0 kg. It follows that in the first case the initial kinetic energy is $K_i = \frac{1}{2}(74.0$ kg$)(4.00$ m/s$)^2 = 592$ J. At the top of the hill all of this kinetic energy is converted to gravitational potential energy, mgh.

In the second case, the initial speed of the snowboarder is 5.00 m/s; thus, the initial kinetic energy is $K_i = \frac{1}{2}(74.0$ kg$)(5.00$ m/s$)^2 = 925$ J. When the snowboarder reaches the top of the hill, 592 J of this kinetic energy is converted to gravitational potential energy, leaving the snowboarder with a final kinetic energy of 925 J $-$ 592 J $=$ 333 J. The corresponding speed is given by

$$\frac{1}{2}mv^2 = 333 \text{ J}$$
$$v = \sqrt{\frac{2(333 \text{ J})}{m}} = \sqrt{\frac{2(333 \text{ J})}{74.0 \text{ kg}}} = \sqrt{9.00 \text{ m}^2/\text{s}^2} = 3.00 \text{ m/s}$$

Thus, as expected, the snowboarder in the second case has a final speed of 3.00 m/s.

We conclude this section with two Examples involving springs.

EXAMPLE 8–8 Spring Time

A 1.70-kg block slides on a horizontal, frictionless surface until it encounters a spring with a force constant of 955 N/m. The block comes to rest after compressing the spring a distance of 4.60 cm. Find the initial speed of the block. (Ignore air resistance and any energy lost when the block initially contacts the spring.)

Picture the Problem
Point i refers to times before the block makes contact with the spring, which means the block has a speed v and the end of the spring is at $x = 0$. Point f refers to the time when the block has come to rest, and the spring is compressed to $x = -d = -4.60$ cm.

We can choose the center of the block to be the $y = 0$ level. With this choice, the gravitational potential energy of the system is zero at all times.

Strategy
Set E_i equal to E_f to find the one unknown, v. Note that the initial energy, E_i, is the kinetic energy of the block before it reaches the spring. The final energy, E_f, is the potential energy of the compressed spring.

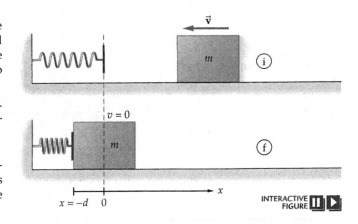

INTERACTIVE
FIGURE

Solution

1. Write expressions for U_i and K_i. For U, we consider only the potential energy of the spring, $U = \frac{1}{2}kx^2$:

$$U_i = \frac{1}{2}k \cdot 0^2 = 0 \quad K_i = \frac{1}{2}mv^2$$

2. Do the same for U_f and K_f:

$$U_f = \frac{1}{2}k(-d)^2 = \frac{1}{2}kd^2 \quad K_f = \frac{1}{2}m \cdot 0^2 = 0$$

3. Set the initial mechanical energy, $E_i = U_i + K_i$, equal to the final mechanical energy, $E_f = U_f + K_f$, and solve for v:

$$U_i + K_i = U_f + K_f$$
$$0 + \frac{1}{2}mv^2 = \frac{1}{2}kd^2 + 0$$
$$v = d\sqrt{\frac{k}{m}}$$

4. Substitute numerical values:

$$v = d\sqrt{\frac{k}{m}} = (0.0460 \text{ m})\sqrt{\frac{955 \text{ N/m}}{1.70 \text{ kg}}} = 1.09 \text{ m/s}$$

continued on next page

Science Fundamentals Second Edition

continued from previous page

Insight
After the block comes to rest, the spring expands again, converting its potential energy back into the kinetic energy of the block. When the block leaves the spring, moving to the right, its speed is once again 1.09 m/s.

Practice Problem
What is the compression distance, d, if the block's initial speed is 0.500 m/s?   [**Answer:** 2.11 cm]

Some related homework problems: Problem 22, Problem 24

ACTIVE EXAMPLE 8–1 Find the Speed of the Block

Suppose the spring and block in Example 8–8 are oriented vertically, as shown here. Initially, the spring is compressed 4.60 cm and the block is at rest. When the block is released, it accelerates upward. Find the speed of the block when the spring has returned to its equilibrium position.

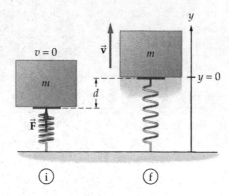

Solution *(Test your understanding by performing the calculations indicated in each step.)*

1. Write an expression for the initial mechanical energy E_i:

$$E_i = U_i + K_i = -mgd + \tfrac{1}{2}kd^2 + 0$$

2. Write an expression for the final mechanical energy E_f:

$$E_f = U_f + K_f = 0 + 0 + \tfrac{1}{2}mv^2$$

3. Set E_i equal to E_f and solve for v:

$$-mgd + \tfrac{1}{2}kd^2 = \tfrac{1}{2}mv^2$$
$$v = \sqrt{kd^2/m - 2gd}$$

4. Substitute numerical values:

$$v = 0.535 \text{ m/s}$$

Insight
In this system, part of the initial potential energy of the spring ($\tfrac{1}{2}kd^2$) goes into increasing the gravitational potential energy of the block (mgd). The remainder of the initial energy, $\tfrac{1}{2}kd^2 - mgd$, is converted into the block's kinetic energy.

Your Turn
What is the speed of the block when the spring is only halfway back to its equilibrium position?

*(Answers to **Your Turn** problems are given in the back of the book.)*

8–4 Work Done by Nonconservative Forces

Nonconservative forces change the amount of mechanical energy in a system. They might decrease the mechanical energy by converting it to thermal energy, or increase it by converting muscular work to kinetic or potential energy. In some systems, both types of processes occur at the same time.

To see the connection between the work done by a nonconservative force, W_{nc}, and the mechanical energy, E, we return once more to the work-energy theorem, which says that the *total* work is equal to the change in kinetic energy:

$$W_{total} = \Delta K$$

Suppose, for instance, that a system has one conservative and one nonconservative force. In this case, the total work is the sum of the conservative work W_c and the nonconservative work W_{nc}:

$$W_{total} = W_c + W_{nc}$$

Recalling that conservative work is related to the change in potential energy by the definition given in Equation 8–1, $W_c = -\Delta U$, we have

$$W_{total} = -\Delta U + W_{nc} = \Delta K$$

Solving this relation for the nonconservative work yields

$$W_{nc} = \Delta U + \Delta K$$

Finally, since the total mechanical energy is $E = U + K$, it follows that the *change* in mechanical energy is $\Delta E = \Delta U + \Delta K$. As a result, the nonconservative work is simply the change in mechanical energy:

$$W_{nc} = \Delta E = E_f - E_i \qquad \text{8–9}$$

If more than one nonconservative force acts, we simply add the nonconservative work done by each such force to obtain W_{nc}.

At this point it may be useful to collect the three "working relationships" that have been introduced in the last two chapters:

$$W_{total} = \Delta K$$
$$W_c = -\Delta U$$
$$W_{nc} = \Delta E \qquad \text{8–10}$$

Note that positive nonconservative work increases the total mechanical energy of a system, while negative nonconservative work decreases the mechanical energy—and converts it to other forms. In the next Example, for instance, part of the initial mechanical energy of a leaf is converted to heat and other forms of energy by air resistance as it falls to the ground.

PROBLEM-SOLVING NOTE

Nonconservative Systems

Start by sketching the system and labeling the initial and final points with i and f, respectively. The initial and final mechanical energies are related to the nonconservative work by $W_{nc} = E_f - E_i$.

EXAMPLE 8–9 A Leaf Falls in the Forest: Find the Nonconservative Work

Deep in the forest, a 17.0-g leaf falls from a tree and drops straight to the ground. If its initial height was 5.30 m and its speed on landing was 1.3 m/s, how much nonconservative work was done on the leaf?

Picture the Problem
The leaf drops from rest at a height $y = h = 5.30$ m and lands with a speed $v = 1.3$ m/s at $y = 0$. These two points are labeled i and f, respectively.

Strategy
To begin, calculate the initial mechanical energy, E_i, and the final mechanical energy, E_f. Once these energies have been determined, the nonconservative work is $W_{nc} = \Delta E = E_f - E_i$.

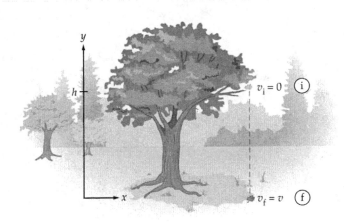

Solution

1. Evaluate U_i, K_i, and E_i:

$U_i = mgh = (0.0170 \text{ kg})(9.81 \text{ m/s}^2)(5.30 \text{ m}) = 0.884 \text{ J}$
$K_i = \frac{1}{2}m \cdot 0^2 = 0$
$E_i = U_i + K_i = 0.884 \text{ J}$

2. Next, evaluate U_f, K_f, and E_f.

$U_f = mg \cdot 0 = 0$
$K_f = \frac{1}{2}mv^2 = \frac{1}{2}(0.0170 \text{ kg})(1.3 \text{ m/s})^2 = 0.014 \text{ J}$
$E_f = U_f + K_f = 0.014 \text{ J}$

3. Use $W_{nc} = \Delta E$ to find the nonconservative work:

$W_{nc} = \Delta E = E_f - E_i = 0.014 \text{ J} - 0.884 \text{ J} = -0.87 \text{ J}$

continued on next page

continued from previous page

Insight

Note that most of the initial mechanical energy is dissipated as the leaf falls. This is indicated in the histograms to the right. The small amount that remains (only about 1.6%) appears as the kinetic energy of the leaf just before it lands. If a cherry had fallen from the tree, it would have struck the ground with a considerably greater speed—perhaps five times the speed of the leaf. In that case, the percentage of the initial potential energy remaining as kinetic energy would have been $5^2 = 25$ times greater than the percentage retained by the leaf.

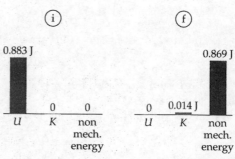

Practice Problem

What was the average nonconservative force exerted on the leaf as it fell? **[Answer:** $W_{nc} = -Fh$, $F = -W_{nc}/h = 0.16$ N, upward]

Some related homework problems: Problem 30, Problem 31

In the following Active Example, we use a knowledge of the nonconservative work to find the depth at which a diver comes to rest.

ACTIVE EXAMPLE 8–2 Find the Diver's Depth

A 95.0-kg diver steps off a diving board and drops into the water 3.00 m below. At some depth d below the water's surface, the diver comes to rest. If the nonconservative work done on the diver is $W_{nc} = -5120$ J, what is the depth, d?

Solution *(Test your understanding by performing the calculations indicated in each step.)*

1. Write the initial mechanical energy, E_i: $E_i = mgh + 0 = mgh$

2. Write the final mechanical energy, E_f: $E_f = mg(-d) + 0 = -mgd$

3. Set W_{nc} equal to ΔE: $W_{nc} = \Delta E = E_f - E_i = -mgd - mgh$

4. Solve for d: $d = -(W_{nc} + mgh)/mg$

5. Substitute numerical values: $d = 2.49$ m

Insight
Another way to write step 3 is $E_f = E_i + W_{nc}$. In words, this equation says that the final mechanical energy is the initial mechanical energy plus the nonconservative work done on the system. In this case, $W_{nc} < 0$; hence the final mechanical energy is less than the initial mechanical energy.

Your Turn
Suppose the diver descends to a depth of 3.50 m. How much nonconservative work is done in this case?

(Answers to **Your Turn** *problems are given in the back of the book.)*

We now present a Conceptual Checkpoint that further examines the relationship between nonconservative work and distance.

CONCEPTUAL CHECKPOINT 8–3   Judging a Putt

A golfer badly misjudges a putt, sending the ball only one-quarter of the distance to the hole. The original putt gave the ball an initial speed of v_0. If the force of resistance due to the grass is constant, would an initial speed of (a) $2v_0$, (b) $3v_0$, or (c) $4v_0$ be needed to get the ball to the hole from its original position?

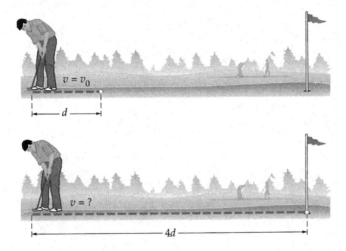

Reasoning and Discussion
In the original putt, the ball started with a kinetic energy of $\frac{1}{2}mv_0^2$ and came to rest in the distance d. The kinetic energy was dissipated by the nonconservative force due to grass resistance, F, which does the work $W_{nc} = -Fd$. Since the change in mechanical energy is $\Delta E = 0 - \frac{1}{2}mv_0^2 = -\frac{1}{2}mv_0^2$, it follows from $W_{nc} = \Delta E$ that $Fd = \frac{1}{2}mv_0^2$. Therefore, to go four times the distance, $4d$, we need to give the ball four times as much kinetic energy. Noting that kinetic energy is proportional to v^2, we see that the initial speed need only be doubled.

Answer:
(a) The initial speed should be doubled to $2v_0$.

A common example of a nonconservative force is kinetic friction. In the next Example, we show how to include the effects of friction in a system that also includes kinetic energy and gravitational potential energy.

EXAMPLE 8–10 Landing with a Thud

A block of mass m_1 = 2.40 kg is connected to a second block of mass m_2 = 1.80 kg, as shown here. When the blocks are released from rest, they move through a distance d = 0.500 m, at which point m_2 hits the floor. Given that the coefficient of kinetic friction between m_1 and the horizontal surface is μ_k = 0.450, find the speed of the blocks just before m_2 lands.

Picture the Problem
We choose y = 0 to be at floor level; therefore, the gravitational potential energy of m_2 is zero when it lands. The potential energy of m_1 doesn't change during this process; it is always m_1gh. Thus, it isn't necessary to know the value of h. Note that we label the beginning and ending points with i and f, respectively.

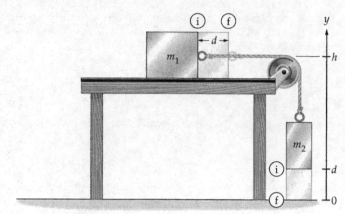

INTERACTIVE FIGURE

Strategy
Since a nonconservative force (friction) is doing work in this system, we use $W_{nc} = \Delta E = E_f - E_i$. Thus, we must calculate not only the mechanical energies, E_i and E_f, but also the nonconservative work, W_{nc}. Note that E_f can be written in terms of the unknown speed of the blocks just before m_2 lands. Therefore, we can set W_{nc} equal to ΔE and solve for the final speed.

Solution

1. Evaluate U_i, K_i, and E_i. Be sure to include contributions from both masses:

$$U_i = m_1gh + m_2gd$$
$$K_i = \tfrac{1}{2}m_1 \cdot 0^2 + \tfrac{1}{2}m_2 \cdot 0^2 = 0$$
$$E_i = U_i + K_i = m_1gh + m_2gd$$

2. Next, evaluate U_f, K_f, and E_f. Note that E_f depends on the unknown speed, v:

$$U_f = m_1gh + 0$$
$$K_f = \tfrac{1}{2}m_1v^2 + \tfrac{1}{2}m_2v^2$$
$$E_f = U_f + K_f = m_1gh + \tfrac{1}{2}m_1v^2 + \tfrac{1}{2}m_2v^2$$

3. Calculate the nonconservative work, W_{nc}. Recall that the force of friction is $f_k = \mu_k N = \mu_k m_1g$, and that it points opposite to the displacement of distance d:

$$W_{nc} = -f_k d = -\mu_k m_1 g d$$

4. Set W_{nc} equal to $\Delta E = E_f - E_i$. Notice that m_1gh cancels because it occurs in both E_i and E_f.

$$W_{nc} = E_f - E_i$$
$$-\mu_k m_1 g d = \tfrac{1}{2}m_1v^2 + \tfrac{1}{2}m_2v^2 - m_2gd$$

5. Solve for v:

$$v = \sqrt{\frac{2(m_2 - \mu_k m_1)gd}{m_1 + m_2}}$$

6. Substitute numerical values:

$$v = \sqrt{\frac{2[1.80 \text{ kg} - (0.450)(2.40 \text{ kg})](9.81 \text{ m/s}^2)(0.500 \text{ m})}{1.80 \text{ kg} + 2.40 \text{ kg}}}$$
$$= 1.30 \text{ m/s}$$

Insight
Note that step 4 can be rearranged as follows: $\tfrac{1}{2}m_1v^2 + \tfrac{1}{2}m_2v^2 = m_2gd - \mu_k m_1 g d$. Translating this to words, we can say that the final kinetic energy of the blocks is equal to the initial gravitational potential energy of m_2, minus the energy dissipated by friction.

Practice Problem
Find the coefficient of kinetic friction if the final speed of the blocks is 0.950 m/s.   [**Answer:** μ_k = 0.589]

Some related homework problems: Problem 35, Problem 36

Finally, we present an Active Example for the common situation of a system in which two different nonconservative forces do work.

ACTIVE EXAMPLE 8–3 Marathon Man: Find the Height of the Hill

An 80.0-kg jogger starts from rest and runs uphill into a stiff breeze. At the top of the hill the jogger has done the work $W_{nc1} = +1.80 \times 10^4$ J, air resistance has done the work $W_{nc2} = -4420$ J, and the jogger's speed is 3.50 m/s. Find the height of the hill.

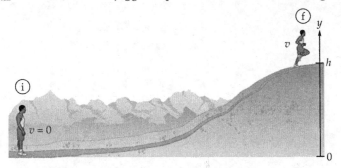

Solution *(Test your understanding by performing the calculations indicated in each step.)*

1. Write the initial mechanical energy, E_i: $E_i = U_i + K_i = 0 + 0 = 0$

2. Write the final mechanical energy, E_f: $E_f = U_f + K_f = mgh + \frac{1}{2}mv^2$

3. Set W_{nc} equal to ΔE: $W_{nc} = \Delta E = mgh + \frac{1}{2}mv^2$

4. Use $W_{nc} = \Delta E$ to solve for h: $h = (W_{nc} - \frac{1}{2}mv^2)/mg$

5. Calculate the total nonconservative work: $W_{nc} = W_{nc1} + W_{nc2} = 13{,}600$ J

6. Substitute numerical values to determine h: $h = 16.7$ m

Insight
As usual when dealing with energy calculations, our final result is independent of the shape of the hill.

Your Turn
Suppose the jogger's mass had been 90.0 kg rather than 80.0 kg. What would be the height of the hill in this case?

*(Answers to **Your Turn** problems are given in the back of the book.)*

▲ Highways that descend steeply are often provided with escape ramps that enable truck drivers whose brakes fail to bring their rigs to a safe stop. These ramps provide a perfect illustration of the conservation of energy. From a physics point of view, the driver's problem is to get rid of an enormous amount of kinetic energy in the safest possible way. The ramps run uphill, so some of the kinetic energy is simply converted back into gravitational potential energy (just as in a roller coaster). In addition, the ramps are typically surfaced with sand or gravel, allowing much of the initial kinetic energy to be dissipated by friction into other forms of energy, such as sound and heat.

Waves and Sound

14–1 Types of Waves   431
14–2 Waves on a String   433
*14–3 Harmonic Wave Functions   436
14–4 Sound Waves   437
14–5 Sound Intensity   441

Have you ever wondered why a grand piano has this somewhat peculiar shape? It's not just tradition—there's also a physical reason, having to do with the way vibrating strings produce sound. But to understand this and other aspects of sound, it is first necessary to learn about waves in general—for sound, as we shall see, is merely a particular kind of wave, though one that has a special importance in our lives.

In the last chapter, we studied the behavior of an oscillator. Here, we consider the behavior of a series of oscillators that are connected to one another. Connecting oscillators leads to an assortment of new phenomena, including waves on a string, water waves, and sound. In this chapter, we focus our attention on the behavior of such waves, and in particular on the way they propagate, their speed of propagation, and their interactions with one another. Later, in Chapter 25, we shall see that light is also a type of wave, and that it displays many of the same phenomena exhibited by the waves considered in this chapter.

430

14–1 Types of Waves

Consider a group of swings in a playground swing set. We know that each swing by itself behaves like a simple pendulum; that is, like an oscillator. Now, let's connect the swings to one another. To be specific, suppose we tie a rope from the seat of the first swing to its neighbor, and then another rope from the second swing to the third swing, and so on. When the swings are at rest—in equilibrium—the connecting ropes have no effect. If you now sit in the first swing and begin oscillating—thus "disturbing" the equilibrium—the connecting ropes cause the other swings along the line to start oscillating as well. You have created a traveling disturbance.

In general, a disturbance that propagates from one place to another is referred to as a **wave**. Waves propagate with well-defined speeds determined by the properties of the material through which they travel. In addition, waves carry energy. For example, part of the energy you put into sound waves when you speak is carried to the ears of others, where some of the sound energy is converted into electrical energy carried by nerve impulses to the brain which, in turn, creates the sensation of hearing.

It is important to distinguish between the motion of the wave itself and the motion of the individual particles that make up the wave. Common examples include the waves that propagate through a field of wheat. The individual wheat stalks sway back and forth as a wave passes, but they do not change their location. Similarly, a "wave" at a ball game may propagate around the stadium more quickly than a person can run, but the individual people making up the wave simply stand and sit in one place. From these simple examples it is clear that waves can come in a variety of types. We discuss some of the more common types in this section. In addition, we show how the speed of a wave is related to some of its basic properties.

▲ A wave can be viewed as a disturbance that propagates through space. Although the wave itself moves steadily in one direction, the particles that create the wave do not share in this motion. Instead, they oscillate back and forth about their equilibrium positions. The water in an ocean wave, for example, moves mainly up and down—as it passes, you bob up and down with it rather than being carried onto the shore. Similarly, the people in a human "wave" at a ballpark simply stand or raise their arms in place—they do not travel around the stadium.

Transverse Waves

Perhaps the easiest type of wave to visualize is a wave on a string, as illustrated in **Figure 14–1**. To generate such a wave, start by tying one end of a long string or rope to a wall. Pull on the free end with your hand, producing a tension in the string, and then move your hand up and down. As you do so, a wave will travel along the string toward the wall. In fact, if your hand moves up and down with simple harmonic motion, the wave on the string will have the shape of a sine or a cosine; we refer to such a wave as a **harmonic wave**.

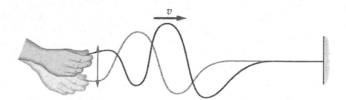

◀ FIGURE 14–1 **A wave on a string**
A wave on a string can be generated by vibrating one end of the string with an up-and-down motion.

Note that the wave travels in the horizontal direction, even though your hand oscillates vertically about one spot. In fact, if you look at any point on the string, it too moves vertically up and down, with no horizontal motion at all. This is shown in **Figure 14–2**, where we see the location of an individual point on a string as a wave travels past. Notice, in particular, that the displacement of particles in a string is at right angles to the direction of propagation of the wave. A wave with this property is called a **transverse wave**:

In a transverse wave, the displacement of individual particles is at *right angles* to the direction of propagation of the wave.

Other examples of transverse waves include light and radio waves. These will be discussed in detail in Chapter 25.

Science Fundamentals Second Edition

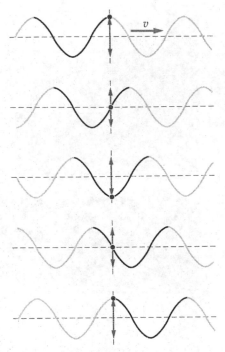

▲ FIGURE 14–2 The motion of a wave on a string

As a wave on a string moves horizontally, all points on the string vibrate in the vertical direction, as indicated by the blue arrow.

▲ FIGURE 14–4 Water waves from a disturbance

An isolated disturbance in a pool of water, caused by a pebble dropped into the water, creates waves that propagate symmetrically away from the disturbance. The crests and troughs form circles on the surface of the water as they move outward.

Longitudinal Waves

Longitudinal waves differ from transverse waves in the way that particles in the wave move. In particular, a longitudinal wave is defined as follows:

> In a longitudinal wave, the displacement of individual particles is parallel to the direction of propagation of the wave.

The classic example of a longitudinal wave is sound. When you speak, for example, the vibrations in your vocal cords create a series of compressions and expansions (rarefactions) in the air. The same kind of situation occurs with a loudspeaker, as illustrated in **Figure 14–3**. Here we see a speaker diaphragm vibrating horizontally with simple harmonic motion. As it moves to the right it compresses the air momentarily; as it moves to the left it rarefies the air. A series of compressions and rarefactions then travel horizontally away from the loudspeaker with the speed of sound.

Figure 14–3 also indicates the motion of an individual particle in the air as a sound wave passes. Note that the particle moves back and forth horizontally; that is, in the same direction as the propagation of the wave. The particle does not travel with the wave—each individual particle simply oscillates about a given position in space.

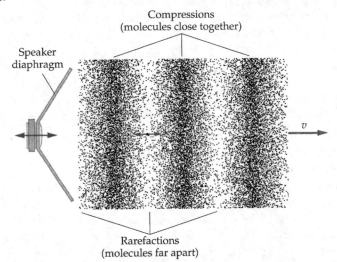

▲ FIGURE 14–3 Sound produced by a speaker

As the diaphragm of a speaker vibrates back and forth, it alternately compresses and rarefies the surrounding air. These regions of high and low density propagate away from the speaker with the speed of sound. Individual particles in the air oscillate back and forth about a given position, as indicated by the blue arrow.

Water Waves

If a pebble is dropped into a pool of water, a series of concentric waves move away from the drop point. This is illustrated in **Figure 14–4**. To visualize the movement of the water as a wave travels by, place a small piece of cork into the water. As a wave passes, the motion of the cork will trace out the motion of the water itself, as indicated in **Figure 14–5**.

Notice that the cork moves in a roughly circular path, returning to approximately its starting point. Thus, each element of water moves both vertically and horizontally as the wave propagates by in the horizontal direction. In this sense, a water wave is a combination of both transverse and longitudinal waves. This makes the water wave more difficult to analyze. Hence, most of our results will refer to the simpler cases of purely transverse and purely longitudinal waves.

Wavelength, Frequency, and Speed

A simple wave can be thought of as a regular, rhythmic disturbance that propagates from one point to another, repeating itself both in *space* and in *time*. We now

▶ **FIGURE 14–5 The motion of a water wave**
As a water wave passes a given point, a molecule (or a small piece of cork) moves in a roughly circular path. This means that the water molecules move both vertically and horizontally. In this sense, the water wave has characteristics of both transverse and longitudinal waves.

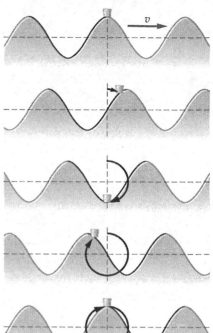

show that the repeat length and the repeat time of a wave are directly related to its speed of propagation.

We begin by considering the snapshots of a wave shown in **Figure 14–6**. Points on the wave corresponding to maximum upward displacement are referred to as **crests**; points corresponding to maximum downward displacement are called **troughs**. The distance from one crest to the next, or from one trough to the next, is the repeat length—or **wavelength, λ**—of the wave.

Definition of Wavelength, λ

λ = distance over which a wave repeats

SI unit: m

Similarly, the repeat time—or **period, T**—of a wave is the time required for one wavelength to pass a given point, as illustrated in Figure 14–6. Closely related to the period of a wave is its **frequency, f**, which, as with oscillations, is defined by the relation $f = 1/T$.

Combining these observations, we see that a wave travels a distance λ in the time T. Applying the definition of speed—distance divided by time—it follows that the speed of a wave is

Speed of a Wave

$$v = \frac{\text{distance}}{\text{time}} = \frac{\lambda}{T} = \lambda f \qquad \text{14–1}$$

SI unit: m/s

This result applies to all waves.

EXERCISE 14–1

Sound waves travel in air with a speed of 343 m/s. The lowest frequency sound we can hear is 20.0 Hz; the highest frequency is 20.0 kHz. Find the wavelength of sound for frequencies of 20.0 Hz and 20.0 kHz.

Solution

Solve Equation 14–1 for λ:

$$\lambda = \frac{v}{f} = \frac{343 \text{ m/s}}{20.0 \text{ s}^{-1}} = 17.2 \text{ m}$$

$$\lambda = \frac{v}{f} = \frac{343 \text{ m/s}}{20{,}000 \text{ s}^{-1}} = 1.72 \text{ cm}$$

14–2 Waves on a String

In this section we consider some of the basic properties of waves traveling on a string, a rope, a wire, or any similar linear medium.

The Speed of a Wave on a String

The speed of a wave is determined by the properties of the medium through which it propagates. In the case of a string of length L, there are two basic characteristics that determine the speed of a wave: (i) the tension in the string, and (ii) the mass of the string.

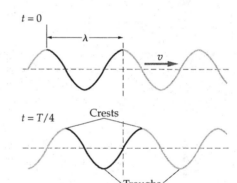

$t = 0$

$t = T/4$ Crests

$t = T/2$ Troughs

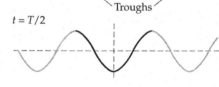

$t = 3T/4$

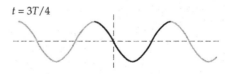

$t = T$

▲ **FIGURE 14–6 The speed of a wave**
A wave repeats over a distance equal to the wavelength, λ. The time necessary for a wave to move one wavelength is the period, T. Thus, the speed of a wave is $v = \lambda/T = \lambda f$.

Let's begin with the tension, which is the force F transmitted through the string (we will use F for the tension rather than T, to avoid confusion between the tension and the period). Clearly, there must be a tension in a string in order for it to propagate a wave. Imagine, for example, that a string lies on a smooth floor with both ends free. If you take one end into your hand and shake it, the portions of the string near your hand will oscillate slightly, but no wave will travel to the other end of the string. If someone else takes hold of the other end of the string and pulls enough to set up a tension, then any movement you make on your end will propagate to the other end. In fact, if the tension is increased—so that the string becomes less slack—waves will travel through the string more rapidly.

Next, we consider the mass m of the string. A heavy string responds slowly to a given disturbance because of its inertia. Thus, if you try sending a wave through a kite string or a large rope, both under the same tension, you will find that the wave in the rope travels more slowly. In general, the heavier a rope or string the slower the speed of waves in it. Of course, the total mass of a string doesn't really matter; a longer string has more mass, but its other properties are basically the same. What is important is the mass of the string per length. We give this quantity the label μ:

Definition of Mass per Length, μ

μ = mass per length = m/L

SI unit: kg/m

To summarize, we expect the speed v to increase with the tension F and decrease with the mass per length, μ. Assuming these are the only factors determining the speed of a wave on a string, we can obtain the dependence of v on F and μ using dimensional analysis (see Chapter 1, Section 3). First, we identify the dimensions of v, F, and μ:

$$[v] = \text{m/s}$$
$$[F] = \text{N} = \text{kg} \cdot \text{m/s}^2$$
$$[\mu] = \text{kg/m}$$

Next, we seek a combination of F and μ that has the dimensions of v; namely, m/s. Suppose, for example, that v depends on F to the power a and μ to the power b. Then, we have

$$v = F^a \mu^b$$

In terms of dimensions, this equation is

$$\text{m/s} = (\text{kg} \cdot \text{m/s}^2)^a (\text{kg/m})^b = \text{kg}^{a+b} \text{m}^{a-b} \text{s}^{-2a}$$

Comparing dimensions, we see that kg does not appear on the left side of the equation; therefore, we conclude that $a + b = 0$ so that kg does not appear on the right side of the equation. Hence, $a = -b$. Looking at the time dimension, s, we see that on the left we have s^{-1}; thus on the right side we must have $-2a = -1$, or $a = \frac{1}{2}$. It follows that $b = -a = -\frac{1}{2}$. This gives the following result:

Speed of a Wave on a String, v

$$v = \sqrt{\frac{F}{\mu}}$$

14–2

SI unit: m/s

As expected, the speed increases with F and decreases with μ.

Dimensional analysis does not guarantee that this is the complete, final result; there could be a dimensionless factor like $\frac{1}{2}$ or 2π left unaccounted for. It turns out, however, that a complete analysis based on Newton's laws gives precisely the same result.

EXERCISE 14-2

A 5.0-m length of rope, with a mass of 0.52 kg, is pulled taut with a tension of 46 N. Find the speed of waves on the rope.

Solution

First, calculate the mass per length, μ:

$$\mu = m/L = (0.52 \text{ kg})/(5.0 \text{ m}) = 0.10 \text{ kg/m}$$

Now, substitute μ and F into Equation 14-2:

$$v = \sqrt{\frac{F}{\mu}} = \sqrt{\frac{46 \text{ N}}{0.10 \text{ kg/m}}} = 21 \text{ m/s}$$

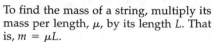

PROBLEM-SOLVING NOTE

Mass versus Mass-per-Length

To find the mass of a string, multiply its mass per length, μ, by its length L. That is, $m = \mu L$.

EXAMPLE 14-1 A Wave on a Rope

A 12-m rope is pulled tight with a tension of 92 N. When one end of the rope is given a "thunk" it takes 0.45 s for the disturbance to propagate to the other end. What is the mass of the rope?

Picture the Problem

Our sketch shows a wave pulse traveling with a speed v from one end of the rope to the other, a distance of 12 m. The tension in the rope is 92 N, and the travel time of the pulse is 0.45 s.

Strategy

We know that the speed of waves (disturbances) on a rope is determined by the tension and the mass per length. Thus, we first calculate the speed of the wave with the information given in the problem statement. Next, we solve for the mass per length, then multiply by the length to get the mass.

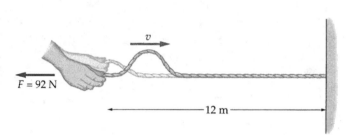

Solution

1. Calculate the speed of the wave:

$$v = \frac{d}{t} = \frac{12 \text{ m}}{0.45 \text{ s}} = 27 \text{ m/s}$$

2. Use $v = \sqrt{F/\mu}$ to solve for the mass per length:

$$\mu = F/v^2$$

3. Substitute numerical values for F and v:

$$\mu = \frac{F}{v^2} = \frac{92 \text{ N}}{(27 \text{ m/s})^2} = 0.13 \text{ kg/m}$$

4. Multiply μ by $L = 12$ m to find the mass:

$$m = \mu L = (0.13 \text{ kg/m})(12 \text{ m}) = 1.6 \text{ kg}$$

Insight

Note that the speed of a wave on this rope (about 60 mi/h) is comparable to the speed of a car on a highway. This speed could be increased even further by pulling harder on the rope, thus increasing its tension.

Practice Problem

If the tension in this rope is doubled, how long will it take for the thunk to travel from one end to the other? [**Answer:** In this case the wave speed is $v = 38$ m/s; hence the time is $t = 0.32$ s.]

Some related homework problems: Problem 9, Problem 10, Problem 11

In the following Conceptual Checkpoint, we consider the speed of a wave on a vertical rope of finite mass.

CONCEPTUAL CHECKPOINT 14–1   Speed of a Wave

A rope of length L and mass M hangs from a ceiling. If the bottom of the rope is given a gentle wiggle, a wave will travel to the top of the rope. As the wave travels upward does its speed (a) increase, (b) decrease, or (c) stay the same?

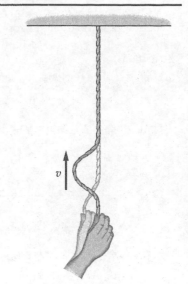

Reasoning and Discussion
The speed of the wave is determined by the tension in the rope and its mass per length. The mass per length is the same from bottom to top, but not the tension. In particular, the tension at any point in the rope is equal to the weight of rope below that point. Thus, the tension increases from almost zero near the bottom to essentially Mg near the top. Since the tension increases with height, so too does the speed, according to Equation 14–2.

Answer:
(a) The speed increases.

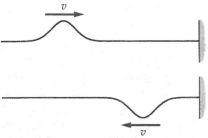

▲ **FIGURE 14–7 A reflected wave pulse: fixed end**

A wave pulse on a string is inverted when it reflects from an end that is tied down.

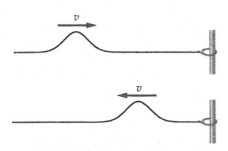

▲ **FIGURE 14–8 A reflected wave pulse: free end**

A wave pulse on a string whose end is free to move is reflected without inversion.

Reflections

Thus far we have discussed only the situation in which a wave travels along a string; but at some point the wave must reach the end of the string. What happens then? Clearly, we expect the wave to be reflected, but the precise way in which the reflection occurs needs to be considered.

Suppose, for example, that the far end of a string is anchored firmly into a wall, as shown in **Figure 14–7**. If you give a flick to your end of the string, you set up a wave "pulse" that travels toward the far end. When it reaches the end, it exerts an upward force on the wall, trying to pull it up into the pulse. Since the end is tied down, however, the wall exerts an equal and opposite downward force to keep the end at rest. Thus, the wall exerts a downward force on the string that is just the *opposite* of the upward force you exerted when you created the pulse. As a result, the reflection is an inverted, or upside-down, pulse, as indicated in Figure 14–7. We shall encounter this same type of inversion under reflection when we consider the reflection of light in Chapter 28.

Another way to tie off the end of the string is shown in **Figure 14–8**. In this case, the string is tied to a small ring that slides vertically with little friction on a vertical pole. In this way, the string still has a tension in it, since it pulls on the ring, but it is also free to move up and down.

Consider a pulse moving along such a string, as in Figure 14–8. When the pulse reaches the end, it lifts the ring upward and then lowers it back down. In fact, the pulse flicks the far end of the string in the *same* way that you flicked it when you created the pulse. Therefore, the far end of the string simply creates a new pulse, identical to the first, only traveling in the opposite direction. This is illustrated in the figure.

Thus, when waves reflect, they may or may not be inverted, depending on how the reflection occurs.

*14–3 Harmonic Wave Functions

If a wave is generated by oscillating one end of a string with simple harmonic motion, the waves will have the shape of a sine or a cosine. This is shown in **Figure 14–9**, where the y direction denotes the vertical displacement of the string, and $y = 0$ corresponds to the flat string with no wave present. In what follows, we consider the mathematical formula that describes y as a function of time, t, and position, x, for such a harmonic wave.

First, note that the harmonic wave in Figure 14–9 repeats when x increases by an amount equal to the wavelength, λ. Thus, the dependence of the wave on x must be of the form

$$y(x) = A \cos\left(\frac{2\pi}{\lambda}x\right) \qquad \text{14–3}$$

To see that this is the correct dependence, note that replacing x with $x + \lambda$ gives the same value for y:

$$y(x + \lambda) = A \cos\left[\frac{2\pi}{\lambda}(x + \lambda)\right] = A \cos\left(\frac{2\pi}{\lambda}x + 2\pi\right) = A \cos\left(\frac{2\pi}{\lambda}x\right) = y(x)$$

It follows that Equation 14–3 describes a vertical displacement that repeats with a wavelength λ, as desired for a wave.

This is only part of the "wave function," however, since we have not yet described the way the wave changes with time. This is illustrated in Figure 14–9, where we see a harmonic wave at time $t = 0$, $t = T/4$, $t = T/2$, $t = 3T/4$, and $t = T$. Note that the peak in the wave that was originally at $x = 0$ at $t = 0$ moves to $x = \lambda/4$, $x = \lambda/2$, $x = 3\lambda/4$, and $x = \lambda$ for the times just given. Thus, the position x of this peak can be written as follows:

$$x = \lambda\frac{t}{T}$$

Equivalently, we can say that the peak that was at $x = 0$ is now at the location given by

$$x - \lambda\frac{t}{T} = 0$$

Similarly, the peak that was originally at $x = \lambda$ at $t = 0$ is at the following position at the general time t:

$$x - \lambda\frac{t}{T} = \lambda$$

In general, if the position of a given point on a wave at $t = 0$ is $x(0)$, and its position at the time t is $x(t)$, the relation between these positions is $x(t) - \lambda t/T = x(0)$. Therefore, to take into account the time dependence of a wave, we replace $x = x(0)$ in Equation 14–3 with $x(0) = x - \lambda t/T$. This yields the harmonic wave function:

$$y(x, t) = A \cos\left[\frac{2\pi}{\lambda}\left(x - \lambda\frac{t}{T}\right)\right] = A \cos\left(\frac{2\pi}{\lambda}x - \frac{2\pi}{T}t\right) \qquad \text{14–4}$$

Note that the wave function, $y(x, t)$, depends on both time and position, and that the wave repeats whenever position increases by the wavelength, λ, or time increases by the period, T.

14–4 Sound Waves

The first thing we do when we come into this world is make a sound. It is many years later before we realize that sound is a wave propagating through the air at a speed of about 770 mi/h. More years are required to gain an understanding of the physics of a sound wave.

A useful mechanical model of a sound wave is provided by a Slinky. If we oscillate one end of a Slinky back and forth horizontally, as in **Figure 14–10**, we send out a longitudinal wave that also travels in the horizontal direction. The wave consists of regions where the coils of the Slinky are compressed alternating with regions where the coils are more widely spaced.

In close analogy with the Slinky model, a speaker produces sound waves by oscillating a diaphragm back and forth horizontally, as we saw in Figure 14–3. Just as with the Slinky, a wave travels away from the source horizontally. The wave consists of compressed regions alternating with rarefied regions.

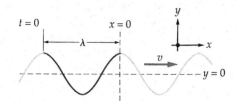

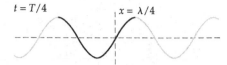

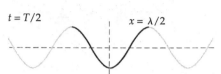

▲ **FIGURE 14–9 A harmonic wave moving to the right**
As a wave moves, the peak that was at $x = 0$ at time $t = 0$ moves to the position $x = \lambda t/T$ at the time t.

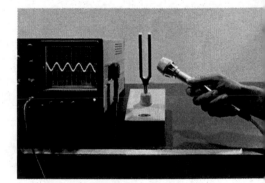

▲ An oscilloscope connected to a microphone can be used to display the wave form of a pure tone, created here by a tuning fork. The trace on the screen shows that the wave form is sinusoidal.

Science Fundamentals Second Edition

▶ **FIGURE 14–10 A wave on a Slinky**
If one end of a Slinky is oscillated back and forth, a series of longitudinal waves are produced. These Slinky waves are analogous to sound waves.

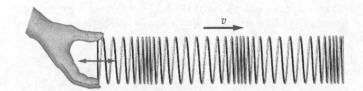

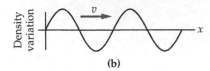

(a)

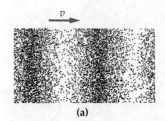

(b)

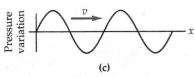

(c)

▲ **FIGURE 14–11 Wave properties of sound**
A sound wave moving through the air **(a)** produces a wavelike disturbance in the **(b)** density and **(c)** pressure of the air.

At first glance, the sound wave seems very different from the wave on a string. In particular, the sound wave doesn't seem to have the nice, sinusoidal shape of a wave. Certainly, Figure 14–3 gives no hint of such a wavelike shape.

If we plot the appropriate quantities, however, the classic wave shape emerges. For example, in **Figure 14–11 (a)** we plot the rarefactions and compressions of a typical sound wave, while in **Figure 14–11 (b)** we plot the fluctuations in the density of the air versus x. Clearly, the density oscillates in a wavelike fashion. Similarly, **Figure 14–11 (c)** shows a plot of the fluctuations in the pressure of the air as a function of x. In regions where the density is high, the pressure is also high; and where the density is low, the pressure is low. Thus, pressure versus position again shows that a sound wave has the usual wave-like properties.

Just like the speed of a wave on a string, the speed of sound is determined by the properties of the medium through which it propagates. In air, under normal atmospheric pressure and temperature, the speed of sound is approximately the following:

Speed of Sound in Air (at room temperature, 20°C)

$v = 343 \text{ m/s} \approx 770 \text{ mi/h}$

SI unit: m/s

When we refer to the speed of sound in this text we will always assume the value is 343 m/s, unless stated specifically otherwise.

As we shall see in Chapter 17, where we study the kinetic theory of gases, the speed of sound in air is directly related to the speed of the molecules themselves. Did you know, for example, that the air molecules colliding with your body at this moment have speeds that are essentially the speed of sound? As the air is heated the molecules will move faster, and hence the speed of sound also increases with temperature.

In a solid, the speed of sound is determined in part by how stiff the material is. The stiffer the material, the faster the sound wave, just as having more tension in a string causes a faster wave. Thus the speed of sound in plastic is rather large (2680 m/s), and in steel it is greater still (5960 m/s). Both speeds are much higher than the speed in air, which is certainly a "squishy" material in comparison. Table 14–1 gives a sampling of sound speed in a range of different materials.

TABLE 14–1
Speed of Sound in Various Materials

Material	Speed (m/s)
Aluminum	6420
Granite	6000
Steel	5960
Pyrex glass	5640
Copper	5010
Plastic	2680
Fresh water (20 °C)	1482
Fresh water (0 °C)	1402
Hydrogen (0 °C)	1284
Helium (0 °C)	965
Air (20 °C)	343
Air (0 °C)	331

CONCEPTUAL CHECKPOINT 14–2   How Far to the Lightning?

Five seconds after a brilliant flash of lightning, thunder shakes the house. Was the lightning **(a)** about a mile away, **(b)** much closer than a mile, or **(c)** much farther away than a mile?

Reasoning and Discussion

As mentioned, the speed of sound is 343 m/s, which is just over 1,000 ft/s. Thus, in five seconds sound travels slightly more than one mile. This gives rise to the following popular rule of thumb: The distance to a lightning strike (in miles) is the time for the thunder to arrive (in seconds) divided by 5.

Notice that we have neglected the travel time of light in our discussion. This is because light propagates with such a large speed (approximately 186,000 mi/s) that its travel time is about a million times less than that of sound.

Answer:
(a) The lightning was about a mile away.

EXAMPLE 14–2 Wishing Well

You drop a stone from rest into a well that is 7.35 m deep. How long does it take before you hear the splash?

Picture the Problem
Our sketch shows the well into which the stone is dropped. Notice that the depth of the well is $d = 7.35$ m. After the stone falls a distance d, the sound from the splash rises the same distance d before it is heard.

Strategy
The time until the splash is heard is the sum of (i) the time, t_1, for the stone to drop a distance d, and (ii) the time, t_2, for sound to travel a distance d.

For the time of drop, we use one-dimensional kinematics with an initial velocity $v = 0$, since the stone is dropped from rest, and an acceleration g. Therefore, the relationship between distance and time for the stone is $d = \frac{1}{2}gt_1^2$, with $g = 9.81$ m/s^2.

For the sound wave, we use $d = vt_2$, with $v = 343$ m/s.

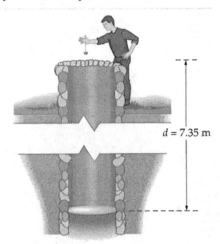

$d = 7.35$ m

Solution

1. Calculate the time for the stone to drop:

$$d = \frac{1}{2}gt_1^2$$

$$t_1 = \sqrt{\frac{2d}{g}} = \sqrt{\frac{2(7.35\text{ m})}{9.81\text{ m/s}^2}} = 1.22\text{ s}$$

2. Calculate the time for sound to travel a distance d:

$$d = vt_2$$

$$t_2 = \frac{d}{v} = \frac{7.35\text{ m}}{343\text{ m/s}} = 0.0214\text{ s}$$

3. Sum the times found above:

$$t = t_1 + t_2 = 1.22\text{ s} + 0.0214\text{ s} = 1.24\text{ s}$$

Insight
Note that the time of travel for the sound is quite small, only a couple hundredths of a second. It is still nonzero, however, and must be taken into account to obtain the correct total time.

In addition, notice that we use the same speed for a sound wave whether it is traveling horizontally, vertically upward, or vertically downward—its speed is independent of its direction of motion. As a result, the waves emanating from a source of sound propagate outward in a spherical pattern, with the wave crests forming concentric spheres around the source.

Practice Problem
You drop a stone into a well and hear the splash 1.47 s later. How deep is the well?   [**Answer:** 10.2 m]

Some related homework problems: Problem 23, Problem 24

The Frequency of a Sound Wave

When we hear a sound, its frequency makes a great impression on us; in fact, the frequency determines the **pitch** of a sound. For example, the keys on a piano produce sound with frequencies ranging from 55 Hz for the key farthest to the left to 4187 Hz for the rightmost key. Similarly, as you hum a song you change

▶ Many animal species use sound waves with frequencies that are too high (ultrasonic) or too low (infrasonic) for human ears to detect. Bats, for example, navigate in the dark and locate their prey by means of a system of biological sonar. They emit a continuous stream of ultrasonic sounds and detect the echoes from objects around them. Blue whales, by contrast, communicate over long distances by means of infrasonic sounds.

REAL-WORLD PHYSICS

Ultrasonic sounds in nature

REAL-WORLD PHYSICS: BIO

Medical applications of ultrasound: ultrasonic scans

REAL-WORLD PHYSICS: BIO

Medical applications of ultrasound: shock wave lithotripsy

REAL-WORLD PHYSICS

Infrasonic communication among animals

the shape and size of your vocal chords slightly to change the frequency of the sound you produce.

The frequency range of human hearing extends well beyond the range of a piano, however. As a rule of thumb, humans can hear sounds between 20 Hz on the low-frequency end and 20,000 Hz on the high-frequency end. Sounds with frequencies above this range are referred to as **ultrasonic,** while those with frequencies lower than 20 Hz are classified as **infrasonic.** Though we are unable to hear ultrasound and infrasound, these frequencies occur commonly in nature, and are used in many technological applications as well.

For example, bats and dolphins produce ultrasound almost continuously as they go about their daily lives. By listening to the echoes of their calls—that is, by using *echolocation*—they are able to navigate about their environment and detect their prey. As a defense mechanism, some of the insects that are preyed upon by bats have the ability to hear the ultrasonic frequency of a hunting bat and take evasive action. For instance, the praying mantis has a specialized ultrasound receptor on its abdomen that allows it to take cover in response to an approaching bat. More dramatically, certain moths fold their wings in flight and drop into a precipitous dive toward the ground when they hear a bat on the prowl.

Medical applications of ultrasound are also common. Perhaps the most familiar is the ultrasound scan that is used to image a fetus in the womb. By sending bursts of ultrasound into the body and measuring the time delay of the resulting echoes—the technological equivalent of echolocation—it is possible to map out the location of structures that lie hidden beneath the skin. In addition to imaging the interior of a body, ultrasound can also produce changes within the body that would otherwise require surgery. For example, in a technique called *shock wave lithotripsy* (SWL), an intense beam of ultrasound is concentrated onto a kidney stone that must be removed. After being hit with as many as 1000 to 3000 pulses of sound (at 23 joules per pulse), the stone is fractured into small pieces that the body can then eliminate on its own.

As for infrasound, it has been discovered in recent years that elephants can communicate with one another using sounds with frequencies as low as 15 Hz. In fact, it may be that *most* elephant communication is infrasonic. These sounds, which humans feel as vibration rather than hear as sound, can carry over an area of about thirty square kilometers on the dry African savanna. And elephants are not alone in this ability. Whales, such as the blue and the finback, produce powerful infrasonic calls as well. Since sound generally travels farther in water than in

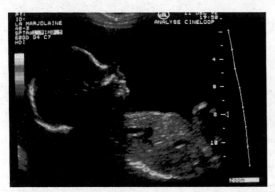 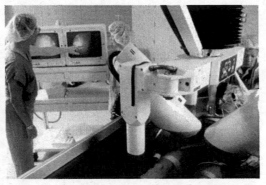

▲ Ultrasound is used in medicine both as an imaging medium and for therapeutic purposes. Ultrasound scans, or sonograms, are created by beaming ultrasonic pulses into the body and measuring the time required for the echoes to return. This technique is commonly used to evaluate heart function (echocardiograms) and to visualize the fetus in the uterus, as shown above (left). In shock wave lithotripsy (right), pulses of high-frequency sound waves are used to shatter kidney stones into fragments that can be passed in the urine.

air, the whale calls can be heard by others of their species over distances of thousands of kilometers.

One final example of infrasound is related to a dramatic event that occurred in southern New Mexico about a decade ago. At 12:47 in the afternoon of October 10, 1997, a meteor shining as bright as the full Moon streaked across the sky for a few brief moments. The event was observed not just visually, however, but with infrasound as well. An array of special microphones at the Los Alamos National Laboratory—originally designed to listen for clandestine nuclear weapons tests—heard the infrasonic boom created by the meteor. By tracking the sonic signals of such meteors it may be possible to recover fragments that manage to reach the ground. The Los Alamos detector is in constant operation, and it detects about 10 rather large objects (2 m or more in diameter) entering the Earth's atmosphere each year.

It should be noted, in light of the wide range of frequencies observed in sound, that the speed of sound is the same for all frequencies. Thus, in the relation

$$v = \lambda f$$

the speed v remains fixed. For example, if the frequency of a wave is doubled, its wavelength is halved, so that the speed v stays the same. The fact that different frequencies travel with the same speed is evident when we listen to an orchestra in a large room. Different instruments are producing sounds of different frequencies, but we hear the sounds at the same time. Otherwise, listening to music from a distance would be quite a different and inharmonious experience.

REAL-WORLD PHYSICS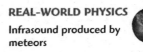

Infrasound produced by meteors

14–5 Sound Intensity

The noise made by a jackhammer is much louder than the song of a sparrow. On this we can all agree. But how do we express such an observation physically? What physical quantity determines the loudness of a sound? We address these questions in this section, and we also present a quantitative scale by which loudness may be measured.

Intensity

The loudness of a sound is determined by its **intensity**; that is, by the amount of energy that passes through a given area in a given time. This is illustrated in **Figure 14–12**. If the energy E passes through the area A in the time t, the intensity, I, of the wave carrying the energy is

$$I = \frac{E}{At}$$

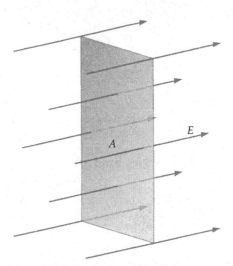

▲ **FIGURE 14–12 Intensity of a wave**
If a wave carries an energy E through an area A in the time t, the corresponding intensity is $I = E/At = P/A$, where $P = E/t$ is the power.

Science Fundamentals Second Edition

TABLE 14–2	Sound Intensities (W/m²)
Loudest sound produced in laboratory	10^9
Saturn V rocket at 50 m	10^8
Rupture of the eardrum	10^4
Jet engine at 50 m	10
Threshold of pain	1
Rock concert	10^{-1}
Jackhammer at 1 m	10^{-3}
Heavy street traffic	10^{-5}
Conversation at 1 m	10^{-6}
Classroom	10^{-7}
Whisper at 1 m	10^{-10}
Normal breathing	10^{-11}
Threshold of hearing	10^{-12}

Recalling that power is energy per time, $P = E/t$, we can express the intensity as follows:

Definition of Intensity, I

$$I = \frac{P}{A}$$

SI unit: W/m²

14–5

The units are those of power (watts, W) divided by area (meters squared, m²).

Though we have introduced the concept of intensity in terms of sound, it applies to all types of waves. For example, the intensity of light from the Sun as it reaches the Earth's upper atmosphere is about 1380 W/m². If this intensity could be heard as sound, it would be painfully loud—roughly the equivalent of four jet airplanes taking off simultaneously. By comparison, the intensity of microwaves in a microwave oven is even greater, about 6000 W/m², whereas the intensity of a whisper is an incredibly tiny 10^{-10} W/m². A selection of representative intensities is given in Table 14–2.

EXERCISE 14–3

A loudspeaker puts out 0.15 W of sound through a square area 2.0 m on each side. What is the intensity of this sound?

Solution

Applying Equation 14–5, with $A = (2.0 \text{ m})^2$, we find

$$I = \frac{P}{A} = \frac{0.15 \text{ W}}{(2.0 \text{ m})^2} = 0.038 \text{ W/m}^2$$

When we listen to a source of sound, such as a person speaking or a radio playing a song, we notice that the loudness of the sound decreases as we move away from the source. This means that the intensity of the sound is also decreasing. The reason for this reduction in intensity is simply that the energy emitted per time by the source spreads out over a larger area—just as spreading a certain amount of jam over a larger piece of bread reduces the intensity of the taste.

In **Figure 14–13** we show a source of sound (a bat) and two observers (moths) listening at the distances r_1 and r_2. Notice that the waves emanating from the bat propagate outward spherically, with the wave crests forming a series of concentric spheres. Assuming no reflections of sound, and a power output by the bat equal to P, the intensity detected by the first moth is

$$I_1 = \frac{P}{4\pi r_1^{\,2}}$$

▲ **FIGURE 14–13 Echolocation**
Two moths, at distances r_1 and r_2, hear the sonar signals sent out by a bat. The intensity of the signal decreases with the square of the distance from the bat. The bat, in turn, hears the echoes sent back by the moths. It can then use the direction and intensity of the returning echoes to locate its prey.

In writing this expression, we have used the fact that the area of a sphere of radius r is $A = 4\pi r^2$. Similarly, the second moth hears the same sound with an intensity of

$$I_2 = \frac{P}{4\pi r_2^{\,2}}$$

The power P is the same in each case—it simply represents the amount of sound emitted by the bat. Solving for the intensity at moth 2 in terms of the intensity at moth 1 we find

$$I_2 = \left(\frac{r_1}{r_2}\right)^2 I_1$$

14–6

In words, the intensity falls off with the square of the distance; doubling the distance reduces the intensity by a factor of 4.

Science Fundamentals Second Edition

To summarize, the intensity a distance r from a point source of power P is

Intensity with Distance from a Point Source

$$I = \frac{P}{4\pi r^2}$$

SI unit: W/m^2

14–7

This result assumes that no sound is reflected—which could increase the amount of energy passing through a given area—that no sound is absorbed, and that the sound propagates outward spherically. These assumptions are applied in the next Example.

PROBLEM-SOLVING NOTE

Intensity Variation with Distance

Suppose the intensity of a point source is I_1 at a distance r_1. This is enough information to find its intensity at any other distance. For example, to find the intensity I_2 at a distance r_2 we use the relation $I_2 = (r_1/r_2)^2 I_1$.

EXAMPLE 14–3 The Power of Song

Two people relaxing on a deck listen to a songbird sing. One person, only 1.00 m from the bird, hears the sound with an intensity of $2.80 \times 10^{-6}\ W/m^2$. **(a)** What intensity is heard by the second person, who is 4.25 m from the bird? Assume that no reflected sound is heard by either person. **(b)** What is the power output of the bird's song?

Picture the Problem
Our sketch shows the two observers, one at a distance of $r_1 = 1.00$ m from the bird, the other at a distance of $r_2 = 4.25$ m. The sound emitted by the bird is assumed to spread out spherically, with no reflections.

Strategy

a. The two intensities are related by Equation 14–6, with $r_1 = 1.00$ m and $r_2 = 4.25$ m.

b. The power output can be obtained from the definition of intensity, $I = P/A$. We can calculate P for either observer, noting that $A = 4\pi r^2$.

Solution

Part (a)

1. Substitute numerical values into Equation 14–6:

$$I_2 = \left(\frac{r_1}{r_2}\right)^2 I_1 = \left(\frac{1.00\ m}{4.25\ m}\right)^2 (2.80 \times 10^{-6}\ W/m^2)$$
$$= 1.55 \times 10^{-7}\ W/m^2$$

Part (b)

2. Solve $I = P/A$ for the power, P, using data for observer 1:

$$I_1 = P/A_1$$
$$P = I_1 A_1 = (2.80 \times 10^{-6}\ W/m^2)[4\pi(1.00\ m)^2]$$
$$= 3.52 \times 10^{-5}\ W$$

3. As a check, repeat the calculation for observer 2:

$$I_2 = P/A_2$$
$$P = I_2 A_2 = (1.55 \times 10^{-7}\ W/m^2)[4\pi(4.25\ m)^2]$$
$$= 3.52 \times 10^{-5}\ W$$

Insight
The intensity at observer 1 is $4.25^2 = 18.1$ times the intensity at observer 2. Even so, the bird only *seems* to be about 2.5 times louder to observer 1. The connection between intensity and perceived (subjective) loudness is discussed in detail later in this section.

Practice Problem
If the intensity at observer 2 were $7.40 \times 10^{-7}\ W/m^2$, how far would he be from the bird?   [**Answer:** $r_2 = 1.95$ m]

Some related homework problems: Problem 28, Problem 33

ACTIVE EXAMPLE 14–1 The Big Hit: Find the Intensity

Ken Griffey, Jr. connects with a fast ball and sends it out of the park. A fan in the outfield bleachers, 140 m away, hears the hit with an intensity of $3.80 \times 10^{-7}\ W/m^2$. Assuming no reflected sounds, what is the intensity heard by the first-base umpire, 90 ft (27.4 m) away from home plate?

continued on next page

Science Fundamentals Second Edition

continued from previous page

Solution *(Test your understanding by performing the calculations indicated in each step.)*

1. Label the data given in the problem. Let the umpire be observer 1 and the fan be observer 2:

$$r_1 = 27.4 \text{ m}$$
$$r_2 = 140 \text{ m}$$
$$I_2 = 3.80 \times 10^{-7} \text{ W/m}^2$$

2. Solve Equation 14–6 for I_1:

$$I_1 = (r_2/r_1)^2 I_2$$

3. Substitute numerical values:

$$I_1 = 9.9 \times 10^{-6} \text{ W/m}^2$$

Insight

For the fan, the sound from the hit is somewhat less intense than normal conversation. For the umpire it is comparable to the sound of a busy street.

Your Turn

Find the distance at which the sound of the hit has the intensity of a whisper. Refer to Table 14–2 for the necessary information.

(Answers to Your Turn problems are given in the back of the book.)

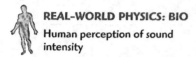

REAL-WORLD PHYSICS: BIO

Human perception of sound intensity

PROBLEM-SOLVING NOTE

Intensity versus Intensity Level

When reading a problem statement, be sure to note carefully whether it refers to the intensity, I, or to the intensity level, β. These two quantities have similar names but completely different meanings and units, as indicated in the following table:

Physical quantity	Physical meaning	Units
Intensity, I	Energy per time per area	W/m^2
Intensity level, β	A measure of relative loudness	dB

Human Perception of Sound

Hearing, like most of our senses, is incredibly versatile and sensitive. We can detect sounds that are about a million times fainter than a typical conversation, and listen to sounds that are a million times louder before experiencing pain. In addition, we are able to hear sounds over a wide range of frequencies, from 20 Hz to 20,000 Hz.

When detecting the faintest of sounds, our hearing is more sensitive than one would ever guess. For example, a faint sound, with an intensity of about 10^{-11} W/m^2, causes a displacement of molecules in the air of about 10^{-10} m. This displacement is roughly the diameter of an atom!

Equally interesting is the way we perceive the loudness of a sound. As an example, suppose you hear a sound of intensity I_1. Next, you listen to a second sound of intensity I_2, and this sound seems to be "twice as loud" as the first. If the two intensities are measured, it turns out that I_2 is about 10 times I_1. Similarly, a third sound, twice as loud as I_2, has an intensity I_3 that is 10 times greater than I_2. Thus, $I_2 = 10 I_1$ and $I_3 = 10 I_2 = 100 I_1$.

Our perception of sound, then, is such that uniform increases in loudness correspond to intensities that increase by multiplicative factors. For this reason, a convenient scale to measure loudness depends on the logarithm of intensity, as we discuss next.

Intensity Level and Decibels

In the study of sound, loudness is measured by the **intensity level** of a wave. Designated by the symbol β, the intensity level is defined as follows:

Definition of Intensity Level, β

$$\beta = (10 \text{ dB}) \log(I/I_0) \qquad\qquad 14\text{–}8$$

SI unit: decibel (dB), which is dimensionless

In this expression, log indicates the logarithm to the base 10, and I_0 is the intensity of the faintest sounds that can be heard. Experiments show this lowest detectable intensity to be

$$I_0 = 10^{-12} \text{ W/m}^2$$

Note that β is dimensionless; the only dimensions that enter into the definition are those of intensity, and they cancel in the logarithm. Still, just as with radians, it is convenient to label the values of intensity level with a name. The name we use—the bel—honors the work of Alexander Graham Bell (1847–1922), the inventor of the telephone. Since the bel is a fairly large unit, it is more common to measure β in units that are one-tenth of a bel. This unit is referred to as the **decibel,** and its abbreviation is dB.

To get a feeling for the decibel scale, let's start with the faintest sounds. If a sound has an intensity $I = I_0$, the corresponding intensity level is

$$\beta = (10 \text{ dB}) \log(I_0/I_0) = 10 \log(1) = 0$$

Increasing the intensity by a factor of 10 makes the sound seem twice as loud. In terms of decibels, we have

$$\beta = (10 \text{ dB}) \log(10I_0/I_0) = (10 \text{ dB}) \log(10) = 10 \text{ dB}$$

Going up in intensity by another factor of 10 doubles the loudness of the sound again, and yields

$$\beta = (10 \text{ dB}) \log(100I_0/I_0) = (10 \text{ dB}) \log(100) = 20 \text{ dB}$$

Thus, *the loudness of a sound doubles with each increase in intensity level of 10 dB.* The *smallest* increase in intensity level that can be detected by the human ear is about 1 dB.

The intensity of a number of independent sound sources is simply the sum of the individual intensities. We use this fact in the following Example.

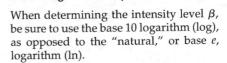

PROBLEM-SOLVING NOTE

Calculating the Intensity Level

When determining the intensity level β, be sure to use the base 10 logarithm (log), as opposed to the "natural," or base e, logarithm (ln).

EXAMPLE 14-4 Pass the Pacifier

A crying child emits sound with an intensity of $8.0 \times 10^{-6} \text{ W/m}^2$. Find **(a)** the intensity level in decibels for the child's sounds, and **(b)** the intensity level for this child and its twin, both crying with identical intensities.

Picture the Problem
We consider the crying sounds of either one or two children. Each child emits sound with an intensity $I = 8.0 \times 10^{-6} \text{ W/m}^2$. If two children are crying together, the total intensity of their sound is $2I$.

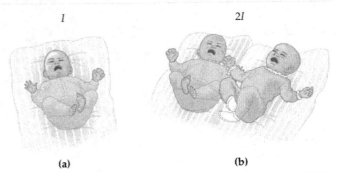

I $2I$

(a)   (b)

Strategy
The intensity level, β, is obtained by applying Equation 14-8.

Solution

Part (a)

1. Calculate β for $I = 8.0 \times 10^{-6} \text{ W/m}^2$:

$$\beta = (10 \text{ dB}) \log(I/I_0)$$
$$= (10 \text{ dB}) \log\left(\frac{8.0 \times 10^{-6} \text{ W/m}^2}{10^{-12} \text{ W/m}^2}\right) = (10 \text{ dB}) \log(8.0 \times 10^6)$$
$$= (10 \text{ dB}) \log(8.0) + (10 \text{ dB}) \log(10^6) = 69 \text{ dB}$$

Part (b)

2. Repeat the calculation with I replaced by $2I$:

$$\beta = (10 \text{ dB}) \log(2I/I_0)$$
$$= (10 \text{ dB}) \log(2) + (10 \text{ dB}) \log(I/I_0)$$
$$= 3.0 \text{ dB} + 69 \text{ dB} = 72 \text{ dB}$$

Insight
Note that the intensity level is increased by $(10 \text{ dB}) \log(2) = 3 \text{ dB}$. This is a general rule: When the intensity is doubled, the intensity level, β, increases by 3 dB. Similarly, when the intensity is halved, β decreases by 3 dB.

Practice Problem
What is the intensity level of four identically crying quadruplets? **[Answer: $\beta = 75 \text{ dB}$]**

Some related homework problems: Problem 30, Problem 31

Even though a change of 3 dB is relatively small—after all, a change of 10 dB is required to make a sound seem twice as loud—it still requires changing the intensity by a factor of two. For example, suppose a large nursery in a hospital has so many crying babies that the intensity level is 6 dB above the safe value, as determined by OSHA (Occupational Safety and Health Administration). To reduce

Science Fundamentals Second Edition

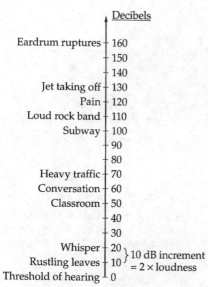

A FIGURE 14–14 Representative intensity levels for common sounds

the level by 6 dB it would be necessary to remove three-quarters of the children, leaving only one-quarter the original number. To our ears, however, the nursery will *sound* only 40 percent quieter!

Figure 14–14 shows the decibel scale with representative values indicated for a variety of common sounds.

Fluids

15–1	Density	477
15–2	Pressure	477
15–3	Static Equilibrium in Fluids: Pressure and Depth	481
15–4	Archimedes' Principle and Buoyancy	486
15–5	Applications of Archimedes' Principle	488
15–6	Fluid Flow and Continuity	493
15–7	Bernoulli's Equation	495
15–8	Applications of Bernoulli's Equation	498

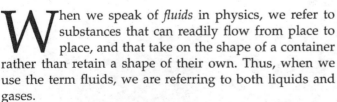

Each of these common household liquids (from top to bottom: corn oil, water, shampoo, dish detergent, antifreeze, maple syrup) has a slightly different density, which determines its order in the vessel. In this chapter we'll see how density is related to buoyancy and other properties of fluids.

When we speak of *fluids* in physics, we refer to substances that can readily flow from place to place, and that take on the shape of a container rather than retain a shape of their own. Thus, when we use the term fluids, we are referring to both liquids and gases.

It is hard to think of a subject more relevant to our everyday lives than fluids. After all, we begin life as a fluid-filled cell suspended in a fluid. We live our independent lives immersed in a fluid that we breathe. In fact, fluids coursing through our circulatory system are literally the lifeblood of our existence. If it were not for the gases in our atmosphere and the liquid water on the Earth's surface, we could not exist.

In this chapter, we examine some of the fundamental physical principles that apply to fluids. All of these principles derive from the basic physics we have learned to this point. For example, straightforward considerations of force and weight lead to an understanding of buoyancy. Similarly, the work–energy theorem results in an understanding of how fluids behave when they flow. As such, fluids provide a wonderful opportunity for us to apply our knowledge of physics to a whole new array of interesting physical systems.

476

15-1 Density

The properties of a fluid can be hard to pin down, given that it can flow, change shape, and either split into smaller portions or combine into a larger system. Thus, one of the best ways to quantify a fluid is in terms of its **density**. Specifically, the density, ρ, of a material (fluid or not) is defined as the mass, M, per volume, V:

TABLE 15-1	
Densities of Common Substances	

Substance	Density (kg/m^3)
Gold	19,300
Mercury	13,600
Lead	11,300
Silver	10,500
Iron	7860
Aluminum	2700
Ebony (wood)	1220
Ethylene glycol (antifreeze)	1114
Whole blood (37 °C)	1060
Seawater	1025
Freshwater	1000
Olive oil	920
Ice	917
Ethyl alcohol	806
Cherry (wood)	800
Balsa (wood)	120
Styrofoam	100
Oxygen	1.43
Air	1.29
Helium	0.179

Definition of Density, ρ

$$\rho = M/V \qquad\qquad 15\text{-}1$$

SI unit: kg/m^3

The denser a material, the more mass it has in any given volume. Note, however, that the density of a substance is the same regardless of the total amount we have in a system.

To get a feel for densities in common substances, we start with water. For example, to fill a cubic container one meter on a side would take over 2000 pounds of water. More precisely, water has the following density:

$$\rho_w = \text{density of water} = 1000 \text{ kg/m}^3$$

A gallon (1 gallon = 3.79 L = 3.79×10^{-3} m^3) of water, then, has a mass of

$$M = \rho V = (1000 \text{ kg/m}^3)(3.79 \times 10^{-3} \text{ m}^3) = 3.79 \text{ kg}$$

As a rule of thumb, a gallon of water weighs just over 8 pounds.

In comparison, the helium in a helium-filled balloon has a density of only about 0.179 kg/m^3, and the density of the air in your room is roughly 1.29 kg/m^3. On the higher end of the density scale, solid gold "weighs" in with a hefty 19,300 kg/m^3. Further examples of densities for common materials are given in Table 15–1.

CONCEPTUAL CHECKPOINT 15-1

One day you look in your refrigerator and find nothing but a dozen eggs (44 g each). A quick measurement shows that the inside of the refrigerator is 1.0 m by 0.60 m by 0.75 m. Is the weight of the *air* in your refrigerator (a) much less than, (b) about the same as, or (c) much more than the weight of the *eggs*?

Reasoning and Discussion
At first it might seem that the "thin air" in the refrigerator weighs practically nothing compared with a carton full of eggs. A brief calculation shows this is not the case. For the eggs, we have

$$m_{eggs} = 12(44 \text{ g}) = 0.53 \text{ kg}$$

For the air,

$$m_{air} = \rho V = (1.29 \text{ kg/m}^3)(1.0 \text{ m} \times 0.60 \text{ m} \times 0.75 \text{ m}) = 0.58 \text{ kg}$$

Thus, the air, with a mass of 0.58 kg (1.28 lb), actually weighs slightly more than the eggs, which have a mass of 0.53 kg (1.17 lb)!

Answer:
(b) The air and the eggs weigh about the same.

15-2 Pressure

If you have ever pushed a button, or pressed a key on a keyboard, you have applied pressure. Now, you might object that you simply exerted a force on the button, or the key, which is correct. That force is spread out over an area, however. For example, when you press a button, the tip of your finger contacts the button over a small but finite area. **Pressure**, P, is a measure of the amount of force, F, per area A:

Definition of Pressure, P

$$P = F/A \qquad\qquad 15\text{-}2$$

SI unit: N/m^2

Science Fundamentals Second Edition

PROBLEM-SOLVING NOTE

Pressure Is Force per Area

Remember that pressure is proportional to the applied force and *inversely* proportional to the area over which it acts.

Pressure is increased if the force applied to a given area is increased, or if a given force is applied to a smaller area. For example, if you press your finger against a balloon, not much happens—your finger causes a small indentation. On the other hand, if you push a needle against the balloon with the same force, you get an explosive pop. The difference is that the same force applied to the small area of a needle tip causes a large enough pressure to rupture the balloon.

EXAMPLE 15–1 Popping a Balloon

Find the pressure exerted on the skin of a balloon if you press with a force of 2.1 N using **(a)** your finger or **(b)** a needle. Assume the area of your fingertip is 1.0×10^{-4} m^2, and the area of the needle tip is 2.5×10^{-7} m^2. **(c)** Find the minimum force necessary to pop the balloon with the needle, given that the balloon pops with a pressure of 3.0×10^5 N/m^2.

Picture the Problem
Our sketch shows a balloon deformed by the press of a finger and of a needle. The difference is not the amount of force that is applied but the area over which it is applied. In the case of the needle, the force may be sufficient to pop the balloon.

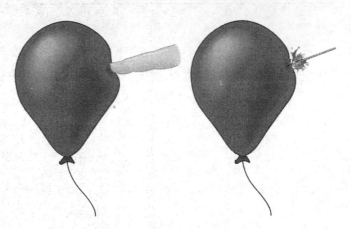

Strategy
(a), **(b)** The force F and the area A are given in the problem statement. We can find the pressure, then, by applying its definition, $P = F/A$.

(c) Rearrange $P = F/A$ to find the force corresponding to a given pressure and area.

Solution

Part (a)

1. Calculate the pressure exerted by the finger:

$$P = \frac{F}{A} = \frac{2.1 \text{ N}}{1.0 \times 10^{-4} \text{ m}^2} = 2.1 \times 10^4 \text{ N/m}^2$$

Part (b)

2. Calculate the pressure exerted by the needle:

$$P = \frac{F}{A} = \frac{2.1 \text{ N}}{2.5 \times 10^{-7} \text{ m}^2} = 8.4 \times 10^6 \text{ N/m}^2$$

Part (c)

3. Solve Equation 15–2 for the force:

$$F = PA$$

4. Substitute numerical values:

$$F = (3.0 \times 10^5 \text{ N/m}^2)(2.5 \times 10^{-7} \text{ m}^2) = 0.075 \text{ N}$$

Insight
Note that the pressure exerted by the needle in part (b) is 400 times greater than the pressure due to the finger in part (a). This increase in pressure with decreasing area accounts for the sharp tips to be found on such disparate objects as nails, pens and pencils, and syringes.

Practice Problem
Find the area that a force of 2.1 N would have to act on to produce a pressure of 3.0×10^5 N/m^2.   [**Answer:** $A = 7.0 \times 10^{-6}$ m^2]

Some related homework problems: Problem 8, Problem 9

REAL-WORLD PHYSICS: BIO

Walking on lily pads

An interesting example of force, area, and pressure in nature is provided by the family of small aquatic birds referred to as rails, and in particular by the gallinule. This bird has exceptionally long toes that are spread out over a large area. The result is that the weight of the bird causes only a relatively small pressure as it walks on the soft, muddy shorelines encountered in its habitat. In some species, the pressure exerted while walking is so small that the birds can actually walk across lily pads without sinking into the water.

Science Fundamentals Second Edition

Atmospheric Pressure and Gauge Pressure

We are all used to working under pressure—about 14.7 pounds per square inch to be precise. This is **atmospheric pressure**, P_{at}, a direct result of the weight of the air above us. In SI units, atmospheric pressure has the following value:

Atmospheric Pressure, P_{at}

$$P_{at} = 1.01 \times 10^5 \, N/m^2 \qquad\qquad 15\text{–}3$$

SI unit: N/m^2

A shorthand unit for N/m^2 is the **pascal** (Pa):

$$1 \, Pa = 1 \, N/m^2 \qquad\qquad 15\text{–}4$$

The pascal honors the pioneering studies of fluids by the French scientist Blaise Pascal (1623–1662). Thus, atmospheric pressure can be written as

$$P_{at} = 101 \, kPa$$

In British units, pressure is measured in pounds per square inch, and

$$P_{at} = 14.7 \, lb/in^2$$

Finally, a common unit for atmospheric pressure in weather forecasting is the **bar**, defined as follows:

$$1 \, bar = 10^5 \, Pa \approx 1 \, P_{at}$$

▲ This bird exerts only a small pressure on the lily pad on which it walks because its weight is spread out over a large area by its long toes. Since the pressure is not enough to sink a lily pad, the bird can seemingly "walk on water."

EXERCISE 15–1

Find the force exerted on the palm of your hand by atmospheric pressure. Assume your palm measures 0.080 m by 0.10 m.

Solution

Applying Equations 15–3 and 15–2, we find

$$F = P_{at}A = (1.01 \times 10^5 \, Pa)(0.080 \, m)(0.10 \, m) = 810 \, N$$

Thus, the atmosphere pushes on the palm of your hand with a force of approximately 180 pounds! Of course, it also pushes on the back of your hand with essentially the same force, but in the opposite direction.

Figure 15–1 illustrates the forces exerted on your hand by atmospheric pressure. If your hand is vertical, atmospheric pressure pushes to the right and to the

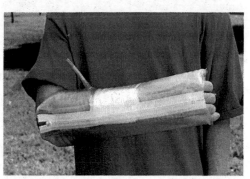

▲ The air around you exerts a force of about 14.7 pounds on every square inch of your body. Because this force is the same in all directions and is opposed by an equal pressure inside your body, you are generally unaware of it. However, when the air is pumped out of a sealed can (left), atmospheric pressure produces an inward force that is unopposed. The resulting collapse of the can vividly illustrates the pressure that is all around us. An air splint (right) utilizes the same principle of unequal pressure. A plastic sleeve is placed around an injured limb and inflated to a pressure greater than that of the atmosphere—and thus of the body's internal pressure. The increased external pressure retards bleeding from the injured area, and also tends to immobilize the limb in case it might be fractured. (Air splints are carried by hikers and others who might be in need of emergency treatment far from professional medical facilities. Before it is inflated, the air splint is about the size and weight of a credit card.)

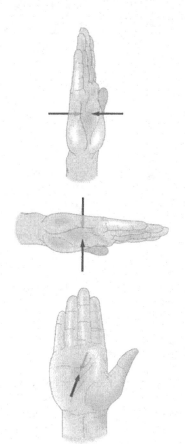

▲ **FIGURE 15–1 Pressure is the same in all directions**

The forces exerted on the two sides of a hand cancel, regardless of the hand's orientation. Hence, pressure acts equally in all directions.

Science Fundamentals Second Edition

left equally, so your hand feels zero net force. If your hand is horizontal, atmospheric pressure exerts upward and downward forces on your hand that are essentially the same in magnitude, again giving zero net force. This cancellation of forces occurs no matter what the orientation of your hand; thus, we can conclude the following:

> The pressure in a fluid acts equally in all directions, and acts at right angles to any surface.

In many cases we are interested in the difference between a given pressure and atmospheric pressure. For example, a flat tire does not have zero pressure in it; the pressure in the tire is atmospheric pressure. To inflate the tire to 241 kPa (35 lb/in²), the pressure inside the tire must be greater than atmospheric pressure by this amount; that is, $P = 241$ kPa $+ P_{at} = 342$ kPa.

To deal with such situations, we introduce the **gauge pressure, P_g**, defined as follows:

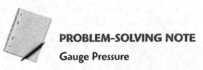

PROBLEM-SOLVING NOTE

Gauge Pressure

If a problem gives you the gauge pressure, recall that the actual pressure is the gauge pressure *plus* atmospheric pressure.

$$P_g = P - P_{at} \qquad\qquad 15\text{–}5$$

It is the gauge pressure, then, that is determined by a tire gauge. Many problems in this chapter refer to the gauge pressure. Hence it must be remembered that the actual pressure in these cases is greater by the amount P_{at}.

EXAMPLE 15–2 Pressuring the Ball: Estimate the Gauge Pressure

Estimate the gauge pressure in a basketball by pushing down on it and noting the area of contact it makes with the surface on which it rests.

Picture the Problem
Our sketch shows the basketball both in its original state, and when a force F pushes downward on it. In the latter case, the ball flattens out on the bottom, forming a circular area of contact with the floor of diameter d.

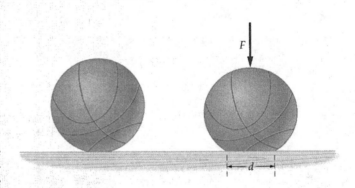

Strategy
To solve this problem, we have to make reasonable estimates of the force applied to the ball and the area of contact.

Suppose, for example, that we push down with a moderate force of 22 N (about 5 lb). The circular area of contact will probably have a diameter of about 2.0 centimeters. This can be verified by carrying out the experiment. Thus, given $F = 22$ N and $A = \pi(d/2)^2$ we can find the gauge pressure.

Solution

1. Using these estimates, calculate the gauge pressure, P_g:
$$P_g = \frac{F}{A} = \frac{22 \text{ N}}{\pi\left(\dfrac{0.020 \text{ m}}{2}\right)^2} = 7.0 \times 10^4 \text{ Pa}$$

Insight
Given that a pressure of one atmosphere, $P_{at} = 101$ kPa $= 1.01 \times 10^5$ Pa, corresponds to 14.7 lb/in², it follows that the gauge pressure of the ball, $P_g = 7.0 \times 10^4$ Pa, corresponds to a pressure of roughly 10 lb/in². Thus, a basketball will typically have a gauge pressure in the neighborhood of 10 lb/in², and hence a total pressure inside the ball of about 25 lb/in².

Practice Problem
What is the diameter of the circular area of contact if a basketball with a 12 lb/in² gauge pressure is pushed down with a force of 44 N (about 10 lb)?   [**Answer:** $d = 2.6$ cm]

Some related homework problems: Problem 11, Problem 12

15–3 Static Equilibrium in Fluids: Pressure and Depth

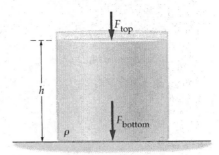

Countless war movies have educated us on the perils of taking a submarine too deep. The hull creaks and groans, rivets start to pop, water begins to spray into the ship, and the captain keeps a close eye on the depth gauge. But what causes the pressure to increase as a submarine dives, and how much does it go up for a given increase in depth?

The answer to the first question is that the increased pressure is due to the added weight of water pressing on the submarine as it goes deeper. To see how this works, consider a cylindrical container filled to a height h with a fluid of density ρ, as in **Figure 15–2**. The top surface of the fluid is open to the atmosphere, with a pressure P_{at}. If the cross-sectional area of the container is A, the downward force exerted on the top surface by the atmosphere is

$$F_{top} = P_{at}A$$

Now, at the bottom of the container, the downward force is F_{top} *plus* the weight of the fluid. Recalling that $M = \rho V$, and that $V = hA$ for a cylinder of height h and area A, this weight is

$$W = Mg = \rho V g = \rho(hA)g$$

Hence, we have

$$F_{bottom} = F_{top} + W = P_{at}A + \rho(hA)g$$

Finally, the pressure at the bottom is obtained by dividing F_{bottom} by the area A:

$$P_{bottom} = \frac{F_{bottom}}{A} = \frac{P_{at}A + \rho(hA)g}{A} = P_{at} + \rho g h$$

Of course, this relation holds not only for the bottom of the container, but for *any depth h below the surface*. Thus, the answer to the second question is that if the depth increases by the amount h, the pressure increases by the amount $\rho g h$. At a depth h below the surface of a fluid, then, the pressure P is given by

$$P = P_{at} + \rho g h \qquad \text{15–6}$$

This expression holds for any fluid with constant density ρ and a pressure P_{at} at its upper surface.

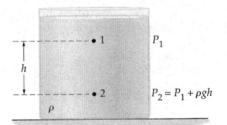

▲ **FIGURE 15–2 Pressure and the weight of a fluid**

The force pushing down on the bottom of the flask is greater than the force pushing down on the surface of the fluid. The difference in force is the weight of fluid in the flask.

▲ **FIGURE 15–3 Pressure variation with depth**

If point 2 is deeper than point 1 by the amount h, its pressure is greater by the amount $\rho g h$.

EXERCISE 15–2

The *Titanic* was found in 1985 lying on the bottom of the North Atlantic at a depth of 2.5 miles. What is the pressure at this depth?

REAL-WORLD PHYSICS

Pressure at the wreck of the *Titanic*

Solution

Applying Equation 15–6 with $\rho = 1025 \text{ kg/m}^3$, we have

$$P = P_{at} + \rho g h = 1.01 \times 10^5 \text{ Pa} + (1025 \text{ kg/m}^3)(9.81 \text{ m/s}^2)\left(\frac{1609 \text{ m}}{1 \text{ mi}}\right)$$

$$= 4.1 \times 10^7 \text{ Pa}$$

This is about 400 atmospheres.

The relation $P = P_{at} + \rho g h$ can be applied to any two points in a fluid. For example, if the pressure at one point is P_1, the pressure P_2 at a depth h below that point is the following:

Dependence of Pressure on Depth

$$P_2 = P_1 + \rho g h \qquad \text{15–7}$$

This relation is illustrated in **Figure 15–3**, and utilized in the next Example.

PROBLEM-SOLVING NOTE

Pressure Depends Only on Depth

The pressure in a static fluid depends only on the depth of the fluid. It is independent of the shape of the container.

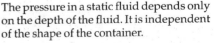

Science Fundamentals Second Edition

EXAMPLE 15–3 Pressure and Depth

A cubical box 20.00 cm on a side is completely immersed in a fluid. At the top of the box the pressure is 105.0 kPa; at the bottom the pressure is 106.8 kPa. What is the density of the fluid?

Picture the Problem

Our sketch shows the box at an unknown depth d below the surface of the fluid. The important dimension for this problem is the height of the box, which is 20.00 cm. We are also given that the pressures at the top and bottom of the box are $P_1 = 105.0$ kPa and $P_2 = 106.8$ kPa, respectively.

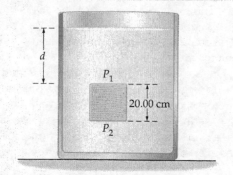

Strategy

The pressures at the top and bottom of the box are related by $P_2 = P_1 + \rho g h$. Since the pressures and the height of the box are given, this relation can be solved for the unknown density, ρ.

Solution

1. Solve $P_2 = P_1 + \rho g h$ for the density:

$$\rho = \frac{P_2 - P_1}{gh}$$

2. Substitute numerical values:

$$\rho = \frac{1.068 \times 10^5 \text{ Pa} - 1.050 \times 10^5 \text{ Pa}}{(9.81 \text{ m/s}^2)(0.2000 \text{ m})} = 920 \text{ kg/m}^3$$

Insight

Comparing with Table 15–1, it appears that the fluid in question may be olive oil. If the box had been immersed in water instead, with its greater density, the difference in pressure between the top and bottom of the box would have been greater as well.

Practice Problem

Given the density obtained above, what is the depth of fluid, d, at the top of the box?   [**Answer:** $d = 0.44$ m]

Some related homework problems: Problem 13, Problem 18

CONCEPTUAL CHECKPOINT 15–2   The Size of Bubbles

One day, while swimming below the surface of the ocean, you let out a small bubble of air from your mouth. As the bubble rises toward the surface, does its diameter (**a**) increase, (**b**) decrease, or (**c**) stay the same?

Reasoning and Discussion

As the bubble rises, the pressure in the surrounding water decreases. This allows the air in the bubble to expand and occupy a larger volume.

Answer:

(**a**) The diameter of the bubble increases.

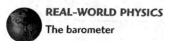

REAL-WORLD PHYSICS

The barometer

An interesting application of the variation of pressure with depth is the **barometer**, which can be used to measure atmospheric pressure. We consider here the simplest type of barometer, which was first proposed by Evangelista Torricelli (1608–1647) in 1643. First, fill a long glass tube—open at one end and closed at the other—with a fluid of density ρ. Next, invert the tube and place its open end below the surface of the same fluid in a bowl, as shown in **Figure 15–4**. Some of the fluid in the tube will flow into the bowl, leaving an empty space (vacuum) at the top. Enough will remain, however, to create a difference in level, h, between the fluid in the bowl and that in the tube.

The basic idea of the barometer is that this height difference is directly related to the atmospheric pressure that pushes down on the fluid in the bowl. To see how this works, first note that the pressure in the vacuum at the top of the tube is zero.

Science Fundamentals Second Edition

Hence, the pressure in the tube at a depth h below the vacuum is $0 + \rho gh = \rho gh$. Now, at the level of the fluid in the bowl we know that the pressure is one atmosphere, P_{at}. Therefore, it follows that

$$P_{at} = \rho gh$$

If these pressures were not the same, there would be a pressure difference between the fluid in the tube and that in the bowl, resulting in a net force and a flow of fluid. Thus, a measurement of h immediately gives atmospheric pressure.

A fluid that is often used in such a barometer is mercury (Hg), with a density of $\rho = 1.3595 \times 10^4 \, kg/m^3$. The corresponding height for a column of mercury is

$$h = \frac{P_{at}}{\rho g} = \frac{1.013 \times 10^5 \, Pa}{(1.3595 \times 10^4 \, kg/m^3)(9.81 \, m/s^2)} = 760 \text{ mm}$$

In fact, atmospheric pressure is *defined* in terms of millimeters of mercury (mmHg):

$$1 \text{ atmosphere} = P_{at} = 760 \text{ mmHg}$$

Table 15–2 summarizes the various expressions we have developed for atmospheric pressure.

Water Seeks Its Own Level

We are all familiar with the aphorism that water seeks its own level. In order for this to hold true, however, it is necessary that the pressure at the surface of the water (or other fluid) be the same everywhere on the surface. This was not the case for the barometer just discussed, where the pressure was P_{at} on one portion of the surface and zero on another. Let's take a moment, then, to consider the level assumed by a fluid with constant pressure on its surface. In doing so, we shall apply considerations involving force, pressure, and energy.

First, the force–pressure point of view. In **Figure 15–5 (a)** we show a U-shaped tube containing a quantity of fluid of density ρ. The fluid rises to the same level in each arm of the U, where it is open to the atmosphere. Therefore, the pressure at the base of each arm is the same; $P_{at} + \rho gh$. Thus, the fluid in the horizontal section of the U is pushed with equal force from each side, giving zero net force. As a result, the fluid remains at rest.

On the other hand, in **Figure 15–5 (b)** the two arms of the U are filled to different levels. Therefore, the pressure at the base of the two arms is different, with the greater pressure at the base of the right arm. The fluid in the horizontal section, then, will experience a net force to the left, causing it to move in that direction. This will tend to equalize the fluid levels of the two arms.

We can arrive at the same conclusion on the basis of energy minimization. Consider a U tube that is initially filled to the same level in both arms, as in Figure 15–5 (a). Now, consider moving a small element of fluid from one arm to the other, to create different levels, as in **Figure 15–6**. In moving this fluid element to the other arm, it is necessary to lift it upward. This, in turn, causes its potential energy to increase. Since nothing else in the system has changed its position, the only change in potential energy is the increase experienced by the element. Thus, we conclude that the system has a minimum energy when the fluid levels are the same and a higher energy when the levels are different. Just as a ball rolls to the bottom of a hill, where its energy is minimized, the fluid seeks its own level and a minimum energy.

If two different liquids, with different densities, are combined in the same U tube, the levels in the arms are not the same. Still, the pressures at the base of each arm must be equal, as before. This is discussed in the next Example.

▶ **FIGURE 15–5 Fluids seek their own level**
(a) When the levels are equal, the pressure is the same at the base of each arm of the U tube. As a result, the fluid in the horizontal section of the U is in equilibrium. (b) With unequal heights, the pressures are different. In this case, the pressure is greater at the base of the right arm, hence fluid will flow toward the left and the levels will equalize.

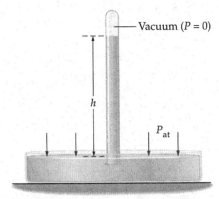

▲ **FIGURE 15–4 A simple barometer**
Atmospheric pressure, P_{at}, is related to the height of fluid in the tube by the relation $P_{at} = \rho gh$.

TABLE 15–2 Atmospheric Pressure

1 atmosphere $= P_{at}$
$= 760$ mmHg
(definition)
$= 14.7 \, lb/in^2$
$= 101 \, kPa$
$= 101 \, kN/m^2$
$\sim 1 \, bar = 100 \, kPa$

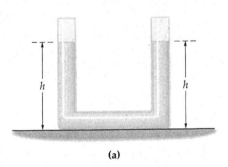

(a)

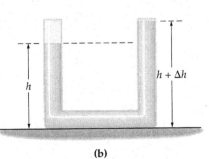

(b)

Science Fundamentals Second Edition

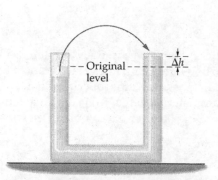

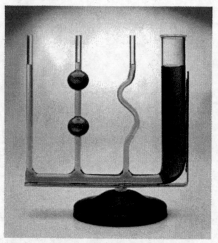

▲ **FIGURE 15–6 Gravitational potential energy of a fluid**
In order to create unequal levels in the two arms of the U tube, an element of fluid must be raised by the height Δh. This increases the gravitational potential energy of the system. The lowest potential energy corresponds to equal levels.

▲ The containers shown here are connected at the bottom by a hollow tube, which allows fluid to flow freely between them. As a result the fluid level is the same in each container regardless of its shape and size.

EXAMPLE 15–4 Oil and Water Don't Mix

A U-shaped tube is filled mostly with water, but a small amount of vegetable oil has been added to one side, as shown in the sketch. The density of the water is 1.00×10^3 kg/m^3, and the density of the vegetable oil is 9.20×10^2 kg/m^3. If the depth of the oil is 5.00 cm, what is the difference in level h between the top of the oil on one side of the U and the top of the water on the other side?

Picture the Problem
The U-shaped tube and the relevant dimensions are shown in our sketch. In particular, note that the depth of the oil is 5.00 cm, and that the oil rises to a greater height on its side of the U than the water does on its side. This is due to the oil having the lower density. Both sides of the U are open to the atmosphere, so the pressure at the top surfaces is P_{at}.

Strategy
For the system to be in equilibrium, it is necessary that the pressure be the same at the bottom of each side of the U; that is, at points C and D. If the pressure is the same at C and D, it will remain equal as one moves up through the water to the points A and B. Above this point the pressures will differ because of the presence of the oil.

Therefore, setting the pressure at point A equal to the pressure at point B determines the depth h_1 in terms of the known depth h_2. It follows that the difference in level between the two sides of the U is simply $h = h_2 - h_1$.

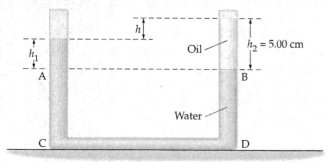

INTERACTIVE FIGURE

Solution

1. Find the pressure at point A, where the depth of the water is h_1:

$$P_A = P_{at} + \rho_{water}gh_1$$

2. Find the pressure at point B, where the depth of the oil is $h_2 = 5.00$ cm:

$$P_B = P_{at} + \rho_{oil}gh_2$$

3. Set P_A equal to P_B:

$$P_{at} + \rho_{water}gh_1 = P_{at} + \rho_{oil}gh_2$$

4. Solve for the depth of the water, h_1, and substitute numerical values:

$$h_1 = h_2\left(\frac{\rho_{oil}}{\rho_{water}}\right)$$

$$= (5.00 \text{ cm})\left(\frac{9.20 \times 10^2 \text{ kg/m}^3}{1.00 \times 10^3 \text{ kg/m}^3}\right) = 4.60 \text{ cm}$$

5. Calculate the difference in levels between the water and oil sides of the U:

$$h = h_2 - h_1 = 5.00 \text{ cm} - 4.60 \text{ cm} = 0.40 \text{ cm}$$

Insight

Note that the weight of the height h_1 of water is equal to the weight of the height h_2 of oil. This is a special case, however, and is due to the fact that our U has equal diameters on its two sides. If the oil side of the U had been wider, for example, the weight of the oil would have been greater, though the difference in height still would have been $h = 0.40$ cm. It is the pressure that matters in a system like this, not the weight. (For a similar situation, see the photo on page 484.)

Practice Problem

Find the pressure at points A and B.   [**Answer:** $P_A = P_B = P_{at} + 451$ Pa]

Some related homework problems: Problem 16, Problem 22, Problem 23

Pascal's Principle

Recall from Equation 15–6 that if the surface of a fluid of density ρ is exposed to the atmosphere with a pressure P_{at}, the pressure at a depth h below the surface is

$$P = P_{at} + \rho g h$$

Suppose, now, that atmospheric pressure is increased from P_{at} to $P_{at} + \Delta P$. As a result, the pressure at the depth h is

$$P = P_{at} + \Delta P + \rho g h = (P_{at} + \rho g h) + \Delta P$$

Thus, by increasing the pressure at the top of the fluid by the amount ΔP, we have increased it by the same amount everywhere in the fluid. This is **Pascal's principle:**

> An external pressure applied to an enclosed fluid is transmitted unchanged to every point within the fluid.

A classic example of Pascal's principle at work is the **hydraulic lift,** which is shown schematically in **Figure 15–7**. Here we see two cylinders, one of cross-sectional area A_1, the other of cross-sectional area $A_2 > A_1$. The cylinders, each of which is fitted with a piston, are connected by a tube and filled with a fluid. Initially the pistons are at the same level and exposed to the atmosphere.

Now, suppose we push down on piston 1 with the force F_1. This increases the pressure in that cylinder by the amount

$$\Delta P = F_1/A_1$$

By Pascal's principle, the pressure in cylinder 2 increases by the *same* amount. Therefore, the increased upward force on piston 2 due to the fluid is

$$F_2 = (\Delta P)A_2$$

Substituting the increase in pressure, $\Delta P = F_1/A_1$, we find

$$F_2 = (F_1/A_1)A_2 = F_1\left(\frac{A_2}{A_1}\right) > F_1 \qquad \text{15–8}$$

REAL-WORLD PHYSICS

The hydraulic lift

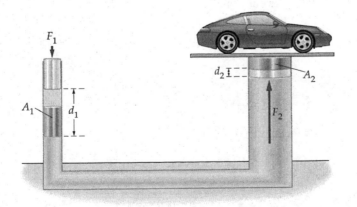

◄ **FIGURE 15–7 A hydraulic lift**
A force F_1 exerted on the small piston causes a much larger force, F_2, to act on the large piston.

To be specific, let's assume that A_2 is 100 times greater than A_1. Then, by pushing down on piston 1 with a force F_1, we push upward on piston 2 with a force of $100F_1$. Our force has been magnified 100 times!

If this sounds too good to be true, rest assured that we are not getting something for nothing. Just as with a lever, there is a tradeoff between the distance through which a force must be applied and the force magnification. This is illustrated in Figure 15–7, where we show piston 1 being pushed down through a distance d_1. This displaces a volume of fluid equal to A_1d_1. The same volume flows into cylinder 2, where it causes piston 2 to rise through a distance d_2. Equating the two volumes, we have

$$A_1d_1 = A_2d_2$$

or

$$d_2 = d_1\left(\frac{A_1}{A_2}\right)$$

Thus, in the example just given, if we move piston 1 down a distance d_1, piston 2 rises a distance $d_2 = d_1/100$. Our force at piston 2 has been magnified 100 times, but the distance it moves has been reduced 100 times.

EXERCISE 15–3

To inspect a 14,500-N car, it is raised with a hydraulic lift. If the radius of the small piston in Figure 15–7 is 4.0 cm, and the radius of the large piston is 17 cm, find the force that must be exerted on the small piston to lift the car.

Solution

Solving Equation 15–8 for F_1, and noting that the area is πr^2, we find

$$F_1 = F_2\left(\frac{A_1}{A_2}\right) = (14{,}500 \text{ N})\left[\frac{\pi(0.040 \text{ m})^2}{\pi(0.17 \text{ m})^2}\right] = 800 \text{ N}$$

15–4 Archimedes' Principle and Buoyancy

The fact that a fluid's pressure increases with depth leads to many interesting consequences. Among them is the fact that a fluid exerts a net upward force on any object it surrounds. This is referred to as a **buoyant force.**

To see the origin of buoyancy, consider a cubical block immersed in a fluid of density ρ, as in **Figure 15–8**. The surrounding fluid exerts normal forces on all of its faces. Clearly, the horizontal forces pushing to the right and to the left are equal, hence they cancel and have no effect on the block.

The situation is quite different for the vertical forces, however. Note, for example, that the downward force exerted on the top face is less than the upward force exerted on the lower face, since the pressure at the lower face is greater. This difference in forces gives rise to a net upward force—the buoyant force.

Let's calculate the buoyant force acting on the block. First, we assume that the cubical block is of length L on a side, and that the pressure on the top surface is P_1. The downward force on the block, then, is

$$F_1 = P_1A = P_1L^2$$

Note that we have used the fact that the area of a square face of side L is L^2. Next, we consider the bottom face. The pressure there is given by Equation 15–7, with a difference in depth of $h = L$:

$$P_2 = P_1 + \rho g L$$

Therefore, the upward force exerted on the bottom face of the cube is

$$F_2 = P_2A = (P_1 + \rho g L)L^2 = P_1L^2 + \rho g L^3 = F_1 + \rho g L^3$$

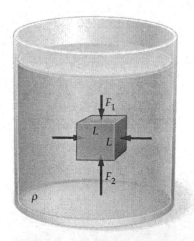

▲ FIGURE 15–8 Buoyant force due to a fluid

A fluid surrounding an object exerts a buoyant force in the upward direction. This is due to the fact that pressure increases with depth, and hence the upward force on the object, F_2, is greater than the downward force, F_1. Forces acting to the left and to the right cancel.

If we take upward as the positive direction, the net vertical force exerted by the fluid on the block—that is, the buoyant force, F_b—is

$$F_b = F_2 - F_1 = \rho g L^3$$

As expected, the block experiences a net upward force from the surrounding fluid.

The precise value of the buoyant force is of some significance, as we now show. First, note that the volume of the cube is L^3. It follows that $\rho g L^3$ is the weight of *fluid* that would occupy the same volume as the cube. Therefore, the buoyant force is equal to the weight of fluid that is displaced by the cube. This is a special case of **Archimedes' principle:**

> An object completely immersed in a fluid experiences an upward buoyant force equal in magnitude to the weight of fluid displaced by the object.

More generally, if a volume V of an object is immersed in a fluid of density ρ_{fluid}, the buoyant force can be expressed as follows:

Buoyant Force When a Volume *V* Is Submerged in a Fluid of Density ρ_{fluid}

$$F_b = \rho_{fluid} g V \qquad\qquad 15\text{–}9$$

SI unit: N

The volume V may be the total volume of the object, or any fraction of the total volume.

To see that Archimedes' principle is completely general, consider the submerged object shown in **Figure 15–9 (a)**. If we were to replace this object with an equivalent volume of fluid, as in **Figure 15–9 (b)**, the container would hold nothing but fluid and would be in static equilibrium. As a result, we conclude that the net buoyant force acting on this "fluid object" must be upward and equal in magnitude to its weight. Now here is the key idea: Since the original object and the fluid object occupy the same position, the forces acting on their surfaces are identical, and hence the net buoyant force is the same for both objects. Therefore, the original object experiences a buoyant force equal to the weight of fluid that it displaces—that is, equal to the weight of the fluid object.

PROBLEM-SOLVING NOTE

The Buoyant Force

Note that the buoyant force is equal to the weight of displaced fluid. It does not depend on the weight of the object that displaces the fluid.

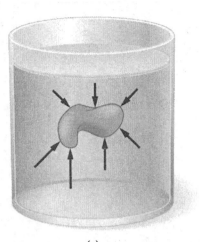

(a)

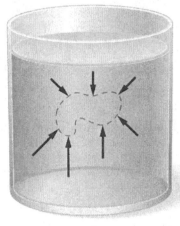

(b)

▶ **FIGURE 15–9 Buoyant force equals the weight of displaced fluid**
The buoyant force acting on the object in **(a)** is equal to the weight of the "fluid object" (with the same size and shape) in **(b)**. This is because the fluid in (b) is at rest; hence the buoyant force acting on the fluid object must cancel its weight. The same forces act on the original object in (a), however, and therefore the buoyant force it experiences is also equal to the weight of the fluid object.

CONCEPTUAL CHECKPOINT 15–3   How Is the Scale Reading Affected?

A flask of water rests on a scale. If you dip your finger into the water, without touching the flask, does the reading on the scale **(a)** increase, **(b)** decrease, or **(c)** stay the same?

Reasoning and Discussion
Your finger experiences an upward buoyant force when it is dipped into the water. By Newton's third law, the water experiences an equal and opposite reaction force acting downward. This downward force is transmitted to the scale, which in turn gives a higher reading.

Another way to look at this result is to note that when you dip your finger into the water, its depth increases. This results in a greater pressure at the bottom of the flask, and hence a greater downward force on the flask. The scale reads this increased downward force.

Answer:
(a) The reading on the scale increases.

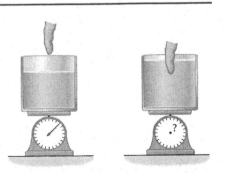

Science Fundamentals Second Edition

15-5 Applications of Archimedes' Principle

In this section we consider a variety of applications of Archimedes' principle. We begin with situations in which an object is fully immersed. Later we consider systems in which an object floats.

Complete Submersion

An interesting application of complete submersion can be found in an apparatus commonly used in determining a person's body-fat percentage. We consider the basic physics of the apparatus and the measurement procedure in the next Example. Following the Example, we derive the relation between overall body density and the body-fat percentage.

EXAMPLE 15-5 Measuring the Body's Density

REAL-WORLD PHYSICS: BIO A person who weighs 720.0 N in air is lowered into a tank of water to about chin level. He sits in a harness of negligible mass suspended from a scale that reads his apparent weight. He now exhales as much air as possible and dunks his head underwater, submerging his entire body. If his apparent weight while submerged is 34.3 N, find **(a)** his volume and **(b)** his density.

Picture the Problem

The scale, the tank, and the person are shown in our sketch. We also show the free-body diagram for the person. Note that the weight of the person in air is designated by $W = mg = 720.0$ N, and the apparent weight in water, which is the upward force exerted by the scale on the person, is designated by $W_a = 34.3$ N. The buoyant force exerted by the water on the person is F_b.

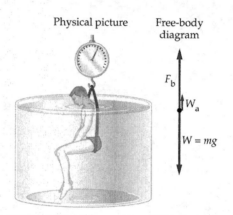

Physical picture   Free-body diagram

Strategy

To find the volume, V_p, and density, ρ_p, of the person, we must use two separate conditions. They are as follows:

(a) When the person is submerged, the surrounding water exerts an upward buoyant force given by Archimedes' principle: $F_b = \rho_{water}V_p g$. This relation, and Newton's second law, can be used to determine V_p.

(b) The weight of the person in air is $W = mg = \rho_p V_p g$. Combining this relation with the volume, V_p, found in part (a) allows us to determine the density, ρ_p.

Solution

Part (a)

1. Apply Newton's second law to the person. Note that the person remains at rest, and therefore the net force acting on him is zero:

$$W_a + F_b - W = 0$$

2. Substitute $F_b = \rho_{water}V_p g$ and solve for V_p:

$$W_a + \rho_{water}V_p g - W = 0$$
$$V_p = \frac{W - W_a}{\rho_{water}g} = \frac{720.0 \text{ N} - 34.3 \text{ N}}{(1.00 \times 10^3 \text{ kg/m}^3)(9.81 \text{ m/s}^2)}$$
$$= 6.99 \times 10^{-2} \text{ m}^3$$

Part (b)

3. Use $W = \rho_p V_p g$ to solve for the density of the person, ρ_p:

$$W = \rho_p V_p g$$
$$\rho_p = \frac{W}{V_p g} = \frac{720.0 \text{ N}}{(6.99 \times 10^{-2} \text{ m}^3)(9.81 \text{ m/s}^2)}$$
$$= 1050 \text{ kg/m}^3$$

Insight

As in Conceptual Checkpoint 15-3, the water exerts an upward buoyant force on the person, and an equal and opposite reaction force acts downward on the tank and water, making it press against the floor with a greater force.

In addition, notice that the density of the person (1050 kg/m^3) is only slightly greater than the density of seawater (1025 kg/m^3), as given in Table 15-1.

Practice Problem

The person can float in water if his lungs are partially filled with air, increasing the volume of his body. What volume must his body have to just float? **[Answer: $V_p = 7.34 \times 10^{-2} \text{ m}^3$]**

Some related homework problems: Problem 33, Problem 34

Once the overall density of the body is determined, the percentage of body fat can be obtained by noting that body fat has a density of $\rho_f = 9.00 \times 10^2 \, \text{kg/m}^3$, whereas the lean body mass (muscles and bone) has a density of $\rho_1 = 1.10 \times 10^3 \, \text{kg/m}^3$. Suppose, for example, that a fraction x_f of the total body mass M is fat mass, and a fraction $(1 - x_f)$ is lean mass; that is, the fat mass is $m_f = x_f M$ and the lean mass is $m_1 = (1 - x_f)M$. The total volume of the body is $V = V_f + V_1$. Using the fact that $V = m/\rho$, we can write the total volume as $V = m_f/\rho_f + m_1/\rho_1 = x_f M/\rho_f + (1 - x_f)M/\rho_1$. Combining these results, the overall density of a person's body, ρ_p, is

$$\rho_p = \frac{M}{V} = \frac{1}{\dfrac{x_f}{\rho_f} + \dfrac{(1 - x_f)}{\rho_1}}$$

Solving for the body-fat fraction, x_f, yields

$$x_f = \frac{1}{\rho_p}\left(\frac{\rho_1 \rho_f}{\rho_1 - \rho_f}\right) - \frac{\rho_f}{\rho_1 - \rho_f}$$

Finally, substituting the values for ρ_f and ρ_1, we find

$$x_f = \frac{(4950 \, \text{kg/m}^3)}{\rho_p} - 4.50$$

This result is known as *Siri's formula*. For example, if $\rho_p = 900 \, \text{kg/m}^3$ (all fat), we find $x_f = 1$; if $\rho_p = 1100 \, \text{kg/m}^3$ (no fat), we find $x_f = 0$. In the case of Example 15–5, where $\rho_p = 1050 \, \text{kg/m}^3$, we find that this person's body-fat fraction is $x_f = 0.214$, for a percentage of 21.4%. This is a reasonable value for a healthy adult male.

A recent refinement to the measurement of body-fat percentage is the Bod Pod, an egg-shaped, air-tight chamber in which a person sits comfortably—high and dry, surrounded only by air. This device works on the same physical principle as submerging a person in water, only it uses air instead of water. Since air is about a thousand times less dense than water, the measurements of apparent weight must be roughly a thousand times more sensitive. Fortunately, this is possible with today's technology, allowing for a much more convenient means of measurement.

Next we consider a low-density object, such as a piece of wood, held down below the surface of a denser fluid.

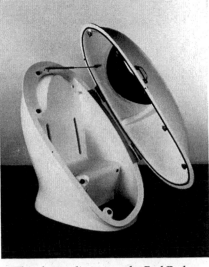

▲ This device, known as the Bod Pod, measures the body-fat percentage of a person inside it by varying the air pressure in the chamber and measuring the corresponding changes in the person's apparent weight. Archimedes' principle is at work here, just as it is in Example 15–5.

REAL-WORLD PHYSICS: BIO

Measuring body fat

ACTIVE EXAMPLE 15–1 Find the Tension in the String

A piece of wood with a density of 706 kg/m^3 is tied with a string to the bottom of a water-filled flask. The wood is completely immersed, and has a volume of $8.00 \times 10^{-6} \, \text{m}^3$. What is the tension in the string?

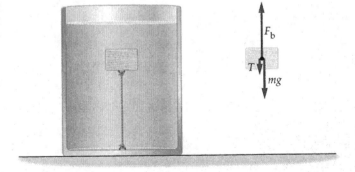

Solution *(Test your understanding by performing the calculations indicated in each step.)*

1. Apply Newton's second law to the wood: $F_b - T - mg = 0$

2. Solve for the tension, T: $T = F_b - mg$

3. Calculate the weight of the wood: $mg = 0.0554 \, \text{N}$

4. Calculate the buoyant force: $F_b = 0.0785 \, \text{N}$

5. Subtract to obtain the tension: $T = 0.0231 \, \text{N}$

Insight
Since the wood floats in water, its buoyant force when completely immersed is greater than its weight.

Your Turn
What is the tension in the string if the piece of wood has a density of 822 kg/m^3?

*(Answers to **Your Turn** problems can be found in the back of the book.)*

Science Fundamentals Second Edition

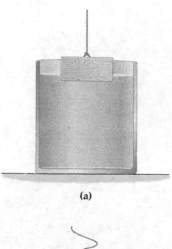

(a)

(b)

▲ **FIGURE 15–10 Floatation**

(a) The block of wood displaces some water, but not enough to equal its weight. Thus, the block would not float at this position. **(b)** The weight of displaced water equals the weight of the block in this case. The block floats now.

Floatation

When an object floats, the buoyant force acting on it equals its weight. For example, suppose we slowly lower a block of wood into a flask of water. At first, as in **Figure 15–10 (a)**, only a small amount of water is displaced and the buoyant force is a fraction of the block's weight. If we were to release the block now, it would drop farther into the water. As we continue to lower the block, more water is displaced, increasing the buoyant force.

Eventually, we reach the situation pictured in **Figure 15–10 (b)**, where the block begins to float. In this case, the buoyant force equals the weight of the wood. This, in turn, means that the weight of the displaced water is equal to the weight of the wood. In general,

> An object floats when it displaces an amount of fluid whose weight is equal to the weight of the object.

This is illustrated in **Figure 15–11 (a)**, where we show the volume of water equal to the weight of a block of wood. Similarly, in **Figure 15–11 (b)** we show the amount of water necessary to have the same weight as a block of metal. Clearly, if the metal is completely submerged, the buoyant force is only a fraction of its weight, and so it sinks. On the other hand, if the metal is formed into the shape of a bowl, as in **Figure 15–11 (c)**, it can displace a volume of water equal to its weight and float.

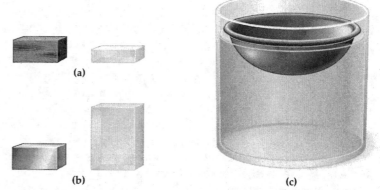

(a)

(b)   (c)

▲ **FIGURE 15–11 Floating an object that is more dense than water**

(a) A wood block and the volume of water that has the same weight. Because the wood has a larger volume than this, it floats. **(b)** A metal block and the volume of water that has the same weight. Since the metal displaces less water than this, it sinks. **(c)** If the metal in (b) is shaped like a bowl, it can displace more water than the volume of the metal itself. In fact, it can displace enough water to float.

▲ Although steel is denser than water, a ship's bowl-like hull (left) displaces enough water to allow it to float, so long as it is not too heavily loaded. (The boundary between the red and black areas of the hull is the Plimsoll line, which indicates where the ship should ride in the water when carrying its maximum safe load—see Conceptual Checkpoint 15–4.) For balloons (right), the key to buoyancy is the lower density and greater volume of hot air. As the air in the balloon is heated, it expands the bag, increasing the volume of air that the balloon displaces. At the same time, heated air spills out of the balloon, decreasing its weight. Eventually, the average density of the balloon plus the hot air it contains becomes lower than that of the surrounding air, and it starts to float.

▲ The water of the Dead Sea is unusually dense because of its great salt content. As a result, swimmers can float higher in the water than they are accustomed and engage in recreational activities that we don't ordinarily associate with a dip in the ocean.

Science Fundamentals Second Edition

Another way to change the buoyancy of an object is to alter its overall density. Consider, for example, the *Cartesian diver* shown in **Figure 15–12**. As illustrated, the diver is simply a small glass tube with an air bubble trapped inside. Initially, the overall density of the tube and the air bubble is less than the density of water, and the diver floats. When the bottle containing the diver is squeezed, however, the pressure in the water rises, and the air bubble is compressed to a smaller volume. Now, the overall density of the tube and air bubble is greater than that of water, and the diver descends. By adjusting the pressure on the bottle, the diver can be made to float at any depth in the bottle.

The same principle applies to the swim bladder of ray-finned bony fishes. The swim bladder is basically an air sac whose volume can be controlled by the fish. By adjusting the size of the swim bladder, the fish can give itself "neutral buoyancy"—that is, the fish can float without effort at a given depth, just like the Cartesian diver. Similar considerations apply to certain diving sea mammals, such as the bottlenose dolphin, Weddell seal, elephant seal, and blue whale. All of these animals are capable of diving to great depths—in fact, some of the seals have been observed at depths of nearly 400 m. In order to conserve energy on their long dives, they take advantage of the fact that the pressure of the surrounding water compresses their bodies and flattens the air sacs in their lungs. Just as with the Cartesian diver, this decreases their buoyancy to the point where they begin to sink. As a result, they can glide effortlessly to the desired depth, saving energy for the swim back to the surface.

REAL-WORLD PHYSICS: BIO
The swim bladder in fish

REAL-WORLD PHYSICS: BIO
Diving sea mammals

ACTIVE EXAMPLE 15–2 Floating a Block of Wood

How much water (density $1.00 \times 10^3 \text{ kg/m}^3$) must be displaced to float a cubical block of wood (density 655 kg/m^3) that is 15.0 cm on a side?

Solution *(Test your understanding by performing the calculations indicated in each step.)*

1. Calculate the volume of the wood: $V_{\text{wood}} = 3.38 \times 10^{-3} \text{ m}^3$

2. Find the weight of the wood: $\rho_{\text{wood}} V_{\text{wood}} g = 21.7 \text{ N}$

3. Write an expression for the weight of a volume of water: $\rho_{\text{water}} V_{\text{water}} g$

4. Set the weight of water equal to the weight of the wood: $\rho_{\text{water}} V_{\text{water}} g = 21.7 \text{ N}$

5. Solve for the volume of water: $V_{\text{water}} = 2.21 \times 10^{-3} \text{ m}^3$

Insight
As expected, only a fraction of the wood must be submerged in order for it to float.

Your Turn
What volume of water must be displaced if the density of the wood is 955 kg/m^3? Compare this volume to the volume of the wood itself.

(Answers to **Your Turn** *problems can be found in the back of the book.)*

▲ **FIGURE 15–12 A Cartesian diver**
A Cartesian diver floats because of the bubble of air trapped within it. When the bottle is squeezed, increasing the pressure in the water, the bubble is reduced in size and the diver sinks.

CONCEPTUAL CHECKPOINT 15–4   The Plimsoll Mark

On the side of a cargo ship you may see a horizontal line indicating "maximum load." (It is sometimes known as the "Plimsoll mark," after the nineteenth-century British legislator who caused it to be adopted.) When a ship is loaded to capacity, the maximum load line is at water level. The ship shown here has two maximum load lines, one for fresh water and one for salt water. Which line should be marked "maximum load for salt water": (**a**) the top line or (**b**) the bottom line?

Reasoning and Discussion
If a ship sails from fresh water into salt water it floats higher, just as it is easier for you to float in an ocean than in a lake. The reason is that salt water is denser than fresh water; hence less of it needs to be displaced to provide a given buoyant force. Since the ship floats higher in salt water, the bottom line should be used to indicate maximum load.

Answer:
(**b**) The bottom line should be used in salt water.

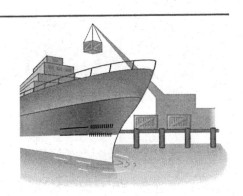

▲ **FIGURE 15–13 Submerged volume of a floating object**
A solid, of volume V_s and density ρ_s, floats in a fluid of density ρ_f. The volume of the solid that is submerged is $V_{sub} = V_s(\rho_s/\rho_f)$.

▲ Most people know that the bulk of an iceberg lies below the surface of the water. But as with ships and swimmers, the actual proportion that is submerged depends on whether the water is fresh or salt (see Example 15–6).

Tip of the Iceberg

As we have seen, an object floats when its weight is equal to the weight of the fluid it displaces. Let's use this condition to determine just how much of a floating object is submerged. We will then apply our result to the classic case of an iceberg.

Consider, then, a solid of density ρ_s floating in a fluid of density ρ_f, as in **Figure 15–13**. If the solid has a volume V_s, its total weight is

$$W_s = \rho_s V_s g$$

Similarly, the weight of a volume V_f of displaced fluid is

$$W_f = \rho_f V_f g$$

Equating these weights, we find the following:

$$W_s = W_f$$
$$\rho_s V_s g = \rho_f V_f g$$

Canceling g, and solving for the volume of displaced fluid, we have

$$V_f = V_s(\rho_s/\rho_f)$$

Since, by definition, the volume of displaced fluid, V_f, is the same as the volume of the solid that is submerged, V_{sub}, we find

Submerged Volume V_{sub} for a Solid of Volume V_s and Density ρ_s Floating in a Fluid of Density ρ_f

$$V_{sub} = V_s(\rho_s/\rho_f) \qquad\qquad 15\text{–}10$$

SI unit: m^3

Note that this relation agrees with the results of Active Example 15–2.
We now apply this result to ice floating in water.

EXAMPLE 15–6 The Tip of the Iceberg

 REAL-WORLD PHYSICS   What percentage of a floating chunk of ice projects above the level of the water? Assume a density of $917\ kg/m^3$ for the ice and $1.00 \times 10^3\ kg/m^3$ for the water.

Picture the Problem
Our sketch shows a chunk of ice floating in a glass of water. In this case the solid object is ice, with a density $\rho_s = \rho_{ice} = 917\ kg/m^3$, and the fluid is water, with a density $\rho_f = \rho_{water} = 1.00 \times 10^3\ kg/m^3$.

Strategy
We can apply Equation 15–10 to this system. First, the fraction of the total volume of the ice, V_s, that is submerged is $V_{sub}/V_s = \rho_s/\rho_f$. Hence the fraction that is above the water is $1 - V_{sub}/V_s = 1 - \rho_s/\rho_f$. Multiplying this fraction by 100 yields the percentage above water.

Solution

1. Calculate the fraction of the total volume of the ice that is submerged:

$$\frac{V_{sub}}{V_s} = \frac{\rho_s}{\rho_f} = \frac{917\ kg/m^3}{1.00 \times 10^3\ kg/m^3} = 0.917$$

2. Calculate the fraction of the ice that is above water:

$$1 - \frac{\rho_s}{\rho_f} = 1 - 0.917 = 0.083$$

3. Multiply by 100 to obtain a percentage:

$$100\left(1 - \frac{\rho_s}{\rho_f}\right) = 100(0.083) = 8.3\%$$

Insight

Because we seek a percentage, it is not necessary to know the total volume of the ice. Thus, our result that 8.3% of the ice is above the water applies whether we are talking about an ice cube in a drinking glass, or an iceberg floating in a freshwater lake. If an iceberg floats in the ocean, however, it will float higher due to the higher density of seawater. We consider this case in the following Practice Problem.

Practice Problem

What percentage of an ice chunk is above water level if it floats in seawater? (The density of seawater can be found in Table 15–1.) [**Answer:** 10.5%]

Some related homework problems: Problem 36, Problem 37

CONCEPTUAL CHECKPOINT 15–5   The New Water Level I

A cup is filled to the brim with water and a floating ice cube. When the ice melts, which of the following occurs? (a) Water overflows the cup, (b) the water level decreases, or (c) the water level remains the same.

Reasoning and Discussion

Since the ice cube floats, it displaces a volume of water equal to its weight. But when it melts, it becomes water, and its weight is the same. Hence, the melted water fills exactly the same volume that the ice cube displaced when floating. As a result, the water level is unchanged.

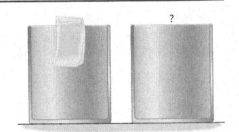

Answer:
(c) The water level remains the same.

CONCEPTUAL CHECKPOINT 15–6   The New Water Level II

A cup is filled to the brim with water and a floating ice cube. Resting on top of the ice cube is a small pebble. When the ice melts, which of the following occurs? (a) Water overflows the cup, (b) the water level decreases, or (c) the water level remains the same.

Reasoning and Discussion

We know from the previous Conceptual Checkpoint that the ice itself makes no difference to the water level. As for the pebble, when it floats on the ice it displaces an amount of water equal to its *weight*. When the ice melts, the pebble drops to the bottom of the cup, where it displaces a volume of water equal to its own *volume*. Since the volume of the pebble is less than the volume of water with the same weight, we conclude that less water is displaced after the ice melts. Hence, the water level decreases.

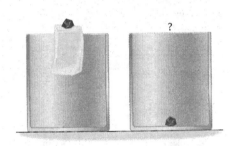

Answer:
(b) The water level decreases.

15–6 Fluid Flow and Continuity

Suppose you want to water the yard, but you don't have a spray nozzle for the end of the hose. Without a nozzle the water flows rather slowly from the hose and hits the ground within half a meter. But if you place your thumb over the end of the hose, narrowing the opening to a fraction of its original size, the water sprays out with a high speed and a large range. Why does decreasing the size of the opening have this effect?

To answer this question, we begin by considering a simple system that shows the same behavior. Imagine, then, that a fluid flows with a speed v_1 through a cylindrical pipe of cross-sectional area A_1, as in the left-hand portion of **Figure 15–14**. If the pipe narrows to a cross-sectional area A_2, as in the right-hand portion of Figure 15–14, the fluid will flow with a new speed, v_2.

We can find the speed in the narrow section of the pipe by assuming that any amount of fluid that passes point 1 in a given time, Δt, must also flow past the point 2 in the same time. If this were not the case, the system would be gaining or losing fluid. To find the mass of fluid passing point 1 in the time Δt, note that the fluid moves through a distance $v_1 \Delta t$ in this time. As a result, the volume of fluid going past point 1 is

$$\Delta V_1 = A_1 v_1 \Delta t$$

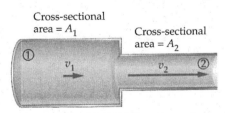

▲ **FIGURE 15–14 Fluid flow through a pipe of varying diameter**

As a fluid flows from a large pipe to a small pipe, the same mass of fluid passes a given point in a given amount of time. Thus, the speed in the small pipe is greater than it is in the large pipe.

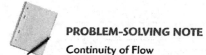

▲ Narrowing the opening in a hose with a nozzle (or thumb) increases the velocity of flow, as one would expect from the equation of continuity.

Hence, the mass of fluid passing point 1 is

$$\Delta m_1 = \rho_1 \Delta V_1 = \rho_1 A_1 v_1 \Delta t$$

Similarly, the mass passing point 2 in the time Δt is

$$\Delta m_2 = \rho_2 \Delta V_2 = \rho_2 A_2 v_2 \Delta t$$

Note that we have allowed for the possibility of the fluid having different densities at points 1 and 2.

Finally, equating these two masses yields the relation between v_1 and v_2:

$$\Delta m_1 = \Delta m_2$$
$$\rho_1 A_1 v_1 \Delta t = \rho_2 A_2 v_2 \Delta t$$

Canceling Δt we find

Equation of Continuity

$$\rho_1 A_1 v_1 = \rho_2 A_2 v_2 \qquad \text{15–11}$$

This relation is referred to as the **equation of continuity.**

Most gases are readily compressed, which means that their densities can change. In contrast, most liquids are practically incompressible, so their densities are essentially constant. Unless stated otherwise, we will assume all liquids discussed in this text to be perfectly incompressible. Thus, for liquids, ρ_1 and ρ_2 are the same in Equation 15–11, and the equation of continuity reduces to the following:

Equation of Continuity for an Incompressible Fluid

$$A_1 v_1 = A_2 v_2 \qquad \text{15–12}$$

We next apply this relation to the case of water flowing through the nozzle of a fire hose.

PROBLEM-SOLVING NOTE

Continuity of Flow

The speed of an incompressible fluid is inversely proportional to the area through which it flows.

EXAMPLE 15–7 Spray I

Water travels through a 9.6-cm diameter fire hose with a speed of 1.3 m/s. At the end of the hose, the water flows out through a nozzle whose diameter is 2.5 cm. What is the speed of the water coming out of the nozzle?

Picture the Problem

In our sketch, we label the speed of the water in the hose with v_1 and the speed of the water coming out the nozzle with v_2. We are given that $v_1 = 1.3$ m/s. We also know that the diameter of the hose is $d_1 = 9.6$ cm and the diameter of the nozzle is $d_2 = 2.5$ cm.

Strategy

We can find the water speed in the nozzle by applying $A_1 v_1 = A_2 v_2$. In addition, we assume that the hose and nozzle are circular in cross section; hence, their areas are given by $A = \pi d^2/4$, where d is the diameter.

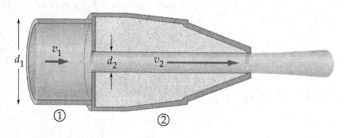

Solution

1. Solve Equation 15–12 for v_2, the speed of the water in the nozzle:

$$v_2 = v_1(A_1/A_2)$$

2. Replace the areas with $A = \pi d^2/4$:

$$v_2 = v_1\left(\frac{\pi d_1^2/4}{\pi d_2^2/4}\right) = v_1\left(\frac{d_1^2}{d_2^2}\right)$$

3. Substitute numerical values:

$$v_2 = v_1\left(\frac{d_1^2}{d_2^2}\right) = (1.3 \text{ m/s})\left(\frac{9.6 \text{ cm}}{2.5 \text{ cm}}\right)^2 = 19 \text{ m/s}$$

Insight

Note that a small-diameter nozzle can give very high speeds. In fact, the speed depends inversely on the diameter squared.

Practice Problem

What nozzle diameter would be required to give the water a speed of 21 m/s? [**Answer:** $d_2 = 2.4$ cm]

Some related homework problems: Problem 41, Problem 46, Problem 47

15–7 Bernoulli's Equation

In this section, we apply the work–energy theorem to fluids. The result is a relation between the pressure of a fluid, its speed, and its height. This relation is known as **Bernoulli's equation**.

Change in Speed

We begin by considering a system in which the speed of the fluid changes. To be specific, the system of interest is the same as that shown in Figure 15–14. We have already shown that the speed of the fluid increases as it flows from region 1 to region 2; we now investigate the corresponding change in pressure.

Our plan of attack is to first calculate the total work done on the fluid as it moves from one region to the next. This result will depend on the pressure in the fluid. Once the total work is obtained, the work-energy theorem allows us to equate it to the change in kinetic energy of the fluid. This will give the pressure-speed relationship we desire.

Consider an element of fluid of length Δx_1, as shown in **Figure 15–15**. This element is pushed in the direction of motion by the pressure P_1. Thus, the pressure does positive work, ΔW_1, on the fluid element. Noting that the force exerted on the element is $F_1 = P_1 A_1$, and that work is force times distance, the work done on the element is

$$\Delta W_1 = F_1 \Delta x_1 = P_1 A_1 \Delta x_1$$

The volume of the fluid element is $\Delta V_1 = A_1 \Delta x_1$, so the work done by P_1 is

$$\Delta W_1 = P_1 \Delta V_1$$

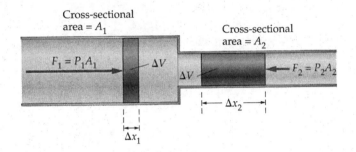

Cross-sectional area = A_1

Cross-sectional area = A_2

$F_1 = P_1 A_1$ ΔV

ΔV $F_2 = P_2 A_2$

Δx_2

Δx_1

◀ **FIGURE 15–15 Work done on a fluid element**

As an incompressible fluid element of volume ΔV moves from pipe 1 to pipe 2, the pressure P_1 does a positive work $P_1 \Delta V$ and the pressure P_2 does a negative work $P_2 \Delta V$. Since P_1 is greater than P_2, the net result is that positive work is done, and the fluid element speeds up.

Next, when the fluid element emerges into region 2, it experiences a force opposite to its direction of motion due to the pressure P_2. Thus, P_2 does negative work on the element. Following the same steps given previously, we can write the work done by P_2 as

$$\Delta W_2 = -P_2 \Delta V_2$$

Now, for an incompressible fluid, the volume of the element does not change as it goes from region 1 to region 2. Therefore,

$$\Delta V_1 = \Delta V_2 = \Delta V$$

Using this result, we can write the total work done on the fluid element as follows:

$$\Delta W_{\text{total}} = \Delta W_1 + \Delta W_2 = P_1 \Delta V - P_2 \Delta V = (P_1 - P_2) \Delta V$$

The final step is to equate the total work to the change in kinetic energy:

$$\Delta W_{\text{total}} = (P_1 - P_2) \Delta V = K_{\text{final}} - K_{\text{initial}} = K_2 - K_1 \qquad \textbf{15–13}$$

What is the kinetic energy of the fluid element? Well, the mass of the element is

$$\Delta m = \rho \Delta V$$

Thus, its kinetic energy is simply

$$K = \tfrac{1}{2}(\Delta m)v^2 = \tfrac{1}{2}(\rho \Delta V)v^2$$

Using this expression in Equation 15–13, we have

$$\Delta W_{\text{total}} = (P_1 - P_2)\Delta V = \left(\tfrac{1}{2}\rho v_2{}^2 - \tfrac{1}{2}\rho v_1{}^2\right)\Delta V$$

Science Fundamentals Second Edition

Canceling the common factor ΔV, and rearranging, we find

$$P_1 + \tfrac{1}{2}\rho v_1{}^2 = P_2 + \tfrac{1}{2}\rho v_2{}^2 \qquad \text{15-14}$$

Equation 15–14 is equivalent to saying that $P + \tfrac{1}{2}\rho v^2$ is constant. Thus, there is a tradeoff between the pressure in a fluid and its speed—as the fluid speeds up, its pressure decreases. If this seems odd, recall that P_1 acts to increase the speed of the fluid element and P_2 acts to decrease its speed. The element will speed up, then, only if P_2 is less than P_1.

EXAMPLE 15–8 Spray II

Referring to Example 15–7, suppose the pressure in the fire hose is 350 kPa. What is the pressure in the nozzle?

Picture the Problem

In our sketch, we use the same numbering system as in Example 15–7; that is, 1 refers to the hose, 2 to the nozzle. Therefore, $P_1 = 350$ kPa, and P_2 is to be determined.

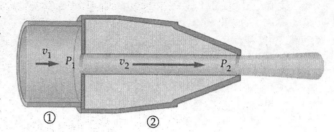

Strategy

We are given P_1, v_1, and the diameters of the hose and nozzle. From the equation of continuity, Equation 15–12, we find v_2 (as in Example 15–7). Now we use this result, plus Equation 15–14, to determine P_2.

Solution

1. Solve Equation 15–14 for the pressure in the nozzle, P_2: $P_2 = P_1 + \tfrac{1}{2}\rho(v_1{}^2 - v_2{}^2)$

2. Substitute numerical values, including v_2 from Example 15–7:

$P_2 = 350 \text{ kPa} + \tfrac{1}{2}(1.00 \times 10^3 \text{ kg/m}^3)[(1.3 \text{ m/s})^2 - (19 \text{ m/s})^2]$
$= 170 \text{ kPa}$

Insight

Note that the pressure in the nozzle is less than the pressure in the hose by roughly a factor of 2. What has happened is that part of the energy associated with the high pressure in the hose has been converted to kinetic energy as the water passes through the nozzle. The connection between pressure and energy will be explored in more detail later in this section.

Practice Problem

What nozzle speed would be required to give a nozzle pressure of 110 kPa? [**Answer:** $v_2 = 22$ m/s]

Some related homework problems: Problem 50, Problem 51

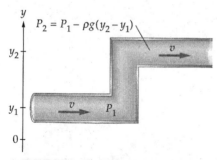

▲ FIGURE 15–16 Fluid pressure in a pipe of varying elevation
Fluid of density ρ flows in a pipe of uniform cross-sectional area from height y_1 to height y_2. As it does so, its pressure decreases by the amount $\rho g(y_2 - y_1)$.

Change in Height

If a fluid flows through the pipe shown in **Figure 15–16**, its height increases from y_1 to y_2 as it goes from one region to the next. Since the cross-sectional area of the pipe is constant, however, the speed of the fluid is unchanged, according to Equation 15–12. Thus, the change in kinetic energy of the fluid element shown in Figure 15–16 is zero.

The total work done on the fluid element is the sum of the works done by the pressure in each of the two regions, plus the work done by gravity. As before, the work done by pressure is

$$\Delta W_{\text{pressure}} = \Delta W_1 + \Delta W_2 = (P_1 - P_2)\Delta V$$

As the fluid element rises, gravity does negative work on it. Recalling that the mass of the element is

$$\Delta m = \rho \Delta V$$

the work done by gravity is

$$\Delta W_{\text{gravity}} = -\Delta m g(y_2 - y_1) = -\rho \Delta V g(y_2 - y_1)$$

Setting the total work equal to zero (since $\Delta K = 0$), yields

$$\Delta W_{\text{total}} = \Delta W_{\text{pressure}} + \Delta W_{\text{gravity}}$$
$$= (P_1 - P_2)\Delta V - \rho g(y_2 - y_1)\Delta V = 0$$

Canceling ΔV and rearranging gives

$$P_1 + \rho g y_1 = P_2 + \rho g y_2 \qquad \text{15-15}$$

Science Fundamentals Second Edition

In this case, it is $P + \rho gy$ that is constant—hence, pressure decreases as the height within a fluid increases. Note, in fact, that Equation 15–15 is precisely the same as Equation 15–7, which was obtained using force considerations. Here we obtained the result using the work-energy theorem.

EXERCISE 15–4

Water flows with constant speed through a garden hose that goes up a step 20.0-cm high. If the water pressure is 143 kPa at the bottom of the step, what is its pressure at the top of the step?

Solution

Apply Equation 15–15, letting subscript 1 refer to the bottom of the step and subscript 2 refer to the top of the step. Solve for P_2:

$$P_2 = P_1 + \rho g(y_1 - y_2)$$
$$= 143 \text{ kPa} + (1.00 \times 10^3 \text{ kg/m}^3)(9.81 \text{ m/s}^2)(0 - 0.200 \text{ m}) = 141 \text{ kPa}$$

This is precisely the pressure difference that would be observed if the water had been at rest.

General Case

In a more general case, both the height of a fluid and its speed may change. Combining the results obtained in Equations 15–14 and 15–15 yields the full form of Bernoulli's equation:

Bernoulli's Equation

$$P_1 + \tfrac{1}{2}\rho v_1^2 + \rho gy_1 = P_2 + \tfrac{1}{2}\rho v_2^2 + \rho gy_2 \qquad \text{15–16}$$

Thus, in general, the quantity $P + \tfrac{1}{2}\rho v^2 + \rho gy$ is a constant within a fluid. This is basically a statement of energy conservation. For example, recalling the definition of density in Equation 15–1, we find that $\tfrac{1}{2}\rho v^2$ is $\tfrac{1}{2}(M/V)v^2 = \left(\tfrac{1}{2}Mv^2\right)/V$. Clearly, this term represents the kinetic energy per volume of the fluid. Similarly, the term ρgy can be written as $(M/V)gy = (Mgy)/V$, which is the gravitational potential energy per volume.

Finally, the first term in Bernoulli's equation—the pressure—can also be thought of as an energy per volume. Recall that $P = F/A$. If we multiply numerator and denominator by a distance, d, we have $P = Fd/Ad$. But Fd is the work done by the force F as it acts through the distance d, and Ad is the volume swept out by an area A moved through a distance d. Therefore, the pressure can be thought of as work (energy) per volume: $P = W/V$.

As a result, Bernoulli's equation is simply a restatement of the work–energy theorem in terms of quantities per volume. Of course, this relation holds only as long as we can ignore frictional losses, which would lead to heating. We will consider the energy aspects of heat in Chapter 16.

ACTIVE EXAMPLE 15–3 Find the Pressure

Repeat Exercise 15–4 with the following additional information: **(a)** the cross-sectional area of the hose on top of the step is half that at the bottom of the step, and **(b)** the speed of the water at the bottom of the step is 1.20 m/s.

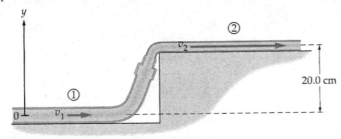

continued on next page

Science Fundamentals Second Edition

197

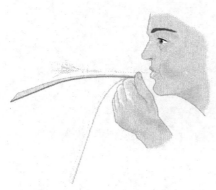

▲ **FIGURE 15-17 The Bernoulli effect on a sheet of paper**

If you hold a piece of paper by its end, it will bend downward. Blowing across the top of the paper reduces the pressure there, resulting in a net upward force which lifts the paper to a nearly horizontal position.

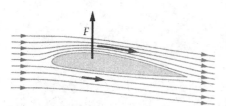

▲ **FIGURE 15-18 Airflow and lift in an airplane wing**

Cross section of an airplane wing with air flowing past it. The wing is shaped so that air flows more rapidly over the top of the wing than along the bottom. As a result, the pressure on top of the wing is reduced, and a net upward force (lift) is generated.

▲ **FIGURE 15-19 Force on a roof due to wind speed**

Wind blows across the roof of a house, but the air inside is at rest. The pressure over the roof is therefore less than the pressure inside, resulting in a net upward force on the roof.

continued from previous page

Solution *(Test your understanding by performing the calculations indicated in each step.)*

1. Use the continuity equation to find the water's speed on top of the step: $v_2 = 2v_1 = 2.40$ m/s

2. Solve Bernoulli's equation for P_2: $P_2 = P_1 - \rho g(y_2 - y_1) - \frac{1}{2}\rho(v_2^2 - v_1^2)$

3. Substitute numerical values: $P_2 = 139$ kPa

Insight

The pressure on top of the step is less than in Exercise 15–4. This is to be expected because, in this case, the water speeds up as it rises over the step.

Your Turn

For what step height will the pressure at the top of the step be equal to atmospheric pressure?

*(Answers to **Your Turn** problems can be found in the back of the book.)*

15-8 Applications of Bernoulli's Equation

We now consider a variety of real-world examples that illustrate the application of Bernoulli's equation.

Pressure and Speed

As mentioned, it often seems counterintuitive that a fast-moving fluid should have less pressure than a slow-moving one. Remember, however, that pressure can be thought of as a form of energy. From this point of view, there is an energy tradeoff between pressure and kinetic energy.

Perhaps the easiest way to demonstrate the dependence of pressure on speed is to blow across the top of a piece of paper. If you hold the paper as shown in **Figure 15-17**, then blow over the top surface, the paper will lift upward. The reason is that there is a difference in air speed between the top and the bottom of the paper, with the higher speed on top. As a result, the pressure above the paper is lower. This pressure difference, in turn, results in a net upward force, referred to as **lift**, and the paper rises.

A similar example of pressure and speed is provided by the airplane wing. A cross section of a typical wing is shown in **Figure 15-18**. The shape of the wing is designed so that air flows more rapidly over the top surface than the lower surface. As a result, the pressure is less on top. As with the piece of paper, the pressure difference results in a net upward force (lift) on the wing.

Note that lift is a dynamic effect; it requires a flow of air. The greater the speed difference, the greater the upward force.

EXERCISE 15-5

During a windstorm, a 35.5 m/s wind blows across the flat roof of a small home, as in **Figure 15-19**. Find the difference in pressure between the air inside the home and the air just above the roof, assuming the doors and windows of the house are closed. (The density of air is 1.29 kg/m³.)

Solution

Use Bernoulli's equation with point 1 just under the roof and point 2 just above the roof. Since there is little difference in elevation between these points, $y_1 = y_2 = y$. Thus,

$$P_1 + 0 + \rho g y = P_2 + \frac{1}{2}\rho v_2^2 + \rho g y$$

Solving for the pressure difference, $P_1 - P_2$, we find

$$P_1 - P_2 = \frac{1}{2}\rho v_2^2 = \frac{1}{2}(1.29 \text{ kg/m}^3)(35.5 \text{ m/s})^2 = 813 \text{ Pa}$$

A difference in pressure of 813 Pa might seem rather small, considering that atmospheric pressure is 101 kPa. However, it can still cause a significant force on a relatively large area, such as a roof. If a typical roof has an area of about 150 m², for example, a pressure difference of 813 Pa results in an upward force of over 27,000 pounds! This is why roofs are often torn from houses during severe windstorms.

On a lighter note, prairie dogs seem to *benefit* from the effects of Bernoulli's equation. A schematic prairie dog burrow is pictured in **Figure 15–20**. Note that one of the entrance/exit mounds is higher than the other. This is significant because the speed of air flow due to the incessant prairie winds varies with height; the speed goes to zero right at ground level, and increases to its maximum value within a few feet above the surface. As a result, the speed of air over the higher mound is greater than that over the lower mound. This causes the pressure to be less over the higher mound. With a pressure difference between the two mounds, air is drawn through the burrow, giving a form of natural air conditioning.

Similar effects are seen in an atomizer, which sprays perfume in a fine mist. As the bulb shoots a gust of air, as in **Figure 15–21**, it passes through a narrow orifice, which causes the air speed to increase. The pressure decreases as a result, and perfume is drawn up by the pressure difference into the stream of air.

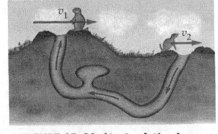

▲ **FIGURE 15–20 Air circulation in a prairie dog burrow**
A prairie dog burrow typically has a high mound on one end and a low mound on the other. Since the wind speed increases with height above the ground, the pressure is smaller at the high-mound end of the burrow. The result is a very convenient circulation of fresh air through the burrow.

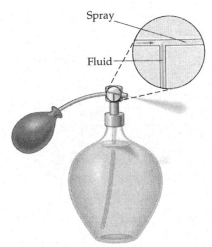

CONCEPTUAL CHECKPOINT 15–7   A Ragtop Roof

A small ranger vehicle has a soft, ragtop roof. When the car is at rest, the roof is flat. When the car is cruising at highway speeds with its windows rolled up, does the roof **(a)** bow upward, **(b)** remain flat, or **(c)** bow downward?

Reasoning and Discussion
When the car is in motion, air flows over the top of the roof, while the air inside the car is at rest—since the windows are closed. Thus, there is less pressure over the roof than under it. As a result, the roof bows upward.

Answer:
(a) The roof bows upward.

▲ **FIGURE 15–21 An atomizer**
The operation of an "atomizer" can be understood in terms of Bernoulli's equation. The high-speed jet of air created by squeezing the bulb creates a low pressure at the top of the vertical tube. This causes fluid to be drawn up the tube and expelled with the air jet as a fine spray.

▲ We often say that a hurricane or tornado "blew the roof off a house." However, the house at left lost its roof not because of the great pressure exerted by the wind, but rather the opposite. In accordance with the Bernoulli effect, the high speed of the wind passing over the roof created a region of reduced pressure. Normal atmospheric pressure inside the house then blew the roof off. The same phenomenon is exploited by prairie dogs to ventilate their burrows. One end of the burrow is always situated at a greater height than the other. Because the prairie wind blows much faster a few feet above ground level, the pressure at the elevated end of the burrow is reduced. The resulting pressure difference produces a flow of air through the burrow.

Science Fundamentals Second Edition

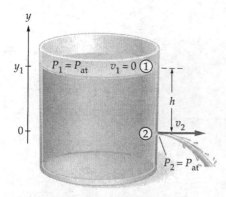

▲ FIGURE 15–22 Fluid emerging from a hole in a container

Since the fluid exiting the hole is in contact with the atmosphere, the pressure there is just as it is on the top surface of the fluid.

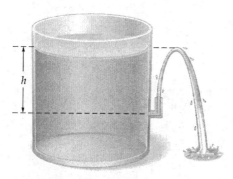

▲ FIGURE 15–23 Maximum height of a stream of water

If the fluid emerging from a hole in a container is directed upward, it has just enough speed to reach the surface level of the fluid. This is an example of energy conservation.

Torricelli's Law

Our final example of Bernoulli's equation deals with the speed of a fluid as it flows through a hole in a container. Consider, for example, the tank of water shown in **Figure 15–22**. If a hole is poked through the side of the tank at a depth h below the surface, what is the speed of the water as it emerges?

To answer this question, we apply Bernoulli's equation to the two points shown in the figure. First, at point 1 we note that the water is open to the atmosphere; thus $P_1 = P_{at}$. Next, with the origin at the level of the hole, the height of the water surface is $y_1 = h$. Finally, if the hole is relatively small and the tank is large, the top surface of the water will have essentially zero speed; thus we can set $v_1 = 0$. Collecting these results, we have the following for point 1:

$$P_1 + \tfrac{1}{2}\rho v_1^2 + \rho g y_1 = P_{at} + 0 + \rho g h$$

Now for point 2. At this point the height is $y_2 = 0$, by definition of the origin, and the speed of the escaping water is the unknown, v_2. Here is the key step: The pressure P_2 is *atmospheric pressure*, because the hole opens the water to the atmosphere. Thus, for point 2 we have the following:

$$P_2 + \tfrac{1}{2}\rho v_2^2 + \rho g y_2 = P_{at} + \tfrac{1}{2}\rho v_2^2 + 0$$

Equating these results yields

$$P_1 + \tfrac{1}{2}\rho v_1^2 + \rho g y_1 = P_2 + \tfrac{1}{2}\rho v_2^2 + \rho g y_2$$

$$P_{at} + \rho g h = P_{at} + \tfrac{1}{2}\rho v_2^2$$

Eliminating P_{at} and ρ we find

$$v_2 = \sqrt{2gh} \qquad\qquad 15\text{–}17$$

This result is known as **Torricelli's law**.

This expression for v_2 should look familiar; it is the speed of an object that falls freely through a distance h. That is, the water emerges from the tank with the same speed as if it had fallen from the surface of the water to the hole. Similarly, if the emerging stream of water were to be directed upward, as in **Figure 15–23**, it would have just enough speed to rise through a height h—right back to the water's surface. This is precisely what one would expect on the basis of energy conservation.

EXAMPLE 15–9 A Water Fountain

In designing a backyard water fountain, a gardener wants a stream of water to exit from the bottom of one tub and land in a second one, as shown in the sketch. The top of the second tub is 0.500 m below the hole in the first tub, which has water in it to a depth of 0.150 m. How far to the right of the first tub must the second one be placed to catch the stream of water?

Picture the Problem
Our sketch labels the various pertinent quantities for this problem. We know that $h = 0.150$ m and $H = 0.500$ m. The distance D is to be found. We have also chosen an appropriate coordinate system, with the y direction vertical and the x direction horizontal.

Strategy
This problem combines Torricelli's law and kinematics. First, we find the speed v of the stream of water as it leaves the first can, using Equation 15–17. Next, we find the time t required for the stream to fall freely through a distance H. Finally, since the stream moves with constant speed in the x direction, the distance D is given by $D = vt$.

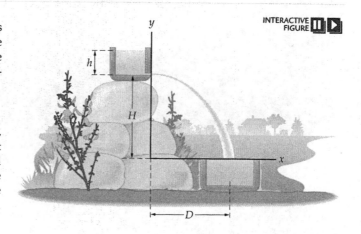

Science Fundamentals Second Edition

Solution

1. Find the speed v of the stream when it leaves the first can: $\quad v = \sqrt{2gh} = \sqrt{2(9.81 \text{ m/s}^2)(0.150 \text{ m})} = 1.72 \text{ m/s}$

2. Find the time t for free fall through a height H: $\quad\quad\quad y = H - \frac{1}{2}gt^2 = 0$

$$t = \sqrt{\frac{2H}{g}} = \sqrt{\frac{2(0.500 \text{ m})}{9.81 \text{ m/s}^2}} = 0.319 \text{ s}$$

3. Multiply v times t to find the distance D: $\quad\quad\quad x = vt = (1.72 \text{ m/s})(0.319 \text{ s}) = 0.549 \text{ m} = D$

Insight
Note that our solution for x can also be written as $x = vt = \sqrt{2gh}(\sqrt{2H/g}) = 2\sqrt{hH}$. Thus, if the values of h and H are interchanged, the distance D remains the same. Note also that x is independent of the acceleration of gravity; therefore, the fountain would work just as well on the Moon.

Practice Problem
Find the distance D for $h = 0.500$ m and $H = 0.150$ m. [**Answer:** $D = 2\sqrt{hH} = 0.548$ m, as expected.]

Some related homework problems: Problem 54, Problem 94

16-2 Temperature Scales

A variety of temperature scales is commonly used in both everyday situations and in physics. Some are related to familiar reference points, such as the temperature of boiling or freezing water. Others have more complex, historical rationale for their values. Here we consider three of the more frequently used temperature scales. We also examine the connections between them.

Later in this chapter we will discuss some of the physical phenomena—such as thermal expansion—that can be used to construct a thermometer. With a properly calibrated thermometer, we can determine the temperature on any of these scales. In the next chapter, we will explore more fully the question of just what temperature means on a conceptual and microscopic level.

The Celsius Scale

Perhaps the easiest temperature scale to remember is the Celsius scale, named in honor of the Swedish astronomer Anders Celsius (1701–1744). Originally, Celsius assigned zero degrees to boiling water and 100 degrees to freezing water. These values were later reversed by the biologist Carolus Linnaeus (1707–1778). Thus, today we say that water freezes at zero degrees Celsius, which we abbreviate as 0 °C, and boils at 100 °C.

Note that the choice of zero level for a temperature scale is quite arbitrary, as is the number of degrees between any two reference points. In the Celsius scale, as in others, there is no upper limit to the value a temperature may have. There is a lower limit, however. For the Celsius scale, the lowest possible temperature is −273.15 °C, as we shall see later in this section.

One bit of notation should be pointed out before we continue. When we write a Celsius temperature, we give a numerical value followed by the degree symbol, °, and the capital letter C. For example, 5 °C is the temperature five degrees Celsius. On the other hand, if the temperature of an object is *changed* by a given amount, we use the notation C°. Thus, if we increase the temperature by five degrees on the Celsius scale, we say that the change in temperature is 5 C°; that is, five Celsius degrees. This is summarized below:

> A temperature T of five degrees is 5 °C
> (five degrees Celsius)
>
> A temperature change ΔT of five degrees is 5 C°
> (five Celsius degrees)

The Fahrenheit Scale

The Fahrenheit scale was developed by Gabriel Fahrenheit (1686–1736), who chose zero to be the lowest temperature he was able to achieve in his laboratory. He also chose 96 degrees to be body temperature, though why he made this choice is not known. In the modern version of the Fahrenheit scale body temperature is 98.6 °F; in addition, water freezes at 32 °F and boils at 212 °F. Lastly, using the same convention as for °C and C°, we say that an increase of 180 F° is required to bring water from freezing to boiling.

Note that the Fahrenheit scale not only has a different zero than the Celsius scale, it also has a different "size" for its degree. As just noted, 180 Fahrenheit degrees are required for the same change in temperature as 100 Celsius degrees. Hence, the Fahrenheit degrees are smaller by a factor of $100/180 = 5/9$.

To convert between a Fahrenheit temperature, T_F, and a Celsius temperature, T_C, we start by writing a linear relation between them. Thus, let

$$T_F = aT_C + b$$

We would like to determine the constants a and b. This requires two independent pieces of information, which we have in the freezing and boiling points of water. Using the freezing point, we find

$$32\ °\text{F} = a(0\ °\text{C}) + b = b$$

Thus, b is 32 °F. Next, the boiling point gives

$$212\ °\text{F} = a(100\ °\text{C}) + 32\ °\text{F}$$

Solving for the constant a we find

$$a = (212\ °\text{F} - 32\ °\text{F})/(100\ °\text{C}) = \frac{180\ \text{F}°}{100\ \text{C}°} = \tfrac{9}{5}\text{F}°/\text{C}°$$

Combining our results gives the following conversion relationship:

Conversion Between Degrees Celsius and Degrees Fahrenheit

$$T_F = (\tfrac{9}{5}\text{F}°/\text{C}°)T_C + 32\ °\text{F} \qquad\qquad \text{16-1}$$

Similarly, this relation can be rearranged to convert from Fahrenheit to Celsius:

Conversion Between Degrees Fahrenheit and Degrees Celsius

$$T_C = (\tfrac{5}{9}\text{C}°/\text{F}°)(T_F - 32\ °\text{F}) \qquad\qquad \text{16-2}$$

Since conversion factors like $\tfrac{9}{5}\text{F}°/\text{C}°$ are a bit clumsy and tend to clutter up an equation, we will generally drop the degree symbols until the final result. For example, to convert 10 °C to degrees Fahrenheit, we write

$$T_F = \tfrac{9}{5}T_C + 32 = \tfrac{9}{5}(10) + 32 = 50\ °\text{F}$$

EXAMPLE 16-1 Temperature Conversions

(a) On a fine spring day you notice that the temperature is 75 °F. What is the corresponding temperature on the Celsius scale?
(b) If the temperature on a brisk winter morning is −2.0 °C, what is the corresponding Fahrenheit temperature?

Picture the Problem
Our sketch shows a circular thermometer with both a Fahrenheit and a Celsius scale. The range of the scales extends well beyond the temperatures 75 °F and −2.0 °C needed for the problem.

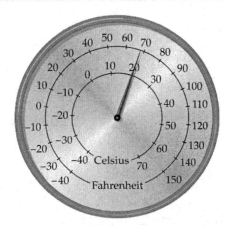

Strategy
The conversions asked for in this problem are straightforward applications of the relations between T_F and T_C. In particular, for **(a)** we use $T_C = (5/9)(T_F - 32)$, and for **(b)** we use $T_F = \tfrac{9}{5}T_C + 32$.

Solution

Part (a)

1. Substitute $T_F = 75\ °\text{F}$ into Equation 16–2: $\qquad T_C = \tfrac{5}{9}(75 - 32) = 24\ °\text{C}$

Part (b)

2. Substitute $T_C = -2.0\ °\text{C}$ in Equation 16–1: $\qquad T_F = \tfrac{9}{5}(-2.0) + 32 = 28\ °\text{F}$

continued on next page

Science Fundamentals Second Edition

continued from previous page

Insight
Note that the results given here agree with the scales shown in the drawing.

Practice Problem
Find the Celsius temperature that corresponds to 110 °F.   [**Answer:** $T_C = 43$ °C]

Some related homework problems: Problem 1, Problem 2

ACTIVE EXAMPLE 16–1 Same Temperature
What temperature is the same on both the Celsius and Fahrenheit scales?

Solution *(Test your understanding by performing the calculations indicated in each step.)*

1. Set $T_F = T_C = t$ in Equation 16–1: $t = 9t/5 + 32$

2. Move all terms involving t to the left side $-4t/5 = 32$
   of the equation:

3. Solve for t: $t = -40$

4. As a check, substitute $T_F = -40$ °F in $T_C = (5/9)(-40 - 32) = -40$ °C
   Equation 16–2:

Insight
Thus, -40 °F is the same as -40 °C. This is consistent with the scale shown in Example 16–1.

Your Turn
Find the Fahrenheit temperature whose numerical value is three times greater than the corresponding Celsius temperature.

*(Answers to **Your Turn** problems can be found in the back of the book.)*

Absolute Zero

Experiments show conclusively that there is a lowest temperature below which it is impossible to cool an object. This is referred to as **absolute zero.** Though absolute zero can be approached from above arbitrarily closely, it can never be attained.

To give an idea of just where absolute zero is on the Celsius scale, we start with the following observation: If a given volume V of air—say the air in a balloon—is cooled from 100 °C to 0 °C, its volume decreases by roughly $V/4$. Imagine this trend continuing uninterrupted. In this case, cooling from 0 °C to -100 °C would reduce the volume by another $V/4$, from -100 °C to -200 °C by another $V/4$, and finally, from -200 °C to -300 °C by another $V/4$, which brings the volume down to zero. Clearly, it doesn't make sense for the volume to be less than zero, and hence absolute zero must be roughly -300 °C.

This result, though crude, is in the right ballpark. A precise determination of absolute zero can be made with a device known as a **constant-volume gas thermometer.** This instrument is shown in **Figure 16–2.** The basic idea is that by adjusting the level of mercury in the right-hand tube, the level of mercury in the left-hand tube can be set to a fixed reference level. With the mercury so adjusted, the gas occupies a constant volume and its pressure is simply $P_{gas} = P_{at} + \rho g h$ (Equation 15–7), where ρ is the density of mercury.

As the temperature of the gas is changed, the mercury level in the right-hand tube can be readjusted as described. The gas pressure can be determined again, and the process repeated. The results of a series of such measurements are shown in **Figure 16–3.**

Note that as a gas is cooled its pressure decreases, as one would expect. In fact, the decrease in pressure is approximately linear. At low enough temperatures the gas eventually liquefies, and its behavior changes, but if we extrapolate the

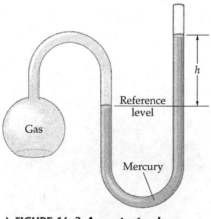

▲ **FIGURE 16–2 A constant-volume gas thermometer**
By adjusting the height of mercury in the right-hand tube, the level in the left-hand tube can be set at the reference level. This assures that the gas occupies a constant volume.

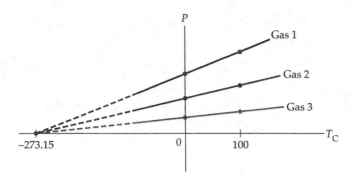

◀ **FIGURE 16–3 Determining absolute zero**
Different gases have different pressures at any given temperature. However, they all extend down to zero pressure at precisely the same temperature, −273.15 °C. This is the location of absolute zero.

straight line obtained before liquefaction, we see that it reaches zero pressure (the lowest pressure possible) at −273.15 °C.

What is remarkable about this result is that it is independent of the gas we use in the thermometer. For example, gas 2 and gas 3 in Figure 16–3 have pressures that are different from one another, and from gas 1. Yet all three gases extrapolate to zero pressure at precisely the same temperature. Thus, we conclude that there is indeed a *unique* value of absolute zero, below which further cooling is not possible.

EXAMPLE 16–2 It's a Gas

The gas in a constant-volume gas thermometer has a pressure of 80.0 kPa at 0.00 °C. Assuming ideal behavior, as in Figure 16–3, what is the pressure of this gas at 105 °C?

Picture the Problem

Our sketch plots the pressure of the gas as a function of temperature. Note that at $T_C = 0.00$ °C the pressure is 80.0 kPa, and that at $T_C = -273.15$ °C the pressure extrapolates linearly to zero. We also indicate the point corresponding to 105 °C on the graph.

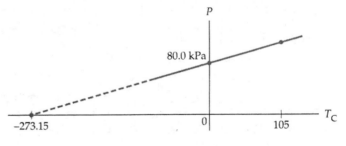

Strategy

We assume that the pressure lies on a straight line, as in Figure 16–3. To find the pressure at $T_C = 105$ °C we simply extend the straight line.

Thus, we start with the information that the pressure increases linearly from 0 to 80.0 kPa when the temperature increases from −273.15 °C to 0.00 °C. This rate of increase in pressure must also apply to an increase in temperature from −273.15 °C to 105 °C. Using this rate we can find the desired pressure.

Solution

1. Calculate the rate at which pressure increases for this gas:

$$\text{rate} = \frac{80.0 \text{ kPa}}{273.15 \text{ C}^\circ} = 0.293 \text{ kPa/C}^\circ$$

2. Multiply this rate by the temperature change from −273.15 °C to 105 °C:

$$(0.293 \text{ kPa/C}^\circ)(378 \text{ C}^\circ) = 111 \text{ kPa}$$

Insight

The pressure of this gas increases from slightly less than one atmosphere at 0.00 °C to slightly more than one atmosphere at 105 °C.

An alternative solution to this problem is to calculate the pressure difference from 0.00 °C to 105 °C. Specifically, we can say that $P = 80.0 \text{ kPa} + (0.293 \text{ kPa/C}^\circ)(105 \text{ C}^\circ) = 111 \text{ kPa}$.

Practice Problem

Find the temperature at which the pressure of the gas is 70.0 kPa. [**Answer:** $T_C = -34.1$ °C]

Some related homework problems: Problem 7, Problem 8

The Kelvin Scale

The Kelvin temperature scale, named for the Scottish physicist William Thomson, Lord Kelvin (1824–1907), is based on the existence of absolute zero. In fact, the zero of the Kelvin scale, abbreviated 0 K, is set exactly at absolute zero. Thus, in this scale there are no negative equilibrium temperatures. The Kelvin scale is also chosen to have the same degree size as the Celsius scale.

As mentioned, absolute zero occurs at $-273.15\,°C$, hence the conversion between a Kelvin-scale temperature, T, and a Celsius temperature, T_C, is as follows:

Conversion Between a Celsius Temperature and a Kelvin Temperature

$$T = T_C + 273.15$$

16–3

Note that the difference between the Celsius and Kelvin scales is simply a difference in the zero level.

The notation for the Kelvin scale differs somewhat from that for the Celsius and Fahrenheit scales. In particular, by international agreement, the degree terminology and the degree symbol, °, are not used in the Kelvin scale. Instead, a temperature of 5 K is read simply as 5 kelvin. In addition, a change in temperature of 5 kelvin is written 5 K, the same as for a temperature of 5 kelvin.

Though the Celsius and Fahrenheit scales are the ones most commonly used in everyday situations, the Kelvin scale is used more than any other in physics. This stems from the fact that the Kelvin scale incorporates the significant concept of absolute zero. As a result, the thermal energy of a system depends in a very simple way on the Kelvin temperature. This will be discussed in detail in the next chapter.

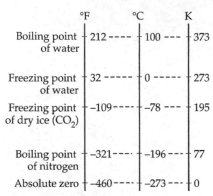

	°F	°C	K
Boiling point of water	212	100	373
Freezing point of water	32	0	273
Freezing point of dry ice (CO_2)	–109	–78	195
Boiling point of nitrogen	–321	–196	77
Absolute zero	–460	–273	0

▲ **FIGURE 16–4 Temperature scales**
A comparison of the Fahrenheit, Celsius, and Kelvin temperature scales. Physically significant temperatures, such as the freezing and boiling points of water, are indicated for each scale.

EXERCISE 16–1

Convert 55 °F to the Kelvin temperature scale.

Solution

First, convert from °F to °C:

$$T_C = \tfrac{5}{9}(55 - 32) = 13\,°C$$

Next, convert °C to K:

$$T = 13 + 273.15 = 286\,K$$

The three temperature scales presented in this section are shown side by side in **Figure 16–4**. Temperatures of particular interest are indicated as well. This permits a useful visual comparison between the scales.

16–4 Heat and Mechanical Work

In this section we consider the connection between heat and mechanical work. We also discuss the conservation of energy as it regards heat.

As mentioned previously, heat is the energy *transferred* from one object to another. At one time it was thought—erroneously—that an object contained a certain amount of "heat fluid," or caloric, that could flow from one place to another. This idea was overturned by the observations of Benjamin Thompson (1753–1814), also known as Count Rumford, the American-born physicist, spy, and social reformer who at one point in his eclectic career supervised the boring of cannon barrels by large drills. He observed that as long as mechanical work was done to turn the drill bits, they continued to produce heat in unlimited quantities. Clearly, the unlimited heat observed in boring the cannons was not present initially in the metal, but instead was produced by continually turning the drill bit.

With this observation, it became clear that heat was simply another form of energy that must be taken into account when applying conservation of energy. For example, if you rub sandpaper back and forth over a piece of wood, you do work. The energy associated with that work is not lost; instead, it produces an increase in temperature. Taking into account the energy associated with this temperature change, we find that energy is indeed conserved. In fact, no observation has ever indicated a situation in which energy is not conserved.

The equivalence between work and heat was first explored quantitatively by James Prescott Joule (1818–1889), the British physicist. In one of his experiments, Joule observed the increase in temperature in a device similar to that shown in **Figure 16–8**. Here, a total mass $2m$ falls through a certain distance h, during which gravity does the mechanical work, $2mgh$. As the mass falls, it turns the paddles in the water, which results in a slight warming of the water. By measuring the mechanical work, $2mgh$, and the increase in the water's temperature, ΔT, Joule was able to show that energy was indeed conserved—it had been converted from gravitational potential energy to an increased energy of the water, as indicated by a higher temperature. Joule's experiments established the precise amount of mechanical work that has the same effect as a given transfer of heat.

Before Joule's work, heat was measured in a unit called the calorie (cal). In particular, one kilocalorie (kcal) was defined as the amount of heat needed to raise the temperature of 1 kg of water from 14.5 °C to 15.5 °C. With his experiments,

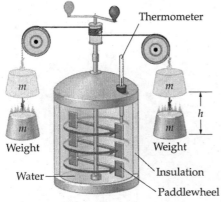

▲ **FIGURE 16–8 The mechanical equivalent of heat**
A device of this type was used by James Joule to measure the mechanical equivalent of heat.

Joule was able to show that 1 kcal = 4186 J, or equivalently, that one calorie of heat transfer is the equivalent of 4.186 J of mechanical work. This is referred to as the **mechanical equivalent of heat:**

The Mechanical Equivalent of Heat

1 cal = 4.186 J   16–8

SI unit: J

In studies of nutrition a different calorie is used. It is the Calorie, with a capital C, and it is simply a kilocalorie; that is, 1 C = 1 kcal. Perhaps this helps people to feel a little better about their calorie intake. After all, a 250 C candy bar sounds a lot better than a 250,000 cal candy bar. They are equivalent, however.

Another common unit for measuring heat is the British thermal unit (Btu). By definition, a Btu is the energy required to heat 1 lb of water from 63 °F to 64 °F. In terms of calories and joules, a Btu is as follows:

$$1 \text{ Btu} = 0.252 \text{ kcal} = 1055 \text{ J} \qquad\qquad 16\text{–}9$$

Finally, we shall use the symbol Q to denote heat:

Heat, Q

Q = heat = energy transferred due to temperature differences   16–10

SI unit: J

Using the mechanical equivalent of heat as the conversion factor, we will typically give heat in either calories or joules.

EXAMPLE 16–4 Stair Master

A 74.0-kg person drinks a thick, rich, 305-C milkshake. How many stairs must this person climb to work off the shake? Let the height of a stair be 20.0 cm.

Picture the Problem
Our sketch shows the person climbing the stairs after drinking the milkshake. Note that each step has a height h = 20.0 cm. In addition, the total height to which the person climbs to work off the milkshake is designated by H. (As we noted in Conceptual Checkpoint 7–1, the horizontal distance is irrelevant here, as it does not affect the work done against gravity.)

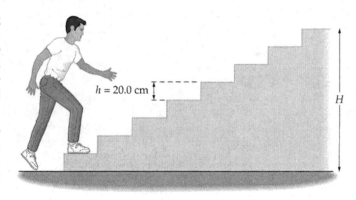

Strategy
We know that the energy intake by drinking the milkshake is the equivalent of the heat Q = 305,000 cal. This energy can be converted to joules by using the relation 1 cal = 4.186 J. Finally, we set the energy of the shake equal to the work done against gravity, mgH, in climbing to a height H.

Solution

1. Convert the energy of the milkshake to joules:

$$Q = 305{,}000 \text{ cal} = 305{,}000 \text{ cal}\left(\frac{4.186 \text{ J}}{1 \text{ cal}}\right) = 1.28 \times 10^6 \text{ J}$$

2. Equate the energy of the milkshake with the work done against gravity:

$$Q = mgH$$

   Solve for the height H:

$$H = Q/mg$$

3. Substitute numerical values:

$$H = \frac{Q}{mg} = \frac{1.28 \times 10^6 \text{ J}}{(74.0 \text{ kg})(9.81 \text{ m/s}^2)} = 1760 \text{ m}$$

4. Divide by the height of a stair to get the number of stairs:

$$\frac{1760 \text{ m}}{0.200 \text{ m/stair}} = 8800 \text{ stairs}$$

continued on next page

Science Fundamentals Second Edition

continued from previous page

Insight
This is clearly a lot of stairs, and a significant height. In fact, 1760 m is more than a mile. Even assuming a metabolic efficiency of 25 percent, a height of about a quarter of a mile must be climbed to work off the shake. Put another way, the shake would be enough "fuel" for you to walk to the top of the Empire State Building with a little left over.

Practice Problem
If the person in the problem climbs 100 stairs, how many Calories have been burned? Assume 100 percent efficiency.
[**Answer:** 3.47 C]

Some related homework problems: Problem 23, Problem 24

16–5 Specific Heats

In the previous section, we mentioned that it takes 4186 J of heat to raise the temperature of 1 kg of water by 1 C°. We have to be clear about the fact that we are heating water, however, because the heat required for a 1 C° increase varies considerably from one substance to another. For example, it takes only 128 J of heat to increase the temperature of 1 kg of lead by 1 C°. In general, the heat required for a given increase in temperature is given by the **heat capacity** of a substance.

Heat Capacity

Suppose we add the heat Q to a given object, and its temperature increases by the amount ΔT. The heat capacity, C, of this object is defined as follows:

Definition of Heat Capacity, C

$$C = \frac{Q}{\Delta T}$$ 16–11

SI unit: J/K = J/C°

Note that the units of heat capacity are joules per kelvin (J/K). Equivalently, since the degree size is the same for the Kelvin and Celsius scales, C can be expressed in units of joules per Celsius degree (J/C°).

The name "heat capacity" is perhaps a bit unfortunate. It derives from the mistaken idea of a "heat fluid," mentioned in the previous section. Objects were imagined to "contain" a certain amount of this nonexistent fluid. Today, we know that an object can readily gain or release heat when it is in thermal contact with other objects—objects cannot be thought of as holding a certain amount of heat.

Instead, the heat capacity should be viewed as the amount of heat necessary for a given temperature change. An object with a large heat capacity, like water, requires a large amount of heat for each increment in temperature. Just the opposite is true for an object with a small heat capacity, like a piece of lead.

To find the heat required for a given ΔT, we simply rearrange Equation 16–11 to solve for Q. This yields

$$Q = C\Delta T$$ 16–12

It should be noted that the *heat capacity is always positive*—just like a speed. Thus, Equation 16–12 shows that the heat Q and the temperature change ΔT have the same sign. This observation leads to the following sign conventions for Q:

Q is positive if ΔT is positive; that is, if heat is *added* to a system.

Q is negative if ΔT is negative; that is, if heat is *removed* from a system.

EXERCISE 16–3

The heat capacity of 1.00 kg of water is 4186 J/K. What is the temperature change of the water if **(a)** 505 J of heat is added to the system, or **(b)** 1010 J of heat is removed?

Science Fundamentals Second Edition

Solution

a. Calculate ΔT for $Q = 505$ J:

$$\Delta T = \frac{Q}{C} = \frac{505 \text{ J}}{4186 \text{ J/K}} = 0.121 \text{ K}$$

b. Since heat is removed in this case, $Q = -1010$ J:

$$\Delta T = \frac{Q}{C} = \frac{-1010 \text{ J}}{4186 \text{ J/K}} = -0.241 \text{ K}$$

Specific Heat

Since it takes 4186 J to increase the temperature of one kilogram of water by one degree Celsius, it takes twice that much to make the same temperature change in two kilograms of water, and so on. Thus, the heat capacity varies not only with the type of substance, but also with the mass of the substance.

We can therefore define a new quantity—the **specific heat,** c—that depends only on the substance, and not on its mass, as follows:

Definition of Specific Heat, c

$$c = \frac{Q}{m\Delta T}$$

16-13

SI unit: $J/(kg \cdot K) = J/(Kg \cdot C°)$

Thus, for example, the specific heat of water is

$$c_{\text{water}} = 4186 \text{ J}/(kg \cdot K)$$

Specific heats for common substances are listed in Table 16–2. Note that the specific heat of water is by far the largest of any common material. This is just another of the many unusual properties of water. Having such a large specific heat means that water can give off or take in large quantities of heat with little change in temperature. It is for this reason that if you take a bite of a pie that is just out of the oven, you are much more likely to burn your tongue on the fruit filling (which has a high water content) than on the much drier crust.

Water's unusually large specific heat also accounts for the moderate climates experienced in regions near great bodies of water. In particular, the enormous volume and large heat capacity of an ocean serve to maintain a nearly constant temperature in the water, which in turn acts to even out the temperature of adjacent coastal areas. For example, the West Coast of the United States benefits from the moderating effect of the Pacific Ocean, aided by the prevailing breezes that come from the ocean onto the coastal regions. In the Midwest, on the other hand, temperature variations can be considerably greater as the land (with a relatively small specific heat) quickly heats up in the summer and cools off in the winter.

Calorimetry

Let's use the specific heat to solve a practical problem. Suppose a block of mass m_b, specific heat c_b, and initial temperature T_b is dropped into a **calorimeter** (basically, a lightweight, insulated flask) containing water. If the water has a mass m_w, a specific heat c_w, and an initial temperature T_w, find the final temperature of the block and the water. Assume that the calorimeter is light enough that it can be ignored, and that no heat is transferred from the calorimeter to its surroundings.

There are two basic ideas involved in solving this problem: (a) the final temperatures of the block and water are equal, since the system will be in thermal equilibrium; and (b) the total energy of the system is conserved. In particular, the second condition means that the amount of heat lost by the block is equal to the heat gained by the water—or vice versa if the water's initial temperature is higher.

TABLE 16–2
Specific Heats at Atmospheric Pressure

Substance	Specific heat, $c[J/(kg \cdot K)]$
Water	4186
Ice	2090
Steam	2010
Beryllium	1820
Air	1004
Aluminum	900
Glass	837
Silicon	703
Iron (steel)	448
Copper	387
Silver	234
Gold	129
Lead	128

REAL-WORLD PHYSICS
Water and the climate

PROBLEM-SOLVING NOTE

Heat Flow and Thermal Equilibrium

To find the temperature of thermal equilibrium when two objects with different temperatures are brought into thermal contact, we simply use the idea that the heat that flows *out* of one of the objects flows *into* the other object.

Science Fundamentals Second Edition

Mathematically, we can write these conditions as follows:

$$Q_b + Q_w = 0 \qquad\qquad 16\text{--}14$$

This means that the heat flow from the block is equal and opposite to the heat flow from the water; in other words, energy is conserved. If we write the heats Q in terms of the specific heats and temperatures, letting the final temperature be T, we have

$$m_b c_b(T - T_b) + m_w c_w(T - T_w) = 0$$

Note that for each heat the change in temperature is T_{final} minus $T_{initial}$, as it should be. Solving for the final temperature, T, we find

$$T = \frac{m_b c_b T_b + m_w c_w T_w}{m_b c_b + m_w c_w} \qquad\qquad 16\text{--}15$$

This result need not be memorized, of course. Whenever solving a problem of this sort, one simply writes down energy conservation and solves for the desired unknown.

In some cases, we may wish to consider the influence of the container itself. This is illustrated in the following Active Example.

ACTIVE EXAMPLE 16–2 Find the Final Temperature

Suppose 550 g of water at 32 °C are poured into a 210-g aluminum can with an initial temperature of 15 °C. Find the final temperature of the system, assuming no heat is exchanged with the surroundings.

Solution *(Test your understanding by performing the calculations indicated in each step.)*

1. Write an expression for the heat flow out of the water: $\qquad Q_w = m_w c_w(T - T_w)$

2. Write an expression for the heat flow into the aluminum: $\qquad Q_a = m_a c_a(T - T_a)$

3. Apply energy conservation: $\qquad Q_w + Q_a = 0$

4. Solve for the final temperature: $\qquad T = 31 \ °C$

Insight
As one might expect from water's large specific heat, the final common temperature (T) is much closer to the initial temperature of the water (T_w) than that of the aluminum (T_a).

Your Turn
Suppose the can is made from iron rather than aluminum. In this case, do you expect the final temperature to be greater than or less than the value for aluminum? Find the final temperature for the case of an iron can.

(Answers to **Your Turn** *problems can be found in the back of the book.)*

EXAMPLE 16–5 Cooling Off

A 0.50-kg block of metal with an initial temperature of 54.5 °C is dropped into a container holding 1.1 kg of water at 20.0 °C. If the final temperature of the block-water system is 21.4 °C, what is the specific heat of the metal? Assume the container can be ignored, and that no heat is exchanged with the surroundings.

Picture the Problem
Initially, when the block is first dropped into the water, the temperatures of the block and water are $T_b = 54.5$ °C and $T_w = 20.0$ °C, respectively. When thermal equilibrium is established, both the block and the water have the same temperature, $T = 21.4$ °C.

Strategy
Heat flows from the block to the water. Setting the heat flow *out of the block* plus the heat flow *into the water* equal to zero (conservation of energy) yields the block's specific heat.

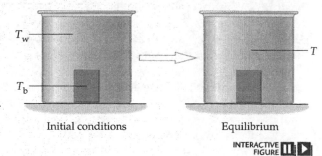

Initial conditions   Equilibrium

INTERACTIVE FIGURE

Solution

1. Write an expression for the heat flow out of the block. Note that Q_{block} is negative, since T is less than T_b:

$$Q_{block} = m_b c_b (T - T_b)$$

2. Write an expression for the heat flow into the water. Note that Q_{water} is positive, since T is greater than T_w:

$$Q_{water} = m_w c_w (T - T_w)$$

3. Set the sum of the heats equal to zero:

$$Q_{block} + Q_{water} = m_b c_b (T - T_b) + m_w c_w (T - T_w) = 0$$

4. Solve for the specific heat of the block, c_b:

$$c_b = \frac{m_w c_w (T - T_w)}{m_b (T_b - T)}$$

5. Substitute numerical values:

$$c_b = \frac{(1.1 \text{ kg})[4186 \text{ J}/(\text{kg} \cdot \text{K})](21.4 \,^\circ\text{C} - 20.0 \,^\circ\text{C})}{(0.50 \text{ kg})(54.5 \,^\circ\text{C} - 21.4 \,^\circ\text{C})}$$

$$= 390 \text{ J}/(\text{kg} \cdot \text{K})$$

Insight

We note from Table 16–2 that the block is probably made of copper.

In addition, note that the final temperature is much closer to the initial temperature of the water than to the initial temperature of the block. This is due in part to the fact that the mass of the water is about twice that of the block; more important, however, is the fact that the water's specific heat is more than 10 times greater than that of the block. In the following Practice Problem we set the mass of the water equal to the mass of the block, so that we can see clearly the effect of the different specific heats.

Practice Problem

If the mass of the water is also 0.50 kg, what is the equilibrium temperature? [**Answer:** $T = 23 \,^\circ\text{C}$. Still much closer to the water's initial temperature than to the block's.]

Some related homework problems: Problem 31, Problem 32

16–6 Conduction, Convection, and Radiation

Heat can be exchanged in a variety of ways. The Sun, for example, warms the Earth from across 93 million miles of empty space by a process known as radiation. As the sunlight strikes the ground and raises its temperature, the ground-level air gets warmer and begins to rise, producing a further exchange of heat by means of convection. Finally, if you walk across the ground in bare feet, you will feel the warming effect of heat entering your body by conduction. In this section we consider each of these three mechanisms of heat exchange in detail.

Conduction

Perhaps the most familiar form of heat exchange is **conduction,** which is the flow of heat directly through a physical material. For example, if you hold one end of a metal rod and put the other end in a fire, it doesn't take long before you begin to feel warmth on your end. The heat you feel is transported along the rod by conduction.

Let's consider this observation from a microscopic point of view. To begin, when you placed one end of the rod into the fire, the high temperature at that location caused the molecules to vibrate with an increased amplitude. These molecules in turn jostle their neighbors and cause them to vibrate with greater amplitude as well. Eventually, the effect travels from molecule to molecule across the length of the rod, resulting in the macroscopic phenomenon of conduction.

If you were to repeat the experiment, this time with a wooden rod, the hot end of the rod would heat up so much that it might even catch on fire, but your end would still be comfortably cool. Thus, conduction depends on the type of material involved. Some materials, called **conductors,** conduct heat very well, whereas other materials, called **insulators,** conduct heat poorly.

Just how much heat flows as a result of conduction? To answer this question we consider the simple system shown in **Figure 16–9**. Here we show a rod of

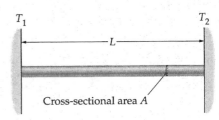

▲ **FIGURE 16–9 Heat conduction through a rod**

The amount of heat that flows through a rod of length L and cross-sectional area A per time is proportional to $A(T_2 - T_1)/L$.

▲ Maintaining proper body temperature in an environment that is often too hot or too cold is a problem for many animals. When the sand is blazing hot, this lizard (left) keeps its contact with the ground to a minimum. By standing on two legs instead of four, it reduces conduction of heat from the ground to its body. Polar bears (right) have the opposite problem. The loss of precious body heat to their surroundings is retarded by their thick fur, which is actually made up of hollow fibers. Air trapped within these fibers provides enhanced insulation, just as it does in our thermal blankets and double-paned windows.

length L and cross-sectional area A, with one end at the temperature T_1 and the other at the temperature $T_2 > T_1$. Experiments show that the amount of heat Q that flows through this rod:

- increases in proportion to the rod's cross-sectional area, A;
- increases in proportion to the temperature difference, $\Delta T = T_2 - T_1$;
- increases steadily with time, t;
- decreases with the length of the rod, L.

Combining these observations in a mathematical expression gives:

Heat Flow by Conduction

$$Q = kA\left(\frac{\Delta T}{L}\right)t \qquad\qquad 16\text{--}16$$

The constant k is referred to as the **thermal conductivity** of the rod. It varies from material to material, as indicated in Table 16–3.

PROBLEM-SOLVING NOTE

Area and Length in Heat Conduction

When applying Equation 16–16, note that A is the area through which the heat flows. Thus, the plane of the area A is perpendicular to the direction of heat flow. The length L is the distance from the high-temperature side of an object to its low-temperature side.

TABLE 16–3 Thermal Conductivities

Substance	Thermal conductivity, $k[\text{W}/(\text{m}\cdot\text{K})]$
Silver	417
Copper	395
Gold	291
Aluminum	217
Steel, low carbon	66.9
Lead	34.3
Stainless steel— alloy 302	16.3
Ice	1.6
Concrete	1.3
Glass	0.84
Water	0.60
Asbestos	0.25
Wood	0.10
Wool	0.040
Air	0.0234

CONCEPTUAL CHECKPOINT 16–3   The Feel of Tile

You get up in the morning and walk barefoot from the bedroom to the bathroom. In the bedroom you walk on carpet, but in the bathroom the floor is tile. Does the tile feel (a) warmer, (b) cooler, or (c) the same temperature as the carpet?

Reasoning and Discussion

Everything in the house is at the same temperature, so it might seem that the carpet and the tile would feel the same. As you probably know from experience, however, the tile feels cooler. The reason is that tile has a much larger thermal conductivity than the carpet, which is actually a fairly good insulator. As a result, more heat flows from your skin to the tile than from your skin to the carpet. To your feet, then, it is as if the tile were much cooler than the carpet.

To get an idea of the thermal conductivities that would apply in this case, let's examine Table 16–3. For the tile, we might expect a thermal conductivity of roughly 0.84, the value appropriate for glass. For the carpet, the thermal conductivity might be as low as 0.04, the thermal conductivity of wool. Thus, the tile could have a thermal conductivity that is 20 times larger than that of the carpet.

Answer:
(b) The tile feels cooler.

Thermal conductivity is an important consideration when insulating a home. We consider some of these issues in the next Example.

EXAMPLE 16–6 What a Pane

One of the windows in a house has the shape of a square 1.0 m on a side. The glass in the window is 0.50 cm thick. How much heat is lost through this window in one day if the temperature in the house is 21 °C and the temperature outside is 0.0 °C?

Picture the Problem
The glass from the window is shown in our sketch, along with its relevant dimensions. Heat flows from the 21 °C side of the window to the 0.0 °C side.

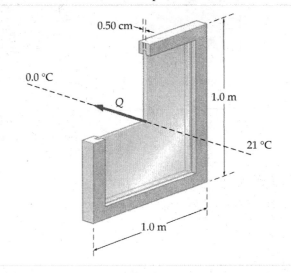

0.50 cm

0.0 °C

Q

1.0 m

21 °C

1.0 m

Strategy
The heat flow is given by Equation 16–16. Note that the area is $(1.0 \text{ m})^2$ and that the length over which heat is conducted is, in this case, the thickness of the glass. Thus, $L = 0.0050$ m. The temperature difference is 21 C° = 21 K, and the thermal conductivity of glass (from Table 16–3) is 0.84 W/(m·K). (Recall from Section 7–4 that 1 W = 1 J/s.)

Solution

1. Calculate the heat flow for a given time, t:

$$Q = kA\left(\frac{\Delta T}{L}\right)t$$

$$= [0.84 \text{ W}/(\text{m} \cdot \text{K})](1.0 \text{ m})^2\left(\frac{21 \text{ K}}{0.0050 \text{ m}}\right)t = (3500 \text{ W})t$$

2. Substitute the number of seconds in a day, 86,400 s, for the time t in the expression for Q:

$$Q = (3500 \text{ W})t = (3500 \text{ W})(86{,}400 \text{ s}) = 3.0 \times 10^8 \text{ J}$$

Insight
This is a sizable amount of heat, roughly equivalent to the energy released in burning a gallon of gasoline. A considerable reduction in heat loss can be obtained by using a double-pane window, which has an insulating layer of air (actually argon or krypton) sandwiched between the two panes of glass. This is discussed in more detail later in this section, and is explored in Problems 42 and 73.

Practice Problem
Suppose the window is replaced with a plate of solid silver. How thick must this plate be to have the same heat flow in a day as the glass? [**Answer:** The silver must have a thickness of $L = 2.5$ m.]

Some related homework problems: Problem 38, Problem 39

Now we consider the heat flow through a combination of two different materials with different thermal conductivities.

CONCEPTUAL CHECKPOINT 16–4   Compare the Heat Flow

Two metal rods are to be used to conduct heat from a region at 100 °C to a region at 0 °C. The rods can be placed in parallel, as shown on the left, or in series, as on the right. Is the heat conducted in the parallel arrangement **(a)** greater than, **(b)** less than, or **(c)** the same as the heat conducted with the rods in series?

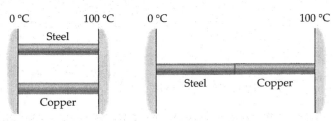

0 °C   100 °C   0 °C   100 °C

Steel

Copper

Steel   Copper

continued on next page

Science Fundamentals Second Edition

continued from previous page

Reasoning and Discussion
The parallel arrangement conducts more heat for two reasons. First, the cross-sectional area available for heat flow is twice as large for the parallel rods. A greater cross-sectional area gives a greater heat flow—everything else being equal. Second, more heat flows through each rod in the parallel configuration because they both have the full temperature difference of 100 C° between their ends. In the series configuration, each rod has a smaller temperature difference between its ends, so less heat flows.

Answer:
(a) More heat is conducted when the rods are in parallel.

In the next Example, we consider the case of heat conduction when two rods are placed in parallel. In the homework we shall consider the corresponding case of the same two rods conducting heat in series.

EXAMPLE 16–7 Parallel Rods

Two 0.525-m rods, one lead the other copper, are connected between metal plates held at 2.00 °C and 106 °C. The rods have a square cross section, 1.50 cm on a side. How much heat flows through the two rods in 1.00 s? Assume that no heat is exchanged between the rods and the surroundings, except at the ends.

Picture the Problem
The lead and the copper rods, each 0.525 m long, are shown in the sketch. Note that both rods have a temperature difference of 104 C° = 104 K between their ends.

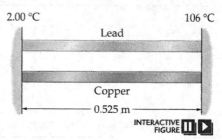

Strategy
The heat flowing through each rod can be calculated using $Q = kA(\Delta T/L)t$ and the value of k given in Table 16–3. The total heat flow is simply the sum of that calculated for each rod.

Solution

1. Calculate the heat flow in one second through the lead rod:

$$Q_l = k_l A\left(\frac{\Delta T}{L}\right)t$$

$$= [34.3 \text{ W}/(\text{m} \cdot \text{K})](0.0150 \text{ m})^2\left(\frac{104 \text{ K}}{0.525 \text{ m}}\right)(1.00 \text{ s})$$

$$= 1.53 \text{ J}$$

2. Calculate the heat flow in one second through the copper rod:

$$Q_c = k_c A\left(\frac{\Delta T}{L}\right)t$$

$$= [395 \text{ W}/(\text{m} \cdot \text{K})](0.0150 \text{ m})^2\left(\frac{104 \text{ K}}{0.525 \text{ m}}\right)(1.00 \text{ s})$$

$$= 17.6 \text{ J}$$

3. Sum the heats found in steps 1 and 2 to get the total heat: $Q_{\text{total}} = Q_l + Q_c = 1.53 \text{ J} + 17.6 \text{ J} = 19.1 \text{ J}$

Insight
As our results show, the copper rod is by far the better conductor of heat. It is also a very good conductor of electricity, as we shall see in Chapter 21.

Practice Problem
What temperature difference would be required for the total heat flow in one second to be 15.0 J?
[**Answer:** $\Delta T = 81.5 \text{ C}° = 81.5 \text{ K}$]

Some related homework problems: Problem 43, Problem 44

As we shall see in Problem 45, the heat conducted by the same two rods connected in series is only 1.41 J, which is less than either of the two rods conduct when placed in parallel. This verifies the conclusion stated in Conceptual Checkpoint 16–4.

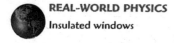

REAL-WORLD PHYSICS
Insulated windows

An application of thermal conductivity in series can be found in the *insulated window*. Most homes today have insulated windows as a means of increasing their energy efficiency. If you look closely at one of these windows, you will see that it

Science Fundamentals Second Edition

is actually constructed from two panes of glass separated by an air-filled gap. Thus, heat flows through three different materials in series as it passes into or out of a home. The fact that the thermal conductivity of air is about 40 times smaller than that of glass means that the insulated window results in significantly less heat flow than would be experienced with a single pane of glass.

As a final example of conduction, we note that many biological systems transfer heat by a mechanism known as *countercurrent exchange*. Consider, for example, an egret or other wading bird standing in cool water all day. As warm blood flows through the arteries on its way to the legs and feet of the bird, it passes through constricted regions where the legs join to the body. Here, where the arteries and veins are packed closely together, the body-temperature arterial blood flowing into the legs transfers heat to the much cooler venous blood returning to the body. Thus, the counter-flowing streams of blood serve to maintain the core body temperature of the bird, while at the same time keeping the legs and feet at much cooler temperatures. The feet still receive the oxygen and nutrients carried by the blood, but they stay at a relatively low temperature to reduce the amount of heat lost to the water.

Similar effects occur in humans. It is common, for example, to hear complaints that a person's hands or feet are cold. There is good reason for this, since they are in fact much cooler than the core body temperature. Just as with the wading birds, the warm arterial blood flowing to the hands and feet exchanges heat with the cool venous blood flowing in the opposite direction (**Figure 16–10**). This helps to reduce the heat loss to our surroundings, and to maintain the desired temperature in the core of the body.

Convection

Suppose you want to heat a small room. To do so, you bring a portable electric heater into the room and turn it on. As the heating coils get red hot, they heat the air in their vicinity; as this air warms, it expands, becoming less dense. Because of its lower density, the warm air rises, to be replaced by cold dense air descending from overhead. This sets up a circulating flow of air that transports heat from the heating coils to the air throughout the room. Heat exchange of this type is referred to as **convection.**

In general, convection occurs when a fluid is unevenly heated. As with the room heater, the warm portions of the fluid rise because of their lower density and the cool portions sink because of their higher density. Thus, in convection, temperature differences result in a flow of fluid. It is this physical flow of matter that carries heat throughout the system.

Convection occurs on an enormous range of length scales. For example, the same type of uneven heating produced by an electric heater in a room can occur in the atmosphere of the Earth as well. The common seashore occurrence of sea breezes during the day and land breezes in the evening is one such example. (See **Figure 16–11** for an illustration of this effect.) On a larger scale, the Sun causes greater warming near the equator than near the poles; as a result, warm equatorial air rises, cool polar air descends, and global convection patterns are established. Similar convection patterns occur in ocean waters, and plate tectonics

REAL-WORLD PHYSICS: BIO
Countercurrent exchange

REAL-WORLD PHYSICS: BIO
Cold hands and feet

▲ Many wading birds use countercurrent exchange in their circulatory systems. This mechanism allows them to keep the temperature of their legs well below that of their bodies. In this way they reduce the conductive loss of body heat to the water.

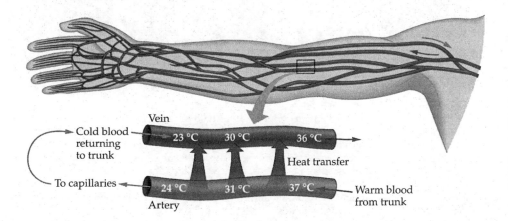

◀ FIGURE 16–10 **Countercurrent heat exchange in the human arm**
Arteries bringing warm blood to the limbs lie close to veins returning cooler blood to the body. This arrangement assures that a temperature difference (gradient) is maintained over the entire length that the vessels run parallel to one another, maximizing heat exchange between the warm arterial blood and the cooler venous blood.

Science Fundamentals Second Edition

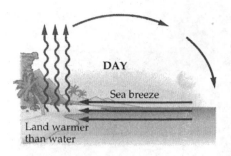

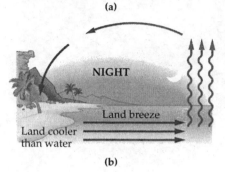

(a) During the day, the sun warms the land more rapidly than the water. This is because the land, which is mostly rocks, has a lower specific heat than the water. The warm land heats the air above it, which becomes less dense and rises. Cooler air from over the water flows in to take its place, producing a "sea breeze." **(b)** At night, the land cools off more rapidly than the water—again because of its lower specific heat. Now it is the air above the relatively warm water that rises and is replaced by cooler air from over the land, producing a "land breeze."

is believed to be caused, at least in part, by convection currents in the Earth's mantle. The Sun also has convection currents, due to the intense heating that occurs in its interior, and disturbances in these currents are often visible as sunspots.

Radiation

Though convection and conduction occur primarily in specific situations, *all* objects give off energy as a result of **radiation**. The energy radiated by an object is in the form of electromagnetic waves (Chapter 25), which include visible light as well as infrared and ultraviolet radiation. Thus, unlike convection and conduction, radiation has no need for a physical material to mediate the energy transfer, since electromagnetic waves can propagate through empty space—that is, through a vacuum. Therefore, the heat you feel radiated from a hot furnace would reach you even if the air were suddenly removed—just as radiant energy from the Sun reaches the Earth across 150 million kilometers of vacuum.

Since radiation can include visible light, it is often possible to "see" the temperature of an object. This is the physical basis of the **optical pyrometer,** invented by Josiah Wedgwood (1730–1795), the renowned English potter. When objects are about 800 °C they appear to be a dull "red hot." Examples include the heating coils in a range or oven. The filament in an incandescent lightbulb glows "yellow hot" at about 3000 °C, about the same temperature as the surface of the red supergiant star Betelgeuse in the constellation Orion. The surface of the Sun, in comparison, is about 6000 °C. Very hot stars, with surface temperatures in the vicinity of 10,000 to 30,000 °C, are "blue hot" and actually appear bluish in the night sky. Rigel, also in the constellation Orion, is an example of such a star. Look above and to the left of Orion's "belt" to see the red Betelgeuse, and below and to the right to see the blue Rigel.

The energy radiated per time by an object—that is, the radiated power, P—is proportional to the surface area, A, over which the radiation occurs. It also depends on the temperature of the object. In fact, the dependence is on the fourth power of the temperature, T^4, where T is the Kelvin-scale temperature. Thus, for

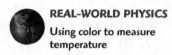

REAL-WORLD PHYSICS
Using color to measure temperature

REAL-WORLD PHYSICS
Temperatures of the stars

▲ Stars have colors that are indicative of their surface temperatures. Thus, the blue supergiant Rigel (lower right) in the constellation Orion is much hotter than the red supergiant Betelgeuse (upper left).

▲ Red-hot volcanic lava is just hot enough (about 1000 °C) to radiate in the visible range. Even when it cools enough to stop glowing, it still emits energy, but most of it is in the form of invisible infrared radiation. Infrared radiation is also given off by the finned "radiators" attached to the supports of the Alaska pipeline. These fins are designed to prevent melting of the environmentally sensitive permafrost over which the pipeline runs. They function much like the radiator that cools your car engine, absorbing heat from the warm oil in the pipeline and dissipating it by radiation and convection into the atmosphere. (What design features can you see that facilitate this function?)

instance, if T is doubled, the radiated power increases by a factor of 16. All this behavior is contained in the **Stefan–Boltzmann law:**

Stefan–Boltzmann Law for Radiated Power, P

$$P = e\sigma A T^4$$ 16–17

SI unit: W

The constant σ in this expression is a fundamental physical constant, the **Stefan–Boltzmann constant:**

$$\sigma = 5.67 \times 10^{-8}\ \text{W}/(\text{m}^2 \cdot \text{K}^4)$$ 16–18

The other constant in the Stefan–Boltzmann law is the **emissivity, e.** The emissivity is a dimensionless number between 0 and 1 that indicates how effective the object is in radiating energy. A value of 1 means that the object is a perfect radiator. In general, a dark-colored object will have an emissivity near 1, and a light-colored object will have an emissivity closer to 0.

▲ Wear black in the desert? It actually helps, by radiating heat away from the wearer more efficiently.

EXERCISE 16–4

Calculate the radiated power from a sphere with a radius of 5.00 cm at the temperature 355 K. Assume the emissivity is unity.

Solution

Using $A = 4\pi r^2$ for a sphere, we have

$$P = e\sigma A T^4 = (1)[5.67 \times 10^{-8}\ \text{W}/(\text{m}^2 \cdot \text{K}^4)]4\pi(0.0500\ \text{m})^2(355\ \text{K})^4 = 28.3\ \text{W}$$

Experiments show that objects absorb radiation from their surroundings according to the same law, the Stefan–Boltzmann law, by which they emit radiation. Thus, if the temperature of an object is T, and its surroundings are at the temperature T_s, the *net* power radiated by the object is

---

Net Radiated Power, P_{net}

$$P_{\text{net}} = e\sigma A(T^4 - T_s{}^4)$$ 16–19

SI unit: W

If the object's temperature is greater than its surroundings, it radiates more energy than it absorbs and P_{net} is positive. On the other hand, if its temperature is less than the surroundings, it absorbs more energy than it radiates and P_{net} is negative. When the object has the same temperature as its surroundings, it is in equilibrium and the net power is zero.

PROBLEM-SOLVING NOTE

Radiated Power

To correctly calculate the radiated power, Equations 16–17 and 16–19, the temperatures must be expressed in the Kelvin scale.

EXAMPLE 16–8   Human Polar Bears

On New Year's Day, several human "polar bears" prepare for their annual dip into the icy waters of Narragansett Bay. One of these hardy souls has a surface area of 1.15 m^2 and a surface temperature of 303 K ($\sim$30 °C). Find the net radiated power from this person **(a)** in a dressing room, where the temperature is 293 K ($\sim$20 °C), and **(b)** outside, where the temperature is 273 K ($\sim$0 °C). Assume an emissivity of 0.900 for the person's skin.

Picture the Problem
Our sketch shows the person radiating power in a room where the surroundings are at 293 K, and outside where the temperature is 273 K. The person also absorbs radiation from the surroundings; hence the net radiated power is greater when the surroundings are cooler.

Strategy
A straightforward application of $P_{\text{net}} = e\sigma A(T^4 - T_s{}^4)$ can be used to find the net power for both parts (a) and (b). The only difference is the temperature of the surroundings, T_s.

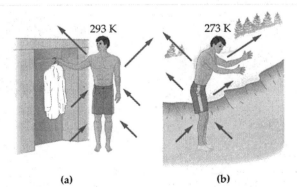

(a)   (b)

continued on next page

Science Fundamentals Second Edition

continued from previous page

Solution

Part (a)

1. Calculate the net power using Equation 16–19 and $T_s = 293$ K:

$$P_{net} = e\sigma A(T^4 - T_s^4)$$
$$= (0.900)[5.67 \times 10^{-8} \text{ W/(m}^2 \cdot \text{K}^4)](1.15 \text{ m}^2)$$
$$\times [(303 \text{ K})^4 - (293 \text{ K})^4]$$
$$= 62.1 \text{ W}$$

Part (b)

2. Calculate the net power using Equation 16–19 and $T_s = 273$ K:

$$P_{net} = e\sigma A(T^4 - T_s^4)$$
$$= (0.900)[5.67 \times 10^{-8} \text{ W/(m}^2 \cdot \text{K}^4)](1.15 \text{ m}^2)$$
$$\times [(303 \text{ K})^4 - (273 \text{ K})^4]$$
$$= 169 \text{ W}$$

Insight

In the warm room the net radiated power is roughly that of a small lightbulb (about 60 W); outdoors, the net radiated power has more than doubled, and is comparable to that of a 150-W lightbulb.

Practice Problem

What temperature must the surroundings have if the net radiated power is to be 155 W?   [**Answer:** $T = 276$ K $\approx 3\,^{\circ}$C]

Some related homework problems: Problem 40, Problem 48

Note that the same emissivity e applies to both the emission and absorption of energy. Thus, a perfect emitter ($e = 1$) is also a perfect absorber. Such an object is referred to as a **blackbody**. As we shall see later, in Chapter 30, the study of blackbody radiation near the turn of the twentieth century ultimately led to one of the most fundamental revolutions in science—the introduction of quantum physics.

The opposite of a blackbody is an ideal reflector, which absorbs *no* radiation ($e = 0$). It follows that an ideal reflector also radiates no energy. This is why the inside of a Thermos bottle is highly reflective. As an almost ideal reflector, the inside of the bottle radiates very little of the energy contained in the hot liquid that it holds. In addition to its shiny interior, a Thermos bottle also has a vacuum between its inner and outer walls, as shown in **Figure 16–12**. This limits the flow of heat to radiation only, since convection and conduction cannot occur in a vacuum. This type of double-walled insulating container was invented by Sir James Dewar (1842–1923), a Scottish physicist and chemist.

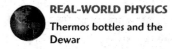

REAL-WORLD PHYSICS

Thermos bottles and the Dewar

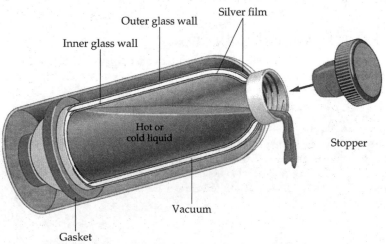

▲ **FIGURE 16–12 The Thermos bottle**
The hot or cold liquid stored in a Thermos bottle is separated from the outside world by a vacuum between the inner and outer glass walls. In addition, the inner glass wall has a reflective coating so that it is a good reflector and a poor radiator.

Science Fundamentals Second Edition

21 Electric Current and Direct-Current Circuits

A battery is a device that uses chemical energy to separate positive and negative charge, producing a potential difference between its terminals. In this case, the chemical energy comes from reactions that take place between the metal electrodes and the acid in the lemon juice. The potential difference causes a current to flow in the wires, which is measured by the attached meter. This chapter explores simple electrical circuits, like the one seen here, and shows how to analyze more complex ones as well.

As you read this paragraph, your heart is pumping blood through the arteries and veins in your body. In a way, your heart is acting like a battery in an electrical circuit: A battery causes electric charge to flow through a closed circuit of wires; your heart causes blood to flow through your body. Just as the flow of blood is important to life, the flow of electric charge is of central importance to modern technology. In this chapter we consider some of the basic properties of moving electric charges, and we apply these results to simple electric circuits.

695

21–1 Electric Current

A flow of electric charge from one place to another is referred to as an **electric current**. Often, the charge is carried by electrons moving through a metal wire. Though the analogy should not be pushed too far, the electrons flowing through a wire are much like water molecules flowing through a garden hose or blood cells flowing through an artery.

To be specific, suppose a charge ΔQ flows past a given point in a wire in a time Δt. In such a case, we say that the electric current, I, in the wire is:

Definition of Electric Current, I

$$I = \frac{\Delta Q}{\Delta t}$$

21–1

SI unit: coulomb per second, C/s = ampere, A

The unit of current, the ampere (A) or *amp* for short, is named for the French physicist André-Marie Ampère (1775–1836) and is defined simply as 1 coulomb per second:

$$1\,A = 1\,C/s$$

The following Example shows that the number of electrons involved in typical electric circuits, with currents of roughly an amp, is extremely large—not unlike the large number of water molecules flowing through a garden hose.

EXAMPLE 21–1 Mega Blaster

The disk drive in a portable CD player is connected to a battery that supplies it with a current of 0.22 A. How many electrons pass through the drive in 4.5 s?

Picture the Problem
Our sketch shows the CD drive with a current $I = 0.22\,A$ flowing through it. Also indicated is the time $\Delta t = 4.5\,s$ during which the current flows.

Strategy
Since we know both the current, I, and the length of time, Δt, we can use the definition of current, $I = \Delta Q/\Delta t$, to find the charge, ΔQ, that flows through the player. Once we know the charge, the number of electrons, N, is simply ΔQ divided by the magnitude of the electron's charge: $N = \Delta Q/e$.

Solution

1. Calculate the charge, ΔQ, that flows through the drive:

$$\Delta Q = I\,\Delta t = (0.22\,A)(4.5\,s) = 0.99\,C$$

2. Divide by the magnitude of the electron's charge, e, to find the number of electrons:

$$N = \frac{\Delta Q}{e} = \frac{0.99\,C}{1.60 \times 10^{-19}\,C/electron}$$
$$= 6.2 \times 10^{18}\,electrons$$

Insight
Thus, even a modest current flowing for a brief time corresponds to the transport of an extremely large number of electrons.

Practice Problem
How long must this current last if 7.5×10^{18} electrons are to flow through the disk drive?   [**Answer:** 5.5 s]

Some related homework problems: Problem 1, Problem 2

When charge flows through a closed path and returns to its starting point, we refer to the closed path as an *electric circuit*. In this chapter we consider **direct-current circuits**, also known as DC circuits, in which the current always flows in the same direction. Circuits with currents that periodically reverse their direction

Science Fundamentals Second Edition

▲ Electric currents are not confined to the wires in our houses and machines, but occur in nature as well. A lightning bolt is simply an enormous, brief current. It flows when the difference in electric potential between cloud and ground (or cloud and cloud) becomes so great that it exceeds the breakdown strength of air. An enormous quantity of charge then leaps across the gap in a fraction of a second. Some organisms, such as this electric torpedo ray, have internal organic "batteries" that can produce significant electrical potentials. The resulting current is used to stun their prey.

are referred to as **alternating-current circuits.** These AC circuits are considered in detail in Chapter 24.

Batteries and Electromotive Force

Although electrons move rather freely in metal wires, they do not flow unless the wires are connected to a source of electrical energy. A close analogy is provided by water in a garden hose. Imagine that you and a friend each hold one end of a garden hose filled with water. If the two ends are held at the same level, as in **Figure 21–1 (a)**, the water does not flow. If, however, one end is raised above the other, as in **Figure 21–1 (b)**, water flows from the high end—where the gravitational potential energy is high—to the low end.

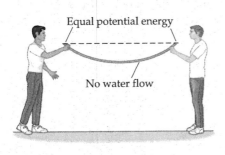
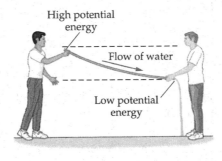

(a)

(b)

◀ **FIGURE 21–1 Water flow as an analogy for electric current**
Water can flow quite freely through a garden hose, but if both ends are at the same level **(a)**, there is no flow. If the ends are held at different levels **(b)**, the water flows from the region where the gravitational potential energy is high to the region where it is low.

A **battery** performs a similar function in an electric circuit. To put it simply, a battery uses chemical reactions to produce a difference in electric potential between its two ends, or **terminals.** The symbol for a battery is ⊣⊢. The terminal corresponding to a high electric potential is denoted by a +, and the terminal corresponding to a low electric potential is denoted by a −. When the battery is connected to a circuit, electrons move in a closed path from the negative terminal of the battery, through the circuit, and back to the positive terminal.

A simple example of an electrical system is shown in **Figure 21–2 (a)**, where we show a battery, a switch, and a lightbulb as they might be connected in a flashlight. In the schematic circuit shown in **Figure 21–2 (b)**, the switch is "open"—creating an **open circuit**—which means there is no closed path through which the electrons can flow. As a result, the light is off. When the switch is closed—which "closes" the circuit—charge flows around the circuit, causing the light to glow.

A mechanical analog to the flashlight circuit is shown in **Figure 21–3**. In this system, the person raising the water from a low to a high level is analogous to the battery, the paddle wheel is analogous to the lightbulb, and the water is analogous

Science Fundamentals Second Edition

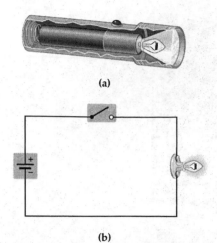

(a)

(b)

▲ **FIGURE 21–2 The flashlight: A simple electrical circuit**

(a) A simple flashlight, consisting of a battery, a switch, and a lightbulb.
(b) When the switch is in the open position, the circuit is "broken," and no charge can flow. When the switch is closed, electrons flow through the circuit and the light glows.

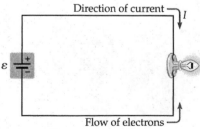

▲ **FIGURE 21–3 A mechanical analog to the flashlight circuit**

The person lifting the water corresponds to the battery in Figure 21–2, and the paddle wheel corresponds to the lightbulb.

to the electric charge. Notice that the person does work in raising the water; later, as the water falls to its original level, it does work on the external world by turning the paddle wheel.

When a battery is disconnected from a circuit and carries no current, the difference in electric potential between its terminals is referred to as its *electromotive force*, or *emf* ($\mathcal{E}$). It follows that the units of emf are the same as those of electric potential, namely, volts. Clearly, then, the electromotive force is not really a force at all. Instead, the emf determines the amount of work a battery does to move a certain amount of charge around a circuit (like the person lifting water in Figure 21–3). To be specific, the magnitude of the work done by a battery of emf $\mathcal{E}$ as a charge ΔQ moves from one of its terminals to the other is given by Equation 20–2:

$$W = \Delta Q \mathcal{E}$$

We apply this relation to a flashlight circuit in the following Active Example.

ACTIVE EXAMPLE 21–1 Operating a Flashlight: Find the Charge and the Work

A battery with an emf of 1.5 V delivers a current of 0.44 A to a flashlight bulb for 64 s (see Figure 21–2). Find **(a)** the charge that passes through the circuit and **(b)** the work done by the battery.

Solution *(Test your understanding by performing the calculations indicated in each step.)*

Part (a)

1. Use the definition of current, $I = \Delta Q/\Delta t$, to find the charge that flows through the circuit: $\Delta Q = 28\,\text{C}$

Part (b)

2. Once we know ΔQ, we can use $W = \Delta Q \mathcal{E}$ to find the work: $W = 42\,\text{J}$

Insight
Note that the more charge a battery moves through a circuit, the more work it does. Similarly, the greater the emf, the greater the work. We can see, then, that a car battery that operates at 12 volts and delivers several amps of current, does much more work than a flashlight battery—as expected.

Your Turn
How long must the flashlight battery operate to do 150 J of work?

(Answers to **Your Turn** *problems are given in the back of the book.)*

The emf of a battery is the potential difference it can produce between its terminals under ideal conditions. In real batteries, however, there is always some internal loss, leading to a potential difference that is less than the ideal value. In fact, the greater the current flowing through a battery the greater the reduction in potential difference between its terminals, as we shall see in Section 21–4. Only when the current is zero can a real battery produce its full emf. Because most batteries have relatively small internal losses, we shall treat batteries as ideal—always producing a potential difference precisely equal to $\mathcal{E}$—unless specifically stated otherwise.

When we draw an electric circuit, it will be useful to draw an arrow indicating the flow of current. By convention, the direction of the current arrow is given in terms of a positive test charge, in much the same way that the direction of the electric field is determined:

> The direction of the current in an electrical circuit is the direction in which a *positive* test charge would move.

▲ **FIGURE 21–4 Direction of current and electron flow**

In the flashlight circuit, electrons flow from the negative terminal of the battery to the positive terminal. The direction of the current, I, is just the opposite: from the positive terminal to the negative terminal.

Of course, in typical circuits the charges that flow are actually *negatively* charged electrons. As a result, the flow of electrons and the current arrow point in opposite directions, as indicated in **Figure 21–4**. Notice that a positive charge will flow from a region of high electric potential, near the positive terminal of the battery, to a region of low electric potential, near the negative terminal, as one would expect.

Science Fundamentals Second Edition

Finally, surprising as it may seem, electrons move rather slowly through a typical wire. They suffer numerous collisions with the atoms in the wire, and hence their path is rather tortuous and roundabout, as indicated in **Figure 21–5**. Like a car contending with a series of speed bumps, the electron's average speed, or **drift speed** as it is often called, is limited by the repeated collisions—in fact, their average speed is commonly about 10^{-4} m/s. Thus, if you switch on the headlights of a car, for example, an electron leaving the battery will take about an hour to reach the lightbulb, yet the lights seem to shine from the instant the switch is turned on. How is this possible?

The answer is that as an electron begins to move away from the battery, it exerts a force on its neighbors, causing them to move in the same general direction and, in turn, to exert a force on their neighbors, and so on. This process generates a propagating influence that travels through the wire at nearly the speed of light. The phenomenon is analogous to a bowling ball's hitting one end of a line of balls; the effect of the colliding ball travels through the line at roughly the speed of sound, although the individual balls have very little displacement. Similarly, the electrons in a wire move with a rather small average velocity as they collide with and bounce off the atoms making up the wire, whereas the influence they have on one another races ahead and causes the light to shine.

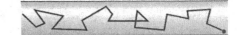

▲ FIGURE 21–5 **Path of an electron in a wire**

Typical path of an electron as it bounces off atoms in a metal wire. Because of the tortuous path the electron follows, its average velocity is rather small.

Electromagnetic Waves

25–1 The Production of Electromagnetic
      Waves   838

25–2 The Propagation of Electromagnetic
      Waves   841

25–3 The Electromagnetic Spectrum   845

Most people think they know exactly what the world looks like—all you have to do, after all, is open your eyes and look. There's more to it than that, however. We all know, for example, that the simple yellow flower shown here (left) is a daisy. But is that really what a daisy looks like? To a bee—with its ability to see ultraviolet light invisible to us—the very same daisy is a flower with three concentric circles forming a "bull's-eye" centered on the nectar (right). Such "nectar guides" are a common feature of flowers as viewed by bees, but are generally invisible to humans. This chapter explores the nature and properties of electromagnetic radiation—the kind we know as visible light, and many other kinds as well.

Electricity and magnetism can seem very different in many ways, but they are actually intimately related—in fact, electric and magnetic fields can be considered as different aspects of the same thing, like the two sides of a coin. For example, we have seen that an electric current produces a magnetic field, and a changing magnetic field produces an electric field. Because of fundamental connections like these, we refer to the phenomena of electricity and magnetism together as **electromagnetism.**

In this chapter we consider one of the most significant manifestations of electromagnetism; namely, that electric and magnetic fields can work together to create traveling waves called **electromagnetic waves.** As we shall see, these waves are responsible for everything from radio and TV signals, to the visible light we see all around us, to the X-rays that reveal our internal structure, and much more. In addition, the prediction, discovery, and technological development of electromagnetic waves is a fascinating success story in the history of science.

837

25–1 The Production of Electromagnetic Waves

Electromagnetic waves were predicted, and their properties were studied theoretically, decades before they were first produced with electrical circuits in the lab. The prediction came from Scottish physicist James Clerk Maxwell (1831–1879), who, in 1864, hypothesized that since a changing magnetic field produces an electric field (Faraday's law) a changing electric field should similarly produce a magnetic field. In effect, Maxwell suggested a sort of "symmetry" between electric and magnetic fields.

Maxwell followed up on his suggestion by working out its mathematical consequences. Among these was that electric and magnetic fields, acting together, could produce an *electromagnetic wave* that travels with the speed of light. As a result, he proposed that visible light—which had previously been thought of as a completely separate phenomenon from electricity and magnetism—was, in fact, an electromagnetic wave. His theory also implied that electromagnetic waves would not be limited to visible light and that it should be possible to produce them with oscillating electric circuits similar to those studied in the previous chapter.

The first production and observation of electromagnetic waves in the lab was carried out by the German physicist Heinrich Hertz (1857–1894) in 1887. Hertz used what was basically an *LC* circuit to generate an alternating current and found that energy could be transferred from this circuit to a similar circuit several meters away. He was able to show, in addition, that the energy transfer exhibited such standard wave phenomena as reflection, refraction, interference, diffraction, and polarization. There could be no doubt that waves were produced by the first circuit and that they propagated across the room to the second circuit. Even more significantly, he was able to show that the speed of the waves was roughly the speed of light, as predicted by Maxwell.

It took only a few years for Hertz's experimental apparatus to be refined and improved to the point where it could be used in practical applications. The first to do so was Guglielmo Marconi (1874–1937), who immediately recognized the implications of the electromagnetic-wave experiments—namely, that waves could be used for communications, eliminating the wires necessary for telegraphy. He patented his first system in 1896 and gained worldwide attention when, in 1901, he received a radio signal in St. John's, Newfoundland, that had been sent from Cornwall, England. When Maxwell died, electromagnetic waves were still just a theory; twenty years later, they were revolutionizing communications.

To gain an understanding of electromagnetic waves, consider the simple electrical circuit shown in **Figure 25–1**. Here we show an ac generator of period T connected to the center of an antenna, which is basically a long, straight wire with a break in the middle. Suppose at time $t = 0$ the generator gives the upper segment of the antenna a maximum positive charge and the lower segment a maximum negative charge, as shown in Figure 25–1 (a). A positive test charge placed on the x axis at point P will experience a downward force; hence, the electric field there is downward. A short time later, when the charge on the antenna is reduced in magnitude, the electric field at P also has a smaller magnitude. We show this result in Figure 25–1 (b).

More importantly, Figure 25–1 (b) also shows that the electric field produced at time $t = 0$ has not vanished, nor has it simply been replaced with the new, reduced-magnitude field. Instead, the original field has *moved farther away from the antenna*, to point Q. The reason that the reduction in charge on the antenna is felt at point P *before* it is felt at point Q is simply that it takes a finite time for this change in charge to be felt at a distance. This is analogous to the fact that a person near a lightning strike hears the thunder before a person who is half a mile away, or that a wave pulse on a string takes a finite time to move from one end of the string to the other.

After the generator has completed one-quarter of a cycle, at time $t = \frac{1}{4}T$, the antenna is uncharged and the field vanishes, as in Figure 25–1 (c). Still later the charges on the antenna segments change sign, giving rise to an electric field that

▲ Electromagnetic waves are produced by (and detected as) oscillating electric currents in a wire or similar conducting element. The actual antenna is often much smaller than is commonly imagined—the bowl-shaped structures that we tend to think of as antennas, such as these microwave relay dishes, serve to focus the transmitted beam in a particular direction or concentrate the received signal on the actual detector.

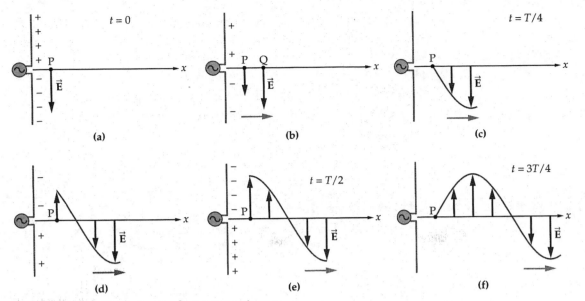

▲ FIGURE 25-1 Producing an electromagnetic wave

A traveling electromagnetic wave produced by an ac generator attached to an antenna. **(a)** At $t = 0$ the electric field at point P is downward. **(b)** A short time later, the electric field at P is still downward, but now with a reduced magnitude. Note that the field created at $t = 0$ has moved to point Q. **(c)** After one quarter of a cycle, at $t = \frac{1}{4}T$, the electric field at P vanishes. **(d)** The charge on the antenna has reversed polarity now, and the electric field at P points upward. **(e)** When the oscillator has completed half a cycle, $t = \frac{1}{2}T$, the field at point P is upward and of maximum magnitude. **(f)** At $t = \frac{3}{4}T$ the field at P vanishes again. The fields produced at earlier times continue to move away from the antenna.

points upward, as we see in Figures 25-1 (d) and (e). The field vanishes again after three-quarters of a cycle, at $t = \frac{3}{4}T$, as shown in Figure 25-1 (f). Immediately after this time, the electric field begins to point downward once more. The net result is a wavelike electric field moving steadily away from the antenna. To summarize,

> The electric field produced by an antenna connected to an ac gener-
> ator propagates away from the antenna, analogous to a wave on a
> string moving away from your hand as you wiggle it up and down.

This is really only half of the electromagnetic wave, however; the other half is a similar wave in the magnetic field. To see this, consider **Figure 25-2**, where we show the current in the antenna flowing upward at a time when the upper segment is positive. Pointing the thumb of the right hand in the direction of the current, and curling the fingers around the wire, as specified in the magnetic field RHR, we see that $\vec{B}$ points into the page at the same time that $\vec{E}$ points downward. It follows, then, that $\vec{E}$ and $\vec{B}$ are at right angles to each other. A more detailed analysis shows that $\vec{E}$ and $\vec{B}$ are perpendicular to each other at all times, and that they are also in phase; that is, when the magnitude of $\vec{E}$ is at its maximum, so is the magnitude of $\vec{B}$.

Combining the preceding results, we can represent the electric and magnetic fields in an electromagnetic wave as shown in **Figure 25-3**. Notice that not only

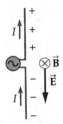

▲ FIGURE 25-2 Field directions in an electromagnetic wave

At a time when the electric field produced by the antenna points downward, the magnetic field points into the page. In general, the electric and magnetic fields in an electromagnetic wave are always at right angles to each other.

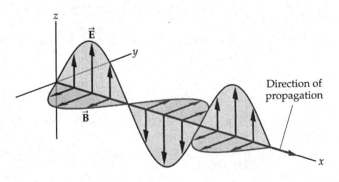

► FIGURE 25-3 The right-hand rule applied to an electromagnetic wave

An electromagnetic wave propagating in the positive x direction. Note that $\vec{E}$ and $\vec{B}$ are perpendicular to each other and in phase. The direction of propagation is given by the thumb of the right hand, after pointing the fingers in the direction of $\vec{E}$ and curling them toward $\vec{B}$.

Science Fundamentals Second Edition

are $\vec{E}$ and $\vec{B}$ perpendicular to each other, they are also perpendicular to the direction of propagation; hence, electromagnetic waves are **transverse** waves. (See Section 14–1 for a comparison of various types of waves.) Finally, the direction of propagation is given by another right-hand rule:

Direction of Propagation for Electromagnetic Waves

Point the fingers of your right hand in the direction of $\vec{E}$, curl your fingers toward $\vec{B}$, and your thumb will point in the direction of propagation.

This rule is consistent with the direction of propagation shown in Figure 25–3.

CONCEPTUAL CHECKPOINT 25–1   **Direction of Magnetic Field**

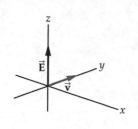

An electromagnetic wave propagates in the positive y direction, as shown in the sketch. If the electric field at the origin is in the positive z direction, is the magnetic field at the origin in (a) the positive x direction, (b) the negative x direction, or (c) the negative y direction?

Reasoning and Discussion

Pointing the fingers of the right hand in the positive z direction (the direction of $\vec{E}$), we see that in order for the thumb to point in the direction of propagation (the positive y direction) the fingers must be curled toward the positive x direction. Therefore, $\vec{B}$ points in the positive x direction.

Answer:

(a) $\vec{B}$ is in the positive x direction.

▶ **FIGURE 25–4 Receiving radio waves**
Basic elements of a tuning circuit used to receive radio waves. First, an incoming wave sets up an alternating current in the antenna. Next, the resonance frequency of the *LC* circuit is adjusted to match the frequency of the radio wave, resulting in a relatively large current in the circuit. This current is then fed into an amplifier to further increase the signal.

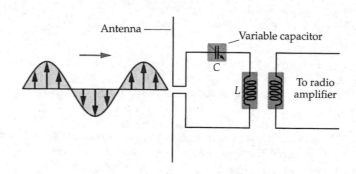

Electromagnetic waves can be detected in much the same way they are generated. Suppose, for instance, that an electromagnetic wave moves to the right, as in **Figure 25–4.** As the wave continues to move, its electric field exerts a force on electrons in the antenna that is alternately up and down, resulting in an alternating current. Thus the electromagnetic field makes the antenna behave much like an ac generator. If the antenna is connected to an *LC* circuit, as indicated in the figure, the resulting current can be relatively large if the resonant frequency of the circuit matches the frequency of the wave. This is the basic principle behind radio and television tuners. In fact, when you turn the tuning knob on a radio, you are actually changing the capacitance or the inductance in an *LC* circuit and, therefore, changing the resonance frequency.

Finally, though we have discussed the production of electromagnetic waves by means of an electric circuit and an antenna, this is certainly not the only way such waves can be generated. In fact, any time an electric charge is accelerated, it will radiate:

Accelerated charges radiate electromagnetic waves.

REAL-WORLD PHYSICS
Radio and television communications

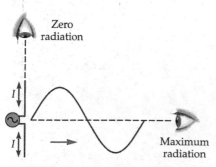

▲ **FIGURE 25–5 Electromagnetic waves and the line of sight**
Electromagnetic radiation is greatest when charges accelerate at right angles to the line of sight. Zero radiation is observed when the charges accelerate along the line of sight. These observations apply to electromagnetic waves of all frequencies.

This condition applies no matter what the cause of the acceleration. In addition, the intensity of radiated electromagnetic waves depends on the orientation of the acceleration relative to the viewer. For example, viewing the antenna perpendicular to its length, so that the charges accelerate at right angles to the line of sight, results in maximum intensity, as illustrated in **Figure 25–5**. Conversely, viewing the antenna straight down from above, in the same direction as the acceleration, results in zero intensity.

25–2 The Propagation of Electromagnetic Waves

A sound wave or a wave on a string requires a medium through which it can propagate. For example, when the air is pumped out of a jar containing a ringing bell, its sound can no longer be heard. In contrast, we can still *see* that the bell is ringing. Thus, light can propagate through a vacuum, as can all other types of electromagnetic waves, such as radio waves and microwaves. In fact, electromagnetic waves travel through a vacuum with the maximum speed that *any* form of energy can have, as we discuss in detail in Chapter 29.

The Speed of Light

All electromagnetic waves travel through a vacuum with precisely the same speed, c. Since light is the form of electromagnetic wave most familiar to us, we refer to c as the *speed of light in a vacuum*. The approximate value of this speed is as follows:

Speed of Light in a Vacuum

$$c = 3.00 \times 10^8 \text{ m/s}$$

25–1

This is a large speed, corresponding to about 186,000 mi/s. Put another way, a beam of light could travel around the world about seven times in a single second. In air the speed of light is slightly less than it is in a vacuum, and in denser materials, such as glass or water, the speed of light is reduced to about two-thirds of its vacuum value.

EXERCISE 25–1

The distance between Earth and the Sun is 1.50×10^{11} m. How long does it take for light to cover this distance?

Solution

Recalling that speed is distance divided by time, it follows that the time t to cover a distance d is $t = d/v$. Using $v = c$, we find

$$t = \frac{d}{c} = \frac{1.50 \times 10^{11} \text{ m}}{3.00 \times 10^8 \text{ m/s}} = 500 \text{ s}$$

Noting that 500 s is $8\frac{1}{3}$ min, we say that Earth is about 8 light-minutes from the Sun.

Because the speed of light is so large, its value is somewhat difficult to determine. The first scientific attempt to measure the speed of light was made by Galileo (1564–1642), who used two lanterns for the experiment. Galileo opened the shutters of one lantern, and an assistant a considerable distance away was instructed to open the shutter on the second lantern as soon as he observed the light from Galileo's lantern. Galileo then attempted to measure the time that elapsed before he saw the light from his assistant's lantern. Since there was no perceptible time lag, beyond the normal human reaction time, Galileo could conclude only that the speed of light must be very great indeed.

The first to give a finite, numerical value to the speed of light was the Danish astronomer Ole Romer (1644–1710), though he did not set out to measure the speed of light at all. Romer was measuring the times at which the moons of Jupiter disappeared behind the planet, and he noticed that these eclipses occurred earlier when Earth was closer to Jupiter and later when Earth was farther away from Jupiter. This difference is illustrated in **Figure 25–6**. From the results of Exercise 25–1, we know that light requires about 16 minutes to travel from one side of Earth's orbit to the other, and this is roughly the discrepancy in eclipse times observed by Romer. In 1676 he announced a value for the speed of light of 2.25×10^8 m/s.

The first laboratory measurement of the speed of light was performed by the French scientist Armand Fizeau (1819–1896). The basic elements of his experiment, shown in **Figure 25–7**, are a mirror and a rotating, notched wheel. Light passing through one notch travels to a mirror a considerable distance away, is reflected

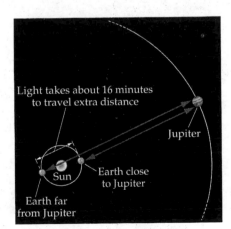

▲ **FIGURE 25–6 Using Jupiter to determine the speed of light**

When the Earth is at its greatest distance from Jupiter, light takes about 16 minutes longer to travel between them. This time lag allowed Ole Romer to estimate the speed of light.

Science Fundamentals Second Edition

▶ FIGURE 25–7 Fizeau's experiment to measure the speed of light

If the time required for light to travel to the far mirror and back is equal to the time it takes the wheel to rotate from one notch to the next, light will pass through the wheel and on to the observer.

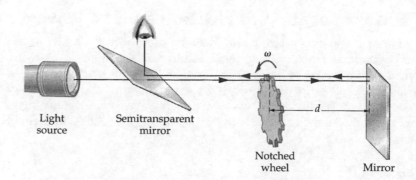

Light source   Semitransparent mirror   Notched wheel   Mirror

back, and then, if the rotational speed of the wheel is adjusted properly, passes through the *next notch* in the wheel. By measuring the rotational speed of the wheel and the distance from the wheel to the mirror, Fizeau was able to obtain a value of 3.13×10^8 m/s for the speed of light.

Today, experiments to measure the speed of light have been refined to such a degree that we now use it to *define* the meter, as was mentioned in Chapter 1. Thus, by definition, the speed of light in a vacuum is

$$c = 299\ 792\ 458 \text{ m/s}$$

For most routine calculations, however, the value $c = 3.00 \times 10^8$ m/s is adequate.

Maxwell's theoretical description of electromagnetic waves allowed him to obtain a simple expression for c in terms of previously known physical quantities. In particular, he found that c could be written as follows:

$$c = \frac{1}{\sqrt{\varepsilon_0 \mu_0}} \qquad\qquad 25\text{–}2$$

Recall that $\varepsilon_0 = 8.85 \times 10^{-12}$ C²/(N·m²) occurs in the expression for the electric field due to a point charge; in fact, ε_0 determines the strength of the electric field. The constant $\mu_0 = 4\pi \times 10^{-7}$ T·m/A plays an equivalent role for the magnetic field. Thus, Maxwell was able to show that these two constants, which were determined by electrostatic and magnetostatic measurements, also combine to yield the speed of light—again demonstrating the symmetrical role that electric and magnetic fields play in electromagnetic waves. Substituting the values for ε_0 and μ_0 we find

$$c = \frac{1}{\sqrt{(8.85 \times 10^{-12}\ \text{C}^2/(\text{N}\cdot\text{m}^2))(4\pi \times 10^{-7}\ \text{T}\cdot\text{m/A})}} = 3.00 \times 10^8 \text{ m/s}$$

Clearly, Maxwell's theoretical expression agrees with experiment.

EXAMPLE 25–1 Fizeau's Results

Consider a Fizeau experiment in which the wheel has 450 notches and rotates with a speed of 35 rev/s. Light passing through one notch travels to the mirror and back just in time to pass through the next notch. If the distance from the wheel to the mirror is 9500 m, what is the speed of light obtained by this measurement?

Picture the Problem
Our sketch shows an experimental setup similar to Fizeau's. The notched wheel is 9500 m from a mirror and spins with an angular speed of 35 rev/s. We show a few notches in our sketch, which represent the 450 notches on the actual wheel.

Strategy
The speed of light is the distance traveled, $2d$, divided by the time required, Δt. To find the time, we note that the wheel rotates from one notch to the next during this time; that is, it rotates through an angle $\Delta\theta = (1/450)$ rev. Knowing the rotational speed, ω, of the wheel, we can find the time using the relation $\Delta\theta = \omega \Delta t$ (Section 10–1).

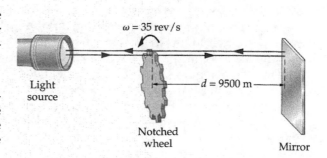

$\omega = 35$ rev/s

Light source   Notched wheel $d = 9500$ m   Mirror

Solution

1. Find the time required for the wheel to rotate from one notch to the next:

$$\Delta t = \frac{\Delta \theta}{\omega} = \frac{(1/450)\ \text{rev}}{35\ \text{rev/s}} = 6.3 \times 10^{-5}\ \text{s}$$

2. Divide the time into the distance to find the speed of light:

$$c = \frac{2d}{\Delta t} = \frac{2(9500\ \text{m})}{6.3 \times 10^{-5}\ \text{s}} = 3.0 \times 10^{8}\ \text{m/s}$$

Insight

Note that even with a rather large distance for the round trip, the travel time of the light is small, only 0.063 milliseconds. This illustrates the great difficulty experimentalists faced in attempting to make an accurate measurement of c.

Practice Problem

If the wheel has 430 notches, what rotational speed is required for the return beam of light to pass through the next notch? [**Answer:** $\omega = 37\ \text{rev/s}$]

Some related homework problems: Problem 14, Problem 15

Although the speed of light is enormous by earthly standards, it is useful to look at it from an astronomical perspective. Imagine, for example, that you could shrink the solar system to fit onto a football field, with the Sun at one end zone and Pluto at the other. On this scale, Earth would be a grain of sand located at the 2.5-yard line from the Sun, and light would take 8 min to cover that distance. To travel to Pluto, at the other end of the field, light would require about 5.5 hr. Thus, on this scale, the speed of light is like the crawl of a small caterpillar. When one recalls that the solar system is but a speck on the outskirts of the Milky Way galaxy, and that the nearest major galaxy to our own—the Andromeda galaxy—is about 2.2 million light-years away, the speed of light doesn't appear so great after all.

The Doppler Effect

In Section 14–5 we discussed the Doppler effect for sound waves—the familiar increase or decrease in frequency as a source of sound approaches or recedes. A similar Doppler effect applies to electromagnetic waves. There are two fundamental differences, however. First, sound waves require a medium through which to travel, whereas light can propagate across a vacuum. Second, the speed of sound

 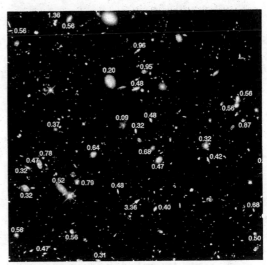

▲ Even traveling at 300 million meters per second, light from the Andromeda galaxy (left) takes over 2 million years to reach us. Yet Andromeda is one of our nearest cosmic neighbors. A sense of the true vastness of the universe is provided by the image known as the Hubble Deep Field (right). This long-exposure photograph, taken from orbit by the Hubble Space Telescope, shows over 1600 galaxies when examined closely. Most of them exhibit a Doppler red-shift—that is, their light is shifted to lower frequencies by the Doppler effect, indicating that they are receding from Earth as the universe expands. The red shifts marked on the photo correspond to distances ranging from about 1.3 billion light years to over 13 billion light years (nearly 10^{23} miles).

Science Fundamentals Second Edition

can be different for different observers. For example, an observer approaching a source of sound measures an increased speed of sound, whereas an observer detecting sound from a moving source measures the usual speed of sound. For this reason, the Doppler effect with sound is different for a moving observer than it is for a moving source (see Figure 14–18 for a direct comparison). In contrast, the speed of electromagnetic waves is *independent* of the motion of the source and observer, as we shall see in Chapter 29. Therefore, there is just one Doppler effect for electromagnetic waves, and it depends only on the *relative speed* between the observer and source.

For source speeds u that are small compared with the speed of light, the observed frequency f' from a source with frequency f is

$$f' = f\left(1 \pm \frac{u}{c}\right) \qquad 25\text{–}3$$

PROBLEM-SOLVING NOTE

Evaluating the Doppler Shift

Since everyday objects generally move with speeds much less than the speed of light, the Doppler-shifted frequency differs little from the original frequency. To see the Doppler effect more clearly, it is often useful to calculate the difference in frequency, $f' - f$, rather than the Doppler-shifted frequency itself.

Note that u in this expression is a speed and hence is always positive. The appropriate sign in front of the term u/c is chosen for a given situation—the plus sign applies to a source that is approaching the observer, the minus sign to a receding source. In addition, u is a *relative* speed between the source and the observer, both of which may be moving. For example, if an observer is moving in the positive x direction with a speed of 5 m/s, and a source ahead of the observer is moving in the positive x direction with a speed of 12 m/s, the relative speed is $u = 12$ m/s $-$ 5 m/s $=$ 7 m/s. Since the distance between the observer and source is increasing with time in this case, we would choose the minus sign in Equation 25–3.

EXERCISE 25–2

An FM radio station broadcasts at a frequency of 88.5 MHz. If you drive your car toward the station at 32.0 m/s, what change in frequency do you observe?

Solution

We can find the change in frequency, $f' - f$, using Equation 25–3:

$$f' - f = f\frac{u}{c} = (88.5 \times 10^6 \text{ Hz})\frac{32.0 \text{ m/s}}{3.00 \times 10^8 \text{ m/s}} = 9.44 \text{ Hz}$$

Thus, the frequency changes by only 9.44 Hz = 0.00000944 MHz.

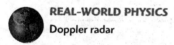

REAL-WORLD PHYSICS

Doppler radar

Common applications of the Doppler effect include the radar units used to measure the speed of automobiles, and the Doppler radar that is used to monitor the weather. In Doppler radar, electromagnetic waves are sent out into the atmosphere and are reflected back to the receiver. The change in frequency of the reflected beam relative to the outgoing beam provides a way of measuring the speed of the clouds and precipitation that reflected the beam. Thus, Doppler radar gives more information than just where a rainstorm is located; it also tells how it is moving. Measurements of this type are particularly important for airports, where information regarding areas of possible wind shear can be crucial for safety.

EXAMPLE 25–2 Nexrad

REAL-WORLD PHYSICS The Doppler weather radar used by the National Weather Service is referred to as Nexrad, which stands for next generation radar. Nexrad commonly operates at a frequency of 2.7 GHz. If a Nexrad wave reflects from an approaching weather system moving with a speed of 28 m/s, find the difference in frequency between the outgoing and returning waves.

Picture the Problem

Our sketch shows the outgoing radar waves, the incoming weather system, and the returning radar waves. The speed of the weather system relative to the radar station is $u = 28$ m/s, and the frequency of the outgoing waves is $f = 2.7$ GHz.

Strategy

Two Doppler effects are involved in this system. First, the outgoing wave is seen to have a frequency $f' = f(1 + u/c)$ by the weather system, since it is moving toward the source. The waves reflected by the weather system, then, have the frequency f'. Since the weather system acts like a moving source of radar with frequency f', an observer at the radar facility detects a frequency $f'' = f'(1 + u/c)$. Thus, given u and f, we can calculate the difference, $f'' - f$.

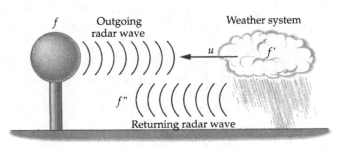

Solution

1. Use $f' = f(1 + u/c)$ to calculate the difference in frequency, $f' - f$:

$$f' - f = fu/c = \frac{(2.7 \times 10^9 \text{ Hz})(28 \text{ m/s})}{3.00 \times 10^8 \text{ m/s}} = 250 \text{ Hz}$$

2. Now, use $f'' = f'(1 + u/c)$ to find the difference between f'' and f':

$$f'' - f' = f'u/c$$

3. Use the results of step 1 to replace f' with $f + 250$ Hz:

$$f'' - (f + 250 \text{ Hz}) = (f + 250 \text{ Hz})u/c$$

4. Solve for the frequency difference, $f'' - f$:

$$f'' - f = (f + 250 \text{ Hz})u/c + 250 \text{ Hz}$$
$$= \frac{(2.7 \times 10^9 \text{ Hz} + 250 \text{ Hz})(28 \text{ m/s})}{3.00 \times 10^8 \text{ m/s}} + 250 \text{ Hz}$$
$$= 500 \text{ Hz}$$

Insight

Notice that we focus on the *difference* in frequency between the very large numbers $f = 2{,}700{,}000{,}000$ Hz and $f'' = 2{,}700{,}000{,}500$ Hz. Clearly, it is more convenient to simply write $f'' - f = 500$ Hz.

In addition, note that the two Doppler shifts in this problem are analogous to the two Doppler shifts we found for the case of a train approaching a tunnel in Example 14–6.

Practice Problem

Find the difference in frequency if the weather system is receding with a speed of 21 m/s. [**Answer:** $f'' - f = -380$ Hz]

Some related homework problems: Problem 21, Problem 23

25–3 The Electromagnetic Spectrum

When white light passes through a prism it spreads out into a rainbow of colors, with red on one end and violet on the other. All these various colors of light are electromagnetic waves, of course; they differ only in their frequency and, hence, their wavelength. The relationship between frequency and wavelength for any wave with a speed v is simply $v = f\lambda$, as was shown in Section 14–11. Because all electromagnetic waves in a vacuum have the same speed, c, it follows that f and λ are related as follows:

$$c = f\lambda \qquad\qquad \text{25–4}$$

Thus, as the frequency of an electromagnetic wave increases, its wavelength decreases.

In the following Example we calculate the frequency of red and violet light, given the corresponding wavelengths. Notice that the wavelengths are given in units of nanometers (nm), where 1 nm $= 10^{-9}$ m. Occasionally the wavelength of light is given in terms of a non-SI unit referred to as the *angstrom* (Å), defined as follows: 1Å $= 10^{-10}$ m.

EXAMPLE 25-3 Roses are Red, Violets are Violet

Find the frequency of red light, with a wavelength of 700.0 nm, and violet light, with a wavelength of 400.0 nm.

Picture the Problem

The visible electromagnetic spectrum, along with representative wavelengths, is shown in our diagram. In addition to the wavelengths of 700.0 nm for red light and 400.0 nm for violet light, we include 600.0 nm for yellowish orange light and 500.0 nm for greenish blue light.

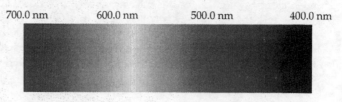

700.0 nm   600.0 nm   500.0 nm   400.0 nm

Strategy

We obtain the frequency by rearranging $c = f\lambda$ to yield $f = c/\lambda$.

Solution

1. Substitute $\lambda = 700.0$ nm for red light:

$$f = \frac{c}{\lambda} = \frac{3.00 \times 10^8 \text{ m/s}}{700.0 \times 10^{-9} \text{ m}} = 4.29 \times 10^{14} \text{ Hz}$$

2. Substitute $\lambda = 400.0$ nm for violet light:

$$f = \frac{c}{\lambda} = \frac{3.00 \times 10^8 \text{ m/s}}{400.0 \times 10^{-9} \text{ m}} = 7.50 \times 10^{14} \text{ Hz}$$

Insight

The frequency of visible light is extremely large. In fact, even for the relatively low frequency of red light, it takes only 2.33×10^{-15} s to complete one cycle. The *range* of visible frequencies is relatively small, however, when compared with other portions of the electromagnetic spectrum.

Practice Problem

What is the wavelength of light with a frequency of 5.25×10^{14} Hz? **[Answer: 571 nm]**

Some related homework problems: Problem 25, Problem 26

In principle, the frequency of an electromagnetic wave can have any positive value, and this full range of frequencies is known as the **electromagnetic spectrum.** Certain bands of the spectrum are given special names, as indicated in **Figure 25–8**. For example, we have just seen that visible light occupies a relatively narrow band of frequencies from 4.29×10^{14} Hz to 7.50×10^{14} Hz. In what follows, we discuss the various regions of the electromagnetic spectrum of most relevance to humans and our technology, in order of increasing frequency.

Radio Waves

($f \sim 10^6$ Hz to 10^9 Hz, $\lambda \sim 300$ m to 0.3 m) The lowest-frequency electromagnetic waves of practical importance are *radio* and *television waves* in the frequency range of roughly 10^6 Hz to 10^9 Hz. Waves in this frequency range are produced in a variety of ways. For example, molecules and accelerated electrons in space give off radio waves, which radio astronomers detect with large dish receivers. Radio waves are also produced as a piece of adhesive tape is slowly peeled from a surface, as you can confirm by holding a transistor radio near the tape and listening for pops and snaps coming from the speaker. Most commonly, the radio waves we pick up with our radios and televisions are produced by alternating currents in metal antennas.

▲ Since the development of the first radiotelescopes in the 1950s, the radio portion of the electromagnetic spectrum has provided astronomers with a valuable new window on the universe. These antennas are part of the Very Large Array (VLA), located in San Augustin, New Mexico.

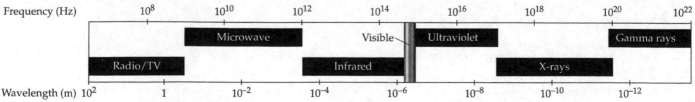

Frequency (Hz) 10^8 10^{10} 10^{12} 10^{14} 10^{16} 10^{18} 10^{20} 10^{22}

Microwave   Visible   Ultraviolet   Gamma rays

Radio/TV   Infrared   X-rays

Wavelength (m) 10^2 1 10^{-2} 10^{-4} 10^{-6} 10^{-8} 10^{-10} 10^{-12}

▲ **FIGURE 25–8 The electromagnetic spectrum**

Note that the visible portion of the spectrum is relatively narrow. The boundaries between various bands of the spectrum are not sharp but, instead, are somewhat arbitrary.

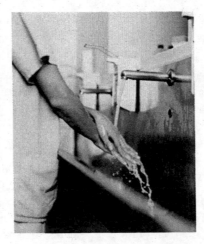

◀ We use infrared rays all the time, even though they are invisible to us. If you change the channel with a remote control, your signal is sent by an infrared ray; if you move your hand in front of a no-touch water faucet, an infrared ray detects the motion. In contrast, snakes called pit vipers can actually "see" infrared rays with the "pit" organs located just in front of their eyes. What must a remote control look like to one of these creatures?

Microwaves

($f \sim 10^9$ Hz to 10^{12} Hz, $\lambda \sim$ 300 mm to 0.3 mm) Electromagnetic radiation with frequencies from 10^9 Hz to about 10^{12} Hz are referred to as *microwaves*. Waves in this frequency range are used to carry long-distance telephone conversations, as well as to cook our food. Microwaves, with wavelengths of about 1 mm to 30 cm, are the highest-frequency electromagnetic waves that can be produced by electronic circuitry.

Infrared Waves

($f \sim 10^{12}$ Hz to 4.3×10^{14} Hz, $\lambda \sim$ 0.3 mm to 700 nm) Electromagnetic waves with frequencies just below that of red light—roughly 10^{12} Hz to 4.3×10^{14} Hz—are known as *infrared* rays. These waves can be felt as heat on our skin but cannot be seen with our eyes. Many creatures, including various types of pit vipers, have specialized infrared receptors that allow them to "see" the infrared rays given off by a warm-blooded prey animal, even in total darkness. Infrared rays are often generated by the rotations and vibrations of molecules. In turn, when infrared rays are absorbed by an object, its molecules rotate and vibrate more vigorously, resulting in an increase in the object's temperature. Finally, many remote controls—for items ranging from TVs to DVD players to gas fireplaces—operate on a beam of infrared light with a wavelength of about 1000 nm. This infrared light is so close to the visible spectrum and so low in intensity that it cannot be felt as heat.

REAL-WORLD PHYSICS: BIO

Infrared receptors in pit vipers

Visible Light

($f \sim 4.3 \times 10^{14}$ Hz to 7.5×10^{14} Hz, $\lambda \sim$ 700 nm to 400 nm) The portion of the electromagnetic spectrum most familiar to us is the spectrum of visible light, represented by the full range of colors seen in a rainbow. Each of the different colors, as perceived by our eyes and nervous system, is nothing more than an electromagnetic wave with a different frequency. Waves in this frequency range

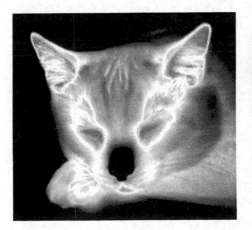

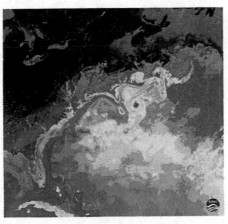

◀ Photographs made with infrared radiation are often called thermograms, since most infrared wavelengths can be felt as heat by the human skin. Thermograms provide a useful remote sensing technique for measuring temperature. In the photo on the left, the areas of the cat's head that are warmest (pink) and coolest (blue) can be clearly identified. In the photo on the right, an infrared satellite image of the Atlantic Ocean off the coast of North America, warmer colors are used to indicate higher sea surface temperatures. The swirling red streak running from lower left toward the upper right is the Gulf Stream.

Science Fundamentals Second Edition

(4.3 × 10^14 to 7.5 × 10^14 Hz) are produced primarily by electrons changing their positions within an atom, as we discuss in detail in Chapter 31.

Ultraviolet Light

($f \sim 7.5 \times 10^{14}$ **Hz to** 10^{17} **Hz,** $\lambda \sim$ **400 nm to 3 nm)** When electromagnetic waves have frequencies just above that of violet light—from about 7.5×10^{14} Hz to 10^{17} Hz—they are called *ultraviolet* or *UV rays*. Although these rays are invisible, they often make their presence known by causing suntans with moderate exposure. More prolonged or intense exposure to UV rays can have harmful consequences, including an increased probability of developing a skin cancer. Fortunately, most of the UV radiation that reaches Earth from the Sun is absorbed in the upper atmosphere by ozone (O_3) and other molecules. A significant reduction in the ozone concentration in the stratosphere could result in an unwelcome increase of UV radiation on Earth's surface.

X-Rays

($f \sim 10^{17}$ **Hz to** 10^{20} **Hz,** $\lambda \sim$ **3 nm to 0.003 nm)** As the frequency of electromagnetic waves is raised even higher, into the range between about 10^{17} Hz to 10^{20} Hz, we reach the part of the spectrum known as *X-rays*. Typically, the X-rays used in medicine are generated by the rapid deceleration of high-speed electrons projected against a metal target, as we show in Section 31–17. These energetic rays, which are only weakly absorbed by the skin and soft tissues, pass through our bodies rather freely, except when they encounter bones, teeth, or other relatively dense material. This property makes X-rays most valuable for medical diagnosis, research, and treatment. Still, X-rays can cause damage to human tissue, and it is desirable to reduce unnecessary exposure to these rays as much as possible.

Gamma Rays

($f \sim 10^{20}$ **Hz and higher,** $\lambda \sim$ **0.003 nm and smaller)** Finally, electromagnetic waves with frequencies above about 10^{20} Hz are generally referred to as *gamma* (γ) *rays*. These rays, which are even more energetic than X-rays, are often produced as neutrons and protons rearrange themselves within a nucleus, or when a particle collides with its antiparticle, and the two annihilate each other. These processes are discussed in detail in Chapter 32. Gamma rays are also highly penetrating and destructive to living cells. It is for this reason that they are used to kill cancer cells and, more recently, microorganisms in food. Irradiated food, however, is a concept that has yet to become popular with the general public, even though NASA has irradiated astronauts' food since the 1960s. If you happen to see irradiated food in the grocery store, you will know that it has been exposed to γ rays from cobalt-60 for 20 to 30 minutes.

Notice that the visible part of the electromagnetic spectrum, so important to life on Earth, is actually the smallest of the frequency bands we have named. This accounts for the fact that a rainbow produces only a narrow band of color in the sky—if the visible band were wider, the rainbow would be wider as well. It should be remembered, however, that there is nothing particularly special about the visible band; in fact, it is even species dependent. For example, some bees and butterflies can see ultraviolet light, and, as mentioned previously, certain snakes can form images from infrared radiation.

One of the main factors in determining the visible range of frequencies is Earth's atmosphere. For example, if one examines the transparency of the atmosphere as a function of frequency, it is found that there is a relatively narrow range of frequencies for which the atmosphere is highly transparent. As eyes evolved in living systems on Earth, they could have evolved to be sensitive to various different frequency ranges. It so happens, however, that the range of frequencies that most animal eyes can detect match nicely with the range of frequencies that the atmosphere allows to reach Earth's surface. This is a nice example of natural adaptation.

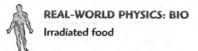

REAL WORLD-PHYSICS: BIO
Biological effects of ultraviolet light

▲ Most ultraviolet radiation cannot penetrate Earth's atmosphere, but ultraviolet astronomical photographs, such as the one shown above, have been taken by cameras in orbit. The bright spots in this image of a spiral galaxy are areas of intense star formation, populated by hot young stars that radiate heavily in the ultraviolet.

REAL-WORLD PHYSICS: BIO
Irradiated food

▲ The use of radiation to preserve food can be quite effective, but the technique is still controversial. Both boxes of strawberries shown here were stored for about 2 weeks at refrigerator temperature. Before storage, the box at right was irradiated to kill microorganisms and mold spores.

Quantum Physics

30–1 Blackbody Radiation and Planck's Hypothesis of Quantized Energy 1004

30–2 Photons and the Photoelectric Effect 1007

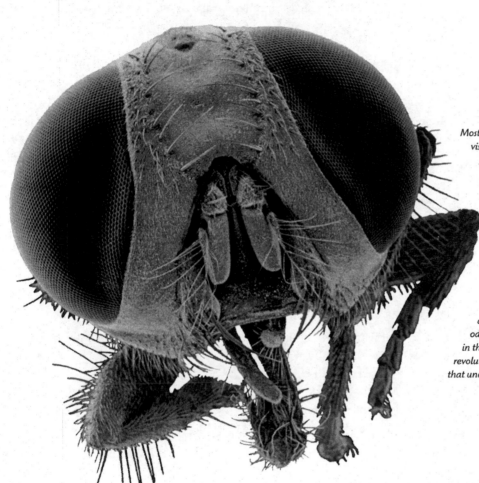

Most of the images that we encounter are made with visible light. Even those that are not, such as thermograms and X-rays, employ other kinds of electromagnetic radiation. Until about 80 years ago, the idea of making a picture by means of particles rather than radiation would have seemed absurd—like trying to create a portrait by bouncing paintballs off the subject and onto a canvas. Yet by the 1920s, physicists discovered that light waves often behave like particles and, conversely, that particles, such as electrons, often behave like waves. Indeed, the wave properties of electrons can be exploited to create remarkably detailed images, such as this scanning electron micrograph of a housefly. This chapter explores the sometimes odd-seeming laws that describe the behavior of nature in the atomic and subatomic realms, and the series of revolutions in physics between the 1890s and the 1930s that uncovered them.

To understand the behavior of nature at the atomic level, it is necessary to introduce a number of new concepts to physics and to modify many others. In this chapter we consider the basic ideas of quantum physics and show that they lead to a deeper understanding of microscopic systems—in much the same way that relativity extends physics into the realm of high speeds. Relativity and quantum physics, taken together, provide the basis for what we refer to today as modern physics.

We begin this chapter by introducing the concept of *quantization*, in which a physical quantity—such as energy—varies in discrete steps rather than continuously, as in classical physics. This concept leads to the idea of the *photon*, which can be thought of as a "particle" of light. Next, we find that just as light can behave like a particle, particles—such as electrons, protons, and neutrons—can behave like waves. Finally, the wave nature of matter introduces a fundamental uncertainty to our knowledge of physical quantities and allows for such classically "forbidden" behavior as *quantum tunneling*.

1003

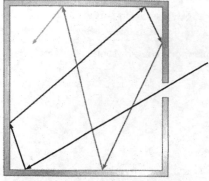

▲ **FIGURE 30–1 An ideal blackbody**
In an ideal blackbody, incident light is completely absorbed. In the case shown here, the absorption occurs as the result of multiple reflections within a cavity. The blackbody, and the electromagnetic radiation it contains, are in thermal equilibrium at a temperature T.

30–1 Blackbody Radiation and Planck's Hypothesis of Quantized Energy

If you have ever looked through a small opening into a hot furnace, you have seen the glow of light associated with its high temperature. As unlikely as it may seem, this light played a central role in the revolution of physics that occurred in the early 1900s. It was through the study of such systems that the idea of *energy quantization*—energy taking on only discrete values—was first introduced to physics.

More precisely, physicists in the late 1800s were actively studying the electromagnetic radiation given off by a physical system known as a **blackbody**. An example of a blackbody is illustrated in **Figure 30–1**. Note that this blackbody has a cavity with a small opening to the outside world—much like a furnace. Light that enters the cavity through the opening is reflected multiple times from the interior walls until it is completely absorbed. It is for this reason that the system is referred to as "black," even though the material from which it is made need not be black at all.

> An ideal blackbody absorbs all the light that is incident on it.

Objects that absorb much of the incident light—though not all of it—are reasonable approximations to a blackbody; objects that are highly reflective and shiny are poor representations of a blackbody.

As we saw in Section 16–6, objects that are effective at absorbing radiation are also effective at giving off radiation. Thus an ideal blackbody is also an ideal radiator. In fact, the basic experiment performed with a blackbody is the following: Heat the blackbody to a fixed temperature, T, and measure the amount of electromagnetic radiation it gives off at a given frequency, f. Repeat this measurement for a number of different frequencies, then plot the intensity of radiation versus frequency. The results of a typical blackbody experiment are shown in **Figure 30–2**, for a variety of different temperatures. Note that there is little radiation at small frequencies, a peak in the radiation at intermediate frequencies, and finally a fall-off to little radiation again at high frequencies.

Now, what is truly remarkable about the blackbody experiment is the following:

> The distribution of energy in blackbody radiation is *independent* of the material from which the blackbody is constructed—it depends only on the temperature, T.

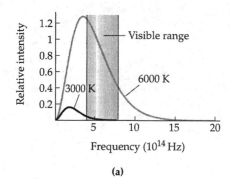

Therefore, a blackbody of steel and one of wood give precisely the same results when held at the same temperature. When physicists observe a phenomenon that is independent of the details of the system, it is a clear signal that they are observing something of fundamental significance. This was certainly the case with blackbody radiation.

Two aspects of the blackbody curves in Figure 30–2 are of particular importance. First, note that as the temperature is increased, the area under the curve increases. Since the total area under the curve is a measure of the total energy emitted by the blackbody, it follows that an object radiates more energy as it becomes hotter.

Second, note that the peak in the blackbody curve moves to higher frequency as the absolute temperature T is increased. This movement, or displacement, of the peak with temperature is described by **Wien's displacement law**:

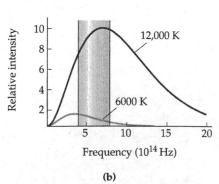

▲ **FIGURE 30–2 Blackbody radiation**
Blackbody radiation as a function of frequency for various temperatures. **(a)** 3000 K and 6000 K. **(b)** 6000 K and 12,000 K. Note that as the temperature is increased, the peak in the radiation shifts toward higher frequency.

Wien's Displacement Law

$$f_{peak} = (5.88 \times 10^{10}\ \text{s}^{-1} \cdot \text{K}^{-1})T \qquad 30\text{–}1$$

SI unit: $\text{Hz} = \text{s}^{-1}$

Thus, there is a direct connection between the temperature of an object and the frequency of radiation it emits most strongly.

Science Fundamentals Second Edition

CONCEPTUAL CHECKPOINT 30-1   Compare Temperatures

Betelgeuse is a red-giant star in the constellation Orion; Rigel is a bluish white star in the same constellation. Is the surface temperature of Betelgeuse **(a)** greater than, **(b)** less than, or **(c)** the same as the surface temperature of Rigel?

Reasoning and Discussion
Recall that red light has a lower frequency than blue light, as can be seen in Figure 25-8. It follows, from Wien's displacement law, that a red star has a lower temperature than a blue star. Therefore, Betelgeuse has the lower surface temperature.

Answer:
(b) The surface temperature of Betelgeuse is less than that of Rigel.

▲ All objects emit electromagnetic radiation over a range of frequencies. The frequency that is radiated most intensely depends on the object's temperature, as specified by Wien's law. The glowing bolt in this picture radiates primarily in the infrared part of the spectrum, but it is hot enough (a few thousand kelvin) so that a significant portion of its radiation falls within the red end of the visible region. The other bolts are too cool to radiate any detectable amount of visible light.

To be more specific about the conclusion given in Conceptual Checkpoint 30-1, let's consider Figure 30-2 in greater detail. At the lowest temperature shown, 3000 K, the radiation is more intense at the red end of the visible spectrum than at the blue end. An object at this temperature—like the heating coil on a stove, for example—would appear "red hot" to the eye. Even so, most of the radiation at this temperature is in the infrared, and thus is not visible to the eye at all. A blackbody at 6000 K, like the surface of the Sun, gives out strong radiation throughout the visible spectrum, though there is still more radiation at the red end than at the blue end. As a result, the light of the Sun appears somewhat yellowish. Finally, at 12,000 K a blackbody appears bluish white, and most of its radiation is in the ultraviolet. The temperature of the star Rigel is determined from the location of its radiation peak in the following Exercise.

EXERCISE 30-1

Find the surface temperature of Rigel, given that its radiation peak occurs at a frequency of 1.17×10^{15} Hz.

Solution
Solving Equation 30-1 for T, we find

$$T = \frac{f_{\text{peak}}}{5.88 \times 10^{10}\ \text{s}^{-1} \cdot \text{K}^{-1}} = \frac{1.17 \times 10^{15}\ \text{Hz}}{5.88 \times 10^{10}\ \text{s}^{-1} \cdot \text{K}^{-1}} = 19{,}900\ \text{K}$$

This is a little more than three times the surface temperature of the Sun. Thus blackbody radiation allows us to determine the temperature of a distant star that we may never visit.

REAL-WORLD PHYSICS

Measuring the temperature of a star

Planck's Quantum Hypothesis

Although experimental understanding of blackbody radiation was quite extensive in the late 1800s, there was a problem. Attempts to explain the blackbody curves of Figure 30-2 theoretically, using classical physics, failed—and failed miserably. To see the problem, consider the curves shown in **Figure 30-3**. The green curve is the experimental result for a blackbody at a given temperature. In contrast, the blue curve shows the prediction of classical physics. Clearly, the classical result cannot be valid, since its curve diverges to infinity at high frequency, which in turn implies that the blackbody radiates an infinite amount of energy. This unphysical divergence at high frequencies is referred to as the *ultraviolet catastrophe*.

The German physicist Max Planck (1858–1947) worked long and hard on this problem. Eventually, he was able to construct a mathematical formula that agreed with experiment for all frequencies. His next problem was to "derive" the equation. The only way he could do this, it turned out, was to make the following bold and unprecedented assumption: The radiation energy in a blackbody at the frequency f must be an integral multiple of a constant (h) times the frequency; that is, energy is *quantized*:

Quantized Energy	
$E_n = nhf \qquad n = 0, 1, 2, 3, \dots$	30-2

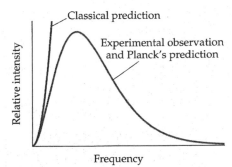

▲ **FIGURE 30-3 The ultraviolet catastrophe**
Classical physics predicts a blackbody radiation curve that rises without limit as the frequency increases. This outcome is referred to as the ultraviolet catastrophe. By assuming energy quantization, Planck was able to derive a curve in agreement with experimental results.

The constant, h, in this expression is known as **Planck's constant**, and it has the following value:

Planck's Constant, h

$$h = 6.63 \times 10^{-34} \, \text{J} \cdot \text{s}$$

SI unit: J·s

30–3

This constant is recognized today as one of the fundamental constants of nature, on an equal footing with other such constants as the speed of light in a vacuum and the rest mass of an electron.

The assumption of energy quantization is quite a departure from classical physics, in which energy can take on any value at all and is related to the amplitude of a wave rather than its frequency. In Planck's calculation, the energy can have only the discrete values hf, $2hf$, $3hf$, and so on. Because of this quantization, it follows that the energy can change only in *quantum jumps* of energy no smaller than hf as the system goes from one quantum state to another. The fundamental increment, or *quantum*, of energy, hf, is incredibly small, as can be seen from the small magnitude of Planck's constant. The next Example explores the size of the quantum and the value of the *quantum number, n*, for a typical macroscopic system.

EXAMPLE 30–1 Quantum Numbers

Suppose the maximum speed of a 1.2-kg mass attached to a spring with a force constant of 35 N/m is 0.95 m/s. **(a)** Find the frequency of oscillation and total energy of this mass–spring system. **(b)** Determine the size of one quantum of energy in this system. **(c)** Assuming the energy of this system satisfies $E_n = nhf$, find the quantum number, n.

Picture the Problem

Our sketch shows a 1.2-kg mass oscillating on a spring with a force constant of 35 N/m. The mass has its maximum speed of $v_{max} = 0.95$ m/s when it passes through the equilibrium position. At this moment, the total energy of the system is simply the kinetic energy of the mass.

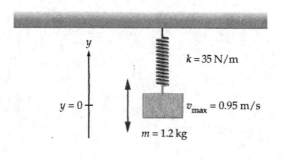

Strategy

a. We can find the frequency of oscillation using $\omega = \sqrt{k/m}$ (Equation 13–10) and $\omega = 2\pi f$ (Equation 13–15). The total energy is simply the kinetic energy as the mass passes through equilibrium, $E = K_{max} = \frac{1}{2}mv_{max}^2$.

b. The energy of one quantum is hf, where f is the frequency found in part (a).

c. We determine the quantum number by solving $E_n = nhf$ for n.

Solution

Part (a)

1. Calculate the frequency of oscillation using $\omega = \sqrt{k/m} = 2\pi f$:

$$\omega = \sqrt{\frac{k}{m}} = 2\pi f$$

$$f = \frac{1}{2\pi}\sqrt{\frac{k}{m}} = \frac{1}{2\pi}\sqrt{\frac{35 \, \text{N/m}}{1.2 \, \text{kg}}} = 0.86 \, \text{Hz}$$

2. Calculate the maximum kinetic energy of the mass $\left(\frac{1}{2}mv_{max}^2\right)$ to find the total energy, E, of the system:

$$E = \frac{1}{2}mv_{max}^2 = \frac{1}{2}(1.2 \, \text{kg})(0.95 \, \text{m/s})^2 = 0.54 \, \text{J}$$

Part (b)

3. The energy of one quantum is hf, where $f = 0.86$ Hz:

$$hf = (6.63 \times 10^{-34} \, \text{J} \cdot \text{s})(0.86 \, \text{Hz}) = 5.7 \times 10^{-34} \, \text{J}$$

Part (c)

4. Set $E_n = nhf$ equal to the total energy of the system and solve for n:

$$E_n = nhf$$

$$n = \frac{E_n}{hf} = \frac{0.54 \, \text{J}}{5.7 \times 10^{-34} \, \text{J}} = 9.5 \times 10^{32}$$

Insight

The numbers found in parts (b) and (c) are incredible for their size. For example, the quantum is on the order of 10^{-34} J, as compared with the energy required to break a bond in a DNA molecule, which is on the order of 10^{-20} J. Thus the quantum for a macroscopic system is about 10^{14} times smaller than the energy needed to affect a molecule. Similarly, the number of quanta in the system, roughly 10^{33}, is comparable to the number of atoms in four Olympic-size swimming pools.

Practice Problem

If the quantum of energy for a 1.5-kg mass on a spring is 0.80×10^{-33} J, what is the force constant of the spring? [**Answer:** $k = 86$ N/m]

Some related homework problems: Problem 9, Problem 72

Clearly, then, the quantum numbers in typical macroscopic systems are incredibly large. As a result, a change of one in the quantum number is completely insignificant and undetectable. Similarly, the change in energy from one quantum state to the next is so small that it cannot be measured in a typical experiment; hence, for all practical purposes, the energy of a macroscopic system seems to change continuously, even though it actually changes by small increments. In contrast, in an atomic system, the energy jumps are of great importance, as we shall see in the next section.

Returning to the ultraviolet catastrophe for a moment, we can now see how Planck's hypothesis removes the unphysical divergence at high frequency predicted by classical physics. In Planck's theory, the higher the frequency f, the greater the quantum of energy, hf. Therefore, as the frequency is increased, the amount of energy required for even the smallest quantum jump increases as well. Since a blackbody has only a finite amount of energy, however, it simply cannot supply the large amount of energy required to produce an extremely high-frequency quantum jump. As a result, the amount of radiation at high frequency drops off toward zero.

Planck's theory of energy quantization leads to an adequate description of the experimental results for blackbody radiation. Still, the theory was troubling and somewhat unsatisfying to Planck and to many other physicists as well. Although the idea of energy quantization worked, at least in this case, it seemed ad hoc and more of a mathematical trick than a true representation of nature. With the work of Einstein, however, which we present in the next section, the well-founded misgivings about quantum theory began to fade away.

30–2 Photons and the Photoelectric Effect

From Max Planck's point of view, energy quantization in a blackbody was probably related to quantized vibrations of atoms in the walls of the blackbody. We are familiar, for example, with the fact that a string tied at both ends can produce standing waves at only certain discrete frequencies (Chapter 14), so perhaps atoms vibrating in a blackbody behave in a similar way, vibrating only with certain discrete energies. Certainly, Planck did not think the light in a blackbody had a quantized energy, since most physicists thought of light as being a wave, which can have any energy.

A brash young physicist named Albert Einstein, however, took the idea of quantized energy seriously and applied it to the radiation in the blackbody. Einstein proposed that light comes in bundles of energy, called **photons**, that obey Planck's hypothesis of energy quantization; that is, light of frequency f consists of photons with an energy given by the following relation:

Energy of a Photon of Frequency *f*

$$E = hf \qquad\qquad\qquad 30\text{–}4$$

SI unit: J

Thus the energy in a beam of light of frequency f can have only the values hf, $2hf$, $3hf$, and so on. Planck's initial reaction to Einstein's suggestion was that he had

Science Fundamentals Second Edition

Low-intensity light beam

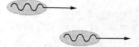

High-intensity light beam

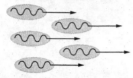

▲ **FIGURE 30-4 The photon model of light**

In the photon model of light, a beam of light consists of many photons, each with an energy hf. The more intense the beam, the more tightly packed the photons.

gone too far with the idea of quantization. As it turns out, nothing could have been further from the truth.

In Einstein's photon model, a beam of light can be thought of as a beam of particles, each carrying the energy hf, as indicated in **Figure 30-4**. If the beam of light is made more intense while keeping the frequency the same, the result is that the photons in the beam are more tightly packed, so that more photons pass a given point in a given time. In this way, more photons shine on a given surface in a given time, increasing the energy delivered to the surface per time. Even so, each photon in the more intense beam has exactly the same amount of energy as those in the less intense beam. The energy of a typical photon of visible light is calculated in the next Exercise.

EXERCISE 30-2

Calculate the energy of a photon of yellow light with a frequency of 5.25×10^{14} Hz. Give the energy in both joules and electron volts.

Solution

Applying Equation 30-4, we find

$$E = hf = (6.63 \times 10^{-34} \, \text{J} \cdot \text{s})(5.25 \times 10^{14} \, \text{s}^{-1}) = 3.48 \times 10^{-19} \, \text{J}$$

$$= 3.48 \times 10^{-19} \, \text{J} \left(\frac{1 \, \text{eV}}{1.60 \times 10^{-19} \, \text{J}} \right) = 2.18 \, \text{eV}$$

Note that the energy of a visible photon is on the order of an electron volt (eV). This is also the typical energy scale for atomic and molecular systems, as we show in detail in the following Example.

EXAMPLE 30-2 When Oxygens Split

Molecular oxygen (O_2) is a diatomic molecule. The energy required to dissociate 1 mol of O_2 to form 2 mol of atomic oxygen is 118 kcal. **(a)** Find the energy (in joules and electron volts) required to dissociate one O_2 molecule. **(b)** Assuming the dissociation energy for one molecule is supplied by a single photon, find the frequency of the photon.

Picture the Problem

In our sketch we show a single photon dissociating an O_2 molecule to form two O atoms. The energy of the photon is $E = hf$.

Strategy

a. This part of the problem is simply a matter of converting from kcal per mole to joules per molecule. This can be accomplished by using the fact that 1 kcal = 4186 J and that Avogadro's number (Section 17-1) is 6.02×10^{23} molecules/mol. We can then convert to electron volts using 1 eV = 1.60×10^{-19} J.

b. We can find the frequency of the photon by setting hf equal to the energy E found in part (a). Since Planck's constant is given in units of J · s, we must use the energy expressed in joules from part (a).

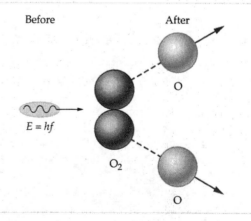

Solution

Part (a)

1. Convert 118 kcal/mol to J/molecule:

$$\left(118 \frac{\text{kcal}}{\text{mol}} \right) \left(\frac{4186 \, \text{J}}{1 \, \text{kcal}} \right) \left(\frac{1}{6.02 \times 10^{23} \, \text{molecules/mol}} \right)$$

$$= 8.21 \times 10^{-19} \, \text{J/molecule}$$

2. Convert the preceding result to eV/molecule:

$$8.21 \times 10^{-19} \frac{\text{J}}{\text{molecule}} \left(\frac{1 \, \text{eV}}{1.60 \times 10^{-19} \, \text{J}} \right)$$

$$= 5.13 \, \text{eV/molecule}$$

Part (b)

3. Use $E = 8.21 \times 10^{-19} \text{ J} = hf$ to solve for the frequency, f: $\qquad f = \dfrac{E}{h} = \dfrac{8.21 \times 10^{-19} \text{ J}}{6.63 \times 10^{-34} \text{ J} \cdot \text{s}} = 1.24 \times 10^{15} \text{ Hz}$

Insight

This frequency is in the ultraviolet. In fact, ultraviolet rays in Earth's upper atmosphere cause O_2 molecules to dissociate, freeing up atomic oxygen which can then combine with O_2 to form ozone, O_3.

Practice Problem

An infrared photon has a frequency of 1.00×10^{13} Hz. How much energy is carried by one mole of these photons? **[Answer:** 3990 J = 0.953 kcal**]**

Some related homework problems: Problem 19, Problem 20

Since photons typically have rather small amounts of energy on a macro-scopic scale, it follows that enormous numbers of photons must be involved in everyday situations, as demonstrated in the following Active Example.

ACTIVE EXAMPLE 30–1 Dark Vision: Find the Number of Photons

Dark-adapted (scotopic) vision is possible in humans with as little as 4.00×10^{-11} W/m^2 of 505-nm light entering the eye. If light of this intensity and wavelength enters the eye through a pupil that is 6.00 mm in diameter, how many photons enter the eye per second?

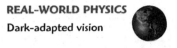

REAL-WORLD PHYSICS
Dark-adapted vision

Solution *(Test your understanding by performing the calculations indicated in each step.)*

1. Calculate the area of the pupil: $\qquad\qquad\qquad\qquad$ 2.83×10^{-5} m^2

2. Multiply the intensity by the area of the pupil $\qquad\qquad$ 1.13×10^{-15} J/s
to find the energy entering the eye per second:

3. Calculate the energy of a photon: $\qquad\qquad\qquad\quad$ 3.94×10^{-19} J

4. Divide the energy of a photon into the energy per $\qquad$ 2870 photons/s
second to find the number of photons per second:

Insight

Thus, even though a typical lightbulb gives off roughly 10^{18} photons per second, we need only about 10^3 photons per second to see. Our eyes are extraordinary instruments, sensitive to an incredibly wide range of intensities.

Finally, suppose an astronomer views a dim, distant galaxy with scotopic vision. The 2870 photons that enter the astronomer's eye each second are separated from one another by about 65 miles. It follows that only one photon at a time from the distant galaxy traverses the astronomer's telescope.

Your Turn

Suppose we consider light with a wavelength greater than 505 nm by a factor of 1.25. Will more or fewer photons be required per second with this new wavelength? By what factor will the required number of photons per second change?

(Answers to **Your Turn** *problems are given in the back of the book.)*

The Photoelectric Effect

Einstein applied his photon model of light to the **photoelectric effect,** in which a beam of light (photo-) hits the surface of a metal and ejects an electron (-electric). The effect can be measured using a device like that pictured in **Figure 30–5**. Note that incoming light ejects an electron—referred to as a photoelectron—from a metal plate called the emitter (E); the electron is then attracted to a collector plate (C), which is at a positive potential relative to the emitter. The result is an electric current that can be measured with an ammeter.

The minimum amount of energy necessary to eject an electron from a particular metal is referred to as the **work function,** W_0, for that metal. Work functions

▶ **FIGURE 30–5 The photoelectric effect**
The photoelectric effect can be studied with a device like that shown. Light shines on a metal plate, ejecting electrons, which are then attracted to a positively charged "collector" plate. The result is an electric current that can be measured with an ammeter.

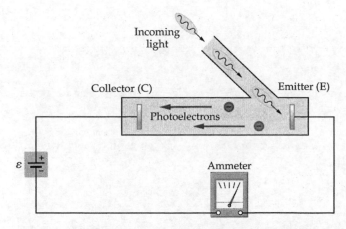

vary from metal to metal but are typically on the order of a few electron volts. If an electron is given an energy E by the beam of light that is greater than W_0, the excess energy goes into kinetic energy of the ejected electron. The maximum kinetic energy (K) a photoelectron can have, then, is

$$K_{max} = E - W_0 \qquad \text{30–5}$$

Just as with blackbody radiation, the photoelectric effect exhibits behavior that is at odds with classical physics. Two of the main areas of disagreement are the following:

- Classical physics predicts that a beam of light of *any* color (frequency) can eject electrons, as long as the beam has sufficient intensity. That is, if a beam is intense enough, the energy it delivers to an electron will exceed the work function and cause it to be ejected.

- Classical physics also predicts that the maximum kinetic energy of an ejected electron should increase as the intensity of the light beam is increased. In particular, the more energy the beam delivers to the metal, the more energy that any given electron can have as it is ejected.

Although both of these predictions are reasonable—necessary, in fact, from the classical physics point of view—they simply do not agree with experiments on the photoelectric effect. In fact, experiments show the following behavior:

- To eject electrons, the incident light beam must have a frequency greater than a certain minimum value, referred to as the **cutoff frequency,** f_0. If the frequency of the light is less than f_0, it will not eject electrons, no matter how intense the beam.

- If the frequency of light is greater than the cutoff frequency, f_0, the effect of increasing the intensity is to increase the *number* of electrons that are emitted per second. The maximum kinetic energy of the electrons does not increase with the intensity of the light; the kinetic energy depends only on the frequency of the light.

As we shall see, these observations are explained quite naturally with the photon model.

First, in Einstein's model each photon has an energy determined solely by its frequency. Therefore, making a beam of a given frequency more intense simply means increasing the number of photons hitting the metal in a given time—not increasing the energy carried by a photon. An electron, then, is ejected only if an incoming photon has an energy that is at least equal to the work function: $E = hf_0 = W_0$. The *cutoff frequency* is thus defined as follows:

Cutoff Frequency, f_0

$$f_0 = \frac{W_0}{h} \qquad \text{30–6}$$

SI unit: Hz = s^{-1}

If the frequency of the light is greater than f_0, the electron can leave the metal with a finite kinetic energy; if the frequency is less than f_0, no electrons are ejected, no matter how intense the beam. We determine a typical cutoff frequency in the next Exercise.

EXERCISE 30–3

The work function for a gold surface is 4.58 eV. Find the cutoff frequency, f_0, for a gold surface.

Solution

Substitution in Equation 30–6 yields

$$f_0 = \frac{W_0}{h} = \frac{(4.58\ \text{eV})\left(\dfrac{1.60 \times 10^{-19}\ \text{J}}{1\ \text{eV}}\right)}{6.63 \times 10^{-34}\ \text{J} \cdot \text{s}} = 1.11 \times 10^{15}\ \text{Hz}$$

This frequency is in the near ultraviolet.

Second, the fact that a more intense beam of monochromatic light delivers more photons per time to the metal just means that more electrons are ejected per time. Since each electron receives precisely the same amount of energy, however, the maximum kinetic energy is the same regardless of the intensity. In fact, if we return to Equation 30–5 and replace the energy, E, with the energy of a photon, hf, we find

$$K_{max} = hf - W_0 \qquad\qquad 30\text{–}7$$

Note that K_{max} depends linearly on the frequency but is independent of the intensity. A plot of K_{max} for sodium (Na) and gold (Au) is given in **Figure 30–6**. Clearly, both lines have the same slope, h, as expected from Equation 30–7, but have different cutoff frequencies. Therefore, with the result given in Equation 30–7, Einstein was able to show that Planck's constant, h, appears in a natural way in the photoelectric effect and is not limited in applicability to the blackbody.

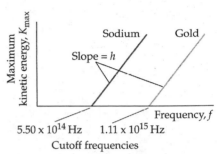

▲ **FIGURE 30–6 The kinetic energy of photoelectrons**
The maximum kinetic energy of photo-electrons as a function of the frequency of light. Note that sodium and gold have different cutoff frequencies, as one might expect for different materials. On the other hand, the slope of the two lines is the same, h, as predicted by Einstein's photon model of light.

EXAMPLE 30–3 White Light on Sodium

A beam of white light containing frequencies between 4.00×10^{14} Hz and 7.90×10^{14} Hz is incident on a sodium surface, which has a work function of 2.28 eV. **(a)** What is the range of frequencies in this beam of light for which electrons are ejected from the sodium surface? **(b)** Find the maximum kinetic energy of the "photoelectrons" that are ejected from this surface.

Picture the Problem
Our sketch shows a beam of white light, represented by photons with different frequencies, incident on a sodium surface. Photoelectrons are ejected from this surface with a kinetic energy that depends on the frequency of the photon that was absorbed.

Strategy

a. We can find the cutoff frequency, f_0, for sodium using $f_0 = W_0/h$, with $W_0 = 2.28$ eV. Frequencies between the cutoff frequency and the maximum frequency in the beam of light, 7.90×10^{14} Hz, will eject electrons.

b. We can obtain the maximum kinetic energy for a given frequency, f, from Equation 30–7: $K_{max} = hf - W_0$. Clearly, the higher the frequency, the greater the maximum kinetic energy. It follows, then, that the greatest possible maximum kinetic energy corresponds to the highest frequency in the beam, 7.90×10^{14} Hz.

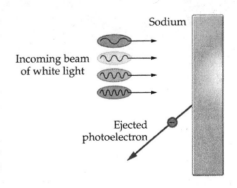

Solution
Part (a)

1. Use $f_0 = W_0/h$ to calculate the cutoff frequency for sodium:

$$f_0 = \frac{W_0}{h} = \frac{(2.28\ \text{eV})\left(\dfrac{1.60 \times 10^{-19}\ \text{J}}{1\ \text{eV}}\right)}{6.63 \times 10^{-34}\ \text{J} \cdot \text{s}} = 5.50 \times 10^{14}\ \text{Hz}$$

2. The frequencies that eject electrons are those between the cutoff frequency and the highest frequency in the beam:

frequencies in this beam that eject electrons:
5.50×10^{14} Hz to 7.90×10^{14} Hz

continued on next page

Science Fundamentals Second Edition

continued from previous page

Part (b)

3. Using $K_{max} = hf - W_0$, calculate K_{max} for the maximum frequency in the beam, $f = 7.90 \times 10^{14}$ Hz:

$$K_{max} = hf - W_0$$
$$= (6.63 \times 10^{-34} \text{ J} \cdot \text{s})(7.90 \times 10^{14} \text{ Hz})$$
$$- (2.28 \text{ eV})\left(\frac{1.60 \times 10^{-19} \text{ J}}{1 \text{ eV}}\right) = 1.59 \times 10^{-19} \text{ J}$$

Insight

Note that most of the photons in a beam of white light will eject electrons from sodium, and that the maximum kinetic energy of one of these photoelectrons is about 1 eV.

Practice Problem

What frequency of light would be necessary to give a maximum kinetic energy of 2.00 eV to the photoelectrons from this surface? [**Answer:** 1.03×10^{15} Hz]

Some related homework problems: Problem 25, Problem 26, Problem 27

CONCEPTUAL CHECKPOINT 30–2   Ejected Electrons

Consider a photoelectric experiment such as the one illustrated in Figure 30–5. A beam of light with a frequency greater than the cutoff frequency shines on the emitter. If the frequency of this beam is increased while the intensity is held constant, does the number of electrons ejected per second from the metal surface (a) increase, (b) decrease, or (c) stay the same?

Reasoning and Discussion

Increasing the frequency of the beam means that each photon carries more energy; however, we know that the intensity of the beam remains constant. It follows, then, that fewer photons hit the surface per time—otherwise the intensity would increase. Since fewer photons hit the surface per time, fewer electrons are ejected per time.

Answer:
(b) The number of electrons ejected per second decreases.

Applications of the photoelectric effect are in common use all around us. For example, if you have ever dashed into an elevator as its doors were closing, you were probably saved from being crushed by the photoelectric effect. Many elevators and garage-door systems use a beam of light and a photoelectric device known as a *photocell* as a safety feature. As long as the beam of light strikes the photocell, the photoelectric effect generates enough ejected electrons to produce a detectable electric current. When the light beam is blocked—by a late arrival at the elevator, for example—the electric current produced by the photocell is interrupted and the doors are signaled to open. Similar photocells automatically turn on streetlights at dusk and measure the amount of light entering a camera.

REAL-WORLD PHYSICS
Photocells

▶ The photoelectric effect is the basic mechanism used by photovoltaic cells, which are now used to power both terrestrial devices such as pay phones (left) and the solar panels that supply electricity to the Hubble Space Telescope (right).

Photocells are also the basic unit in the *solar energy panels* that convert some of the energy in sunlight into electrical energy. A small version of a solar energy panel can be found on many pocket calculators. These panels are efficient enough to operate their calculators with nothing more than dim indoor lighting. Larger outdoor panels can operate billboards and safety lights in remote areas far from commercial power lines. Truly large solar panels, 240 ft in length, power the International Space Station and are so large that they make the station visible to the naked eye from Earth's surface. These applications of solar panels may only hint at the potential for solar energy in the future, however, especially when one considers that sunlight delivers about 200,000 times more energy to Earth each day than all the world's electrical energy production combined.

Finally, it is interesting to note that though Einstein is best known for his development of the theory of relativity, he was awarded the Nobel Prize in physics not for relativity but for the photoelectric effect.

REAL-WORLD PHYSICS
Solar energy panels

Atomic Physics

A number of animals, including many species of coral, sponges, and even scorpions, emit beautiful and sometimes eerie colors when illuminated by ultraviolet light. We do not ordinarily expect rabbits to fall into this category. However, scientists recently inserted a jellyfish gene that directs the production of green fluorescent protein (GFP) into the fertilized egg of a rabbit. The result was Alba, the "GFP bunny"—the world's first fluorescent rabbit. This chapter explores our modern understanding of the structure of the atom, which makes it possible to explain not only the phenomenon of fluorescence but many others as well, including the properties of the chemical elements and the generation of laser light.

In today's world it is taken for granted that we, along with everything else on Earth, are made of atoms. Although it may seem surprising at first, this belief in atoms has not always been universal. As recently as the first part of the twentieth century there was still serious debate about the microscopic nature of matter. With the advent of quantum physics, however, the debate quickly faded away as atomic structure came to be understood in ever greater detail.

In this chapter we begin by developing the quantum model of the simplest of all atoms—the hydrogen atom. We then show that the basic features of hydrogen apply to more complex atoms as well. As a result, we are able to understand—in detail—the arrangement of elements in the periodic table. That quantum physics can describe the structure of an atom, and show why the various elements have their characteristic properties, is one of the greatest successes of modern science.

Science Fundamentals Second Edition

31-1 Early Models of the Atom

Speculations about the microscopic structure of matter have intrigued humankind for thousands of years. Ancient Greek philosophers, including Leucippus and Democritus, considered the question of what would happen if you took a small object, like a block of copper, and cut it in half, then cut it in half again, and again, for many subsequent divisions. They reasoned that eventually you would reduce the block to a single speck of copper that could not be divided further. This smallest piece of an element was called the **atom** (a + tom), which means, literally, "without division."

It was not until the late nineteenth century, however, that the question of atoms began to yield to direct scientific investigation. We now consider some of the more important early developments in atomic models that helped lead to our current understanding.

The Thomson Model: Plum Pudding

In 1897 the English physicist J. J. Thomson (1856-1940) discovered a "particle" that is smaller in size and thousands of times less massive than even the smallest atom. The **electron,** as this particle was named, was also found to have a negative electric charge—in contrast with atoms, which are electrically neutral. Thomson proposed, therefore, that atoms have an internal structure that includes both electrons and a quantity of positively charged matter. The latter would account for most of the mass of an atom, and would have a charge equal in magnitude to the charge on the electrons.

The picture of an atom that Thomson settled on is one he referred to as the "plum-pudding model." In this model, electrons are embedded in a more or less uniform distribution of positive charge—like raisins spread throughout a pudding. This model is illustrated in **Figure 31-1**. Although the plum-pudding model was in agreement with everything Thomson knew about atoms at the time, new experiments were soon to rule out this model and replace it with one that was more like the solar system than a pudding.

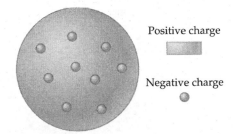

Positive charge

Negative charge

▲ FIGURE 31-1 **The plum-pudding model of an atom**

The model of an atom proposed by J. J. Thomson consists of a uniform positive charge, which accounts for most of the mass of an atom, with small negatively charged electrons scattered throughout, like raisins in a pudding.

The Rutherford Model: A Miniature Solar System

Inspired by the findings and speculations of Thomson, other physicists began to investigate atomic structure. In 1909, Ernest Rutherford (1871-1937) and his coworkers Hans Geiger (1882-1945) and Ernest Marsden (1889-1970) (at that time a twenty-year-old undergraduate) decided to test Thomson's model by directing a beam of positively charged particles, known as **alpha particles,** at a thin gold foil. Since alpha particles—which were later found to be the nuclei of helium atoms—carry a positive charge, they should be deflected as they pass through the positively charged "pudding" in the gold foil. The deflection should have the following properties: (i) it should be relatively small, since the alpha particles have a substantial mass and the positive charge in the atom is spread out; and (ii) all the alpha particles should be deflected in roughly the same way, since the positive pudding fills virtually all space.

When Geiger and Marsden performed the experiment, their results were not in agreement with these predictions. In fact, most of the alpha particles passed right through the foil as if it were not there—as if the atoms in the foil were mostly empty space. Because the results were rather surprising, Rutherford suggested that the experiment be modified to look not only for alpha particles with small angles of deflection—as originally expected—but for ones with large deflections as well.

This suggestion turned out to be an inspired hunch. Not only were large-angle deflections observed, but some of the alpha particles, in fact, were found to have practically reversed their direction of motion. Rutherford was stunned. In his own words, "It was almost as incredible as if you fired a fifteen-inch shell at a piece of tissue paper and it came back and hit you."

Science Fundamentals Second Edition

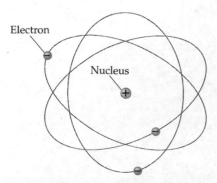

Electron

Nucleus

▲ **FIGURE 31–2 The solar system model of an atom**
Ernest Rutherford proposed that an atom is like a miniature solar system, with a massive positively charged nucleus orbited by lightweight negatively charged electrons.

To account for the results of these experiments, Rutherford proposed that an atom has a structure similar to that of the solar system, as illustrated in **Figure 31–2**. In particular, he imagined that the lightweight, negatively charged electrons orbit a small, positively charged **nucleus** containing almost all the atom's mass. In this nuclear model of the atom, most of the atom is indeed empty space, allowing the majority of the alpha particles to pass right through. Furthermore, the positive charge of the atom is now highly concentrated in a small nucleus, rather than spread throughout the atom. This means that an alpha particle that happens to make a head-on collision with the nucleus can actually be turned around, as observed in the experiments.

To see just how small the nucleus must be in his model, Rutherford combined the experimental data with detailed theoretical calculations. His result was that the radius of a nucleus must be smaller than the diameter of the atom by a factor of about 10,000. To put this value into perspective, imagine an atom magnified in size until its nucleus is as large as the Sun. At what distance would an electron orbit in this "atomic" solar system? Using the factor given by Rutherford, we find that the orbit of the electron would have a radius essentially the same as the orbit of Pluto—inside this radius would be only empty space and the nucleus. Thus an atom must have an even larger fraction of empty space than the solar system!

Although Rutherford's nuclear model of the atom seems reasonable, it contains fatal flaws. First, an orbiting electron undergoes a centripetal acceleration toward the nucleus (Chapter 6). As we know from Section 25–1, however, any electric charge that accelerates gives off energy in the form of electromagnetic radiation. Thus, an electron continually radiating energy as it orbits is similar to a satellite losing energy to air resistance when it orbits too close to the Earth's atmosphere. Just as in the case of a satellite, an electron would spiral inward and eventually plunge into the nucleus. Since the entire process of collapse would occur in a fraction of a second (about 10^{-9} s in fact), the atoms in Rutherford's model would simply not be stable—in contrast with the observed stability of atoms in nature.

Even if we ignore the stability problem for a moment, there is another serious discrepancy between Rutherford's model and experiment. Maxwell's equations state that the frequency of radiation from an orbiting electron should be the same as the frequency of its orbit. In the case of an electron spiraling inward the frequency would increase continuously. Thus if we look at light coming from an atom, the Rutherford model indicates that we should see a continuous range of frequencies. This prediction is in striking contrast with experiments, which show that light coming from an atom has only certain discrete frequencies and wavelengths, as we discuss in the next section.

Nuclear Physics and Nuclear Radiation

32–1   The Constituents and Structure
         of Nuclei   1072

32–2   Radioactivity   1076

32–3   Half-Life and Radioactive Dating   1083

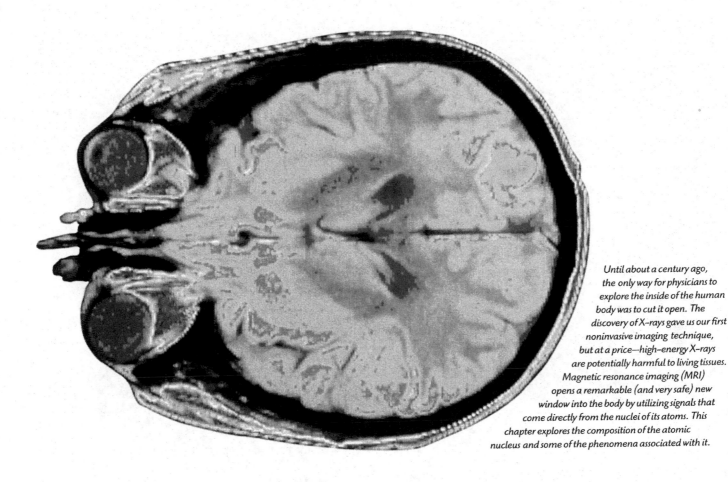

Until about a century ago, the only way for physicians to explore the inside of the human body was to cut it open. The discovery of X–rays gave us our first noninvasive imaging technique, but at a price—high–energy X–rays are potentially harmful to living tissues. Magnetic resonance imaging (MRI) opens a remarkable (and very safe) new window into the body by utilizing signals that come directly from the nuclei of its atoms. This chapter explores the composition of the atomic nucleus and some of the phenomena associated with it.

In the previous chapter our focus was almost entirely on the electrons in an atom. We studied their orbits and energies, their jumps from orbit to orbit, and the photons they emitted or absorbed. The nucleus played little role in these considerations. It was treated as a point object at the center of the atom, providing the electrostatic force necessary to hold the atom together.

The nucleus is much more than a point, however. Most nuclei contain a number of strongly interacting particles packed closely together in a more or less spherical assembly. The energies associated with changes inside a nucleus are orders of magnitude greater than those involved in chemical reactions, which involve only the electrons. It is for this reason that the Sun, which is powered by nuclear reactions, can burn for many billions of years—if the Sun were powered by chemical reactions it would have burned out after giving off light for only a few million years. This chapter considers the physics at play in the nucleus, discusses the nuclear reactions that occur in the Sun and in nuclear power plants, and describes a number of biomedical applications related to the nucleus.

1071

32–1 The Constituents and Structure of Nuclei

The simplest nucleus is that of the hydrogen atom. This nucleus consists of a single **proton**, whose mass is about 1836 times greater than the mass of an electron and whose electric charge is $+e$. All other nuclei contain neutrons in addition to protons. The **neutron** is an electrically neutral particle (its electric charge is zero) with a mass just slightly greater than that of the proton. No other particles are found in nuclei. Collectively, protons and neutrons are referred to as **nucleons.**

Nuclei are characterized by the number and type of nucleons they contain. First, the **atomic number,** Z, is defined as the number of protons in a nucleus. In an electrically neutral atom, the number of electrons will also be equal to Z. Next, the number of neutrons in a nucleus is designated by the **neutron number,** N. Finally, the total number of nucleons in a nucleus is the **mass number,** A. These definitions are summarized in Table 32–1. Clearly, the mass number is the sum of the atomic number and the neutron number:

$$A = Z + N \qquad\qquad 32\text{–}1$$

A special notation is used to indicate the composition of a nucleus. Consider, for example, an unstable but very useful form of carbon known as carbon-14. The nucleus of carbon-14 is written as follows:

$$^{14}_{6}\text{C}$$

In this expression, C represents the chemical element carbon. The number 6 is the atomic number of carbon, $Z = 6$, and the number 14 is the mass number of this nucleus, $A = 14$. This means that carbon-14 has 14 nucleons in its nucleus. The neutron number can be found by solving Equation 32–1 for N: $N = A - Z = 14 - 6 = 8$. Thus the nucleus of carbon-14 consists of 6 protons and 8 neutrons. The most common form of carbon is carbon-12, whose nucleus is designated as follows: $^{12}_{6}\text{C}$. This nucleus has 6 protons and 6 neutrons.

In general, the nucleus of an arbitrary element, X, with atomic number Z and mass number A, is represented as

$$^{A}_{Z}X$$

Note that once a given element is specified, the value of Z is known. As a result, the subscript Z is sometimes omitted.

TABLE 32–1
Numbers That Characterize a Nucleus

Z	Atomic number = number of protons in nucleus
N	Neutron number = number of neutrons in nucleus
A	Mass number = number of nucleons in nucleus

EXERCISE 32–1

    a. Give the symbol for a nucleus of aluminum that contains 14 neutrons.

    b. Tritium is a type of "heavy hydrogen." The nucleus of tritium can be written as $^{3}_{1}\text{H}$. What is the number of protons and neutrons in a tritium nucleus?

Solution

    a. Looking up aluminum in the periodic table in Appendix E, we find that $Z = 13$. In addition, we are given that $N = 14$. Therefore, $A = Z + N = 27$, and hence the symbol for this nucleus is $^{27}_{13}\text{Al}$.

    b. We obtain the number of protons from the subscript; therefore, $Z = 1$. The number of neutrons, from Equation 32–1, is $N = A - Z$, where A is the superscript. Therefore, the number of neutrons is $N = 3 - 1 = 2$.

All nuclei of a given element have the same number of protons, Z. They may have different numbers of neutrons, N, however. Nuclei with the same value of Z but different values of N are referred to as **isotopes.** For example, $^{12}_{6}\text{C}$ and $^{13}_{6}\text{C}$ are two isotopes of carbon, with $^{12}_{6}\text{C}$ being the most common one, constituting about 98.89% of naturally occurring carbon. About 1.11% of natural carbon is $^{13}_{6}\text{C}$. Values for the percentage abundance of various isotopes can be found in Appendix F.

Also given in Appendix F are the atomic masses of many common isotopes. These masses are given in terms of the **atomic mass unit,** u, defined so that the

Science Fundamentals Second Edition

mass of one atom of $^{12}_{6}C$ is exactly 12 u. The value of u is as follows:

Definition of Atomic Mass Unit, u

$$1\,u = 1.660540 \times 10^{-27}\,kg \qquad\qquad 32\text{--}2$$

SI unit: kg

Protons have a mass just slightly greater than 1 u, and the neutron is slightly more massive than the proton. The precise masses of the proton and neutron are given in Table 32–2, along with the mass of the electron.

TABLE 32–2 Mass and Charge of Particles in the Atom

Particle	Mass (kg)	Mass (MeV/c^2)	Mass (u)	Charge (C)
Proton	1.672623×10^{-27}	938.28	1.007276	$+1.6022 \times 10^{-19}$
Neutron	1.674929×10^{-27}	939.57	1.008665	0
Electron	9.109390×10^{-31}	0.511	0.0005485799	-1.6022×10^{-19}

When we consider nuclear reactions later in this chapter, an important consideration will be the energy equivalent of a given mass, as given by Einstein's famous relation, $E = mc^2$ (Equation 30–7). The energy equivalent of one atomic mass unit is

$$E = mc^2 = (1\,u)c^2$$

$$= (1.660540 \times 10^{-27}\,kg)(2.998 \times 10^8\,m/s)^2\left(\frac{1\,eV}{1.6022 \times 10^{-19}\,J}\right)$$

$$= 931.5\,MeV$$

where $1\,MeV = 10^6\,eV$. When we consider that the ionization energy of hydrogen is only 13.6 eV, it is clear that the energy equivalent of nucleons is enormous compared with typical atomic energies. In general, energies involving the nucleus are on the order of MeV, and energies associated with the electrons in an atom are on the order of eV. Finally, because mass and energy can be converted from one form to the other, it is common to express the atomic mass unit in terms of energy as follows:

$$1\,u = 931.5\,MeV/c^2 \qquad\qquad 32\text{--}3$$

The masses of the proton, neutron, and electron are also given in units of MeV/c^2 in Table 32–2.

Nuclear Size and Density

To obtain an estimate for the size of a nucleus, Rutherford did a simple calculation using energy conservation. He considered the case of a particle of charge $+q$ and mass m approaching a nucleus of charge $+Ze$ with a speed v. He further assumed that the approach was head-on. At some distance, d, from the center of the nucleus, the incoming particle comes to rest instantaneously, before turning around. It follows that the radius of the nucleus is less than d. In Example 32–1 we obtain a symbolic expression for the distance d.

EXAMPLE 32–1 Setting a Limit on the Radius of a Nucleus

A particle of mass m, charge $+q$, and speed v heads directly toward a distant, stationary nucleus of charge $+Ze$. Find the distance of closest approach between the incoming particle and the center of the nucleus.

Picture the Problem
The incoming particle moves on a line that passes through the center of the nucleus. Far from the nucleus, the particle's speed is v. The particle turns around (comes to rest instantaneously) a distance d from the center of the nucleus.

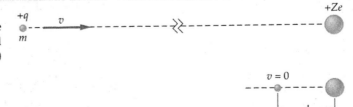

continued on next page

continued from previous page

Strategy

We can find the distance d by applying energy conservation. In particular, the initial energy of the system is the kinetic energy of the particle, $\frac{1}{2}mv^2$, assuming the particle approaches the nucleus from infinity. The final energy is the electric potential energy, $U = kq_1q_2/r = k(Ze)q/d$. Setting these energies equal to each other allows us to solve for d.

Solution

1. Write an expression for the initial energy of the system:

$$E_i = \tfrac{1}{2}mv^2$$

2. Write an expression for the final energy of the system:

$$E_f = \frac{k(Ze)q}{d}$$

3. Set the final energy equal to the initial energy and solve for d:

$$\tfrac{1}{2}mv^2 = \frac{k(Ze)q}{d}$$

$$d = \frac{kZeq}{\left(\tfrac{1}{2}mv^2\right)}$$

Insight

Notice that the distance of closest approach is inversely proportional to the initial kinetic energy of the incoming particle and directly proportional to the charge on the nucleus.

Practice Problem

Find the distance at which the speed of the incoming particle is equal to $\tfrac{1}{2}v$. **[Answer:** $\dfrac{kZeq}{\frac{3}{4}\left(\frac{1}{2}mv^2\right)}$**]**

Some related homework problems: Problem 6, Problem 7

Using the result obtained in Example 32–1, Rutherford found that for an alpha particle approaching a gold nucleus in one of his experiments, the distance of closest approach was 3.2×10^{-14} m. A similar calculation for alpha particles fired at silver atoms gives a closest approach distance of 2.0×10^{-14} m. This suggests that the size of the nucleus varies from element to element; in particular, the nucleus of silver is smaller than that of gold. In fact, more careful measurements since Rutherford's time have established that the average radius of a nucleus of mass number A is given approximately by the following expression:

$$r = (1.2 \times 10^{-15}\ \text{m})A^{1/3} \qquad \text{32–4}$$

Notice that the length scale of the nucleus is on the order of 10^{-15} m, as opposed to the length scale of an atom, which is on the order of 10^{-10} m. Recall that 10^{-15} m is referred to as a *femtometer* (fm). To honor the pioneering work of Enrico Fermi (1901–1954) in the field of nuclear physics, the femtometer is often referred to as the **fermi**:

Definition of the Fermi, fm

1 fermi = 1 fm = 10^{-15} m

SI unit: m

We now use Equation 32–4 to find the radius of a particular nucleus.

EXERCISE 32–2

Find the radius of a $^{14}_{6}$C nucleus.

Solution

Substitute $A = 14$ in Equation 32–4:

$$r = (1.2 \times 10^{-15}\ \text{m})(14)^{1/3} = 2.9 \times 10^{-15}\ \text{m} = 2.9\ \text{fm}$$

The fact that the radius of a nucleus depends on $A^{1/3}$ has interesting consequences for the density of the nucleus, and these are explored in the next Example.

EXAMPLE 32–2 Nuclear Density

Using the expression $r = (1.2 \times 10^{-15}\,\text{m})A^{1/3}$, calculate the density of a nucleus with mass number A.

Picture the Problem
Our sketch shows a collection of neutrons and protons in a densely packed nucleus of radius r.

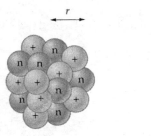

 Proton

 Neutron

Strategy
To find the density of a nucleus, we must divide its mass, M, by its volume, V. Ignoring the small difference in mass between a neutron and a proton, we can express the mass of a nucleus as $M = Am$, where $m = 1.67 \times 10^{-27}$ kg. The volume of a nucleus is simply the volume of a sphere of radius r; $V = 4\pi r^3/3$.

Solution

1. Write an expression for the mass of a nucleus:

$$M = Am = A(1.67 \times 10^{-27}\,\text{kg})$$

2. Write an expression for the volume of a nucleus:

$$V = \tfrac{4}{3}\pi r^3 = \tfrac{4}{3}\pi[(1.2 \times 10^{-15}\,\text{m})A^{1/3}]^3$$
$$= \tfrac{4}{3}\pi(1.7 \times 10^{-45}\,\text{m}^3)A$$

3. Divide the mass by the volume to find the density:

$$\rho = \frac{M}{V} = \frac{Am}{\tfrac{4}{3}\pi(1.7 \times 10^{-45}\,\text{m}^3)A}$$
$$= \frac{(1.67 \times 10^{-27}\,\text{kg})}{\tfrac{4}{3}\pi(1.7 \times 10^{-45}\,\text{m}^3)} = 2.3 \times 10^{17}\,\text{kg/m}^3$$

Insight
Note that the density of a nucleus is found to be *independent* of the mass number, A. This means that a nucleus can be thought of as a collection of closely packed nucleons, much like a group of marbles in a bag. The neutrons in a nucleus serve to separate the protons, thereby reducing their mutual electrostatic repulsion.

The density of a nucleus is incredibly large. For example, a single teaspoon of nuclear matter would weigh about a trillion tons.

Practice Problem
Find the surface area of a nucleus in terms of the mass number, A, assuming it to be a sphere.
[**Answer:** area = $(1.8 \times 10^{-29}\,\text{m}^2)A^{2/3}$]

Some related homework problems: Problem 8, Problem 9

Nuclear Stability

We know that like charges repel one another, and that the force of repulsion increases rapidly with decreasing distance. It follows that protons in a nucleus, with a separation of only about a fermi, must exert relatively large forces on one another. Applying Coulomb's law (Equation 19–5), we find the following force for two protons (charge $+e$) separated by a distance of 10^{-15} m:

$$F = \frac{ke^2}{r^2} = 230\,\text{N}$$

The acceleration such a force would give to a proton is $a = F/m = (230\,\text{N})/(1.67 \times 10^{-27}\,\text{kg}) = 1.4 \times 10^{29}\,\text{m/s}^2$, which is about 10^{28} times greater than the acceleration of gravity! Thus, if protons in the nucleus experienced only the electrostatic force, the nucleus would fly apart in an instant. It follows that large attractive forces must also act within the nucleus.

The attractive force that holds a nucleus together is called the **strong nuclear force**. This force has the following properties:

- The strong force is short range, acting only to distances of a couple fermis.
- The strong force is attractive and acts with nearly equal strength between protons and protons, protons and neutrons, and neutrons and neutrons.

In addition, the strong nuclear force does not act on electrons. As a result, it has no effect on the chemical properties of an atom.

Science Fundamentals Second Edition

▶ **FIGURE 32–1 *N* and *Z* for stable and unstable nuclei**

Stable nuclei with proton numbers less than 104 are indicated by small red dots. Notice that large nuclei have significantly more neutrons, N, than protons, Z. The inset shows unstable nuclei and their decay modes for proton numbers between 65 and 80.

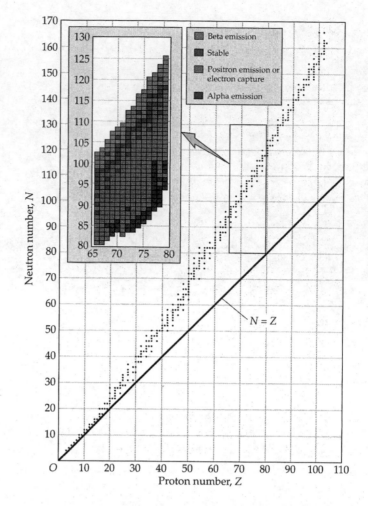

It is the competition between the repulsive electrostatic forces and the attractive strong nuclear forces that determines whether a given nucleus is stable. **Figure 32–1** shows the neutron number, N, and atomic number (proton number), Z, for nuclei that are stable. Note that nuclei of relatively small atomic number are most stable when the numbers of protons and neutrons in the nucleus are approximately equal, $N = Z$. For example, $^{12}_{6}C$ and $^{13}_{6}C$ are both stable. As the atomic number increases, however, we see that the points corresponding to stable nuclei deviate from the line $N = Z$. In fact, we see that large stable nuclei tend to contain significantly more neutrons than protons, as in the case of $^{185}_{75}Re$. Since all nucleons experience the strong nuclear force, but only the protons experience the electrostatic force, the neutrons effectively "dilute" the nuclear charge density, reducing the effect of the repulsive forces that otherwise would make the nucleus disintegrate.

As the number of protons in a nucleus increases, however, a point is reached at which the strong nuclear forces are no longer able to compensate for the repulsive forces between protons. In fact, the largest number of protons in a stable nucleus is $Z = 83$, corresponding to the element bismuth. Nuclei with more than 83 protons are simply not stable, as can be seen by noting that all elements with $Z > 83$ in Appendix F decay in a finite time—that is, they have a finite half-life. (We shall discuss the half-life of unstable nuclei in detail in Section 32–3.) The nuclei of many well-known elements, such as radon and uranium, disintegrate—decay—in a finite time. We turn now to a discussion of the various ways in which an unstable nucleus decays.

32–2 Radioactivity

An unstable nucleus does not last forever—sooner or later it changes its composition by emitting a particle of one type or another. Alternatively, a nucleus in an excited state may rearrange its nucleons into a lower-energy state and emit a high-energy photon. We refer to such processes as the **decay** of a nucleus, and the various emissions that result are known collectively as **radioactivity.**

When a nucleus undergoes radioactive decay, the mass of the system decreases. That is, the mass of the initial nucleus before decay is greater than the mass of the resulting nucleus plus the mass of the emitted particle. The difference in mass, $\Delta m < 0$, appears as a release of energy, according to the relation $E = |\Delta m|c^2$. The mass difference for any given decay can be determined by referring to Appendix F. Note that the atomic masses listed in Appendix F are the masses of neutral atoms; that is, the values given in the table include the mass of the electrons in an atom. This factor must be considered whenever the mass difference of a reaction is calculated, as we shall see later in this section.

Three types of particles with mass are given off during the various processes of radioactive decay. They are as follows:

- Alpha (α) particles, which are the nuclei of $^4_2$He. Note that an alpha particle consists of two protons and two neutrons. When a nucleus decays by giving off alpha particles, we say that it emits α rays.
- Electrons, also referred to as beta (β) particles. The electrons given off by a nucleus are called β rays, or β^- rays to be more precise. (The minus sign is a reminder that the charge of an electron is $-e$.)
- **Positrons,** which have the same mass as an electron but a charge of $+e$. If a nucleus gives off positrons, we say that it emits β^+ rays. (A positron, which is short for "positive electron," is the **antiparticle** of the ordinary electron. Positrons will be considered in greater detail in Section 32–7.)

Finally, radioactivity may take the form of a photon rather than a particle with nonzero mass:

- A nucleus in an excited state may emit a high-energy photon, a gamma (γ) ray, and drop to a lower-energy state.

The following Conceptual Checkpoint examines the behavior of radioactivity in a magnetic field.

CONCEPTUAL CHECKPOINT 32–1   Identify the Radiation

A sample of radioactive material is placed at the bottom of a small hole drilled into a piece of lead. The sample emits α rays, β^- rays, and γ rays into a region of constant magnetic field. It is observed that the radiation follows three distinct paths, 1, 2, and 3, as shown in the sketch. Identify each path with the corresponding type of radiation: (a) path 1, α rays; path 2, β^- rays; path 3, γ rays; (b) path 1, β^- rays; path 2, γ rays; path 3, α rays; or (c) path 1, α rays; path 2, γ rays; path 3, β^- rays.

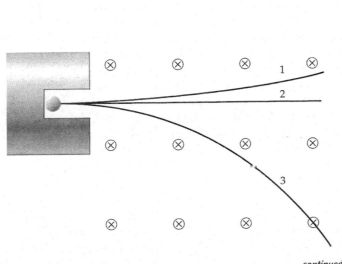

continued on next page

Science Fundamentals Second Edition

continued from previous page

Reasoning and Discussion

First, because γ rays are uncharged, they are not deflected by the magnetic field. It follows that path 2 corresponds to γ rays.

Next, the right-hand rule for the magnetic force (Section 22–2) indicates that positively charged particles will be deflected upward, and negatively charged particles will be deflected downward. As a result, path 1 corresponds to α rays, and path 3 corresponds to β⁻ rays.

Answer:
(c) Path 1, α rays; path 2, γ rays; path 3, β⁻ rays.

Radioactivity was discovered by the French physicist Antoine Henri Becquerel (1852–1908) in 1896 when he observed that uranium was able to expose photographic emulsion, even when the emulsion was covered. Thus radioactivity has the ability to penetrate various materials. In fact, the various types of radioactivity were initially named according to their ability to penetrate, starting with α rays, which are the least penetrating. Typical penetrating abilities for α, β, and γ rays are as follows:

- α rays can barely penetrate a sheet of paper.
- β rays (both β⁻ and β⁺) can penetrate a few millimeters of aluminum.
- γ rays can penetrate several centimeters of lead.

We turn now to a detailed examination of each of these types of decay.

Alpha Decay

When a nucleus decays by giving off an α particle ($^4_2$He), it loses two protons and two neutrons. As a result, its atomic number, Z, decreases by 2, and its mass number decreases by 4. Symbolically, we can write this process as follows:

$$^A_Z X \longrightarrow \, ^{A-4}_{Z-2} Y + ^4_2 He$$

where X is referred to as the **parent nucleus,** and Y is the **daughter nucleus.** Notice that the sum of the atomic numbers on the right side of this process is equal to the atomic number on the left side; similar remarks apply to the mass numbers.

The next Example considers the alpha decay of uranium-238. We first use conservation of atomic number and mass number to determine the identity of the daughter nucleus. Next, we use the mass difference to calculate the amount of energy released by the decay.

PROBLEM-SOLVING NOTE

The Effects of Alpha Decay

In alpha decay, the total number of protons is the same before and after the reaction. The same is true of the total number of neutrons. On the other hand, the mass number of the daughter nucleus is 4 less than the mass number of the parent nucleus. Similarly, the atomic number of the daughter nucleus is 2 less than the atomic number of the parent nucleus.

PROBLEM-SOLVING NOTE

Atomic Masses Include Electrons

When calculating the mass difference in a nuclear reaction, be sure to note that the atomic masses in Appendix F include the electrons that would be present in a neutral atom. The only item in Appendix F to which this does *not* apply is the neutron.

EXAMPLE 32–3 Uranium Decay

Determine (a) the daughter nucleus and (b) the energy released when $^{238}_{92}$U undergoes alpha decay.

Picture the Problem

Our sketch shows the specified decay of $^{238}_{92}$U into a daughter nucleus plus an α particle. Note that the number of neutrons and protons is indicated for $^{238}_{92}$U. The α particle consists of two neutrons and two protons.

Strategy

a. We can identify the daughter nucleus by requiring that the total number of neutrons and protons be the same before and after the decay.

b. To find the energy, we first calculate the mass before and after the decay. The magnitude of the difference in mass, $|\Delta m|$, times the speed of light squared, c^2, gives the amount of energy released.

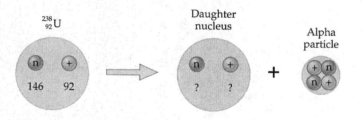

Solution

Part (a)

1. Determine the number of neutrons and protons in the daughter nucleus. Add these numbers together to obtain the mass number of the daughter nucleus:

$$N = 146 - 2 = 144$$
$$Z = 92 - 2 = 90$$
$$A = N + Z = 144 + 90 = 234$$

2. Referring to Appendix F, we see that the daughter nucleus is thorium-234:

$$^{234}_{90}\text{Th}$$

Part (b)

3. Use Appendix F to find the initial mass of the system; that is, the mass of a $^{238}_{92}$U atom:

$$m_i = 238.050786 \text{ u}$$

4. Use Appendix F to find the final mass of the system; that is, the mass of a $^{234}_{90}$Th atom plus the mass of a $^4_2$He atom:

$$m_f = 234.043596 \text{ u} + 4.002603 \text{ u} = 238.046199 \text{ u}$$

5. Calculate the mass difference and the corresponding energy release (recall that 1 u = 931.5 MeV/c^2):

$$\Delta m = m_f - m_i$$
$$= 238.046199 \text{ u} - 238.050786 \text{ u} = -0.004587 \text{ u}$$

$$E = |\Delta m|c^2 = (0.004587 \text{ u})\left(\frac{931.5 \text{ MeV}/c^2}{1 \text{ u}}\right)c^2$$

$$= 4.273 \text{ MeV}$$

Insight

Each of the masses used in this decay includes the electrons of the corresponding neutral atom. Since the number of electrons initially (92) is the same as the number of electrons in a thorium atom (90) plus the number of electrons in a helium atom (2), the electrons make no contribution to the total mass difference, Δm.

Practice Problem

Find the daughter nucleus and energy released when $^{226}_{88}$Ra undergoes alpha decay.   [**Answer:** $^{222}_{86}$Rn, 4.871 MeV]

Some related homework problems: Problem 16, Problem 17

A considerable amount of energy is released in the alpha decay of uranium-238. As indicated in **Figure 32–2**, this energy appears as kinetic energy of the daughter nucleus and the α particle as they move off in opposite directions. The following Conceptual Checkpoint compares the kinetic energy of the daughter nucleus with that of the α particle.

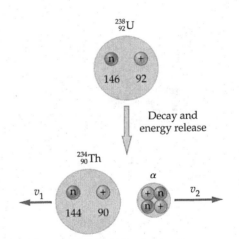

▲ **FIGURE 32–2 Alpha decay of uranium-238**
When $^{238}_{92}$U decays into $^{234}_{90}$Th and an alpha particle, the mass of the system decreases. The "lost" mass is actually converted into energy; it appears as the kinetic energy of the $^{234}_{90}$Th nucleus and the alpha particle.

CONCEPTUAL CHECKPOINT 32–2   Compare Kinetic Energies

When a stationary $^{238}_{92}$U nucleus decays into a $^{234}_{90}$Th nucleus and an α particle, is the kinetic energy of the α particle (a) greater than, (b) less than, or (c) the same as the kinetic energy of the $^{234}_{90}$Th nucleus?

Reasoning and Discussion

Because no external forces are involved in the decay process, it follows that the momentum of the system is conserved. Letting subscript 1 refer to the $^{234}_{90}$Th nucleus, and subscript 2 to the α particle, the condition for momentum conservation is $m_1v_1 = m_2v_2$. Solving for the speed of the α particle, we have $v_2 = (m_1/m_2)v_1$; that is, the α particle has the greater speed, since m_1 is greater than m_2.

The fact that the α particle has the greater speed does not, in itself, ensure that its kinetic energy is the larger of the two. After all, the α particle also has the smaller mass. To compare the kinetic energies, note that the kinetic energy of the $^{234}_{90}$Th nucleus is $\frac{1}{2}m_1v_1^2$. The kinetic energy of the α particle is $\frac{1}{2}m_2v_2^2 = \frac{1}{2}m_2[(m_1/m_2)v_1]^2 = \frac{1}{2}m_1v_1^2(m_1/m_2) > \frac{1}{2}m_1v_1^2$. Therefore, the α particle carries away the majority of the kinetic energy released in the decay. In this particular case, the α particle has a kinetic energy that is $m_1/m_2 = 234/4 = 58.5$ times greater than the kinetic energy of the $^{234}_{90}$Th nucleus.

Answer:

(a) The α particle has the greater kinetic energy.

REAL-WORLD PHYSICS

Smoke detector

Although you may not be aware of it, many homes are protected from the hazards of fire by a small device—a smoke detector—that uses the alpha decay

of a manmade radioactive isotope, $^{241}_{95}$Am. In this type of smoke detector, a minute quantity of $^{241}_{95}$Am is placed between two metal plates connected to a battery or other source of emf. The α particles emitted by the radioactive source ionize the air, allowing a measurable electric current to flow between the plates. As long as this current flows, the smoke detector remains silent. When smoke enters the detector, however, the ionized air molecules tend to stick to the smoke particles and become neutralized. This reduces the current and triggers the alarm. These "ionization" smoke detectors are more sensitive than the "photoelectric" detectors that rely on the thickness of smoke to dim a beam of light.

▲ Smoke detectors like this one make use of a synthetic radioactive isotope, americium-241. The alpha particles emitted when this isotope decays ionize air molecules, making them able to conduct a small current. Smoke particles neutralize the ions, interrupting the current and setting off an alarm.

Beta Decay

The basic process that occurs in beta decay is the conversion of a neutron to a proton and an electron:

$$^{1}_{0}n \longrightarrow {}^{1}_{1}p + e^-$$

Thus when a nucleus decays by giving off an electron, its mass number is unchanged (since protons and neutrons count equally in determining A), but its atomic number increases by 1. This process can be represented as follows:

$$^{A}_{Z}X \longrightarrow {}^{A}_{Z+1}Y + e^-$$

Similarly, if a nucleus undergoes a different type of decay in which it gives off a positron, the process can be written

$$^{A}_{Z}X \longrightarrow {}^{A}_{Z-1}Y + e^+$$

In the next Example we determine the energy that is released as carbon-14 undergoes beta decay.

EXAMPLE 32–4 Beta Decay of Carbon-14

Find **(a)** the daughter nucleus and **(b)** the energy released when $^{14}_{6}$C undergoes β^- decay.

Picture the Problem
In our sketch we show $^{14}_{6}$C giving off a β^- particle and converting into a daughter nucleus. The number of neutrons and protons in the $^{14}_{6}$C nucleus is indicated. Note that the β^- particle is not a nucleon.

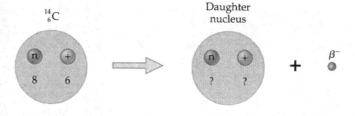

Strategy

a. We can identify the daughter nucleus by requiring that the total number of nucleons be the same before and after the decay. The number of neutrons will be decreased by one, and the number of protons will be increased by one.

b. To find the energy, we begin by calculating the mass before and after the decay. The magnitude of the difference in mass, $|\Delta m|$, times the speed of light squared, c^2, gives the amount of energy released.

Solution

Part (a)

1. Determine the number of neutrons and protons in the daughter nucleus. Add these numbers together to obtain the mass number of the daughter nucleus:

$N = 8 - 1 = 7$
$Z = 6 + 1 = 7$
$A = N + Z = 7 + 7 = 14$

2. Referring to Appendix F, we see that the daughter nucleus is nitrogen-14:

$^{14}_{7}$N

Part (b)

3. Use Appendix F to find the initial mass of the system; that is, the mass of a $^{14}_{6}C$ atom:

$$m_i = 14.003242 \text{ u}$$

4. Use Appendix F to find the final mass of the system, which is simply the mass of a $^{14}_{7}N$ atom (the mass of the β^- particle is included in the mass of $^{14}_{7}N$, as we point out in the Insight):

$$m_f = 14.003074 \text{ u}$$
$$\Delta m = m_f - m_i$$
$$= 14.003074 \text{ u} - 14.003242 \text{ u} = -0.000168 \text{ u}$$

5. Calculate the mass difference and the corresponding energy release (recall that 1 u = 931.5 MeV/c^2):

$$E = |\Delta m| c^2 = (0.000168 \text{ u})\left(\frac{931.5 \text{ MeV}/c^2}{1 \text{ u}}\right)c^2$$
$$= 0.156 \text{ MeV}$$

Insight

With regard to the masses used in this calculation, note that the mass of $^{14}_{6}C$ includes the mass of its 6 electrons. Similarly, the mass of $^{14}_{7}N$ includes the mass of 7 electrons in the neutral $^{14}_{7}N$ atom. However, when the $^{14}_{6}C$ nucleus converts to a $^{14}_{7}N$ nucleus, the number of electrons orbiting the nucleus is still 6. In effect, the newly created $^{14}_{7}N$ atom is missing one electron; that is, the mass of the $^{14}_{7}N$ atom includes the mass of one too many electrons. Therefore, it is not necessary to add the mass of an electron (representing the β^- particle) to the final mass of the system, because this extra electron mass is already included in the mass of the $^{14}_{7}N$ atom.

Practice Problem

Find the daughter nucleus and the energy released when $^{234}_{90}Th$ undergoes β^- decay.　　[**Answer:** $^{234}_{91}Pa$, 0.274 MeV]

Some related homework problems: Problem 18, Problem 20

Referring to Conceptual Checkpoint 32–2, we would expect the kinetic energy of an electron emitted during beta decay to account for most of the energy released by the decay process. In fact, energy conservation allows us to predict the precise amount of kinetic energy the electron should have. It turns out, however, that when the kinetic energy of emitted electrons is measured, a range of values is obtained, as indicated in **Figure 32–3**. Specifically, we find that all electrons given off in beta decay have energies that are less than would be predicted by energy conservation. On closer examination it is found that beta decay seems to violate conservation of linear and angular momentum as well! For these reasons, beta decay was an interesting and intriguing puzzle for physicists.

The resolution of this puzzle was given by Pauli in 1930, when he proposed that the "missing" energy and momentum were actually carried off by a particle that was not observed in the experiments. For this particle to have been unobserved, it must have zero charge and little or no mass. Fermi dubbed Pauli's hypothetical particle the **neutrino,** meaning, literally, "little neutral one." We now know that neutrinos do in fact exist and that they account exactly for the missing energy and momentum. They interact so weakly with matter, however, that it wasn't until 1950 that they were observed experimentally. Recent experiments on neutrinos given off by the Sun provide the best evidence yet that the mass of a neutrino is in fact finite—though extremely small. In fact, the best estimate of the neutrino mass at this time is that it is less than about 7 eV/c^2. For comparison, the mass of the electron is 511,000 eV/c^2.

To give an indication of just how weakly neutrinos interact with matter, only one in every 200 million neutrinos that pass through the Earth interacts with it in any way. As far as the neutrinos are concerned, it is almost as if the Earth did not exist. Right now, in fact, billions of neutrinos are passing through your body every second without the slightest effect.

We can now write the correct expression for the decay of a neutron. Indicating the electron neutrino with the symbol ν_e, we have the following:

$$^{1}_{0}n \longrightarrow {}^{1}_{1}p + e^- + \bar{\nu}_e \qquad\qquad \text{32–5}$$

The bar over the neutrino symbol indicates that the neutrino given off in β^- decay is actually an **antineutrino,** the antiparticle counterpart of the neutrino

PROBLEM-SOLVING NOTE

The Effects of Beta Decay

In β^- decay, the number of neutrons decreases by 1, and the number of protons increases by 1. The mass number is unchanged.

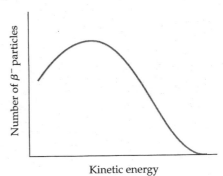

▲ **FIGURE 32–3 Energy of electrons emitted in β^- decay**

When electrons are emitted during β^- decay, they come off with a range of energies. This indicates that another particle (the neutrino) must also be taking away some of the energy.

(just as the positron is the antiparticle of the electron). The neutrino itself is given off in β^+ decay.

Gamma Decay

An atom in an excited state can emit a photon when one of its electrons drops to a lower-energy level. Similarly, a nucleus in an excited state can emit a photon as it decays to a state of lower energy. Since nuclear energies are so much greater than typical atomic energies, the photons given off by a nucleus are highly energetic. In fact, these photons have energies that place them well beyond X-rays in the electromagnetic spectrum. We refer to such high-energy photons as **gamma (γ) rays.**

As an example of a situation in which a γ ray can be given off, consider the following beta decay:

$$^{14}_{6}C \longrightarrow {}^{14}_{7}N^* + e^- + \bar{\nu}_e$$

The asterisk on the nitrogen symbol indicates that the nitrogen nucleus has been left in an excited state as a result of the beta decay. Subsequently, the nitrogen nucleus may decay to its ground state with the emission of a γ ray:

$$^{14}_{7}N^* \longrightarrow {}^{14}_{7}N + \gamma$$

Notice that neither the atomic number nor the mass number is changed by the emission of a γ ray.

ACTIVE EXAMPLE 32–1 Gamma-Ray Emission: Find the Change in Mass

A $^{226}_{88}Ra$ nucleus in an excited state emits a γ ray with a wavelength of 6.67×10^{-12} m. Find the decrease in mass of the $^{226}_{88}Ra$ nucleus as a result of this process.

Solution *(Test your understanding by performing the calculations indicated in each step.)*

1. Find the frequency of the γ ray: $\quad\quad\quad\quad\quad\quad\quad\quad f = c/\lambda = 4.50 \times 10^{19}$ Hz

2. Calculate the energy of the γ ray photon: $\quad\quad\quad\quad E = hf = 0.186$ MeV

3. Determine the mass difference corresponding $\quad\quad |\Delta m| = E/c^2 = 0.000200$ u
   to the energy of the photon:

Insight

As a result of emitting this γ ray, the mass of the $^{226}_{88}Ra$ nucleus decreases by an amount that is about one-third the mass of the electron.

Your Turn

If the wavelength of the emitted gamma ray is doubled, by what factor does the mass difference change?

*(Answers to **Your Turn** problems are given in the back of the book.)*

Radioactive Decay Series

Consider an unstable nucleus that decays and produces a daughter nucleus. If the daughter nucleus is also unstable, it will eventually decay and produce its own daughter nucleus, which may in turn be unstable. In such cases, an original parent nucleus can produce a series of related nuclei referred to as a **radioactive decay series.** An example of a radioactive decay series is shown in **Figure 32–4**. In this case, the parent nucleus is $^{235}_{92}U$, and the final nucleus of the series is $^{207}_{82}Pb$, which is stable.

Notice that several of the intermediate nuclei in this series can decay in two different ways—either by alpha decay or by beta decay. Thus there is a variety of "paths" a $^{235}_{92}U$ nucleus can follow as it transforms into a $^{207}_{82}Pb$ nucleus. In addition, the intermediate nuclei in this series decay fairly rapidly, at least on a geological time scale. For example, any actinium-227 that was present when the Earth formed would have decayed away long ago. The fact that actinium-227 is still found on the Earth today in natural uranium deposits is due to its continual production in this and other decay series.

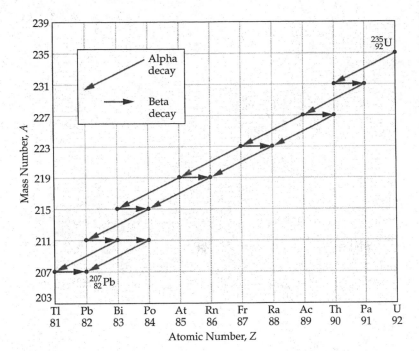

◄ FIGURE 32–4 Radioactive decay series of $^{235}_{92}$U

When $^{235}_{92}$U decays, it passes through a number of intermediate nuclei before reaching the stable end of the series, $^{207}_{82}$Pb. Note that some intermediary nuclei can decay in only one way, whereas others have two decay possibilities.

Activity

The rate at which nuclear decay occurs—that is, the number of decays per second—is referred to as the **activity**. A highly active material has many nuclear decays occurring every second. For example, a typical sample of radium (usually a fraction of a gram) might have 10^5 to 10^{10} decays per second.

The unit we use to measure activity is the curie, named in honor of Pierre (1859–1906) and Marie (1867–1934) Curie, pioneers in the study of radioactivity. The **curie (Ci)** is defined as follows:

$$1 \text{ curie} = 1 \text{ Ci} = 3.7 \times 10^{10} \text{ decays/s} \qquad \textbf{32–6}$$

The reason for this choice is that 1 Ci is roughly the activity of 1 g of radium. In SI units, we measure activity in terms of the **becquerel** (Bq):

$$1 \text{ becquerel} = 1 \text{ Bq} = 1 \text{ decay/s} \qquad \textbf{32–7}$$

The units of activity most often encountered in practical applications are the millicurie ($1 \text{ mCi} = 10^{-3} \text{ Ci}$) and the microcurie ($1 \, \mu\text{Ci} = 10^{-6} \text{ Ci}$).

EXERCISE 32–3

A sample of radium has an activity of 15 μCi. How many decays per second occur in this sample?

Solution

Using the definition given in Equation 32–6, we find

$$15 \, \mu\text{Ci} = 15 \times 10^{-6} \text{ Ci}$$

$$= (15 \times 10^{-6} \text{ Ci})\left(\frac{3.7 \times 10^{10} \text{ decays/s}}{1 \text{ Ci}}\right) = 5.6 \times 10^5 \text{ decays/s}$$

32–3 Half-Life and Radioactive Dating

The phenomenon of radioactive decay, though fundamentally random in its behavior, has certain properties that make it useful as a type of "nuclear clock." In fact, it has been discovered that radioactive decay can be used to date numerous items of interest from the recent—and not so recent—past. In this section we

▶ **FIGURE 32–5 Tossing coins as an analogy for nuclear decay**

The points on this graph show the number of coins remaining (on average) if one starts with 64 coins and removes half with each round of tosses. The curve is a plot of the mathematical function $64e^{-(0.693)t}$, where $t = 1$ means one round of tosses, $t = 2$ means two rounds, and so on.

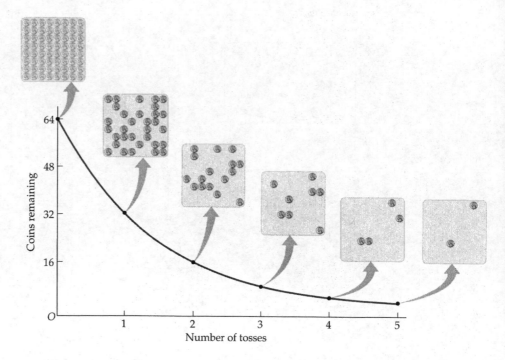

consider the behavior of radioactive decay as a function of time, introduce the concept of a half-life, and show explicitly how these concepts can be applied to dating.

To begin, consider an analogy in which coins represent nuclei, and the side that comes up when a given coin is tossed determines whether the corresponding nucleus decays. Suppose, for example, that we toss a group of 64 coins and remove any coin that comes up tails. We expect that—on average—32 coins will be removed after the first round of tosses. Which coins will be removed—and the precise number that will be removed—cannot be known, because the flip of a coin, like the decay of a nucleus, is a random process. When we toss the remaining 32 coins, we expect an average of 16 more to be removed, and so on, with each round of tosses decreasing the number of coins by a factor of 2. The results after the first few rounds are shown by the points in **Figure 32–5**.

Also shown in Figure 32–5 is a smooth curve representing the following mathematical function:

$$N = (64)e^{-(\ln 2)t} = (64)e^{-(0.693)t} \qquad \text{32-8}$$

where N represents the number of coins, and the time variable, t, represents the number of rounds of tosses. For example, if we set $t = 1$ in Equation 32–8, we find $N = 32$, and if we set $t = 2$, we find $N = 16$. This type of "exponential dependence" is a general feature whenever the number of some quantity increases or decreases by a constant factor with each constant interval of time. Examples include the balance in a bank account with compounding interest and the population of the Earth as a function of time.

When nuclei decay, their behavior is much like that of the coins in our analogy. Which nucleus will decay in a given interval of time, and the precise number that will decay, are controlled by a random process that causes the decay—on average—of a given fraction of the original number of nuclei. Thus the number of nuclei, N, remaining at time t is given by an expression analogous to Equation 32–8:

$$N = N_0 e^{-\lambda t} \qquad \text{32-9}$$

PROBLEM-SOLVING NOTE

Consistent Units and the Decay Constant

When calculating the number of nuclei present at a given time, be sure to use consistent units for the time, t, and the decay constant, λ. For example, if you express λ in units of y^{-1}, measure the time in units of y.

where N_0 is the number of nuclei present at time $t = 0$, and the constant λ is referred to as the **decay constant.** In the analogy of the coins, $N_0 = 64$ and $\lambda = 0.693 \text{ s}^{-1}$. Note that the larger the value of the decay constant, the more rapidly the number of nuclei decreases with time. **Figure 32–6** shows the dependence on λ graphically.

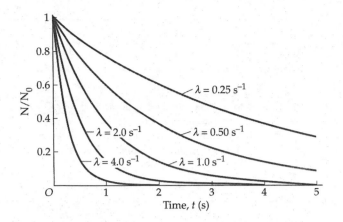

The larger the decay constant, λ, the more rapidly the population of a group of nuclei decreases. In this plot, the value of λ doubles as we move downward from one curve to the next.

ACTIVE EXAMPLE 32–2 Find the Radon Level

Radon can pose a health risk when high levels become trapped in the basement of a house. Suppose 4.75×10^7 radon atoms are in a basement at a time when it is sealed to prevent any additional radon from entering. Given that the decay constant of radon is 0.181 d^{-1}, how many radon atoms remain in the basement after **(a)** 7 d and **(b)** 14 d?

Solution *(Test your understanding by performing the calculations indicated in each step.)*

Part (a)

1. Evaluate Equation 32–9 with $t = 7$ d: $\qquad\qquad\qquad N = 1.34 \times 10^7$

Part (b)

2. Evaluate Equation 32–9 with $t = 14$ d: $\qquad\qquad\qquad N = 3.77 \times 10^6$

Insight

Notice that after 7 d the number of radon atoms has decreased by a factor of about 3.55. After 14 d, the number has decreased by a factor of about $3.55^2 = 12.6$. It follows that every 7 d the number of radon atoms decreases by another factor of 3.55.

Your Turn

What period of time is required for the number of radon atoms to decrease by a factor of 2.00?

(Answers to **Your Turn** *problems are given in the back of the book.)*

A useful way to characterize the rate at which a given type of nucleus decays is in terms of its half-life, which is defined as follows:

> The **half-life** of a given type of radioactive nucleus is the time required for the number of such nuclei to decrease by a factor of 2; that is, for the number to decrease from N_0 to $\frac{1}{2}N_0$, from $\frac{1}{2}N_0$ to $\frac{1}{4}N_0$, and so on.

We can solve for this time, call it $T_{1/2}$, by setting $N = \frac{1}{2}N_0$ in Equation 32–9:

$$\tfrac{1}{2}N_0 = N_0 e^{-\lambda T_{1/2}}$$

Canceling N_0 and taking the natural logarithm of both sides of the equation, we find

$$T_{1/2} = \frac{\ln 2}{\lambda} = \frac{0.693}{\lambda} \qquad\qquad \text{32–10}$$

Notice that a large decay constant corresponds to a short half-life, in agreement with the plots shown in Figure 32–6.

▲ Radon-222 ($^{222}_{86}\text{Rn}$) is an isotope produced in a radioactive decay series that includes uranium-238 and radium-226. Since uranium is naturally present in certain kinds of rocks and the soils derived from them, radon, which is a gas, can accumulate in basements and similar enclosed underground spaces that lack adequate ventilation. Radon-222 is itself radioactive, undergoing alpha decay with a half-life of about 4 days, and although its concentration is generally small, it may produce radiation levels great enough to be a health hazard if exposure is prolonged. Homeowners in many parts of the country use test kits to monitor the radiation levels produced by radon.

CONCEPTUAL CHECKPOINT 32-3 How Many Nuclei?

A system consists of N_0 radioactive nuclei at time $t = 0$. The number of nuclei remaining after *half* a half-life (that is, at time $t = \frac{1}{2}T_{1/2}$) is (a) $\frac{1}{4}N_0$, (b) $\frac{3}{4}N_0$, or (c) $\frac{1}{\sqrt{2}}N_0$?

Reasoning and Discussion

Referring to the Insight following Active Example 32-2, we note that if the number of nuclei decreases by a factor f in the time $\frac{1}{2}T_{1/2}$, it will decrease by the factor f^2 in the time $2\left(\frac{1}{2}T_{1/2}\right) = T_{1/2}$. We know, however, that the number of nuclei remaining at the time $T_{1/2}$ is $\frac{1}{2}N_0$. It follows that $f^2 = \frac{1}{2}$, or that $f = \frac{1}{\sqrt{2}}$. Therefore, the number of nuclei remaining at the time $\frac{1}{2}T_{1/2}$ is $\frac{1}{\sqrt{2}}N_0$.

Answer:

(c) At half a half-life, the number of nuclei remaining is $\frac{1}{\sqrt{2}}N_0$.

Now, the property that makes radioactivity so useful as a clock is that its **decay rate, R,** or **activity,** depends on time in a straightforward way. To see this, think back to the analogy of the coins. The number of coins that decay (are removed) on the first round of tosses is $32 = \frac{1}{2}(64)$, the number that decay on the second round is $16 = \frac{1}{2}(32)$, and so on. That is, the number that decay in any given interval of time is proportional to the number present at the beginning of the interval.

The same type of analysis applies to nuclei. Therefore, the number of nuclei that decay, ΔN, in a given time interval, Δt, is proportional to the number, N, that is present at time t:

$$R = \left| \frac{\Delta N}{\Delta t} \right| = \lambda N \qquad \qquad 32\text{--}11$$

There are two points to note regarding this equation. First, observe that the number of nuclei is decreasing, $\Delta N < 0$. It is for this reason that we take the absolute value of the quantity $\Delta N/\Delta t$. Second, notice that the proportionality constant is simply λ, the decay constant. That λ is the correct constant of proportionality can be shown using calculus.

Combining Equation 32-11 with Equation 32-9, we obtain the time dependence of the activity, R:

$$R = \lambda N_0 e^{-\lambda t} = R_0 e^{-\lambda t} \qquad \qquad 32\text{--}12$$

Note that $R_0 = \lambda N_0$ is the initial value of the activity. We apply this relation in the following Active Example.

ACTIVE EXAMPLE 32-3 Find the Activity of Radon

Referring to Active Example 32-2, calculate how many radon atoms disintegrate per second (a) initially and (b) after 7 d.

Solution *(Test your understanding by performing the calculations indicated in each step.)*

Part (a)

1. Calculate the activity for $N_0 = 4.75 \times 10^7$. Be sure to convert the decay constant to the unit s^{-1}: $R = \lambda N_0 = 99.5$ decays/s

Part (b)

2. Repeat the calculation for $N = 1.34 \times 10^7$: $R = \lambda N = 28.1$ decays/s

Insight

We see that the initial activity (number of decays per time) is 99.5 Bq. In terms of the curie, the initial activity is 0.00269 μCi.

Your Turn

How long does it take after the basement is sealed for the activity of the radon to decrease to 10.0 Bq?

*(Answers to **Your Turn** problems are given in the back of the book.)*

Science Fundamentals Second Edition

Referring to Equation 32–12, we see that the basic idea of radioactive dating is simply this: If we know the initial activity of a sample, R_0, and we also know the sample's activity now, R, we can find the corresponding time, t, as follows:

$$\frac{R}{R_0} = e^{-\lambda t}$$

$$t = -\frac{1}{\lambda}\ln\frac{R}{R_0} = \frac{1}{\lambda}\ln\frac{R_0}{R} \qquad \textbf{32–13}$$

The current activity, R, can be measured in the lab, but how can we know the initial activity, R_0? We address the question next for the specific case of carbon-14.

Carbon-14 Dating

To determine the initial activity of carbon-14 requires a basic knowledge of the role it plays in Earth's biosphere. First, we note that carbon-14 is unstable, with a half-life of 5730 y. It follows that the carbon-14 initially present in any *closed* system will decay away to practically nothing in a time of several half-lives, yet the ratio of carbon-14 to carbon-12 in Earth's atmosphere remains approximately constant at the value 1.20×10^{-12}. Evidently, Earth's atmosphere is not a closed system, at least as far as carbon-14 is concerned.

This is indeed the case. Cosmic rays, which are high-energy particles from outer space, are continuously entering Earth's upper atmosphere and initiating nuclear reactions in nitrogen-14 (a stable isotope). These reactions result in a steady production of carbon-14. Thus, the steady level of carbon-14 in the atmosphere is a result of the balance between the *production rate* due to cosmic rays and the *decay rate* due to the properties of the carbon-14 nucleus.

We note that living organisms have the same ratio of carbon-14 to carbon-12 as the atmosphere, since they continuously exchange carbon with their surroundings. When an organism dies, however, the exchange of carbon ceases and the carbon-14 in the organism (wood, bone, shell, etc.) begins to decay. This process is illustrated in **Figure 32–7**, where we see that the carbon-14 activity of an organism is constant until it dies, at which point it decreases exponentially with a half-life of 5730 y.

All that remains to implement carbon-14 dating is to determine the initial activity, R_0. For convenience, we calculate R_0 for a 1-g sample of carbon. As we know from Chapter 31, 12 g of carbon-12 consists of Avogadro's number of atoms, 6.02×10^{23}. Therefore, 1 g consists of $(6.02 \times 10^{23})/12 = 5.02 \times 10^{22}$ carbon-12 atoms. Multiplying this number of atoms by the ratio of carbon-14 to carbon-12, 1.20×10^{-12}, shows that the number of carbon-14 atoms in the 1-g sample is 6.02×10^{10}. Next, we need the decay constant, which we obtain by rearranging Equation 32–10:

$$\lambda = \frac{\ln 2}{T_{1/2}} = \frac{0.693}{T_{1/2}}$$

▲ The Iceman, found in the Italian Alps in 1991. His age was established by means of radiocarbon dating.

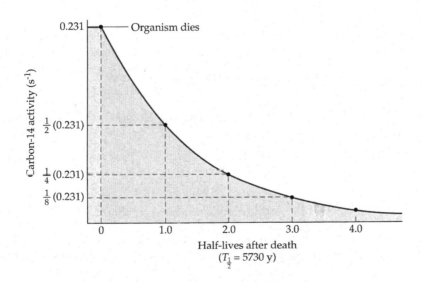

▲ **FIGURE 32–7 Activity of carbon-14**
While an organism is living and exchanging carbon with the atmosphere, its carbon-14 activity remains constant. When the organism dies, the carbon-14 activity decays exponentially with a half-life of 5730 years.

Science Fundamentals Second Edition

269

Using $T_{1/2} = 5730$ y $= 1.81 \times 10^{11}$ s, we find $\lambda = 3.83 \times 10^{-12}$ s^{-1}. Finally, the initial activity of a 1-g sample of carbon is

$$R_0 = \lambda N_0 = (3.83 \times 10^{-12} \text{ s}^{-1})(6.02 \times 10^{10}) = 0.231 \text{ Bq} \qquad \textbf{32-14}$$

This is the initial activity used in Figure 32–7. It follows that 5730 y after an organism dies, its carbon-14 activity per gram of carbon will have decreased to about $\frac{1}{2}(0.231 \text{ Bq}) = 0.116$ Bq.

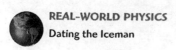

REAL-WORLD PHYSICS

Dating the Iceman

The next Example applies this basic idea to a real-world case of some interest— the Iceman of the Alps.

EXAMPLE 32–5 Age of the Iceman: You Don't Look a Day over 5000

Early in the afternoon of September 19, 1991, a German couple hiking in the Italian Alps noticed something brown sticking out of the ice 8 to 10 m ahead of them. At first they took the object to be a doll or some rubbish. As they got closer, however, it became apparent that the object they had discovered was the body of a person trapped in the ice, with only the top part of the body exposed. Subsequent investigation revealed the remarkably well-preserved body to be that of a Stone Age man who had died in the mountains and become entombed in the ice. When the carbon-14 dating method was applied to the remains of the Iceman and some of the materials he had carried with him, it was found that the carbon-14 activity was about 0.121 Bq per gram of carbon. Using this information, date the remains of the Iceman.

Picture the Problem
Our sketch shows the decay of the carbon-14 activity of a gram of carbon as a function of time. The initial activity of carbon-14 in such a sample is 0.231 Bq.

Strategy
We can obtain the age of the remains directly from Equation 32–13: $t = (1/\lambda) \ln(R_0/R)$. In this case, $R_0 = 0.231$ Bq, and $R = 0.121$ Bq. Since an answer in years would be most useful, we express the decay constant as $\lambda = 0.693/T_{1/2}$, with $T_{1/2} = 5730$ y.

Note that the observed activity of 0.121 Bq is slightly greater than $\frac{1}{2}(0.231 \text{ Bq}) = 0.116$ Bq; hence, we expect the age of the remains to be slightly less than the half-life of 5730 y.

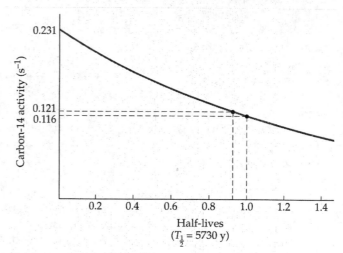

Solution

1. Determine the value of the decay constant, λ, in units of y^{-1}:

$$\lambda = \frac{0.693}{5730 \text{ y}} = 1.21 \times 10^{-4} \text{ y}^{-1}$$

2. Substitute λ, R_0, and R into Equation 32–13:

$$t = \frac{1}{\lambda} \ln\left(\frac{R_0}{R}\right)$$

$$= \frac{1}{(1.21 \times 10^{-4} \text{ y}^{-1})} \ln\left(\frac{0.231 \text{ Bq}}{0.121 \text{ Bq}}\right) = 5340 \text{ y}$$

Insight
We conclude that the Iceman, who has been dubbed Ötzi, died in the mountains during the Stone Age, some 5340 y ago. Detailed examination of Ötzi's body and possessions indicate he was probably an itinerant sheepherder and/or hunter. He met his end in a violent fashion, however. Recent CT scans confirm that Ötzi was killed by an arrow that entered through his shoulder blade and lodged less than an inch from his left lung.

Practice Problem
If the remains of another iceman of the same age are found in the year 2991, what will be the carbon-14 activity of 1 g of carbon? **[Answer:** 0.107 Bq]

Some related homework problems: Problem 29, Problem 30

As useful as carbon-14 dating is, it is limited to time spans of only a few half-lives, say, 10,000 to 15,000 y. Beyond that range, the current activity will be so small that accurate measurements will be difficult. To measure dates on different time scales, different radioactive isotopes must be used. Other frequently used isotopes and their half-lives are $^{210}_{82}\text{Pb}(22.3 \text{ y})$, $^{40}_{19}\text{K}(1.28 \times 10^9 \text{ y})$, and $^{238}_{92}\text{U}(4.468 \times 10^9 \text{ y})$.

We see that it takes about 8.5 MeV to separate the nucleons of tritium. Compare this with the fact that only 13.6 eV is required to remove the electron from tritium. As we have noted before, nuclear processes typically involve energies in the MeV range, whereas atomic processes require energies in the eV range.

Science Fundamentals Second Edition

Chemistry

CHAPTER 1

1.1 The Study of Chemistry

1.2 Classifications of Matter

1.3 Properties of Matter

1.4 Units of Measurement

1.5 Uncertainty in Measurement

1.6 Dimensional Analysis

WHAT'S AHEAD

- We begin by providing a very brief perspective of what chemistry is about and why it is useful to learn chemistry. *(Section 1.1)*

- Next, we examine some fundamental ways to classify materials, distinguishing between *pure substances* and *mixtures* and noting that there are two fundamentally different kinds of pure substances: *elements* and *compounds*. *(Section 1.2)*

- We then consider some of the different kinds of characteristics, or *properties*, that we use to characterize, identify, and separate substances. *(Section 1.3)*

- Many properties rely on quantitative measurements, involving both numbers and units. The units of measurement used throughout science are those of the *metric system*, a decimal system of measurement. *(Section 1.4)*

- The uncertainties inherent in all measured quantities and those obtained from calculations involving measured quantities are expressed by the number of *significant figures* used to report the number. *(Section 1.5)*

- Units as well as numbers are carried through calculations, and obtaining correct units for the result of a calculation is an important way to check whether the calculation is correct. *(Section 1.6)*

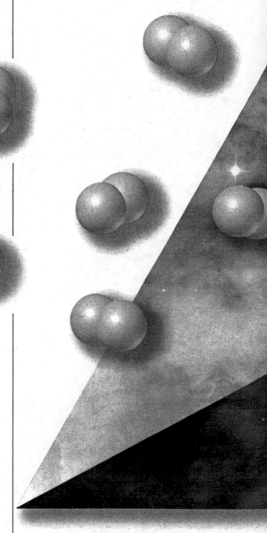

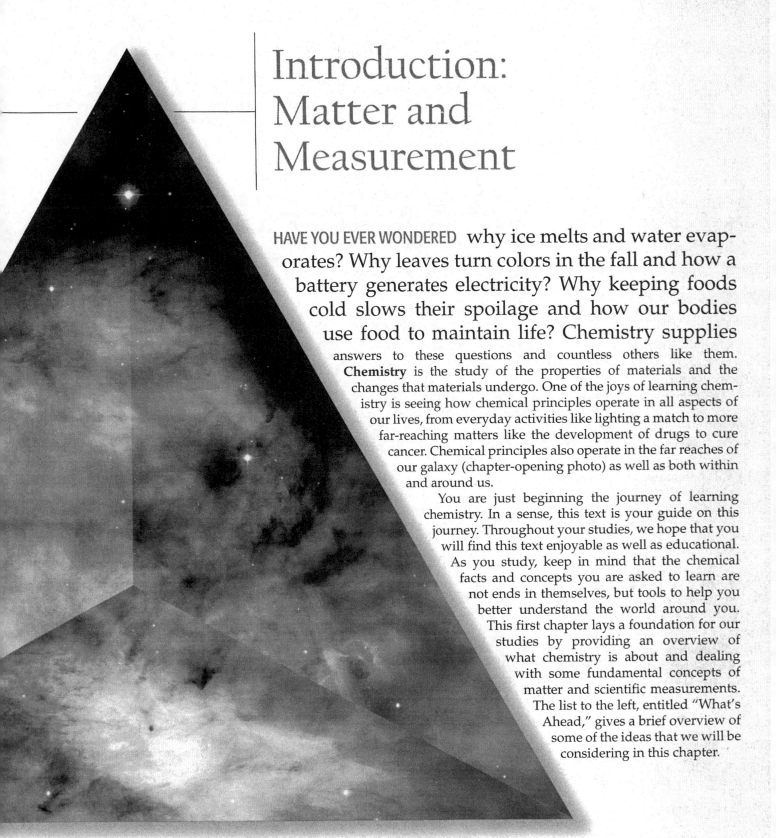

Introduction: Matter and Measurement

HAVE YOU EVER WONDERED why ice melts and water evaporates? Why leaves turn colors in the fall and how a battery generates electricity? Why keeping foods cold slows their spoilage and how our bodies use food to maintain life? Chemistry supplies answers to these questions and countless others like them. **Chemistry** is the study of the properties of materials and the changes that materials undergo. One of the joys of learning chemistry is seeing how chemical principles operate in all aspects of our lives, from everyday activities like lighting a match to more far-reaching matters like the development of drugs to cure cancer. Chemical principles also operate in the far reaches of our galaxy (chapter-opening photo) as well as both within and around us.

You are just beginning the journey of learning chemistry. In a sense, this text is your guide on this journey. Throughout your studies, we hope that you will find this text enjoyable as well as educational. As you study, keep in mind that the chemical facts and concepts you are asked to learn are not ends in themselves, but tools to help you better understand the world around you. This first chapter lays a foundation for our studies by providing an overview of what chemistry is about and dealing with some fundamental concepts of matter and scientific measurements. The list to the left, entitled "What's Ahead," gives a brief overview of some of the ideas that we will be considering in this chapter.

HUBBLE SPACE TELESCOPE IMAGE of the Omega Nebula, which resides 5,500 light-years away in the constellation Sagittarius. Ultraviolet radiation from young, massive stars in the region cause atoms to emit light. Hydrogen, the simplest and most plentiful element, occurs as molecules in cool regions, as atoms in hotter regions, and as ions in the hottest regions. The processes that occur within stars are responsible for creating other chemical elements from hydrogen.

1

1.1 | The Study of Chemistry

Before traveling to an unfamiliar city, you might look at a map to get some sense of where you are heading. Because chemistry may be unfamiliar to you, it's useful to get a general idea of what lies ahead before you embark on your journey. In fact, you might even ask why you are taking the trip.

The Atomic and Molecular Perspective of Chemistry

Chemistry involves studying the properties and behavior of matter. **Matter** is the physical material of the universe; it is anything that has mass and occupies space. A **property** is any characteristic that allows us to recognize a particular type of matter and to distinguish it from other types. This book, your body, the clothes you are wearing, and the air you are breathing are all samples of matter. Not all forms of matter are so common or so familiar, but countless experiments have shown that the tremendous variety of matter in our world is due to combinations of only about 100 very basic, or elementary, substances called **elements**. As we proceed through this text, we will seek to relate the properties of matter to its composition, that is, to the particular elements it contains.

Chemistry also provides a background to understanding the properties of matter in terms of **atoms**, the almost infinitesimally small building blocks of matter. Each element is composed of a unique kind of atom. We will see that the properties of matter relate not only to the kinds of atoms it contains (*composition*), but also to the arrangements of these atoms (*structure*).

Atoms can combine to form **molecules** in which two or more atoms are joined together in specific shapes. Throughout this text you will see molecules represented using colored spheres to show how their component atoms connect to each other (Figure 1.1 ▼). The color merely provides a convenient way to distinguish between the atoms of different elements. As examples, compare the molecules of ethanol and ethylene glycol, which are depicted in Figure 1.1. Notice that these molecules differ somewhat in composition. Ethanol contains one red sphere, which represents one oxygen atom, whereas ethylene glycol contains two.

Even apparently minor differences in the composition or structure of molecules can cause profound differences in their properties. Ethanol, also called grain alcohol, is the alcohol in beverages such as beer and wine. Ethylene glycol, on the other hand, is a viscous liquid used as automobile antifreeze. The properties of these two substances differ in a great number of ways, including the temperatures at which they freeze and boil. One of the challenges that chemists undertake is to alter the composition or structure of molecules in a controlled way, creating new substances with different properties.

Every change in the observable world—from boiling water to the changes that occur as our bodies combat invading viruses—has its basis in the world of atoms and molecules. Thus, as we proceed with our study of chemistry, we will find

3-D MODELS
Oxygen, Water, Carbon Dioxide, Ethanol, Ethylene Glycol, Aspirin

▼ **Figure 1.1 Molecular models.** The white, dark gray, and red spheres represent atoms of hydrogen, carbon, and oxygen, respectively.

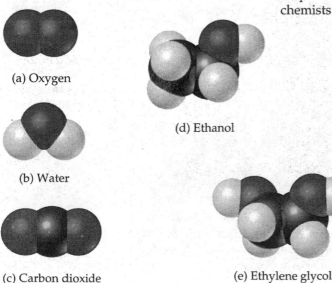

(a) Oxygen

(b) Water

(c) Carbon dioxide

(d) Ethanol

(e) Ethylene glycol

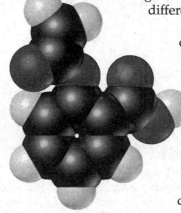

(f) Aspirin

ourselves thinking in two realms, the *macroscopic* realm of ordinary-sized objects (*macro* = large) and the *submicroscopic* realm of atoms and molecules. We make our observations in the macroscopic world—in the laboratory and in our every-day surroundings. In order to understand that world, however, we must visualize how atoms and molecules behave at the submicroscopic level. Chemistry is the science that seeks to understand the properties and behavior of matter by studying the properties and behavior of atoms and molecules.

 GIVE IT SOME THOUGHT

(a) In round numbers, about how many elements are there? (b) What submicroscopic particles are the building blocks of matter?

Why Study Chemistry?

Chemistry provides important understanding of our world and how it works. It is an extremely practical science that greatly impacts our daily living. Indeed, chemistry lies near the heart of many matters of public concern: improvement of health care, conservation of natural resources, protection of the environment, and provision of our everyday needs for food, clothing, and shelter. Using chemistry, we have discovered pharmaceutical chemicals that enhance our health and prolong our lives. We have increased food production through the development of fertilizers and pesticides. We have developed plastics and other materials that are used in almost every facet of our lives. Unfortunately, some chemicals also have the potential to harm our health or the environment. It is in our best interest as educated citizens and consumers to understand the profound effects, both positive and negative, that chemicals have on our lives and to strike an informed balance about their uses.

Most of you are studying chemistry, however, not merely to satisfy your curiosity or to become more informed consumers or citizens, but because it is an essential part of your curriculum. Your major might be biology, engineering, agriculture, geology, or some other field. Why do so many diverse subjects share an essential tie to chemistry? The answer is that chemistry, by its very nature, is the *central science*, central to a fundamental understanding of other sciences and technologies. For example, our interactions with the material world raise basic questions about the materials around us. What are their compositions and properties? How do they interact with us and our environment? How, why, and when do they undergo change? These questions are important whether the material is part of high-tech computer chips, an aged pigment used by a Renaissance painter, or the DNA that transmits genetic information in our bodies (Figure 1.2 ▼).

By studying chemistry, you will learn to use the powerful language and ideas that have evolved to describe and enhance our understanding of matter.

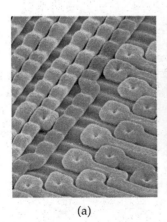

(a)   (b)   (c)

◀ **Figure 1.2 Chemistry helps us better understand materials.** (a) A microscopic view of an EPROM (Erasable Programmable Read-Only Memory) silicon microchip. (b) A Renaissance painting, *Young Girl Reading*, by Vittore Carpaccio (1472–1526). (c) A long strand of DNA that has spilled out of the damaged cell wall of a bacterium.

Science Fundamentals Second Edition

CHEMISTRY AT WORK | Chemistry and the Chemical Industry

Many people are familiar with common household chemicals such as those shown in Figure 1.3 ▶, but few realize the size and importance of the chemical industry. Worldwide sales of chemicals and related products manufactured in the United States total over $450 billion annually. The chemical industry employs over 10% of all scientists and engineers and is a major contributor to the U.S. economy.

Vast amounts of chemicals are produced each year and serve as raw materials for a variety of uses, including the manufacture of metals, plastics, fertilizers, pharmaceuticals, fuels, paints, adhesives, pesticides, synthetic fibers, microprocessor chips, and numerous other products. Table 1.1 ▼ lists the top ten chemicals produced in the United States. We will discuss many of these substances and their uses as the course progresses.

People who have degrees in chemistry hold a variety of positions in industry, government, and academia. Those who work in the chemical industry find positions as laboratory chemists, carrying out experiments to develop new products (research and development), analyzing materials (quality control), or assisting customers in using products (sales and service). Those with more experience or training may work as managers or company directors. There are also alternate careers that a chemistry degree prepares you for such as teaching, medicine, biomedical research, information science, environmental work, technical sales, work with government regulatory agencies, and patent law.

▲ **Figure 1.3   Household chemicals.** Many common supermarket products have very simple chemical compositions.

TABLE 1.1	The Top Ten Chemicals Produced by the Chemical Industry in 2003[a]			
Rank	Chemical	Formula	2003 Production (billions of pounds)	Principal End Uses
1	Sulfuric acid	H_2SO_4	82	Fertilizers, chemical manufacturing
2	Nitrogen	N_2	75	Fertilizers
3	Oxygen	O_2	61	Steel, welding
4	Ethylene	C_2H_4	51	Plastics, antifreeze
5	Lime	CaO	38	Paper, cement, steel
6	Propylene	C_3H_6	31	Plastics
7	Ammonia	NH_3	24	Fertilizers
8	Chlorine	Cl_2	24	Bleaches, plastics, water purification
9	Phosphoric acid	H_3PO_4	24	Fertilizers
10	Sodium hydroxide	$NaOH$	19	Aluminum production, soap

[a]Most data from *Chemical and Engineering News*, July 5, 2004, pp. 51, 54.

The language of chemistry is a universal scientific language that is widely used in other disciplines. Furthermore, an understanding of the behavior of atoms and molecules provides powerful insights in other areas of modern science, technology, and engineering. For this reason, chemistry will probably play a significant role in your future. You will be better prepared for the future if you increase your understanding of chemical principles, and it is our goal to help you achieve this end.

1.2 | Classifications of Matter

Let's begin our study of chemistry by examining some fundamental ways in which matter is classified and described. Two principal ways of classifying matter are according to its physical state (as a gas, liquid, or solid) and according to its composition (as an element, compound, or mixture).

States of Matter

A sample of matter can be a gas, a liquid, or a solid. These three forms of matter are called the **states of matter**. The states of matter differ in some of their simple observable properties. A **gas** (also known as *vapor*) has no fixed volume or shape; rather, it conforms to the volume and shape of its container. A gas can be compressed to occupy a smaller volume, or it can expand to occupy a larger one. A **liquid** has a distinct volume independent of its container but has no specific shape: It assumes the shape of the portion of the container that it occupies. A **solid** has both a definite shape and a definite volume. Neither liquids nor solids can be compressed to any appreciable extent.

The properties of the states can be understood on the molecular level (Figure 1.4 ▶). In a gas the molecules are far apart and are moving at high speeds, colliding repeatedly with each other and with the walls of the container. In a liquid the molecules are packed more closely together, but still move rapidly, allowing them to slide over each other; thus, liquids pour easily. In a solid the molecules are held tightly together, usually in definite arrangements, in which the molecules can wiggle only slightly in their otherwise fixed positions.

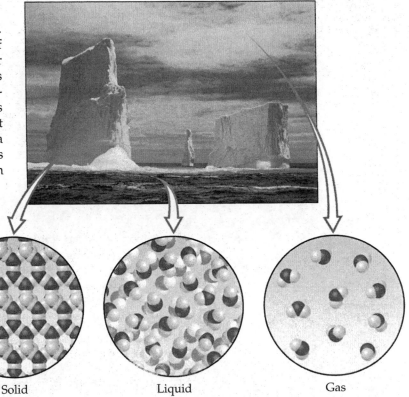

Solid   Liquid   Gas

▲ **Figure 1.4   The three physical states of water–water vapor, liquid water, and ice.** In this photo we see both the liquid and solid states of water. We cannot see water vapor. What we see when we look at steam or clouds is tiny droplets of liquid water dispersed in the atmosphere. The molecular views show that the molecules in the solid are arranged in a more orderly way than in the liquid. The molecules in the gas are much farther apart than those in the liquid or the solid.

ACTIVITY
Phases of Water

Pure Substances

Most forms of matter that we encounter—for example, the air we breathe (a gas), gasoline for cars (a liquid), and the sidewalk on which we walk (a solid)—are not chemically pure. We can, however, resolve, or separate, these forms of matter into different pure substances. A **pure substance** (usually referred to simply as a *substance*) is matter that has distinct properties and a composition that doesn't vary from sample to sample. Water and ordinary table salt (sodium chloride), the primary components of seawater, are examples of pure substances.

All substances are either elements or compounds. **Elements** cannot be decomposed into simpler substances. On the molecular level, each element is composed of only one kind of atom [Figure 1.5(a and b) ▼]. **Compounds** are substances

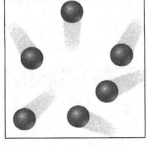

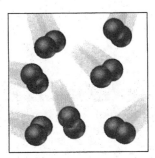

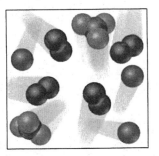

(a) Atoms of an element

(b) Molecules of an element

(c) Molecules of a compound

(d) Mixture of elements and a compound

▲ **Figure 1.5   Molecular comparison of element, compounds, and mixtures.** Each element contains a unique kind of atom. Elements might consist of individual atoms, as in (a), or molecules, as in (b). Compounds contain two or more different atoms chemically joined together, as in (c). A mixture contains the individual units of its components, shown in (d) as both atoms and molecules.

Science Fundamentals Second Edition

▶ **Figure 1.6 Relative abundances of elements.** Elements in percent by mass in (a) Earth's crust (including oceans and atmosphere) and (b) the human body.

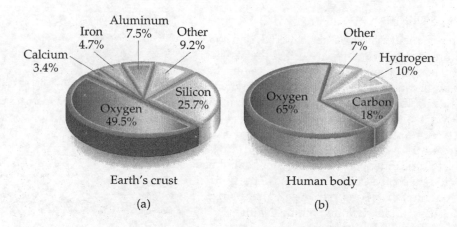

Earth's crust

(a)

Human body

(b)

composed of two or more elements, so they contain two or more kinds of atoms [Figure 1.5(c)]. Water, for example, is a compound composed of two elements, hydrogen and oxygen. Figure 1.5(d) shows a mixture of substances. **Mixtures** are combinations of two or more substances in which each substance retains its own chemical identity.

Elements

At the present time 116 elements are known. These elements vary widely in their abundance, as shown in Figure 1.6 ▲. For example, only five elements account for over 90% of Earth's crust: oxygen, silicon, aluminum, iron, and calcium. In contrast, just three elements (oxygen, carbon, and hydrogen) account for over 90% of the mass of the human body.

Some of the more common elements are listed in Table 1.2 ▼, along with the chemical abbreviations—or chemical *symbols*—used to denote them. All the known elements and their symbols are listed on the front inside cover of this text. The table in which the symbol for each element is enclosed in a box is called the *periodic table*. In the periodic table the elements are arranged in vertical columns so that closely related elements are grouped together. We describe this important tool in more detail in Section 2.5.

The symbol for each element consists of one or two letters, with the first letter capitalized. These symbols are often derived from the English name for the element, but sometimes they are derived from a foreign name instead (last column in Table 1.2). You will need to know these symbols and to learn others as we encounter them in the text.

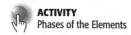 **ACTIVITY**
Phases of the Elements

 GIVE IT SOME THOUGHT

Which element is most abundant in both Earth's crust and in the human body? What is the symbol for this element?

TABLE 1.2	Some Common Elements and Their Symbols				
Carbon	C	Aluminum	Al	Copper	Cu (from *cuprum*)
Fluorine	F	Bromine	Br	Iron	Fe (from *ferrum*)
Hydrogen	H	Calcium	Ca	Lead	Pb (from *plumbum*)
Iodine	I	Chlorine	Cl	Mercury	Hg (from *hydrargyrum*)
Nitrogen	N	Helium	He	Potassium	K (from *kalium*)
Oxygen	O	Lithium	Li	Silver	Ag (from *argentum*)
Phosphorus	P	Magnesium	Mg	Sodium	Na (from *natrium*)
Sulfur	S	Silicon	Si	Tin	Sn (from *stannum*)

Science Fundamentals Second Edition

Compounds

Most elements can interact with other elements to form compounds. For example, consider the fact that when hydrogen gas burns in oxygen gas, the elements hydrogen and oxygen combine to form the compound water. Conversely, water can be decomposed into its component elements by passing an electrical current through it, as shown in Figure 1.7 ▼. Pure water, regardless of its source, consists of 11% hydrogen and 89% oxygen by mass. This macroscopic composition corresponds to the molecular composition, which consists of two hydrogen atoms combined with one oxygen atom:

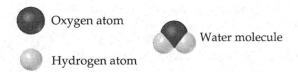

Oxygen atom

Water molecule

Hydrogen atom

The elements hydrogen and oxygen themselves exist naturally as diatomic (two-atom) molecules:

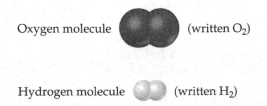

Oxygen molecule   (written O_2)

Hydrogen molecule   (written H_2)

As seen in Table 1.3 ▶, the properties of water bear no resemblance to the properties of its component elements. Hydrogen, oxygen, and water are each unique substances, a consequence of the uniqueness of their respective molecules.

ANIMATION
Electrolysis of Water

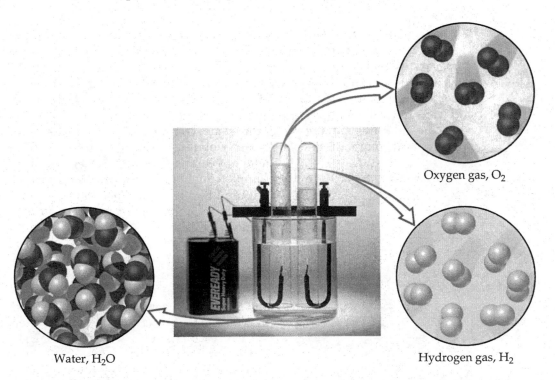

Oxygen gas, O_2

Water, H_2O

Hydrogen gas, H_2

▲ **Figure 1.7 · Electrolysis of water.** Water decomposes into its component elements, hydrogen and oxygen, when a direct electrical current is passed through it. The volume of hydrogen, which is collected in the right tube of the apparatus, is twice the volume of oxygen, which is collected in the left tube.

Science Fundamentals Second Edition

TABLE 1.3 Comparison of Water, Hydrogen, and Oxygen			
	Water	Hydrogen	Oxygen
State[a]	Liquid	Gas	Gas
Normal boiling point	100°C	−253°C	−183°C
Density[a]	1.00 g/mL	0.084 g/L	1.33 g/L
Flammable	No	Yes	No

[a] At room temperature and atmospheric pressure. (See Section 10.2.)

The observation that the elemental composition of a pure compound is always the same is known as the **law of constant composition** (or the **law of definite proportions**). It was first put forth by the French chemist Joseph Louis Proust (1754–1826) in about 1800. Although this law has been known for 200 years, the general belief persists among some people that a fundamental difference exists between compounds prepared in the laboratory and the corresponding compounds found in nature. However, a pure compound has the same composition and properties regardless of its source. Both chemists and nature must use the same elements and operate under the same natural laws. When two materials differ in composition and properties, we know that they are composed of different compounds or that they differ in purity. Occasionally, however, a pure solid substance may have more than one crystalline form, and these may have slightly different properties.

 GIVE IT SOME THOUGHT

Hydrogen, oxygen, and water are all composed of molecules. What is it about the molecules of water that makes water a compound?

Mixtures

Most of the matter we encounter consists of mixtures of different substances. Each substance in a mixture retains its own chemical identity and hence its own properties. Whereas pure substances have fixed compositions, the compositions of mixtures can vary. A cup of sweetened coffee, for example, can contain either a little sugar or a lot. The substances making up a mixture (such as sugar and water) are called *components* of the mixture.

Some mixtures do not have the same composition, properties, and appearance throughout. Both rocks and wood, for example, vary in texture and appearance throughout any typical sample. Such mixtures are *heterogeneous* [Figure 1.8(a) ◄]. Mixtures that are uniform throughout are *homogeneous*. Air is a homogeneous mixture of the gaseous substances nitrogen, oxygen, and smaller amounts of other substances. The nitrogen in air has all the properties that pure nitrogen does because both the pure substance and the mixture contain the same nitrogen molecules. Salt, sugar, and many other substances dissolve in water to form homogeneous mixtures [Figure 1.8(b)]. Homogeneous mixtures are also called **solutions**. Figure 1.9 ► summarizes the classification of matter into elements, compounds, and mixtures.

▼ **Figure 1.8 Mixtures.** (a) Many common materials, including rocks, are heterogeneous. This close-up photo is of *malachite*, a copper mineral. (b) Homogeneous mixtures are called solutions. Many substances, including the blue solid shown in this photo (copper sulfate), dissolve in water to form solutions.

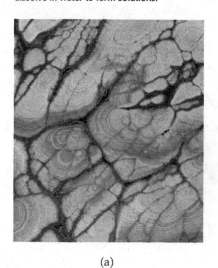

(a)

(b)

Science Fundamentals Second Edition

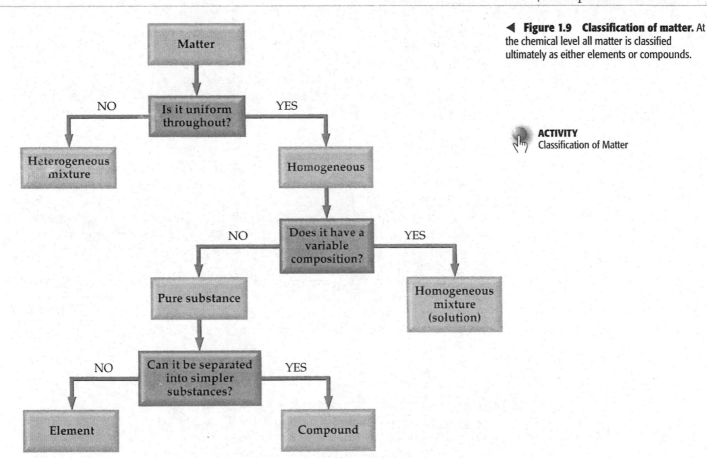

◀ **Figure 1.9 Classification of matter.** At the chemical level all matter is classified ultimately as either elements or compounds.

ACTIVITY
Classification of Matter

■ **SAMPLE EXERCISE 1.1 | Distinguishing among elements, compounds, and mixtures**

"White gold," used in jewelry, contains two elements, gold and palladium. Two different samples of white gold differ in the relative amounts of gold and palladium that they contain. Both are uniform in composition throughout. Without knowing any more about the materials, use Figure 1.9 to characterize and classify white gold.

Solution Because the material is uniform throughout, it is homogeneous. Because its composition differs for the two samples, it cannot be a compound. Instead, it must be a homogeneous mixture. Gold and palladium can be said to form a solid solution with one another.

■ **PRACTICE EXERCISE**

Aspirin is composed of 60.0% carbon, 4.5% hydrogen, and 35.5% oxygen by mass, regardless of its source. Use Figure 1.9 to characterize and classify aspirin.
Answer: It is a compound because it has constant composition and can be separated into several elements.

1.3 | Properties of Matter

Every substance has a unique set of properties. For example, the properties listed in Table 1.3 allow us to distinguish hydrogen, oxygen, and water from one another. The properties of matter can be categorized as physical or chemical. **Physical properties** can be measured without changing the identity and composition of the substance. These properties include color, odor, density, melting point, boiling point, and hardness. **Chemical properties** describe the way a substance may change, or *react*, to form other substances. A common chemical property is flammability, the ability of a substance to burn in the presence of oxygen.

Science Fundamentals Second Edition

Some properties—such as temperature, melting point, and density—do not depend on the amount of the sample being examined. These properties, called **intensive properties**, are particularly useful in chemistry because many can be used to *identify* substances. **Extensive properties** of substances depend on the quantity of the sample, with two examples being mass and volume. Extensive properties relate to the *amount* of substance present.

Physical and Chemical Changes

As with the properties of a substance, the changes that substances undergo can be classified as either physical or chemical. During **physical changes** a substance changes its physical appearance, but not its composition. The evaporation of water is a physical change. When water evaporates, it changes from the liquid state to the gas state, but it is still composed of water molecules, as depicted earlier in Figure 1.4. All **changes of state** (for example, from liquid to gas or from liquid to solid) are physical changes.

In **chemical changes** (also called **chemical reactions**) a substance is transformed into a chemically different substance. When hydrogen burns in air, for example, it undergoes a chemical change because it combines with oxygen to form water. The molecular-level view of this process is depicted in Figure 1.10 ▼.

▼ **Figure 1.10   A chemical reaction.**

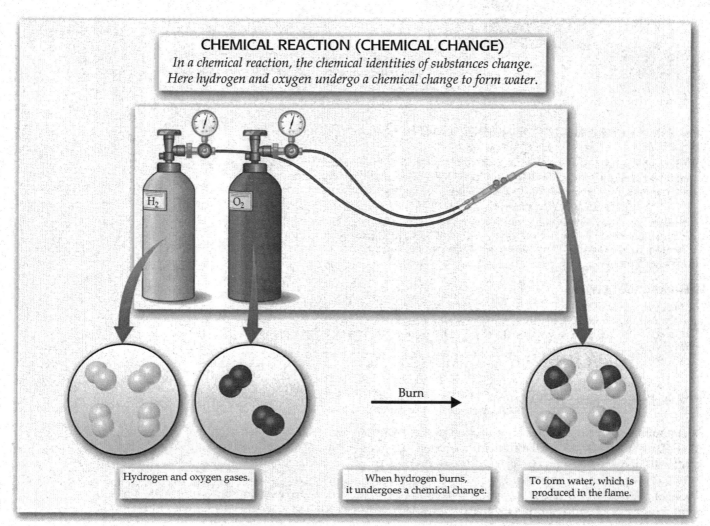

CHEMICAL REACTION (CHEMICAL CHANGE)
In a chemical reaction, the chemical identities of substances change. Here hydrogen and oxygen undergo a chemical change to form water.

H_2

O_2

Burn

Hydrogen and oxygen gases.

When hydrogen burns, it undergoes a chemical change.

To form water, which is produced in the flame.

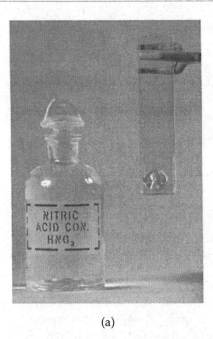

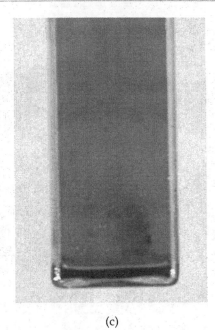

(a)   (b)   (c)

▲ **Figure 1.11 The chemical reaction between a copper penny and nitric acid.** The dissolved copper produces the blue-green solution; the reddish brown gas produced is nitrogen dioxide.

Chemical changes can be dramatic. In the account that follows, Ira Remsen, author of a popular chemistry text published in 1901, describes his first experiences with chemical reactions. The chemical reaction that he observed is shown in Figure 1.11 ▲.

While reading a textbook of chemistry, I came upon the statement "nitric acid acts upon copper," and I determined to see what this meant. Having located some nitric acid, I had only to learn what the words "act upon" meant. In the interest of knowledge I was even willing to sacrifice one of the few copper cents then in my possession. I put one of them on the table, opened a bottle labeled "nitric acid," poured some of the liquid on the copper, and prepared to make an observation. But what was this wonderful thing which I beheld? The cent was already changed, and it was no small change either. A greenish-blue liquid foamed and fumed over the cent and over the table. The air became colored dark red. How could I stop this? I tried by picking the cent up and throwing it out the window. I learned another fact: nitric acid acts upon fingers. The pain led to another unpremeditated experiment. I drew my fingers across my trousers and discovered nitric acid acts upon trousers. That was the most impressive experiment I have ever performed. I tell of it even now with interest. It was a revelation to me. Plainly the only way to learn about such remarkable kinds of action is to see the results, to experiment, to work in the laboratory.

 GIVE IT SOME THOUGHT

Which of the following is a physical change, and which is a chemical change? Explain. (a) Plants use carbon dioxide and water to make sugar. (b) Water vapor in the air on a cold day forms frost.

 **MOVIE**
Sodium and Potassium in Water

Science Fundamentals Second Edition

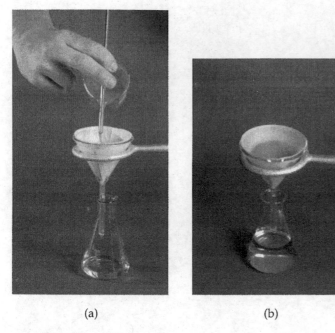

(a)   (b)

▲ **Figure 1.12   Separation by filtration.** A mixture of a solid and a liquid is poured through a porous medium, in this case filter paper. The liquid passes through the paper while the solid remains on the paper.

Separation of Mixtures

Because each component of a mixture retains its own properties, we can separate a mixture into its components by taking advantage of the differences in their properties. For example, a heterogeneous mixture of iron filings and gold filings could be sorted individually by color into iron and gold. A less tedious approach would be to use a magnet to attract the iron filings, leaving the gold ones behind. We can also take advantage of an important chemical difference between these two metals: Many acids dissolve iron, but not gold. Thus, if we put our mixture into an appropriate acid, the iron would dissolve and the gold would be left behind. The two could then be separated by *filtration*, a procedure illustrated in Figure 1.12 ◄. We would have to use other chemical reactions, which we will learn about later, to transform the dissolved iron back into metal.

An important method of separating the components of a homogeneous mixture is *distillation*, a process that depends on the different abilities of substances to form gases. For example, if we boil a solution of salt and water, the water evaporates, forming a gas, and the salt is left behind. The gaseous water can be converted back to a liquid on the walls of a condenser, as shown in the apparatus depicted in Figure 1.13 ▼.

The differing abilities of substances to adhere to the surfaces of various solids such as paper and starch can also be used to separate mixtures. This is the basis of *chromatography* (literally "the writing of colors"), a technique that can give beautiful and dramatic results. An example of the chromatographic separation of ink is shown in Figure 1.14 ►.

MOVIES
Mixtures and Compounds, Paper Chromatography of Ink

► **Figure 1.13   Distillation.** A simple apparatus for the separation of a sodium chloride solution (salt water) into its components. Boiling the solution evaporates the water, which is condensed, then collected in the receiving flask. After all the water has boiled away, pure sodium chloride remains in the boiling flask.

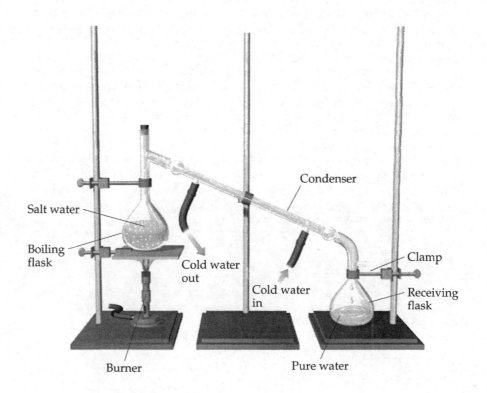

Salt water

Boiling flask

Burner

Cold water out

Cold water in

Condenser

Clamp

Receiving flask

Pure water

Science Fundamentals Second Edition

▲ **Figure 1.14 Separation of ink into components by paper chromatography.** (a) Water begins to move up the paper. (b) Water moves past the ink spot, dissolving different components of the ink at different rates. (c) Water has separated the ink into its several different components.

 A CLOSER LOOK | The Scientific Method

Although two scientists rarely approach the same problem in exactly the same way, there are guidelines for the practice of science that have come to be known as the **scientific method**. These guidelines are outlined in Figure 1.15 ▼. We begin by collecting information, or *data*, by observation and experiment. The collection of information, however, is not the ultimate goal. The goal is to find a pattern or sense of order in our observations and to understand the origin of this order.

As we perform our experiments, we may begin to see patterns that lead us to a *tentative explanation*, or **hypothesis**, that guides us in planning further experiments. Eventually, we may be able to tie together a great number of observations in a single statement or equation called a scientific law. A **scientific law** *is a concise verbal statement or a mathematical equation that summarizes a broad variety of observations and experiences.* We tend to think of the laws of nature as the basic rules under which nature operates. However, it is not so much that matter obeys the laws of nature, but rather that the laws of nature describe the behavior of matter.

At many stages of our studies we may propose explanations of why nature behaves in a particular way. If a hypothesis is sufficiently general and is continually effective in predicting facts yet to be observed, it is called a theory. A **theory** *is an explanation of the general causes of certain phenomena,*

with considerable evidence or facts to support it. For example, Einstein's theory of relativity was a revolutionary new way of thinking about space and time. It was more than just a simple hypothesis, however, because it could be used to make predictions that could be tested experimentally. When these experiments were conducted, the results were generally in agreement with the predictions and were not explainable by earlier theories. Thus, the theory of relativity was supported, but not proven. Indeed, theories can never be proven to be absolutely correct.

As we proceed through this text, we will rarely have the opportunity to discuss the doubts, conflicts, clashes of personalities, and revolutions of perception that have led to our present ideas. We need to be aware that just because we can spell out the results of science so concisely and neatly in textbooks does not mean that scientific progress is smooth, certain, and predictable. Some of the ideas we present in this text took centuries to develop and involved large numbers of scientists. We gain our view of the natural world by standing on the shoulders of the scientists who came before us. Take advantage of this view. As you study, exercise your imagination. Don't be afraid to ask daring questions when they occur to you. You may be fascinated by what you discover!

Related Exercise: 1.59

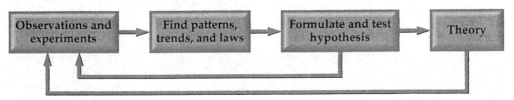

▲ **Figure 1.15 The scientific method.** The scientific method is a general approach to problems that involves making observations, seeking patterns in the observations, formulating hypotheses to explain the observations, and testing these hypotheses by further experiments. Those hypotheses that withstand such tests and prove themselves useful in explaining and predicting behavior become known as theories.

Science Fundamentals Second Edition

▲ **Figure 1.16 Metric units.** Metric measurements are increasingly common in the United States, as exemplified by the volume printed on this one-liter soda bottle.

1.4 | Units of Measurement

Many properties of matter are *quantitative*; that is, they are associated with numbers. When a number represents a measured quantity, the units of that quantity must always be specified. To say that the length of a pencil is 17.5 is meaningless. Expressing the number with its units, 17.5 centimeters (cm), properly specifies the length. The units used for scientific measurements are those of the **metric system**.

The metric system, which was first developed in France during the late eighteenth century, is used as the system of measurement in most countries throughout the world. The United States has traditionally used the English system, although use of the metric system has become more common. For example, the contents of most canned goods and soft drinks in grocery stores are now given in metric as well as in English units as shown in Figure 1.16 ◄.

SI Units

In 1960 an international agreement was reached specifying a particular choice of metric units for use in scientific measurements. These preferred units are called **SI units**, after the French *Système International d'Unités*. This system has seven *base units* from which all other units are derived. Table 1.4 ▼ lists these base units and their symbols. In this chapter we will consider the base units for length, mass, and temperature.

TABLE 1.4 SI Base Units		
Physical Quantity	**Name of Unit**	**Abbreviation**
Mass	Kilogram	kg
Length	Meter	m
Time	Second	s[a]
Temperature	Kelvin	K
Amount of substance	Mole	mol
Electric current	Ampere	A
Luminous intensity	Candela	cd

[a]The abbreviation sec is frequently used.

In the metric system, prefixes are used to indicate decimal fractions or multiples of various units. For example, the prefix *milli-* represents a 10^{-3} fraction of a unit: A milligram (mg) is 10^{-3} gram (g), a millimeter (mm) is 10^{-3} meter (m), and so forth. Table 1.5 ▼ presents the prefixes commonly encountered in chemistry. In using SI units and in working problems throughout this text, you must be comfortable using exponential notation. If you are unfamiliar with exponential notation or want to review it, refer to Appendix A.1.

TABLE 1.5 Selected Prefixes Used in the Metric System			
Prefix	**Abbreviation**	**Meaning**	**Example**
Giga	G	10^{9}	1 gigameter (Gm) = 1×10^{9} m
Mega	M	10^{6}	1 megameter (Mm) = 1×10^{6} m
Kilo	k	10^{3}	1 kilometer (km) = 1×10^{3} m
Deci	d	10^{-1}	1 decimeter (dm) = 0.1 m
Centi	c	10^{-2}	1 centimeter (cm) = 0.01 m
Milli	m	10^{-3}	1 millimeter (mm) = 0.001 m
Micro	μ[a]	10^{-6}	1 micrometer (μm) = 1×10^{-6} m
Nano	n	10^{-9}	1 nanometer (nm) = 1×10^{-9} m
Pico	p	10^{-12}	1 picometer (pm) = 1×10^{-12} m
Femto	f	10^{-15}	1 femtometer (fm) = 1×10^{-15} m

[a]This is the Greek letter mu (pronounced "mew").

Although non-SI units are being phased out, there are still some that are commonly used by scientists. Whenever we first encounter a non-SI unit in the text, the proper SI unit will also be given.

GIVE IT SOME THOUGHT

Which of the following quantities is the smallest: 1 mg, 1 μg, or 1 pg?

Length and Mass

The SI base unit of *length* is the meter (m), a distance only slightly longer than a yard. The relations between the English and metric system units that we will use most frequently in this text appear on the back inside cover. We will discuss how to convert English units into metric units, and vice versa, in Section 1.6.

Mass* is a measure of the amount of material in an object. The SI base unit of mass is the kilogram (kg), which is equal to about 2.2 pounds (lb). This base unit is unusual because it uses a prefix, *kilo-*, instead of the word *gram* alone. We obtain other units for mass by adding prefixes to the word *gram*.

SAMPLE EXERCISE 1.2 | Using metric prefixes

What is the name given to the unit that equals (a) 10^{-9} gram, (b) 10^{-6} second, (c) 10^{-3} meter?

Solution In each case we can refer to Table 1.5, finding the prefix related to each of the decimal fractions: (a) nanogram, ng, (b) microsecond, μs, (c) millimeter, mm.

PRACTICE EXERCISE

(a) What decimal fraction of a second is a picosecond, ps? (b) Express the measurement 6.0×10^3 m using a prefix to replace the power of ten. (c) Use exponential notation to express 3.76 mg in grams.
Answers: (a) 10^{-12} second, (b) 6.0 km, (c) 3.76×10^{-3} g

Temperature

Temperature is a measure of the hotness or coldness of an object. Indeed, temperature is a physical property that determines the direction of heat flow. Heat always flows spontaneously from a substance at higher temperature to one at lower temperature. Thus, we feel the influx of heat when we touch a hot object, and we know that the object is at a higher temperature than our hand.

The temperature scales commonly employed in scientific studies are the Celsius and Kelvin scales. The **Celsius scale** is also the everyday scale of temperature in most countries (Figure 1.17 ▶). It was originally based on the assignment of 0°C to the freezing point of water and 100°C to its boiling point at sea level (Figure 1.18 ▶).

The **Kelvin scale** is the SI temperature scale, and the SI unit of temperature is the kelvin (K). Historically, the Kelvin scale was based on the properties of gases; its origins will be considered in Chapter 10. Zero on this scale is the lowest attainable temperature, −273.15°C, a temperature referred to as *absolute zero*. Both the Celsius and Kelvin scales have equal-sized units—that is, a kelvin is the same size as a degree Celsius. Thus, the Kelvin and Celsius scales are related as follows:

$$K = °C + 273.15 \qquad [1.1]$$

▲ **Figure 1.17 Australian stamp.** Many countries employ the Celsius temperature scale in everyday use, as illustrated by this stamp.

---

* Mass and weight are not interchangeable terms and are often incorrectly thought to be the same. The weight of an object is the force that its mass exerts due to gravity. In space, where gravitational forces are very weak, an astronaut can be weightless, but he or she cannot be massless. In fact, the astronaut's mass in space is the same as it is on Earth.

▶ **Figure 1.18 Comparison of the Kelvin, Celsius, and Fahrenheit temperature scales.** The freezing point and boiling point of water as well as normal human body temperature is indicated on each of the scales.

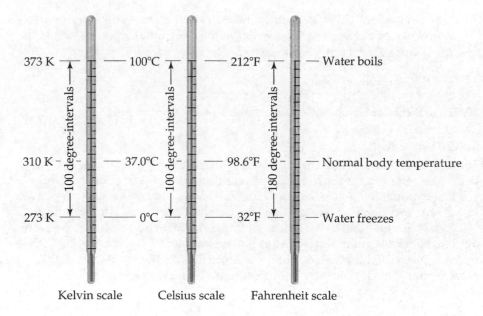

Kelvin scale   Celsius scale   Fahrenheit scale

ACTIVITY
Temperature

The freezing point of water, 0°C, is 273.15 K (Figure 1.18). Notice that we do not use a degree sign (°) with temperatures on the Kelvin scale.

The common temperature scale in the United States is the *Fahrenheit scale*, which is not generally used in scientific studies. On the Fahrenheit scale, water freezes at 32°F and boils at 212°F. The Fahrenheit and Celsius scales are related as follows:

$$°C = \frac{5}{9}(°F - 32) \text{ or } °F = \frac{9}{5}(°C) + 32 \qquad [1.2]$$

SAMPLE EXERCISE 1.3 | Converting units of temperature

If a weather forecaster predicts that the temperature for the day will reach 31°C, what is the predicted temperature **(a)** in K, **(b)** in °F?

Solution (a) Using Equation 1.1, we have K = 31 + 273 = 304 K

(b) Using Equation 1.2, we have °F = $\frac{9}{5}$(31) + 32 = 56 + 32 = 88°F

PRACTICE EXERCISE

Ethylene glycol, the major ingredient in antifreeze, freezes at −11.5°C. What is the freezing point in **(a)** K, **(b)** °F?
Answers: **(a)** 261.7 K, **(b)** 11.3°F

Derived SI Units

The SI base units in Table 1.4 are used to derive the units of other quantities. To do so, we use the defining equation for the quantity, substituting the appropriate base units. For example, speed is defined as the ratio of distance traveled to elapsed time. Thus, the SI unit for speed is the SI unit for distance (length) divided by the SI unit for time, m/s, which we read as "meters per second." We will encounter many derived units, such as those for force, pressure, and energy, later in this text. In this chapter we examine the derived units for volume and density.

Volume

The *volume* of a cube is given by its length cubed, (length)³. Thus, the SI unit of volume is the SI unit of length raised to the third power. The cubic meter, or m³, is the volume of a cube that is 1 m on each edge. Smaller units, such as cubic centimeters, cm³ (sometimes written as cc), are frequently used in chemistry. Another unit of volume commonly used in chemistry is the *liter* (L), which equals a cubic decimeter, dm³, and is slightly larger than a quart. The liter is the first metric unit we have encountered that is *not* an SI unit. There are 1000 milliliters (mL) in a liter (Figure 1.19 ▶), and each milliliter is the same volume as a cubic centimeter: 1 mL = 1 cm³. The terms *milliliter* and *cubic centimeter* are used interchangeably in expressing volume.

The devices used most frequently in chemistry to measure volume are illustrated in Figure 1.20 ▼. Syringes, burets, and pipets deliver liquids with more precision than graduated cylinders. Volumetric flasks are used to contain specific volumes of liquid.

Density

Density is a property of matter that is widely used to characterize substances. It is defined as the amount of mass in a unit volume of the substance:

$$\text{Density} = \frac{\text{mass}}{\text{volume}} \qquad [1.3]$$

The densities of solids and liquids are commonly expressed in units of grams per cubic centimeter (g/cm³) or grams per milliliter (g/mL). The densities of some common substances are listed in Table 1.6 ▼. It is no coincidence that the density of water is 1.00 g/mL; the gram was originally defined as the mass of 1 mL of water at a specific temperature. Because most substances change volume when heated or cooled, densities are temperature dependent.

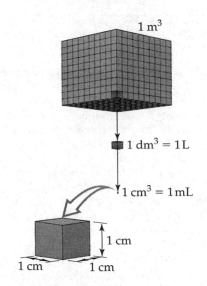

▲ **Figure 1.19 Volume relationships.** The volume occupied by a cube that is 1 m on each edge is a cubic meter, 1 m³ (top). Each cubic meter contains 1000 dm³ (middle). A liter is the same volume as a cubic decimeter, 1 L = 1 dm³. Each cubic decimeter contains 1000 cubic centimeters, 1 dm³ = 1000 cm³. Each cubic centimeter equals a milliliter, 1 cm³ = 1 mL (bottom).

TABLE 1.6 Densities of Some Selected Substances at 25°C	
Substance	**Density (g/cm³)**
Air	0.001
Balsa wood	0.16
Ethanol	0.79
Water	1.00
Ethylene glycol	1.09
Table sugar	1.59
Table salt	2.16
Iron	7.9
Gold	19.32

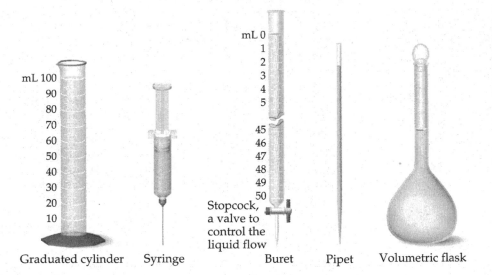

◀ **Figure 1.20 Common volumetric glassware.** The graduated cylinder, syringe, and buret are used in laboratories to deliver variable volumes of liquid; the pipet is used to deliver a specific volume of liquid. The volumetric flask contains a specific volume of liquid when filled to the mark.

Graduated cylinder   Syringe   Buret   Pipet   Volumetric flask

Science Fundamentals Second Edition

CHEMISTRY AT WORK | Chemistry in the News

Chemistry is a very lively, active field of science. Because it is so central to our lives, there are reports on matters of chemical significance in the news nearly every day. Some tell of recent breakthroughs in the development of new pharmaceuticals, materials, and processes. Others deal with environmental and public safety issues. As you study chemistry, we hope you will develop the skills to better understand the impact of chemistry on your life. You need these skills to take part in public discussions and debates about matters related to chemistry that affect your community, the nation, and the world. By way of examples, here are summaries of a few recent stories in which chemistry plays a role.

"Fueling a Miniature Revolution"

The ready availability of electric cars has been delayed for years by problems in finding a suitable energy source. The batteries that are available at reasonable cost are too heavy, and they can propel a car only a limited distance before needing to be recharged. The fuel cell, an electrical device in which fuels are used to directly generate electricity, is an alternative to a battery. Experimental vehicles powered by fuel cells, such as the car shown in Figure 1.21 ▼, are now commonly displayed on the pages of magazines and newspapers, offering hope that someday such vehicles will be a practical means of transportation.

The development of fuel cells for transportation has caused some to propose that fuel cells might also be practical for small electronic devices such as cell phones and notebook computers. As these devices become smaller, faster, and more capable, their power demands increase. Even the best batteries are hard-pressed to meet the need for lightweight, portable power sources that deliver power for an extended period of time. Many people have had the unfortunate experience of having a battery go dead during a cell-phone call or the inconvenience of having to carry extra batteries or charging devices while traveling.

In a fuel cell, the fuel flows through the cell on demand. Once the fuel is consumed, more can be added to make the cell produce more energy. In contrast, batteries are sealed systems, which means that once their chemical reactions are complete, the user has to either recharge the batteries or buy new ones. Small-scale fuel cells for portable electronic devices would be the size of conventional battery packs but weigh considerably less. Until now, successful fuel cells have required the use of hydrogen as a fuel. One of the keys to the commercial development of small cells is the development of practical systems, which convert a hydrogen-containing fuel such as methanol into the hydrogen that the cell can use.

"Biting into Research for New Dental Materials"

Rapid changes are occurring in the materials that dentists use. Research has yielded new and improved ways to bond restorative materials to teeth, improvements in the durability and appearance of materials used to restore or protect teeth, and improved treatments to reduce tooth decay.

For example, new materials are being developed that do not merely plug the cavities caused by decay and the dentist's drill, but are biologically active and stimulate the tooth to repair itself. The new materials contain amorphous calcium phosphate, which releases calcium and phosphate to tooth structures in proportions that form the mineral found naturally in teeth. The composition is not useful for large cavities because it is not as strong as conventional filling materials, but it is useful for fillings in small cavities and to seal pits and fissures in teeth where bits of food can accumulate and cause decay.

"Nanotechnology: Hype and Hope"

The past 15 years have witnessed an explosion of relatively inexpensive equipment and techniques for probing and manipulating materials on the nanometer-length scale. These capabilities have led to optimistic forecasts of futuristic nanotechnologies including molecular-scale machines and robots that can manipulate matter with atomic precision. Many believe that such futuristic visions are mere hype, while others express the conviction that they can be realized.

Nanoscale materials exhibit chemical and physical properties that are different from the properties of bulk materials. For example, carbon can be made to form tubular structures as shown in Figure 1.22 ▶. These tubes, called nanotubes, resemble a cylindrical roll of chicken wire. When nanotubes are perfectly formed, they conduct electricity like a metal.

Scientists have learned that the electric and optical properties of certain nanometer-size particles can be tuned by adjusting the particle size or shape. These particles are therefore of interest for applications in various kinds of electronic devices. For example, scientists at IBM's T. J. Watson Research Center recently generated an electric current in a single carbon nanotube by shining light on it. By developing the means to control light and electrical current, scientists aim to produce tiny optoelectronic devices. Although such applications are still years from commercial fruition, they nevertheless offer the promise of dramatically changing not only the size of

▲ **Figure 1.21   Cutaway view of car powered by fuel cells.**

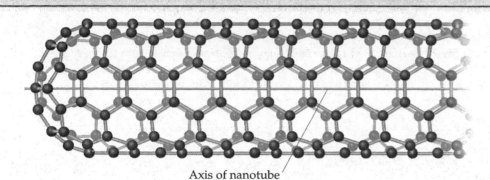

◀ **Figure 1.22   A section of carbon nanotube.** Each intersection in the network represents a carbon atom chemically joined to three others.

Axis of nanotube

electronic devices and many other items but also the way they are manufactured. The results obtained at the IBM labs also suggest that such devices might be assembled from simpler, smaller components such as individual molecules and other nanostructures. This approach is similar to the one nature uses to construct complex biological architectures.

"Got Mercury?"

The Food and Drug Administration (FDA) and the Environmental Protection Agency (EPA) recently issued a joint advisory about fish and shellfish consumption for people at risk from exposure to high mercury levels, namely pregnant women, nursing mothers, and young children. According to the advisory, people in these populations should not eat shark, swordfish, king mackerel, or tilefish, and should limit their intake of other fish as well. The concern is based on the fact that nearly all fish contain at least traces of methylmercury (Figure 1.23 ▼), a biologically active form of mercury.

Tiny amounts of mercury vapor occur in the atmosphere, resulting from both natural sources and pollution. In the United States, coal-fired power plants are the largest unregulated source of mercury that is due to human activities. Mercury in the atmosphere is converted to simple mercury-containing compounds and returned to Earth's surface in rainwater. The mercury compounds are converted to methylmercury by aquatic bacteria. Plankton take up some of the methylmercury, fish eat the plankton, and bigger fish eat them. The resultant accumulation of mercury through the food chain can produce mercury levels a million times greater in fish than in the surrounding waters.

When we eat fish, the methylmercury is absorbed from our gastrointestinal tract and distributed widely throughout our body. Methylmercury produces the greatest damage in the brain and central nervous system where it causes loss of nerve cells, which in turn results in neurological problems. The symptoms of acute mercury poisoning include numbness, difficulty in speaking, and loss of coordination. Fortunately, adults are able to release about 1% of their methylmercury burden daily by a number of different pathways. For infants, however, these mechanisms are not fully developed, leading to greater potential damage.

"New Elements Created"

Two new elements were reported in February 2004 as a result of studies performed at the Joint Institute for Nuclear Research (JINR) in Dubna, Russia. JINR scientists and their collaborators from Lawrence Livermore National Lab in California announced that they had produced 4 atoms of a new superheavy element (element 115) by striking a target of americium atoms (element 95) with a highly energetic beam of calcium atoms in a device called a particle accelerator.

The atoms of element 115 last only 90 milliseconds (90 ms) before decomposing to yet another new element (element 113). Element 113 is also unstable, lasting a little over a second. Although these times seem very short, they are actually long compared with other unstable nuclei of comparable mass. How long a nucleus lasts before falling apart is a measure of its stability. Theory suggests that elements in the vicinity of element 114 in the periodic table should be more stable than other heavy nuclei. Scientists, however, caution that these results will need to be confirmed by others before they are fully accepted.

Methylmercury – CH_3Hg^+

▲ **Figure 1.23   Molecular model of methylmercury.**

When reporting densities, the temperature should be specified. If no temperature is reported, we usually assume that the temperature is 25°C, close to normal room temperature.

The terms *density* and *weight* are sometimes confused. A person who says that iron weighs more than air generally means that iron has a higher density than air; 1 kg of air has the same mass as 1 kg of iron, but the iron occupies a smaller volume, thereby giving it a higher density. If we combine two liquids that do not mix, the less dense one will float on the more dense one.

■ **SAMPLE EXERCISE 1.4** | Determining density and using density to determine volume or mass

(a) Calculate the density of mercury if 1.00×10^2 g occupies a volume of 7.36 cm^3.
(b) Calculate the volume of 65.0 g of the liquid methanol (wood alcohol) if its density is 0.791 g/mL.
(c) What is the mass in grams of a cube of gold (density = 19.32 g/cm^3) if the length of the cube is 2.00 cm?

Solution

(a) We are given mass and volume, so Equation 1.3 yields

$$\text{Density} = \frac{\text{mass}}{\text{volume}} = \frac{1.00 \times 10^2 \text{ g}}{7.36 \text{ cm}^3} = 13.6 \text{ g/cm}^3$$

(b) Solving Equation 1.3 for volume and then using the given mass and density gives

$$\text{Volume} = \frac{\text{mass}}{\text{density}} = \frac{65.0 \text{ g}}{0.791 \text{ g/mL}} = 82.2 \text{ mL}$$

(c) We can calculate the mass from the volume of the cube and its density. The volume of a cube is given by its length cubed:

$$\text{Volume} = (2.00 \text{ cm})^3 = (2.00)^3 \text{ cm}^3 = 8.00 \text{ cm}^3$$

Solving Equation 1.3 for mass and substituting the volume and density of the cube, we have

$$\text{Mass} = \text{volume} \times \text{density} = (8.00 \text{ cm}^3)(19.32 \text{ g/cm}^3) = 155 \text{ g}$$

■ **PRACTICE EXERCISE**

(a) Calculate the density of a 374.5-g sample of copper if it has a volume of 41.8 cm^3. (b) A student needs 15.0 g of ethanol for an experiment. If the density of ethanol is 0.789 g/mL, how many milliliters of ethanol are needed? (c) What is the mass, in grams, of 25.0 mL of mercury (density = 13.6 g/mL)?
Answers: (a) 8.96 g/cm^3, (b) 19.0 mL, (c) 340 g

1.5 | Uncertainty in Measurement

There are two kinds of numbers in scientific work: *exact numbers* (those whose values are known exactly) and *inexact numbers* (those whose values have some uncertainty). Most of the exact numbers that we will encounter in this course have defined values. For example, there are exactly 12 eggs in a dozen, exactly 1000 g in a kilogram, and exactly 2.54 cm in an inch. The number 1 in any conversion factor between units, as in 1 m = 100 cm or 1 kg = 2.2046 lb, is also an exact number. Exact numbers can also result from counting numbers of objects. For example, we can count the exact number of marbles in a jar or the exact number of people in a classroom.

Numbers obtained by measurement are always *inexact*. There are always inherent limitations in the equipment used to measure quantities (equipment errors), and there are differences in how different people make the same measurement (human errors). Suppose that ten students with ten balances are given the same dime and told to determine its mass. The ten measurements will probably vary slightly from one another for various reasons. The balances might be calibrated slightly differently, and there might be differences in how each student reads the mass from the balance. Remember: *Uncertainties always*

ACTIVITY
Uncertainty in Measurement

exist in measured quantities. Counting very large numbers of objects usually has some associated error as well. Consider, for example, how difficult it is to obtain accurate census information for a city or vote counts for an election.

Which of the following is an inexact quantity: (a) the number of people in your chemistry class, (b) the mass of a penny, (c) the number of grams in a kilogram?

Precision and Accuracy

The terms precision and accuracy are often used in discussing the uncertainties of measured values. **Precision** is a measure of how closely individual measurements agree with one another. **Accuracy** refers to how closely individual measurements agree with the correct, or "true," value. The analogy of darts stuck in a dartboard pictured in Figure 1.24 ▶ illustrates the difference between these two concepts.

In the laboratory we often perform several different "trials" of the same experiment. We gain confidence in the accuracy of our measurements if we obtain nearly the same value each time. Figure 1.24 should remind us, however, that precise measurements could be inaccurate. For example, if a very sensitive balance is poorly calibrated, the masses we measure will be consistently either high or low. They will be inaccurate even if they are precise.

Significant Figures

Suppose you determine the mass of a dime on a balance capable of measuring to the nearest 0.0001 g. You could report the mass as 2.2405 ± 0.0001 g. The $\pm$ notation (read "plus or minus") expresses the magnitude of the uncertainty of your measurement. In much scientific work we drop the $\pm$ notation with the understanding that there is always some uncertainty in the last digit of the measured quantity. That is, *measured quantities are generally reported in such a way that only the last digit is uncertain.*

Figure 1.25 ▼ shows a thermometer with its liquid column between the scale marks. We can read the certain digits from the scale and estimate the uncertain one. From the scale marks on the thermometer, we see that the liquid is between the 25°C and 30°C marks. We might estimate the temperature to be 27°C, being somewhat uncertain of the second digit of our measurement.

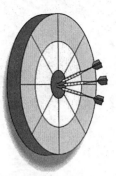

Good accuracy
Good precision

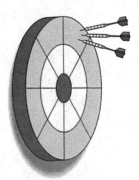

Poor accuracy
Good precision

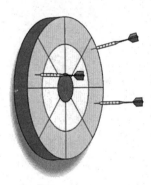

Poor accuracy
Poor precision

▲ **Figure 1.24 Precision and accuracy.** The distribution of darts on a target illustrates the difference between accuracy and precision.

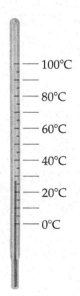

◀ **Figure 1.25 Significant figures in measurements.** The thermometer has markings every 5°C. The temperature is between 25°C and 30°C and is approximately 27°C. The two significant figures in the measurement include the second digit, which is estimated by reading between the scale marks.

Science Fundamentals Second Edition

All digits of a measured quantity, including the uncertain one, are called **significant figures**. A measured mass reported as 2.2 g has two significant figures, whereas one reported as 2.2405 g has five significant figures. The greater the number of significant figures, the greater is the certainty implied for the measurement. When multiple measurements are made of a quantity, the results can be averaged, and the number of significant figures estimated by using statistical methods.

SAMPLE EXERCISE 1.5 | Relating significant figures to the uncertainty of a measurement

What difference exists between the measured values 4.0 g and 4.00 g?

Solution Many people would say there is no difference, but a scientist would note the difference in the number of significant figures in the two measurements. The value 4.0 has two significant figures, while 4.00 has three. This difference implies that the first measurement has more uncertainty. A mass of 4.0 g indicates that the uncertainty is in the first decimal place of the measurement. Thus, the mass might be anything between 3.9 and 4.1 g, which we can represent as 4.0 ± 0.1 g. A measurement of 4.00 g implies that the uncertainty is in the second decimal place. Thus, the mass might be anything between 3.99 and 4.01 g, which we can represent as 4.00 ± 0.01 g. Without further information, we cannot be sure whether the difference in uncertainties of the two measurements reflects the precision or accuracy of the measurement.

PRACTICE EXERCISE

A balance has a precision of ± 0.001 g. A sample that has a mass of about 25 g is placed on this balance. How many significant figures should be reported for this measurement?

Answer: five, as in the measurement 24.995 g

To determine the number of significant figures in a reported measurement, read the number from left to right, counting the digits starting with the first digit that is not zero. *In any measurement that is properly reported, all nonzero digits are significant.* Zeros, however, can be used either as part of the measured value or merely to locate the decimal point. Thus, zeros may or may not be significant, depending on how they appear in the number. The following guidelines describe the different situations involving zeros:

1. Zeros *between* nonzero digits are always significant—1005 kg (four significant figures); 1.03 cm (three significant figures).

"MY GOODNESS, IT'S 12:15:0936420175! TIME FOR LUNCH."

Science Fundamentals Second Edition

2. Zeros *at the beginning* of a number are never significant; they merely indicate the position of the decimal point—0.02 g (one significant figure); 0.0026 cm (two significant figures).

3. Zeros *at the end* of a number are significant if the number contains a decimal point—0.0200 g (three significant figures); 3.0 cm (two significant figures).

A problem arises when a number ends with zeros but contains no decimal point. In such cases, it is normally assumed that the zeros are not significant. Exponential notation (Appendix A) can be used to clearly indicate whether zeros at the end of a number are significant. For example, a mass of 10,300 g can be written in exponential notation showing three, four, or five significant figures depending on how the measurement is obtained:

1.03×10^4 g   (three significant figures)
1.030×10^4 g   (four significant figures)
1.0300×10^4 g   (five significant figures)

In these numbers all the zeros to the right of the decimal point are significant (rules 1 and 3). (The exponential term does not add to the number of significant figures.)

SAMPLE EXERCISE 1.6 | Determining the number of significant figures in a measurement

How many significant figures are in each of the following numbers (assume that each number is a measured quantity): (a) 4.003, (b) 6.023×10^{23}, (c) 5000?

Solution (a) Four; the zeros are significant figures. (b) Four; the exponential term does not add to the number of significant figures. (c) One. We assume that the zeros are not significant when there is no decimal point shown. If the number has more significant figures, a decimal point should be employed or the number written in exponential notation. Thus, 5000. has four significant figures, whereas 5.00×10^3 has three.

PRACTICE EXERCISE

How many significant figures are in each of the following measurements: (a) 3.549 g, (b) 2.3×10^4 cm, (c) 0.00134 m³?
Answers: (a) four, (b) two, (c) three

ACTIVITY
Significant Figures

Significant Figures in Calculations

When carrying measured quantities through calculations, *the least certain measurement limits the certainty of the calculated quantity and thereby determines the number of significant figures in the final answer.* The final answer should be reported with only one uncertain digit. To keep track of significant figures in calculations, we will make frequent use of two rules, one for multiplication and division and another for addition and subtraction.

1. *For multiplication and division*, the result contains the same number of significant figures as the measurement with the fewest significant figures. When the result contains more than the correct number of significant figures, it must be rounded off. For example, the area of a rectangle whose measured edge lengths are 6.221 cm and 5.2 cm should be reported as 32 cm² even though a calculator shows the product of 6.221 and 5.2 to have more digits:

    Area = (6.221 cm)(5.2 cm) = 32.3492 cm² $\Rightarrow$ round off to 32 cm²

    We round off to two significant figures because the least precise number—5.2 cm—has only two significant figures.

2. *For addition and subtraction*, the result has the same number of decimal places as the measurement with the fewest decimal places. Consider the following example in which the uncertain digits appear in color:

This number limits	20.42	← two decimal places
the number of significant	1.322	← three decimal places
figures in the result ⟶	83.1	← one decimal place
	104.842	← round off to 104. 8 (one decimal place)

We report the result as 104.8 because 83.1 has only one decimal place.

Notice that for multiplication and division, significant figures are counted. For addition and subtraction, decimal places are counted. In determining the final answer for a calculated quantity, exact numbers can be treated as if they have an infinite number of significant figures. This rule applies to many definitions between units. Thus, when we say, "There are 12 inches in 1 foot," the number 12 is exact, and we need not worry about the number of significant figures in it.

In *rounding off numbers*, look at the leftmost digit to be removed:

- If the leftmost digit removed is less than 5, the preceding number is left unchanged. Thus, rounding 7.248 to two significant figures gives 7.2.

- If the leftmost digit removed is 5 or greater, the preceding number is increased by 1. Rounding 4.735 to three significant figures gives 4.74, and rounding 2.376 to two significant figures gives 2.4.*

■ SAMPLE EXERCISE 1.7 | Determining the number of significant figures in a calculated quantity

The width, length, and height of a small box are 15.5 cm, 27.3 cm, and 5.4 cm, respectively. Calculate the volume of the box, using the correct number of significant figures in your answer.

Solution The volume of a box is determined by the product of its width, length, and height. In reporting the product, we can show only as many significant figures as given in the dimension with the fewest significant figures, that for the height (two significant figures):

Volume = width × length × height

$$= (15.5 \text{ cm})(27.3 \text{ cm})(5.4 \text{ cm}) = 2285.01 \text{ cm}^3 \Rightarrow 2.3 \times 10^3 \text{ cm}^3$$

When we use a calculator to do this calculation, the display shows 2285.01, which we must round off to two significant figures. Because the resulting number is 2300, it is best reported in exponential notation, 2.3×10^3, to clearly indicate two significant figures.

■ PRACTICE EXERCISE

It takes 10.5 s for a sprinter to run 100.00 m. Calculate the average speed of the sprinter in meters per second, and express the result to the correct number of significant figures.
Answer: 9.52 m/s (3 significant figures)

---

* Your instructor may want you to use a slight variation on the rule when the leftmost digit to be removed is exactly 5, with no following digits or only zeros. One common practice is to round up to the next higher number if that number will be even, and down to the next lower number otherwise. Thus, 4.7350 would be rounded to 4.74, and 4.7450 would also be rounded to 4.74.

■ **SAMPLE EXERCISE 1.8** | Determining the number of significant figures in a calculated quantity

A gas at 25°C fills a container whose volume is 1.05×10^3 cm³. The container plus gas have a mass of 837.6 g. The container, when emptied of all gas, has a mass of 836.2 g. What is the density of the gas at 25°C?

Solution

To calculate the density, we must know both the mass and the volume of the gas. The mass of the gas is just the difference in the masses of the full and empty container:

$$(837.6 - 836.2) \text{ g} = 1.4 \text{ g}$$

In subtracting numbers, we determine the number of significant figures in our result by counting decimal places in each quantity. In this case each quantity has one decimal place. Thus, the mass of the gas, 1.4 g, has one decimal place.

Using the volume given in the question, 1.05×10^3 cm³, and the definition of density, we have

$$\text{Density} = \frac{\text{mass}}{\text{volume}} = \frac{1.4 \text{ g}}{1.05 \times 10^3 \text{ cm}^3}$$
$$= 1.3 \times 10^{-3} \text{ g/cm}^3 = 0.0013 \text{ g/cm}^3$$

In dividing numbers, we determine the number of significant figures in our result by counting the number of significant figures in each quantity. There are two significant figures in our answer, corresponding to the smaller number of significant figures in the two numbers that form the ratio.

■ **PRACTICE EXERCISE**

To how many significant figures should the mass of the container be measured (with and without the gas) in Sample Exercise 1.8 in order for the density to be calculated to three significant figures?
Answer: five (In order for the difference in the two masses to have three significant figures, there must be two decimal places in the masses of the filled and empty containers.)

When a calculation involves two or more steps and you write down answers for intermediate steps, retain at least one additional digit—past the number of significant figures—for the intermediate answers. This procedure ensures that small errors from rounding at each step do not combine to affect the final result. When using a calculator, you may enter the numbers one after another, rounding only the final answer. Accumulated rounding-off errors may account for small differences among results you obtain and answers given in the text for numerical problems.

1.6 | Dimensional Analysis

Throughout the text we use an approach called **dimensional analysis** as an aid in problem solving. In dimensional analysis we carry units through all calculations. Units are multiplied together, divided into each other, or "canceled." Using dimensional analysis helps ensure that the solutions to problems yield the proper units. Moreover, it provides a systematic way of solving many numerical problems and of checking our solutions for possible errors.

The key to using dimensional analysis is the correct use of conversion factors to change one unit into another. A **conversion factor** is a fraction whose numerator and denominator are the same quantity expressed in different units. For example, 2.54 cm and 1 in. are the same length, 2.54 cm = 1 in. This relationship allows us to write two conversion factors:

$$\frac{2.54 \text{ cm}}{1 \text{ in.}} \quad \text{and} \quad \frac{1 \text{ in.}}{2.54 \text{ cm}}$$

We use the first of these factors to convert inches to centimeters. For example, the length in centimeters of an object that is 8.50 in. long is given by

Number of centimeters = (8.50 in.) $\dfrac{2.54 \text{ cm}}{1 \text{ in.}}$ = 21.6 cm

Desired unit

Given unit

The unit inches in the denominator of the conversion factor cancels the unit inches in the given data (8.50 *inches*). The unit centimeters in the numerator of the conversion factor becomes the unit of the final answer. Because the numerator and denominator of a conversion factor are equal, multiplying any quantity by a conversion factor is equivalent to multiplying by the number 1 and so does not change the intrinsic value of the quantity. The length 8.50 in. is the same as the length 21.6 cm.

In general, we begin any conversion by examining the units of the given data and the units we desire. We then ask ourselves what conversion factors we have available to take us from the units of the given quantity to those of the desired one. When we multiply a quantity by a conversion factor, the units multiply and divide as follows:

$$\text{Given unit} \times \frac{\text{desired unit}}{\text{given unit}} = \text{desired unit}$$

If the desired units are not obtained in a calculation, then an error must have been made somewhere. Careful inspection of units often reveals the source of the error.

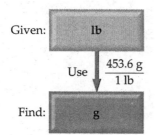

Given: lb

Use $\dfrac{453.6\ g}{1\ lb}$

Find: g

SAMPLE EXERCISE 1.9 | Converting units

If a woman has a mass of 115 lb, what is her mass in grams? (Use the relationships between units given on the back inside cover of the text.)

Solution Because we want to change from lb to g, we look for a relationship between these units of mass. From the back inside cover we have 1 lb = 453.6 g. In order to cancel pounds and leave grams, we write the conversion factor with grams in the numerator and pounds in the denominator:

$$\text{Mass in grams} = (115\ \cancel{lb})\left(\frac{453.6\ g}{1\ \cancel{lb}}\right) = 5.22 \times 10^4\ g$$

The answer can be given to only three significant figures, the number of significant figures in 115 lb. The process we have used is diagrammed in the margin.

PRACTICE EXERCISE

By using a conversion factor from the back inside cover, determine the length in kilometers of a 500.0-mi automobile race.
Answer: 804.7 km

 GIVE IT SOME THOUGHT

How do we determine how many digits to use in conversion factors, such as the one between pounds and grams in Sample Exercise 1.9?

 STRATEGIES IN CHEMISTRY | Estimating Answers

A friend once remarked cynically that calculators let you get the wrong answer more quickly. What he was implying by that remark was that unless you have the correct strategy for solving a problem and have punched in the correct numbers, the answer will be incorrect. If you learn to *estimate* answers, however, you will be able to check whether the answers to your calculations are reasonable.

The idea is to make a rough calculation using numbers that are rounded off in such a way that the arithmetic can be easily performed without a calculator. This approach is often referred to as making a "ballpark" estimate, meaning that while it doesn't give an exact answer, it gives one that is roughly the right size. By working with units using dimensional analysis and by estimating answers, we can readily check the reasonableness of our answers to calculations.

Using Two or More Conversion Factors

It is often necessary to use several conversion factors in solving a problem. As an example, let's convert the length of an 8.00-m rod to inches. The table on the back inside cover doesn't give the relationship between meters and inches. It *does* give the relationship between centimeters and inches (1 in. = 2.54 cm), though, and from our knowledge of metric prefixes we know that 1 cm = 10^{-2} m. Thus, we can convert step by step, first from meters to centimeters, and then from centimeters to inches as diagrammed in the margin.

Combining the given quantity (8.00 m) and the two conversion factors, we have

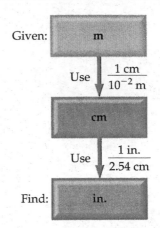

$$\text{Number of inches} = (8.00 \text{ m})\left(\frac{100 \text{ cm}}{1 \text{ m}}\right)\left(\frac{1 \text{ in.}}{2.54 \text{ cm}}\right) = 315 \text{ in.}$$

The first conversion factor is applied to cancel meters and convert the length to centimeters. Thus, meters are written in the denominator and centimeters in the numerator. The second conversion factor is written to cancel centimeters, so it has centimeters in the denominator and inches, the desired unit, in the numerator.

SAMPLE EXERCISE 1.10 | Converting units using two or more conversion factors

The average speed of a nitrogen molecule in air at 25°C is 515 m/s. Convert this speed to miles per hour.

Solution To go from the given units, m/s, to the desired units, mi/hr, we must convert meters to miles and seconds to hours. From the relationships given on the back inside cover of the book, we find that 1 mi = 1.6093 km. From our knowledge of metric prefixes we know that 1 km = 10^3 m. Thus, we can convert m to km and then convert km to mi. From our knowledge of time we know that 60 s = 1 min and 60 min = 1 hr. Thus, we can convert s to min and then convert min to hr.

Applying first the conversions for distance and then those for time, we can set up one long equation in which unwanted units are canceled:

$$\text{Speed in mi/hr} = \left(515\frac{\text{m}}{\text{s}}\right)\left(\frac{1 \text{ km}}{10^3 \text{ m}}\right)\left(\frac{1 \text{ mi}}{1.6093 \text{ km}}\right)\left(\frac{60 \text{ s}}{1 \text{ min}}\right)\left(\frac{60 \text{ min}}{1 \text{ hr}}\right)$$

$$= 1.15 \times 10^3 \text{ mi/hr}$$

Our answer has the desired units. We can check our calculation, using the estimating procedure described in the previous "Strategies" box. The given speed is about 500 m/s. Dividing by 1000 converts m to km, giving 0.5 km/s. Because 1 mi is about 1.6 km, this speed corresponds to 0.5/1.6 = 0.3 mi/s. Multiplying by 60 gives about 0.3 × 60 = 20 mi/min. Multiplying again by 60 gives 20 × 60 = 1200 mi/hr. The approximate solution (about 1200 mi/hr) and the detailed solution (1150 mi/hr) are reasonably close. The answer to the detailed solution has three significant figures, corresponding to the number of significant figures in the given speed in m/s.

PRACTICE EXERCISE

A car travels 28 mi per gallon of gasoline. How many kilometers per liter will it go?
Answer: 12 km/L

Conversions Involving Volume

The conversion factors previously noted convert from one unit of a given measure to another unit of the same measure, such as from length to length. We also have conversion factors that convert from one measure to a different one. The density of a substance, for example, can be treated as a conversion factor between mass and volume. Suppose that we want to know the mass in grams of two cubic inches (2.00 in.^{3}) of gold, which has a density of 19.3 g/cm^3. The density gives us the following factors:

$$\frac{19.3 \text{ g}}{1 \text{ cm}^3} \quad \text{and} \quad \frac{1 \text{ cm}^3}{19.3 \text{ g}}$$

Because the answer we want is a mass in grams, we can see that we will use the first of these factors, which has mass in grams in the numerator. To use this factor, however, we must first convert cubic inches to cubic centimeters. The relationship between in.^{3} and cm^3 is not given on the back inside cover, but the relationship between inches and centimeters is given: 1 in. = 2.54 cm (exactly). Cubing both sides of this equation gives (1 in.)^3 = (2.54 cm)^3 from which we write the desired conversion factor:

$$\frac{(2.54 \text{ cm})^3}{(1 \text{ in.})^3} = \frac{(2.54)^3 \text{ cm}^3}{(1)^3 \text{ in.}^3} = \frac{16.39 \text{ cm}^3}{1 \text{ in.}^3}$$

Notice that both the numbers and the units are cubed. Also, because 2.54 is an exact number, we can retain as many digits of (2.54)^3 as we need. We have used four, one more than the number of digits in the density (19.3 g/cm^3). Applying our conversion factors, we can now solve the problem:

$$\text{Mass in grams} = (2.00 \text{ in.}^3)\left(\frac{16.39 \text{ cm}^3}{1 \text{ in.}^3}\right)\left(\frac{19.3 \text{ g}}{1 \text{ cm}^3}\right) = 633 \text{ g}$$

The procedure is diagrammed below. The final answer is reported to three significant figures, the same number of significant figures as in 2.00 and 19.3.

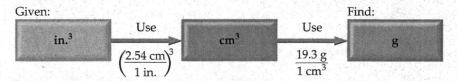

SAMPLE EXERCISE 1.11 | Converting volume units

Earth's oceans contain approximately 1.36×10^9 km^3 of water. Calculate the volume in liters.

Solution This problem involves conversion of km^3 to L. From the back inside cover of the text we find 1 L = 10^{-3} m^3, but there is no relationship listed involving km^3. From our knowledge of metric prefixes, however, we have 1 km = 10^3 m, and we can use this relationship between lengths to write the desired conversion factor between volumes:

$$\left(\frac{10^3 \text{ m}}{1 \text{ km}}\right)^3 = \frac{10^9 \text{ m}^3}{1 \text{ km}^3}$$

Thus, converting from km^3 to m^3 to L, we have

$$\text{Volume in liters} = (1.36 \times 10^9 \text{ km}^3)\left(\frac{10^9 \text{ m}^3}{1 \text{ km}^3}\right)\left(\frac{1 \text{ L}}{10^{-3} \text{ m}^3}\right) = 1.36 \times 10^{21} \text{ L}$$

PRACTICE EXERCISE

If the volume of an object is reported as 5.0 ft^3, what is the volume in cubic meters?
Answer: 0.14 m^3

▄▄ SAMPLE EXERCISE 1.12 | Conversions involving density

What is the mass in grams of 1.00 gal of water? The density of water is 1.00 g/mL.

Solution Before we begin solving this exercise, we note the following:

1. We are given 1.00 gal of water (the known, or given, quantity) and asked to calculate its mass in grams (the unknown).

2. We have the following conversion factors either given, commonly known, or available on the back inside cover of the text:

$$\frac{1.00 \text{ g water}}{1 \text{ mL water}} \quad \frac{1 \text{ L}}{1000 \text{ mL}} \quad \frac{1 \text{ L}}{1.057 \text{ qt}} \quad \frac{1 \text{ gal}}{4 \text{ qt}}$$

The first of these conversion factors must be used as written (with grams in the numerator) to give the desired result, whereas the last conversion factor must be inverted in order to cancel gallons:

$$\text{Mass in grams} = (1.00 \text{ gal})\left(\frac{4 \text{ qt}}{1 \text{ gal}}\right)\left(\frac{1 \text{ L}}{1.057 \text{ qt}}\right)\left(\frac{1000 \text{ mL}}{1 \text{ L}}\right)\left(\frac{1.00 \text{ g}}{1 \text{ mL}}\right)$$

$$= 3.78 \times 10^3 \text{ g water}$$

The units of our final answer are appropriate, and we've also taken care of our significant figures. We can further check our calculation by the estimation procedure. We can round 1.057 off to 1. Focusing on the numbers that don't equal 1 then gives merely $4 \times 1000 = 4000$ g, in agreement with the detailed calculation.

▄▄ PRACTICE EXERCISE

The density of benzene is 0.879 g/mL. Calculate the mass in grams of 1.00 qt of benzene.
Answer: 832 g

 STRATEGIES IN CHEMISTRY | The Importance of Practice

If you've ever played a musical instrument or participated in athletics, you know that the keys to success are practice and discipline. You can't learn to play a piano merely by listening to music, and you can't learn how to play basketball merely by watching games on television. Likewise, you can't learn chemistry by merely watching your instructor do it. Simply reading this book, listening to lectures, or reviewing notes will not usually be sufficient when exam time comes around. Your task is not merely to understand how someone else uses chemistry, but to be able to do it yourself. That takes practice on a regular basis, and anything that you have to do on a regular basis requires self-discipline until it becomes a habit.

Throughout the book, we have provided sample exercises in which the solutions are shown in detail. A practice exercise, for which only the answer is given, accompanies each sample exercise. It is important that you use these exercises as learning aids. End-of-chapter exercises provide additional questions to help you understand the material in the chapter. Red numbers indicate exercises for which answers are given at the back of the book. A review of basic mathematics is given in Appendix A.

The practice exercises in this text and the homework assignments given by your instructor provide the minimal practice that you will need to succeed in your chemistry course. Only by working all the assigned problems will you face the full range of difficulty and coverage that your instructor expects you to master for exams. There is no substitute for a determined and perhaps lengthy effort to work problems on your own. If you do get stuck on a problem, however, get help from your instructor, a teaching assistant, a tutor, or a fellow student. Spending an inordinate amount of time on a single exercise is rarely effective unless you know that it is particularly challenging and requires extensive thought and effort.

SUMMARY AND KEY TERMS

Introduction and Section 1.1 **Chemistry** is the study of the composition, structure, properties, and changes of **matter**. The composition of matter relates to the kinds of **elements** it contains. The structure of matter relates to the ways the **atoms** of these elements are arranged. A **property** is any characteristic that gives a sample of matter its unique identity. A **molecule** is an entity composed of two or more atoms with the atoms attached to one another in a specific **way**.

Section 1.2 Matter exists in three physical states, **gas**, **liquid**, and **solid**, which are known as the **states of matter**. There are two kinds of **pure substances**: elements and **compounds**. Each element has a single kind of atom and is represented by a chemical symbol consisting of one or two letters, with the first letter capitalized. Compounds are composed of two or more elements joined chemically. The **law of constant composition**, also called the **law of definite proportions**, states that the elemental composition of a pure compound is always the same. Most matter consists of a mixture of substances. **Mixtures** have variable compositions and can be either homogeneous or heterogeneous; homogeneous mixtures are called **solutions**.

Section 1.3 Each substance has a unique set of **physical properties** and **chemical properties** that can be used to identify it. During a **physical change**, matter does not change its composition. **Changes of state** are physical changes. In a **chemical change (chemical reaction)** a substance is transformed into a chemically different substance. **Intensive properties** are independent of the amount of matter examined and are used to identify substances. **Extensive properties** relate to the amount of substance present. Differences in physical and chemical properties are used to separate substances.

The **scientific method** is a dynamic process used to answer questions about our physical world. Observations and experiments lead to **scientific laws**, general rules that summarize how nature behaves. Observations also lead to tentative explanations or **hypotheses**. As a hypothesis is tested and refined, a **theory** may be developed.

Section 1.4 Measurements in chemistry are made using the **metric system**. Special emphasis is placed on a particular set of metric units called **SI units**, which are based on the meter, the kilogram, and the second as the basic units of length, **mass**, and time, respectively. The metric system employs a set of prefixes to indicate decimal fractions or multiples of the base units. The SI temperature scale is the **Kelvin scale**, although the **Celsius scale** is frequently used as well. **Density** is an important property that equals mass divided by volume.

Section 1.5 All measured quantities are inexact to some extent. The **precision** of a measurement indicates how closely different measurements of a quantity agree with one another. The **accuracy** of a measurement indicates how well a measurement agrees with the accepted or "true" value. The **significant figures** in a measured quantity include one estimated digit, the last digit of the measurement. The significant figures indicate the extent of the uncertainty of the measurement. Certain rules must be followed so that a calculation involving measured quantities is reported with the appropriate number of significant figures.

Section 1.6 In the **dimensional analysis** approach to problem solving, we keep track of units as we carry measurements through calculations. The units are multiplied together, divided into each other, or canceled like algebraic quantities. Obtaining the proper units for the final result is an important means of checking the method of calculation. When converting units and when carrying out several other types of problems, **conversion factors** can be used. These factors are ratios constructed from valid relations between equivalent quantities.

VISUALIZING CONCEPTS

Visualizing Concepts

The exercises in this section are intended to probe your understanding of key concepts rather than your ability to utilize formulas and perform calculations. Those exercises with red exercise numbers have answers in the back of the book.

1.1 Which of the following figures represents **(a)** a pure element, **(b)** a mixture of two elements, **(c)** a pure compound, **(d)** a mixture of an element and a compound? (More than one picture might fit each description.)

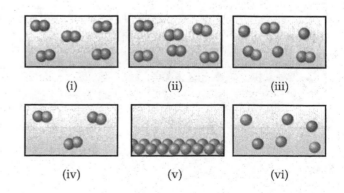

(i)   (ii)   (iii)

(iv)   (v)   (vi)

1.2 Does the following diagram represent a chemical or physical change? How do you know?

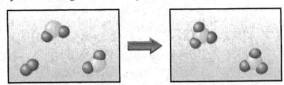

1.3 Identify each of the following as measurements of length, area, volume, mass, density, time, or temperature: **(a)** 5 ns, **(b)** 5.5 kg/m^3, **(c)** 0.88 pm, **(d)** 540 km^2, **(e)** 173 K, **(f)** 2 mm^3, **(g)** 23°C.

1.4 The following dartboards illustrate the types of errors often seen when one measurement is repeated several times. The bull's-eye represents the "true value," and the darts represent the experimental measurements. Which board best represents each of the following scenarios: **(a)** measurements both accurate and precise, **(b)** measurements precise but inaccurate, **(c)** measurements imprecise but yield an accurate average?

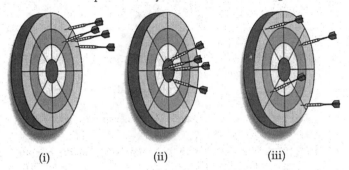

(i)   (ii)   (iii)

1.5 **(a)** What is the length of the pencil in the following figure if the scale reads in centimeters? How many significant figures are there in this measurement? **(b)** An oven thermometer with a circular scale reading degrees Fahrenheit is shown. What temperature does the scale indicate? How many significant figures are in the measurement?

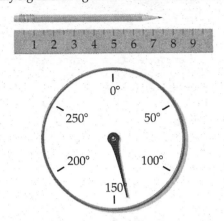

1.6 What is wrong with the following statement? Twenty years ago an ancient artifact was determined to be 1900 years old. It must now be 1920 years old.

1.7 When you convert units, how do you decide which part of the conversion factor is in the numerator and which is in the denominator?

1.8 Draw a logic map indicating the steps you would take to convert miles per hour to kilometers per second. Write down the conversion factor for each step, as done on page 28.

EXERCISES

Classification and Properties of Matter

The following exercises are divided into sections that deal with specific topics in the chapter. These exercises are grouped in pairs, with the answer given in the back of the book to the odd-numbered one, as indicated by the red exercise number. Those exercises whose number appears in brackets are more challenging than the nonbracketed exercises.

1.9 Classify each of the following as a pure substance or a mixture; if a mixture, indicate whether it is homogeneous or heterogeneous: **(a)** rice pudding, **(b)** seawater, **(c)** magnesium, **(d)** gasoline.

1.10 Classify each of the following as a pure substance or a mixture; if a mixture, indicate whether it is homogeneous or heterogeneous: **(a)** air, **(b)** tomato juice, **(c)** iodine crystals, **(d)** sand.

1.11 Give the chemical symbols for the following elements: **(a)** sulfur, **(b)** potassium, **(c)** chlorine, **(d)** copper, **(e)** silicon, **(f)** nitrogen, **(g)** calcium, **(h)** helium.

1.12 Give the chemical symbol for each of the following elements: **(a)** carbon, **(b)** sodium, **(c)** fluorine, **(d)** iron, **(e)** phosphorus, **(f)** argon, **(g)** nickel, **(h)** silver.

1.13 Name the chemical elements represented by the following symbols: **(a)** Li, **(b)** Al, **(c)** Pb, **(d)** S, **(e)** Br, **(f)** Sn, **(g)** Cr, **(h)** Zn.

1.14 Name each of the following elements: **(a)** Co, **(b)** I, **(c)** Kr, **(d)** Hg, **(e)** As, **(f)** Ti, **(g)** K, **(h)** Ge.

1.15 A solid white substance A is heated strongly in the absence of air. It decomposes to form a new white substance B and a gas C. The gas has exactly the same properties as the product obtained when carbon is burned in an excess of oxygen. Based on these observations, can we determine whether solids A and B and the gas C are elements or compounds? Explain your conclusions for each substance.

1.16 In 1807 the English chemist Humphry Davy passed an electric current through molten potassium hydroxide and isolated a bright, shiny reactive substance. He claimed the discovery of a new element, which he named potassium. In those days, before the advent of modern instruments, what was the basis on which one could claim that a substance was an element?

1.17 In the process of attempting to characterize a substance, a chemist makes the following observations: The substance is a silvery white, lustrous metal. It melts at 649°C and boils at 1105°C. Its density at 20°C is 1.738 g/cm^3. The substance burns in air, producing an intense white light. It reacts with chlorine to give a brittle white solid. The substance can be pounded into thin sheets or drawn into wires. It is a good conductor of electricity. Which of these characteristics are physical properties, and which are chemical properties?

1.18 Read the following description of the element zinc, and indicate which are physical properties and which are chemical properties. Zinc is a silver–gray-colored metal that melts at 420°C. When zinc granules are added to dilute sulfuric acid, hydrogen is given off and the metal dissolves. Zinc has a hardness on the Mohs scale of 2.5 and a density of 7.13 g/cm^3 at 25°C. It reacts slowly with oxygen gas at elevated temperatures to form zinc oxide, ZnO.

1.19 Label each of the following as either a physical process or a chemical process: **(a)** corrosion of aluminum metal, **(b)** melting of ice, **(c)** pulverizing an aspirin, **(d)** digesting a candy bar, **(e)** explosion of nitroglycerin.

1.20 A match is lit and held under a cold piece of metal. The following observations are made: **(a)** The match burns. **(b)** The metal gets warmer. **(c)** Water condenses on the metal. **(d)** Soot (carbon) is deposited on the metal. Which of these occurrences are due to physical changes, and which are due to chemical changes?

1.21 Suggest a method of separating each of the following mixtures into two components: **(a)** sugar and sand, **(b)** iron and sulfur.

1.22 A beaker contains a clear, colorless liquid. If it is water, how could you determine whether it contained dissolved table salt? Do *not* taste it!

Units and Measurement

1.23 What decimal power do the following abbreviations represent: **(a)** d, **(b)** c, **(c)** f, **(d)** μ, **(e)** M, **(f)** k, **(g)** n, **(h)** m, **(i)** p?

1.24 Use appropriate metric prefixes to write the following measurements without use of exponents: **(a)** 6.35×10^{-2} L, **(b)** 6.5×10^{-6} s, **(c)** 9.5×10^{-4} m, **(d)** 4.23×10^{-9} m^3, **(e)** 12.5×10^{-8} kg, **(f)** 3.5×10^{-10} g, **(g)** 6.54×10^{9} fs.

1.25 Perform the following conversions: **(a)** 25.5 mg to g, **(b)** 4.0×10^{-10} m to nm, **(c)** 0.575 mm to μm.

1.26 Convert **(a)** 9.5×10^{-2} kg to g, **(b)** 0.0023 μm to nm; **(c)** 7.25×10^{-4} s to ms.

1.27 **(a)** A sample of carbon tetrachloride, a liquid once used in dry cleaning, has a mass of 39.73 g and a volume of 25.0 mL at 25°C. What is its density at this temperature? Will carbon tetrachloride float on water? (Materials that are less dense than water will float.) **(b)** The density of platinum is 21.45 g/cm^3 at 20°C. Calculate the mass of 75.00 cm^3 of platinum at this temperature. **(c)** The density of magnesium is 1.738 g/cm^3 at 20°C. What is the volume of 87.50 g of this metal at this temperature?

1.28 **(a)** A cube of osmium metal 1.500 cm on a side has a mass of 76.31 g at 25°C. What is its density in g/cm^3 at this temperature? **(b)** The density of titanium metal is 4.51 g/cm^3 at 25°C. What mass of titanium displaces 65.8 mL of water at 25°C? **(c)** The density of benzene at 15°C is 0.8787 g/mL. Calculate the mass of 0.1500 L of benzene at this temperature.

1.29 **(a)** To identify a liquid substance, a student determined its density. Using a graduated cylinder, she measured out a 45-mL sample of the substance. She then measured the mass of the sample, finding that it weighed 38.5 g. She knew that the substance had to be either isopropyl alcohol (density 0.785 g/mL) or toluene (density 0.866 g/mL). What are the calculated density and the probable identity of the substance? **(b)** An experiment requires 45.0 g of ethylene glycol, a liquid whose density is 1.114 g/mL. Rather than weigh the sample on a balance, a chemist chooses to dispense the liquid using a graduated cylinder. What volume of the liquid should

he use? **(c)** A cubic piece of metal measures 5.00 cm on each edge. If the metal is nickel, whose density is 8.90 g/cm^3, what is the mass of the cube?

1.30 **(a)** After the label fell off a bottle containing a clear liquid believed to be benzene, a chemist measured the density of the liquid to verify its identity. A 25.0-mL portion of the liquid had a mass of 21.95 g. A chemistry handbook lists the density of benzene at 15°C as 0.8787 g/mL. Is the calculated density in agreement with the tabulated value? **(b)** An experiment requires 15.0 g of cyclohexane, whose density at 25°C is 0.7781 g/mL. What volume of cyclohexane should be used? **(c)** A spherical ball of lead has a diameter of 5.0 cm. What is the mass of the sphere if lead has a density of 11.34 g/cm^3? (The volume of a sphere is $\left(\frac{4}{3}\right)\pi r^3$ where r is the radius.)

[1.31] Gold can be hammered into extremely thin sheets called gold leaf. If a 200-mg piece of gold (density = 19.32 g/cm^3) is hammered into a sheet measuring 2.4×1.0 ft, what is the average thickness of the sheet in meters? How might the thickness be expressed without exponential notation, using an appropriate metric prefix?

[1.32] A cylindrical rod formed from silicon is 16.8 cm long and has a mass of 2.17 kg. The density of silicon is 2.33 g/cm^3. What is the diameter of the cylinder? (The volume of a cylinder is given by $\pi r^2 h$, where r is the radius, and h is its length.)

1.33 Make the following conversions: **(a)** 62°F to °C, **(b)** 216.7°C to °F, **(c)** 233°C to K, **(d)** 315 K to °F, **(e)** 2500°F to K.

1.34 **(a)** The temperature on a warm summer day is 87°F. What is the temperature in °C? **(b)** Many scientific data are reported at 25°C. What is this temperature in kelvins and in degrees Fahrenheit? **(c)** Suppose that a recipe calls for an oven temperature of 175°F. Convert this temperature to degrees Celsius and to kelvins. **(d)** The melting point of sodium bromide (a salt) is 755°C. Calculate this temperature in °F and in kelvins. **(e)** Neon, the gaseous element used to make electronic signs, has a melting point of −248.6°C and a boiling point of −246.1°C. Convert these temperatures to kelvins.

Uncertainty in Measurement

1.35 Indicate which of the following are exact numbers: **(a)** the mass of a paper clip, **(b)** the surface area of a dime, **(c)** the number of inches in a mile, **(d)** the number of ounces in a pound, **(e)** the number of microseconds in a week, **(f)** the number of pages in this book.

1.36 Indicate which of the following are exact numbers: **(a)** the mass of a 32-oz can of coffee, **(b)** the number of students in your chemistry class, **(c)** the temperature of the surface of the sun, **(d)** the mass of a postage stamp, **(e)** the number of milliliters in a cubic meter of water, **(f)** the average height of students in your school.

1.37 What is the number of significant figures in each of the following measured quantities? **(a)** 358 kg, **(b)** 0.054 s, **(c)** 6.3050 cm, **(d)** 0.0105 L, **(e)** 7.0500×10^{-3} m^3.

1.38 Indicate the number of significant figures in each of the following measured quantities: **(a)** 3.7745 km, **(b)** 205 m^2, **(c)** 1.700 cm, **(d)** 350.0 K, **(e)** 307.080 g.

1.39 Round each of the following numbers to four significant figures, and express the result in standard exponential notation: **(a)** 102.53070, **(b)** 656,980, **(c)** 0.008543210, **(d)** 0.000257870, **(e)** −0.0357202.

1.40 **(a)** The diameter of Earth at the equator is 7926.381 mi. Round this number to three significant figures, and express it in standard exponential notation. **(b)** The circumference of Earth through the poles is 40,008 km. Round this number to four significant figures, and express it in standard exponential notation.

1.41 Carry out the following operations, and express the answers with the appropriate number of significant figures: **(a)** 12.0550 + 9.05, **(b)** 257.2 − 19.789, **(c)** $(6.21 \times 10^3)(0.1050)$, **(d)** 0.0577/0.753.

1.42 Carry out the following operations, and express the answer with the appropriate number of significant figures: **(a)** 320.55 − (6104.5/2.3), **(b)** $[(285.3 \times 10^5) - (1.200 \times 10^3)] \times 2.8954$, **(c)** $(0.0045 \times 20{,}000.0) + (2813 \times 12)$, **(d)** $863 \times [1255 - (3.45 \times 108)]$.

Dimensional Analysis

1.43 Using the information on the back inside cover and your knowledge of English units, write down the conversion factors needed to convert **(a)** cm to ft, **(b)** in.^{3} to cm^3.

1.44 Using the information on the back inside cover, write down the conversion factors needed to convert **(a)** mi to km, **(b)** qt to L.

1.45 Perform the following conversions: **(a)** 0.076 L to mL, **(b)** 5.0×10^{-8} m to nm, **(c)** 6.88×10^5 ns to s, **(d)** 0.50 lb to g, **(e)** 1.55 kg/m^3 to g/L, **(f)** 5.850 gal/hr to L/s.

1.46 **(a)** The speed of light in a vacuum is 2.998×10^8 m/s. Calculate its speed in km/hr. **(b)** The Sears Tower in Chicago is 1454 ft tall. Calculate its height in meters. **(c)** The Vehicle Assembly Building at the Kennedy Space Center in Florida has a volume of 3,666,500 m^3. Convert this volume to liters, and express the result in standard exponential notation. **(d)** An individual suffering from a high cholesterol level in her blood has 232 mg of cholesterol per 100 mL of blood. If the total blood volume of the individual is 5.2 L, how many grams of total blood cholesterol does the individual's body contain?

1.47 Perform the following conversions: **(a)** 5.00 days to s, **(b)** 0.0550 mi to m, **(c)** \$1.89/gal to dollars per liter, **(d)** 0.510 in./ms to km/hr, **(e)** 22.50 gal/min to L/s, **(f)** 0.02500 ft^3 to cm^3.

1.48 Carry out the following conversions: **(a)** 0.105 in. to mm, **(b)** 0.870 qt to mL, **(c)** 8.75 μm/s to km/hr, **(d)** 4.733 yd^3 to m^3, **(e)** \$3.99/lb to dollars per kg, **(f)** 8.75 lb/ft^3 to g/mL.

1.49 **(a)** How many liters of wine can be held in a wine barrel whose capacity is 31 gal? **(b)** The recommended adult dose of Elixophyllin®, a drug used to treat asthma, is 6 mg/kg of body mass. Calculate the dose in milligrams for a 150-lb person. **(c)** If an automobile is able to travel 254 mi on 11.2 gal of gasoline, what is the gas mileage in km/L? **(d)** A pound of coffee beans yields 50 cups of coffee (4 cups = 1 qt). How many milliliters of coffee can be obtained from 1 g of coffee beans?

1.50 **(a)** If an electric car is capable of going 225 km on a single charge, how many charges will it need to travel from Boston, Massachusetts, to Miami, Florida, a distance of 1486 mi, assuming that the trip begins with a full charge? **(b)** If a migrating loon flies at an average speed of 14 m/s, what is its average speed in mi/hr? **(c)** What is the engine piston displacement in liters of an engine whose displacement is listed as 450 in.^{3}? **(d)** In March 1989 the *Exxon Valdez* ran aground and spilled 240,000 barrels of crude petroleum off the coast of Alaska. One barrel of petroleum is equal to 42 gal. How many liters of petroleum were spilled?

1.51 The density of air at ordinary atmospheric pressure and 25°C is 1.19 g/L. What is the mass, in kilograms, of the air in a room that measures $12.5 \times 15.5 \times 8.0$ ft?

1.52 The concentration of carbon monoxide in an urban apartment is 48 μg/m^3. What mass of carbon monoxide in grams is present in a room measuring $9.0 \times 14.5 \times 18.8$ ft?

1.53 By using estimation techniques, arrange these items in order from shortest to longest: a 57-cm length of string, a 14-in. long shoe, and a 1.1-m length of pipe.

1.54 By using estimation techniques, determine which of the following is the heaviest and which is the lightest: a 5-lb bag of potatoes, a 5-kg bag of sugar, or 1 gal of water (density = 1.0 g/mL).

[1.55] The Morgan silver dollar has a mass of 26.73 g. By law, it was required to contain 90% silver, with the remainder being copper. **(a)** When the coin was minted in the late 1800s, silver was worth \$1.18 per troy ounce (31.1 g). At this price, what is the value of the silver in the silver dollar? **(b)** Today, silver sells for about \$5.30 per troy ounce. How many Morgan silver dollars are required to obtain \$25.00 worth of pure silver?

[1.56] A copper refinery produces a copper ingot weighing 150 lb. If the copper is drawn into wire whose diameter is 8.25 mm, how many feet of copper can be obtained from the ingot? The density of copper is 8.94 g/cm^3. (Assume that the wire is a cylinder whose volume is $V = \pi r^2 h$, where r is its radius and h is its height or length.)

Additional Exercises

The exercises in this section are not divided by category, although they are roughly in the order of the topics in the chapter. They are not paired.

1.57 What is meant by the terms composition and structure when referring to matter?

1.58 **(a)** Classify each of the following as a pure substance, a solution, or a heterogeneous mixture: a gold coin, a cup of coffee, a wood plank. **(b)** What ambiguities are there in answering part (a) from the descriptions given?

1.59 **(a)** What is the difference between a hypothesis and a theory? **(b)** Explain the difference between a theory and a scientific law. Which addresses how matter behaves, and which addresses why it behaves that way?

1.60 A sample of ascorbic acid (vitamin C) is synthesized in the laboratory. It contains 1.50 g of carbon and 2.00 g of oxygen. Another sample of ascorbic acid isolated from citrus fruits contains 6.35 g of carbon. How many grams of oxygen does it contain? Which law are you assuming in answering this question?

1.61 Two students determine the percentage of lead in a sample as a laboratory exercise. The true percentage is 22.52%. The students' results for three determinations are as follows:
1. 22.52, 22.48, 22.54
2. 22.64, 22.58, 22.62

(a) Calculate the average percentage for each set of data, and tell which set is the more accurate based on the average. (b) Precision can be judged by examining the average of the deviations from the average value for that data set. (Calculate the average value for each data set, then calculate the average value of the absolute deviations of each measurement from the average.) Which set is more precise?

1.62 Is the use of significant figures in each of the following statements appropriate? Why or why not? (a) The 2000 circulation of *National Geographic* was 8,783,752. (b) In July 2003 the population of Cook County, Illinois, was 5,351,552. (c) The average annual rainfall in San Diego, California, is 20.54 cm. (d) In the United States, 0.621% of the population has the surname Brown.

1.63 What type of quantity (for example, length, volume, density) do the following units indicate: (a) mL, (b) cm^2, (c) mm^3, (d) mg/L, (e) ps, (f) nm, (g) K?

1.64 Give the derived SI units for each of the following quantities in base SI units: (a) acceleration = distance/$time^2$; (b) force = mass × acceleration; (c) work = force × distance; (d) pressure = force/area; (e) power = work/time.

1.65 The liquid substances mercury (density = 13.5 g/mL), water (1.00 g/mL), and cyclohexane (0.778 g/mL) do not form a solution when mixed, but separate in distinct layers. Sketch how the liquids would position themselves in a test tube.

1.66 A 40-lb container of peat moss measures 14 × 20 × 30 in. A 40-lb container of topsoil has a volume of 1.9 gal. (a) Calculate the average densities of peat moss and topsoil in units of g/cm^3. Would it be correct to say that peat moss is "lighter" than topsoil? Explain. (b) How many bags of the peat moss are needed to cover an area measuring 10. ft by 20. ft to a depth of 2.0 in.?

1.67 Small spheres of equal mass are made of lead (density = 11.3 g/cm^3), silver (10.5 g/cm^3), and aluminum (2.70 g/cm^3). Which sphere has the largest diameter, and which has the smallest?

1.68 The annual production of sodium hydroxide in the United States in 1999 was 23.2 billion pounds. (a) How many grams of sodium hydroxide were produced in that year? (b) The density of sodium hydroxide is 2.130 g/cm^3. How many cubic kilometers were produced?

1.69 (a) You are given a bottle that contains 4.59 cm^3 of a metallic solid. The total mass of the bottle and solid is 35.66 g. The empty bottle weighs 14.23 g. What is the density of the solid? (b) Mercury is traded by the

"flask," a unit that has a mass of 34.5 kg. What is the volume of a flask of mercury if the density of mercury is 13.5 g/mL? (c) A thief plans to steal a gold sphere with a radius of 28.9 cm from a museum. If the gold has a density of 19.3 g/cm^3, what is the mass of the sphere? [The volume of a sphere is $V = (4/3)\pi r^3$.] Is he likely to be able to walk off with it unassisted?

1.70 Automobile batteries contain sulfuric acid, which is commonly referred to as "battery acid." Calculate the number of grams of sulfuric acid in 0.500 L of battery acid if the solution has a density of 1.28 g/mL and is 38.1% sulfuric acid by mass.

[1.71] A 32.65-g sample of a solid is placed in a flask. Toluene, in which the solid is insoluble, is added to the flask so that the total volume of solid and liquid together is 50.00 mL. The solid and toluene together weigh 58.58 g. The density of toluene at the temperature of the experiment is 0.864 g/mL. What is the density of the solid?

[1.72] Suppose you decide to define your own temperature scale using the freezing point (−11.5°C) and boiling point (197.6°C) of ethylene glycol. If you set the freezing point as 0°G and the boiling point as 100°G, what is the freezing point of water on this new scale?

1.73 Recently, one of the text authors completed an exactly 10-mi road race, in a time of 1 hr, 25 min, and 14 s. (a) What was the runner's average speed in miles per hour? (b) What was the runner's pace in minutes and seconds per mile?

1.74 The distance from Earth to the Moon is approximately 240,000 mi. (a) What is this distance in meters? (b) The *Concorde SST* has an air speed of about 2400 km/hr. If the *Concorde* could fly to the Moon, how many seconds would it take?

1.75 The U.S. quarter has a mass of 5.67 g and is approximately 1.55 mm thick. (a) How many quarters would have to be stacked to reach 575 ft, the height of the Washington Monument? (b) How much would this stack weigh? (c) How much money would this stack contain? (d) In 2004 the national debt was $7.2 trillion. How many stacks like the one described would be necessary to pay off this debt?

1.76 In the United States, water used for irrigation is measured in acre-feet. An acre-foot of water covers an acre to a depth of exactly 1 ft. An acre is 4840 yd^2. An acre-foot is enough water to supply two typical households for 1.00 yr. (a) If desalinated water costs $2480 per acre-foot, how much does desalinated water cost per liter? (b) How much would it cost one household per day if it were the only source of water?

[1.77] A package of aluminum foil contains 50 ft^2 of foil, which weighs approximately 8.0 oz. Aluminum has a density of 2.70 g/cm^3. What is the approximate thickness of the foil in millimeters?

[1.78] A 15.0-cm long cylindrical glass tube, sealed at one end, is filled with ethanol. The mass of ethanol needed to fill the tube is found to be 11.86 g. The density of ethanol is 0.789 g/mL. Calculate the inner diameter of the tube in centimeters.

[1.79] Gold is alloyed (mixed) with other metals to increase its hardness in making jewelry. (a) Consider a piece of gold jewelry that weighs 9.85 g and has a volume of 0.675 cm³. The jewelry contains only gold and silver, which have densities of 19.3 g/cm³ and 10.5 g/cm³, respectively. Assuming that the total volume of the jewelry is the sum of the volumes of the gold and silver that it contains, calculate the percentage of gold (by mass) in the jewelry. **(b)** The relative amount of gold in an alloy is commonly expressed in units of carats. Pure gold is 24-carat, and the percentage of gold in an alloy is given as a percentage of this value. For example, an alloy that is 50% gold is 12-carat. State the purity of the gold jewelry in carats.

[1.80] Suppose you are given a sample of a homogeneous liquid. What would you do to determine whether it is a solution or a pure substance?

[1.81] Chromatography (Figure 1.14) is a simple, but reliable, method for separating a mixture into its constituent substances. Suppose you are using chromatography to separate a mixture of two substances. How would you know whether the separation is successful? Can you propose a means of quantifying how good or how poor the separation is?

[1.82] You are assigned the task of separating a desired granular material, with a density of 3.62 g/cm³, from an undesired granular material that has a density of 2.04 g/cm³. You want to do this by shaking the mixture in a liquid in which the heavier material will fall to the bottom and the lighter material will float. A solid will float on any liquid that is more dense. Using a handbook of chemistry, find the densities of the following substances: carbon tetrachloride, hexane, benzene, and methylene iodide. Which of these liquids will serve your purpose, assuming no chemical interaction between the liquid and the solids?

[1.83] The concepts of accuracy and precision are not always easy to grasp. Here are two sets of studies: **(a)** The mass of a secondary weight standard is determined by weighing it on a very precise balance under carefully controlled laboratory conditions. The average of 18 different weight measurements is taken as the weight of the standard. **(b)** A group of 10,000 males between the ages of 50 and 55 is surveyed to ascertain a relationship between calorie intake and blood cholesterol level. The survey questionnaire is quite detailed, asking the respondents about what they eat, smoking and drinking habits, and so on. The results are reported as showing that for men of comparable lifestyles, there is a 40% chance of the blood cholesterol level being above 230 for those who consume more than 40 calories per gram of body weight per day, as compared with those who consume fewer than 30 calories per gram of body weight per day.

Discuss and compare these two studies in terms of the precision and accuracy of the result in each case. How do the two studies differ in nature in ways that affect the accuracy and precision of the results? What makes for high precision and accuracy in any given study? In each of these studies, what factors might not be controlled that could affect the accuracy and precision? What steps can be taken generally to attain higher precision and accuracy?

eMEDIA EXERCISES

These exercises make use of the interactive objects available online in OneKey or the Companion Website, and on your Accelerator CD. Access to these resources comes in your MediaPak.

1.84 Experiment with the **Phases of the Elements** activity (*1.2*). **(a)** How many elements are liquids at room temperature, and what are they? **(b)** Choose two temperatures—one higher and one lower than room temperature—and determine how many elements are liquids at those temperatures.

1.85 Watch the **Electrolysis of Water** animation (*1.2*). **(a)** How can you tell from this experiment that water is a compound and not an element? **(b)** If you were to perform a similar experiment using liquid bromine instead of liquid water in the apparatus, what would you expect to happen?

1.86 The **Changes of State** animation (*1.3*) shows what happens to a solid when it is heated. **(a)** Describe the changes that occur. **(b)** Is the change from solid to liquid a chemical change or a physical change? **(c)** Is the change from liquid to gas a chemical change or a physical change? **(d)** Is enough information given to determine whether the original solid is an element, a compound, or a mixture? Explain.

1.87 **(a)** Use the **Significant Figures** activity (*1.5*) to verify your answers to Exercises 1.41 and 1.42. **(b)** Is it possible for the sum of a column of numbers, each containing two significant figures, to have more than two significant figures? Explain. **(c)** How many significant figures should there be in the answer to the following calculation? $(35.2 - 30.1) \times 1.23 = \underline{\qquad}$.

2.1 The Atomic Theory of Matter

2.2 The Discovery of Atomic Structure

2.3 The Modern View of Atomic Structure

2.4 Atomic Weights

2.5 The Periodic Table

2.6 Molecules and Molecular Compounds

2.7 Ions and Ionic Compounds

2.8 Naming Inorganic Compounds

2.9 Some Simple Organic Compounds

WHAT'S AHEAD

- We begin by giving a brief history of the notion of *atoms*—the smallest pieces of matter. *(Section 2.1)*

- Next, we look at some of the key experiments that led to the discovery of *electrons* and to the *nuclear model* of the atom. *(Section 2.2)*

- We then discuss the modern theory of atomic structure, including the ideas of *atomic numbers, mass numbers,* and *isotopes. (Section 2.3)*

- We introduce the concept of *atomic weights* and how they relate to the masses of individual atoms. *(Section 2.4)*

- Our discussion of atoms leads to the organization of the elements into the *periodic table,* in which elements are put in order of increasing atomic number and grouped by chemical similarity. *(Section 2.5)*

- Our understanding of atoms allows us to discuss the assemblies of atoms called *molecules* and how their compositions are represented by *empirical and molecular formulas. (Section 2.6)*

- We learn that atoms can gain or lose electrons to form *ions,* and we look at how to use the periodic table to predict the charges on ions and the empirical formulas of *ionic compounds. (Section 2.7)*

- We will see the systematic way in which substances are named, called *nomenclature,* and how this nomenclature is applied to inorganic compounds. *(Section 2.8)*

- Finally, we introduce some basic ideas of *organic chemistry,* which is the chemistry of the element carbon. *(Section 2.9)*

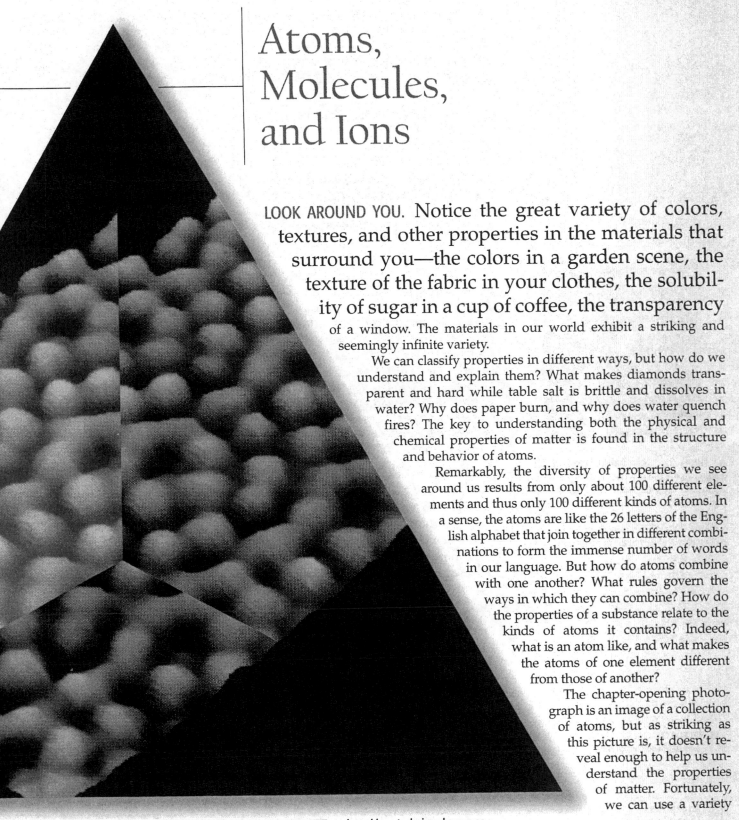

Atoms, Molecules, and Ions

LOOK AROUND YOU. Notice the great variety of colors, textures, and other properties in the materials that surround you—the colors in a garden scene, the texture of the fabric in your clothes, the solubility of sugar in a cup of coffee, the transparency of a window. The materials in our world exhibit a striking and seemingly infinite variety.

We can classify properties in different ways, but how do we understand and explain them? What makes diamonds transparent and hard while table salt is brittle and dissolves in water? Why does paper burn, and why does water quench fires? The key to understanding both the physical and chemical properties of matter is found in the structure and behavior of atoms.

Remarkably, the diversity of properties we see around us results from only about 100 different elements and thus only 100 different kinds of atoms. In a sense, the atoms are like the 26 letters of the English alphabet that join together in different combinations to form the immense number of words in our language. But how do atoms combine with one another? What rules govern the ways in which they can combine? How do the properties of a substance relate to the kinds of atoms it contains? Indeed, what is an atom like, and what makes the atoms of one element different from those of another?

The chapter-opening photograph is an image of a collection of atoms, but as striking as this picture is, it doesn't reveal enough to help us understand the properties of matter. Fortunately, we can use a variety

INDIVIDUAL CARBON ATOMS IN A SAMPLE OF GRAPHITE as viewed by a technique known as scanning tunneling microscopy (STM). Notice the hexagonal arrangements of the atoms in both the STM image and in the adjacent molecular model.

37

of experimental techniques to probe the atom to gain a clearer understanding of what it is like. In this chapter we begin to explore the fascinating world of atoms that we discover by such experiments. We will examine the basic structure of the atom and briefly discuss the formation of molecules and ions, thereby providing a foundation for exploring chemistry more deeply in later chapters.

2.1 | The Atomic Theory of Matter

Philosophers from the earliest times have speculated about the nature of the fundamental "stuff" from which the world is made. Democritus (460–370 BC) and other early Greek philosophers thought that the material world must be made up of tiny indivisible particles that they called *atomos*, meaning "indivisible or uncuttable." Later, Plato and Aristotle formulated the notion that there can be no ultimately indivisible particles. The "atomic" view of matter faded for many centuries during which Aristotelean philosophy dominated Western culture.

The notion of atoms reemerged in Europe during the seventeenth century, when scientists tried to explain the properties of gases. Air is composed of something invisible and in constant motion; we can feel the motion of the wind against us, for example. It is natural to think of tiny invisible particles as giving rise to these familiar effects. Isaac Newton (1642–1727), the most famous scientist of his time, favored the idea of atoms, but thinking of atoms as invisible particles in air is different from thinking of atoms as the fundamental building blocks of elements.

As chemists learned to measure the amounts of elements that reacted with one another to form new substances, the ground was laid for an atomic theory that linked the idea of elements with the idea of atoms. That theory came into being during the period 1803–1807 in the work of an English schoolteacher, John Dalton (Figure 2.1 ◀). Dalton's atomic theory involved the following postulates:

1. Each element is composed of extremely small particles called atoms.
2. All atoms of a given element are identical to one another in mass and other properties, but the atoms of one element are different from the atoms of all other elements.
3. Atoms of an element are not changed into atoms of a different element by chemical reactions; atoms are neither created nor destroyed in chemical reactions.
4. Compounds are formed when atoms of more than one element combine; a given compound always has the same relative number and kind of atoms.

According to Dalton's atomic theory, **atoms** are the smallest particles of an element that retain the chemical identity of the element. ∞ (Section 1.1) As noted in the postulates of Dalton's theory, an element is composed of only one kind of atom, whereas a compound contains atoms of two or more elements.

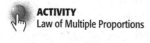

ACTIVITY
Law of Multiple Proportions

Dalton's theory explains several simple laws of chemical combination that were known in his time. One of these was the *law of constant composition*: In a given compound, the relative numbers and kinds of atoms are constant. ∞ (Section 1.2) This law is the basis of Dalton's Postulate 4. Another fundamental chemical law was the *law of conservation of mass* (also known as the *law of conservation of matter*): The total mass of materials present after a chemical reaction is the same as the total mass present before the reaction. This law is the basis for Postulate 3. Dalton proposed that atoms always retain their identities and that atoms taking part in a chemical reaction rearrange to give new chemical combinations.

ANIMATION
Multiple Proportions

A good theory should not only explain the known facts but should also predict new ones. Dalton used his theory to deduce the *law of multiple proportions*: If two elements A and B combine to form more than one compound, the masses of B that can combine with a given mass of A are in the ratio of small whole numbers. We can illustrate this law by considering the substances water and hydrogen peroxide, both of which consist of the elements hydrogen and oxygen. In forming water, 8.0 g of oxygen combines with 1.0 g of hydrogen. In forming hydrogen peroxide, 16.0 g of oxygen combines with 1.0 g of hydrogen. In other words, the ratio of the mass of oxygen per gram of hydrogen in the two compounds is 2:1. Using the atomic theory, we can conclude that hydrogen peroxide contains twice as many atoms of oxygen per hydrogen atom as does water.

 GIVE IT SOME THOUGHT

One compound of carbon and oxygen contains 1.333 g of oxygen per gram of carbon, whereas a second compound contains 2.666 g of oxygen per gram of carbon. (a) What chemical law do these data illustrate? (b) If the first compound has an equal number of oxygen and carbon atoms, what can we conclude about the composition of the second compound?

2.2 | The Discovery of Atomic Structure

Dalton reached his conclusion about atoms on the basis of chemical observations in the macroscopic world of the laboratory. Neither he nor those who followed him during the century after his work was published had direct evidence for the existence of atoms. Today, however, we can use powerful instruments to measure the properties of individual atoms and even provide images of them (Figure 2.2 ▶).

As scientists began to develop methods for more detailed probing of the nature of matter, the atom, which was supposed to be indivisible, began to show signs of a more complex structure: We now know that the atom is composed of still smaller **subatomic particles**. Before we summarize the current model of atomic structure, we will briefly consider a few of the landmark discoveries that led to that model. We'll see that the atom is composed in part of electrically charged particles, some with a positive (+) charge and some with a negative (−) charge. As we discuss the development of our current model of the atom, keep in mind a simple statement of the behavior of charged particles: *Particles with the same charge repel one another, whereas particles with unlike charges are attracted to one another.*

Cathode Rays and Electrons

In the mid-1800s, scientists began to study electrical discharge through partially evacuated tubes (tubes that had been pumped almost empty of air), such as those shown in Figure 2.3 ▼. A high voltage produces radiation within the tube.

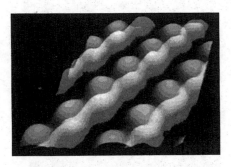

▲ **Figure 2.2   An image of the surface of the semiconductor GaAs (gallium arsenide).** This image was obtained by a technique called scanning tunneling microscopy. The color was added to the image by computer to distinguish the gallium atoms (blue spheres) from the arsenic atoms (red spheres).

▼ **Figure 2.3   Cathode-ray tube.** (a) In a cathode-ray tube, electrons move from the negative electrode (cathode) to the positive electrode (anode). (b) A photo of a cathode-ray tube containing a fluorescent screen to show the path of the cathode rays. (c) The path of the cathode rays is deflected by the presence of a magnet.

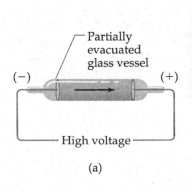

Partially evacuated glass vessel

(−)   (+)

High voltage

(a)

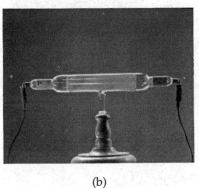

(b)

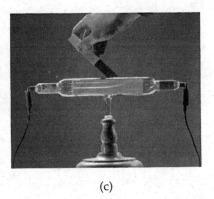

(c)

Science Fundamentals Second Edition

▶ **Figure 2.4 Cathode-ray tube with perpendicular magnetic and electric fields.** The cathode rays (electrons) originate from the negative plate on the left and are accelerated toward the positive plate, which has a hole in its center. A beam of electrons passes through the hole and is then deflected by the magnetic and electric fields. The three paths result from different strengths of the magnetic and electric fields. The charge-to-mass ratio of the electron can be determined by measuring the effects that the magnetic and electric fields have on the direction of the beam.

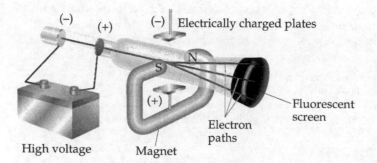

 Thompson Cathode-Ray Experiment

 ANIMATION Millikan Oil-Drop Experiment

 Millikan Oil-Drop Experiment

This radiation became known as **cathode rays** because it originated from the negative electrode, or cathode. Although the rays themselves could not be seen, their movement could be detected because the rays cause certain materials, including glass, to *fluoresce*, or give off light. (Television picture tubes are cathode-ray tubes; a television picture is the result of fluorescence from the television screen.)

Scientists held conflicting views about the nature of the cathode rays. It was not initially clear whether the rays were an invisible stream of particles or a new form of radiation. Experiments showed that cathode rays are deflected by electric or magnetic fields in a way consistent with their being a stream of negative electrical charge [Figure 2.3(c)]. The British scientist J. J. Thomson observed many properties of the rays, including the fact that the rays are the same regardless of the identity of the cathode material. In a paper published in 1897, he summarized his observations and concluded that cathode rays are streams of negatively charged particles. Thomson's paper is generally accepted as the "discovery" of what later became known as the *electron*.

Thomson constructed a cathode-ray tube having a fluorescent screen at one end, such as that shown in Figure 2.4 ▲, so that he could quantitatively measure the effects of electric and magnetic fields on the thin stream of electrons passing through a hole in the positively charged electrode. These measurements made it possible to calculate a value of 1.76×10^8 coulombs per gram for the ratio of the electron's electrical charge to its mass.*

Once the charge-to-mass ratio of the electron was known, measuring either the charge or the mass of an electron would also yield the value of the other quantity. In 1909, Robert Millikan (1868–1953) of the University of Chicago succeeded in measuring the charge of an electron by performing a series of experiments described in Figure 2.5 ▼. He then calculated the mass of the electron by

▶ **Figure 2.5 Millikan's oil-drop experiment.** A representation of the apparatus Millikan used to measure the charge of the electron. Small drops of oil, which had picked up extra electrons, were allowed to fall between two electrically charged plates. Millikan monitored the drops, measuring how the voltage on the plates affected their rate of fall. From these data he calculated the charges on the drops. His experiment showed that the charges were always integral multiples of 1.602×10^{-19} C, which he deduced was the charge of a single electron.

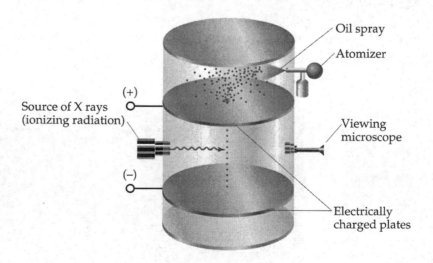

* The coulomb (C) is the SI unit for electrical charge.

Science Fundamentals Second Edition

using his experimental value for the charge, 1.60×10^{-19} C, and Thomson's charge-to-mass ratio, 1.76×10^8 C/g:

$$\text{Electron mass} = \frac{1.60 \times 10^{-19} \text{ C}}{1.76 \times 10^8 \text{ C/g}} = 9.10 \times 10^{-28} \text{ g}$$

This result agrees well with the presently accepted value for the mass of the electron, 9.10938×10^{-28} g. This mass is about 2000 times smaller than that of hydrogen, the lightest atom.

Radioactivity

In 1896 the French scientist Henri Becquerel (1852–1908) was studying a uranium compound when he discovered that it spontaneously emits high-energy radiation. This spontaneous emission of radiation is called **radioactivity**. At Becquerel's suggestion Marie Curie (Figure 2.6 ▶) and her husband, Pierre, began experiments to isolate the radioactive components of the compound.

Further study of the nature of radioactivity, principally by the British scientist Ernest Rutherford (Figure 2.7 ▶), revealed three types of radiation: alpha (α), beta (β), and gamma (γ) radiation. Each type differs in its response to an electric field, as shown in Figure 2.8 ▼. The paths of both α and β radiation are bent by the electric field, although in opposite directions, whereas γ radiation is unaffected.

Rutherford showed that both α and β rays consist of fast-moving particles, which were called α and β particles. In fact, β particles are high-speed electrons and can be considered the radioactive equivalent of cathode rays. They are therefore attracted to a positively charged plate. The α particles have a positive charge and are therefore attracted toward a negative plate. In units of the charge of the electron, β particles have a charge of 1− and α particles a charge of 2+. Each α particle is considerably heavier than an electron, having a mass about 7300 times that of an electron. Gamma radiation is high-energy radiation similar to X rays; it does not consist of particles and carries no charge. We will discuss radioactivity in greater detail in Chapter 21.

The Nuclear Atom

With the growing evidence that the atom is composed of smaller particles, attention was given to how the particles fit together. In the early 1900s Thomson reasoned that because electrons contribute only a very small fraction of the mass of an atom, they probably were responsible for an equally small fraction of the atom's size. He proposed that the atom consisted of a uniform positive sphere of matter in which the electrons were embedded, as shown

▲ **Figure 2.6 Marie Sklodowska Curie (1867–1934).** When M. Curie presented her doctoral thesis, it was described as the greatest single contribution of any doctoral thesis in the history of science. Among other things, two new elements, polonium and radium, had been discovered. In 1903 Henri Becquerel, M. Curie, and her husband, Pierre, were jointly awarded the Nobel Prize in physics. In 1911 M. Curie won a second Nobel Prize, this time in chemistry.

▲ **Figure 2.7 Ernest Rutherford (1871–1937).** Rutherford, whom Einstein called "the second Newton," was born and educated in New Zealand. In 1895 he was the first overseas student ever to be awarded a position at the Cavendish Laboratory at Cambridge University in England, where he worked with J. J. Thomson. In 1898 he joined the faculty of McGill University in Montreal. While at McGill, Rutherford did his research on radioactivity that led to his being awarded the 1908 Nobel Prize in chemistry. In 1907 Rutherford moved back to England to be a faculty member at Manchester University, where in 1910 he performed his famous α-particle scattering experiments that led to the nuclear model of the atom. In 1992 his native New Zealand honored Rutherford by putting his likeness, along with his Nobel Prize medal, on their $100 currency note.

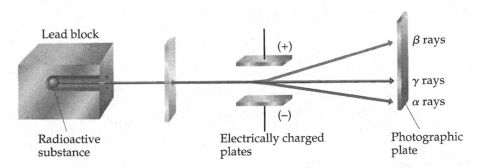

▲ **Figure 2.8 Behavior of alpha (α), beta (β), and gamma (γ) rays in an electric field.** The α rays consist of positively charged particles and are therefore attracted to the negatively charged plate. The β rays consist of negatively charged particles and are attracted to the positively charged plate. The γ rays, which carry no charge, are unaffected by the electric field.

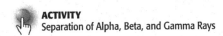

ACTIVITY
Separation of Alpha, Beta, and Gamma Rays

Science Fundamentals Second Edition

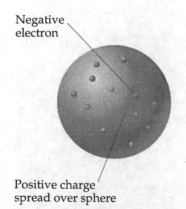

Negative electron

Positive charge spread over sphere

▲ **Figure 2.9   J. J. Thomson's "plum-pudding" model of the atom.** Thomson pictured the small electrons to be embedded in the atom much like raisins in a pudding or like seeds in a watermelon. Ernest Rutherford proved this model wrong.

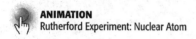

ANIMATION
Rutherford Experiment: Nuclear Atom

Rutherford's Backscattering Experiment

in Figure 2.9 ◄. This so-called "plum-pudding" model, named after a traditional English dessert, was very short-lived.

In 1910, Rutherford and his coworkers performed an experiment that disproved Thomson's model. Rutherford was studying the angles at which α particles were deflected, or *scattered*, as they passed through a thin gold foil a few thousand atoms thick (Figure 2.10 ▼). He and his coworkers discovered that almost all the α particles passed directly through the foil without deflection. A small percentage were found to be slightly deflected, on the order of 1 degree, consistent with Thomson's plum-pudding model. Just for the sake of completeness, Rutherford suggested that Ernest Marsden, an undergraduate student working in the laboratory, look for evidence of scattering at large angles. To everyone's surprise, a small amount of scattering was observed at large angles. Some particles were even scattered back in the direction from which they had come. The explanation for these results was not immediately obvious, but they were clearly inconsistent with Thomson's plum-pudding model.

By 1911, Rutherford was able to explain these observations. He postulated that most of the mass of each gold atom in his foil and all of its positive charge reside in a very small, extremely dense region, which he called the **nucleus**. He postulated further that most of the total volume of an atom is empty space in which electrons move around the nucleus. In the α-scattering experiment, most α particles passed directly through the foil because they did not encounter the minute nucleus of any gold atom; they merely passed through the empty space making up the greatest part of all the atoms in the foil. Occasionally, however, an α particle came close to a gold nucleus. The repulsion between the highly charged gold nucleus and the α particle was strong enough to deflect the less massive α particle, as shown in Figure 2.11 ▶.

Subsequent experimental studies led to the discovery of both positive particles (*protons*) and neutral particles (*neutrons*) in the nucleus. Protons were discovered in 1919 by Rutherford. Neutrons were discovered in 1932 by the British scientist James Chadwick (1891–1972). We examine these particles more closely in Section 2.3.

▶ **Figure 2.10   Rutherford's experiment on the scattering of α particles.** The red lines represent the paths of the α particles. When the incoming beam strikes the gold foil, most particles pass straight through the foil but some are scattered.

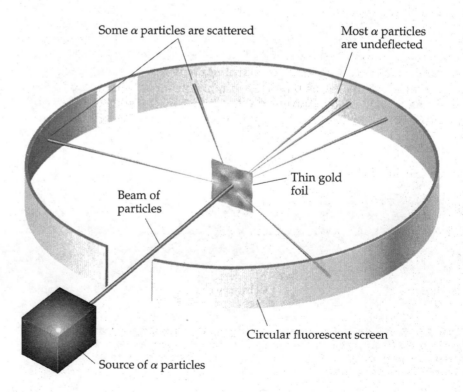

Some α particles are scattered

Most α particles are undeflected

Thin gold foil

Beam of particles

Circular fluorescent screen

Source of α particles

Science Fundamentals Second Edition

GIVE IT SOME THOUGHT

What happens to most of the α particles that strike the gold foil in Rutherford's experiment, and why do they behave that way?

2.3 | The Modern View of Atomic Structure

Since the time of Rutherford, physicists have learned much about the detailed composition of atomic nuclei. In the course of these discoveries, the list of particles that make up nuclei has grown long and continues to increase. As chemists, however, we can take a very simple view of the atom because only three subatomic particles—the **proton**, **neutron**, and **electron**—have a bearing on chemical behavior.

The charge of an electron is -1.602×10^{-19} C, and that of a proton is $+1.602 \times 10^{-19}$ C. The quantity 1.602×10^{-19} C is called the **electronic charge**. For convenience, the charges of atomic and subatomic particles are usually expressed as multiples of this charge rather than in coulombs. Thus, the charge of the electron is $1-$, and that of the proton is $1+$. Neutrons are uncharged and are therefore electrically neutral (which is how they received their name). *Every atom has an equal number of electrons and protons, and so atoms have no net electrical charge.*

Protons and neutrons reside together in the nucleus of the atom, which, as Rutherford proposed, is extremely small. The vast majority of an atom's volume is the space in which the electrons reside. The electrons are attracted to the protons in the nucleus by the force that exists between particles of opposite electrical charge. In later chapters we will see that the strength of the attractive forces between electrons and nuclei can be used to explain many of the differences between different elements.

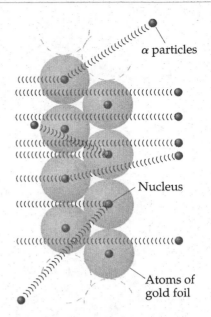

▲ **Figure 2.11 Rutherford's model explaining the scattering of α particles.** The gold foil is several thousand atoms thick. Because most of the volume of each atom is empty space, most α particles pass through the foil without deflection. When an α particle passes very close to a gold nucleus, however, it is repelled, causing its path to be altered.

GIVE IT SOME THOUGHT

(a) If an atom has 15 protons, how many electrons does it have? (b) Where do the protons reside in an atom?

Atoms have extremely small masses. The mass of the heaviest known atom, for example, is on the order of 4×10^{-22} g. Because it would be cumbersome to express such small masses in grams, we use instead the **atomic mass unit**, or amu.* One amu equals 1.66054×10^{-24} g. The masses of the proton and neutron are very nearly equal, and both are much greater than that of the electron: A proton has a mass of 1.0073 amu, a neutron 1.0087 amu, and an electron 5.486×10^{-4} amu. Because it would take 1836 electrons to equal the mass of 1 proton, the nucleus contains most of the mass of an atom. Table 2.1 ▼ summarizes the charges and masses of the subatomic particles. We will have more to say about atomic masses in Section 2.4.

TABLE 2.1 Comparison of the Proton, Neutron, and Electron		
Particle	**Charge**	**Mass (amu)**
Proton	Positive (1+)	1.0073
Neutron	None (neutral)	1.0087
Electron	Negative (1−)	5.486×10^{-4}

* The SI abbreviation for the atomic mass unit is u. We will use the more common abbreviation amu.

Science Fundamentals Second Edition

Atoms are also extremely small. Most atoms have diameters between 1×10^{-10} m and 5×10^{-10} m, or 100–500 pm. A convenient, although non-SI, unit of length used to express atomic dimensions is the **angstrom** (Å). One angstrom equals 10^{-10} m. Thus, atoms have diameters on the order of 1–5 Å. The diameter of a chlorine atom, for example, is 200 pm, or 2.0 Å. Both picometers and angstroms are commonly used to express the dimensions of atoms and molecules.

SAMPLE EXERCISE 2.1 | Illustrating the Size of an Atom

The diameter of a U.S. penny is 19 mm. The diameter of a silver atom, by comparison, is only 2.88 Å. How many silver atoms could be arranged side by side in a straight line across the diameter of a penny?

Solution The unknown is the number of silver (Ag) atoms. We use the relationship 1 Ag atom = 2.88 Å as a conversion factor relating the number of atoms and distance. Thus, we can start with the diameter of the penny, first converting this distance into angstroms and then using the diameter of the Ag atom to convert distance to the number of Ag atoms:

$$\text{Ag atoms} = (19 \text{ mm})\left(\frac{10^{-3} \text{ m}}{1 \text{ mm}}\right)\left(\frac{1 \text{ Å}}{10^{-10} \text{ m}}\right)\left(\frac{1 \text{ Ag atom}}{2.88 \text{ Å}}\right) = 6.6 \times 10^7 \text{ Ag atoms}$$

That is, 66 million silver atoms could sit side by side across a penny!

PRACTICE EXERCISE

The diameter of a carbon atom is 1.54 Å. **(a)** Express this diameter in picometers. **(b)** How many carbon atoms could be aligned side by side in a straight line across the width of a pencil line that is 0.20 mm wide?
Answers: **(a)** 154 pm, **(b)** 1.3×10^6 C atoms

The diameters of atomic nuclei are on the order of 10^{-4} Å, only a small fraction of the diameter of the atom as a whole. You can appreciate the relative sizes of the atom and its nucleus by imagining that if the atom were as large as a football stadium, the nucleus would be the size of a small marble. Because the tiny nucleus carries most of the mass of the atom in such a small volume, it has an incredible density—on the order of 10^{13}–10^{14} g/cm^3. A matchbox full of material of such density would weigh over 2.5 billion tons! Astrophysicists have suggested that the interior of a collapsed star may approach this density.

An illustration of the atom that incorporates the features we have just discussed is shown in Figure 2.12 ▼. The electrons, which take up most of the volume of the atom, play the major role in chemical reactions. The significance of representing the region containing the electrons as an indistinct cloud will become clear in later chapters when we consider the energies and spatial arrangements of the electrons.

▼ **Figure 2.12 The structure of the atom.** The nucleus, which contains protons and neutrons, is the location of virtually all the mass of the atom. The rest of the atom is the space in which the light, negatively charged electrons reside.

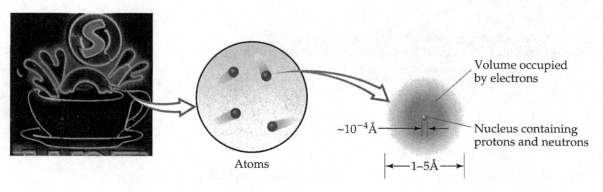

Atoms

$\sim 10^{-4}$ Å

1–5 Å

Volume occupied by electrons

Nucleus containing protons and neutrons

Science Fundamentals Second Edition

A CLOSER LOOK | Basic Forces

There are four basic forces, or interactions, known in nature: gravitational, electromagnetic, strong nuclear, and weak nuclear. *Gravitational forces* are attractive forces that act between all objects in proportion to their masses. Gravitational forces between atoms or between subatomic particles are so small that they are of no chemical significance.

Electromagnetic forces are attractive or repulsive forces that act between either electrically charged or magnetic objects. Electric and magnetic forces are intimately related. Electric forces are of fundamental importance in understanding the chemical behavior of atoms. The magnitude of the electric force between two charged particles is given by *Coulomb's law*: $F = kQ_1Q_2/d^2$, where Q_1 and Q_2 are the magnitudes of the charges on the two particles, d is the distance between their

centers, and k is a constant determined by the units for Q and d. A negative value for the force indicates attraction, whereas a positive value indicates repulsion.

All nuclei except those of hydrogen atoms contain two or more protons. Because like charges repel, electrical repulsion would cause the protons to fly apart if a stronger attractive force did not keep them together. This force is called the *strong nuclear force*. It acts between subatomic particles, as in the nucleus. At this distance, the strong nuclear force is stronger than the electric force, and as a result the nucleus holds together. The *weak nuclear force* is weaker than the electric force but stronger than the gravitational force. We are aware of its existence only because it shows itself in certain types of radioactivity.

Related Exercises: 2.78(b) and 2.83

Atomic Numbers, Mass Numbers, and Isotopes

What makes an atom of one element different from an atom of another element? For example, how does an atom of carbon differ from an atom of oxygen? The significant difference is in their subatomic compositions: The atoms of each element have a characteristic number of protons. Indeed, the number of protons in the nucleus of an atom of any particular element is called that element's **atomic number**. Because an atom has no net electrical charge, the number of electrons it contains must equal the number of protons. All atoms of carbon, for example, have six protons and six electrons, whereas all atoms of oxygen have eight protons and eight electrons. Thus, carbon has atomic number 6, whereas oxygen has atomic number 8. The atomic number of each element is listed with the name and symbol of the element on the front inside cover of the text.

Atoms of a given element can differ in the number of neutrons they contain and consequently in mass. For example, most atoms of carbon have six neutrons, although some have more and some have less. The symbol $^{12}_{6}C$ (read "carbon twelve," carbon-12) represents the carbon atom containing six protons and six neutrons. The atomic number is shown by the subscript, and the superscript, called the **mass number**, is the total number of protons plus neutrons in the atom:

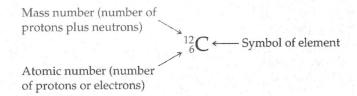

Because all atoms of a given element have the same atomic number, the subscript is redundant and is often omitted. Thus, the symbol for carbon-12 can be represented simply as ^{12}C. As one more example of this notation, atoms that contain six protons and eight neutrons have a mass number of 14 and are represented as $^{14}_{6}C$ or ^{14}C and referred to as carbon-14.

Atoms with identical atomic numbers but different mass numbers (that is, same number of protons but different numbers of neutrons) are called **isotopes**

Science Fundamentals Second Edition

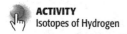

ACTIVITY
Isotopes of Hydrogen

TABLE 2.2 Some Isotopes of Carbon[a]			
Symbol	Number of Protons	Number of Electrons	Number of Neutrons
^{11}C	6	6	5
^{12}C	6	6	6
^{13}C	6	6	7
^{14}C	6	6	8

Almost 99% of the carbon found in nature is ^{12}C.

of one another. Several isotopes of carbon are listed in Table 2.2 ▲. We will generally use the notation with superscripts only when referring to a particular isotope of an element.

■ **SAMPLE EXERCISE 2.2** | Determining the Number of Subatomic Particles in Atoms

How many protons, neutrons, and electrons are in **(a)** an atom of ^{197}Au; **(b)** an atom of strontium-90?

Solution (a) The superscript 197 is the mass number, the sum of the number of protons plus the number of neutrons. According to the list of elements given on the front inside cover, gold has an atomic number of 79. Consequently, an atom of ^{197}Au has 79 protons, 79 electrons, and $197 - 79 = 118$ neutrons. **(b)** The atomic number of strontium (listed on the front inside cover) is 38. Thus, all atoms of this element have 38 protons and 38 electrons. The strontium-90 isotope has $90 - 38 = 52$ neutrons.

■ **PRACTICE EXERCISE**

How many protons, neutrons, and electrons are in **(a)** a ^{138}Ba atom, **(b)** an atom of phosphorus-31?
Answer: **(a)** 56 protons, 56 electrons, and 82 neutrons; **(b)** 15 protons, 15 electrons, and 16 neutrons.

■ **SAMPLE EXERCISE 2.3** | Writing Symbols for Atoms

Magnesium has three isotopes, with mass numbers 24, 25, and 26. **(a)** Write the complete chemical symbol (superscript and subscript) for each of them. **(b)** How many neutrons are in an atom of each isotope?

Solution (a) Magnesium has atomic number 12, and so all atoms of magnesium contain 12 protons and 12 electrons. The three isotopes are therefore represented by $^{24}_{12}Mg$, $^{25}_{12}Mg$, and $^{26}_{12}Mg$. **(b)** The number of neutrons in each isotope is the mass number minus the number of protons. The numbers of neutrons in an atom of each isotope are therefore 12, 13, and 14, respectively.

■ **PRACTICE EXERCISE**

Give the complete chemical symbol for the atom that contains 82 protons, 82 electrons, and 126 neutrons.
Answer: $^{208}_{82}Pb$

2.4 | Atomic Weights

Atoms are small pieces of matter, and so they have mass. In this section we will discuss the mass scale used for atoms and introduce the concept of *atomic weights*. In Section 3.3 we will extend these concepts to show how atomic masses are used to determine the masses of compounds and *molecular weights*.

Science Fundamentals Second Edition

The Atomic Mass Scale

Although scientists of the nineteenth century knew nothing about subatomic particles, they were aware that atoms of different elements have different masses. They found, for example, that each 100.0 g of water contains 11.1 g of hydrogen and 88.9 g of oxygen. Thus, water contains 88.9/11.1 = 8 times as much oxygen, by mass, as hydrogen. Once scientists understood that water contains two hydrogen atoms for each oxygen, they concluded that an oxygen atom must have 2 × 8 = 16 times as much mass as a hydrogen atom. Hydrogen, the lightest atom, was arbitrarily assigned a relative mass of 1 (no units), and atomic masses of other elements were at first determined relative to this value. Thus, oxygen was assigned an atomic mass of 16.

Today we can determine the masses of individual atoms with a high degree of accuracy. For example, we know that the ^{1}H atom has a mass of 1.6735×10^{-24} g and the ^{16}O atom has a mass of 2.6560×10^{-23} g. As we noted in Section 2.3, it is convenient to use the *atomic mass unit* (amu) when dealing with these extremely small masses:

$$1 \text{ amu} = 1.66054 \times 10^{-24} \text{ g and } 1 \text{ g} = 6.02214 \times 10^{23} \text{ amu}$$

The atomic mass unit is presently defined by assigning a mass of exactly 12 amu to an atom of the ^{12}C isotope of carbon. In these units, an ^{1}H atom has a mass of 1.0078 amu and an ^{16}O atom has a mass of 15.9949 amu.

Average Atomic Masses

Most elements occur in nature as mixtures of isotopes. We can determine the *average atomic mass* of an element by using the masses of its various isotopes and their relative abundances. Naturally occurring carbon, for example, is composed of 98.93% ^{12}C and 1.07% ^{13}C. The masses of these isotopes are 12 amu (exactly) and 13.00335 amu, respectively. We calculate the average atomic mass of carbon from the fractional abundance of each isotope and the mass of that isotope:

$$(0.9893)(12 \text{ amu}) + (0.0107)(13.00335 \text{ amu}) = 12.01 \text{ amu}$$

The average atomic mass of each element (expressed in atomic mass units) is also known as its **atomic weight**. Although the term *average atomic mass* is more proper, the term *atomic weight* is more common. The atomic weights of the elements are listed in both the periodic table and the table of elements on the inside front cover of this text.

 GIVE IT SOME THOUGHT

A particular atom of chromium has a mass of 52.94 amu, whereas the atomic weight of chromium is 51.99 amu. Explain the difference in the two masses.

SAMPLE EXERCISE 2.4 | Calculating the Atomic Weight of an Element from Isotopic Abundances

Naturally occurring chlorine is 75.78% ^{35}Cl, which has an atomic mass of 34.969 amu, and 24.22% ^{37}Cl, which has an atomic mass of 36.966 amu. Calculate the average atomic mass (that is, the atomic weight) of chlorine.

Solution The average atomic mass is found by multiplying the abundance of each isotope by its atomic mass and summing these products. Because 75.78% = 0.7578 and 24.22% = 0.2422, we have

$$\text{Average atomic mass} = (0.7578)(34.969 \text{ amu}) + (0.2422)(36.966 \text{ amu})$$

$$= 26.50 \text{ amu} + 8.953 \text{ amu}$$

$$= 35.45 \text{ amu}$$

This answer makes sense: The average atomic mass of Cl is between the masses of the two isotopes and is closer to the value of ^{35}Cl, which is the more abundant isotope.

■ PRACTICE EXERCISE

Three isotopes of silicon occur in nature: ^{28}Si (92.23%), which has an atomic mass of 27.97693 amu; ^{29}Si (4.68%), which has an atomic mass of 28.97649 amu; and ^{30}Si (3.09%), which has an atomic mass of 29.97377 amu. Calculate the atomic weight of silicon.
Answer: 28.09 amu

ACTIVITY
Mass Spectrometer

 A CLOSER LOOK | The Mass Spectrometer

The most direct and accurate means for determining atomic and molecular weights is provided by the **mass spectrometer** (Figure 2.13 ▼). A gaseous sample is introduced at *A* and bombarded by a stream of high-energy electrons at *B*. Collisions between the electrons and the atoms or molecules of the gas produce positively charged particles, mostly with a 1+ charge. These charged particles are accelerated toward a negatively charged wire grid (*C*). After they pass through the grid, the particles encounter two slits that allow only a narrow beam of particles to pass. This beam then passes between the poles of a magnet, which deflects the particles into a curved path, much as electrons are deflected by a magnetic field (Figure 2.4). For charged particles with the same charge, the extent of deflection depends on mass—the more massive the particle, the less the deflection. The particles are thereby separated according to their masses. By changing the strength of the magnetic field or the accelerating voltage on the negatively charged grid, charged particles of various masses can be selected to enter the detector at the end of the instrument.

A graph of the intensity of the detector signal versus particle atomic mass is called a *mass spectrum*. The mass spectrum of chlorine atoms, shown in Figure 2.14 ▼, reveals the presence of two isotopes. Analysis of a mass spectrum gives both the masses of the charged particles reaching the detector and their relative abundances. The abundances are obtained from the signal intensities. Knowing the atomic mass and the abundance of each isotope allows us to calculate the atomic weight of an element, as shown in Sample Exercise 2.4.

Mass spectrometers are used extensively today to identify chemical compounds and analyze mixtures of substances. Any molecule that loses electrons falls apart, forming an array of positively charged fragments. The mass spectrometer measures the masses of these fragments, producing a chemical "fingerprint" of the molecule and providing clues about how the atoms were connected in the original molecule. Thus, a chemist might use this technique to determine the molecular structure of a newly synthesized compound or to identify a pollutant in the environment.
Related Exercises: 2.31, 2.32, 2.33(b), 2.34, 2.86, and 2.87

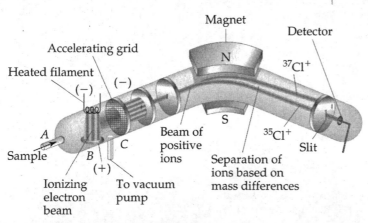

▲ **Figure 2.13 A mass spectrometer.** Cl atoms are introduced on the left side of the spectrometer and are ionized to form Cl^+ ions, which are then directed through a magnetic field. The paths of the ions of the two isotopes of Cl diverge as they pass through the magnetic field. As drawn, the spectrometer is tuned to detect $^{35}Cl^+$ ions. The heavier $^{37}Cl^+$ ions are not deflected enough for them to reach the detector.

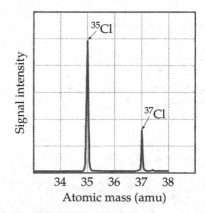

▲ **Figure 2.14 Mass spectrum of atomic chlorine.** The fractional abundances of the ^{35}Cl and ^{37}Cl isotopes of chlorine are indicated by the relative signal intensities of the beams reaching the detector of the mass spectrometer.

2.5 | The Periodic Table

Dalton's atomic theory set the stage for a vigorous growth in chemical experimentation during the early 1800s. As the body of chemical observations grew and the list of known elements expanded, attempts were made to find regular patterns in chemical behavior. These efforts culminated in the development of the periodic table in 1869. We will have much to say about the periodic table in later chapters, but it is so important and useful that you should become acquainted with it now. You will quickly learn that *the periodic table is the most significant tool that chemists use for organizing and remembering chemical facts.*

Many elements show very strong similarities to one another. The elements lithium (Li), sodium (Na), and potassium (K) are all soft, very reactive metals, for example; and the elements helium (He), neon (Ne), and argon (Ar) are all very nonreactive gases. If the elements are arranged in order of increasing atomic number, their chemical and physical properties are found to show a repeating, or periodic, pattern. For example, each of the soft, reactive metals—lithium, sodium, and potassium—comes immediately after one of the nonreactive gases—helium, neon, and argon—as shown in Figure 2.15 ▼.

The arrangement of elements in order of increasing atomic number, with elements having similar properties placed in vertical columns, is known as the **periodic table**. The periodic table is shown in Figure 2.16 ▶ and is also given on the front inside cover of the text. For each element in the table, the atomic number and atomic symbol are given, and the atomic weight is often given as well, as in the following typical entry for potassium:

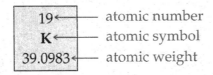

You may notice slight variations in periodic tables from one book to another or between those in the lecture hall and in the text. These are simply matters of style, or they might concern the particular information included; there are no fundamental differences.

The horizontal rows of the periodic table are called **periods**. The first period consists of only two elements, hydrogen (H) and helium (He). The second and third periods, which begin with lithium (Li) and sodium (Na), respectively, consist of eight elements each. The fourth and fifth periods

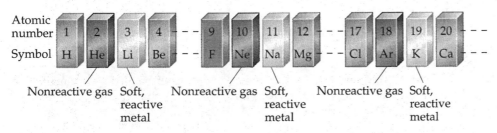

▲ **Figure 2.15 Arranging the elements by atomic number reveals a periodic pattern of properties.** This periodic pattern is the basis of the periodic table.

	1A 1																	8A 18
1	1 H	2A 2											3A 13	4A 14	5A 15	6A 16	7A 17	2 He
2	3 Li	4 Be											5 B	6 C	7 N	8 O	9 F	10 Ne
3	11 Na	12 Mg	3B 3	4B 4	5B 5	6B 6	7B 7	8B 8	8B 9	10	1B 11	2B 12	13 Al	14 Si	15 P	16 S	17 Cl	18 Ar
4	19 K	20 Ca	21 Sc	22 Ti	23 V	24 Cr	25 Mn	26 Fe	27 Co	28 Ni	29 Cu	30 Zn	31 Ga	32 Ge	33 As	34 Se	35 Br	36 Kr
5	37 Rb	38 Sr	39 Y	40 Zr	41 Nb	42 Mo	43 Tc	44 Ru	45 Rh	46 Pd	47 Ag	48 Cd	49 In	50 Sn	51 Sb	52 Te	53 I	54 Xe
6	55 Cs	56 Ba	71 Lu	72 Hf	73 Ta	74 W	75 Re	76 Os	77 Ir	78 Pt	79 Au	80 Hg	81 Tl	82 Pb	83 Bi	84 Po	85 At	86 Rn
7	87 Fr	88 Ra	103 Lr	104 Rf	105 Db	106 Sg	107 Bh	108 Hs	109 Mt	110	111	112	113	114	115	116		

	57 La	58 Ce	59 Pr	60 Nd	61 Pm	62 Sm	63 Eu	64 Gd	65 Tb	66 Dy	67 Ho	68 Er	69 Tm	70 Yb
Metals														
Metalloids	89 Ac	90 Th	91 Pa	92 U	93 Np	94 Pu	95 Am	96 Cm	97 Bk	98 Cf	99 Es	100 Fm	101 Md	102 No
Nonmetals														

▲ **Figure 2.16 Periodic table of the elements.** Different colors are used to show the division of the elements into metals, metalloids, and nonmetals.

ACTIVITY
Periodic Table

contain 18 elements. The sixth period has 32 elements, but in order for it to fit on a page, 14 of these elements (those with atomic numbers 57–70) appear at the bottom of the table. The seventh and last period is incomplete, but it also has 14 of its members placed in a row at the bottom of the table.

The vertical columns of the periodic table are called **groups**. The way in which the groups are labeled is somewhat arbitrary, and three labeling schemes are in common use, two of which are shown in Figure 2.16. The top set of labels, which have A and B designations, is widely used in North America. Roman numerals, rather than Arabic ones, are often employed in this scheme. Group 7A, for example, is often labeled VIIA. Europeans use a similar convention that numbers the columns from 1A through 8A and then from 1B through 8B, thereby giving the label 7B (or VIIB) instead of 7A to the group headed by fluorine (F). In an effort to eliminate this confusion, the International Union of Pure and Applied Chemistry (IUPAC) has proposed a convention that numbers the groups from 1 through 18 with no A or B designations, as shown in the lower set of labels at the top of the table in Figure 2.16. We will use the traditional North American convention with Arabic numerals.

Elements that belong to the same group often exhibit similarities in physical and chemical properties. For example, the "coinage metals"— copper (Cu), silver (Ag), and gold (Au)—all belong to group 1B. As their name suggests, the coinage metals are used throughout the world to make coins. Many other groups in the periodic table also have names, as listed in Table 2.3 ▶.

Group	Name	Elements
1A	Alkali metals	Li, Na, K, Rb, Cs, Fr
2A	Alkaline earth metals	Be, Mg, Ca, Sr, Ba, Ra
6A	Chalcogens	O, S, Se, Te, Po
7A	Halogens	F, Cl, Br, I, At
8A	Noble gases (or rare gases)	He, Ne, Ar, Kr, Xe, Rn

TABLE 2.3 Names of Some Groups in the Periodic Table

We will learn in Chapters 6 and 7 that the elements in a group of the periodic table have similar properties because they have the same arrangement of electrons at the periphery of their atoms. However, we need not wait until then to make good use of the periodic table; after all, the table was invented by chemists who knew nothing about electrons! We can use the table, as they intended, to correlate the behaviors of elements and to aid in remembering many facts. You will find it helpful to refer to the periodic table frequently when studying the remainder of this chapter.

Except for hydrogen, all the elements on the left side and in the middle of the periodic table are **metallic elements**, or **metals**. The majority of elements are metallic, and they all share many characteristic properties, such as luster and high electrical and heat conductivity. All metals, with the exception of mercury (Hg), are solids at room temperature. The metals are separated from the **nonmetallic elements**, or **nonmetals**, by a diagonal steplike line that runs from boron (B) to astatine (At), as shown in Figure 2.16. Hydrogen, although on the left side of the periodic table, is a nonmetal. At room temperature some of the nonmetals are gaseous, some are solid, and one is liquid. Nonmetals generally differ from the metals in appearance (Figure 2.17 ▶) and in other physical properties. Many of the elements that lie along the line that separates metals from nonmetals, such as antimony (Sb), have properties that fall between those of metals and those of nonmetals. These elements are often referred to as **metalloids**.

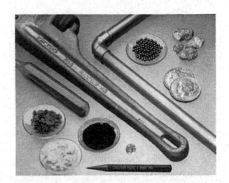

▲ **Figure 2.17 Some familiar examples of metals and nonmetals.** The nonmetals (from bottom left) are sulfur (yellow powder), iodine (dark, shiny crystals), bromine (reddish brown liquid and vapor in glass vial), and three samples of carbon (black charcoal powder, diamonds, and graphite in the pencil lead). The metals are in the form of an aluminum wrench, copper pipe, lead shot, silver coins, and gold nuggets.

 GIVE IT SOME THOUGHT

Chlorine is a halogen. Locate this element in the periodic table. (a) What is its symbol? (b) In what period and in what group is the element located? (c) What is its atomic number? (d) Is chlorine a metal or nonmetal?

SAMPLE EXERCISE 2.5 | Using the Periodic Table

Which two of the following elements would you expect to show the greatest similarity in chemical and physical properties: B, Ca, F, He, Mg, P?

Solution Elements that are in the same group of the periodic table are most likely to exhibit similar chemical and physical properties. We therefore expect that Ca and Mg should be most alike because they are in the same group (2A, the alkaline earth metals).

PRACTICE EXERCISE

Locate Na (sodium) and Br (bromine) on the periodic table. Give the atomic number of each, and label each a metal, metalloid, or nonmetal.
Answer: Na, atomic number 11, is a metal; Br, atomic number 35, is a nonmetal.

A CLOSER LOOK | Glenn Seaborg and Seaborgium

Prior to 1940 the periodic table ended at uranium, element number 92. Since that time, no scientist has had a greater effect on the periodic table than Glenn Seaborg. Seaborg (Figure 2.18 ▶) became a faculty member in the chemistry department at the University of California, Berkeley, in 1937. In 1940 he and his colleagues Edwin McMillan, Arthur Wahl, and Joseph Kennedy succeeded in isolating plutonium (Pu) as a product of the reaction between uranium and neutrons. We will talk about reactions of this type, called *nuclear reactions*, in Chapter 21. We will also discuss the key role that plutonium plays in nuclear fission reactions, such as those that occur in nuclear power plants and atomic bombs.

During the period 1944 through 1958, Seaborg and his coworkers also identified various products of nuclear reactions as being the elements having atomic numbers 95 through 102. All these elements are radioactive and are not found in nature; they can be synthesized only via nuclear reactions. For their efforts in identifying the elements beyond uranium (the *transuranium* elements), McMillan and Seaborg shared the 1951 Nobel Prize in chemistry.

From 1961 to 1971, Seaborg served as the chairman of the U.S. Atomic Energy Commission (now the Department of Energy). In this position he had an important role in establishing international treaties to limit the testing of nuclear weapons. Upon his return to Berkeley he was part of the team that in 1974 first identified element number 106; that discovery was corroborated by another team at Berkeley in 1993. In 1994, to honor Seaborg's many contributions to the discovery of new elements, the American Chemical Society proposed that element number 106 be named "seaborgium," with a proposed

▲ **Figure 2.18   Glenn Seaborg (1912–1999).** The photograph shows Seaborg at Berkeley in 1941 using a Geiger counter to try to detect radiation produced by plutonium. Geiger counters will be discussed in Section 21.5.

symbol of Sg. After several years of controversy about whether an element should be named after a living person, the name seaborgium was officially adopted by the IUPAC in 1997, and Seaborg became the first person to have an element named after him while he was still alive.
Related Exercise: 2.90

2.6 | Molecules and Molecular Compounds

The atom is the smallest representative sample of an element, but only the noble-gas elements are normally found in nature as isolated atoms. Most matter is composed of molecules or ions, both of which are formed from atoms. We examine molecules here and ions in Section 2.7.

A **molecule** is an assembly of two or more atoms tightly bound together. The resultant "package" of atoms behaves in many ways as a single, distinct object, just as a television set composed of many parts can be recognized as a single object. We will discuss the forces that hold the atoms together (the chemical bonds) in Chapters 8 and 9.

Molecules and Chemical Formulas

Many elements are found in nature in molecular form; that is, two or more of the same type of atom are bound together. For example, the oxygen normally found in air consists of molecules that contain two oxygen atoms. We represent this molecular form of oxygen by the **chemical formula** O_2 (read "oh two"). The subscript in the formula tells us that two oxygen atoms are present in each molecule. A molecule that is made up of two atoms is called a **diatomic molecule.** Oxygen also exists in another molecular form known as *ozone*. Molecules of ozone consist of three oxygen atoms, making the chemical formula for this substance O_3. Even though "normal" oxygen (O_2) and ozone

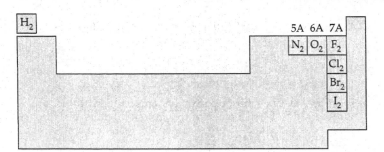

are both composed only of oxygen atoms, they exhibit very different chemical and physical properties. For example, O_2 is essential for life, but O_3 is toxic; O_2 is odorless, whereas O_3 has a sharp, pungent smell.

The elements that normally occur as diatomic molecules are hydrogen, oxygen, nitrogen, and the halogens. Their locations in the periodic table are shown in Figure 2.19 ▲. When we speak of the substance hydrogen, we mean H_2 unless we explicitly indicate otherwise. Likewise, when we speak of oxygen, nitrogen, or any of the halogens, we are referring to O_2, N_2, F_2, Cl_2, Br_2, or I_2. Thus, the properties of oxygen and hydrogen listed in Table 1.3 are those of O_2 and H_2. Other, less common forms of these elements behave much differently.

Compounds that are composed of molecules are called **molecular compounds** and contain more than one type of atom. A molecule of water, for example, consists of two hydrogen atoms and one oxygen atom. It is therefore represented by the chemical formula H_2O. Lack of a subscript on the O indicates one atom of O per water molecule. Another compound composed of these same elements (in different relative proportions) is hydrogen peroxide, H_2O_2. The properties of hydrogen peroxide are very different from the properties of water.

Several common molecules are shown in Figure 2.20 ▶. Notice how the composition of each compound is given by its chemical formula. Notice also that these substances are composed only of nonmetallic elements. *Most molecular substances that we will encounter contain only nonmetals.*

Molecular and Empirical Formulas

Chemical formulas that indicate the actual numbers and types of atoms in a molecule are called **molecular formulas**. (The formulas in Figure 2.20 are molecular formulas.) Chemical formulas that give only the relative number of atoms of each type in a molecule are called **empirical formulas**. The subscripts in an empirical formula are always the smallest possible whole-number ratios. The molecular formula for hydrogen peroxide is H_2O_2, for example, whereas its empirical formula is HO. The molecular formula for ethylene is C_2H_4, and its empirical formula is CH_2. For many substances, the molecular formula and the empirical formula are identical, as in the case of water, H_2O.

Molecular formulas provide more information about molecules than do empirical formulas. Whenever we know the molecular formula of a compound, we can determine its empirical formula. The converse is not true, however; if we know the empirical formula of a substance, we can't determine its molecular formula unless we have more information. So why do chemists bother with empirical formulas? As we will see in Chapter 3, certain common methods of analyzing substances lead to the empirical formula only. Once the empirical formula is known, however, additional experiments can give the information needed to convert the empirical formula to the molecular one. In addition, there are substances, such as the most common forms of elemental carbon, that don't exist as isolated molecules. For these substances, we must rely on empirical formulas. Thus, all the common forms of elemental carbon are represented by the element's chemical symbol, C, which is the empirical formula for all the forms.

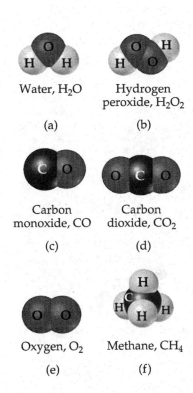

Water, H_2O

(a)

Hydrogen peroxide, H_2O_2

(b)

Carbon monoxide, CO

(c)

Carbon dioxide, CO_2

(d)

Oxygen, O_2

(e)

Methane, CH_4

(f)

▲ **Figure 2.20 Molecular models of some simple molecules.** Notice how the chemical formulas of these substances correspond to their compositions.

ACTIVITY
Representations of Methane

Structural formula

Perspective drawing

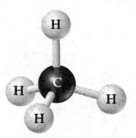

Ball-and-stick model

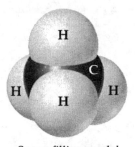

Space-filling model

▲ **Figure 2.21   Different representations of the methane (CH₄) molecule.** Structural formulas, perspective drawings, ball-and-stick models, and space-filling models each help us visualize the ways atoms are attached to each other in molecules. In the perspective drawing, solid lines represent bonds in the plane of the paper, the solid wedge represents a bond that extends out from the plane of the paper, and dashed lines represent bonds behind the paper.

■ **SAMPLE EXERCISE 2.6** | Relating Empirical and Molecular Formulas

Write the empirical formulas for the following molecules: (a) glucose, a substance also known as either blood sugar or dextrose, whose molecular formula is $C_6H_{12}O_6$; (b) nitrous oxide, a substance used as an anesthetic and commonly called laughing gas, whose molecular formula is N_2O.

Solution (a) The subscripts of an empirical formula are the smallest whole-number ratios. The smallest ratios are obtained by dividing each subscript by the largest common factor, in this case 6. The resultant empirical formula for glucose is CH_2O.

(b) Because the subscripts in N_2O are already the lowest integral numbers, the empirical formula for nitrous oxide is the same as its molecular formula, N_2O.

■ **PRACTICE EXERCISE**

Give the empirical formula for the substance called *diborane*, whose molecular formula is B_2H_6.
Answer: BH_3

Picturing Molecules

The molecular formula of a substance summarizes the composition of the substance but does not show how the atoms come together to form the molecule. The **structural formula** of a substance shows which atoms are attached to which within the molecule. For example, the structural formulas for water, hydrogen peroxide, and methane (CH_4) can be written as follows:

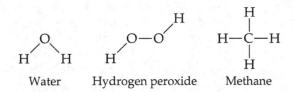

Water   Hydrogen peroxide   Methane

The atoms are represented by their chemical symbols, and lines are used to represent the bonds that hold the atoms together.

A structural formula usually does not depict the actual geometry of the molecule, that is, the actual angles at which atoms are joined together. A structural formula can be written as a *perspective drawing*, however, to give some sense of three-dimensional shape, as shown in Figure 2.21 ◄.

Scientists also rely on various models to help visualize molecules. *Ball-and-stick models* show atoms as spheres and bonds as sticks. This type of model has the advantage of accurately representing the angles at which the atoms are attached to one another within the molecule (Figure 2.21). All atoms may be represented by balls of the same size, or the relative sizes of the balls may reflect the relative sizes of the atoms. Sometimes the chemical symbols of the elements are superimposed on the balls, but often the atoms are identified simply by color.

A *space-filling model* depicts what the molecule would look like if the atoms were scaled up in size (Figure 2.21). These models show the relative sizes of the atoms, but the angles between atoms, which help define their molecular geometry, are often more difficult to see than in ball-and-stick models. As in ball-and-stick models, the identities of the atoms are indicated by their colors, but they may also be labeled with the element's symbol.

2.7 | Ions and Ionic Compounds

The nucleus of an atom is unchanged by chemical processes, but atoms can readily gain or lose electrons. If electrons are removed from or added to a neutral atom, a charged particle called an **ion** is formed. An ion with a positive charge is called a **cation** (pronounced CAT-ion); a negatively charged ion is called an **anion** (AN-ion).

To see how ions form, consider the sodium atom, which has 11 protons and 11 electrons. This atom easily loses one electron. The resulting cation has 11 protons and 10 electrons, which means it has a net charge of 1+.

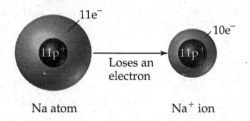

| Na atom | Na$^+$ ion |

The net charge on an ion is represented by a superscript; the superscripts +, 2+, and 3+, for instance, mean a net charge resulting from the loss of one, two, and three electrons, respectively. The superscripts −, 2−, and 3− represent net charges resulting from the gain of one, two, and three electrons, respectively. Chlorine, with 17 protons and 17 electrons, for example, can gain an electron in chemical reactions, producing the Cl$^-$ ion:

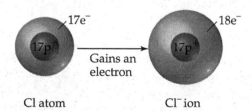

| Cl atom | Cl$^-$ ion |

In general, metal atoms tend to lose electrons to form cations, whereas nonmetal atoms tend to gain electrons to form anions.

SAMPLE EXERCISE 2.7 | Writing Chemical Symbols for Ions

Give the chemical symbol, including mass number, for each of the following ions: **(a)** The ion with 22 protons, 26 neutrons, and 19 electrons; **(b)** the ion of sulfur that has 16 neutrons and 18 electrons.

Solution **(a)** The number of protons (22) is the atomic number of the element, which means this element is titanium (Ti). The mass number of this isotope is $22 + 26 = 48$ (the sum of the protons and neutrons). Because the ion has three more protons than electrons, it has a net charge of 3+. Thus, the symbol for the ion is $^{48}Ti^{3+}$.

 (b) By referring to a periodic table or a table of elements, we see that sulfur (S) has an atomic number of 16. Thus, each atom or ion of sulfur must contain 16 protons. We are told that the ion also has 16 neutrons, meaning the mass number of the ion is $16 + 16 = 32$. Because the ion has 16 protons and 18 electrons, its net charge is 2−. Thus, the symbol for the ion is $^{32}S^{2-}$.

 In general, we will focus on the net charges of ions and ignore their mass numbers unless the circumstances dictate that we specify a certain isotope.

PRACTICE EXERCISE

How many protons and electrons does the Se^{2-} ion possess?
Answer: 34 protons and 36 electrons

In addition to simple ions, such as Na^+ and Cl^-, there are **polyatomic ions**, such as NO_3^- (nitrate ion) and SO_4^{2-} (sulfate ion). These latter ions consist of atoms joined as in a molecule, but they have a net positive or negative charge. We will consider further examples of polyatomic ions in Section 2.8.

It is important to realize that the chemical properties of ions are very different from the chemical properties of the atoms from which the ions are derived. The difference is like the change from Dr. Jekyll to Mr. Hyde: Although a given atom and its ion may be essentially the same (plus or minus a few electrons), the behavior of the ion is very different from that of the atom.

Predicting Ionic Charges

Many atoms gain or lose electrons so as to end up with the same number of electrons as the noble gas closest to them in the periodic table. The members of the noble-gas family are chemically very nonreactive and form very few compounds. We might deduce that this is because their electron arrangements are very stable. Nearby elements can obtain these same stable arrangements by losing or gaining electrons. For example, loss of one electron from an atom of sodium leaves it with the same number of electrons as the neutral neon atom (atomic number 10). Similarly, when chlorine gains an electron, it ends up with 18, the same number of electrons as in argon (atomic number 18). We will use this simple observation to explain the formation of ions until Chapter 8, where we discuss chemical bonding.

SAMPLE EXERCISE 2.8 | Predicting the Charges of Ions

Predict the charge expected for the most stable ion of barium and for the most stable ion of oxygen.

Solution We will assume that these elements form ions that have the same number of electrons as the nearest noble-gas atom. From the periodic table, we see that barium has atomic number 56. The nearest noble gas is xenon, atomic number 54. Barium can attain a stable arrangement of 54 electrons by losing two of its electrons, forming the Ba^{2+} cation.

 Oxygen has atomic number 8. The nearest noble gas is neon, atomic number 10. Oxygen can attain this stable electron arrangement by gaining two electrons, thereby forming the O^{2-} anion.

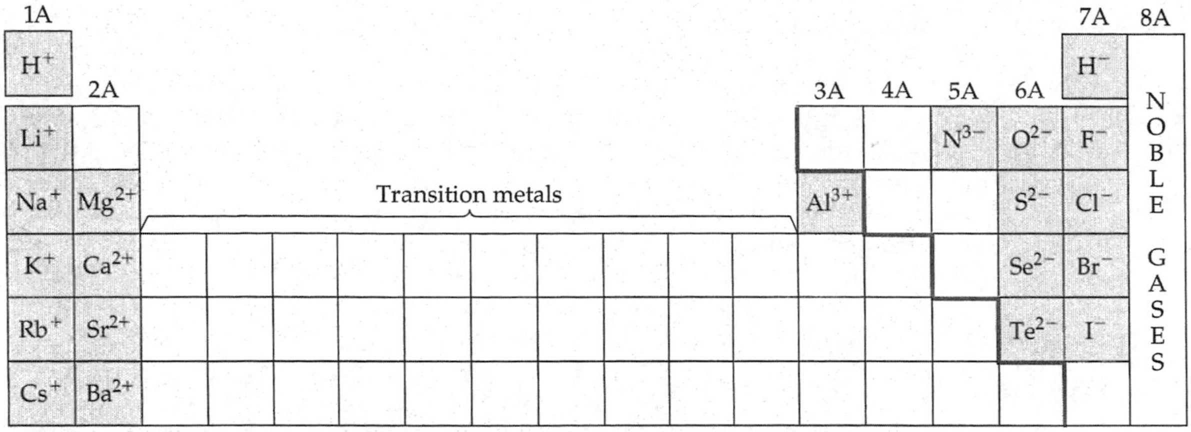

1A														7A	8A
H^+	2A								3A	4A	5A	6A		H^-	N
Li^+											N^{3-}	O^{2-}	F^-		O B
Na^+	Mg^{2+}			Transition metals					Al^{3+}			S^{2-}	Cl^-		L E
K^+	Ca^{2+}											Se^{2-}	Br^-		G A
Rb^+	Sr^{2+}											Te^{2-}	I^-		S E S
Cs^+	Ba^{2+}														

▲ **Figure 2.22 Charges of some common ions.** Notice that the steplike line that divides metals from nonmetals also separates cations from anions.

PRACTICE EXERCISE

Predict the charge expected for the most stable ion of aluminum and for the most stable ion of fluorine.
Answer: 3+ and 1−

The periodic table is very useful for remembering the charges of ions, especially those of the elements on the left and right sides of the table. As Figure 2.22 ▲ shows, the charges of these ions relate in a simple way to their positions in the table. On the left side of the table, for example, the group 1A elements (the alkali metals) form 1+ ions, and the group 2A elements (the alkaline earths) form 2+ ions. On the other side of the table the group 7A elements (the halogens) form 1− ions, and the group 6A elements form 2− ions. As we will see later in the text, many of the other groups do not lend themselves to such simple rules.

Ionic Compounds

A great deal of chemical activity involves the transfer of electrons from one substance to another, and, as we just saw, ions form when one or more electrons transfer from one neutral atom to another. Figure 2.23 ▼ shows that when elemental sodium is allowed to react with elemental chlorine, an electron transfers

▼ **Figure 2.23 The formation of an ionic compound.** (a) The transfer of an electron from a neutral Na atom to a neutral Cl atom leads to the formation of an Na^+ ion and a Cl^- ion. (b) Arrangement of these ions in solid sodium chloride (NaCl). (c) A sample of sodium chloride crystals.

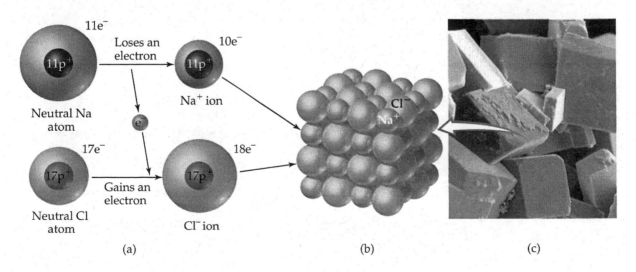

Science Fundamentals Second Edition

from a neutral sodium atom to a neutral chlorine atom. We are left with an Na^+ ion and a Cl^- ion. Because objects of opposite charge attract, the Na^+ and the Cl^- ions bind together to form the compound sodium chloride (NaCl). Sodium chloride, which we know better as common table salt, is an example of an **ionic compound**, a compound that contains both positively and negatively charged ions.

We can often tell whether a compound is ionic (consisting of ions) or molecular (consisting of molecules) from its composition. In general, cations are metal ions, whereas anions are nonmetal ions. Consequently, *ionic compounds are generally combinations of metals and nonmetals*, as in NaCl. In contrast, *molecular compounds are generally composed of nonmetals only*, as in H_2O.

SAMPLE EXERCISE 2.9 | Identifying Ionic and Molecular Compounds

Which of the following compounds would you expect to be ionic: N_2O, Na_2O, $CaCl_2$, SF_4?

Solution We would predict that Na_2O and $CaCl_2$ are ionic compounds because they are composed of a metal combined with a nonmetal. The other two compounds, composed entirely of nonmetals, are predicted (correctly) to be molecular compounds.

PRACTICE EXERCISE

Which of the following compounds are molecular: CBr_4, FeS, P_4O_6, PbF_2?
Answer: CBr_4 and P_4O_6

The ions in ionic compounds are arranged in three-dimensional structures. The arrangement of Na^+ and Cl^- ions in NaCl is shown in Figure 2.23. Because there is no discrete molecule of NaCl, we are able to write only an empirical formula for this substance. In fact, only empirical formulas can be written for most ionic compounds.

We can readily write the empirical formula for an ionic compound if we know the charges of the ions of which the compound is composed. Chemical compounds are always electrically neutral. Consequently, the ions in an ionic compound always occur in such a ratio that the total positive charge equals the total negative charge. Thus, there is one Na^+ to one Cl^- (giving NaCl), one Ba^{2+} to two Cl^- (giving $BaCl_2$), and so forth.

As you consider these and other examples, you will see that if the charges on the cation and anion are equal, the subscript on each ion will be 1. If the charges are not equal, the charge on one ion (without its sign) will become the subscript on the other ion. For example, the ionic compound formed from Mg (which forms Mg^{2+} ions) and N (which forms N^{3-} ions) is Mg_3N_2:

$$Mg^{\textcircled{2}+} \times N^{\textcircled{3}-} \longrightarrow Mg_3N_2$$

GIVE IT SOME THOUGHT

Why don't we write the formula for the compound formed by Ca^{2+} and O^{2-} as Ca_2O_2?

SAMPLE EXERCISE 2.10 | Using Ionic Charge to Write Empirical Formulas for Ionic Compounds

What are the empirical formulas of the compounds formed by **(a)** Al^{3+} and Cl^- ions, **(b)** Al^{3+} and O^{2-} ions, **(c)** Mg^{2+} and NO_3^- ions?

Solution (a) Three Cl⁻ ions are required to balance the charge of one Al^{3+} ion. Thus, the formula is $AlCl_3$.

(b) Two Al^{3+} ions are required to balance the charge of three O^{2-} ions (that is, the total positive charge is 6+, and the total negative charge is 6−). Thus, the formula is Al_2O_3.

(c) Two NO_3^- ions are needed to balance the charge of one Mg^{2+}. Thus, the formula is $Mg(NO_3)_2$. In this case the formula for the entire polyatomic ion NO_3^- must be enclosed in parentheses so that it is clear that the subscript 2 applies to all the atoms of that ion.

▪ PRACTICE EXERCISE
Write the empirical formulas for the compounds formed by the following ions:
(a) Na^+ and PO_4^{3-}, (b) Zn^{2+} and SO_4^{2-}, (c) Fe^{3+} and CO_3^{2-}.
Answers: (a) Na_3PO_4, (b) $ZnSO_4$, (c) $Fe_2(CO_3)_3$

 CHEMISTRY AND LIFE | Elements Required by Living Organisms

Figure 2.24 ▼ shows the elements that are essential for life. More than 97% of the mass of most organisms comprises just six elements—oxygen, carbon, hydrogen, nitrogen, phosphorus, and sulfur. Water (H_2O) is the most common compound in living organisms, accounting for at least 70% of the mass of most cells. Carbon is the most prevalent element (by mass) in the solid components of cells. Carbon atoms are found in a vast variety of organic molecules, in which the carbon atoms are bonded to other carbon atoms or to atoms of other elements, principally H, O, N, P, and S. All proteins, for example, contain the following group of atoms that occurs repeatedly within the molecules:

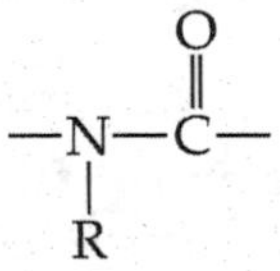

$$-N-\overset{\overset{\displaystyle O}{\|}}{C}-$$
$$\underset{\displaystyle R}{|}$$

(R is either an H atom or a combination of atoms such as CH_3.)

In addition, 23 more elements have been found in various living organisms. Five are ions that are required by all organisms: Ca^{2+}, Cl^-, Mg^{2+}, K^+, and Na^+. Calcium ions, for example, are necessary for the formation of bone and for the transmission of signals in the nervous system, such as those that trigger the contraction of cardiac muscles, causing the heart to beat. Many other elements are needed in only very small quantities and consequently are called *trace* elements. For example, trace quantities of copper are required in the diet of humans to aid in the synthesis of hemoglobin.

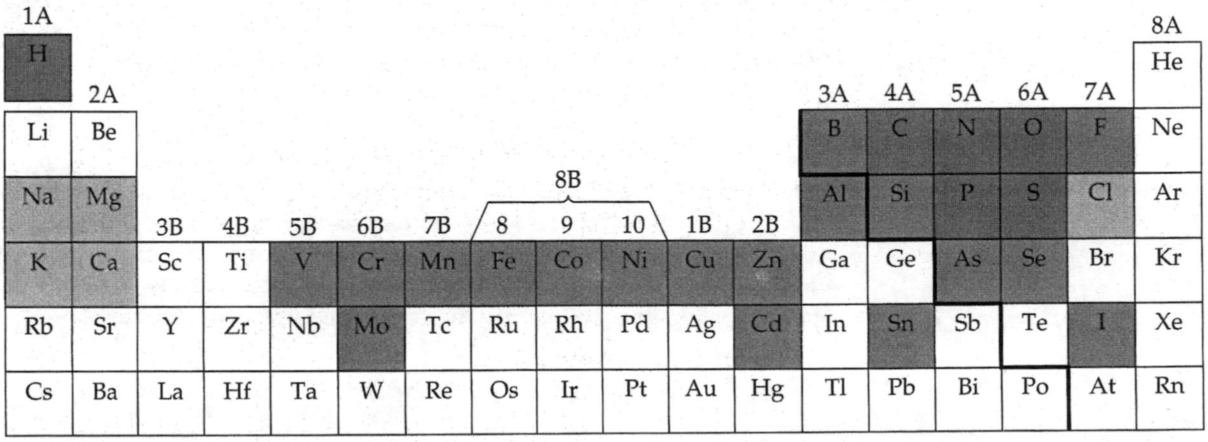

▼ **Figure 2.24 Biologically essential elements.** The elements that are essential for life are indicated by colors. Red denotes the six most abundant elements in living systems (hydrogen, carbon, nitrogen, oxygen, phosphorus, and sulfur). Blue indicates the five next most abundant elements. Green indicates the elements needed in only trace amounts.

1A																	8A
H	2A											3A	4A	5A	6A	7A	He
Li	Be											B	C	N	O	F	Ne
Na	Mg	3B	4B	5B	6B	7B	8B 8	9	10	1B	2B	Al	Si	P	S	Cl	Ar
K	Ca	Sc	Ti	V	Cr	Mn	Fe	Co	Ni	Cu	Zn	Ga	Ge	As	Se	Br	Kr
Rb	Sr	Y	Zr	Nb	Mo	Tc	Ru	Rh	Pd	Ag	Cd	In	Sn	Sb	Te	I	Xe
Cs	Ba	La	Hf	Ta	W	Re	Os	Ir	Pt	Au	Hg	Tl	Pb	Bi	Po	At	Rn

Science Fundamentals Second Edition

STRATEGIES IN CHEMISTRY | Pattern Recognition

Someone once said that drinking at the fountain of knowledge in a chemistry course is like drinking from a fire hydrant. Indeed, the pace can sometimes seem brisk. More to the point, however, we can drown in the facts if we don't see the general patterns. The value of recognizing patterns and learning rules and generalizations is that the patterns, rules, and generalizations free us from learning (or trying to memorize) many individual facts. The patterns, rules, and generalizations tie ideas together so that we don't get lost in the details.

Many students struggle with chemistry because they don't see how the topics relate to one another, how ideas connect together. They therefore treat every idea and problem as being unique instead of as an example or application of a general rule, procedure, or relationship. You can avoid this pitfall by remembering the following: Begin to notice the structure of the topic you are studying. Pay attention to the trends and rules given to summarize a large body of information. Notice, for example, how atomic structure helps us understand the existence of isotopes (as seen in Table 2.2) and how the periodic table aids us in remembering the charges of ions (as seen in Figure 2.22). You may surprise yourself by observing patterns that are not even explicitly spelled out yet. Perhaps you've even noticed certain trends in chemical formulas. Moving across the periodic table from element 11 (Na), we find that the elements form compounds with F having the following compositions: NaF, MgF_2, and AlF_3. Does this trend continue? Do SiF_4, PF_5, and SF_6 exist? Indeed they do. If you have picked up on trends like this from the scraps of information you've seen so far, then you're ahead of the game and you've already prepared yourself for some topics we will address in later chapters.

2.8 | Naming Inorganic Compounds

To obtain information about a particular substance, you must know its chemical formula and name. The names and formulas of compounds are essential vocabulary in chemistry. The system used in naming substances is called **chemical nomenclature** from the Latin words *nomen* (name) and *calare* (to call).

There are now more than 19 million known chemical substances. Naming them all would be a hopelessly complicated task if each had a special name independent of all others. Many important substances that have been known for a long time, such as water (H_2O) and ammonia (NH_3), do have individual, traditional names (so-called "common" names). For most substances, however, we rely on a systematic set of rules that leads to an informative and unique name for each substance, a name based on the composition of the substance.

The rules for chemical nomenclature are based on the division of substances into categories. The major division is between organic and inorganic compounds. *Organic compounds* contain carbon, usually in combination with hydrogen, oxygen, nitrogen, or sulfur. All others are *inorganic compounds*. Early chemists associated organic compounds with plants and animals, and they associated inorganic compounds with the nonliving portion of our world. Although this distinction between living and nonliving matter is no longer pertinent, the classification between organic and inorganic compounds continues to be useful. In this section we consider the basic rules for naming inorganic compounds, and in Section 2.9 we will introduce the names of some simple organic compounds. Among inorganic compounds, we will consider three categories: ionic compounds, molecular compounds, and acids.

Names and Formulas of Ionic Compounds

ACTIVITIES
Naming Cations,
Naming Anions

Recall from Section 2.7 that ionic compounds usually consist of metal ions combined with nonmetal ions. The metals form the positive ions, and the nonmetals form the negative ions. Let's examine the naming of positive ions, then the naming of negative ones. After that, we will consider how to put the names of the ions together to identify the complete ionic compound.

1. *Positive Ions (Cations)*

   (a) *Cations formed from metal atoms have the same name as the metal:*

   Na^+ sodium ion Zn^{2+} zinc ion Al^{3+} aluminum ion

   Ions formed from a single atom are called *monatomic ions*.

(b) *If a metal can form different cations, the positive charge is indicated by a Roman numeral in parentheses following the name of the metal:*

Fe^{2+} iron(II) ion Cu^{+} copper(I) ion

Fe^{3+} iron(III) ion Cu^{2+} copper(II) ion

Ions of the same element that have different charges exhibit different properties, such as different colors (Figure 2.25 ▶).

Most of the metals that can form more than one cation are *transition metals,* elements that occur in the middle block of elements, from group 3B to group 2B in the periodic table. The charges of these ions are indicated by Roman numerals. The metals that form only one cation are those of group 1A (Na^{+}, K^{+}, and Rb^{+}) and group 2A (Mg^{2+}, Ca^{2+}, Sr^{2+}, and Ba^{2+}), as well as Al^{3+} (group 3A) and two transition-metal ions: Ag^{+} (group 1B) and Zn^{2+} (group 2B). Charges are not expressed explicitly when naming these ions. However, if there is any doubt in your mind whether a metal forms more than one cation, use a Roman numeral to indicate the charge. It is never wrong to do so, even though it may be unnecessary.

An older method still widely used for distinguishing between two differently charged ions of a metal is to apply the ending *-ous* or *-ic*. These endings represent the lower and higher charged ions, respectively. They are added to the root of the element's Latin name:

Fe^{2+} ferrous ion Cu^{+} cuprous ion

Fe^{3+} ferric ion Cu^{2+} cupric ion

Although we will only rarely use these older names in this text, you might encounter them elsewhere.

(c) *Cations formed from nonmetal atoms have names that end in -ium:*

NH_4^{+} ammonium ion H_3O^{+} hydronium ion

These two ions are the only ions of this kind that we will encounter frequently in the text. They are both polyatomic. The vast majority of cations are monatomic metal ions.

The names and formulas of some common cations are shown in Table 2.4 ▶ and are also included in a table of common ions that is placed in the back inside cover of the text. The ions listed on the left in Table 2.4 are the monatomic ions that do not have variable charges. Those listed on the right are either polyatomic cations or cations with variable charges. The Hg_2^{2+} ion is unusual because this metal ion is not monatomic. It is called the mercury(I) ion because it can be thought of as two Hg^{+} ions fused together. The cations that you will encounter most frequently are shown in boldface. These are the ones you should learn first.

▲ **Figure 2.25 Ions of the same element with different charges exhibit different properties.** Compounds containing ions of the same element but with different charge can be very different in appearance and properties. Both substances shown are complex compounds of iron that also contain K^{+} and CN^{-} ions. The one on the left is potassium ferrocyanide, which contains Fe(II) bound to CN^{-} ions. The one on the right is potassium ferricyanide, which contains Fe(III) bound to CN^{-} ions. Both substances are used extensively in blueprinting and other dyeing processes.

💡 **GIVE IT SOME THOUGHT**

Why is CrO named using a Roman numeral, chromium(II) oxide, whereas CaO is named without a Roman numeral in the name, calcium oxide?

2. *Negative Ions (Anions)*

(a) *The names of monatomic anions are formed by replacing the ending of the name of the element with -ide:*

H^{-} hydride ion O^{2-} oxide ion N^{3-} nitride ion

A few simple polyatomic anions also have names ending in *-ide*:

OH^{-} hydroxide ion CN^{-} cyanide ion O_2^{2-} peroxide ion

TABLE 2.4   Common Cations*

Charge	Formula	Name	Formula	Name
1+	H^+	**Hydrogen ion**	NH_4^+	**Ammonium ion**
	Li^+	Lithium ion	Cu^+	Copper(I) or cuprous ion
	Na^+	**Sodium ion**		
	K^+	**Potassium ion**		
	Cs^+	Cesium ion		
	Ag^+	**Silver ion**		
2+	Mg^{2+}	**Magnesium ion**	Co^{2+}	Cobalt(II) or cobaltous ion
	Ca^{2+}	**Calcium ion**	Cu^{2+}	**Copper(II) or cupric ion**
	Sr^{2+}	Strontium ion	Fe^{2+}	**Iron(II) or ferrous ion**
	Ba^{2+}	Barium ion	Mn^{2+}	Manganese(II) or manganous ion
	Zn^{2+}	**Zinc ion**	Hg_2^{2+}	Mercury(I) or mercurous ion
	Cd^{2+}	Cadmium ion	Hg^{2+}	**Mercury(II) or mercuric ion**
			Ni^{2+}	Nickel(II) or nickelous ion
			Pb^{2+}	**Lead(II) or plumbous ion**
			Sn^{2+}	Tin(II) or stannous ion
3+	Al^{3+}	**Aluminum ion**	Cr^{3+}	Chromium(III) or chromic ion
			Fe^{3+}	**Iron(III) or ferric ion**

*The most common ions are in boldface.

ACTIVITY
Polyatomic Ions

(b) *Polyatomic anions containing oxygen have names ending in -ate or -ite.* These anions are called **oxyanions**. The ending *-ate* is used for the most common oxyanion of an element. The ending *-ite* is used for an oxyanion that has the same charge but one O atom fewer:

NO_3^- nitrate ion SO_4^{2-} sulfate ion

NO_2^- nitrite ion SO_3^{2-} sulfite ion

Prefixes are used when the series of oxyanions of an element extends to four members, as with the halogens. The prefix *per-* indicates one more O atom than the oxyanion ending in *-ate*; the prefix *hypo-* indicates one O atom fewer than the oxyanion ending in *-ite*:

ClO_4^- perchlorate ion (one more O atom than chlorate)

ClO_3^- **chlorate ion**

ClO_2^- chlorite ion (one O atom fewer than chlorate)

ClO^- hypochlorite ion (one O atom fewer than chlorite)

These rules are summarized in Figure 2.26 ▼.

▼ **Figure 2.26   Summary of the procedure for naming anions.** The root of the name (such as "chlor" for chlorine) goes in the blank.

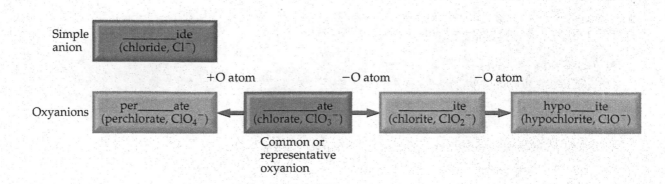

	4A	5A	6A	7A
2	$CO_3{}^{2-}$ Carbonate ion	$NO_3{}^-$ Nitrate ion		
3		$PO_4{}^{3-}$ Phosphate ion	$SO_4{}^{2-}$ Sulfate ion	$ClO_4{}^-$ Perchlorate ion

◀ **Figure 2.27 Common oxyanions.** The composition and charges of common oxyanions are related to their location in the periodic table.

 GIVE IT SOME THOUGHT

What information is conveyed by the endings *-ide*, *-ate*, and *-ite* in the name of an anion?

Students often have a hard time remembering the number of oxygen atoms in the various oxyanions and the charges of these ions. Figure 2.27 ▲ lists the oxyanions of C, N, P, S, and Cl that contain the maximum number of O atoms. There is a periodic pattern to these formulas that can help you remember them. Notice that C and N, which are in the second period of the periodic table, have only three O atoms each, whereas P, S, and Cl, which are in the third period, have four O atoms each. If we begin at the lower right side of the figure, with Cl, we see that the charges increase from right to left, from 1− for Cl ($ClO_4{}^-$) to 3− for P ($PO_4{}^{3-}$). In the second period the charges also increase from right to left, from 1− for N ($NO_3{}^-$) to 2− for C ($CO_3{}^{2-}$). Each anion shown in Figure 2.27 has a name ending in *-ate*. The $ClO_4{}^-$ ion also has a *per-* prefix. If you know the rules summarized in Figure 2.26 and the names and formulas of the five oxyanions in Figure 2.27, you can deduce the names for the other oxyanions of these elements.

 GIVE IT SOME THOUGHT

Predict the formulas for the borate ion and silicate ion, assuming that they contain a single B and Si atom, respectively, and follow the trends shown in Figure 2.27.

SAMPLE EXERCISE 2.11 | Determining the Formula of an Oxyanion from Its Name

Based on the formula for the sulfate ion, predict the formula for **(a)** the selenate ion and **(b)** the selenite ion. (Sulfur and selenium are both members of group 6A and form analogous oxyanions.)

Solution (a) The sulfate ion is $SO_4{}^{2-}$. The analogous selenate ion is therefore $SeO_4{}^{2-}$.
    (b) The ending *-ite* indicates an oxyanion with the same charge but one O atom fewer than the corresponding oxyanion that ends in *-ate*. Thus, the formula for the selenite ion is $SeO_3{}^{2-}$.

PRACTICE EXERCISE

The formula for the bromate ion is analogous to that for the chlorate ion. Write the formula for the hypobromite and perbromate ions.
Answer: BrO^- and $BrO_4{}^-$

(c) *Anions derived by adding H^+ to an oxyanion are named by adding as a prefix the word* hydrogen *or* dihydrogen, *as appropriate:*

$CO_3{}^{2-}$ carbonate ion $PO_4{}^{3-}$ phosphate ion

$HCO_3{}^-$ hydrogen carbonate ion $H_2PO_4{}^-$ dihydrogen phosphate ion

Notice that each H^+ reduces the negative charge of the parent anion by one. An older method for naming some of these ions is to use the prefix *bi-*. Thus, the $HCO_3{}^-$ ion is commonly called the bicarbonate ion, and $HSO_4{}^-$ is sometimes called the bisulfate ion.

Science Fundamentals Second Edition

TABLE 2.5   Common Anions*

Charge	Formula	Name	Formula	Name
1−	H^-	Hydride ion	$C_2H_3O_2^-$	Acetate ion
	F^-	**Fluoride ion**	ClO_3^-	Chlorate ion
	Cl^-	**Chloride ion**	ClO_4^-	**Perchlorate ion**
	Br^-	**Bromide ion**	NO_3^-	**Nitrate ion**
	I^-	**Iodide ion**	MnO_4^-	Permanganate ion
	CN^-	Cyanide ion		
	OH^-	**Hydroxide ion**		
2−	O^{2-}	**Oxide ion**	CO_3^{2-}	**Carbonate ion**
	O_2^{2-}	Peroxide ion	CrO_4^{2-}	Chromate ion
	S^{2-}	**Sulfide ion**	$Cr_2O_7^{2-}$	Dichromate ion
			SO_4^{2-}	**Sulfate ion**
3−	N^{3-}	Nitride ion	PO_4^{3-}	**Phosphate ion**

*The most common ions are in boldface.

The names and formulas of the common anions are listed in Table 2.5 ▲ and on the back inside cover of the text. Those anions whose names end in -*ide* are listed on the left portion of Table 2.5, and those whose names end in -*ate* are listed on the right. The most common of these ions are shown in boldface. These are the ones you should learn first. The formulas of the ions whose names end with -*ite* can be derived from those ending in -*ate* by removing an O atom. Notice the location of the monatomic ions in the periodic table. Those of group 7A always have a 1− charge (F^-, Cl^-, Br^-, and I^-), and those of group 6A have a 2− charge (O^{2-} and S^{2-}).

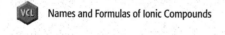

Names and Formulas of Ionic Compounds

3. *Ionic Compounds*

Names of ionic compounds consist of the cation name followed by the anion name:

$CaCl_2$	calcium chloride
$Al(NO_3)_3$	aluminum nitrate
$Cu(ClO_4)_2$	copper(II) perchlorate (or cupric perchlorate)

ACTIVITY
Ionic Compounds

In the chemical formulas for aluminum nitrate and copper(II) perchlorate, parentheses followed by the appropriate subscript are used because the compounds contain two or more polyatomic ions.

SAMPLE EXERCISE 2.12 | Determining the Names of Ionic Compounds from Their Formulas

Name the following compounds: **(a)** K_2SO_4, **(b)** $Ba(OH)_2$, **(c)** $FeCl_3$.

Solution Each compound is ionic and is named using the guidelines we have already discussed. In naming ionic compounds, it is important to recognize polyatomic ions and to determine the charge of cations with variable charge. **(a)** The cation in this compound is K^+, and the anion is SO_4^{2-}. (If you thought the compound contained S^{2-} and O^{2-} ions, you failed to recognize the polyatomic sulfate ion.) Putting together the names of the ions, we have the name of the compound, potassium sulfate. **(b)** In this case the compound is composed of Ba^{2+} and OH^- ions. Ba^{2+} is the barium ion and OH^- is the hydroxide ion. Thus, the compound is called barium hydroxide. **(c)** You must determine the charge of Fe in this compound because an iron atom can form more than one cation. Because the compound contains three Cl^- ions, the cation must be Fe^{3+}, which is the iron(III), or ferric, ion. The Cl^- ion is the chloride ion. Thus, the compound is iron(III) chloride or ferric chloride.

Science Fundamentals Second Edition

PRACTICE EXERCISE

Name the following compounds: (a) NH_4Br, (b) Cr_2O_3, (c) $Co(NO_3)_2$.
Answers: (a) ammonium bromide, (b) chromium(III) oxide, (c) cobalt(II) nitrate

SAMPLE EXERCISE 2.13 | Determining the Formulas of Ionic Compounds from Their Names

Write the chemical formulas for the following compounds: (a) potassium sulfide, (b) calcium hydrogen carbonate, (c) nickel(II) perchlorate.

Solution In going from the name of an ionic compound to its chemical formula, you must know the charges of the ions to determine the subscripts. (a) The potassium ion is K^+, and the sulfide ion is S^{2-}. Because ionic compounds are electrically neutral, two K^+ ions are required to balance the charge of one S^{2-} ion, giving the empirical formula of the compound, K_2S. (b) The calcium ion is Ca^{2+}. The carbonate ion is CO_3^{2-}, so the hydrogen carbonate ion is HCO_3^-. Two HCO_3^- ions are needed to balance the positive charge of Ca^{2+}, giving $Ca(HCO_3)_2$. (c) The nickel(II) ion is Ni^{2+}. The perchlorate ion is ClO_4^-. Two ClO_4^- ions are required to balance the charge on one Ni^{2+} ion, giving $Ni(ClO_4)_2$.

PRACTICE EXERCISE

Give the chemical formula for (a) magnesium sulfate, (b) silver sulfide, (c) lead(II) nitrate.
Answers: (a) $MgSO_4$, (b) Ag_2S, (c) $Pb(NO_3)_2$

Names and Formulas of Acids

Acids are an important class of hydrogen-containing compounds and are named in a special way. For our present purposes, an *acid* is a substance whose molecules yield hydrogen ions (H^+) when dissolved in water. When we encounter the chemical formula for an acid at this stage of the course, it will be written with H as the first element, as in HCl and H_2SO_4.

We can consider an acid to be composed of an anion connected to enough H^+ ions to neutralize, or balance, the anion's charge. Thus, the SO_4^{2-} ion requires two H^+ ions, forming H_2SO_4. The name of an acid is related to the name of its anion, as summarized in Figure 2.28 ▼.

1. *Acids containing anions whose names end in -ide are named by changing the -ide ending to -ic, adding the prefix* hydro- *to this anion name, and then following with the word* acid, *as in the following examples:*

Anion	Corresponding Acid
Cl^- (chloride)	HCl (hydrochloric acid)
S^{2-} (sulfide)	H_2S (hydrosulfuric acid)

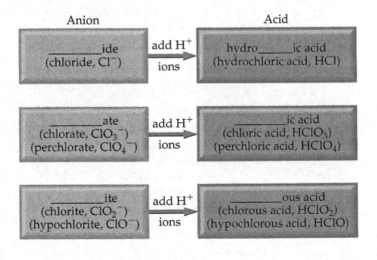

◀ **Figure 2.28 Relating names of anions and acids.** Summary of the way in which anion names and acid names are related. The prefixes *per-* and *hypo-* are retained in going from the anion to the acid.

Science Fundamentals Second Edition

2. *Acids containing anions whose names end in* -ate *or* -ite *are named by changing* -ate *to* -ic *and* -ite *to* -ous, *and then adding the word* acid. Prefixes in the anion name are retained in the name of the acid. These rules are illustrated by the oxyacids of chlorine:

Anion	Corresponding Acid
ClO_4^- (perchlorate)	$HClO_4$ (perchloric acid)
ClO_3^- (chlorate)	$HClO_3$ (chloric acid)
ClO_2^- (chlorite)	$HClO_2$ (chlorous acid)
ClO^- (hypochlorite)	$HClO$ (hypochlorous acid)

SAMPLE EXERCISE 2.14 | Relating the Names and Formulas of Acids

Name the following acids: **(a)** HCN, **(b)** HNO_3, **(c)** H_2SO_4, **(d)** H_2SO_3.

Solution **(a)** The anion from which this acid is derived is CN^-, the cyanide ion. Because this ion has an *-ide* ending, the acid is given a *hydro-* prefix and an *-ic* ending: hydrocyanic acid. Only water solutions of HCN are referred to as hydrocyanic acid: The pure compound, which is a gas under normal conditions, is called hydrogen cyanide. Both hydrocyanic acid and hydrogen cyanide are *extremely* toxic. **(b)** Because NO_3^- is the nitrate ion, HNO_3 is called nitric acid (the *-ate* ending of the anion is replaced with an *-ic* ending in naming the acid). **(c)** Because SO_4^{2-} is the sulfate ion, H_2SO_4 is called sulfuric acid. **(d)** Because SO_3^{2-} is the sulfite ion, H_2SO_3 is sulfurous acid (the *-ite* ending of the anion is replaced with an *-ous* ending).

PRACTICE EXERCISE

Give the chemical formulas for **(a)** hydrobromic acid, **(b)** carbonic acid.
Answers: **(a)** HBr, **(b)** H_2CO_3

Names and Formulas of Binary Molecular Compounds

The procedures used for naming *binary* (two-element) molecular compounds are similar to those used for naming ionic compounds:

1. *The name of the element farther to the left in the periodic table is usually written first.* An exception to this rule occurs in the case of compounds that contain oxygen. Oxygen is always written last except when combined with fluorine.

2. *If both elements are in the same group in the periodic table, the one having the higher atomic number is named first.*

3. *The name of the second element is given an* -ide *ending.*

4. *Greek prefixes (Table 2.6 ◄) are used to indicate the number of atoms of each element.* The prefix *mono-* is never used with the first element. When the prefix ends in *a* or *o* and the name of the second element begins with a vowel (such as *oxide*), the *a* or *o* of the prefix is often dropped.

The following examples illustrate these rules:

Cl_2O	dichlorine monoxide	NF_3	nitrogen trifluoride
N_2O_4	dinitrogen tetroxide	P_4S_{10}	tetraphosphorus decasulfide

It is important to realize that you cannot predict the formulas of most molecular substances in the same way that you predict the formulas of ionic compounds. That is why we name molecular compounds using prefixes that explicitly indicate their composition. Molecular compounds that contain hydrogen and one other element are an important exception, however. These compounds can be treated as if they were neutral substances containing H^+ ions and anions. Thus, you can predict that the substance whose name is hydrogen chloride has the formula HCl, containing one H^+ to balance the charge of one Cl^-.

TABLE 2.6 Prefixes Used in Naming Binary Compounds Formed Between Nonmetals

Prefix	Meaning
Mono-	1
Di-	2
Tri-	3
Tetra-	4
Penta-	5
Hexa-	6
Hepta-	7
Octa-	8
Nona-	9
Deca-	10

(The name hydrogen chloride is used only for the pure compound; water solutions of HCl are called hydrochloric acid.) Similarly, the formula for hydrogen sulfide is H_2S because two H^+ are needed to balance the charge on S^{2-}.

■ **SAMPLE EXERCISE 2.15** | Relating the Names and Formulas of Binary Molecular Compounds

Name the following compounds: **(a)** SO_2, **(b)** PCl_5, **(c)** N_2O_3.

Solution The compounds consist entirely of nonmetals, so they are probably molecular rather than ionic. Using the prefixes in Table 2.6, we have **(a)** sulfur dioxide, **(b)** phosphorus pentachloride, and **(c)** dinitrogen trioxide.

■ **PRACTICE EXERCISE**

Give the chemical formula for **(a)** silicon tetrabromide, **(b)** disulfur dichloride. *Answers:* **(a)** $SiBr_4$, **(b)** S_2Cl_2

2.9 | Some Simple Organic Compounds

The study of compounds of carbon is called **organic chemistry**, and, as noted earlier in the chapter, compounds that contain carbon and hydrogen, often in combination with oxygen, nitrogen, or other elements, are called *organic compounds*. We will examine organic compounds and organic chemistry in some detail in Chapter 25. You will see a number of organic compounds throughout this text; many of them have practical applications or are relevant to the chemistry of biological systems. Here we present a very brief introduction to some of the simplest organic compounds so as to provide you with a sense of what these molecules look like and how they are named.

Alkanes

Compounds that contain only carbon and hydrogen are called **hydrocarbons**. In the most basic class of hydrocarbons, each carbon atom is bonded to four other atoms. These compounds are called **alkanes**. The three simplest alkanes, which contain one, two, and three carbon atoms, respectively, are methane (CH_4), ethane (C_2H_6), and propane (C_3H_8). The structural formulas of these three alkanes are as follows:

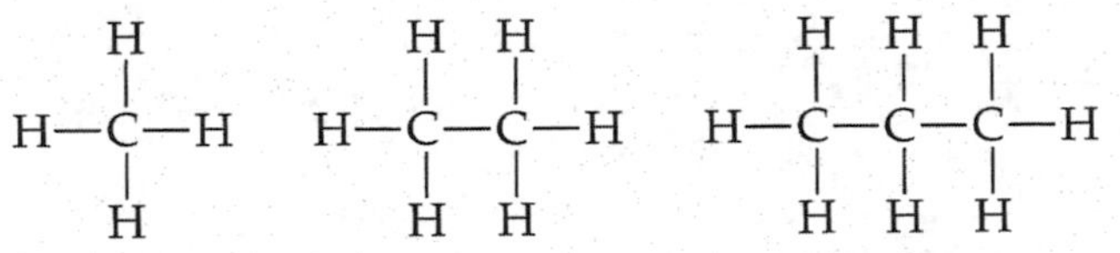

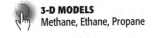

Methane   Ethane   Propane

3-D MODELS
Methane, Ethane, Propane

Longer alkanes can be made by adding additional carbon atoms to the "skeleton" of the molecule.

Although the hydrocarbons are binary molecular compounds, they are not named like the inorganic binary compounds discussed in Section 2.8. Instead, each alkane has a name that ends in *-ane*. For alkanes with five or more carbon atoms, the names are derived from prefixes like those in Table 2.6. An alkane with eight carbon atoms, for example, is called *octane* (C_8H_{18}), where the *octa-* prefix for eight is combined with the *-ane* ending for an alkane. Gasoline consists primarily of octanes, as will be discussed in Chapter 25.

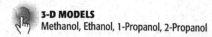

Some Derivatives of Alkanes

Other classes of organic compounds are obtained when hydrogen atoms of alkanes are replaced with *functional groups*, which are specific groups of atoms. An **alcohol**, for example, is obtained by replacing an H atom of an alkane with an —OH group. The name of the alcohol is derived from that of the alkane by adding an *-ol* ending:

$$
\begin{array}{ccc}
\underset{\displaystyle \text{Methanol}}{\text{H}-\overset{\displaystyle \text{H}}{\underset{\displaystyle \text{H}}{\text{C}}}-\text{OH}}
&
\underset{\displaystyle \text{Ethanol}}{\text{H}-\overset{\displaystyle \text{H}}{\underset{\displaystyle \text{H}}{\text{C}}}-\overset{\displaystyle \text{H}}{\underset{\displaystyle \text{H}}{\text{C}}}-\text{OH}}
&
\underset{\displaystyle \text{1-Propanol}}{\text{H}-\overset{\displaystyle \text{H}}{\underset{\displaystyle \text{H}}{\text{C}}}-\overset{\displaystyle \text{H}}{\underset{\displaystyle \text{H}}{\text{C}}}-\overset{\displaystyle \text{H}}{\underset{\displaystyle \text{H}}{\text{C}}}-\text{OH}}
\end{array}
$$

Alcohols have properties that are very different from the properties of the alkanes from which the alcohols are obtained. For example, methane, ethane, and propane are all colorless gases under normal conditions, whereas methanol, ethanol, and propanol are colorless liquids. We will discuss the reasons for these differences in properties in Chapter 11.

The prefix "1" in the name 1-propanol indicates that the replacement of H with OH has occurred at one of the "outer" carbon atoms rather than the "middle" carbon atom. A different compound called 2-propanol (also known as isopropyl alcohol) is obtained if the OH functional group is attached to the middle carbon atom:

$$
\begin{array}{cc}
\underset{\displaystyle \text{1-Propanol}}{\text{H}-\overset{\displaystyle \text{H}}{\underset{\displaystyle \text{H}}{\text{C}}}-\overset{\displaystyle \text{H}}{\underset{\displaystyle \text{H}}{\text{C}}}-\overset{\displaystyle \text{H}}{\underset{\displaystyle \text{H}}{\text{C}}}-\text{OH}}
&
\underset{\displaystyle \text{2-Propanol}}{\text{H}-\overset{\displaystyle \text{H}}{\underset{\displaystyle \text{H}}{\text{C}}}-\overset{\displaystyle \text{H}}{\underset{\displaystyle \text{O}-\text{H}}{\text{C}}}-\overset{\displaystyle \text{H}}{\underset{\displaystyle \text{H}}{\text{C}}}-\text{H}}
\end{array}
$$

Ball-and-stick models of these two molecules are presented in Figure 2.29 ◀.

Much of the richness of organic chemistry is possible because organic compounds can form long chains of carbon–carbon bonds. The series of alkanes that begins with methane, ethane, and propane and the series of alcohols that begins with methanol, ethanol, and propanol can both be extended for as long as we desire, in principle. The properties of alkanes and alcohols change as the chains get longer. Octanes, which are alkanes with eight carbon atoms, are liquids under normal conditions. If the alkane series is extended to tens of thousands of carbon atoms, we obtain *polyethylene*, a solid substance that is used to make thousands of plastic products, such as plastic bags, food containers, and laboratory equipment.

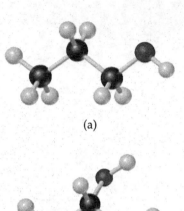

(a)

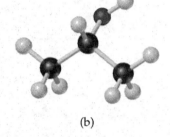

(b)

▲ **Figure 2.29 The two forms of propanol (C_3H_7OH).** (a) 1-Propanol, in which the OH group is attached to one of the end carbon atoms, and (b) 2-propanol, in which the OH group is attached to the middle carbon atom.

SAMPLE EXERCISE 2.16 | Writing Structural and Molecular Formulas for Hydrocarbons

Consider the alkane called *pentane*. **(a)** Assuming that the carbon atoms are in a straight line, write a structural formula for pentane. **(b)** What is the molecular formula for pentane?

Solution (a) Alkanes contain only carbon and hydrogen, and each carbon atom is attached to four other atoms. Because the name pentane contains the prefix *penta-* for five (Table 2.6), we can assume that pentane contains five carbon atoms bonded in a chain. If we then add enough hydrogen atoms to make four bonds to each carbon atom, we obtain the following structural formula:

$$
\text{H}-\overset{\displaystyle \text{H}}{\underset{\displaystyle \text{H}}{\text{C}}}-\overset{\displaystyle \text{H}}{\underset{\displaystyle \text{H}}{\text{C}}}-\overset{\displaystyle \text{H}}{\underset{\displaystyle \text{H}}{\text{C}}}-\overset{\displaystyle \text{H}}{\underset{\displaystyle \text{H}}{\text{C}}}-\overset{\displaystyle \text{H}}{\underset{\displaystyle \text{H}}{\text{C}}}-\text{H}
$$

This form of pentane is often called *n*-pentane, where the *n*- stands for "normal" because all five carbon atoms are in one line in the structural formula.

(b) Once the structural formula is written, we can determine the molecular formula by counting the atoms present. Thus, *n*-pentane has the formula C_5H_{12}.

■ PRACTICE EXERCISE

Butane is the alkane with four carbon atoms. (a) What is the molecular formula of butane? (b) What are the name and molecular formula of an alcohol derived from butane?
Answers: (a) C_4H_{10}, (b) butanol, $C_4H_{10}O$ or C_4H_9OH

SUMMARY AND KEY TERMS

Sections 2.1 and 2.2 Atoms are the basic building blocks of matter; they are the smallest units of an element that can combine with other elements. Atoms are composed of even smaller particles, called **subatomic particles**. Some of these subatomic particles are charged and follow the usual behavior of charged particles: Particles with the same charge repel one another, whereas particles with unlike charges are attracted to one another. We considered some of the important experiments that led to the discovery and characterization of subatomic particles. Thomson's experiments on the behavior of **cathode rays** in magnetic and electric fields led to the discovery of the electron and allowed its charge-to-mass ratio to be measured. Millikan's oil-drop experiment determined the charge of the electron. Becquerel's discovery of **radioactivity**, the spontaneous emission of radiation by atoms, gave further evidence that the atom has a substructure. Rutherford's studies of how thin metal foils scatter α particles showed that the atom has a dense, positively charged **nucleus**.

Section 2.3 Atoms have a nucleus that contains **protons** and **neutrons**; **electrons** move in the space around the nucleus. The magnitude of the charge of the electron, 1.602×10^{-19} C, is called the **electronic charge**. The charges of particles are usually represented as multiples of this charge; thus, an electron has a $1-$ charge, and a proton has a $1+$ charge. The masses of atoms are usually expressed in terms of **atomic mass units** (1 amu = 1.66054×10^{-24} g). The dimensions of atoms are often expressed in units of **angstroms** (1 Å = 10^{-10} m).

Elements can be classified by **atomic number**, the number of protons in the nucleus of an atom. All atoms of a given element have the same atomic number. The **mass number** of an atom is the sum of the numbers of protons and neutrons. Atoms of the same element that differ in mass number are known as **isotopes**.

Section 2.4 The atomic mass scale is defined by assigning a mass of exactly 12 amu to a ^{12}C atom. The **atomic weight** (average atomic mass) of an element can be calculated from the relative abundances and masses of that element's isotopes. The **mass spectrometer** provides the most direct and accurate means of experimentally measuring atomic (and molecular) weights.

Section 2.5 The **periodic table** is an arrangement of the elements in order of increasing atomic number. Elements with similar properties are placed in vertical columns. The elements in a column are known as a periodic **group**. The elements in a horizontal row are known as a **period**. The **metallic elements (metals)**, which comprise the majority of the elements, dominate the left side and the middle of the table; the **nonmetallic elements (nonmetals)** are located on the upper right side. Many of the elements that lie along the line that separates metals from nonmetals are **metalloids**.

Section 2.6 Atoms can combine to form **molecules**. Compounds composed of molecules (**molecular compounds**) usually contain only nonmetallic elements. A molecule that contains two atoms is called a **diatomic molecule**. The composition of a substance is given by its **chemical formula**. A molecular substance can be represented by its **empirical formula**, which gives the relative numbers of atoms of each kind. It is usually represented by its **molecular formula**, however, which gives the actual numbers of each type of atom in a molecule. **Structural formulas** show the order in which the atoms in a molecule are connected. Ball-and-stick models and space-filling models are often used to represent molecules.

Section 2.7 Atoms can either gain or lose electrons, forming charged particles called **ions**. Metals tend to lose electrons, becoming positively charged ions (**cations**). Nonmetals tend to gain electrons, forming negatively charged ions (**anions**). Because **ionic compounds** are electrically neutral, containing both cations and anions, they usually contain both metallic and nonmetallic elements. Atoms that are joined together, as in a molecule, but carry a net charge are called **polyatomic ions**. The chemical formulas used for ionic compounds are empirical formulas, which can be written readily if the charges of the ions are known. The total positive charge of the cations in an ionic compound equals the total negative charge of the anions.

Science Fundamentals Second Edition

Section 2.8 The set of rules for naming chemical compounds is called **chemical nomenclature**. We studied the systematic rules used for naming three classes of inorganic substances: ionic compounds, acids, and binary molecular compounds. In naming an ionic compound, the cation is named first and then the anion. Cations formed from metal atoms have the same name as the metal. If the metal can form cations of differing charges, the charge is given using Roman numerals. Monatomic anions have names ending in -ide. Polyatomic anions containing oxygen and another element (**oxyanions**) have names ending in -ate or -ite.

Section 2.9 **Organic chemistry** is the study of compounds that contain carbon. The simplest class of organic molecules are the **hydrocarbons**, which contain only carbon and hydrogen. Hydrocarbons in which each carbon atom is attached to four other atoms are called **alkanes**. Alkanes have names that end in -ane, such as methane and ethane. Other organic compounds are formed when an H atom of a hydrocarbon is replaced with a functional group. An **alcohol**, for example, is a compound in which an H atom of a hydrocarbon is replaced by an OH functional group. Alcohols have names that end in -ol, such as methanol and ethanol.

VISUALIZING CONCEPTS

2.1 A charged particle is caused to move between two electrically charged plates, as shown below.

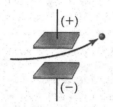

(a) Why does the path of the charged particle bend? **(b)** What is the sign of the electrical charge on the particle? **(c)** As the charge on the plates is increased, would you expect the bending to increase, decrease, or stay the same? **(d)** As the mass of the particle is increased while the speed of the particles remains the same, would you expect the bending to increase, decrease, or stay the same? [Section 2.2]

2.2 Four of the boxes in the following periodic table are colored. Which of these are metals and which are nonmetals? Which one is an alkaline earth metal? Which one is a noble gas? [Section 2.5]

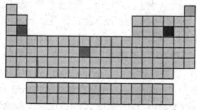

2.3 Does the following drawing represent a neutral atom or an ion? Write its complete chemical symbol including mass number, atomic number, and net charge (if any). [Sections 2.3 and 2.7]

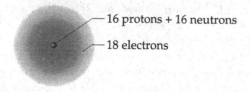

16 protons + 16 neutrons

18 electrons

2.4 Which of the following diagrams is most likely to represent an ionic compound, and which a molecular one? Explain your choice. [Sections 2.6 and 2.7]

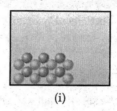 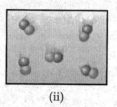

(i)   (ii)

2.5 Write the chemical formula for the following compound. Is the compound ionic or molecular? Name the compound. [Sections 2.6 and 2.8]

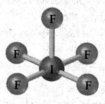

2.6 The following diagram represents an ionic compound in which the cations are indicated by the red spheres and the anions are indicated by the blue spheres. Which of the following formulas is consistent with the drawing: KBr, K_2SO_4, $Ca(NO_3)_2$, $Fe_2(SO_4)_3$? Name the compound. [Sections 2.7 and 2.8]

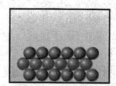

EXERCISES

Atomic Theory and the Discovery of Atomic Structure

2.7 How does Dalton's atomic theory account for the fact that when 1.000 g of water is decomposed into its elements, 0.111 g of hydrogen and 0.889 g of oxygen are obtained regardless of the source of the water?

2.8 Hydrogen sulfide is composed of two elements: hydrogen and sulfur. In an experiment, 6.500 g of hydrogen sulfide is fully decomposed into its elements. **(a)** If 0.384 g of hydrogen is obtained in this experiment, how many grams of sulfur must be obtained? **(b)** What fundamental law does this experiment demonstrate? **(c)** How is this law explained by Dalton's atomic theory?

2.9 A chemist finds that 30.82 g of nitrogen will react with 17.60 g, 35.20 g, 70.40 g, or 88.00 g of oxygen to form four different compounds. **(a)** Calculate the mass of oxygen per gram of nitrogen in each compound. **(b)** How do the numbers in part (a) support Dalton's atomic theory?

2.10 In a series of experiments, a chemist prepared three different compounds that contain only iodine and fluorine and determined the mass of each element in each compound:

Compound	Mass of Iodine (g)	Mass of Fluorine (g)
1	4.75	3.56
2	7.64	3.43
3	9.41	9.86

(a) Calculate the mass of fluorine per gram of iodine in each compound. **(b)** How do the numbers in part (a) support the atomic theory?

2.11 Summarize the evidence used by J. J. Thomson to argue that cathode rays consist of negatively charged particles.

2.12 An unknown particle is caused to move between two electrically charged plates, as illustrated in Figure 2.8. Its path is deflected in the opposite direction from that of a beta particle, and it is deflected by a smaller magnitude. What can you conclude about the charge and mass of this unknown particle?

2.13 **(a)** Figure 2.5 shows the apparatus used in the Millikan oil-drop experiment with the positively charged plate above the negatively charged plate. What do you think would be the effect on the rate of oil drops descending if the charges on the plates were reversed (negative above positive)? **(b)** In his original series of experiments, Millikan measured the charge on 58 separate oil drops. Why do you suppose he chose so many drops before reaching his final conclusions?

2.14 Millikan determined the charge on the electron by studying the static charges on oil drops falling in an electric field. A student carried out this experiment using several oil drops for her measurements and calculated the charges on the drops. She obtained the following data:

Droplet	Calculated Charge (C)
A	1.60×10^{-19}
B	3.15×10^{-19}
C	4.81×10^{-19}
D	6.31×10^{-19}

(a) What is the significance of the fact that the droplets carried different charges? **(b)** What conclusion can the student draw from these data regarding the charge of the electron? **(c)** What value (and to how many significant figures) should she report for the electronic charge?

Modern View of Atomic Structure; Atomic Weights

2.15 The radius of an atom of krypton (Kr) is about 1.9 Å. **(a)** Express this distance in nanometers (nm) and in picometers (pm). **(b)** How many krypton atoms would have to be lined up to span 1.0 mm? **(c)** If the atom is assumed to be a sphere, what is the volume in cm^3 of a single Kr atom?

2.16 An atom of tin (Sn) has a diameter of about 2.8×10^{-8} cm. **(a)** What is the radius of a tin atom in angstroms (Å) and in meters (m)? **(b)** How many Sn atoms would have to be placed side by side to span a distance of 6.0 μm? **(c)** If the atom is assumed to be a sphere, what is the volume in m^3 of a single Sn atom?

2.17 Answer the following questions without referring to Table 2.1: **(a)** What are the main subatomic particles that make up the atom? **(b)** What is the charge, in units of the electronic charge, of each of the particles? **(c)** Which of the particles is the most massive? Which is the least massive?

2.18 Determine whether each of the following statements is true or false; if false, correct the statement to make it true: **(a)** The nucleus has most of the mass and comprises most of the volume of an atom; **(b)** every atom of a given element has the same number of protons; **(c)** the number of electrons in an atom equals the number of neutrons in the atom; **(d)** the protons in the nucleus of the helium atom are held together by a force called the strong nuclear force.

2.19 **(a)** Define atomic number and mass number. **(b)** Which of these can vary without changing the identity of the element?

2.20 **(a)** Which two of the following are isotopes of the same element: $^{31}_{16}X$, $^{31}_{15}X$, $^{32}_{16}X$? **(b)** What is the identity of the element whose isotopes you have selected?

2.21 How many protons, neutrons, and electrons are in the following atoms: **(a)** ^{40}Ar, **(b)** ^{65}Zn, **(c)** ^{70}Ga, **(d)** ^{80}Br, **(e)** ^{184}W, **(f)** ^{243}Am.

2.22 Each of the following isotopes is used in medicine. Indicate the number of protons and neutrons in each isotope: **(a)** phosphorus-32, **(b)** chromium-51, **(c)** cobalt-60, **(d)** technetium-99, **(e)** iodine-131; **(f)** thallium-201.

2.23 Fill in the gaps in the following table, assuming each column represents a neutral atom:

Symbol	^{52}Cr				
Protons		25			82
Neutrons		30	64		
Electrons			48	86	
Mass no.				222	207

2.24 Fill in the gaps in the following table, assuming each column represents a neutral atom:

Symbol	^{121}Sb				
Protons		45			94
Neutrons		58	50		
Electrons			38	52	
Mass no.				127	239

2.25 Write the correct symbol, with both superscript and subscript, for each of the following. Use the list of elements on the front inside cover as needed: **(a)** the isotope of platinum that contains 118 neutrons, **(b)** the isotope of krypton with mass number 84, **(c)** the isotope of arsenic with mass number 75, **(d)** the isotope of magnesium that has an equal number of protons and neutrons.

2.26 One way in which Earth's evolution as a planet can be understood is by measuring the amounts of certain isotopes in rocks. One quantity recently measured is the ratio of ^{129}Xe to ^{130}Xe in some minerals. In what way do these two isotopes differ from one another, and in what respects are they the same?

2.27 **(a)** What isotope is used as the standard in establishing the atomic mass scale? **(b)** The atomic weight of boron is reported as 10.81, yet no atom of boron has the mass of 10.81 amu. Explain.

2.28 **(a)** What is the mass in amu of a carbon-12 atom? **(b)** Why is the atomic weight of carbon reported as 12.011 in the table of elements and the periodic table in the front inside cover of this text?

2.29 Only two isotopes of copper occur naturally, ^{63}Cu (atomic mass = 62.9296 amu; abundance 69.17%) and ^{65}Cu (atomic mass = 64.9278 amu; abundance 30.83%). Calculate the atomic weight (average atomic mass) of copper.

2.30 The element lead (Pb) consists of four naturally occurring isotopes with atomic masses 203.97302, 205.97444, 206.97587, and 207.97663 amu. The relative abundances of these four isotopes are 1.4, 24.1, 22.1, and 52.4%, respectively. From these data, calculate the atomic weight of lead.

2.31 **(a)** In what fundamental way is mass spectrometry related to Thomson's cathode-ray experiments (Figure 2.4)? **(b)** What are the labels on the axes of a mass spectrum? **(c)** In order to measure the mass spectrum of an atom, the atom must first lose or gain one or more electrons. Why is this so?

2.32 **(a)** The mass spectrometer in Figure 2.13 has a magnet as one of its components. What is the purpose of the magnet? **(b)** The atomic weight of Cl is 35.5 amu. However, the mass spectrum of Cl (Figure 2.14) does not show a peak at this mass. Explain. **(c)** A mass spectrum of phosphorus (P) atoms shows only a single peak at a mass of 31. What can you conclude from this observation?

2.33 Naturally occurring magnesium has the following isotopic abundances:

Isotope	Abundance	Atomic mass (amu)
^{24}Mg	78.99%	23.98504
^{25}Mg	10.00%	24.98584
^{26}Mg	11.01%	25.98259

(a) What is the average atomic mass of Mg? **(b)** Sketch the mass spectrum of Mg.

2.34 Mass spectrometry is more often applied to molecules than to atoms. We will see in Chapter 3 that the *molecular weight* of a molecule is the sum of the atomic weights of the atoms in the molecule. The mass spectrum of H_2 is taken under conditions that prevent decomposition into H atoms. The two naturally occurring isotopes of hydrogen are ^{1}H (atomic mass = 1.00783 amu; abundance 99.9885%) and ^{2}H (atomic mass = 2.01410 amu; abundance 0.0115%). **(a)** How many peaks will the mass spectrum have? **(b)** Give the relative atomic masses of each of these peaks. **(c)** Which peak will be the largest, and which the smallest?

The Periodic Table; Molecules and Ions

2.35 For each of the following elements, write its chemical symbol, locate it in the periodic table, and indicate whether it is a metal, metalloid, or nonmetal: **(a)** chromium, **(b)** helium, **(c)** phosphorus, **(d)** zinc, **(e)** magnesium, **(f)** bromine, **(g)** arsenic.

2.36 Locate each of the following elements in the periodic table; indicate whether it is a metal, metalloid, or nonmetal; and give the name of the element: **(a)** Na, **(b)** Ti, **(c)** Ga, **(d)** U, **(e)** Pd, **(f)** Se, **(g)** Kr.

2.37 For each of the following elements, write its chemical symbol, determine the name of the group to which it belongs (Table 2.3), and indicate whether it is a metal, metalloid, or nonmetal: **(a)** potassium, **(b)** iodine, **(c)** magnesium, **(d)** argon, **(e)** sulfur.

2.38 The elements of group 4A show an interesting change in properties moving down the group. Give the name and chemical symbol of each element in the group, and label it as a nonmetal, metalloid, or metal.

2.39 What can we tell about a compound when we know the empirical formula? What additional information is conveyed by the molecular formula? By the structural formula? Explain in each case.

2.40 Two compounds have the same empirical formula. One substance is a gas, the other is a viscous liquid. How is it possible for two substances with the same empirical formula to have markedly different properties?

2.41 Write the empirical formula corresponding to each of the following molecular formulas: **(a)** Al_2Br_6, **(b)** C_8H_{10}, **(c)** $C_4H_8O_2$, **(d)** P_4O_{10}, **(e)** $C_6H_4Cl_2$, **(f)** $B_3N_3H_6$.

2.42 Determine the molecular and empirical formulas of the following: **(a)** The organic solvent *benzene*, which has six carbon atoms and six hydrogen atoms; **(b)** the compound *silicon tetrachloride*, which has a silicon atom and four chlorine atoms and is used in the manufacture of computer chips; **(c)** the reactive substance *diborane*, which has two boron atoms and six hydrogen atoms; **(d)** the sugar called *glucose*, which has six carbon atoms, twelve hydrogen atoms, and six oxygen atoms.

2.43 How many hydrogen atoms are in each of the following: **(a)** C_2H_5OH, **(b)** $Ca(CH_3COO)_2$, **(c)** $(NH_4)_3PO_4$?

2.44 How many of the indicated atoms are represented by each chemical formula: **(a)** carbon atoms in $C_2H_5COOCH_3$, **(b)** oxygen atoms in $Ca(ClO_3)_2$, **(c)** hydrogen atoms in $(NH_4)_2HPO_4$?

2.45 Write the molecular and structural formulas for the compounds represented by the following molecular models:

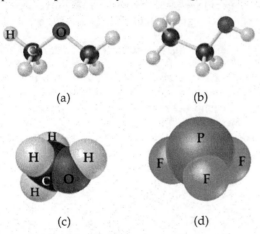

(a)   (b)

(c)   (d)

2.46 Write the molecular and structural formulas for the compounds represented by the following models:

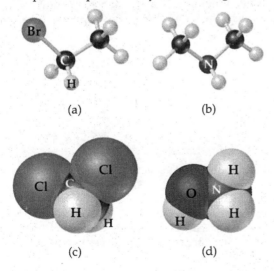

(a)   (b)

(c)   (d)

2.47 Fill in the gaps in the following table:

Symbol	$^{59}Co^{3+}$			
Protons		34	76	80
Neutrons		46	116	120
Electrons		36		78
Net charge			2+	

2.48 Fill in the gaps in the following table:

Symbol	$^{75}As^{3-}$			
Protons		28	53	
Neutrons		31	74	118
Electrons		26		76
Net charge			1−	3+

2.49 Each of the following elements is capable of forming an ion in chemical reactions. By referring to the periodic table, predict the charge of the most stable ion of each: **(a)** Mg, **(b)** Al, **(c)** K, **(d)** S, **(e)** F.

2.50 Using the periodic table, predict the charges of the ions of the following elements: **(a)** Sr, **(b)** Sc, **(c)** P, **(d)** I, **(e)** Se.

2.51 Using the periodic table to guide you, predict the chemical formula and name of the compound formed by the following elements: **(a)** Ga and F, **(b)** Li and H, **(c)** Al and I, **(d)** K and S.

2.52 The most common charge associated with silver in its compounds is 1+. Indicate the chemical formulas you would expect for compounds formed between Ag and **(a)** iodine, **(b)** sulfur, **(c)** fluorine.

2.53 Predict the chemical formula for the ionic compound formed by **(a)** Ca^{2+} and Br^-, **(b)** K^+ and CO_3^{2-}, **(c)** Al^{3+} and $C_2H_3O_2^-$, **(d)** NH_4^+ and SO_4^{2-}, **(e)** Mg^{2+} and PO_4^{3-}.

2.54 Predict the chemical formulas of the compounds formed by the following pairs of ions: **(a)** Cu^+ and S^{2-}, **(b)** Fe^{3+} and O^{2-}, **(c)** Hg_2^{2+} and CO_3^{2-}, **(d)** Ca^{2+} and AsO_4^{3-}, **(e)** NH_4^+ and CO_3^{2-}.

2.55 Predict whether each of the following compounds is molecular or ionic: **(a)** B_2H_6, **(b)** CH_3OH, **(c)** $LiNO_3$, **(d)** Sc_2O_3, **(e)** $CsBr$, **(f)** $NOCl$, **(g)** NF_3, **(h)** Ag_2SO_4.

2.56 Which of the following are ionic, and which are molecular? **(a)** PF_5, **(b)** NaI, **(c)** SCl_2, **(d)** $Ca(NO_3)_2$, **(e)** $FeCl_3$, **(f)** LaP, **(g)** $CoCO_3$, **(h)** N_2O_4.

Naming Inorganic Compounds; Organic Molecules

2.57 Give the chemical formula for (a) chlorite ion, (b) chloride ion, (c) chlorate ion, (d) perchlorate ion, (e) hypochlorite ion.

2.58 Selenium, an element required nutritionally in trace quantities, forms compounds analogous to sulfur. Name the following ions: (a) SeO_4^{2-}, (b) Se^{2-}, (c) HSe^-, (d) $HSeO_3^-$.

2.59 Name the following ionic compounds: (a) MgO, (b) $AlCl_3$, (c) Li_3PO_4, (d) $Ba(ClO_4)_2$, (e) $Cu(NO_3)_2$, (f) $Fe(OH)_2$, (g) $Ca(C_2H_3O_2)_2$, (h) $Cr_2(CO_3)_3$, (i) K_2CrO_4, (j) $(NH_4)_2SO_4$.

2.60 Name the following ionic compounds: (a) Li_2O, (b) NaClO, (c) $Sr(CN)_2$, (d) $Cr(OH)_3$, (e) $Fe_2(CO_3)_3$, (f) $Co(NO_3)_2$, (g) $(NH_4)_2SO_3$, (h) NaH_2PO_4, (i) $KMnO_4$, (j) $Ag_2Cr_2O_7$.

2.61 Write the chemical formulas for the following compounds: (a) aluminum hydroxide, (b) potassium sulfate, (c) copper(I) oxide, (d) zinc nitrate, (e) mercury(II) bromide, (f) iron(III) carbonate, (g) sodium hypobromite.

2.62 Give the chemical formula for each of the following ionic compounds: (a) sodium phosphate, (b) cobalt(II) nitrate, (c) barium bromate, (d) copper(II) perchlorate, (e) magnesium hydrogen carbonate, (f) chromium(III) acetate, (g) potassium dichromate.

2.63 Give the name or chemical formula, as appropriate, for each of the following acids: (a) $HBrO_3$, (b) HBr, (c) H_3PO_4, (d) hypochlorous acid, (e) iodic acid, (f) sulfurous acid.

2.64 Provide the name or chemical formula, as appropriate, for each of the following acids: (a) hydrobromic acid, (b) hydrosulfuric acid, (c) nitrous acid, (d) H_2CO_3, (e) $HClO_3$, (f) $HC_2H_3O_2$.

2.65 Give the name or chemical formula, as appropriate, for each of the following binary molecular substances: (a) SF_6, (b) IF_5, (c) XeO_3, (d) dinitrogen tetroxide, (e) hydrogen cyanide, (f) tetraphosphorus hexasulfide.

2.66 The oxides of nitrogen are very important ingredients in determining urban air pollution. Name each of the following compounds: (a) N_2O, (b) NO, (c) NO_2, (d) N_2O_5, (e) N_2O_4.

2.67 Write the chemical formula for each substance mentioned in the following word descriptions (use the front inside cover to find the symbols for the elements you don't know). (a) Zinc carbonate can be heated to form zinc oxide and carbon dioxide. (b) On treatment with hydrofluoric acid, silicon dioxide forms silicon tetrafluoride and water. (c) Sulfur dioxide reacts with water to form sulfurous acid. (d) The substance phosphorus trihydride, commonly called phosphine, is a toxic gas. (e) Perchloric acid reacts with cadmium to form cadmium(II) perchlorate. (f) Vanadium(III) bromide is a colored solid.

2.68 Assume that you encounter the following phrases in your reading. What is the chemical formula for each substance mentioned? (a) Sodium hydrogen carbonate is used as a deodorant. (b) Calcium hypochlorite is used in some bleaching solutions. (c) Hydrogen cyanide is a very poisonous gas. (d) Magnesium hydroxide is used as a cathartic. (e) Tin(II) fluoride has been used as a fluoride additive in toothpastes. (f) When cadmium sulfide is treated with sulfuric acid, fumes of hydrogen sulfide are given off.

2.69 (a) What is a hydrocarbon? (b) Butane is the alkane with a chain of four carbon atoms. Write a structural formula for this compound, and determine its molecular and empirical formulas.

2.70 (a) What ending is used for the names of alkanes? (b) Hexane is an alkane whose structural formula has all its carbon atoms in a straight chain. Draw the structural formula for this compound, and determine its molecular and empirical formulas. [*Hint:* You might need to refer to Table 2.6.]

2.71 (a) What is a functional group? (b) What functional group characterizes an alcohol? (c) With reference to Exercise 2.69, write a structural formula for 1-butanol, the alcohol derived from butane, by making a substitution on one of the end carbon atoms.

2.72 (a) What do ethane and ethanol have in common? (b) How does 1-propanol differ from propane?

Additional Exercises

2.73 Describe a major contribution to science made by each of the following scientists: (a) Dalton, (b) Thomson, (c) Millikan, (d) Rutherford.

2.74 What is radioactivity? Indicate whether you agree or disagree with the following statement, and indicate your reasons: Henri Becquerel's discovery of radioactivity shows that the atom is not indivisible, as had been believed for so long.

2.75 How did Rutherford interpret the following observations made during his α-particle scattering experiments? (a) Most α particles were not appreciably deflected as they passed through the gold foil. (b) A few α particles were deflected at very large angles. (c) What differences would you expect if beryllium foil were used instead of gold foil in the α-particle scattering experiment?

[2.76] Suppose a scientist repeats the Millikan oil-drop experiment, but reports the charges on the drops using an unusual (and imaginary) unit called the *warmomb* (wa). He obtains the following data for four of the drops:

Droplet	Calculated Charge (wa)
A	3.84×10^{-8}
B	4.80×10^{-8}
C	2.88×10^{-8}
D	8.64×10^{-8}

(a) If all the droplets were the same size, which would fall most slowly through the apparatus? (b) From these data, what is the best choice for the charge of the electron in warmombs? (c) Based on your answer to part (b), how many electrons are there on each of the droplets? (d) What is the conversion factor between warmombs and coulombs?

2.77 The natural abundance of ^{3}He is 0.000137%. **(a)** How many protons, neutrons, and electrons are in an atom of ^{3}He? **(b)** Based on the sum of the masses of their subatomic particles, which is expected to be more massive, an atom of ^{3}He or an atom of ^{3}H (which is also called *tritium*)? **(c)** Based on your answer for part (b), what would need to be the precision of a mass spectrometer that is able to differentiate between peaks that are due to ^{3}He$^+$ and ^{3}H$^+$?

[2.78] An α particle is the nucleus of an ^{4}He atom. **(a)** How many protons and neutrons are in an α particle? **(b)** What force holds the protons and neutrons together in the α particle? **(c)** What is the charge on an α particle in units of electronic charge? **(d)** The charge-to-mass ratio of an α particle is 4.8224×10^4 C/g. Based on the charge on the particle, calculate its mass in grams and in amu. **(e)** By using the data in Table 2.1, compare your answer for part (d) with the sum of the masses of the individual subatomic particles. Can you explain the difference in mass? (If not, we will discuss such mass differences further in Chapter 21.)

[2.79] A cube of gold that is 1.00 cm on a side has a mass of 19.3 g. A single gold atom has a mass of 197.0 amu. **(a)** How many gold atoms are in the cube? **(b)** From the information given, estimate the diameter in Å of a single gold atom. **(c)** What assumptions did you make in arriving at your answer for part (b)?

[2.80] The diameter of a rubidium atom is 4.95 Å. We will consider two different ways of placing the atoms on a surface. In arrangement A, all the atoms are lined up with one another. Arrangement B is called a *close-packed* arrangement because the atoms sit in the "depressions" formed by the previous row of atoms:

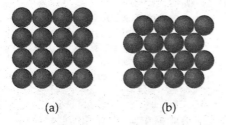

(a)   (b)

(a) Using arrangement A, how many Rb atoms could be placed on a square surface that is 1.0 cm on a side? **(b)** How many Rb atoms could be placed on a square surface that is 1.0 cm on a side, using arrangement B? **(c)** By what factor has the number of atoms on the surface increased in going to arrangement B from arrangement A? If extended to three dimensions, which arrangement would lead to a greater density for Rb metal?

[2.81] **(a)** Assuming the dimensions of the nucleus and atom shown in Figure 2.12, what fraction of the *volume* of the atom is taken up by the nucleus? **(b)** Using the mass of the proton from Table 2.1 and assuming its diameter is 1.0×10^{-15} m, calculate the density of a proton in g/cm^3.

2.82 The element oxygen has three naturally occurring isotopes, with 8, 9, and 10 neutrons in the nucleus, respectively. **(a)** Write the full chemical symbols for these three isotopes. **(b)** Describe the similarities and differences between the three kinds of atoms of oxygen.

2.83 Use Coulomb's law, $F = kQ_1Q_2/d^2$, to calculate the electric force on an electron ($Q = -1.6 \times 10^{-19}$ C) exerted by a single proton if the particles are 0.53×10^{-10} m apart. The constant k in Coulomb's law is 9.0×10^9 N·m^2/C^2. (The unit abbreviated N is the Newton, the SI unit of force.)

2.84 Gallium (Ga) consists of two naturally occurring isotopes with masses of 68.926 and 70.925 amu. **(a)** How many protons and neutrons are in the nucleus of each isotope? Write the complete atomic symbol for each, showing the atomic number and mass number. **(b)** The average atomic mass of Ga is 69.72 amu. Calculate the abundance of each isotope.

[2.85] Using a suitable reference such as the *CRC Handbook of Chemistry and Physics* or http://www.webelements.com, look up the following information for nickel: **(a)** the number of known isotopes, **(b)** the atomic masses (in amu) and the natural abundance of the five most abundant isotopes.

[2.86] There are two different isotopes of bromine atoms. Under normal conditions, elemental bromine consists of Br$_2$ molecules (Figure 2.19), and the mass of a Br$_2$ molecule is the sum of the masses of the two atoms in the molecule. The mass spectrum of Br$_2$ consists of three peaks:

Mass (amu)	Relative Size
157.836	0.2569
159.834	0.4999
161.832	0.2431

(a) What is the origin of each peak (of what isotopes does each consist)? **(b)** What is the mass of each isotope? **(c)** Determine the average molecular mass of a Br$_2$ molecule. **(d)** Determine the average atomic mass of a bromine atom. **(e)** Calculate the abundances of the two isotopes.

2.87 It is common in mass spectrometry to assume that the mass of a cation is the same as that of its parent atom. **(a)** Using data in Table 2.1, determine the number of significant figures that must be reported before the difference in mass of ^{1}H and ^{1}H$^+$ is significant. **(b)** What percentage of the mass of an ^{1}H atom does the electron represent?

2.88 *Bronze* is a metallic alloy often used in decorative applications and in sculpture. A typical bronze consists of copper, tin, and zinc, with lesser amounts of phosphorus and lead. Locate each of these five elements in the periodic table, write their symbols, and identify the group of the periodic table to which they belong.

2.89 From the following list of elements—Ar, H, Ga, Al, Ca, Br, Ge, K, O—pick the one that best fits each description; use each element only once: **(a)** an alkali metal, **(b)** an alkaline earth metal, **(c)** a noble gas, **(d)** a halogen, **(e)** a metalloid, **(f)** a nonmetal listed in group 1A, **(g)** a metal that forms a 3+ ion, **(h)** a nonmetal that forms a 2− ion, **(i)** an element that resembles aluminum.

2.90 The first atoms of seaborgium (Sg) were identified in 1974. The longest-lived isotope of Sg has a mass number of 266. **(a)** How many protons, electrons, and neutrons are in an ^{266}Sg atom? **(b)** Atoms of Sg are very unstable, and it is therefore difficult to study this element's properties. Based on the position of Sg in the periodic table, what element should it most closely resemble in its chemical properties?

2.91 From the molecular structures shown here, identify the one that corresponds to each of the following species: **(a)** chlorine gas; **(b)** propane, **(c)** nitrate ion; **(d)** sulfur trioxide; **(e)** methyl chloride, CH_3Cl.

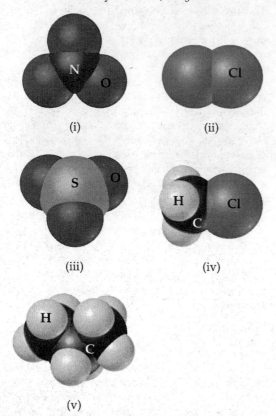

(i)   (ii)

(iii)   (iv)

(v)

2.92 Name each of the following oxides. Assuming that the compounds are ionic, what charge is associated with the metallic element in each case? **(a)** NiO, **(b)** MnO_2, **(c)** Cr_2O_3, **(d)** MoO_3.

2.93 Iodic acid has the molecular formula HIO_3. Write the formulas for the following: **(a)** the iodate anion, **(b)** the periodate anion, **(c)** the hypoiodite anion, **(d)** hypoiodous acid, **(e)** periodic acid.

2.94 Elements in the same group of the periodic table often form oxyanions with the same general formula. The anions are also named in a similar fashion. Based on these observations, suggest a chemical formula or name, as appropriate, for each of the following ions: **(a)** BrO_4^-, **(b)** SeO_3^{2-}, **(c)** arsenate ion, **(d)** hydrogen tellurate ion.

2.95 Give the chemical names of each of the following familiar compounds: **(a)** NaCl (table salt), **(b)** $NaHCO_3$ (baking soda), **(c)** NaOCl (in many bleaches), **(d)** NaOH (caustic soda), **(e)** $(NH_4)_2CO_3$ (smelling salts), **(f)** $CaSO_4$ (plaster of Paris).

2.96 Many familiar substances have common, unsystematic names. For each of the following, give the correct systematic name: **(a)** saltpeter, KNO_3; **(b)** soda ash, Na_2CO_3; **(c)** lime, CaO; **(d)** muriatic acid, HCl; **(e)** Epsom salts, $MgSO_4$; **(f)** milk of magnesia, $Mg(OH)_2$.

2.97 Many ions and compounds have very similar names, and there is great potential for confusing them. Write the correct chemical formulas to distinguish between **(a)** calcium sulfide and calcium hydrogen sulfide, **(b)** hydrobromic acid and bromic acid, **(c)** aluminum nitride and aluminum nitrite, **(d)** iron(II) oxide and iron(III) oxide, **(e)** ammonia and ammonium ion, **(f)** potassium sulfite and potassium bisulfite, **(g)** mercurous chloride and mercuric chloride, **(h)** chloric acid and perchloric acid.

[2.98] Using the *CRC Handbook of Chemistry and Physics*, find the density, melting point, and boiling point for **(a)** PF_3, **(b)** $SiCl_4$, **(c)** ethanol, C_2H_6O.

[2.99] The compound *cyclohexane* is an alkane in which six carbon atoms form a ring. The partial structural formula of the compound is as follows:

(a) Complete the structural formula for cyclohexane. **(b)** Is the molecular formula for cyclohexane the same as that for *n*-hexane, in which the carbon atoms are in a straight line? If possible, comment on the source of any differences. **(c)** Propose a structural formula for *cyclohexanol*, the alcohol derived from cyclohexane.

2.100 The periodic table helps organize the chemical behaviors of the elements. As a class discussion or as a short essay, describe how the table is organized, and mention as many ways as you can think of in which the position of an element in the table relates to the chemical and physical properties of the element.

eMEDIA EXERCISES

These exercises make use of the interactive objects available on-line in OneKey or the Companion Website, and on your Accelerator CD. Access to these resources comes in your MediaPak.

2.101 **(a)** After watching the **Multiple Proportions** animation (2.1), show how the oxygen-to-hydrogen mass ratios of H_2O and H_2O_2 illustrate the law of multiple proportions. **(b)** Refer to Exercise 2.9, and sketch molecular models (similar to those in the movie) of the three N- and O-containing compounds in the exercise. **(c)** Do the same thing for Exercise 2.10, sketching models of the I- and F-containing molecules.

2.102 Prior to Rutherford's gold-foil experiment, the mass and positively charged particles of an atom were thought to be evenly distributed throughout the volume of the atom. **(a)** Watch the animation of the **Rutherford Experiment: Nuclear Atom** (2.2), and describe how the experimental results would have been different if the earlier model had been correct. **(b)** What specific feature of the modern view of atomic structure was illuminated by Rutherford's experiment?

2.103 The **Separation of Alpha, Beta, and Gamma Rays** animation (2.2) shows how three different types of radioactive emissions behave in the presence of an electric field. **(a)** Which of the three types of radiation does not consist of a stream of charged particles? **(b)** In Exercise 2.9 you explained why α and β rays are deflected in opposite directions. In the movie, the difference in the *magnitude* of deflection of α versus β particles is attributed primarily to a difference in mass. How much more massive are α particles than β particles? What factors other than mass influence the magnitude of deflection?

2.104 Give the correct formula and name for the ionic compound formed by each of the indicated combinations: NH_4^+ and Al^{3+} each with Br^-, OH^-, S^{2-}, CO_3^{2-}, NO_3^-, and ClO_4^-. Use the **Ionic Compounds** activity (2.7) to check your answers.

eLABORATORY EXERCISES

These exercises allow students to apply the concepts and skills for this chapter in the simulated laboratory of Virtual ChemLab. Worksheets for each of these exercises are found in the Virtual ChemLab Workbook in your MediaPak.

2.106 *(VCL 2-1) Thomson Cathode-Ray Tube Experiment*
In 1897, Thomson showed that if you could measure how much a beam of electrons was bent in an electric field and measure the magnetic field required to move the beam of electrons back to center, you could determine the charge-to-mass ratio (q/m_e) for the electrons. In this problem, you will duplicate the Thomson cathode-ray tube experiment and calculate the charge-to-mass ratio of an electron.

2.107 *(VCL 2-2) Millikan Oil-Drop Experiment*
In 1909, Robert Millikan and his graduate student Harvey Fletcher showed that they could measure the charge of an electron by making very small oil drops, depositing electrons on these drops, and then applying an electric field. You will get a chance to repeat their experiments and, using the results from the Thomson assignment, be able to experimentally calculate the mass of an electron.

2.108 *(VCL 2-3) Rutherford's Backscattering Experiment*
A key experiment in understanding the nature of atomic structure was completed by Ernest Rutherford in 1911. He set up an experiment that directed a beam of alpha particles (helium nuclei) through a gold foil and then onto a detector screen. According to the plum-pudding atomic model, electrons float around inside a cloud of positive charge. Based on this model, Rutherford expected that almost all the alpha particles should pass through the gold foil and not be deflected. A few of the alpha particles would experience a slight deflection because of the attraction to the negative electrons. Imagine his surprise when a few alpha particles deflected at all angles, even nearly straight backward. You will have a chance to repeat this experiment and observe the number of alpha particles that are deflected at different angles. You will also be able to experiment with other metals and understand why Rutherford selected gold.

2.109 *(VCL 2-4) Investigating the Properties of Alpha and Beta Particles*
As scientists began investigating the properties of atoms, their first discovery was that they could extract negatively charged particles. They called these particles electrons, but they are also known as beta particles in the context of nuclear decay. Robert Millikan used beta particles in his famous oil-drop experiment. Another particle ejected during nuclear decay is the alpha particle. An alpha particle is a helium nucleus, or a helium atom without its two electrons. Consequently, an alpha particle is positively charged. Ernest Rutherford used alpha particles in his gold-foil experiment. In this assignment you will investigate the propeties of alpha and beta particles using the virtual laboratory.

2.110 *(VCL 2-5) Names and Formulas of Ionic Compounds*
In this problem you will go into the virtual laboratory and make a series of ionic compounds containing the cations Ag^+, Pb^+, Ca^{2+}, Fe^{3+}, and Cu^{2+}; observe the reactions and identify the color of the compounds formed; write the chemical formulas; and write the chemical names.

3.1 Chemical Equations

3.2 Some Simple Patterns of Chemical Reactivity

3.3 Formula Weights

3.4 Avogadro's Number and the Mole

3.5 Empirical Formulas from Analyses

3.6 Quantitative Information from Balanced Equations

3.7 Limiting Reactants

WHAT'S AHEAD

- We begin by considering how we can use chemical formulas to write equations that represent chemical reactions. *(Section 3.1)*

- We then examine some simple kinds of chemical reactions: *combination reactions, decomposition reactions*, and *combustion reactions. (Section 3.2)*

- We then use chemical formulas to relate the masses of substances to the numbers of atoms, molecules, or ions contained in the substances, a relationship that leads to the crucially important concept of a mole. A *mole* is 6.022×10^{23} objects (atoms, molecules, ions, or whatever). *(Sections 3.3 and 3.4)*

- We will apply the mole concept to determine chemical formulas from the masses of each element in a given quantity of a compound. *(Section 3.5)*

- We will use the quantitative information inherent in chemical formulas and equations together with the mole concept to predict the amounts of substances consumed and/or produced in chemical reactions. *(Section 3.6)*

- A special situation arises when one of the reactants is used up before the others and the reaction therefore stops, leaving some of the excess starting material unreacted. *(Section 3.7)*

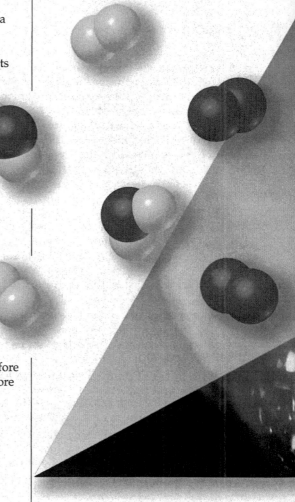

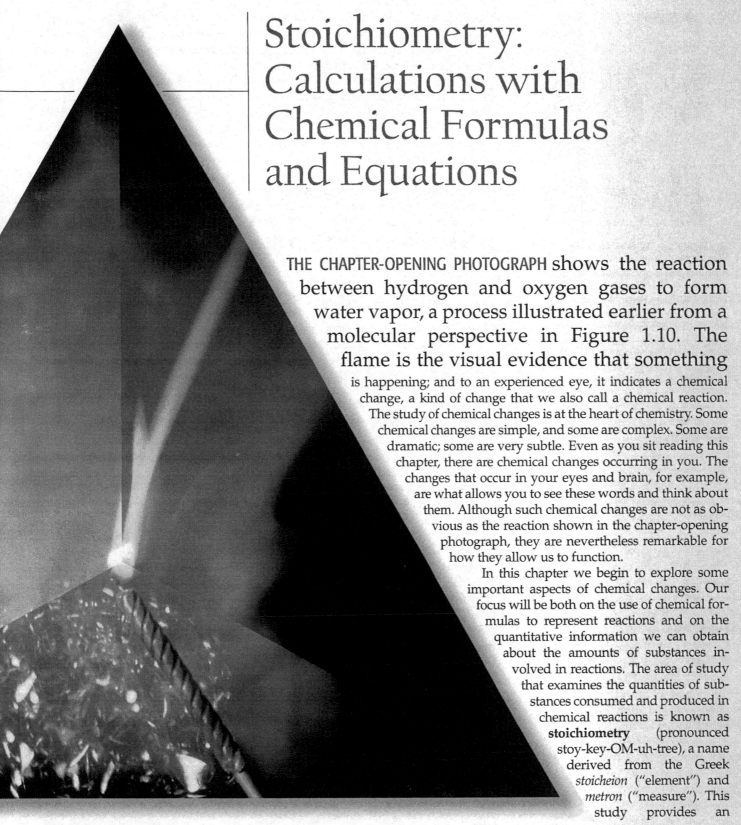

Stoichiometry: Calculations with Chemical Formulas and Equations

THE CHAPTER-OPENING PHOTOGRAPH shows the reaction between hydrogen and oxygen gases to form water vapor, a process illustrated earlier from a molecular perspective in Figure 1.10. The flame is the visual evidence that something is happening; and to an experienced eye, it indicates a chemical change, a kind of change that we also call a chemical reaction. The study of chemical changes is at the heart of chemistry. Some chemical changes are simple, and some are complex. Some are dramatic; some are very subtle. Even as you sit reading this chapter, there are chemical changes occurring in you. The changes that occur in your eyes and brain, for example, are what allows you to see these words and think about them. Although such chemical changes are not as obvious as the reaction shown in the chapter-opening photograph, they are nevertheless remarkable for how they allow us to function.

In this chapter we begin to explore some important aspects of chemical changes. Our focus will be both on the use of chemical formulas to represent reactions and on the quantitative information we can obtain about the amounts of substances involved in reactions. The area of study that examines the quantities of substances consumed and produced in chemical reactions is known as **stoichiometry** (pronounced stoy-key-OM-uh-tree), a name derived from the Greek *stoicheion* ("element") and *metron* ("measure"). This study provides an

COMBUSTION OF HYDROGEN GAS. The gas is bubbled through a soap solution forming hydrogen-filled bubbles. As the bubbles float upwards, they are ignited by a candle on a long pole. The red-orange flame is due to the combustion of the soap bubbles as the hydrogen reacts with oxygen in the air.

Science Fundamentals Second Edition

▲ Figure 3.1   Antoine Lavoisier (1734–1794). Lavoisier conducted many important studies on combustion reactions. Unfortunately, his career was cut short by the French Revolution. He was a member of the French nobility and a tax collector. He was guillotined in 1794 during the final months of the Reign of Terror. He is now generally considered to be the father of modern chemistry because he conducted carefully controlled experiments and used quantitative measurements.

MOVIE
Formation of water

essential set of tools that are widely used in chemistry. Such diverse problems as measuring the concentration of ozone in the atmosphere, determining the potential yield of gold from an ore, and assessing different processes for converting coal into gaseous fuels all use aspects of stoichiometry.

Stoichiometry is built on an understanding of atomic masses (Section 2.4), chemical formulas, and the law of conservation of mass. ∞ (Section 2.1) The French nobleman and scientist Antoine Lavoisier (Figure 3.1 ◄) discovered this important chemical law in the late 1700s. In a chemistry text published in 1789, Lavoisier stated the law in this eloquent way: "We may lay it down as an incontestable axiom that, in all the operations of art and nature, nothing is created; an equal quantity of matter exists both before and after the experiment. Upon this principle, the whole art of performing chemical experiments depends." With the advent of Dalton's atomic theory, chemists came to understand the basis for this law: *Atoms are neither created nor destroyed during any chemical reaction.* The changes that occur during any reaction merely rearrange the atoms. The same collection of atoms is present both before and after the reaction.

3.1 | Chemical Equations

Chemical reactions are represented in a concise way by **chemical equations**. When hydrogen (H_2) burns, for example, it reacts with oxygen (O_2) in the air to form water (H_2O) (chapter-opening photograph). We write the chemical equation for this reaction as follows:

$$2\,H_2 + O_2 \longrightarrow 2\,H_2O \qquad [3.1]$$

We read the + sign as "reacts with" and the arrow as "produces." The chemical formulas to the left of the arrow represent the starting substances, called **reactants**. The chemical formulas to the right of the arrow represent substances produced in the reaction, called **products**. The numbers in front of the formulas are *coefficients*. (As in algebraic equations, the numeral 1 is usually not written.) The coefficients indicate the relative numbers of molecules of each kind involved in the reaction.

Because atoms are neither created nor destroyed in any reaction, a chemical equation must have an equal number of atoms of each element on each side of the arrow. When this condition is met, the equation is said to be *balanced*. On the right side of Equation 3.1, for example, there are two molecules of H_2O, each composed of two atoms of hydrogen and one atom of oxygen. Thus, $2\,H_2O$ (read "two molecules of water") contains $2 \times 2 = 4$ H atoms and $2 \times 1 = 2$ O. Notice that the number of atoms is obtained by multiplying the coefficient and the subscripts in the chemical formula. Because there are four H atoms and two O atoms on each side of the equation, the equation is balanced. We can represent the balanced equation by the following molecular models, which illustrate that the number of atoms of each kind is the same on both sides of the arrow:

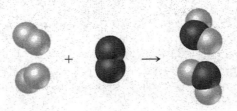

GIVE IT SOME THOUGHT

How many atoms of Mg, O, and H are represented by $3\,Mg(OH)_2$?

Chemical symbol	Meaning		Composition
H_2O	One molecule of water:		Two H atoms and one O atom
$2 H_2O$	Two molecules of water:		Four H atoms and two O atoms
H_2O_2	One molecule of hydrogen peroxide:		Two H atoms and two O atoms

◀ **Figure 3.2 The difference between a subscript in a chemical formula and a coefficient in front of the formula.** Notice how adding the coefficient 2 in front of the formula (line 2) has a different effect on the implied composition than adding the subscript 2 to the formula (in line 3). The number of atoms of each type (listed under composition) is obtained by multiplying the coefficient and the subscript associated with each element in the formula.

Balancing Equations

Once we know the formulas of the reactants and products in a reaction, we can write the unbalanced equation. We then balance the equation by determining the coefficients that provide equal numbers of each type of atom on each side of the equation. For most purposes, a balanced equation should contain the smallest possible whole-number coefficients.

In balancing equations, it is important to understand the difference between a coefficient in front of a formula and a subscript in a formula. Refer to Figure 3.2 ▲. Notice that changing a subscript in a formula—from H_2O to H_2O_2, for example—changes the identity of the chemical. The substance H_2O_2, hydrogen peroxide, is quite different from the substance H_2O, water. *Subscripts should never be changed in balancing an equation.* In contrast, placing a coefficient in front of a formula changes only the *amount* of the substance and not its *identity*. Thus, 2 H_2O means two molecules of water, 3 H_2O means three molecules of water, and so forth.

To illustrate the process of balancing equations, consider the reaction that occurs when methane (CH_4), the principal component of natural gas, burns in air to produce carbon dioxide gas (CO_2) and water vapor (H_2O) (Figure 3.3 ▼). Both of these products contain oxygen atoms that come from O_2 in the air. Thus, O_2 is a reactant, and the unbalanced equation is

$$CH_4 + O_2 \longrightarrow CO_2 + H_2O \qquad \text{(unbalanced)} \qquad [3.2]$$

It is usually best to balance first those elements that occur in the fewest chemical formulas on each side of the equation. In our example both C and H

ACTIVITY
Reading a Chemical Equation

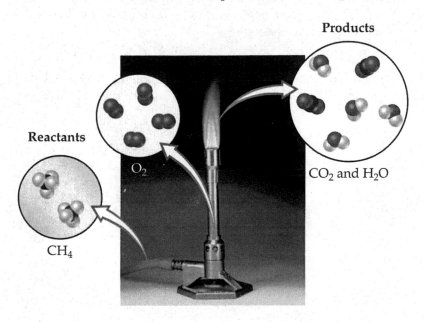

Reactants

CH₄

Products

O₂

CO₂ and H₂O

◀ **Figure 3.3 Methane reacts with oxygen to produce the flame in a Bunsen burner.** The methane (CH_4) in natural gas and oxygen (O_2) from the air are the reactants in the reaction, while carbon dioxide (CO_2) and water (H_2O) are the products.

Science Fundamentals Second Edition

appear in only one reactant and, separately, in one product each, so we begin by focusing on CH_4. Let's consider first carbon and then hydrogen.

One molecule of the reactant CH_4 contains the same number of C atoms (one) as one molecule of the product CO_2. The coefficients for these substances *must* be the same, therefore, and we choose them both to be 1 as we start the balancing process. However, one molecule of CH_4 contains more H atoms (four) than one molecule of the product H_2O (two). If we place a coefficient 2 in front of H_2O, there will be four H atoms on each side of the equation:

$$CH_4 + O_2 \longrightarrow CO_2 + 2\,H_2O \qquad \text{(unbalanced)} \qquad [3.3]$$

At this stage the products have more O atoms (four—two from CO_2 and two from $2\,H_2O$) than the reactants (two). If we place a coefficient 2 in front of the reactant O_2, we complete the balancing by making the number of O atoms equal on both sides of the equation:

$$CH_4 + 2\,O_2 \longrightarrow CO_2 + 2\,H_2O \qquad \text{(balanced)} \qquad [3.4]$$

The molecular view of the balanced equation is shown in Figure 3.4 ▼. We see that there are one C, four H, and four O atoms on both sides of the arrow, indicating the equation is balanced.

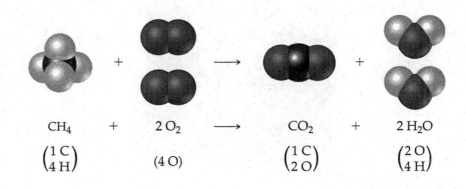

$$CH_4 \quad + \quad 2\,O_2 \quad \longrightarrow \quad CO_2 \quad + \quad 2\,H_2O$$

$$\begin{pmatrix} 1\,C \\ 4\,H \end{pmatrix} \qquad (4\,O) \qquad\qquad \begin{pmatrix} 1\,C \\ 2\,O \end{pmatrix} \qquad \begin{pmatrix} 2\,O \\ 4\,H \end{pmatrix}$$

Science Fundamentals Second Edition

The approach we have taken in arriving at balanced Equation 3.4 is largely trial and error. We balance each kind of atom in succession, adjusting coefficients as necessary. This approach works for most chemical equations.

SAMPLE EXERCISE 3.1 | Interpreting and Balancing Chemical Equations

The following diagram represents a chemical reaction in which the red spheres are oxygen atoms and the blue spheres are nitrogen atoms. **(a)** Write the chemical formulas for the reactants and products. **(b)** Write a balanced equation for the reaction. **(c)** Is the diagram consistent with the law of conservation of mass?

Solution (a) The left box, which represents the reactants, contains two kinds of molecules, those composed of two oxygen atoms (O_2) and those composed of one nitrogen atom and one oxygen atom (NO). The right box, which represents the products, contains only molecules composed of one nitrogen atom and two oxygen atoms (NO_2).

(b) The unbalanced chemical equation is

$$O_2 + NO \longrightarrow NO_2 \quad \text{(unbalanced)}$$

In this equation there are three O atoms on the left side of the arrow and two O atoms on the right side. We can increase the number of O atoms by placing a coefficient 2 on the product side:

$$O_2 + NO \longrightarrow 2\,NO_2 \quad \text{(unbalanced)}$$

Now there are two N atoms and four O atoms on the right. Placing a coefficient 2 in front of NO brings both the N atoms and O atoms into balance:

$$O_2 + 2\,NO \longrightarrow 2\,NO_2 \quad \text{(balanced)}$$

(c) The left box (reactants) contains four O_2 molecules and eight NO molecules. Thus, the molecular ratio is one O_2 for each two NO as required by the balanced equation. The right box (products) contains eight NO_2 molecules. The number of NO_2 molecules on the right equals the number of NO molecules on the left as the balanced equation requires. Counting the atoms, we find eight N atoms in the eight NO molecules in the box on the left. There are also $4 \times 2 = 8$ O atoms in the O_2 molecules and eight O atoms in the NO molecules, giving a total of 16 O atoms. In the box on the right, we find eight N atoms and $8 \times 2 = 16$ O atoms in the eight NO_2 molecules. Because there are equal numbers of both N and O atoms in the two boxes, the drawing is consistent with the law of conservation of mass.

ACTIVITY
Balancing Equations

PRACTICE EXERCISE

In order to be consistent with the law of conservation of mass, how many NH_3 molecules should be shown in the right box of the following diagram?

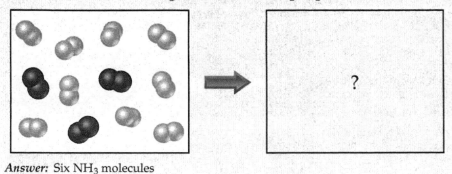

Answer: Six NH_3 molecules

Indicating the States of Reactants and Products

Additional information is often added to the formulas in balanced equations to indicate the physical state of each reactant and product. We use the symbols (g), (l), (s), and (aq) for gas, liquid, solid, and aqueous (water) solution, respectively. Thus, Equation 3.4 can be written

$$CH_4(g) + 2\,O_2(g) \longrightarrow CO_2(g) + 2\,H_2O(g) \qquad [3.5]$$

Sometimes the conditions (such as temperature or pressure) under which the reaction proceeds appear above or below the reaction arrow. The symbol Δ (the Greek uppercase letter delta) is often placed above the arrow to indicate the addition of heat.

■ SAMPLE EXERCISE 3.2 | Balancing Chemical Equations

Balance this equation:
$$Na(s) + H_2O(l) \longrightarrow NaOH(aq) + H_2(g)$$

Solution We begin by counting the atoms of each kind on both sides of the arrow. The Na and O atoms are balanced (one Na and one O on each side), but there are two H atoms on the left and three H atoms on the right. Thus, we need to increase the number of H atoms on the left. As a trial beginning in our effort to balance H, let's place a coefficient 2 in front of H_2O:

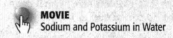
MOVIE
Sodium and Potassium in Water

$$Na(s) + 2\,H_2O(l) \longrightarrow NaOH(aq) + H_2(g)$$

Beginning this way doesn't balance H, but introducing the coefficient 2 does increase the number of H atoms among the reactants, which we need to do. The fact that it causes O to be unbalanced is something we will take care of after we balance H. Now that we have 2 H_2O on the left, we can balance H by putting a coefficient 2 in front of NaOH on the right:

$$Na(s) + 2\,H_2O(l) \longrightarrow 2\,NaOH(aq) + H_2(g)$$

Balancing H in this way fortuitously brings O into balance, but notice that Na is now unbalanced, with one on the left but two on the right. To rebalance Na, we put a coefficient 2 in front of the reactant:

$$2\,Na(s) + 2\,H_2O(l) \longrightarrow 2\,NaOH(aq) + H_2(g)$$

Finally, we check the number of atoms of each element and find that we have two Na atoms, four H atoms, and two O atoms on each side of the equation. The equation is balanced.

Comment: Notice that in balancing this equation, we moved back and forth placing a coefficient in front of H_2O, then NaOH, and finally Na. In balancing equations, we often find ourselves following this pattern of moving back and forth from one side of the arrow to the other, placing coefficients first in front of a formula on one side and then in front of a formula on the other side until the equation is balanced.

■ PRACTICE EXERCISE

Balance the following equations by providing the missing coefficients:

(a) __Fe(s) + __$O_2(g)$ $\longrightarrow$ __$Fe_2O_3(s)$

(b) __$C_2H_4(g)$ + __$O_2(g)$ $\longrightarrow$ __$CO_2(g)$ + __$H_2O(g)$

(c) __Al(s) + __HCl(aq) $\longrightarrow$ __$AlCl_3(aq)$ + __$H_2(g)$

Answers: (a) 4, 3, 2; (b) 1, 3, 2, 2; (c) 2, 6, 2, 3

3.2 | Some Simple Patterns of Chemical Reactivity

In this section we examine three simple kinds of reactions that we will see frequently throughout this chapter. Our first reason for examining these reactions is merely to become better acquainted with chemical reactions and their balanced equations. Our second reason is to consider how we might predict the products of some of these reactions knowing only their reactants. The key to predicting the products formed by a given combination of reactants is recognizing general patterns of chemical reactivity. Recognizing a pattern of reactivity for a class of substances gives you a broader understanding than merely memorizing a large number of unrelated reactions.

Combination and Decomposition Reactions

Table 3.1 ▼ summarizes two simple types of reactions, combination and decomposition reactions. In **combination reactions** two or more substances react to form one product. There are many examples of such reactions, especially those in which elements combine to form compounds. For example, magnesium metal burns in air with a dazzling brilliance to produce magnesium oxide, as shown in Figure 3.5 ▶:

$$2\,Mg(s) + O_2(g) \longrightarrow 2\,MgO(s) \qquad [3.6]$$

This reaction is used to produce the bright flame generated by flares.

When a combination reaction occurs between a metal and a nonmetal, as in Equation 3.6, the product is an ionic solid. Recall that the formula of an ionic compound can be determined from the charges of the ions involved ∞ (Section 2.7). When magnesium reacts with oxygen, for example, the magnesium loses electrons and forms the magnesium ion, Mg^{2+}. The oxygen gains electrons and forms the oxide ion, O^{2-}. Thus, the reaction product is MgO. You should be able to recognize when a reaction is a combination reaction and to predict the products of a combination reaction in which the reactants are a metal and a nonmetal.

 GIVE IT SOME THOUGHT

When Na and S combine in a combination reaction, what is the chemical formula of the product?

TABLE 3.1	Combination and Decomposition Reactions
Combination Reactions	
$A + B \longrightarrow C$ $C(s) + O_2(g) \longrightarrow CO_2(g)$ $N_2(g) + 3\,H_2(g) \longrightarrow 2\,NH_3(g)$ $CaO(s) + H_2O(l) \longrightarrow Ca(OH)_2\,(s)$	Two reactants combine to form a single product. Many elements react with one another in this fashion to form compounds.
Decomposition Reactions	
$C \longrightarrow A + B$ $2\,KClO_3(s) \longrightarrow 2\,KCl(s) + 3\,O_2(g)$ $PbCO_3(s) \longrightarrow PbO(s) + CO_2(g)$ $Cu(OH)_2(s) \longrightarrow CuO(s) + H_2O(l)$	A single reactant breaks apart to form two or more substances. Many compounds react this way when heated.

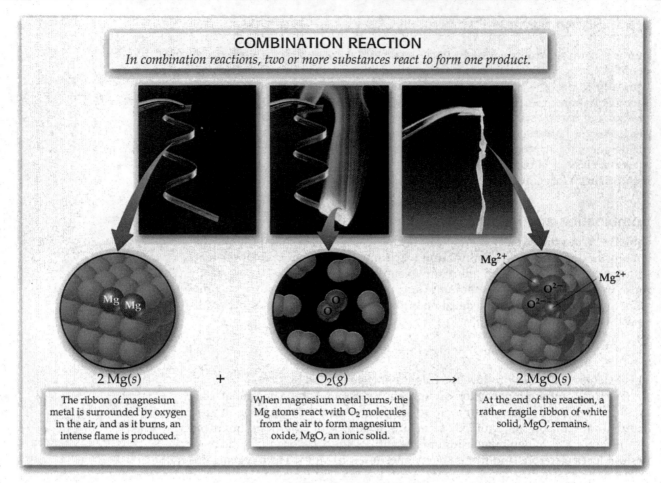

COMBINATION REACTION
In combination reactions, two or more substances react to form one product.

$2 Mg(s)$ + $O_2(g)$ $\longrightarrow$ $2 MgO(s)$

The ribbon of magnesium metal is surrounded by oxygen in the air, and as it burns, an intense flame is produced.

When magnesium metal burns, the Mg atoms react with O_2 molecules from the air to form magnesium oxide, MgO, an ionic solid.

At the end of the reaction, a rather fragile ribbon of white solid, MgO, remains.

▲ **Figure 3.5   Combustion of magnesium metal in air.**

MOVIE
Reactions with Oxygen

ANIMATION
Air Bags

▲ **Figure 3.6   An automobile air bag.**
The decomposition of sodium azide, $NaN_3(s)$, is used to inflate automobile air bags. When properly ignited, the NaN_3 decomposes rapidly, forming nitrogen gas, $N_2(g)$, which expands the air bag.

In a **decomposition reaction** one substance undergoes a reaction to produce two or more other substances. Many compounds undergo decomposition reactions when heated. For example, many metal carbonates decompose to form metal oxides and carbon dioxide when heated:

$$CaCO_3(s) \longrightarrow CaO(s) + CO_2(g) \qquad [3.7]$$

The decomposition of $CaCO_3$ is an important commercial process. Limestone or seashells, which are both primarily $CaCO_3$, are heated to prepare CaO,

which is known as lime or quicklime. About 2×10^{10} kg (20 million tons) of CaO is used in the United States each year, principally in making glass, in obtaining iron from its ores, and in making mortar to bind bricks.

The decomposition of sodium azide (NaN_3) rapidly releases $N_2(g)$, so this reaction is used to inflate safety air bags in automobiles (Figure 3.6 ◄):

$$2 NaN_3(s) \longrightarrow 2 Na(s) + 3 N_2(g) \qquad [3.8]$$

The system is designed so that an impact ignites a detonator cap, which in turn causes NaN_3 to decompose explosively. A small quantity of NaN_3 (about 100 g) forms a large quantity of gas (about 50 L). We will consider the volumes of gases produced in chemical reactions in Section 10.5.

SAMPLE EXERCISE 3.3 | Writing Balanced Equations for Combination and Decomposition Reactions

Write balanced equations for the following reactions: **(a)** The combination reaction that occurs when lithium metal and fluorine gas react. **(b)** The decomposition reaction that occurs when solid barium carbonate is heated. (Two products form: a solid and a gas.)

Solution **(a)** The symbol for lithium is Li. With the exception of mercury, all metals are solids at room temperature. Fluorine occurs as a diatomic molecule (see Figure 2.19). Thus, the reactants are Li(s) and $F_2(g)$. The product will consist of a metal and a nonmetal, so we expect it to be an ionic solid. Lithium ions have a 1+ charge, Li^+, whereas fluoride ions have a 1− charge, F^-. Thus, the chemical formula for the product is LiF. The balanced chemical equation is

$$2\,Li(s) + F_2(g) \longrightarrow 2\,LiF(s)$$

(b) The chemical formula for barium carbonate is $BaCO_3$. As noted in the text, many metal carbonates decompose to form metal oxides and carbon dioxide when heated. In Equation 3.7, for example, $CaCO_3$ decomposes to form CaO and CO_2. Thus, we would expect that $BaCO_3$ decomposes to form BaO and CO_2. Barium and calcium are both in group 2A in the periodic table, moreover, which further suggests they would react in the same way:

$$BaCO_3(s) \longrightarrow BaO(s) + CO_2(g)$$

PRACTICE EXERCISE

Write balanced chemical equations for the following reactions: **(a)** Solid mercury(II) sulfide decomposes into its component elements when heated. **(b)** The surface of aluminum metal undergoes a combination reaction with oxygen in the air.
Answers: **(a)** $HgS(s) \longrightarrow Hg(l) + S(s)$; **(b)** $4\,Al(s) + 3\,O_2(g) \longrightarrow 2\,Al_2O_3(s)$

Combustion in Air

Combustion reactions are rapid reactions that produce a flame. Most of the combustion reactions we observe involve O_2 from air as a reactant. Equation 3.5 and Practice Exercise 3.1(b) illustrate a general class of reactions involving the burning, or combustion, of hydrocarbon compounds (compounds that contain only carbon and hydrogen, such as CH_4 and C_2H_4). ∞ (Section 2.9)

When hydrocarbons are combusted in air, they react with O_2 to form CO_2 and H_2O.* The number of molecules of O_2 required in the reaction and the number of molecules of CO_2 and H_2O formed depend on the composition of the hydrocarbon, which acts as the fuel in the reaction. For example, the combustion of propane (C_3H_8), a gas used for cooking and home heating, is described by the following equation:

$$C_3H_8(g) + 5\,O_2(g) \longrightarrow 3\,CO_2(g) + 4\,H_2O(g) \qquad [3.9]$$

The state of the water, $H_2O(g)$ or $H_2O(l)$, depends on the conditions of the reaction. Water vapor, $H_2O(g)$, is formed at high temperature in an open container. The blue flame produced when propane burns is shown in Figure 3.7 ▶.

Combustion of oxygen-containing derivatives of hydrocarbons, such as CH_3OH, also produces CO_2 and H_2O. The simple rule that hydrocarbons and related oxygen-containing derivatives of hydrocarbons form CO_2 and H_2O when they burn in air summarizes the behavior of about 3 million compounds. Many substances that our bodies use as energy sources, such as the sugar glucose ($C_6H_{12}O_6$), similarly react in our bodies with O_2 to form CO_2 and H_2O.

▲ **Figure 3.7 Propane burning in air.**
The liquid propane, C_3H_8, vaporizes and mixes with air as it escapes through the nozzle. The combustion reaction of C_3H_8 and O_2 produces a blue flame.

---

* When there is an insufficient quantity of O_2 present, carbon monoxide (CO) will be produced along with the CO_2; this is called *incomplete* combustion. If the amount of O_2 is severely restricted, fine particles of carbon that we call soot will be produced. *Complete* combustion produces only CO_2 and H_2O. Unless specifically stated to the contrary, we will always take *combustion* to mean *complete combustion*.

In our bodies, however, the reactions take place in a series of steps that occur at body temperature. The reactions are then described as *oxidation reactions* rather than combustion reactions.

■ SAMPLE EXERCISE 3.4 | Writing Balanced Equations for Combustion Reactions

Write the balanced equation for the reaction that occurs when methanol, $CH_3OH(l)$, is burned in air.

Solution When any compound containing C, H, and O is combusted, it reacts with the $O_2(g)$ in air to produce $CO_2(g)$ and $H_2O(g)$. Thus, the unbalanced equation is

$$CH_3OH(l) + O_2(g) \longrightarrow CO_2(g) + H_2O(g)$$

The C atoms are balanced with one on each side of the arrow. Because CH_3OH has four H atoms, we place a coefficient 2 in front of H_2O to balance the H atoms:

$$CH_3OH(l) + O_2(g) \longrightarrow CO_2(g) + 2 H_2O(g)$$

This balances H but gives four O atoms in the products. Because there are only three O atoms in the reactants (one in CH_3OH and two in O_2), we are not finished yet. We can place the fractional coefficient $\frac{3}{2}$ in front of O_2 to give a total of four O atoms in the reactants (there are $\frac{3}{2} \times 2 = 3$ O atoms in $\frac{3}{2}O_2$):

$$CH_3OH(l) + \tfrac{3}{2}O_2(g) \longrightarrow CO_2(g) + 2 H_2O(g)$$

Although the equation is now balanced, it is not in its most conventional form because it contains a fractional coefficient. If we multiply each side of the equation by 2, we will remove the fraction and achieve the following balanced equation:

$$2 CH_3OH(l) + 3 O_2(g) \longrightarrow 2 CO_2(g) + 4 H_2O(g)$$

■ PRACTICE EXERCISE

Write the balanced equation for the reaction that occurs when ethanol, $C_2H_5OH(l)$, is burned in air.

Answer: $C_2H_5OH(l) + 3 O_2(g) \longrightarrow 2 CO_2(g) + 3 H_2O(g)$

3.3 | Formula Weights

Chemical formulas and chemical equations both have a *quantitative* significance; the subscripts in formulas and the coefficients in equations represent precise quantities. The formula H_2O indicates that a molecule of this substance contains exactly two atoms of hydrogen and one atom of oxygen. Similarly, the coefficients in a balanced chemical equation indicate the relative quantities of reactants and products. But how do we relate the numbers of atoms or molecules to the amounts we measure out in the laboratory? Although we cannot directly count atoms or molecules, we can indirectly determine their numbers if we know their masses. Therefore, before we can pursue the quantitative aspects of chemical formulas or equations, we must examine the masses of atoms and molecules, which we do in this section and the next.

Formula and Molecular Weights

The **formula weight** of a substance is the sum of the atomic weights of each atom in its chemical formula. Using atomic masses from a periodic table, we find, for example, that the formula weight of sulfuric acid (H_2SO_4) is 98.1 amu:*

---

* The abbreviation AW is used for atomic weight, FW for formula weight, and MW for molecular weight.

$$FW \text{ of } H_2SO_4 = 2(AW \text{ of } H) + (AW \text{ of } S) + 4(AW \text{ of } O)$$

$$= 2(1.0 \text{ amu}) + 32.1 \text{ amu} + 4(16.0 \text{ amu})$$

$$= 98.1 \text{ amu}$$

For convenience, we have rounded off all the atomic weights to one place beyond the decimal point. We will round off the atomic weights in this way for most problems.

If the chemical formula is merely the chemical symbol of an element, such as Na, then the formula weight equals the atomic weight of the element. If the chemical formula is that of a molecule, then the formula weight is also called the **molecular weight**. The molecular weight of glucose ($C_6H_{12}O_6$), for example, is

$$MW \text{ of } C_6H_{12}O_6 = 6(12.0 \text{ amu}) + 12(1.0 \text{ amu}) + 6(16.0 \text{ amu}) = 180.0 \text{ amu}$$

Because ionic substances, such as NaCl, exist as three-dimensional arrays of ions (Figure 2.23), it is inappropriate to speak of molecules of NaCl. Instead, we speak of *formula units*, represented by the chemical formula of the substance. The formula unit of NaCl consists of one Na^+ ion and one Cl^- ion. Thus, the formula weight of NaCl is the mass of one formula unit:

$$FW \text{ of } NaCl = 23.0 \text{ amu} + 35.5 \text{ amu} = 58.5 \text{ amu}$$

▬ SAMPLE EXERCISE 3.5 | Calculating Formula Weights

Calculate the formula weight of **(a)** sucrose, $C_{12}H_{22}O_{11}$ (table sugar), and **(b)** calcium nitrate, $Ca(NO_3)_2$.

Solution (a) By adding the atomic weights of the atoms in sucrose, we find it to have a formula weight of 342.0 amu:

12 C atoms = 12(12.0 amu) =	44.0 amu
22 H atoms = 22(1.0 amu) =	22.0 amu
11 O atoms = 11(16.0 amu) =	176.0 amu
	342.0 amu

(b) If a chemical formula has parentheses, the subscript outside the parentheses is a multiplier for all atoms inside. Thus, for $Ca(NO_3)_2$, we have

1 Ca atom = 1(40.1 amu) =	40.1 amu
2 N atoms = 2(14.0 amu) =	28.0 amu
6 O atoms = 6(16.0 amu) =	96.0 amu
	164.1 amu

▬ PRACTICE EXERCISE

Calculate the formula weight of **(a)** $Al(OH)_3$ and **(b)** CH_3OH.
Answers: **(a)** 78.0 amu, **(b)** 32.0 amu

Percentage Composition from Formulas

Occasionally we must calculate the *percentage composition* of a compound (that is, the percentage by mass contributed by each element in the substance). For example, in order to verify the purity of a compound, we may wish to compare the calculated percentage composition of the substance with that found experimentally. Calculating percentage composition is a straightforward matter if the chemical formula is known. The calculation depends on the formula weight of the substance, the atomic weight of the element of interest, and the number of atoms of that element in the chemical formula:

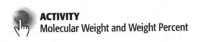
ACTIVITY
Molecular Weight and Weight Percent

$$\% \text{ element} = \frac{(\text{number of atoms of that element})(\text{atomic weight of element})}{\text{formula weight of compound}} \times 100\% \qquad [3.10]$$

SAMPLE EXERCISE 3.6 | Calculating Percentage Composition

Calculate the percentage of carbon, hydrogen, and oxygen (by mass) in $C_{12}H_{22}O_{11}$.

Solution Let's examine this question using the problem-solving steps in the "Strategies in Chemistry: Problem Solving" essay.

Analyze: We are given a chemical formula, $C_{12}H_{22}O_{11}$, and asked to calculate the percentage by mass of its component elements (C, H, and O).

Plan: We can use Equation 3.10, relying on a periodic table to obtain the atomic weight of each component element. The atomic weights are first used to determine the formula weight of the compound. (The formula weight of $C_{12}H_{22}O_{11}$, 342.0 amu, was calculated in Sample Exercise 3.5.) We must then do three calculations, one for each element.

Solve: Using Equation 3.10, we have

$$\%C = \frac{(12)(12.0 \text{ amu})}{342.0 \text{ amu}} \times 100\% = 42.1\%$$

$$\%H = \frac{(22)(1.0 \text{ amu})}{342.0 \text{ amu}} \times 100\% = 6.4\%$$

$$\%O = \frac{(11)(16.0 \text{ amu})}{342.0 \text{ amu}} \times 100\% = 51.5\%$$

Check: The percentages of the individual elements must add up to 100%, which they do in this case. We could have used more significant figures for our atomic weights, giving more significant figures for our percentage composition, but we have adhered to our suggested guideline of rounding atomic weights to one digit beyond the decimal point.

PRACTICE EXERCISE

Calculate the percentage of nitrogen, by mass, in $Ca(NO_3)_2$.
Answer: 17.1%

3.4 | Avogadro's Number and the Mole

Even the smallest samples that we deal with in the laboratory contain enormous numbers of atoms, ions, or molecules. For example, a teaspoon of water (about 5 mL) contains 2×10^{23} water molecules, a number so large that it almost defies comprehension. Chemists, therefore, have devised a special counting unit for describing such large numbers of atoms or molecules.

STRATEGIES IN CHEMISTRY | Problem Solving

The key to success in problem solving is practice. As you practice, you will find that you can improve your skills by following these steps:

Step 1: Analyze the problem. Read the problem carefully for understanding. What does it say? Draw any picture or diagram that will help you visualize the problem. Write down both the data you are given and the quantity that you need to obtain (the unknown).

Step 2: Develop a plan for solving the problem. Consider the possible paths between the given information and the unknown. What principles or equations relate the known data to the unknown? Recognize that some data may not be given explicitly in the problem; you may be expected to know certain quantities (such as Avogadro's number,

which we will soon discuss) or look them up in tables (such as atomic weights). Recognize also that your plan may involve either a single step or a series of steps with intermediate answers.

Step 3: Solve the problem. Use the known information and suitable equations or relationships to solve for the unknown. Dimensional analysis (Section 1.6) is a very useful tool for solving a great number of problems. Be careful with significant figures, signs, and units.

Step 4: Check the solution. Read the problem again to make sure you have found all the solutions asked for in the problem. Does your answer make sense? That is, is the answer outrageously large or small, or is it in the ballpark? Finally, are the units and significant figures correct?

In everyday life we use counting units like dozen (12 objects) and gross (144 objects) to deal with modestly large quantities. In chemistry the unit for dealing with the number of atoms, ions, or molecules in a common-sized sample is the **mole**, abbreviated mol.* A mole is the amount of matter that contains as many objects (atoms, molecules, or whatever objects we are considering) as the number of atoms in exactly 12 g of isotopically pure ^{12}C. From experiments, scientists have determined this number to be 6.0221421×10^{23}. Scientists call this number **Avogadro's number**, in honor of Amedeo Avogadro (1776–1856), an Italian scientist. For most purposes we will use 6.02×10^{23} or 6.022×10^{23} for Avogadro's number throughout the text.

A mole of atoms, a mole of molecules, or a mole of anything else all contain Avogadro's number of these objects:

$$1 \text{ mol } ^{12}C \text{ atoms} = 6.02 \times 10^{23} \text{ } ^{12}C \text{ atoms}$$

$$1 \text{ mol } H_2O \text{ molecules} = 6.02 \times 10^{23} \text{ } H_2O \text{ molecules}$$

$$1 \text{ mol } NO_3^- \text{ ions} = 6.02 \times 10^{23} \text{ } NO_3^- \text{ ions}$$

Avogadro's number is so large that it is difficult to imagine. Spreading 6.02×10^{23} marbles over the entire surface of Earth would produce a layer about 3 mi thick. If Avogadro's number of pennies were placed side by side in a straight line, they would encircle Earth 300 trillion (3×10^{14}) times.

■■ **SAMPLE EXERCISE 3.7** | Estimating Numbers of Atoms

Without using a calculator, arrange the following samples in order of increasing numbers of carbon atoms: 12 g ^{12}C, 1 mol C_2H_2, 9×10^{23} molecules of CO_2.

Solution

Analyze: We are given amounts of different substances expressed in grams, moles, and number of molecules and asked to arrange the samples in order of increasing numbers of C atoms.

Plan: To determine the number of C atoms in each sample, we must convert g ^{12}C, mol C_2H_2, and molecules CO_2 all to numbers of C atoms. To do this converting, we use the definition of mole and Avogadro's number.

Solve: A mole is defined as the amount of matter that contains as many units of the matter as there are C atoms in exactly 12 g of ^{12}C. Thus, 12 g of ^{12}C contains 1 mol of C atoms (that is, 6.02×10^{23} C atoms). In 1 mol C_2H_2, there are 6×10^{23} C_2H_2 molecules. Because there are two C atoms in each C_2H_2 molecule, this sample contains 12×10^{23} C atoms. Because each CO_2 molecule contains one C atom, the sample of CO_2 contains 9×10^{23} C atoms. Hence, the order is 12 g ^{12}C (6×10^{23} C atoms) $< 9 \times 10^{23}$ CO_2 molecules (9×10^{23} C atoms) < 1 mol C_2H_2 (12×10^{23} C atoms).

Check: We can check our results by comparing the number of moles of C atoms in each sample because the number of moles is proportional to the number of atoms. Thus, 12 g of ^{12}C is 1 mol C; 1 mol of C_2H_2 contains 2 mol C, and 9×10^{23} molecules of CO_2 contain 1.5 mol C, giving the same order as above: 12 g ^{12}C (1 mol C) $< 9 \times 10^{23}$ CO_2 molecules (1.5 mol C) < 1 mol C_2H_2 (2 mol C).

■■ **PRACTICE EXERCISE**

Without using a calculator, arrange the following samples in order of increasing number of O atoms: 1 mol H_2O, 1 mol CO_2, 3×10^{23} molecules O_3.
Answer: 1 mol H_2O (6×10^{23} O atoms) $< 3 \times 10^{23}$ molecules O_3 (9×10^{23} O atoms) < 1 mol CO_2 (12×10^{23} O atoms)

---

* The term *mole* comes from the Latin word *moles*, meaning "a mass." The term *molecule* is the diminutive form of this word and means "a small mass."

■ **SAMPLE EXERCISE 3.8** | Converting Moles to Number of Atoms

Calculate the number of H atoms in 0.350 mol of $C_6H_{12}O_6$.

Solution

Analyze: We are given both the amount of a substance (0.350 mol) and its chemical formula ($C_6H_{12}O_6$). The unknown is the number of H atoms in the sample.

Plan: Avogadro's number provides the conversion factor between the number of moles of $C_6H_{12}O_6$ and the number of molecules of $C_6H_{12}O_6$. Once we know the number of molecules of $C_6H_{12}O_6$, we can use the chemical formula, which tells us that each molecule of $C_6H_{12}O_6$ contains 12 H atoms. Thus, we convert moles of $C_6H_{12}O_6$ to molecules of $C_6H_{12}O_6$ and then determine the number of atoms of H from the number of molecules of $C_6H_{12}O_6$:

$$\text{Moles } C_6H_{12}O_6 \longrightarrow \text{molecules } C_6H_{12}O_6 \longrightarrow \text{atoms H}$$

Solve:

H atoms =

$$(0.350 \text{ mol } C_6H_{12}O_6)\left(\frac{6.02 \times 10^{23} \text{ molecules } C_6H_{12}O_6}{1 \text{ mol } C_6H_{12}O_6}\right)\left(\frac{12 \text{ H atoms}}{1 \text{ molecule } C_6H_{12}O_6}\right)$$

$$= 2.53 \times 10^{24} \text{ H atoms}$$

Check: The magnitude of our answer is reasonable: It is a large number about the magnitude of Avogadro's number. We can also make the following ballpark calculation: Multiplying $0.35 \times 6 \times 10^{23}$ gives about 2×10^{23} molecules. Multiplying this result by 12 gives $24 \times 10^{23} = 2.4 \times 10^{24}$ H atoms, which agrees with the previous, more detailed calculation. Because we were asked for the number of H atoms, the units of our answer are correct. The given data had three significant figures, so our answer has three significant figures.

■ **PRACTICE EXERCISE**

How many oxygen atoms are in **(a)** 0.25 mol $Ca(NO_3)_2$ and **(b)** 1.50 mol of sodium carbonate?

Answers: **(a)** 9.0×10^{23}, **(b)** 2.71×10^{24}

Molar Mass

A dozen is the same number (12) whether we have a dozen eggs or a dozen elephants. Clearly, however, a dozen eggs does not have the same mass as a dozen elephants. Similarly, a mole is always the *same number* (6.02×10^{23}), but 1-mole samples of different substances will have *different masses*. Compare, for example, 1 mol of ^{12}C and 1 mol of ^{24}Mg. A single ^{12}C atom has a mass of 12 amu, whereas a single ^{24}Mg atom is twice as massive, 24 amu (to two significant figures). Because a mole always has the same number of particles, a mole of ^{24}Mg must be twice as massive as a mole of ^{12}C. Because a mole of ^{12}C has a mass of 12 g (by definition), then a mole of ^{24}Mg must have a mass of 24 g. This example illustrates a general rule relating the mass of an atom to the mass of Avogadro's number (1 mol) of these atoms: *The mass of a single atom of an element (in amu) is numerically equal to the mass (in grams) of 1 mol of that element.* This statement is true regardless of the element:

1 atom of ^{12}C has a mass of 12 amu $\Rightarrow$ 1 mol ^{12}C has a mass of 12 g

1 atom of Cl has an atomic weight of 35.5 amu $\Rightarrow$ 1 mol Cl has a mass of 35.5 g

1 atom of Au has an atomic weight of 197 amu $\Rightarrow$ 1 mol Au has a mass of 197 g

Notice that when we are dealing with a particular isotope of an element, we use the mass of that isotope; otherwise we use the atomic weight (the average atomic mass) of the element.

Science Fundamentals Second Edition

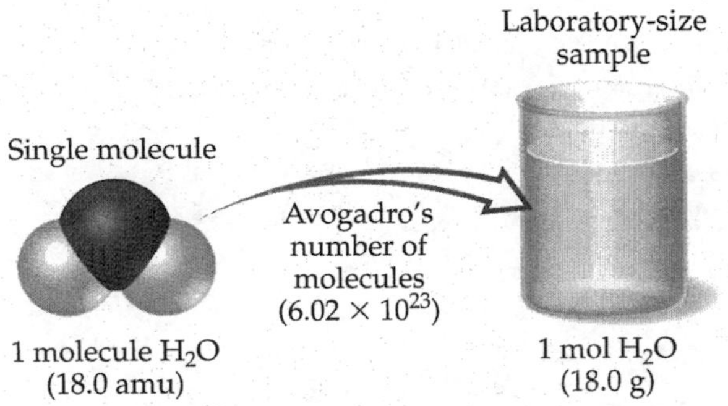

Laboratory-size
sample

Single molecule

Avogadro's
number of
molecules
(6.02×10^{23})

1 molecule H_2O
(18.0 amu)

1 mol H_2O
(18.0 g)

▲ **Figure 3.8   Comparing the mass of 1 molecule H_2O and 1 mol H_2O.** Notice that the masses are numerically equal but have different units (18.0 amu compared to 18.0 g) representing the huge difference in mass.

For other kinds of substances, the same numerical relationship exists between the formula weight (in amu) and the mass (in grams) of one mole of that substance:

1 H_2O molecule has a mass of 18.0 amu $\Rightarrow$ 1 mol H_2O has a mass of 18.0 g

1 NO_3^- ion has a mass of 62.0 amu $\Rightarrow$ 1 mol NO_3^- has a mass of 62.0 g

1 NaCl unit has a mass of 58.5 amu $\Rightarrow$ 1 mol NaCl has a mass of 58.5 g

Figure 3.8 ▲ illustrates the relationship between the mass of a single molecule of H_2O and that of a mole of H_2O.

The mass in grams of one mole of a substance (that is, the mass in grams per mol) is called the **molar mass** of the substance. *The molar mass (in g/mol) of any substance is always numerically equal to its formula weight (in amu).* The substance NaCl, for example, has formula weight of 58.5 amu and a molar mass of 58.5 g/mol. Further examples of mole relationships are shown in Table 3.2 ▼. Figure 3.9 ▶ shows 1-mole quantities of several common substances.

The entries in Table 3.2 for N and N_2 point out the importance of stating the chemical form of a substance exactly when we use the mole concept. Suppose you read that 1 mol of nitrogen is produced in a particular reaction. You might interpret this statement to mean 1 mol of nitrogen atoms (14.0 g). Unless otherwise stated, however, what is probably meant is 1 mol of nitrogen molecules, N_2 (28.0 g), because N_2 is the usual chemical form of the element. To avoid ambiguity, it is important to state explicitly the chemical form being discussed. Using the chemical formula N_2 avoids ambiguity.

▲ **Figure 3.9   One mole each of a solid, a liquid, and a gas.** One mole of NaCl, the solid, has a mass of 58.45 g. One mole of H_2O, the liquid, has a mass of 18.0 g and occupies a volume of 18.0 mL. One mole of O_2, the gas, has a mass of 32.0 g and occupies a balloon whose diameter is 35 cm.

TABLE 3.2 Mole Relationships				
Name of substance	Formula	Formula Weight (amu)	Molar Mass (g/mol)	Number and Kind of Particles in One Mole
Atomic nitrogen	N	14.0	14.0	6.022×10^{23} N atoms
Molecular nitrogen	N_2	28.0	28.0	$\begin{cases} 6.022 \times 10^{23} \, N_2 \text{ molecules} \\ 2(6.022 \times 10^{23}) \, N \text{ atoms} \end{cases}$
Silver	Ag	107.9	107.9	6.022×10^{23} Ag atoms
Silver ions	Ag^+	107.9[a]	107.9	$6.022 \times 10^{23} \, Ag^+$ ions
Barium chloride	$BaCl_2$	208.2	208.2	$\begin{cases} 6.022 \times 10^{23} \, BaCl_2 \text{ units} \\ 6.022 \times 10^{23} \, Ba^{2+} \text{ ions} \\ 2(6.022 \times 10^{23}) \, Cl^- \text{ ions} \end{cases}$

[a]Recall that the electron has negligible mass; thus, ions and atoms have essentially the same mass.

Science Fundamentals Second Edition

■■ SAMPLE EXERCISE 3.9 | Calculating Molar Mass

What is the mass in grams of 1.000 mol of glucose, $C_6H_{12}O_6$?

Solution

Analyze: We are given a chemical formula and asked to determine its molar mass.

Plan: The molar mass of a substance is found by adding the atomic weights of its component atoms.

Solve:

$$
\begin{array}{rll}
6\text{ C atoms} &= 6(12.0\text{ amu}) &= 72.0\text{ amu} \\
12\text{ H atoms} &= 12(\ 1.0\text{ amu}) &= 12.0\text{ amu} \\
6\text{ O atoms} &= 6(16.0\text{ amu}) &= \underline{96.0\text{ amu}} \\
& & 180.0\text{ amu}
\end{array}
$$

Because glucose has a formula weight of 180.0 amu, one mole of this substance has a mass of 180.0 g. In other words, $C_6H_{12}O_6$ has a molar mass of 180.0 g/mol.

Check: The magnitude of our answer seems reasonable, and g/mol is the appropriate unit for the molar mass.

Comment: Glucose is sometimes called dextrose. Also known as blood sugar, glucose is found widely in nature, occurring, for example, in honey and fruits. Other types of sugars used as food are converted into glucose in the stomach or liver before they are used by the body as energy sources. Because glucose requires no conversion, it is often given intravenously to patients who need immediate nourishment.

■■ PRACTICE EXERCISE

Calculate the molar mass of $Ca(NO_3)_2$.
Answer: 164.1 g/mol

Interconverting Masses and Moles

Conversions of mass to moles and of moles to mass are frequently encountered in calculations using the mole concept. These calculations are made easy through dimensional analysis, as shown in Sample Exercises 3.10 and 3.11.

■■ SAMPLE EXERCISE 3.10 | Converting Grams to Moles

Calculate the number of moles of glucose ($C_6H_{12}O_6$) in 5.380 g of $C_6H_{12}O_6$.

Solution

Analyze: We are given the number of grams of a substance and its chemical formula and asked to calculate the number of moles.

Plan: The molar mass of a substance provides the factor for converting grams to moles. The molar mass of $C_6H_{12}O_6$ is 180.0 g/mol (Sample Exercise 3.9).

Solve: Using 1 mol $C_6H_{12}O_6$ = 180.0 g $C_6H_{12}O_6$ to write the appropriate conversion factor, we have

$$
\text{Moles } C_6H_{12}O_6 = (5.380 \text{ g } C_6H_{12}O_6)\left(\frac{1 \text{ mol } C_6H_{12}O_6}{180.0 \text{ g } C_6H_{12}O_6}\right) = 0.02989 \text{ mol } C_6H_{12}O_6
$$

Check: Because 5.380 g is less than the molar mass, it is reasonable that our answer is less than one mole. The units of our answer (mol) are appropriate. The original data had four significant figures, so our answer has four significant figures.

■■ PRACTICE EXERCISE

How many moles of sodium bicarbonate ($NaHCO_3$) are there in 508 g of $NaHCO_3$?
Answer: 6.05 mol $NaHCO_3$

■■ SAMPLE EXERCISE 3.11 | Converting Moles to Grams

Calculate the mass, in grams, of 0.433 mol of calcium nitrate.

Solution

Analyze: We are given the number of moles and name of a substance and asked to calculate the number of grams in the sample.

Plan: In order to convert moles to grams, we need the molar mass, which we can calculate using the chemical formula and atomic weights.

Solve: Because the calcium ion is Ca^{2+} and the nitrate ion is NO_3^-, calcium nitrate is $Ca(NO_3)_2$. Adding the atomic weights of the elements in the compound gives a formula weight of 164.1 amu. Using 1 mol $Ca(NO_3)_2$ = 164.1 g $Ca(NO_3)_2$ to write the appropriate conversion factor, we have

$$\text{Grams } Ca(NO_3)_2 = \left(0.433 \text{ mol } Ca(NO_3)_2\right)\left(\frac{164.1 \text{ g } Ca(NO_3)_2}{1 \text{ mol } Ca(NO_3)_2}\right) = 71.1 \text{ g } Ca(NO_3)_2$$

Check: The number of moles is less than 1, so the number of grams must be less than the molar mass, 164.1 g. Using rounded numbers to estimate, we have $0.5 \times 150 = 75$ g. Thus, the magnitude of our answer is reasonable. Both the units (g) and the number of significant figures (3) are correct.

▇ PRACTICE EXERCISE

What is the mass, in grams, of **(a)** 6.33 mol of $NaHCO_3$ and **(b)** 3.0×10^{-5} mol of sulfuric acid?
Answers: **(a)** 532 g, **(b)** 2.9×10^{-3} g

Interconverting Masses and Numbers of Particles

The mole concept provides the bridge between masses and numbers of particles. To illustrate how we can interconvert masses and numbers of particles, let's calculate the number of copper atoms in an old copper penny. Such a penny weighs about 3 g, and we'll assume that it is 100% copper:

$$\text{Cu atoms} = (3 \text{ g Cu})\left(\frac{1 \text{ mol Cu}}{63.5 \text{ g Cu}}\right)\left(\frac{6.02 \times 10^{23} \text{ Cu atoms}}{1 \text{ mol Cu}}\right)$$
$$= 3 \times 10^{22} \text{ Cu atoms}$$

Notice how dimensional analysis (Section 1.6) provides a straightforward route from grams to numbers of atoms. The molar mass and Avogadro's number are used as conversion factors to convert grams $\longrightarrow$ moles $\longrightarrow$ atoms. Notice also that our answer is a very large number. Any time you calculate the number of atoms, molecules, or ions in an ordinary sample of matter, you can expect the answer to be very large. In contrast, the number of moles in a sample will usually be much smaller, often less than 1. The general procedure for interconverting mass and number of formula units (atoms, molecules, ions, or whatever is represented by the chemical formula) of a substance is summarized in Figure 3.10 ▼.

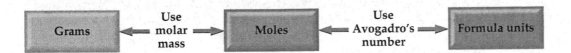

▲ **Figure 3.10   Procedure for interconverting the mass and the number of formula units of a substance.** The number of moles of the substance is central to the calculation; thus, the mole concept can be thought of as the bridge between the mass of a substance in grams and the number of formula units.

▇ SAMPLE EXERCISE 3.12 | Calculating the Number of Molecules and Number of Atoms from Mass

(a) How many glucose molecules are in 5.23 g of $C_6H_{12}O_6$? **(b)** How many oxygen atoms are in this sample?

Solution
Analyze: We are given the number of grams and chemical formula and asked to calculate **(a)** the number of molecules and **(b)** the number of O atoms in the sample.
(a) Plan: The strategy for determining the number of molecules in a given quantity of a substance is summarized in Figure 3.10. We must convert 5.23 g $C_6H_{12}O_6$ to moles $C_6H_{12}O_6$, which can then be converted to molecules $C_6H_{12}O_6$. The first conversion uses the molar mass of $C_6H_{12}O_6$: 1 mol $C_6H_{12}O_6$ = 180.0 g $C_6H_{12}O_6$. The second conversion uses Avogadro's number.

Solve: Molecules $C_6H_{12}O_6$

$$= (5.23 \text{ g } C_6H_{12}O_6)\left(\frac{1 \text{ mol } C_6H_{12}O_6}{180.0 \text{ g } C_6H_{12}O_6}\right)\left(\frac{6.022 \times 10^{23} \text{ molecules } C_6H_{12}O_6}{1 \text{ mol } C_6H_{12}O_6}\right)$$

$$= 1.75 \times 10^{22} \text{ molecules } C_6H_{12}O_6$$

Check: The magnitude of the answer is reasonable. Because the mass we began with is less than a mole, there should be less than 6.02×10^{23} molecules. We can make a ballpark estimate of the answer: $5/200 = 2.5 \times 10^{-2}$ mol; $2.5 \times 10^{-2} \times 6 \times 10^{23} = 15 \times 10^{21} = 1.5 \times 10^{22}$ molecules. The units (molecules) and significant figures (three) are appropriate.

(b) Plan: To determine the number of O atoms, we use the fact that there are six O atoms in each molecule of $C_6H_{12}O_6$. Thus, multiplying the number of molecules $C_6H_{12}O_6$ by the factor (6 atoms O/1 molecule $C_6H_{12}O_6$) gives the number of O atoms.

Solve:

$$\text{Atoms O} = (1.75 \times 10^{22} \text{ molecules } C_6H_{12}O_6)\left(\frac{6 \text{ atoms O}}{1 \text{ molecule } C_6H_{12}O_6}\right)$$

$$= 1.05 \times 10^{23} \text{ atoms O}$$

Check: The answer is simply 6 times as large as the answer to part (a). The number of significant figures (three) and the units (atoms O) are correct.

▬ PRACTICE EXERCISE

(a) How many nitric acid molecules are in 4.20 g of HNO_3? **(b)** How many O atoms are in this sample?
Answers: **(a)** 4.01×10^{22} molecules HNO_3, **(b)** 1.20×10^{23} atoms O

3.5 | Empirical Formulas from Analyses

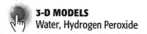

3-D MODELS
Water, Hydrogen Peroxide

As we learned in Section 2.6, the empirical formula for a substance tells us the relative number of atoms of each element it contains. Thus, the empirical formula H_2O indicates that water contains two H atoms for each O atom. This ratio also applies on the molar level: 1 mol of H_2O contains 2 mol of H atoms and 1 mol of O atoms. Conversely, the ratio of the number of moles of each element in a compound gives the subscripts in a compound's empirical formula. Thus, the mole concept provides a way of calculating the empirical formulas of chemical substances, as shown in the following examples.

Mercury and chlorine combine to form a compound that is 73.9% mercury and 26.1% chlorine by mass. This means that if we had a 100.0-g sample of the solid, it would contain 73.9 g of mercury (Hg) and 26.1 g of chlorine (Cl). (Any size sample can be used in problems of this type, but we will generally use 100.0 g to simplify the calculation of mass from percentage.) Using the atomic weights of the elements to give us molar masses, we can calculate the number of moles of each element in the sample:

$$(73.9 \text{ g Hg})\left(\frac{1 \text{ mol Hg}}{200.6 \text{ g Hg}}\right) = 0.368 \text{ mol Hg}$$

$$(26.1 \text{ g Cl})\left(\frac{1 \text{ mol Cl}}{35.5 \text{ g Cl}}\right) = 0.735 \text{ mol Cl}$$

We then divide the larger number of moles (0.735) by the smaller (0.368) to obtain a Cl : Hg mole ratio of 1.99 : 1:

$$\frac{\text{moles of Cl}}{\text{moles of Hg}} = \frac{0.735 \text{ mol Cl}}{0.368 \text{ mol Hg}} = \frac{1.99 \text{ mol Cl}}{1 \text{ mol Hg}}$$

Given:

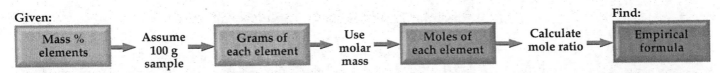

Because of experimental errors, the results may not lead to exact integers for the ratios of moles. The number 1.99 is very close to 2, so we can confidently conclude that the empirical formula for the compound is $HgCl_2$. This is the empirical formula because its subscripts are the smallest integers that express the *ratios* of atoms present in the compound. ∞∞ (Section 2.6) The general procedure for determining empirical formulas is outlined in Figure 3.11 ▲.

▲ **Figure 3.11 Procedure for calculating an empirical formula from percentage composition.** The central part of the calculation is determining the number of moles of each element in the compound. The procedure is also summarized as "percent to mass, mass to mole, divide by small, multiply 'til whole."

ACTIVITY
Empirical Formula Determination: C_8H_6O

SAMPLE EXERCISE 3.13 | Calculating an Empirical Formula

Ascorbic acid (vitamin C) contains 40.92% C, 4.58% H, and 54.50% O by mass. What is the empirical formula of ascorbic acid?

Solution
Analyze: We are to determine an empirical formula of a compound from the mass percentages of its elements.
Plan: The strategy for determining the empirical formula involves the three steps given in Figure 3.11.
Solve: We *first* assume, for simplicity, that we have exactly 100 g of material (although any mass can be used). In 100 g of ascorbic acid, we have

40.92 g C, 4.58 g H, and 54.50 g O.

Second, we calculate the number of moles of each element:

$$\text{Moles C} = (40.92 \text{ g C})\left(\frac{1 \text{ mol C}}{12.01 \text{ g C}}\right) = 3.407 \text{ mol C}$$

$$\text{Moles H} = (4.58 \text{ g H})\left(\frac{1 \text{ mol H}}{1.008 \text{ g H}}\right) = 4.54 \text{ mol H}$$

$$\text{Moles O} = (54.50 \text{ g O})\left(\frac{1 \text{ mol O}}{16.00 \text{ g O}}\right) = 3.406 \text{ mol O}$$

Third, we determine the simplest whole-number ratio of moles by dividing each number of moles by the smallest number of moles, 3.406:

$$\text{C:} \frac{3.407}{3.406} = 1.000 \quad \text{H:} \frac{4.54}{3.406} = 1.33 \quad \text{O:} \frac{3.406}{3.406} = 1.000$$

The ratio for H is too far from 1 to attribute the difference to experimental error; in fact, it is quite close to $1\frac{1}{3}$. This suggests that if we multiply the ratio by 3, we will obtain whole numbers:

$$\text{C:H:O} = 3(1:1.33:1) = 3:4:3$$

The whole-number mole ratio gives us the subscripts for the empirical formula:

$$C_3H_4O_3$$

Check: It is reassuring that the subscripts are moderately sized whole numbers. Otherwise, we have little by which to judge the reasonableness of our answer.

PRACTICE EXERCISE

A 5.325-g sample of methyl benzoate, a compound used in the manufacture of perfumes, is found to contain 3.758 g of carbon, 0.316 g of hydrogen, and 1.251 g of oxygen. What is the empirical formula of this substance?
Answer: C_4H_4O

Molecular Formula from Empirical Formula

For any compound, the formula obtained from percentage compositions is always the empirical formula. We can obtain the molecular formula from the empirical formula if we are given the molecular weight or molar mass of the compound. *The subscripts in the molecular formula of a substance are always a whole-number multiple of the corresponding subscripts in its empirical formula.* ∞ (Section 2.6) This multiple can be found by comparing the empirical formula weight with the molecular weight:

$$\text{Whole-number multiple} = \frac{\text{molecular weight}}{\text{empirical formula weight}} \qquad [3.11]$$

In Sample Exercise 3.13, for example, the empirical formula of ascorbic acid was determined to be $C_3H_4O_3$, giving an empirical formula weight of 3(12.0 amu) + 4(1.0 amu) + 3(16.0 amu) = 88.0 amu. The experimentally determined molecular weight is 176 amu. Thus, the molecular weight is 2 times the empirical formula weight (176/88.0 = 2.00), and the molecular formula must therefore have twice as many of each kind of atom as the empirical formula. Consequently, we multiply the subscripts in the empirical formula by 2 to obtain the molecular formula: $C_6H_8O_6$.

■ SAMPLE EXERCISE 3.14 | Determining a Molecular Formula

Mesitylene, a hydrocarbon that occurs in small amounts in crude oil, has an empirical formula of C_3H_4. The experimentally determined molecular weight of this substance is 121 amu. What is the molecular formula of mesitylene?

Solution
Analyze: We are given an empirical formula and molecular weight and asked to determine a molecular formula.
Plan: The subscripts in the molecular formula of a compound are whole-number multiples of the subscripts in its empirical formula. To find the appropriate multiple, we must compare the molecular weight with the formula weight of the empirical formula.
Solve: First, we calculate the formula weight of the empirical formula, C_3H_4:

$$3(12.0 \text{ amu}) + 4(1.0 \text{ amu}) = 40.0 \text{ amu}$$

Next, we divide the molecular weight by the empirical formula weight to obtain the multiple used to multiply the subscripts in C_3H_4:

$$\frac{\text{Molecular weight}}{\text{Empirical formula weight}} = \frac{121}{40.0} = 3.02$$

Only whole-number ratios make physical sense because we must be dealing with whole atoms. The 3.02 in this case results from a small experimental error in the molecular weight. We therefore multiply each subscript in the empirical formula by 3 to give the molecular formula: C_9H_{12}.
Check: We can have confidence in the result because dividing the molecular weight by the formula weight yields nearly a whole number.

■ PRACTICE EXERCISE

Ethylene glycol, the substance used in automobile antifreeze, is composed of 38.7% C, 9.7% H, and 51.6% O by mass. Its molar mass is 62.1 g/mol. **(a)** What is the empirical formula of ethylene glycol? **(b)** What is its molecular formula?
Answers: **(a)** CH_3O, **(b)** $C_2H_6O_2$

Combustion Analysis

The empirical formula of a compound is based on experiments that give the number of moles of each element in a sample of the compound. That is why we use the word "empirical," which means "based on observation and experiment." Chemists have devised a number of experimental techniques to determine

Science Fundamentals Second Edition

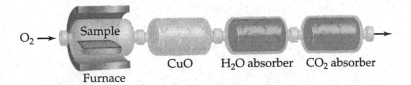

▲ Figure 3.12 Apparatus to determine percentages of carbon and hydrogen in a compound.
The compound is combusted to form CO_2 and H_2O. Copper oxide helps to oxidize traces of carbon and carbon monoxide to carbon dioxide and to oxidize hydrogen to water.

empirical formulas. One of these is combustion analysis, which is commonly used for compounds containing principally carbon and hydrogen as their component elements.

When a compound containing carbon and hydrogen is completely combusted in an apparatus such as that shown in Figure 3.12 ▲ the carbon in the compound is converted to CO_2, and the hydrogen is converted to H_2O. ∞ (Section 3.2) The amounts of CO_2 and H_2O produced are determined by measuring the mass increase in the CO_2 and H_2O absorbers. From the masses of CO_2 and H_2O we can calculate the number of moles of C and H in the original compound and thereby the empirical formula. If a third element is present in the compound, its mass can be determined by subtracting the masses of C and H from the compound's original mass. Sample Exercise 3.15 shows how to determine the empirical formula of a compound containing C, H, and O.

■■ SAMPLE EXERCISE 3.15 | Determining Empirical Formula by Combustion Analysis

Isopropyl alcohol, a substance sold as rubbing alcohol, is composed of C, H, and O. Combustion of 0.255 g of isopropyl alcohol produces 0.561 g of CO_2 and 0.306 g of H_2O. Determine the empirical formula of isopropyl alcohol.

Solution

Analyze: We are told that isopropyl alcohol contains C, H, and O atoms and given the quantities of CO_2 and H_2O produced when a given quantity of the alcohol is combusted. We must use this information to determine the empirical formula for isopropyl alcohol, a task that requires us to calculate the number of moles of C, H, and O in the sample.

Plan: We can use the mole concept to calculate the number of grams of C present in the CO_2 and the number of grams of H present in the H_2O. These are the quantities of C and H present in the isopropyl alcohol before combustion. The number of grams of O in the compound equals the mass of the isopropyl alcohol minus the sum of the C and H masses. Once we have the number of grams of C, H, and O in the sample, we can then proceed as in Sample Exercise 3.13: Calculate the number of moles of each element, and determine the mole ratio, which gives the subscripts in the empirical formula.

Solve: To calculate the number of grams of C, we first use the molar mass of CO_2, 1 mol CO_2 = 44.0 g CO_2, to convert grams of CO_2 to moles of CO_2. Because there is only 1 C atom in each CO_2 molecule, there is 1 mol of C atoms per mole of CO_2 molecules. This fact allows us to convert the moles of CO_2 to moles of C. Finally, we use the molar mass of C, 1 mol C = 12.0 g C, to convert moles of C to grams of C. Combining the three conversion factors, we have:

$$\text{Grams C} = (0.561\ \text{g CO}_2)\left(\frac{1\ \text{mol CO}_2}{44.0\ \text{g CO}_2}\right)\left(\frac{1\ \text{mol C}}{1\ \text{mol CO}_2}\right)\left(\frac{12.0\ \text{g C}}{1\ \text{mol C}}\right) = 0.153\ \text{g C}$$

The calculation of the number of grams of H from the grams of H_2O is similar, although we must remember that there are 2 mol of H atoms per 1 mol of H_2O molecules:

$$\text{Grams H} = (0.306\ \text{g H}_2\text{O})\left(\frac{1\ \text{mol H}_2\text{O}}{18.0\ \text{g H}_2\text{O}}\right)\left(\frac{2\ \text{mol H}}{1\ \text{mol H}_2\text{O}}\right)\left(\frac{1.01\ \text{g H}}{1\ \text{mol H}}\right) = 0.0343\ \text{g H}$$

The total mass of the sample, 0.255 g, is the sum of the masses of the C, H, and O. Thus, we can calculate the mass of O as follows:

$$\text{Mass of O} = \text{mass of sample} - (\text{mass of C} + \text{mass of H})$$
$$= 0.255\ \text{g} - (0.153\ \text{g} + 0.0343\ \text{g}) = 0.068\ \text{g O}$$

Science Fundamentals Second Edition

We then calculate the number of moles of C, H, and O in the sample:

$$\text{Moles C} = (0.153 \text{ g C})\left(\frac{1 \text{ mol C}}{12.0 \text{ g C}}\right) = 0.0128 \text{ mol C}$$

$$\text{Moles H} = (0.0343 \text{ g H})\left(\frac{1 \text{ mol H}}{1.01 \text{ g H}}\right) = 0.0340 \text{ mol H}$$

$$\text{Moles O} = (0.068 \text{ g O})\left(\frac{1 \text{ mol O}}{16.0 \text{ g O}}\right) = 0.0043 \text{ mol O}$$

To find the empirical formula, we must compare the relative number of moles of each element in the sample. The relative number of moles of each element is found by dividing each number by the smallest number, 0.0043. The mole ratio of C:H:O so obtained is 2.98:7.91:1.00. The first two numbers are very close to the whole numbers 3 and 8, giving the empirical formula C_3H_8O.
Check: The subscripts work out to be moderately sized whole numbers, as expected.

PRACTICE EXERCISE

(a) Caproic acid, which is responsible for the foul odor of dirty socks, is composed of C, H, and O atoms. Combustion of a 0.225-g sample of this compound produces 0.512 g CO_2 and 0.209 g H_2O. What is the empirical formula of caproic acid? **(b)** Caproic acid has a molar mass of 116 g/mol. What is its molecular formula?
Answers: **(a)** C_3H_6O, **(b)** $C_6H_{12}O_2$

GIVE IT SOME THOUGHT

In Sample Exercise 3.15, how do you explain the fact that the ratios C:H:O are 2.98:7.91:1.00, rather than exact integers 3:8:1?

3.6 | Quantitative Information from Balanced Equations

The coefficients in a chemical equation represent the relative numbers of molecules involved in a reaction. The mole concept allows us to convert this information to the masses of the substances. Consider the following balanced equation:

$$2 H_2(g) + O_2(g) \longrightarrow 2 H_2O(l) \qquad [3.12]$$

The coefficients indicate that two molecules of H_2 react with each molecule of O_2 to form two molecules of H_2O. It follows that the relative numbers of moles are identical to the relative numbers of molecules:

$$\begin{array}{ccccc}
2 H_2(g) & + & O_2(g) & \longrightarrow & 2 H_2O(l) \\
\text{2 molecules} & & \text{1 molecule} & & \text{2 molecules} \\
2(6.02 \times 10^{23} \text{ molecules}) & & 1(6.02 \times 10^{23} \text{ molecules}) & & 2(6.02 \times 10^{23} \text{ molecules}) \\
\text{2 mol} & & \text{1 mol} & & \text{2 mol}
\end{array}$$

We can generalize this observation for all balanced chemical equations: *The coefficients in a balanced chemical equation indicate both the relative numbers of molecules (or formula units) involved in the reaction and the relative numbers of moles.* Table 3.3 ▼ further summarizes this result and also shows how it corresponds

TABLE 3.3 Information from a Balanced Equation				
Equation:	$2 H_2(g)$	+ $O_2(g)$	$\longrightarrow$	$2 H_2O(l)$
Molecules:	2 molecules H_2	+ 1 molecule O_2	$\longrightarrow$	2 molecules H_2O
Mass (amu):	4.0 amu H_2	+ 32.0 amu O_2	$\longrightarrow$	36.0 amu H_2O
Amount (mol):	2 mol H_2	+ 1 mol O_2	$\longrightarrow$	2 mol H_2O
Mass (g):	4.0 g H_2	+ 32.0 g O_2	$\longrightarrow$	36.0 g H_2O

to the law of conservation of mass. Notice that the total mass of the reactants (4.0 g + 32.0 g) equals the total mass of the products (36.0 g).

The quantities 2 mol H_2, 1 mol O_2, and 2 mol H_2O, which are given by the coefficients in Equation 3.12, are called *stoichiometrically equivalent quantities*. The relationship between these quantities can be represented as

$$2 \text{ mol } H_2 \simeq 1 \text{ mol } O_2 \simeq 2 \text{ mol } H_2O$$

where the $\simeq$ symbol means "is stoichiometrically equivalent to." In other words, Equation 3.12 shows 2 mol of H_2 and 1 mol of O_2 forming 2 mol of H_2O. These stoichiometric relations can be used to convert between quantities of reactants and products in a chemical reaction. For example, the number of moles of H_2O produced from 1.57 mol of O_2 can be calculated as follows:

$$\text{Moles } H_2O = (1.57 \text{ mol } O_2)\left(\frac{2 \text{ mol } H_2O}{1 \text{ mol } O_2}\right) = 3.14 \text{ mol } H_2O$$

 GIVE IT SOME THOUGHT

When 1.57 mol O_2 reacts with H_2 to form H_2O, how many moles of H_2 are consumed in the process?

As an additional example, consider the combustion of butane (C_4H_{10}), the fuel in disposable cigarette lighters:

$$2 C_4H_{10}(l) + 13 O_2(g) \longrightarrow 8 CO_2(g) + 10 H_2O(g) \qquad [3.13]$$

Let's calculate the mass of CO_2 produced when 1.00 g of C_4H_{10} is burned. The coefficients in Equation 3.13 tell how the amount of C_4H_{10} consumed is related to the amount of CO_2 produced: 2 mol $C_4H_{10} \simeq 8$ mol CO_2. In order to use this relationship, however, we must use the molar mass of C_4H_{10} to convert grams of C_4H_{10} to moles of C_4H_{10}. Because 1 mol $C_4H_{10} = 58.0$ g C_4H_{10}, we have

$$\text{Moles } C_4H_{10} = (1.00 \text{ g } C_4H_{10})\left(\frac{1 \text{ mol } C_4H_{10}}{58.0 \text{ g } C_4H_{10}}\right)$$

$$= 1.72 \times 10^{-2} \text{ mol } C_4H_{10}$$

We can then use the stoichiometric factor from the balanced equation, 2 mol $C_4H_{10} \simeq 8$ mol CO_2, to calculate moles of CO_2:

$$\text{Moles } CO_2 = (1.72 \times 10^{-2} \text{ mol } C_4H_{10})\left(\frac{8 \text{ mol } CO_2}{2 \text{ mol } C_4H_{10}}\right)$$

$$= 6.88 \times 10^{-2} \text{ mol } CO_2$$

Finally, we can calculate the mass of the CO_2, in grams, using the molar mass of CO_2 (1 mol $CO_2 = 44.0$ g CO_2):

$$\text{Grams } CO_2 = (6.88 \times 10^{-2} \text{ mol } CO_2)\left(\frac{44.0 \text{ g } CO_2}{1 \text{ mol } CO_2}\right)$$

$$= 3.03 \text{ g } CO_2$$

Thus, the conversion sequence is

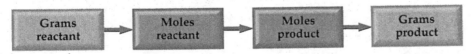

► **Figure 3.13 The procedure for calculating amounts of reactants or products in a reaction.** The number of grams of a reactant consumed or of a product formed in a reaction can be calculated, starting with the number of grams of one of the other reactants or products. Notice how molar masses and the coefficients in the balanced equation are used.

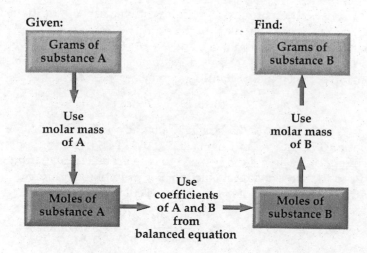

ACTIVITY
Stoichiometry Calculation

These steps can be combined in a single sequence of factors:

$$\text{Grams CO}_2 = (1.00 \text{ g C}_4\text{H}_{10})\left(\frac{1 \text{ mol C}_4\text{H}_{10}}{58.0 \text{ g C}_4\text{H}_{10}}\right)\left(\frac{8 \text{ mol CO}_2}{2 \text{ mol C}_4\text{H}_{10}}\right)\left(\frac{44.0 \text{ g CO}_2}{1 \text{ mol CO}_2}\right)$$

$$= 3.03 \text{ g CO}_2$$

Similarly, we can calculate the amount of O_2 consumed or H_2O produced in this reaction. For example, to calculate the amount of O_2 consumed, we again rely on the coefficients in the balanced equation to give us the appropriate stoichiometric factor: 2 mol $C_4H_{10} \simeq$ 13 mol O_2:

$$\text{Grams O}_2 = (1.00 \text{ g C}_4\text{H}_{10})\left(\frac{1 \text{ mol C}_4\text{H}_{10}}{58.0 \text{ g C}_4\text{H}_{10}}\right)\left(\frac{13 \text{ mol O}_2}{2 \text{ mol C}_4\text{H}_{10}}\right)\left(\frac{32.0 \text{ g O}_2}{1 \text{ mol O}_2}\right)$$

$$= 3.59 \text{ g O}_2$$

Figure 3.13 ▲ summarizes the general approach used to calculate the quantities of substances consumed or produced in chemical reactions. The balanced chemical equation provides the relative numbers of moles of reactants and products involved in the reaction.

SAMPLE EXERCISE 3.16 | Calculating Amounts of Reactants and Products
How many grams of water are produced in the oxidation of 1.00 g of glucose, $C_6H_{12}O_6$?

$$C_6H_{12}O_6(s) + 6 \text{ O}_2(g) \longrightarrow 6 \text{ CO}_2(g) + 6 \text{ H}_2\text{O}(l)$$

Solution
Analyze: We are given the mass of a reactant and are asked to determine the mass of a product in the given equation.
Plan: The general strategy, as outlined in Figure 3.13, requires three steps. First, the amount of $C_6H_{12}O_6$ must be converted from grams to moles. We can then use the balanced equation, which relates the moles of $C_6H_{12}O_6$ to the moles of H_2O: 1 mol $C_6H_{12}O_6 \simeq$ 6 mol H_2O. Finally, the moles of H_2O must be converted to grams.

Solve: First, use the molar mass of $C_6H_{12}O_6$ to convert from grams $C_6H_{12}O_6$ to moles $C_6H_{12}O_6$:

$$\text{Moles C}_6\text{H}_{12}\text{O}_6 = (1.00 \text{ g C}_6\text{H}_{12}\text{O}_6)\left(\frac{1 \text{ mol C}_6\text{H}_{12}\text{O}_6}{180.0 \text{ g C}_6\text{H}_{12}\text{O}_6}\right)$$

Second, use the balanced equation to convert moles of $C_6H_{12}O_6$ to moles of H_2O:

$$\text{Moles H}_2\text{O} = (1.00 \text{ g C}_6\text{H}_{12}\text{O}_6)\left(\frac{1 \text{ mol C}_6\text{H}_{12}\text{O}_6}{180.0 \text{ g C}_6\text{H}_{12}\text{O}_6}\right)\left(\frac{6 \text{ mol H}_2\text{O}}{1 \text{ mol C}_6\text{H}_{12}\text{O}_6}\right)$$

Third, use the molar mass of H_2O to convert from moles of H_2O to grams of H_2O:

$$\text{Grams H}_2\text{O} = (1.00 \text{ g C}_6\text{H}_{12}\text{O}_6)\left(\frac{1 \text{ mol C}_6\text{H}_{12}\text{O}_6}{180.0 \text{ g C}_6\text{H}_{12}\text{O}_6}\right)\left(\frac{6 \text{ mol H}_2\text{O}}{1 \text{ mol C}_6\text{H}_{12}\text{O}_6}\right)\left(\frac{18.0 \text{ g H}_2\text{O}}{1 \text{ mol H}_2\text{O}}\right)$$

$$= 0.600 \text{ g H}_2\text{O}$$

Science Fundamentals Second Edition

The steps can be summarized in a diagram like that in Figure 3.13:

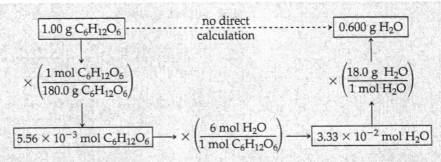

$$1.00 \text{ g } C_6H_{12}O_6 \xrightarrow{\text{no direct calculation}} 0.600 \text{ g } H_2O$$

$$\times \left(\frac{1 \text{ mol } C_6H_{12}O_6}{180.0 \text{ g } C_6H_{12}O_6} \right) \qquad \times \left(\frac{18.0 \text{ g } H_2O}{1 \text{ mol } H_2O} \right)$$

$$5.56 \times 10^{-3} \text{ mol } C_6H_{12}O_6 \xrightarrow{\times \left(\frac{6 \text{ mol } H_2O}{1 \text{ mol } C_6H_{12}O_6} \right)} 3.33 \times 10^{-2} \text{ mol } H_2O$$

Check: An estimate of the magnitude of our answer, 18/180 = 0.1 and 0.1 × 6 = 0.6, agrees with the exact calculation. The units, grams H_2O, are correct. The initial data had three significant figures, so three significant figures for the answer is correct.
Comment: An average person ingests 2 L of water daily and eliminates 2.4 L. The difference between 2 L and 2.4 L is produced in the metabolism of foodstuffs, such as in the oxidation of glucose. (*Metabolism* is a general term used to describe all the chemical processes of a living animal or plant.) The desert rat (kangaroo rat), on the other hand, apparently never drinks water. It survives on its metabolic water.

■ PRACTICE EXERCISE

The decomposition of $KClO_3$ is commonly used to prepare small amounts of O_2 in the laboratory: $2 KClO_3(s) \longrightarrow 2 KCl(s) + 3 O_2(g)$. How many grams of O_2 can be prepared from 4.50 g of $KClO_3$?
Answer: 1.77 g

CHEMISTRY AT WORK | CO_2 and the Greenhouse Effect

Coal and petroleum provide the fuels that we use to generate electricity and power our industrial machinery. These fuels are composed primarily of hydrocarbons and other carbon-containing substances. As we have seen, the combustion of 1.00 g of C_4H_{10} produces 3.03 g of CO_2. Similarly, a gallon (3.78 L) of gasoline (density = 0.70 g/mL and approximate composition C_8H_{18}) produces about 8 kg (18 lb) of CO_2. Combustion of such fuels releases about 20 billion tons of CO_2 into the atmosphere annually.

Much CO_2 is absorbed into oceans or used by plants in photosynthesis. Nevertheless, we are now generating CO_2 much faster than it is being absorbed. Chemists have monitored atmospheric CO_2 concentrations since 1958. Analysis of air trapped in ice cores taken from Antarctica and Greenland makes it possible to determine the atmospheric levels of CO_2 during the past 160,000 years. These measurements reveal that the level of CO_2 remained fairly constant from the last Ice Age, some 10,000 years ago, until roughly the beginning of the Industrial Revolution, about 300 years ago. Since that time the concentration of CO_2 has increased by about 25% (Figure 3.14 ▼).

Although CO_2 is a minor component of the atmosphere, it plays a significant role by absorbing radiant heat, acting much like the glass of a greenhouse. For this reason, we often refer to CO_2 and other heat-trapping gases as greenhouse gases, and we call the warming caused by these gases the *greenhouse effect*. Most atmospheric scientists believe that the accumulation of CO_2 and other heat-trapping gases has begun to change the climate of our planet. Still, it is recognized that the factors affecting climate are complex and incompletely understood.

We will examine the greenhouse effect more closely in Chapter 18.
Related Exercises: 3.64, 3.96, 3.99, and 3.103

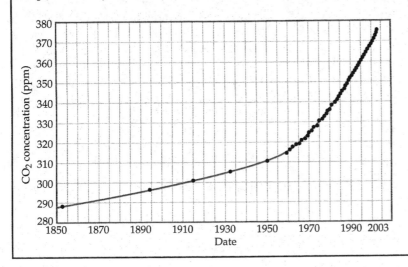

◀ **Figure 3.14 Increasing concentration of atmospheric CO_2.** The world-wide concentration of CO_2 has increased from about 290 ppm to over 370 ppm over the past 150 years. The concentration in ppm is the number of molecules of CO_2 per million (10^6) molecules of air. Data before 1958 came from analyses of air trapped in bubbles of glacial ice.

Science Fundamentals Second Edition

■ SAMPLE EXERCISE 3.17 | Calculating Amounts of Reactants and Products

Solid lithium hydroxide is used in space vehicles to remove exhaled carbon dioxide. The lithium hydroxide reacts with gaseous carbon dioxide to form solid lithium carbonate and liquid water. How many grams of carbon dioxide can be absorbed by 1.00 g of lithium hydroxide?

Solution

Analyze: We are given a verbal description of a reaction and asked to calculate the number of grams of one reactant that reacts with 1.00 g of another.

Plan: The verbal description of the reaction can be used to write a balanced equation:

$$2 \text{ LiOH}(s) + CO_2(g) \longrightarrow Li_2CO_3(s) + H_2O(l)$$

We are given the grams of LiOH and asked to calculate grams of CO_2. We can accomplish this task by using the following sequence of conversions:

$$\text{Grams LiOH} \longrightarrow \text{moles LiOH} \longrightarrow \text{moles } CO_2 \longrightarrow \text{grams } CO_2.$$

The conversion from grams of LiOH to moles of LiOH requires the molar mass of LiOH (6.94 + 16.00 + 1.01 = 23.95 g/mol). The conversion of moles of LiOH to moles of CO_2 is based on the balanced chemical equation: 2 mol LiOH $\simeq$ 1 mol CO_2. To convert the number of moles of CO_2 to grams, we must use the molar mass of CO_2: 12.01 + 2(16.00) = 44.01 g/mol.

Solve:

$$(1.00 \text{ g LiOH})\left(\frac{1 \text{ mol LiOH}}{23.95 \text{ g LiOH}}\right)\left(\frac{1 \text{ mol } CO_2}{2 \text{ mol LiOH}}\right)\left(\frac{44.01 \text{ g } CO_2}{1 \text{ mol } CO_2}\right) = 0.919 \text{ g } CO_2$$

Check: Notice that 23.95 $\approx$ 24, 24 × 2 = 48, and 44/48 is slightly less than 1. Thus, the magnitude of the answer is reasonable based on the amount of starting LiOH; the significant figures and units are appropriate, too.

■ PRACTICE EXERCISE

Propane, C_3H_8, is a common fuel used for cooking and home heating. What mass of O_2 is consumed in the combustion of 1.00 g of propane?
Answer: 3.64 g

3.7 | Limiting Reactants

Suppose you wish to make several sandwiches using one slice of cheese and two slices of bread for each sandwich. Using Bd = bread, Ch = cheese, and Bd_2Ch = sandwich, the recipe for making a sandwich can be represented like a chemical equation:

$$2 \text{ Bd} + \text{Ch} \longrightarrow Bd_2Ch$$

If you have 10 slices of bread and 7 slices of cheese, you will be able to make only five sandwiches before you run out of bread. You will have 2 slices of cheese left over. The amount of available bread limits the number of sandwiches.

An analogous situation occurs in chemical reactions when one of the reactants is used up before the others. The reaction stops as soon as any one of the reactants is totally consumed, leaving the excess reactants as leftovers. Suppose, for example, that we have a mixture of 10 mol H_2 and 7 mol O_2, which react to form water:

$$2 H_2(g) + O_2(g) \longrightarrow 2 H_2O(g)$$

Because 2 mol H_2 $\simeq$ 1 mol O_2, the number of moles of O_2 needed to react with all the H_2 is

$$\text{Moles } O_2 = (10 \text{ mol } H_2)\left(\frac{1 \text{ mol } O_2}{2 \text{ mol } H_2}\right) = 5 \text{ mol } O_2$$

Science Fundamentals Second Edition

Before reaction   After reaction

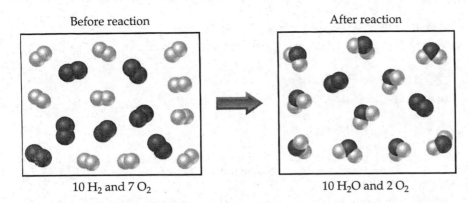

10 H_2 and 7 O_2 10 H_2O and 2 O_2

▲ **Figure 3.15 Example illustrating a limiting reactant.** Because the H_2 is completely consumed, it is the limiting reagent in this case. Because there is a stoichiometric excess of O_2, some is left over at the end of the reaction. The amount of H_2O formed is related directly to the amount of H_2 consumed.

Because 7 mol O_2 was available at the start of the reaction, 7 mol O_2 − 5 mol O_2 = 2 mol O_2 will still be present when all the H_2 is consumed. The example we have considered is depicted on a molecular level in Figure 3.15 ▲.

The reactant that is completely consumed in a reaction is called either the **limiting reactant** or *limiting reagent* because it determines, or limits, the amount of product formed. The other reactants are sometimes called either *excess reactants* or *excess reagents*. In our example, H_2 is the limiting reactant, which means that once all the H_2 has been consumed, the reaction stops. O_2 is the excess reactant, and some is left over when the reaction stops.

There are no restrictions on the starting amounts of the reactants in any reaction. Indeed, many reactions are carried out using an excess of one reagent. The quantities of reactants consumed and the quantities of products formed, however, are restricted by the quantity of the limiting reactant. When a combustion reaction takes place in the open air, oxygen is plentiful and is therefore the excess reactant. You may have had the unfortunate experience of running out of gasoline while driving. The car stops because you've run out of the limiting reactant in the combustion reaction, the fuel.

Before we leave our present example, let's summarize the data in a tabular form:

ANIMATION
Limiting Reagent

	2 $H_2(g)$	+	$O_2(g)$	⟶	2 $H_2O(g)$
Initial quantities:	10 mol		7 mol		0 mol
Change (reaction):	−10 mol		−5 mol		+10 mol
Final quantities:	0 mol		2 mol		10 mol

The initial amounts of the reactants are what we started with (10 mol H_2 and 7 mol O_2). The second line in the table (change) summarizes the amounts of the reactants consumed and the amount of the product formed in the reaction. These quantities are restricted by the quantity of the limiting reactant and depend on the coefficients in the balanced equation. The mole ratio $H_2 : O_2 : H_2O = 10 : 5 : 10$ conforms to the ratio of the coefficients in the balanced equation, $2 : 1 : 2$. The changes are negative for the reactants because they are consumed during the reaction and positive for the product because it is formed during the reaction. Finally, the quantities in the third line of the table (final quantities) depend on the initial quantities and their changes, and these entries are found by adding the entries for the initial quantity and change for each column. There is none of the limiting reactant (H_2) left at the end of the reaction. All that remains is 2 mol O_2 and 10 mol H_2O.

ACTIVITY
Limiting Reagents

Science Fundamentals Second Edition

SAMPLE EXERCISE 3.18 | Calculating the Amount of Product Formed from a Limiting Reactant

The most important commercial process for converting N_2 from the air into nitrogen-containing compounds is based on the reaction of N_2 and H_2 to form ammonia (NH_3):

$$N_2(g) + 3 H_2(g) \longrightarrow 2 NH_3(g)$$

How many moles of NH_3 can be formed from 3.0 mol of N_2 and 6.0 mol of H_2?

Solution

Analyze: We are asked to calculate the number of moles of product, NH_3, given the quantities of each reactant, N_2 and H_2, available in a reaction. Thus, this is a limiting reactant problem.

Plan: If we assume that one reactant is completely consumed, we can calculate how much of the second reactant is needed in the reaction. By comparing the calculated quantity with the available amount, we can determine which reactant is limiting. We then proceed with the calculation, using the quantity of the limiting reactant.

Solve: The number of moles of H_2 needed for complete consumption of 3.0 mol of N_2 is

$$\text{Moles } H_2 = (3.0 \text{ mol } N_2)\left(\frac{3 \text{ mol } H_2}{1 \text{ mol } N_2}\right) = 9.0 \text{ mol } H_2$$

Because only 6.0 mol H_2 is available, we will run out of H_2 before the N_2 is gone, and H_2 will be the limiting reactant. We use the quantity of the limiting reactant, H_2, to calculate the quantity of NH_3 produced:

$$\text{Moles } NH_3 = (6.0 \text{ mol } H_2)\left(\frac{2 \text{ mol } NH_3}{3 \text{ mol } H_2}\right) = 4.0 \text{ mol } NH_3$$

Comment: The table on the right summarizes this example:

	$N_2(g)$ +	$3 H_2(g) \longrightarrow$	$2 NH_3(g)$
Initial quantities:	3.0 mol	6.0 mol	0 mol
Change (reaction):	−2.0 mol	−6.0 mol	+4.0 mol
Final quantities:	1.0 mol	0 mol	4.0 mol

Notice that we can calculate not only the number of moles of NH_3 formed but also the number of moles of each of the reactants remaining after the reaction. Notice also that although the number of moles of H_2 present at the beginning of the reaction is greater than the number of moles of N_2 present, the H_2 is nevertheless the limiting reactant because of its larger coefficient in the balanced equation.

Check: The summarizing table shows that the mole ratio of reactants used and product formed conforms to the coefficients in the balanced equation, $1:3:2$. Also, because H_2 is the limiting reactant, it is completely consumed in the reaction, leaving 0 mol at the end. Because 2.0 mol H_2 has two significant figures, our answer has two significant figures.

PRACTICE EXERCISE

Consider the reaction $2 Al(s) + 3 Cl_2(g) \longrightarrow 2 AlCl_3(s)$. A mixture of 1.50 mol of Al and 3.00 mol of Cl_2 is allowed to react. **(a)** Which is the limiting reactant? **(b)** How many moles of $AlCl_3$ are formed? **(c)** How many moles of the excess reactant remain at the end of the reaction?

Answers: **(a)** Al, **(b)** 1.50 mol, **(c)** 0.75 mol Cl_2

SAMPLE EXERCISE 3.19 | Calculating the Amount of Product Formed from a Limiting Reactant

Consider the following reaction:

$$2 Na_3PO_4(aq) + 3 Ba(NO_3)_2(aq) \longrightarrow Ba_3(PO_4)_2(s) + 6 NaNO_3(aq)$$

Suppose a solution containing 3.50 g of Na_3PO_4 is mixed with a solution containing 6.40 g of $Ba(NO_3)_2$. How many grams of $Ba_3(PO_4)_2$ can be formed?

Solution

Analyze: We are asked to calculate the amount of a product, given the amounts of two reactants, so this is a limiting reactant problem.

Plan: We must first identify the limiting reagent. To do so, we can calculate the number of moles of each reactant and compare their ratio with that required by the balanced equation. We then use the quantity of the limiting reagent to calculate the mass of $Ba_3(PO_4)_2$ that forms.

Solve: From the balanced equation, we have the following stoichiometric relations:

$$2 \text{ mol } Na_3PO_4 \simeq 3 \text{ mol } Ba(NO_3)_2 \simeq 1 \text{ mol } Ba_3(PO_4)_2$$

Using the molar mass of each substance, we can calculate the number of moles of each reactant:

$$\text{Moles Na}_3\text{PO}_4 = (3.50 \text{ g Na}_3\text{PO}_4)\left(\frac{1 \text{ mol Na}_3\text{PO}_4}{164 \text{ g Na}_3\text{PO}_4}\right) = 0.0213 \text{ mol Na}_3\text{PO}_4$$

$$\text{Moles Ba(NO}_3)_2 = (6.40 \text{ g Ba(NO}_3)_2)\left(\frac{1 \text{ mol Ba(NO}_3)_2}{261 \text{ g Ba(NO}_3)_2}\right) = 0.0245 \text{ mol Ba(NO}_3)_2$$

Thus, there are slightly more moles of $Ba(NO_3)_2$ than moles of Na_3PO_4. The coefficients in the balanced equation indicate, however, that the reaction requires 3 mol $Ba(NO_3)_2$ for each 2 mol Na_3PO_4. [That is, 1.5 times more moles of $Ba(NO_3)_2$ are needed than moles of Na_3PO_4.] Thus, there is insufficient $Ba(NO_3)_2$ to completely consume the Na_3PO_4. That means that $Ba(NO_3)_2$ is the limiting reagent. We therefore use the quantity of $Ba(NO_3)_2$ to calculate the quantity of product formed. We can begin this calculation with the grams of $Ba(NO_3)_2$, but we can save a step by starting with the moles of $Ba(NO_3)_2$ that were calculated previously in the exercise:

$$\text{Grams Ba}_3(\text{PO}_4)_2 = (0.0245 \text{ mol Ba(NO}_3)_2)\left(\frac{1 \text{ mol Ba}_3(\text{PO}_4)_2}{3 \text{ mol Ba(NO}_3)_2}\right)\left(\frac{602 \text{ g Ba}_3(\text{PO}_4)_2}{1 \text{ mol Ba}_3(\text{PO}_4)_2}\right)$$

$$= 4.92 \text{ g Ba}_3(\text{PO}_4)_2$$

Check: The magnitude of the answer seems reasonable: Starting with the numbers in the two conversion factors on the right, we have $600/3 = 200$; $200 \times 0.025 = 5$. The units are correct, and the number of significant figures (three) corresponds to the number in the quantity of $Ba(NO_3)_2$.

Comment: The quantity of the limiting reagent, $Ba(NO_3)_2$, can also be used to determine the quantity of $NaNO_3$ formed (4.16 g) and the quantity of Na_3PO_4 used (2.67 g). The number of grams of the excess reagent, Na_3PO_4, remaining at the end of the reaction equals the starting amount minus the amount consumed in the reaction, $3.50 \text{ g} - 2.67 \text{ g} = 0.82 \text{ g}$.

▮ PRACTICE EXERCISE

A strip of zinc metal having a mass of 2.00 g is placed in an aqueous solution containing 2.50 g of silver nitrate, causing the following reaction to occur:

$$\text{Zn}(s) + 2\,\text{AgNO}_3(aq) \longrightarrow 2\,\text{Ag}(s) + \text{Zn(NO}_3)_2(aq)$$

(a) Which reactant is limiting? **(b)** How many grams of Ag will form? **(c)** How many grams of $Zn(NO_3)_2$ will form? **(d)** How many grams of the excess reactant will be left at the end of the reaction?
Answers: **(a)** $AgNO_3$, **(b)** 1.59 g, **(c)** 1.39 g, **(d)** 1.52 g Zn

Theoretical Yields

The quantity of product that is calculated to form when all of the limiting reactant reacts is called the **theoretical yield**. The amount of product actually obtained in a reaction is called the *actual yield*. The actual yield is almost always less than (and can never be greater than) the theoretical yield. There are many reasons for this difference. Part of the reactants may not react, for example, or they may react in a way different from that desired (side reactions). In addition, it is not always possible to recover all of the product from the reaction mixture. The **percent yield** of a reaction relates the actual yield to the theoretical (calculated) yield:

$$\text{Percent yield} = \frac{\text{actual yield}}{\text{theoretical yield}} \times 100\% \qquad [3.14]$$

In the experiment described in Sample Exercise 3.19, for example, we calculated that 4.92 g of $Ba_3(PO_4)_2$ should form when 3.50 g of Na_3PO_4 is mixed with 6.40 g of $Ba(NO_3)_2$. The 4.92 g is the theoretical yield of $Ba_3(PO_4)_2$ in the reaction. If the actual yield turned out to be 4.70 g, the percent yield would be

$$\frac{4.70 \text{ g}}{4.92 \text{ g}} \times 100\% = 95.5\%$$

STRATEGIES IN CHEMISTRY | How to Take a Test

At about this time in your study of chemistry, you are likely to face your first hour-long examination. The best way to prepare for the exam is to study and do homework diligently and to make sure you get help from the instructor on any material that is unclear or confusing. (See the advice for learning and studying chemistry presented in the preface of the book.) We present here some general guidelines for taking tests.

Depending on the nature of your course, the exam could consist of a variety of different types of questions. Let's consider some of the more common types and how they can best be addressed.

1. Multiple-choice questions

In large-enrollment courses, the most common kind of testing device is the multiple-choice question. You are given the problem and usually presented with four or five possible answers from which you must select the correct one. The first thing to realize is that the instructor has written the question so that all of the answer choices appear at first glance to be correct. (There would be little point in offering choices you could tell were wrong even

without knowing much about the concept being tested.) Thus, you should not jump to the conclusion that because one of the choices looks correct, it must be so.

If a multiple-choice question involves a calculation, perform the calculation, quickly double-check your work, and *only then* compare your answer with the choices. If you find a match, you have probably found the correct answer. Keep in mind, though, that your instructor has anticipated the most common errors one can make in solving a given problem and has probably listed the incorrect answers resulting from those errors. Thus, always double-check your reasoning and make sure to use dimensional analysis to arrive at the correct answer, with the correct units.

In multiple-choice questions that don't involve calculations, one way to proceed if you are not sure of the correct choice is to eliminate all the choices you know for sure to be incorrect. Additionally, the reasoning you used in eliminating incorrect choices will help you in reasoning about which is the one correct choice.

■ SAMPLE EXERCISE 3.20 | Calculating the Theoretical Yield and Percent Yield for a Reaction

Adipic acid, $H_2C_6H_8O_4$, is used to produce nylon. The acid is made commercially by a controlled reaction between cyclohexane (C_6H_{12}) and O_2:

$$2\,C_6H_{12}(l) + 5\,O_2(g) \longrightarrow 2\,H_2C_6H_8O_4(l) + 2\,H_2O(g)$$

(a) Assume that you carry out this reaction starting with 25.0 g of cyclohexane and that cyclohexane is the limiting reactant. What is the theoretical yield of adipic acid?

(b) If you obtain 33.5 g of adipic acid from your reaction, what is the percent yield of adipic acid?

Solution

Analyze: We are given a chemical equation and the quantity of the limiting reactant (25.0 g of C_6H_{12}). We are asked first to calculate the theoretical yield of a product ($H_2C_6H_8O_4$) and then to calculate its percent yield if only 33.5 g of the substance is actually obtained.

Plan:

(a) The theoretical yield, which is the calculated quantity of adipic acid formed in the reaction, can be calculated using the following sequence of conversions:

$$g\,C_6H_{12} \longrightarrow mol\,C_6H_{12} \longrightarrow mol\,H_2C_6H_8O_4 \longrightarrow g\,H_2C_6H_8O_4.$$

(b) The percent yield is calculated by comparing the actual yield (33.5 g) to the theoretical yield using Equation 3.14.

Solve:

(a) Grams $H_2C_6H_8O_4$ = $(25.0\ \cancel{g\,C_6H_{12}})\left(\dfrac{1\ \cancel{mol\,C_6H_{12}}}{84.0\ \cancel{g\,C_6H_{12}}}\right)$

$$\times \left(\dfrac{2\ \cancel{mol\,H_2C_6H_8O_4}}{2\ \cancel{mol\,C_6H_{12}}}\right)\left(\dfrac{146.0\ g\,H_2C_6H_8O_4}{1\ \cancel{mol\,H_2C_6H_8O_4}}\right)$$

$$= 43.5\ g\,H_2C_6H_8O_4$$

(b) Percent yield = $\dfrac{\text{actual yield}}{\text{theoretical yield}} \times 100\% = \dfrac{33.5\ g}{43.5\ g} \times 100\% = 77.0\%$

Check: Our answer in (a) has the appropriate magnitude, units, and significant figures. In (b) the answer is less than 100% as necessary.

2. **Calculations in which you must show your work**
Your instructor may present you with a numerical problem in which you are to show your work in arriving at a solution. In questions of this kind, you may receive partial credit even if you don't arrive at the correct answer, depending on whether the instructor can follow your line of reasoning. It is important, therefore, to be as neat and organized as you can be, given the pressures of exam taking. It is helpful in approaching such questions to take a few moments to think about the direction you are going to take in solving the problem, and you may even want to write a few words or a diagram on the test paper to indicate your plan of attack. Then write out your calculations as neatly as you can. Show the units for every number you write down, and use dimensional analysis as much as you can, showing how units cancel.

3. **Questions requiring drawings**
Sometimes a test question will require you to draw a chemical structure, a diagram related to chemical bonding, or a figure showing some kind of chemical process. Questions of this kind will come later in the course, but it

is useful to talk about them here. (You should review this box before each exam you take, to remind yourself of good exam-taking practices.) Be sure to label your drawing as completely as possible.

4. **Other types of questions**
Other exam questions you might encounter include true-false questions and ones in which you are given a list and asked to indicate which members of the list match some criterion given in the question. Often students answer such questions incorrectly because, in their haste, they misunderstand the nature of the question. Whatever the question form, ask yourself this: What is the instructor testing here? What material am I supposed to know that this question covers?

Finally, if you find that you simply don't see how to arrive at a reasoned response to a question, don't linger over the question. Put a check next to it and go on to the next one. If time permits, you can come back to the unanswered questions, but lingering over a question when nothing is coming to mind is wasting time you may need to finish the exam.

PRACTICE EXERCISE

Imagine that you are working on ways to improve the process by which iron ore containing Fe_2O_3 is converted into iron. In your tests you carry out the following reaction on a small scale:

$$Fe_2O_3(s) + 3 CO(g) \longrightarrow 2 Fe(s) + 3 CO_2(g)$$

(a) If you start with 150 g of Fe_2O_3 as the limiting reagent, what is the theoretical yield of Fe? **(b)** If the actual yield of Fe in your test was 87.9 g, what was the percent yield? *Answers:* **(a)** 105 g Fe, **(b)** 83.7%

SUMMARY AND KEY TERMS

Introduction and Section 3.1 The study of the quantitative relationships between chemical formulas and chemical equations is known as **stoichiometry**. One of the important concepts of stoichiometry is the law of conservation of mass, which states that the total mass of the products of a chemical reaction is the same as the total mass of the reactants. The same numbers of atoms of each type are present before and after a chemical reaction. A balanced **chemical equation** shows equal numbers of atoms of each element on each side of the equation. Equations are balanced by placing coefficients in front of the chemical formulas for the **reactants** and **products** of a reaction, *not* by changing the subscripts in chemical formulas.

Section 3.2 Among the reaction types described in this chapter are (1) **combination reactions**, in which two reactants combine to form one product; (2) **decomposition reactions**, in which a single reactant forms two or more

products; and (3) **combustion reactions** in oxygen, in which a hydrocarbon or related compound reacts with O_2 to form CO_2 and H_2O.

Section 3.3 Much quantitative information can be determined from chemical formulas and balanced chemical equations by using atomic weights. The **formula weight** of a compound equals the sum of the atomic weights of the atoms in its formula. If the formula is a molecular formula, the formula weight is also called the **molecular weight**. Atomic weights and formula weights can be used to determine the elemental composition of a compound.

Section 3.4 A **mole** of any substance is **Avogadro's number** (6.02×10^{23}) of formula units of that substance. The mass of a mole of atoms, molecules, or ions (the **molar mass**) equals the formula weight of that material expressed in grams. The mass of one molecule of H_2O, for example, is 18 amu, so the mass of 1 mol of H_2O is 18 g. That is, the molar mass of H_2O is 18 g/mol.

Science Fundamentals Second Edition

Section 3.5 The empirical formula of any substance can be determined from its percent composition by calculating the relative number of moles of each atom in 100 g of the substance. If the substance is molecular in nature, its molecular formula can be determined from the empirical formula if the molecular weight is also known.

Sections 3.6 and 3.7 The mole concept can be used to calculate the relative quantities of reactants and products involved in chemical reactions. The coefficients in a balanced equation give the relative numbers of moles of the reactants and products. To calculate the number of grams of a product from the number of grams of a reactant, therefore, first convert grams of reactant to moles of reactant. We then use the coefficients in the balanced equation to convert the number of moles of reactant to moles of product. Finally, we convert moles of product to grams of product.

A **limiting reactant** is completely consumed in a reaction. When it is used up, the reaction stops, thus limiting the quantities of products formed. The **theoretical yield** of a reaction is the quantity of product calculated to form when all of the limiting reagent reacts. The actual yield of a reaction is always less than the theoretical yield. The **percent yield** compares the actual and theoretical yields.

VISUALIZING CONCEPTS

3.1 The reaction between reactant A (blue spheres) and reactant B (red spheres) is shown in the following diagram:

Based on this diagram, which equation best describes the reaction? [Section 3.1]
(a) $A_2 + B \longrightarrow A_2B$ **(b)** $A_2 + 4B \longrightarrow 2AB_2$
(c) $2A + B_4 \longrightarrow 2AB_2$ **(d)** $A + B_2 \longrightarrow AB_2$

3.2 Under appropriate experimental conditions, H_2 and CO undergo a combination reaction to form CH_3OH. The drawing below represents a sample of H_2. Make a corresponding drawing of the CO needed to react completely with the H_2. How did you arrive at the number of CO molecules in your drawing? [Section 3.2]

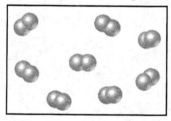

3.3 The following diagram represents the collection of elements formed by decomposition reaction. **(a)** If the blue spheres represent N atoms and the red ones represent O atoms, what was the empirical formula of the original compound? **(b)** Could you draw a diagram representing the molecules of the compound that had been decomposed? Why or why not? [Section 3.2]

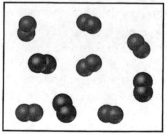

3.4 The following diagram represents the collection of CO_2 and H_2O molecules formed by complete combustion of a hydrocarbon. What is the empirical formula of the hydrocarbon? [Section 3.2]

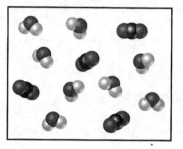

3.5 Glycine, an amino acid used by organisms to make proteins, is represented by the molecular model below. **(a)** Write its molecular formula. **(b)** Determine its molecular mass. **(c)** Calculate the percent nitrogen by mass in glycine. [Section 3.3 and 3.5]

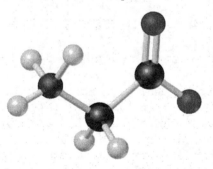

3.6 The following diagram represents a high-temperature reaction between CH_4 and H_2O. Based on this reaction, how many moles of each product can be obtained starting with 4.0 mol CH_4? [Section 3.6]

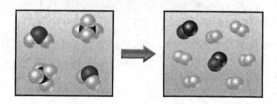

3.7 Nitrogen (N_2) and hydrogen (H_2) react to form ammonia (NH_3). Consider the mixture of N_2 and H_2 shown in the accompanying diagram. The blue spheres represent N, and the white ones represent H. Draw a representation of the product mixture, assuming that the reaction goes to completion. How did you arrive at your representation? What is the limiting reactant in this case? [Section 3.7]

3.8 Nitrogen monoxide and oxygen react to form nitrogen dioxide. Consider the mixture of NO and O_2 shown in the accompanying diagram. The blue spheres represent N, and the red ones represent O. (a) Draw a representation of the product mixture, assuming that the reaction goes to completion. What is the limiting reactant in this case? (b) How many NO_2 molecules would you draw as products if the reaction had a percent yield of 75%? [Section 3.7]

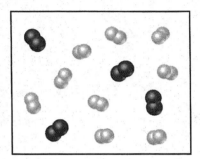

EXERCISES

Balancing Chemical Equations

3.9 (a) What scientific principle or law is used in the process of balancing chemical equations? (b) In balancing equations, why shouldn't subscripts in chemical formulas be changed? (c) What are the symbols used to represent gases, liquids, solids, and aqueous solutions in chemical equations?

3.10 (a) What is the difference between adding a subscript 2 to the end of the formula for CO to give CO_2 and adding a coefficient in front of the formula to give 2 CO? (b) Is the following chemical equation, as written, consistent with the law of conservation of mass?

$$3\,Mg(OH)_2(s) + 2\,H_3PO_4(aq) \longrightarrow$$
$$Mg_3(PO_4)_2(s) + 6\,H_2O(l)$$

Why or why not?

3.11 Balance the following equations:
(a) $CO(g) + O_2(g) \longrightarrow CO_2(g)$
(b) $N_2O_5(g) + H_2O(l) \longrightarrow HNO_3(aq)$
(c) $CH_4(g) + Cl_2(g) \longrightarrow CCl_4(l) + HCl(g)$
(d) $Al_4C_3(s) + H_2O(l) \longrightarrow Al(OH)_3(s) + CH_4(g)$
(e) $C_5H_{10}O_2(l) + O_2(g) \longrightarrow CO_2(g) + H_2O(g)$
(f) $Fe(OH)_3(s) + H_2SO_4(aq) \longrightarrow Fe_2(SO_4)_3(aq) + H_2O(l)$
(g) $Mg_3N_2(s) + H_2SO_4(aq) \longrightarrow$
$$MgSO_4(aq) + (NH_4)_2SO_4(aq)$$

3.12 Balance the following equations:
(a) $Li(s) + N_2(g) \longrightarrow Li_3N(s)$
(b) $La_2O_3(s) + H_2O(l) \longrightarrow La(OH)_3(aq)$
(c) $NH_4NO_3(s) \longrightarrow N_2(g) + O_2(g) + H_2O(g)$

(d) $Ca_3P_2(s) + H_2O(l) \longrightarrow Ca(OH)_2(aq) + PH_3(g)$
(e) $Ca(OH)_2(aq) + H_3PO_4(aq) \longrightarrow Ca_3(PO_4)_2(s) + H_2O(l)$
(f) $AgNO_3(aq) + Na_2SO_4(aq) \longrightarrow$
$$Ag_2SO_4(s) + NaNO_3(aq)$$
(g) $CH_3NH_2(g) + O_2(g) \longrightarrow CO_2(g) + H_2O(g) + N_2(g)$

3.13 Write balanced chemical equations to correspond to each of the following descriptions: (a) Solid calcium carbide, CaC_2, reacts with water to form an aqueous solution of calcium hydroxide and acetylene gas, C_2H_2. (b) When solid potassium chlorate is heated, it decomposes to form solid potassium chloride and oxygen gas. (c) Solid zinc metal reacts with sulfuric acid to form hydrogen gas and an aqueous solution of zinc sulfate. (d) When liquid phosphorus trichloride is added to water, it reacts to form aqueous phosphorous acid, $H_3PO_3(aq)$, and aqueous hydrochloric acid. (e) When hydrogen sulfide gas is passed over solid hot iron(III) hydroxide, the resultant reaction produces solid iron(III) sulfide and gaseous water.

3.14 Convert these descriptions into balanced equations: (a) When sulfur trioxide gas reacts with water, a solution of sulfuric acid forms. (b) Boron sulfide, $B_2S_3(s)$, reacts violently with water to form dissolved boric acid, H_3BO_3, and hydrogen sulfide gas. (c) Phosphine, $PH_3(g)$, combusts in oxygen gas to form gaseous water and solid tetraphosphorus decoxide. (d) When solid mercury(II) nitrate is heated, it decomposes to form solid mercury(II) oxide, gaseous nitrogen dioxide, and oxygen. (e) Copper metal reacts with hot concentrated sulfuric acid solution to form aqueous copper(II) sulfate, sulfur dioxide gas, and water.

Patterns of Chemical Reactivity

3.15 (a) When the metallic element sodium combines with the nonmetallic element bromine, $Br_2(l)$, how can you determine the chemical formula of the product? How do you know whether the product is a solid, liquid, or gas at room temperature? Write the balanced chemical equation for the reaction. (b) When a hydrocarbon burns in air, what reactant besides the hydrocarbon is involved in the reaction? What products are formed? Write a balanced chemical equation for the combustion of benzene, $C_6H_6(l)$, in air.

3.16 (a) Determine the chemical formula of the product formed when the metallic element calcium combines with the nonmetallic element oxygen, O_2. Write the balanced chemical equation for the reaction. (b) What products form when a compound containing C, H, and O is completely combusted in air? Write a balanced chemical equation for the combustion of acetone, $C_3H_6O(l)$, in air.

3.17 Write a balanced chemical equation for the reaction that occurs when (a) $Mg(s)$ reacts with $Cl_2(g)$; (b) barium carbonate decomposes into barium oxide and carbon dioxide gas when heated; (c) the hydrocarbon styrene, $C_8H_8(l)$, is combusted in air; (d) dimethylether, $CH_3OCH_3(g)$, is combusted in air.

3.18 Write a balanced chemical equation for the reaction that occurs when (a) aluminum metal undergoes a combination reaction with $O_2(g)$; (b) copper(II) hydroxide decomposes into copper(II) oxide and water when heated;

(c) heptane, $C_7H_{16}(l)$, burns in air; (d) the gasoline additive MTBE (methyl tert-butyl ether), $C_5H_{12}O(l)$, burns in air.

3.19 Balance the following equations, and indicate whether they are combination, decomposition, or combustion reactions:
(a) $Al(s) + Cl_2(g) \longrightarrow AlCl_3(s)$
(b) $C_2H_4(g) + O_2(g) \longrightarrow CO_2(g) + H_2O(g)$
(c) $Li(s) + N_2(g) \longrightarrow Li_3N(s)$
(d) $PbCO_3(s) \longrightarrow PbO(s) + CO_2(g)$
(e) $C_7H_8O_2(l) + O_2(g) \longrightarrow CO_2(g) + H_2O(g)$

3.20 Balance the following equations, and indicate whether they are combination, decomposition, or combustion reactions:
(a) $C_3H_6(g) + O_2(g) \longrightarrow CO_2(g) + H_2O(g)$
(b) $NH_4NO_3(s) \longrightarrow N_2O(g) + H_2O(g)$
(c) $C_5H_6O(l) + O_2(g) \longrightarrow CO_2(g) + H_2O(g)$
(d) $N_2(g) + H_2(g) \longrightarrow NH_3(g)$
(e) $K_2O(s) + H_2O(l) \longrightarrow KOH(aq)$

Formula Weights

3.21 Determine the formula weights of each of the following compounds: (a) N_2O_5, (b) $CuSO_4$, (c) $(NH_4)_3PO_4$, (d) $Ca(HCO_3)_2$, (e) aluminum sulfide, (f) iron(III) sulfate, (g) disilicon hexabromide.

3.22 Determine the formula weights of each of the following compounds: (a) nitrous oxide, N_2O, known as laughing gas and used as an anesthetic in dentistry; (b) benzoic acid, $HC_7H_5O_2$, a substance used as a food preservative; (c) $Mg(OH)_2$, the active ingredient in milk of magnesia; (d) urea, $(NH_2)_2CO$, a compound used as a nitrogen fertilizer; (e) isopentyl acetate, $CH_3CO_2C_5H_{11}$, responsible for the odor of bananas.

3.23 Calculate the percentage by mass of oxygen in the following compounds: (a) SO_3; (b) CH_3COOCH_3; (c) $Cr(NO_3)_3$; (d) sodium sulfate; (e) ammonium nitrate.

3.24 Calculate the percentage by mass of the indicated element in the following compounds: (a) carbon in acetylene, C_2H_2, a gas used in welding; (b) hydrogen in ascorbic acid, $HC_6H_7O_6$, also known as vitamin C; (c) hydrogen in ammonium sulfate, $(NH_4)_2SO_4$, a substance used as a nitrogen fertilizer; (d) platinum in $PtCl_2(NH_3)_2$, a chemotherapy agent called cisplatin; (e) oxygen in the female sex hormone estradiol, $C_{18}H_{24}O_2$; (f) carbon in capsaicin, $C_{18}H_{27}NO_3$, the compound that gives the hot taste to chili peppers.

3.25 Based on the following structural formulas, calculate the percentage of carbon by mass present in each compound:

(a)
Benzaldehyde
(almond fragrance)

(b)
Vanillin
(vanilla flavor)

(c)
Isopentyl acetate
(banana flavor)

3.26 Calculate the percentage of carbon by mass in each of the compounds represented by the following models:

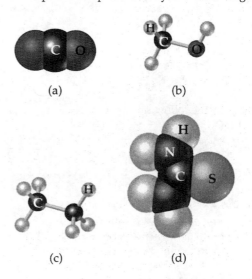

(a)   (b)

(c)   (d)

Avogadro's Number and the Mole

3.27 **(a)** What is Avogadro's number, and how is it related to the mole? **(b)** What is the relationship between the formula weight of a substance and its molar mass?

3.28 **(a)** What is the mass, in grams, of a mole of ^{12}C? **(b)** How many carbon atoms are present in a mole of ^{12}C?

3.29 Without doing any detailed calculations (but using a periodic table to give atomic weights), rank the following samples in order of increasing number of atoms: 0.50 mol H_2O, 23 g Na, 6.0×10^{23} N_2 molecules.

3.30 Without doing any detailed calculations (but using a periodic table to give atomic weights), rank the following samples in order of increasing number of atoms: 3.0×10^{23} molecules of H_2O_2, 2.0 mol CH_4, 32 g O_2.

3.31 What is the mass, in kilograms, of an Avogadro's number of Olympic shot-put balls if each one has a mass of 16 lb? How does this compare with the mass of Earth, 5.98×10^{24} kg?

3.32 If Avogadro's number of pennies is divided equally among the 292 million men, women, and children in the United States, how many dollars would each receive? How does this compare with the national debt of the United States, which was $7.0 trillion at the time of the writing of this text?

3.33 Calculate the following quantities:
(a) mass, in grams, of 0.773 mol CaH_2
(b) moles of $Mg(NO_3)_2$ in 5.35 g of this substance
(c) number of molecules in 0.0305 mol CH_3OH
(d) number of C atoms in 0.585 mol C_4H_{10}

3.34 Calculate the following quantities:
(a) mass, in grams, of 1.906×10^{-2} mol BaI_2
(b) number of moles of NH_4Cl in 48.3 g of this substance
(c) number of molecules in 0.05752 mol $HCHO_2$
(d) number of O atoms in 4.88×10^{-3} mol $Al(NO_3)_3$

3.35 **(a)** What is the mass, in grams, of 2.50×10^{-3} mol of ammonium phosphate?
(b) How many moles of chloride ions are in 0.2550 g of aluminum chloride?
(c) What is the mass, in grams, of 7.70×10^{20} molecules of caffeine, $C_8H_{10}N_4O_2$?
(d) What is the molar mass of cholesterol if 0.00105 mol weighs 0.406 g?

3.36 **(a)** What is the mass, in grams, of 0.0714 mol of iron(III) sulfate?
(b) How many moles of ammonium ions are in 8.776 g of ammonium carbonate?
(c) What is the mass, in grams, of 6.52×10^{21} molecules of aspirin, $C_9H_8O_4$?
(d) What is the molar mass of diazepam (Valium®) if 0.05570 mol weighs 15.86 g?

3.37 The molecular formula of allicin, the compound responsible for the characteristic smell of garlic, is $C_6H_{10}OS_2$. **(a)** What is the molar mass of allicin? **(b)** How many moles of allicin are present in 5.00 mg of this substance? **(c)** How many molecules of allicin are in 5.00 mg of this substance? **(d)** How many S atoms are present in 5.00 mg of allicin?

3.38 The molecular formula of aspartame, the artificial sweetener marketed as NutraSweet®, is $C_{14}H_{18}N_2O_5$. **(a)** What is the molar mass of aspartame? **(b)** How many moles of aspartame are present in 1.00 mg of aspartame? **(c)** How many molecules of aspartame are present in 1.00 mg of aspartame? **(d)** How many hydrogen atoms are present in 1.00 mg of aspartame?

3.39 A sample of glucose, $C_6H_{12}O_6$, contains 1.250×10^{21} atoms of carbon. **(a)** How many atoms of hydrogen does it contain? **(b)** How many molecules of glucose does it contain? **(c)** How many moles of glucose does it contain? **(d)** What is the mass of this sample in grams?

3.40 A sample of the male sex hormone testosterone, $C_{19}H_{28}O_2$, contains 7.08×10^{20} atoms of hydrogen. **(a)** How many atoms of carbon does it contain? **(b)** How many molecules of testosterone does it contain? **(c)** How many moles of testosterone does it contain? **(d)** What is the mass of this sample in grams?

3.41 The allowable concentration level of vinyl chloride, C_2H_3Cl, in the atmosphere in a chemical plant is 2.0×10^{-6} g/L. How many moles of vinyl chloride in each liter does this represent? How many molecules per liter?

3.42 At least 25 μg of tetrahydrocannabinol (THC), the active ingredient in marijuana, is required to produce intoxication. The molecular formula of THC is $C_{21}H_{30}O_2$. How many moles of THC does this 25 μg represent? How many molecules?

Empirical Formulas

3.43 Give the empirical formula of each of the following compounds if a sample contains **(a)** 0.0130 mol C, 0.0390 mol H, and 0.0065 mol O; **(b)** 11.66 g iron and 5.01 g oxygen; **(c)** 40.0% C, 6.7% H, and 53.3% O by mass.

3.44 Determine the empirical formula of each of the following compounds if a sample contains **(a)** 0.104 mol K, 0.052 mol C, and 0.156 mol O; **(b)** 5.28 g Sn and 3.37 g F; **(c)** 87.5% N and 12.5% H by mass.

3.45 Determine the empirical formulas of the compounds with the following compositions by mass:
(a) 10.4% C, 27.8% S, and 61.7% Cl
(b) 21.7% C, 9.6% O, and 68.7% F
(c) 32.79% Na, 13.02% Al, and 54.19% F

3.46 Determine the empirical formulas of the compounds with the following compositions by mass:
(a) 55.3% K, 14.6% P, and 30.1% O
(b) 24.5% Na, 14.9% Si, and 60.6% F
(c) 62.1% C, 5.21% H, 12.1% N, and 20.7% O

3.47 What is the molecular formula of each of the following compounds?
(a) empirical formula CH_2, molar mass = 84 g/mol
(b) empirical formula NH_2Cl, molar mass = 51.5 g/mol

3.48 What is the molecular formula of each of the following compounds?
(a) empirical formula HCO_2, molar mass = 90.0 g/mol
(b) empirical formula C_2H_4O, molar mass = 88 g/mol

3.49 Determine the empirical and molecular formulas of each of the following substances:

(a) Styrene, a compound substance used to make Styrofoam® cups and insulation, contains 92.3% C and 7.7% H by mass and has a molar mass of 104 g/mol.

(b) Caffeine, a stimulant found in coffee, contains 49.5% C, 5.15% H, 28.9% N, and 16.5% O by mass and has a molar mass about 195 g/mol.

(c) Monosodium glutamate (MSG), a flavor enhancer in certain foods, contains 35.51% C, 4.77% H, 37.85% O, 8.29% N, and 13.60% Na, and has a molar mass of 169 g/mol.

3.50 Determine the empirical and molecular formulas of each of the following substances:

(a) Ibuprofen, a headache remedy, contains 75.69% C, 8.80% H, and 15.51% O by mass, and has a molar mass about 206 g/mol.

(b) Cadaverine, a foul smelling substance produced by the action of bacteria on meat, contains 58.55% C, 13.81% H, and 27.40% N by mass; its molar mass is 102.2 g/mol.

(c) Epinephrine (adrenaline), a hormone secreted into the bloodstream in times of danger or stress, contains 59.0% C, 7.1% H, 26.2% O, and 7.7% N by mass; its MW is about 180 amu.

3.51 (a) Combustion analysis of toluene, a common organic solvent, gives 5.86 mg of CO_2 and 1.37 mg of H_2O. If the compound contains only carbon and hydrogen, what is its empirical formula? (b) Menthol, the substance we can smell in mentholated cough drops, is composed of C, H,

and O. A 0.1005-g sample of menthol is combusted, producing 0.2829 g of CO_2 and 0.1159 g of H_2O. What is the empirical formula for menthol? If the compound has a molar mass of 156 g/mol, what is its molecular formula?

3.52 (a) The characteristic odor of pineapple is due to ethyl butyrate, a compound containing carbon, hydrogen, and oxygen. Combustion of 2.78 mg of ethyl butyrate produces 6.32 mg of CO_2 and 2.58 mg of H_2O. What is the empirical formula of the compound? (b) Nicotine, a component of tobacco, is composed of C, H, and N. A 5.250-mg sample of nicotine was combusted, producing 14.242 mg of CO_2 and 4.083 mg of H_2O. What is the empirical formula for nicotine? If the substance has a molar mass of 60 ± 5 g/mol, what is its molecular formula?

3.53 Washing soda, a compound used to prepare hard water for washing laundry, is a hydrate, which means that a certain number of water molecules are included in the solid structure. Its formula can be written as $Na_2CO_3 \cdot xH_2O$, where x is the number of moles of H_2O per mole of Na_2CO_3. When a 2.558-g sample of washing soda is heated at 25°C, all the water of hydration is lost, leaving 0.948 g of Na_2CO_3. What is the value of x?

3.54 Epsom salts, a strong laxative used in veterinary medicine, is a hydrate, which means that a certain number of water molecules are included in the solid structure. The formula for Epsom salts can be written as $MgSO_4 \cdot xH_2O$, where x indicates the number of moles of H_2O per mole of $MgSO_4$. When 5.061 g of this hydrate is heated to 250°C, all the water of hydration is lost, leaving 2.472 g of $MgSO_4$. What is the value of x?

Calculations Based on Chemical Equations

3.55 Why is it essential to use balanced chemical equations when determining the quantity of a product formed from a given quantity of a reactant?

3.56 What parts of balanced chemical equations give information about the relative numbers of moles of reactants and products involved in a reaction?

3.57 Hydrofluoric acid, HF(aq), cannot be stored in glass bottles because compounds called silicates in the glass are attacked by the HF(aq). Sodium silicate (Na_2SiO_3), for example, reacts as follows:

$$Na_2SiO_3(s) + 8\,HF(aq) \longrightarrow$$

$$H_2SiF_6(aq) + 2\,NaF(aq) + 3\,H_2O(l)$$

(a) How many moles of HF are needed to react with 0.300 mol of Na_2SiO_3?

(b) How many grams of NaF form when 0.500 mol of HF reacts with excess Na_2SiO_3?

(c) How many grams of Na_2SiO_3 can react with 0.800 g of HF?

3.58 The fermentation of glucose ($C_6H_{12}O_6$) produces ethyl alcohol (C_2H_5OH) and CO_2:

$$C_6H_{12}O_6(aq) \longrightarrow 2\,C_2H_5OH(aq) + 2\,CO_2(g)$$

(a) How many moles of CO_2 are produced when 0.400 mol of $C_6H_{12}O_6$ reacts in this fashion?

(b) How many grams of $C_6H_{12}O_6$ are needed to form 7.50 g of C_2H_5OH?

(c) How many grams of CO_2 form when 7.50 g of C_2H_5OH are produced?

3.59 Several brands of antacids use $Al(OH)_3$ to react with stomach acid, which contains primarily HCl:

$$Al(OH)_3(s) + HCl(aq) \longrightarrow AlCl_3(aq) + H_2O(l)$$

(a) Balance this equation.

(b) Calculate the number of grams of HCl that can react with 0.500 g of $Al(OH)_3$.

(c) Calculate the number of grams of $AlCl_3$ and the number of grams of H_2O formed when 0.500 g of $Al(OH)_3$ reaacts.

(d) Show that your calculations in parts (b) and (c) are consistent with the law of conservation of mass.

3.60 An iron ore sample contains Fe_2O_3 together with other substances. Reaction of the ore with CO produces iron metal:

$$Fe_2O_3(s) + CO(g) \longrightarrow Fe(s) + CO_2(g)$$

(a) Balance this equation.

(b) Calculate the number of grams of CO that can react with 0.150 kg of Fe_2O_3.

(c) Calculate the number of grams of Fe and the number of grams of CO_2 formed when 0.150 kg of Fe_2O_3 reacts.

(d) Show that your calculations in parts (b) and (c) are consistent with the law of conservation of mass.

3.61 Aluminum sulfide reacts with water to form aluminum hydroxide and hydrogen sulfide. **(a)** Write the balanced chemical equation for this reaction. **(b)** How many grams of aluminum hydroxide are obtained from 6.75 g of aluminum sulfide?

3.62 Calcium hydride reacts with water to form calcium hydroxide and hydrogen gas. **(a)** Write a balanced chemical equation for the reaction. **(b)** How many grams of calcium hydride are needed to form 8.500 g of hydrogen?

3.63 Automotive air bags inflate when sodium azide, NaN_3, rapidly decomposes to its component elements:

$$2\,NaN_3(s) \longrightarrow 2\,Na(s) + 3\,N_2(g)$$

(a) How many moles of N_2 are produced by the decomposition of 1.50 mol of NaN_3?

(b) How many grams of NaN_3 are required to form 10.0 g of nitrogen gas?

(c) How many grams of NaN_3 are required to produce 10.0 ft^3 of nitrogen gas if the gas has a density of 1.25 g/L?

3.64 The complete combustion of octane, C_8H_{18}, a component of gasoline, proceeds as follows:

$$2\,C_8H_{18}(l) + 25\,O_2(g) \longrightarrow 16\,CO_2(g) + 18\,H_2O(g)$$

(a) How many moles of O_2 are needed to burn 1.25 mol of C_8H_{18}?

(b) How many grams of O_2 are needed to burn 10.0 g of C_8H_{18}?

(c) Octane has a density of 0.692 g/mL at 20°C. How many grams of O_2 are required to burn 1.00 gal of C_8H_{18}?

3.65 A piece of aluminum foil 1.00 cm square and 0.550 mm thick is allowed to react with bromine to form aluminum bromide as shown in the accompanying photo.

(a) How many moles of aluminum were used? (The density of aluminum is 2.699 g/cm^3.) **(b)** How many grams of aluminum bromide form, assuming that the aluminum reacts completely?

3.66 Detonation of nitroglycerin proceeds as follows:

$$4\,C_3H_5N_3O_9(l) \longrightarrow$$
$$12\,CO_2(g) + 6\,N_2(g) + O_2(g) + 10\,H_2O(g)$$

(a) If a sample containing 2.00 mL of nitroglycerin (density = 1.592 g/mL) is detonated, how many total moles of gas are produced? **(b)** If each mole of gas occupies 55 L under the conditions of the explosion, how many liters of gas are produced? **(c)** How many grams of N_2 are produced in the detonation?

Limiting Reactants; Theoretical Yields

3.67 **(a)** Define the terms *limiting reactant* and *excess reactant*. **(b)** Why are the amounts of products formed in a reaction determined only by the amount of the limiting reactant?

3.68 **(a)** Define the terms *theoretical yield, actual yield,* and *percent yield.* **(b)** Why is the actual yield in a reaction almost always less than the theoretical yield?

3.69 A manufacturer of bicycles has 4815 wheels, 2305 frames, and 2255 handlebars. **(a)** How many bicycles can be manufactured using these parts? **(b)** How many parts of each kind are left over? **(c)** Which part limits the production of bicycles?

3.70 A bottling plant has 121,515 bottles with a capacity of 355 mL, 122,500 caps, and 40,875 L of beverage. **(a)** How many bottles can be filled and capped? **(b)** How much of each item is left over? **(c)** Which component limits the production?

3.71 Sodium hydroxide reacts with carbon dioxide as follows:

$$2\,NaOH(s) + CO_2(g) \longrightarrow Na_2CO_3(s) + H_2O(l)$$

Which reagent is the limiting reactant when 1.85 mol NaOH and 1.00 mol CO_2 are allowed to react? How many moles of Na_2CO_3 can be produced? How many moles of the excess reactant remain after the completion of the reaction?

3.72 Aluminum hydroxide reacts with sulfuric acid as follows:

$$2\,Al(OH)_3(s) + 3\,H_2SO_4(aq) \longrightarrow$$
$$Al_2(SO_4)_3(aq) + 6\,H_2O(l)$$

Which reagent is the limiting reactant when 0.500 mol $Al(OH)_3$ and 0.500 mol H_2SO_4 are allowed to react? How many moles of $Al_2(SO_4)_3$ can form under these conditions? How many moles of the excess reactant remain after the completion of the reaction?

3.73 The fizz produced when an Alka-Seltzer® tablet is dissolved in water is due to the reaction between sodium bicarbonate ($NaHCO_3$) and citric acid ($H_3C_6H_5O_7$):

$$3\,NaHCO_3(aq) + H_3C_6H_5O_7(aq) \longrightarrow$$
$$3\,CO_2(g) + 3\,H_2O(l) + Na_3C_6H_5O_7(aq)$$

In a certain experiment 1.00 g of sodium bicarbonate and 1.00 g of citric acid are allowed to react. **(a)** Which is the limiting reactant? **(b)** How many grams of carbon dioxide form? **(c)** How many grams of the excess reactant remain after the limiting reactant is completely consumed?

3.74 One of the steps in the commercial process for converting ammonia to nitric acid is the conversion of NH_3 to NO:

$$4\,NH_3(g) + 5\,O_2(g) \longrightarrow 4\,NO(g) + 6\,H_2O(g)$$

In a certain experiment, 1.50 g of NH_3 reacts with 2.75 g of O_2. **(a)** Which is the limiting reactant? **(b)** How many grams of NO and of H_2O form? **(c)** How many grams of the excess reactant remain after the limiting reactant is completely consumed? **(d)** Show that your calculations in parts (b) and (c) are consistent with the law of conservation of mass.

3.75 Solutions of sodium carbonate and silver nitrate react to form solid silver carbonate and a solution of sodium nitrate. A solution containing 3.50 g of sodium carbonate is mixed with one containing 5.00 g of silver nitrate. How many grams of sodium carbonate, silver nitrate, silver carbonate, and sodium nitrate are present after the reaction is complete?

3.76 Solutions of sulfuric acid and lead(II) acetate react to form solid lead(II) sulfate and a solution of acetic acid. If 7.50 g of sulfuric acid and 7.50 g of lead(II) acetate are mixed, calculate the number of grams of sulfuric acid, lead(II) acetate, lead(II) sulfate, and acetic acid present in the mixture after the reaction is complete.

3.77 When benzene (C_6H_6) reacts with bromine (Br_2), bromobenzene (C_6H_5Br) is obtained:

$$C_6H_6 + Br_2 \longrightarrow C_6H_5Br + HBr$$

(a) What is the theoretical yield of bromobenzene in this reaction when 30.0 g of benzene reacts with 65.0 g of bromine? **(b)** If the actual yield of bromobenzene was 56.7 g, what was the percentage yield?

3.78 When ethane (C_2H_6) reacts with chlorine (Cl_2), the main product is C_2H_5Cl; but other products containing Cl, such as $C_2H_4Cl_2$, are also obtained in small quantities. The formation of these other products reduces the yield of C_2H_5Cl. **(a)** Calculate the theoretical yield of C_2H_5Cl when 125 g of C_2H_6 reacts with 255 g of Cl_2, assuming that C_2H_6 and Cl_2 react only to form C_2H_5Cl and HCl. **(b)** Calculate the percent yield of C_2H_5Cl if the reaction produces 206 g of C_2H_5Cl.

3.79 Lithium and nitrogen react to produce lithium nitride:

$$6\,Li(s) + N_2(g) \longrightarrow 2\,Li_3N(s)$$

If 5.00 g of each reactant undergoes a reaction with a 88.5% yield, how many grams of Li_3N are obtained from the reaction?

3.80 When hydrogen sulfide gas is bubbled into a solution of sodium hydroxide, the reaction forms sodium sulfide and water. How many grams of sodium sulfide are formed if 1.50 g of hydrogen sulfide is bubbled into a solution containing 2.00 g of sodium hydroxide, assuming that the sodium sulfide is made in 92.0% yield?

Additional Exercises

3.81 Write the balanced chemical equation for **(a)** the complete combustion of butyric acid, $HC_4H_7O_2(l)$, a compound produced when butter becomes rancid; **(b)** the decomposition of solid nickel(II) hydroxide into solid nickel(II) oxide and water vapor; **(c)** the combination reaction between zinc metal and chlorine gas.

3.82 The effectiveness of nitrogen fertilizers depends on both their ability to deliver nitrogen to plants and the amount of nitrogen they can deliver. Four common nitrogen-containing fertilizers are ammonia, ammonium nitrate, ammonium sulfate, and urea [$(NH_2)_2CO$]. Rank these fertilizers in terms of the mass percentage nitrogen they contain.

3.83 **(a)** Diamond is a natural form of pure carbon. How many moles of carbon are in a 1.25-carat diamond (1 carat = 0.200 g)? How many atoms are in this diamond? **(b)** The molecular formula of acetylsalicylic acid (aspirin), one of the most common pain relievers, is $HC_9H_7O_4$. How many moles of $HC_9H_7O_4$ are in a 0.500-g tablet of aspirin? How many molecules of $HC_9H_7O_4$ are in this tablet?

3.84 **(a)** One molecule of the antibiotic known as penicillin G has a mass of 5.342×10^{-21} g. What is the molar mass of penicillin G? **(b)** Hemoglobin, the oxygen-carrying protein in red blood cells, has four iron atoms per molecule and contains 0.340% iron by mass. Calculate the molar mass of hemoglobin.

3.85 Very small crystals composed of 1000 to 100,000 atoms, called quantum dots, are being investigated for use in electronic devices.

(a) Calculate the mass in grams of a quantum dot consisting of 10,000 atoms of silicon.
(b) Assuming that the silicon in the dot has a density of 2.3 g/cm^3, calculate its volume.
(c) Assuming that the dot has the shape of a cube, calculate the length of each edge of the cube.

3.86 Serotonin is a compound that conducts nerve impulses in the brain. It contains 68.2 mass percent C, 6.86 mass percent H, 15.9 mass percent N, and 9.08 mass percent O. Its molar mass is 176 g/mol. Determine its molecular formula.

3.87 The koala dines exclusively on eucalyptus leaves. Its digestive system detoxifies the eucalyptus oil, a poison to other animals. The chief constituent in eucalyptus oil is a substance called eucalyptol, which contains 77.87% C, 11.76% H, and the remainder O. **(a)** What is the empirical formula for this substance? **(b)** A mass spectrum of eucalyptol shows a peak at about 154 amu. What is the molecular formula of the substance?

3.88 Vanillin, the dominant flavoring in vanilla, contains C, H, and O. When 1.05 g of this substance is completely combusted, 2.43 g of CO_2 and 0.50 g of H_2O are produced. What is the empirical formula of vanillin?

[3.89] An organic compound was found to contain only C, H, and Cl. When a 1.50-g sample of the compound was completely combusted in air, 3.52 g of CO_2 was formed. In a separate experiment the chlorine in a 1.00-g sample of the compound was converted to 1.27 g of AgCl. Determine the empirical formula of the compound.

[3.90] An oxybromate compound, $KBrO_x$, where x is unknown, is analyzed and found to contain 52.92% Br. What is the value of x?

[3.91] An element X forms an iodide (XI_3) and a chloride (XCl_3). The iodide is quantitatively converted to the chloride when it is heated in a stream of chlorine:

$$2\,XI_3 + 3\,Cl_2 \longrightarrow 2\,XCl_3 + 3\,I_2$$

If 0.5000 g of XI_3 is treated, 0.2360 g of XCl_3 is obtained. **(a)** Calculate the atomic weight of the element X. **(b)** Identify the element X.

3.92 If 1.5 mol of each of the following compounds is completely combusted in oxygen, which one will produce the largest number of moles of H_2O? Which will produce the least? Explain. C_2H_5OH, C_3H_8, $CH_3CH_2COCH_3$

3.93 A method used by the Environmental Protection Agency (EPA) for determining the concentration of ozone in air is to pass the air sample through a "bubbler" containing sodium iodide, which removes the ozone according to the following equation:

$$O_3(g) + 2\,NaI(aq) + H_2O(l) \longrightarrow$$
$$O_2(g) + I_2(s) + 2\,NaOH(aq)$$

(a) How many moles of sodium iodide are needed to remove 3.8×10^{-5} mol O_3? **(b)** How many grams of sodium iodide are needed to remove 0.550 mg of O_3?

3.94 A chemical plant uses electrical energy to decompose aqueous solutions of NaCl to give Cl_2, H_2, and NaOH:

$$2\,NaCl(aq) + 2\,H_2O(l) \longrightarrow$$
$$2\,NaOH(aq) + H_2(g) + Cl_2(g)$$

If the plant produces 1.5×10^6 kg (1500 metric tons) of Cl_2 daily, estimate the quantities of H_2 and NaOH produced.

3.95 The fat stored in the hump of a camel is a source of both energy and water. Calculate the mass of H_2O produced by metabolism of 1.0 kg of fat, assuming the fat consists entirely of tristearin ($C_{57}H_{110}O_6$), a typical animal fat, and assuming that during metabolism, tristearin reacts with O_2 to form only CO_2 and H_2O.

[3.96] When hydrocarbons are burned in a limited amount of air, both CO and CO_2 form. When 0.450 g of a particular hydrocarbon was burned in air, 0.467 g of CO, 0.733 g of CO_2, and 0.450 g of H_2O were formed.

(a) What is the empirical formula of the compound? **(b)** How many grams of O_2 were used in the reaction? **(c)** How many grams would have been required for complete combustion?

3.97 A mixture of $N_2(g)$ and $H_2(g)$ reacts in a closed container to form ammonia, $NH_3(g)$. The reaction ceases before either reactant has been totally consumed. At this stage 2.0 mol N_2, 2.0 mol H_2, and 2.0 mol NH_3 are present. How many moles of N_2 and H_2 were present originally?

[3.98] A mixture containing $KClO_3$, K_2CO_3, $KHCO_3$, and KCl was heated, producing CO_2, O_2, and H_2O gases according to the following equations:

$$2\,KClO_3(s) \longrightarrow 2\,KCl(s) + 3\,O_2(g)$$
$$2\,KHCO_3(s) \longrightarrow K_2O(s) + H_2O(g) + 2\,CO_2(g)$$
$$K_2CO_3(s) \longrightarrow K_2O(s) + CO_2(g)$$

The KCl does not react under the conditions of the reaction. If 100.0 g of the mixture produces 1.80 g of H_2O, 13.20 g of CO_2, and 4.00 g of O_2, what was the composition of the original mixture? (Assume complete decomposition of the mixture.)

3.99 When a mixture of 10.0 g of acetylene (C_2H_2) and 10.0 g of oxygen (O_2) is ignited, the resultant combustion reaction produces CO_2 and H_2O. **(a)** Write the balanced chemical equation for this reaction. **(b)** Which is the limiting reactant? **(c)** How many grams of C_2H_2, O_2, CO_2, and H_2O are present after the reaction is complete?

3.100 Aspirin ($C_9H_8O_4$) is produced from salicylic acid ($C_7H_6O_3$) and acetic anhydride ($C_4H_6O_3$):

$$C_7H_6O_3 + C_4H_6O_3 \longrightarrow C_9H_8O_4 + HC_2H_3O_2$$

(a) How much salicylic acid is required to produce 1.5×10^2 kg of aspirin, assuming that all of the salicylic acid is converted to aspirin? **(b)** How much salicylic acid would be required if only 80% of the salicylic acid is converted to aspirin? **(c)** What is the theoretical yield of aspirin if 185 kg of salicylic acid is allowed to react with 125 kg of acetic anhydride? **(d)** If the situation described in part (c) produces 182 kg of aspirin, what is the percentage yield?

Integrative Exercises

(These exercises require skills from earlier chapters as well as skills from the present chapter.)

3.101 Consider a sample of calcium carbonate in the form of a cube measuring 2.005 in. on each edge. If the sample has a density of 2.71 g/cm³, how many oxygen atoms does it contain?

3.102 **(a)** You are given a cube of silver metal that measures 1.000 cm on each edge. The density of silver is 0.49 g/cm³. How many atoms are in this cube? **(b)** Because atoms are spherical, they cannot occupy all of the space of the cube. The silver atoms pack in the solid in such a way that 74% of the volume of the solid is actually filled with the silver atoms. Calculate the volume of a single silver atom. **(c)** Using the volume of a silver atom and the formula for the volume of a sphere, calculate the radius in angstroms of a silver atom.

3.103 If an automobile travels 225 mi with a gas mileage of 20.5 mi/gal, how many kilograms of CO_2 are produced?

Assume that the gasoline is composed of octane, $C_8H_{18}(l)$, whose density is 0.69 g/mL.

3.104 In 1865 a chemist reported that he had reacted a weighed amount of pure silver with nitric acid and had recovered all the silver as pure silver nitrate. The mass ratio of silver to silver nitrate was found to be 0.634985. Using only this ratio and the presently accepted values for the atomic weights of silver and oxygen, calculate the atomic weight of nitrogen. Compare this calculated atomic weight with the currently accepted value.

3.105 A particular coal contains 2.5% sulfur by mass. When this coal is burned, the sulfur is converted into sulfur dioxide gas. The sulfur dioxide reacts with calcium oxide to form solid calcium sulfite. **(a)** Write the balanced chemical equation for the reaction. **(b)** If the coal is burned in a power plant that uses 2000 tons of coal per day, what is the daily production of calcium sulfite?

3.106 Copper is an excellent electrical conductor widely used in making electric circuits. In producing a printed circuit board for the electronics industry, a layer of copper is laminated on a plastic board. A circuit pattern is then printed on the board using a chemically resistant polymer. The board is then exposed to a chemical bath that reacts with the exposed copper, leaving the desired copper circuit, which has been protected by the overlaying polymer. Finally, a solvent removes the polymer. One reaction used to remove the exposed copper from the circuit board is

$$Cu(s) + Cu(NH_3)_4Cl_2(aq) + 4 NH_3(aq) \longrightarrow$$

$$2 Cu(NH_3)_4Cl(aq)$$

A plant needs to produce 5000 circuit boards, each with a surface area measuring 2.0 in. × 3.0 in. The boards are covered with a 0.65-mm layer of copper. In subsequent processing, 85% of the copper is removed. Copper has a density of 8.96 g/cm^3. Calculate the masses of $Cu(NH_3)_4Cl_2$ and NH_3 needed to produce the circuit boards, assuming that the reaction used gives a 97% yield.

3.107 Hydrogen cyanide, HCN, is a poisonous gas. The lethal dose is approximately 300 mg HCN per kilogram of air when inhaled. (a) Calculate the amount of HCN that gives the lethal dose in a small laboratory room measuring 12 × 15 × 8.0 ft. The density of air at 26°C is 0.00118 g/cm^3. (b) If the HCN is formed by reaction of NaCN with an acid such as H_2SO_4, what mass of NaCN gives the lethal dose in the room?

$$2 NaCN(s) + H_2SO_4(aq) \longrightarrow Na_2SO_4(aq) + 2 HCN(g)$$

(c) HCN forms when synthetic fibers containing Orlon® or Acrilan® burn. Acrilan® has an empirical formula of CH_2CHCN, so HCN is 50.9% of the formula by mass. A rug measures 12 × 15 ft and contains 30 oz of Acrilan® fibers per square yard of carpet. If the rug burns, will a lethal dose of HCN be generated in the room? Assume that the yield of HCN from the fibers is 20% and that the carpet is 50% consumed.

eMEDIA EXERCISES

These exercises make use of the interactive objects available online in OneKey or the Companion Website, and on your Accelerator CD. Access to these resources comes in your MediaPak.

3.108 (a) Balance the three reactions available in the **Balancing Equations** activity (3.1). (b) If, in the case of the reduction of Fe_2O_3 you were to multiply each coefficient in the balanced equation by the same number, would the reaction still be balanced? (c) Would it still be balanced if you were to square each coefficient? (d) What would the coefficients be in the balanced equation if the reduction reaction produced carbon *mon*oxide instead of carbon *di*oxide?

3.109 Calculate the percentage composition of each compound in Exercise 3.22. Use the **Molecular Weight and Weight Percent** activity (3.3) to check your answers.

3.110 Consider the reaction of zinc metal with hydrochloric acid shown in the animation **Limiting Reagent** (3.7). (a) What would the limiting reagent have been if 100 mg of Zn had been combined with 2.0 × 10^{-3} mol of HCl?

(b) What volume of hydrogen gas would the reaction have produced? (c) For the purposes of the limiting reagent experiment shown in the movie, why is it important that the hydrogen gas have a low solubility in water? How would the apparent yield of a reaction be affected if the evolved gas were very soluble in (or reactive with) water?

3.111 Write the balanced equation and predict the masses of products and remaining reactant for each of the following combinations. Use the **Limiting Reagents** (3.7) activity to check your answers. (a) 50 g $Pb(NO_3)_2$ and 55 g K_2CrO_4 to form $PbCrO_4$ and KNO_3; (b) 150 g $FeCl_2$ and 125 g Na_2S to form FeS and NaCl; (c) 96 g $Ca(NO_3)_2$ and 62 g Na_2CO_3 to form $CaCO_3$ and $NaNO_3$.

3.112 (a) In the reaction between $FeCl_3$ and NaOH to produce $Fe(OH)_3$ and NaCl, what mass of sodium hydroxide would be required to completely consume 50 g of iron(III) chloride? (b) Use the **Limiting Reagents** activity (3.7) to combine 50 g $FeCl_3$ with as close as you can get to the stoichiometric amount of sodium hydroxide, making sure that you add enough to completely consume the $FeCl_3$. How much sodium hydroxide is left over?

⬡ eLABORATORY EXERCISES

These exercises allow students to apply the concepts and skills for this chapter in the simulated laboratory of Virtual ChemLab. Worksheets for each of these exercises are found in the Virtual ChemLab Workbook in your MediaPak.

3.113 *(VCL 3-1) Counting Atoms*

It is a common problem for students to be asked to calculate the number of atoms in a pure elemental material or compound, given the mass of the sample. In this problem you will go into the virtual laboratory, retrieve a sample of gold (Au), use an analytical balance to measure its mass, and then calculate the number of atoms in the sample.

3.114 *(VCL 3-2) Counting Atoms*

In this problem you will go into the virtual laboratory, retrieve a sample of lead (Pb) and of uranium (U), use an analytical balance to measure the mass of each sample, and then calculate the number of atoms in each sample.

3.115 *(VCL 3-3) Counting Atoms*

In this problem you will go into the virtual laboratory; retrieve samples of erbium (Er), sodium (Na), tungsten (W), and a fourth sample of your choice; use an analytical balance to measure the mass of each sample; and then calculate the number of atoms in each sample.

3.116 *(VCL 3-4) Counting Molecules*

In this problem you will go into the virtual laboratory and retrieve a bottle of NaCl, weigh out approximately 1 g of the sample on an analytical balance, and then calculate the number of atoms of Na and Cl in the sample.

3.117 *(VCL 3-5) Counting Molecules*

In this problem you will go into the virtual laboratory and retrieve a bottle of sugar, weigh out approximately 1 g of the sample on an analytical balance, and then calculate the number of atoms of C, H, and O in the sample. You will also repeat this with a bottle of NH_4Cl.

3.118 *(VCL 3-6) Counting Protons, Neutrons, and Electrons*

In this problem you will enter the virtual laboratory and weigh out an isotopically pure sample of scandium (^{45}Sc), calculate the number of moles in the sample, and then calculate the number of protons, neutrons, and electrons.

3.119 *(VCL 3-7) Counting Protons, Neutrons, and Electrons*

In this problem you will enter the virtual laboratory and weigh out an isotopically pure sample of bismuth (^{209}Bi), calculate the number of moles in the sample, and then calculate the number of protons, neutrons, and electrons in $^{209}Bi^{5+}$.

3.120 *(VCL 3-8) Writing Balanced Precipitation Reactions*

It is an important skill that students be able to write balanced net ionic reactions for reactions that are observed in the laboratory. In this problem you will go into the virtual laboratory and perform a series of precipitation reactions using Ag^+, Pb^{2+}, and Sb^{3+}. After observing the reactions, you will write the net ionic equations representing these reactions and then balance them.

CHAPTER 4

4.1 General Properties
of Aqueous Solutions

4.2 Precipitation Reactions

4.3 Acid-Base Reactions

4.4 Oxidation-Reduction Reactions

4.5 Concentrations of Solutions

4.6 Solution Stoichiometry
and Chemical Analysis

WHAT'S AHEAD

- We begin by examining the nature of the substances dissolved in water, whether they exist in water as ions, molecules, or some mixture of the two. This information is necessary to understand the nature of reactants in aqueous solutions. *(Section 4.1)*

Three major types of chemical processes occur in aqueous solution:

- *Precipitation reactions* are those in which soluble reactants yield an insoluble product. *(Section 4.2)*

- *Acid-base reactions* are those in which H^+ ions are transferred between reactants. *(Section 4.3)*

- *Oxidation-reduction reactions* are those in which electrons are transferred between reactants. *(Section 4.4)*

- Reactions between ions can be represented by *ionic equations* that show, for example, how ions can combine to form precipitates, or how they are removed from the solution or changed in some other way. *(Section 4.2)*

- After examining the common types of chemical reactions and how they are recognized and described, we consider how the *concentrations* of solutions can be expressed. *(Section 4.5)*

- We conclude the chapter by examining how the concepts of stoichiometry and concentration can be used to determine the amounts or concentrations of various substances. *(Section 4.6)*

Science Fundamentals Second Edition

Aqueous Reactions and Solution Stoichiometry

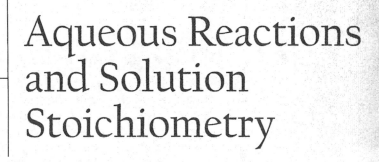

THE WATERS OF THE PACIFIC OCEAN, seen in this chapter-opening photograph of the California coast, are part of the World Ocean that covers almost two-thirds of our planet. Water has been the key to much of Earth's evolutionary history. Life itself almost certainly originated in water, and the need for water by all forms of life has helped determine diverse biological structures. Your own body is about 60% water by mass. We will see repeatedly throughout this text that water possesses many unusual properties essential to supporting life on Earth.

The waters of the World Ocean may not appear to be any different from those of Lake Tahoe or the water that flows from your kitchen faucet, but a taste of seawater is all it takes to demonstrate that there is an important difference. Water has an exceptional ability to dissolve a wide variety of substances. Water in nature—whether it is drinking water from the tap, water from a clear mountain stream, or seawater—invariably contains a variety of dissolved substances. Solutions in which water is the dissolving medium are called **aqueous solutions**. Seawater differs from what we call "freshwater" in having a much higher total concentration of dissolved ionic substances.

Water is the medium for most of the chemical reactions that take place within us and around us. Nutrients dissolved in blood are carried to our cells, where they enter into reactions that help keep us alive. Automobile parts rust when they come into frequent contact with aqueous solutions that contain various

A VIEW OF THE PACIFIC OCEAN from along the California coastline.

121

▲ **Figure 4.1 Limestone cave.** When CO_2 dissolves in water, the resulting solution is slightly acidic. Limestone caves are formed by the dissolving action of this acidic solution acting on $CaCO_3$ in the limestone.

dissolved substances. Spectacular limestone caves (Figure 4.1 ◄) are formed by the dissolving action of underground water containing carbon dioxide, $CO_2(aq)$:

$$CaCO_3(s) + H_2O(l) + CO_2(aq) \longrightarrow Ca(HCO_3)_2(aq) \qquad [4.1]$$

We saw in Chapter 3 a few simple types of chemical reactions and how they are described. In this chapter we continue to examine chemical reactions by focusing on aqueous solutions. A great deal of important chemistry occurs in aqueous solutions, and we need to learn the vocabulary and concepts used to describe and understand this chemistry. In addition, we will extend the concepts of stoichiometry that we learned in Chapter 3 by considering how solution concentrations can be expressed and used.

4.1 | General Properties of Aqueous Solutions

A *solution* is a homogeneous mixture of two or more substances. ∞∞ (Section 1.2) The substance present in greatest quantity is usually called the **solvent**. The other substances in the solution are known as the **solutes**; they are said to be dissolved in the solvent. When a small amount of sodium chloride (NaCl) is dissolved in a large quantity of water, for example, the water is the solvent and the sodium chloride is the solute.

Electrolytic Properties

Imagine preparing two aqueous solutions—one by dissolving a teaspoon of table salt (sodium chloride) in a cup of water and the other by dissolving a teaspoon of table sugar (sucrose) in a cup of water. Both solutions are clear and colorless. How do they differ? One way, which might not be immediately obvious, is in their electrical conductivity: The salt solution is a good conductor of electricity, whereas the sugar solution is not.

Whether or not a solution conducts electricity can be determined by using a device such as that shown in Figure 4.2 ▶. To light the bulb, an electric current must flow between the two electrodes that are immersed in the solution. Although water itself is a poor conductor of electricity, the presence of ions causes aqueous solutions to become good conductors. Ions carry electrical charge from one electrode to the other, completing the electrical circuit. Thus, the conductivity of NaCl solutions indicates the presence of ions in the solution, and the lack of conductivity of sucrose solutions indicates the absence of ions. When NaCl dissolves in water, the solution contains Na^+ and Cl^- ions, each surrounded by water molecules. When sucrose ($C_{12}H_{22}O_{11}$) dissolves in water, the solution contains only neutral sucrose molecules surrounded by water molecules.

A substance (such as NaCl) whose aqueous solutions contain ions is called an **electrolyte**. A substance (such as $C_{12}H_{22}O_{11}$) that does not form ions in solution is called a **nonelectrolyte**. The difference between NaCl and $C_{12}H_{22}O_{11}$ arises largely because NaCl is ionic, whereas $C_{12}H_{22}O_{11}$ is molecular.

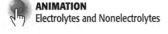

ANIMATION
Electrolytes and Nonelectrolytes

Ionic Compounds in Water

Recall from Section 2.7 and especially Figure 2.23 that solid NaCl consists of an orderly arrangement of Na^+ and Cl^- ions. When NaCl dissolves in water, each ion separates from the solid structure and disperses throughout the solution as shown in Figure 4.3(a) ▶. The ionic solid *dissociates* into its component ions as it dissolves.

Water is a very effective solvent for ionic compounds. Although water is an electrically neutral molecule, one end of the molecule (the O atom) is rich in electrons and thus possesses a partial negative charge, denoted by $\delta-$.

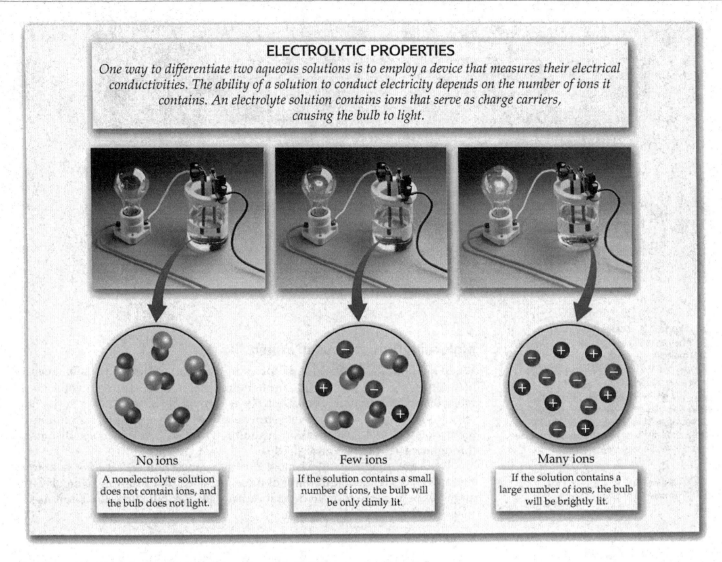

ELECTROLYTIC PROPERTIES

One way to differentiate two aqueous solutions is to employ a device that measures their electrical conductivities. The ability of a solution to conduct electricity depends on the number of ions it contains. An electrolyte solution contains ions that serve as charge carriers, causing the bulb to light.

No ions

A nonelectrolyte solution does not contain ions, and the bulb does not light.

Few ions

If the solution contains a small number of ions, the bulb will be only dimly lit.

Many ions

If the solution contains a large number of ions, the bulb will be brightly lit.

▲ **Figure 4.2 Measuring ion concentrations using conductivity.**

The other end (the H atoms) has a partial positive charge, denoted by δ+. Positive ions (cations) are attracted by the negative end of H_2O, and negative ions (anions) are attracted by the positive end.

As an ionic compound dissolves, the ions become surrounded by H_2O molecules as shown in Figure 4.3(a). The ions are said to be solvated. The **solvation** process helps stabilize the ions in solution and prevents cations and anions from recombining. Furthermore, because the ions and their shells of surrounding water molecules are free to move about, the ions become dispersed uniformly throughout the solution.

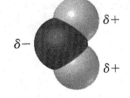

We can usually predict the nature of the ions present in a solution of an ionic compound from the chemical name of the substance. Sodium sulfate (Na_2SO_4), for example, dissociates into sodium ions (Na^+) and sulfate ions (SO_4^{2-}). You must remember the formulas and charges of common ions (Tables 2.4 and 2.5) to understand the forms in which ionic compounds exist in aqueous solution.

GIVE IT SOME THOUGHT

What dissolved species are present in a solution of (a) KCN, (b) $NaClO_4$?

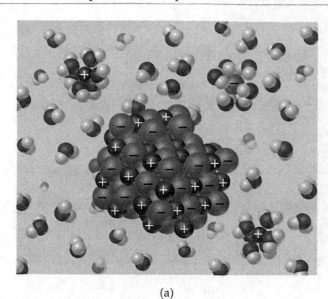

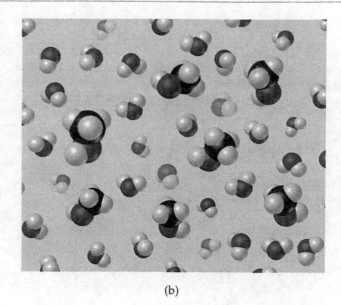

(a)   (b)

▲ **Figure 4.3   Dissolution in water.**
(a) When an ionic compound dissolves in water, H_2O molecules separate, surround, and disperse the ions into the liquid. (b) Methanol, CH_3OH, a molecular compound, dissolves without forming ions. The methanol molecules can be found by looking for the black spheres, which represent carbon atoms. In both parts (a) and (b) the water molecules have been moved apart so the solute particles can be seen more clearly.

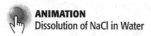
ANIMATION
Dissolution of NaCl in Water

MOVIE
Strong and Weak Electrolytes

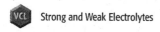
Strong and Weak Electrolytes

Molecular Compounds in Water

When a molecular compound dissolves in water, the solution usually consists of intact molecules dispersed throughout the solution. Consequently, most molecular compounds are nonelectrolytes. As we have seen, table sugar (sucrose) is an example of a nonelectrolyte. As another example, a solution of methanol (CH_3OH) in water consists entirely of CH_3OH molecules dispersed throughout the water [Figure 4.3(b)].

There are, however, a few molecular substances whose aqueous solutions contain ions. The most important of these are acids. For example, when $HCl(g)$ dissolves in water to form hydrochloric acid, $HCl(aq)$, it *ionizes*; that is, it dissociates into $H^+(aq)$ and $Cl^-(aq)$ ions.

Strong and Weak Electrolytes

There are two categories of electrolytes, strong and weak, which differ in the extent to which they conduct electricity. **Strong electrolytes** are those solutes that exist in solution completely or nearly completely as ions. Essentially all soluble ionic compounds (such as NaCl) and a few molecular compounds (such as HCl) are strong electrolytes. **Weak electrolytes** are those solutes that exist in solution mostly in the form of molecules with only a small fraction in the form of ions. For example, in a solution of acetic acid ($HC_2H_3O_2$) most of the solute is present as $HC_2H_3O_2$ molecules. Only a small fraction (about 1%) of the $HC_2H_3O_2$ is present as $H^+(aq)$ and $C_2H_3O_2^-(aq)$ ions.

We must be careful not to confuse the extent to which an electrolyte dissolves with whether it is strong or weak. For example, $HC_2H_3O_2$ is extremely soluble in water but is a weak electrolyte. $Ba(OH)_2$, on the other hand, is not very soluble, but the amount of the substance that does dissolve dissociates almost completely, so $Ba(OH)_2$ is a strong electrolyte.

When a weak electrolyte such as acetic acid ionizes in solution, we write the reaction in the following manner:

$$HC_2H_3O_2(aq) \rightleftharpoons H^+(aq) + C_2H_3O_2^-(aq) \qquad [4.2]$$

The double arrow means that the reaction is significant in both directions. At any given moment some $HC_2H_3O_2$ molecules are ionizing to form H^+ and $C_2H_3O_2^-$. At the same time, H^+ and $C_2H_3O_2^-$ ions are recombining to form $HC_2H_3O_2$. The balance between these opposing processes determines the relative numbers of ions and neutral molecules. This balance produces a state of **chemical equilibrium** that varies from one weak electrolyte to another. Chemical equilibria are extremely important, and we will devote Chapters 15–17 to examining them in detail.

Chemists use a double arrow to represent the ionization of weak electrolytes and a single arrow to represent the ionization of strong electrolytes. Because HCl is a strong electrolyte, we write the equation for the ionization of HCl as follows:

$$HCl(aq) \longrightarrow H^+(aq) + Cl^-(aq) \qquad [4.3]$$

The absence of a reverse arrow indicates that the H^+ and Cl^- ions have no tendency to recombine in water to form HCl molecules.

In the sections ahead we will begin to look more closely at how we can use the composition of a compound to predict whether it is a strong electrolyte, weak electrolyte, or nonelectrolyte. For the moment, it is important only to remember that *soluble ionic compounds are strong electrolytes*. We identify ionic compounds as being ones composed of metals and nonmetals [such as NaCl, $FeSO_4$, and $Al(NO_3)_3$], or compounds containing the ammonium ion, NH_4^+ [such as NH_4Br and $(NH_4)_2CO_3$].

GIVE IT SOME THOUGHT

Which solute will cause the lightbulb in the experiment shown in Figure 4.2 to glow more brightly, CH_3OH or $MgBr_2$?

■■ SAMPLE EXERCISE 4.1 | Relating Relative Numbers of Anions and Cations to Chemical Formulas

The diagram on the right represents an aqueous solution of one of the following compounds: $MgCl_2$, KCl, or K_2SO_4. Which solution does it best represent?

Solution
Analyze: We are asked to associate the charged spheres in the diagram with ions present in a solution of an ionic substance.
Plan: We examine the ionic substances given in the problem to determine the relative numbers and charges of the ions that each contains. We then correlate these charged ionic species with the ones shown in the diagram.
Solve: The diagram shows twice as many cations as anions, consistent with the formulation K_2SO_4.
Check: Notice that the total net charge in the diagram is zero, as it must be if it is to represent an ionic substance.

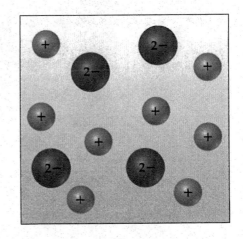

■■ PRACTICE EXERCISE

If you were to draw diagrams (such as that shown on the right) representing aqueous solutions of each of the following ionic compounds, how many anions would you show if the diagram contained six cations? **(a)** $NiSO_4$, **(b)** $Ca(NO_3)_2$, **(c)** Na_3PO_4, **(d)** $Al_2(SO_4)_3$
Answers: **(a)** 6, **(b)** 12, **(c)** 2, **(d)** 9

4.2 | Precipitation Reactions

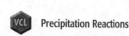
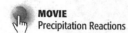
Figure 4.4 ▼ shows two clear solutions being mixed, one containing lead nitrate [Pb(NO₃)₂] and the other containing potassium iodide (KI). The reaction between these two solutes produces an insoluble yellow product. Reactions that result in the formation of an insoluble product are known as **precipitation reactions**. A **precipitate** is an insoluble solid formed by a reaction in solution. In Figure 4.4 the precipitate is lead iodide (PbI_2), a compound that has a very low solubility in water:

$$Pb(NO_3)_2(aq) + 2\,KI(aq) \longrightarrow PbI_2(s) + 2\,KNO_3(aq) \qquad [4.4]$$

The other product of this reaction, potassium nitrate, remains in solution.

Precipitation reactions occur when certain pairs of oppositely charged ions attract each other so strongly that they form an insoluble ionic solid. To predict whether certain combinations of ions form insoluble compounds, we must consider some guidelines concerning the solubilities of common ionic compounds.

▼ **Figure 4.4   A Precipitation Reaction.**

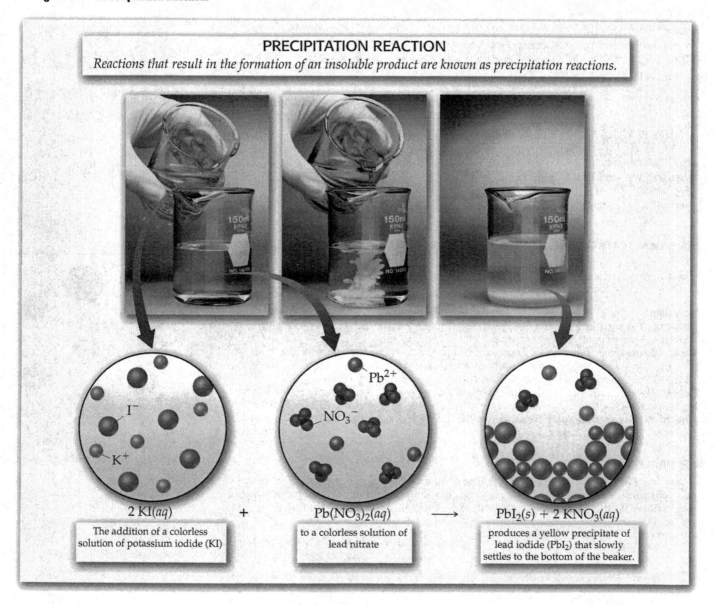

PRECIPITATION REACTION
Reactions that result in the formation of an insoluble product are known as precipitation reactions.

$2\,KI(aq)$ + $Pb(NO_3)_2(aq)$ $\longrightarrow$ $PbI_2(s) + 2\,KNO_3(aq)$

| The addition of a colorless solution of potassium iodide (KI) | to a colorless solution of lead nitrate | produces a yellow precipitate of lead iodide (PbI_2) that slowly settles to the bottom of the beaker. |

TABLE 4.1 Solubility Guidelines for Common Ionic Compounds in Water	
Soluble Ionic Compounds	**Important Exceptions**
Compounds containing NO_3^-	None
$C_2H_3O_2^-$	None
Cl^-	Compounds of Ag^+, Hg_2^{2+}, and Pb^{2+}
Br^-	Compounds of Ag^+, Hg_2^{2+}, and Pb^{2+}
I^-	Compounds of Ag^+, Hg_2^{2+}, and Pb^{2+}
SO_4^{2-}	Compounds of Sr^{2+}, Ba^{2+}, Hg_2^{2+}, and Pb^{2+}
Insoluble Ionic Compounds	**Important Exceptions**
Compounds containing S^{2-}	Compounds of NH_4^+, the alkali metal cations, and Ca^{2+}, Sr^{2+}, and Ba^{2+}
CO_3^{2-}	Compounds of NH_4^+ and the alkali metal cations
PO_4^{3-}	Compounds of NH_4^+ and the alkali metal cations
OH^-	Compounds of the alkali metal cations, and NH_4^+, Ca^{2+}, Sr^{2+}, and Ba^{2+}

Solubility Guidelines for Ionic Compounds

The **solubility** of a substance at a given temperature is the amount of that substance that can be dissolved in a given quantity of solvent at that temperature. For instance, only 1.2×10^{-3} mol of PbI_2 dissolves in a liter of water at 25°C. In our discussions any substance with a solubility less than 0.01 mol/L will be referred to as *insoluble*. In those cases the attraction between the oppositely charged ions in the solid is too great for the water molecules to separate them to any significant extent, and the substance remains largely undissolved.

Unfortunately, there are no rules based on simple physical properties such as ionic charge to guide us in predicting whether a particular ionic compound will be soluble. Experimental observations, however, have led to guidelines for predicting solubility for ionic compounds. For example, experiments show that all common ionic compounds that contain the nitrate anion, NO_3^-, are soluble in water. Table 4.1 ▲ summarizes the solubility guidelines for common ionic compounds. The table is organized according to the anion in the compound, but it reveals many important facts about cations. Note that *all common ionic compounds of the alkali metal ions (group 1A of the periodic table) and of the ammonium ion (NH_4^+) are soluble in water.*

ACTIVITY
Ionic Compounds

SAMPLE EXERCISE 4.2 | Using Solubility Rules

Classify the following ionic compounds as soluble or insoluble in water: **(a)** sodium carbonate (Na_2CO_3), **(b)** lead sulfate ($PbSO_4$).

Solution
Analyze: We are given the names and formulas of two ionic compounds and asked to predict whether they are soluble or insoluble in water.
Plan: We can use Table 4.1 to answer the question. Thus, we need to focus on the anion in each compound because the table is organized by anions.
Solve: (a) According to Table 4.1, most carbonates are insoluble, but carbonates of the alkali metal cations (such as sodium ion) are an exception to this rule and are soluble. Thus, Na_2CO_3 is soluble in water.
(b) Table 4.1 indicates that although most sulfates are water soluble, the sulfate of Pb^{2+} is an exception. Thus, $PbSO_4$ is insoluble in water.

To predict whether a precipitate forms when we mix aqueous solutions of two strong electrolytes, we must (1) note the ions present in the reactants, (2) consider the possible combinations of the cations and anions, and (3) use Table 4.1 to determine if any of these combinations is insoluble. For example, will a precipitate form when solutions of $Mg(NO_3)_2$ and $NaOH$ are mixed? Both $Mg(NO_3)_2$ and $NaOH$ are soluble ionic compounds, and they are both strong electrolytes. Mixing $Mg(NO_3)_2(aq)$ and $NaOH(aq)$ first produces a solution containing Mg^{2+}, NO_3^-, Na^+, and OH^- ions. Will either of the cations interact with either of the anions to form an insoluble compound? In addition to the reactants, the other possible interactions are Mg^{2+} with OH^- and Na^+ with NO_3^-. From Table 4.1 we see that hydroxides are generally insoluble. Because Mg^{2+} is not an exception, $Mg(OH)_2$ is insoluble and will thus form a precipitate. $NaNO_3$, however, is soluble, so Na^+ and NO_3^- will remain in solution. The balanced equation for the precipitation reaction is

$$Mg(NO_3)_2(aq) + 2\,NaOH(aq) \longrightarrow Mg(OH)_2(s) + 2\,NaNO_3(aq) \qquad [4.5]$$

Exchange (Metathesis) Reactions

Notice in Equation 4.5 that the cations in the two reactants exchange anions—Mg^{2+} ends up with OH^-, and Na^+ ends up with NO_3^-. The chemical formulas of the products are based on the charges of the ions—two OH^- ions are needed to give a neutral compound with Mg^{2+}, and one NO_3^- ion is needed to give a neutral compound with Na^+. ∞ (Section 2.7) It is only after the chemical formulas of the products have been determined that the equation can be balanced.

Reactions in which positive ions and negative ions appear to exchange partners conform to the following general equation:

$$AX + BY \longrightarrow AY + BX \qquad [4.6]$$

Example: $\qquad AgNO_3(aq) + KCl(aq) \longrightarrow AgCl(s) + KNO_3(aq)$

Such reactions are known as **exchange reactions**, or **metathesis reactions** (meh-TATH-eh-sis, which is the Greek word for "to transpose"). Precipitation reactions conform to this pattern, as do many acid-base reactions, as we will see in Section 4.3.

To complete and balance a metathesis equation, we follow these steps:

1. Use the chemical formulas of the reactants to determine the ions that are present.
2. Write the chemical formulas of the products by combining the cation from one reactant with the anion of the other. (Use the charges of the ions to determine the subscripts in the chemical formulas.)
3. Finally, balance the equation.

SAMPLE EXERCISE 4.3 | Predicting a Metathesis Reaction

(a) Predict the identity of the precipitate that forms when solutions of $BaCl_2$ and K_2SO_4 are mixed.
(b) Write the balanced chemical equation for the reaction.

Solution
Analyze: We are given two ionic reactants and asked to predict the insoluble product that they form.
Plan: We need to write down the ions present in the reactants and to exchange the anions between the two cations. Once we have written the chemical formulas for these products, we can use Table 4.1 to determine which is insoluble in water. Knowing the products also allows us to write the equation for the reaction.
Solve: (a) The reactants contain Ba^{2+}, Cl^-, K^+, and SO_4^{2-} ions. If we exchange the anions, we will have $BaSO_4$ and KCl. According to Table 4.1, most compounds of SO_4^{2-} are soluble but those of Ba^{2+} are not. Thus, $BaSO_4$ is insoluble and will precipitate from solution. KCl, on the other hand, is soluble.

(b) From part (a) we know the chemical formulas of the products, $BaSO_4$ and KCl. The balanced equation with phase labels shown is

$$BaCl_2(aq) + K_2SO_4(aq) \longrightarrow BaSO_4(s) + 2\,KCl(aq)$$

▮ PRACTICE EXERCISE

(a) What compound precipitates when solutions of $Fe_2(SO_4)_3$ and $LiOH$ are mixed?
(b) Write a balanced equation for the reaction. (c) Will a precipitate form when solutions of $Ba(NO_3)_2$ and KOH are mixed?
Answers: (a) $Fe(OH)_3$; (b) $Fe_2(SO_4)_3(aq) + 6\,LiOH(aq) \longrightarrow 2\,Fe(OH)_3(s) + 3\,Li_2SO_4(aq)$; (c) no (both possible products are water soluble)

Ionic Equations

In writing chemical equations for reactions in aqueous solution, it is often useful to indicate explicitly whether the dissolved substances are present predominantly as ions or as molecules. Let's reconsider the precipitation reaction between $Pb(NO_3)_2$ and 2 KI, shown previously in Figure 4.4:

$$Pb(NO_3)_2(aq) + 2\,KI(aq) \longrightarrow PbI_2(s) + 2\,KNO_3(aq)$$

An equation written in this fashion, showing the complete chemical formulas of the reactants and products, is called a **molecular equation** because it shows the chemical formulas of the reactants and products without indicating their ionic character. Because $Pb(NO_3)_2$, KI, and KNO_3 are all soluble ionic compounds and therefore strong electrolytes, we can write the chemical equation to indicate explicitly the ions that are in the solution:

$$Pb^{2+}(aq) + 2\,NO_3^-(aq) + 2\,K^+(aq) + 2\,I^-(aq) \longrightarrow$$

$$PbI_2(s) + 2\,K^+(aq) + 2\,NO_3^-(aq) \quad [4.7]$$

An equation written in this form, with all soluble strong electrolytes shown as ions, is known as a **complete ionic equation**.

Notice that $K^+(aq)$ and $NO_3^-(aq)$ appear on both sides of Equation 4.7. Ions that appear in identical forms among both the reactants and products of a complete ionic equation are called **spectator ions**. They are present but play no direct role in the reaction. When spectator ions are omitted from the equation (they cancel out like algebraic quantities), we are left with the **net ionic equation**:

$$Pb^{2+}(aq) + 2\,I^-(aq) \longrightarrow PbI_2(s) \quad [4.8]$$

A net ionic equation includes only the ions and molecules directly involved in the reaction. Charge is conserved in reactions, so the sum of the charges of the ions must be the same on both sides of a balanced net ionic equation. In this case the 2+ charge of the cation and the two 1− charges of the anions add to give zero, the charge of the electrically neutral product. *If every ion in a complete ionic equation is a spectator, then no reaction occurs.*

Net ionic equations are widely used to illustrate the similarities between large numbers of reactions involving electrolytes. For example, Equation 4.8 expresses the essential feature of the precipitation reaction between any strong electrolyte containing Pb^{2+} and any strong electrolyte containing I^-: The $Pb^{2+}(aq)$ and $I^-(aq)$ ions combine to form a precipitate of PbI_2. Thus, a net ionic equation demonstrates that more than one set of reactants can lead to the same net reaction. Aqueous solutions of KI and MgI_2 share many chemical similarities because both contain I^- ions. The complete equation, on the other hand, identifies the actual reactants that participate in a reaction.

The following steps summarize the procedure for writing net ionic equations:

1. Write a balanced molecular equation for the reaction.
2. Rewrite the equation to show the ions that form in solution when each soluble strong electrolyte dissociates into its component ions. *Only strong electrolytes dissolved in aqueous solution are written in ionic form.*
3. Identify and cancel spectator ions.

ACTIVITY
Writing a Net Ionic Equation

SAMPLE EXERCISE 4.4 | Writing a Net Ionic Equation

Write the net ionic equation for the precipitation reaction that occurs when solutions of calcium chloride and sodium carbonate are mixed.

Solution

Analyze: Our task is to write a net ionic equation for a precipitation reaction, given the names of the reactants present in solution.

Plan: We first need to write the chemical formulas of the reactants and products and to determine which product is insoluble. Then we write and balance the molecular equation. Next, we write each soluble strong electrolyte as separated ions to obtain the complete ionic equation. Finally, we eliminate the spectator ions to obtain the net ionic equation.

Solve: Calcium chloride is composed of calcium ions, Ca^{2+}, and chloride ions, Cl^-; hence an aqueous solution of the substance is $CaCl_2(aq)$. Sodium carbonate is composed of Na^+ ions and CO_3^{2-} ions; hence an aqueous solution of the compound is $Na_2CO_3(aq)$. In the molecular equations for precipitation reactions, the anions and cations appear to exchange partners. Thus, we put Ca^{2+} and CO_3^{2-} together to give $CaCO_3$ and Na^+ and Cl^- together to give NaCl. According to the solubility guidelines in Table 4.1, $CaCO_3$ is insoluble and NaCl is soluble. The balanced molecular equation is

$$CaCl_2(aq) + Na_2CO_3(aq) \longrightarrow CaCO_3(s) + 2\,NaCl(aq)$$

In a complete ionic equation, *only* dissolved strong electrolytes (such as soluble ionic compounds) are written as separate ions. As the *(aq)* designations remind us, $CaCl_2$, Na_2CO_3, and NaCl are all dissolved in the solution. Furthermore, they are all strong electrolytes. $CaCO_3$ is an ionic compound, but it is not soluble. We do not write the formula of any insoluble compound as its component ions. Thus, the complete ionic equation is

$$Ca^{2+}(aq) + 2\,Cl^-(aq) + 2\,Na^+(aq) + CO_3^{2-}(aq) \longrightarrow$$
$$CaCO_3(s) + 2\,Na^+(aq) + 2\,Cl^-(aq)$$

Cl^- and Na^+ are spectator ions. Canceling them gives the following net ionic equation:

$$Ca^{2+}(aq) + CO_3^{2-}(aq) \longrightarrow CaCO_3(s)$$

Check: We can check our result by confirming that both the elements and the electric charge are balanced. Each side has one Ca, one C, and three O, and the net charge on each side equals 0.

Comment: If none of the ions in an ionic equation is removed from solution or changed in some way, then they all are spectator ions and a reaction does not occur.

PRACTICE EXERCISE

Write the net ionic equation for the precipitation reaction that occurs when aqueous solutions of silver nitrate and potassium phosphate are mixed.
Answers: $3\,Ag^+(aq) + PO_4^{3-}(aq) \longrightarrow Ag_3PO_4(s)$

4.3 | Acid-Base Reactions

Many acids and bases are industrial and household substances (Figure 4.5 ▶), and some are important components of biological fluids. Hydrochloric acid, for example, is not only an important industrial chemical but also the main constituent of gastric juice in your stomach. Acids and bases also happen to be common electrolytes.

▲ **Figure 4.5 Some common household acids (left) and bases (right).**

Acids

Acids are substances that ionize in aqueous solutions to form hydrogen ions, thereby increasing the concentration of $H^+(aq)$ ions. Because a hydrogen atom consists of a proton and an electron, H^+ is simply a proton. Thus, acids are often called proton donors. Molecular models of three common acids, HCl, HNO_3, and $HC_2H_3O_2$, are shown in the margin.

Just as cations are surrounded and bound by water molecules (see Figure 4.3[a]), the proton is also solvated by water molecules. The nature of the proton in water is discussed in detail in Section 16.2. In writing chemical equations involving the proton in water, we represent it simply as $H^+(aq)$.

Molecules of different acids can ionize to form different numbers of H^+ ions. Both HCl and HNO_3 are *monoprotic* acids, which yield one H^+ per molecule of acid. Sulfuric acid, H_2SO_4, is a *diprotic* acid, one that yields two H^+ per molecule of acid. The ionization of H_2SO_4 and other diprotic acids occurs in two steps:

$$H_2SO_4(aq) \longrightarrow H^+(aq) + HSO_4^-(aq) \qquad [4.9]$$

$$HSO_4^-(aq) \rightleftharpoons H^+(aq) + SO_4^{2-}(aq) \qquad [4.10]$$

Although H_2SO_4 is a strong electrolyte, only the first ionization is complete. Thus, aqueous solutions of sulfuric acid contain a mixture of $H^+(aq)$, $HSO_4^-(aq)$, and $SO_4^{2-}(aq)$.

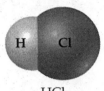

HCl

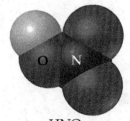

HNO_3

Bases

Bases are substances that accept (react with) H^+ ions. Bases produce hydroxide ions (OH^-) when they dissolve in water. Ionic hydroxide compounds such as NaOH, KOH, and $Ca(OH)_2$ are among the most common bases. When dissolved in water, they dissociate into their component ions, introducing OH^- ions into the solution.

Compounds that do not contain OH^- ions can also be bases. For example, ammonia (NH_3) is a common base. When added to water, it accepts an H^+ ion from the water molecule and thereby produces an OH^- ion (Figure 4.6 ▶):

$$NH_3(aq) + H_2O(l) \rightleftharpoons NH_4^+(aq) + OH^-(aq) \qquad [4.11]$$

Because only a small fraction of the NH_3 (about 1%) forms NH_4^+ and OH^- ions, ammonia is a weak electrolyte.

$HC_2H_3O_2$

Strong and Weak Acids and Bases

Acids and bases that are strong electrolytes (completely ionized in solution) are called **strong acids** and **strong bases**. Those that are weak electrolytes (partly ionized) are called **weak acids** and **weak bases**. Strong acids are more reactive than weak acids when the reactivity depends only on the concentration of $H^+(aq)$. The reactivity of an acid, however, can depend on the anion as well as on $H^+(aq)$. For example, hydrofluoric acid (HF) is a weak acid (only partly ionized in aqueous solution), but it is very reactive and vigorously attacks many substances, including glass. This reactivity is due to the combined action of $H^+(aq)$ and $F^-(aq)$.

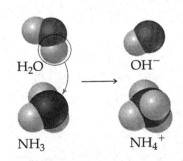

H_2O → OH^-

NH_3 → NH_4^+

▲ **Figure 4.6 Hydrogen ion transfer.** An H_2O molecule acts as a proton donor (acid), and NH_3 as a proton acceptor (base). Only a fraction of the NH_3 reacts with H_2O; NH_3 is a weak electrolyte.

TABLE 4.2 Common Strong Acids and Bases	
Strong Acids	**Strong Bases**
Hydrochloric, HCl	Group 1A metal hydroxides (LiOH, NaOH, KOH, RbOH, CsOH)
Hydrobromic, HBr	Heavy group 2A metal hydroxides [$Ca(OH)_2$, $Sr(OH)_2$, $Ba(OH)_2$]
Hydroiodic, HI	
Chloric, $HClO_3$	
Perchloric, $HClO_4$	
Nitric, HNO_3	
Sulfuric, H_2SO_4	

ANIMATION
Introduction to Aqueous Acids

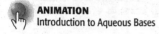

ANIMATION
Introduction to Aqueous Bases

Table 4.2 ▲ lists the common strong acids and bases. You should commit these to memory. As you examine this table, notice that some of the most common acids, such as HCl, HNO_3, and H_2SO_4, are strong. Three of the strong acids are the hydrogen compounds of the halogen family. (HF, however, is a weak acid.) The list of strong acids is very short. Most acids are weak. The only common strong bases are the hydroxides of Li^+, Na^+, K^+, Rb^+, and Cs^+ (the alkali metals, group 1A) and the hydroxides of Ca^{2+}, Sr^{2+}, and Ba^{2+} (the heavy alkaline earths, group 2A). These are the common soluble metal hydroxides. Most other metal hydroxides are insoluble in water. The most common weak base is NH_3, which reacts with water to form OH^- ions (Equation 4.11).

 GIVE IT SOME THOUGHT

Which of the following is a strong acid: H_2SO_3, HBr, $HC_2H_3O_2$?

SAMPLE EXERCISE 4.5 | Comparing Acid Strengths

The following diagrams represent aqueous solutions of three acids (HX, HY, and HZ) with water molecules omitted for clarity. Rank them from strongest to weakest.

HX   HY   HZ

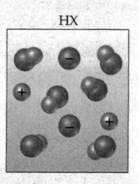   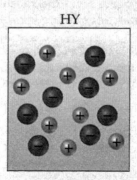   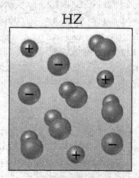

Solution
Analyze: We are asked to rank three acids from strongest to weakest, based on schematic drawings of their solutions.
Plan: We can examine the drawings to determine the relative numbers of uncharged molecular species present. The strongest acid is the one with the most H^+ ions and fewest undissociated acid molecules in solution. The weakest is the one with the largest number of undissociated molecules.
Solve: The order is HY > HZ > HX. HY is a strong acid because it is totally ionized (no HY molecules in solution), whereas both HX and HZ are weak acids, whose solutions consist of a mixture of molecules and ions. Because HZ contains more H^+ ions and fewer molecules than HX, it is a stronger acid.

PRACTICE EXERCISE

Imagine a diagram showing ten Na^+ ions and ten OH^- ions. If this solution were mixed with the one pictured on the previous page for HY, what would the diagram look like that represents the solution after any possible reaction? (H^+ ions will react with OH^- ions to form H_2O.)
Answer: The final diagram would show ten Na^+ ions, two OH^- ions, eight Y^- ions, and eight H_2O molecules.

TABLE 4.3 Summary of the Electrolytic Behavior of Common Soluble Ionic and Molecular Compounds

	Strong Electrolyte	Weak Electrolyte	Nonelectrolyte
Ionic	All	None	None
Molecular	Strong acids (see Table 4.2)	Weak acids (H ...) Weak bases (NH_3)	All other compounds

Identifying Strong and Weak Electrolytes

If we remember the common strong acids and bases (Table 4.2) and also remember that NH_3 is a weak base, we can make reasonable predictions about the electrolytic strength of a great number of water-soluble substances. Table 4.3 ▲ summarizes our observations about electrolytes. To classify a soluble substance as a strong electrolyte, weak electrolyte, or nonelectrolyte, we simply work our way down and across this table. We first ask ourselves whether the substance is ionic or molecular. If it is ionic, it is a strong electrolyte because the second column of Table 4.3 tells us that all ionic compounds are strong electrolytes. If the substance we want to classify is molecular, we ask whether it is an acid or a base. (Does it have H first in the chemical formula?) If it is an acid, we rely on the memorized list from Table 4.2 to determine whether it is a strong or weak electrolyte: All strong acids are strong electrolytes, and all weak acids are weak electrolytes. If an acid is not listed in Table 4.2, it is probably a weak acid and therefore a weak electrolyte. For example, H_3PO_4, H_2SO_3, and $HC_7H_5O_2$ are not listed in Table 4.2 and are weak acids. If the substance we want to classify is a base, we again turn to Table 4.2 to determine whether it is one of the listed strong bases. NH_3 is the only molecular base that we consider in this chapter, and Table 4.3 tells us it is a weak electrolyte. (There are compounds called amines that are related to NH_3 and are also molecular bases, but we will not consider them until Chapter 16.) Finally, any molecular substance that we encounter in this chapter that is not an acid or NH_3 is probably a nonelectrolyte.

SAMPLE EXERCISE 4.6 | Identifying Strong, Weak, and Nonelectrolytes

Classify each of the following dissolved substances as a strong electrolyte, weak electrolyte, or nonelectrolyte: $CaCl_2$, HNO_3, C_2H_5OH (ethanol), $HCHO_2$ (formic acid), KOH.

Solution
Analyze: We are given several chemical formulas and asked to classify each substance as a strong electrolyte, weak electrolyte, or nonelectrolyte.
Plan: The approach we take is outlined in Table 4.3. We can predict whether a substance is ionic or molecular, based on its composition. As we saw in Section 2.7, most ionic compounds we encounter in this text are composed of a metal and a nonmetal, whereas most molecular compounds are composed only of nonmetals.
Solve: Two compounds fit the criteria for ionic compounds: $CaCl_2$ and KOH. As Table 2.3 tells us that all ionic compounds are strong electrolytes, that is how we classify these two substances. The three remaining compounds are molecular.

Two, HNO_3 and $HCHO_2$, are acids. Nitric acid, HNO_3, is a common strong acid, as shown in Table 4.2, and therefore is a strong electrolyte. Because most acids are weak acids, our best guess would be that $HCHO_2$ is a weak acid (weak electrolyte). This is correct. The remaining molecular compound, C_2H_5OH, is neither an acid nor a base, so it is a nonelectrolyte.

Comment: Although C_2H_5OH has an OH group, it is not a metal hydroxide; thus, it is not a base. Rather, it is a member of a class of organic compounds that have C—OH bonds, which are known as alcohols. ∞ (Section 2.9)

▬ PRACTICE EXERCISE

Consider solutions in which 0.1 mol of each of the following compounds is dissolved in 1 L of water: $Ca(NO_3)_2$ (calcium nitrate), $C_6H_{12}O_6$ (glucose), $NaC_2H_3O_2$ (sodium acetate), and $HC_2H_3O_2$ (acetic acid). Rank the solutions in order of increasing electrical conductivity, based on the fact that the greater the number of ions in solution, the greater the conductivity.

Answers: $C_6H_{12}O_6$ (nonelectrolyte) < $HC_2H_3O_2$ (weak electrolyte, existing mainly in the form of molecules with few ions) < $NaC_2H_3O_2$ (strong electrolyte that provides two ions, Na^+ and $C_2H_3O_2^-$) < $Ca(NO_3)_2$ (strong electrolyte that provides three ions, Ca^{2+} and $2\ NO_3^-$)

Neutralization Reactions and Salts

The properties of acidic solutions are quite different from those of basic solutions. Acids have a sour taste, whereas bases have a bitter taste.* Acids can change the colors of certain dyes in a specific way that differs from the effect of a base (Figure 4.7 ◄). The dye known as litmus, for example, is changed from blue to red by an acid, and from red to blue by a base. In addition, acidic and basic solutions differ in chemical properties in several important ways that we will explore in this chapter and in later chapters.

When a solution of an acid and a solution of a base are mixed, a **neutralization reaction** occurs. The products of the reaction have none of the characteristic properties of either the acidic solution or the basic solution. For example, when hydrochloric acid is mixed with a solution of sodium hydroxide, the following reaction occurs:

▲ **Figure 4.7 The acid-base indicator bromthymol blue.** The indicator is blue in basic solution and yellow in acidic solution. The left flask shows the indicator in the presence of a base, aqueous ammonia (labeled as ammonium hydroxide). The right flask shows the indicator in the presence of hydrochloric acid, HCl.

$$\underset{\text{(acid)}}{HCl(aq)} + \underset{\text{(base)}}{NaOH(aq)} \longrightarrow \underset{\text{(water)}}{H_2O(l)} + \underset{\text{(salt)0}}{NaCl(aq)} \qquad [4.12]$$

Water and table salt, NaCl, are the products of the reaction. By analogy to this reaction, the term **salt** has come to mean any ionic compound whose cation comes from a base (for example, Na^+ from NaOH) and whose anion comes from an acid (for example, Cl^- from HCl). In general, *a neutralization reaction between an acid and a metal hydroxide produces water and a salt.*

Because HCl, NaOH, and NaCl are all soluble strong electrolytes, the complete ionic equation associated with Equation 4.12 is

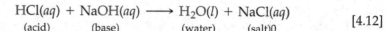

$$H^+(aq) + Cl^-(aq) + Na^+(aq) + OH^-(aq) \longrightarrow H_2O(l) + Na^+(aq) + Cl^-(aq) \qquad [4.13]$$

Therefore, the net ionic equation is

$$H^+(aq) + OH^-(aq) \longrightarrow H_2O(l) \qquad [4.14]$$

Equation 4.14 summarizes the essential feature of the neutralization reaction between any strong acid and any strong base: $H^+(aq)$ and $OH^-(aq)$ ions combine to form H_2O.

---

* Tasting chemical solutions is not a good practice. However, we have all had acids such as ascorbic acid (vitamin C), acetylsalicylic acid (aspirin), and citric acid (in citrus fruits) in our mouths, and we are familiar with their characteristic sour taste. Soaps, which are basic, have the characteristic bitter taste of bases.

(a)

(b)

(c)

Figure 4.8 ▲ shows the reaction between hydrochloric acid and the base $Mg(OH)_2$, which is insoluble in water. A milky white suspension of $Mg(OH)_2$ called milk of magnesia is seen dissolving as the neutralization reaction occurs:

Molecular equation:

$$Mg(OH)_2(s) + 2\,HCl(aq) \longrightarrow MgCl_2(aq) + 2\,H_2O(l) \qquad [4.15]$$

Net ionic equation:

$$Mg(OH)_2(s) + 2\,H^+(aq) \longrightarrow Mg^{2+}(aq) + 2\,H_2O(l) \qquad [4.16]$$

Notice that the OH^- ions (this time in a solid reactant) and H^+ ions combine to form H_2O. Because the ions exchange partners, neutralization reactions between acids and metal hydroxides are also metathesis reactions.

▲ **Figure 4.8 Reaction of $Mg(OH)_2(s)$ with acid.** (a) Milk of magnesia is a suspension of magnesium hydroxide, $Mg(OH)_2(s)$, in water. (b) The magnesium hydroxide dissolves upon the addition of hydrochloric acid, $HCl(aq)$. (c) The final clear solution contains soluble $MgCl_2(aq)$, shown in Equation 4.15.

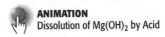

ANIMATION
Dissolution of $Mg(OH)_2$ by Acid

■■■ SAMPLE EXERCISE 4.7 | Writing Chemical Equations for a Neutralization Reaction

(a) Write a balanced molecular equation for the reaction between aqueous solutions of acetic acid ($HC_2H_3O_2$) and barium hydroxide [$Ba(OH)_2$]. **(b)** Write the net ionic equation for this reaction.

Solution
Analyze: We are given the chemical formulas for an acid and a base and asked to write a balanced molecular equation and then a net ionic equation for their neutralization reaction.
Plan: As Equation 4.12 and the italicized statement that follows it indicate, neutralization reactions form two products, H_2O and a salt. We examine the cation of the base and the anion of the acid to determine the composition of the salt.

Solve: (a) The salt will contain the cation of the base (Ba^{2+}) and the anion of the acid ($C_2H_3O_2^-$). Thus, the formula of the salt is $Ba(C_2H_3O_2)_2$. According to the solubility guidelines in Table 4.1, this compound is soluble. The unbalanced molecular equation for the neutralization reaction is

$$HC_2H_3O_2(aq) + Ba(OH)_2(aq) \longrightarrow H_2O(l) + Ba(C_2H_3O_2)_2(aq)$$

To balance this molecular equation, we must provide two molecules of $HC_2H_3O_2$ to furnish the two $C_2H_3O_2^-$ ions and to supply the two H^+ ions needed to combine with the two OH^- ions of the base. The balanced molecular equation is

$$2\,HC_2H_3O_2(aq) + Ba(OH)_2(aq) \longrightarrow 2\,H_2O(l) + Ba(C_2H_3O_2)_2(aq)$$

(b) To write the net ionic equation, we must determine whether each compound in aqueous solution is a strong electrolyte. $HC_2H_3O_2$ is a weak electrolyte (weak acid), $Ba(OH)_2$ is a strong electrolyte, and $Ba(C_2H_3O_2)_2$ is also a strong electrolyte (ionic compound). Thus, the complete ionic equation is

$$2\,HC_2H_3O_2(aq) + Ba^{2+}(aq) + 2\,OH^-(aq) \longrightarrow 2\,H_2O(l) + Ba^{2+}(aq) + 2\,C_2H_3O_2{}^-(aq)$$

Eliminating the spectator ions gives

$$2\,HC_2H_3O_2(aq) + 2\,OH^-(aq) \longrightarrow 2\,H_2O(l) + 2\,C_2H_3O_2{}^-(aq)$$

Simplifying the coefficients gives the net ionic equation:

$$HC_2H_3O_2(aq) + OH^-(aq) \longrightarrow H_2O(l) + C_2H_3O_2{}^-(aq)$$

Check: We can determine whether the molecular equation is correctly balanced by counting the number of atoms of each kind on both sides of the arrow. (There are ten H, six O, four C, and one Ba on each side.) However, it is often easier to check equations by counting groups: There are two $C_2H_3O_2$ groups, as well as one Ba, and four additional H atoms and two additional O atoms on each side of the equation. The net ionic equation checks out because the numbers of each kind of element and the net charge are the same on both sides of the equation.

PRACTICE EXERCISE

(a) Write a balanced molecular equation for the reaction of carbonic acid (H_2CO_3) and potassium hydroxide (KOH). (b) Write the net ionic equation for this reaction.
Answers: (a) $H_2CO_3(aq) + 2\,KOH(aq) \longrightarrow 2\,H_2O(l) + K_2CO_3(aq)$;   (b) $H_2CO_3(aq) + 2\,OH^-(aq) \longrightarrow 2\,H_2O(l) + CO_3{}^{2-}(aq)$. ($H_2CO_3$ is a weak acid and therefore a weak electrolyte, whereas KOH, a strong base, and K_2CO_3, an ionic compound, are strong electrolytes.)

Acid-Base Reactions with Gas Formation

There are many bases besides OH^- that react with H^+ to form molecular compounds. Two of these that you might encounter in the laboratory are the sulfide ion and the carbonate ion. Both of these anions react with acids to form gases that have low solubilities in water. Hydrogen sulfide (H_2S), the substance that gives rotten eggs their foul odor, forms when an acid such as HCl(aq) reacts with a metal sulfide such as Na_2S:

Molecular equation: $2\,HCl(aq) + Na_2S(aq) \longrightarrow H_2S(g) + 2\,NaCl(aq)$ [4.17]

Net ionic equation: $2\,H^+(aq) + S^{2-}(aq) \longrightarrow H_2S(g)$ [4.18]

Carbonates and bicarbonates react with acids to form CO_2 gas. Reaction of $CO_3{}^{2-}$ or $HCO_3{}^-$ with an acid first gives carbonic acid (H_2CO_3). For example, when hydrochloric acid is added to sodium bicarbonate, the following reaction occurs:

$$HCl(aq) + NaHCO_3(aq) \longrightarrow NaCl(aq) + H_2CO_3(aq) \qquad [4.19]$$

Carbonic acid is unstable; if present in solution in sufficient concentrations, it decomposes to form CO_2, which escapes from the solution as a gas.

$$H_2CO_3(aq) \longrightarrow H_2O(l) + CO_2(g) \qquad [4.20]$$

The decomposition of H_2CO_3 produces bubbles of CO_2 gas, as shown in Figure 4.9 ◄. The overall reaction is summarized by the following equations:

Molecular equation:
$$HCl(aq) + NaHCO_3(aq) \longrightarrow NaCl(aq) + H_2O(l) + CO_2(g) \qquad [4.21]$$

Net ionic equation: $H^+(aq) + HCO_3{}^-(aq) \longrightarrow H_2O(l) + CO_2(g)$ [4.22]

Both $NaHCO_3$ and Na_2CO_3 are used as acid neutralizers in acid spills. The bicarbonate or carbonate salt is added until the fizzing due to the formation of

▲ **Figure 4.9   Carbonates react with acids to form carbon dioxide gas.** Here $NaHCO_3$ (white solid) reacts with hydrochloric acid; the bubbles contain CO_2.

CHEMISTRY AT WORK | Antacids

The stomach secretes acids to help digest foods. These acids, which include hydrochloric acid, contain about 0.1 mol of H^+ per liter of solution. The stomach and digestive tract are normally protected from the corrosive effects of stomach acid by a mucosal lining. Holes can develop in this lining, however, allowing the acid to attack the underlying tissue, causing painful damage. These holes, known as ulcers, can be caused by the secretion of excess acids or by a weakness in the digestive lining. Recent studies indicate, however, that many ulcers are caused by bacterial infection. Between 10 and 20% of Americans suffer from ulcers at some point in their lives, and many others experience occasional indigestion or heartburn that is due to digestive acids entering the esophagus.

We can address the problem of excess stomach acid in two simple ways: (1) removing the excess acid, or (2) decreasing the production of acid. Those substances that remove excess acid are called *antacids*, whereas those that decrease the production of acid are called *acid inhibitors*. Figure 4.10 ▶ shows several common, over-the-counter drugs of both types.

Antacids are simple bases that neutralize digestive acids. Their ability to neutralize acids is due to the hydroxide, carbonate, or bicarbonate ions they contain. Table 4.4 ◀ lists the active ingredients in some antacids.

The newer generation of antiulcer drugs, such as Tagamet® and Zantac®, are acid inhibitors. They act on acid-producing cells in the lining of the stomach. Formulations that control acid in this way are now available as over-the-counter drugs.

Related Exercise: 4.93

TABLE 4.4 Some Common Antacids

Commercial Name	Acid-Neutralizing Agents
Alka-Seltzer®	$NaHCO_3$
Amphojel®	$Al(OH)_3$
Di-Gel®	$Mg(OH)_2$ and $CaCO_3$
Milk of Magnesia	$Mg(OH)_2$
Maalox®	$Mg(OH)_2$ and $Al(OH)_3$
Mylanta®	$Mg(OH)_2$ and $Al(OH)_3$
Rolaids®	$NaAl(OH)_2CO_3$
Tums®	$CaCO_3$

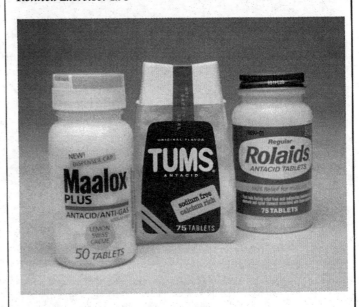

▲ **Figure 4.10 Antacids.** These products all serve as acid-neutralizing agents in the stomach.

$CO_2(g)$ stops. Sometimes sodium bicarbonate is used as an antacid to soothe an upset stomach. In that case the HCO_3^- reacts with stomach acid to form $CO_2(g)$. The fizz when Alka-Seltzer® tablets are added to water arises from the reaction of sodium bicarbonate and citric acid.

 GIVE IT SOME THOUGHT

By analogy to examples already given in the text, predict what gas forms when $Na_2SO_3(s)$ is treated with $HCl(aq)$.

4.4 | Oxidation-Reduction Reactions

In precipitation reactions cations and anions come together to form an insoluble ionic compound. In neutralization reactions H^+ ions and OH^- ions come together to form H_2O molecules. Now let's consider a third important kind of reaction, one in which electrons are transferred between reactants. Such reactions are called **oxidation-reduction**, or *redox*, **reactions**.

Oxidation and Reduction

The corrosion of iron (rusting) and of other metals, such as the corrosion of the terminals of an automobile battery, are familiar processes. What we call *corrosion* is the conversion of a metal into a metal compound by a reaction between the metal and some substance in its environment. Rusting, as shown in Figure 4.11 ▲, involves the reaction of oxygen with iron in the presence of water.

When a metal corrodes, it loses electrons and forms cations. For example, calcium is vigorously attacked by acids to form calcium ions:

MOVIE
Reduction of CuO

ANIMATIONS
Oxidation-Reduction Reactions - Part I
Oxidation-Reduction Reactions - Part II

$$Ca(s) + 2\,H^+(aq) \longrightarrow Ca^{2+}(aq) + H_2(g) \qquad [4.23]$$

When an atom, ion, or molecule has become more positively charged (that is, when it has lost electrons), we say that it has been oxidized. *Loss of electrons by a substance is called* **oxidation**. Thus, Ca, which has no net charge, is *oxidized* (undergoes oxidation) in Equation 4.23, forming Ca^{2+}.

The term oxidation is used because the first reactions of this sort to be studied thoroughly were reactions with oxygen. Many metals react directly with O_2 in air to form metal oxides. In these reactions the metal loses electrons to oxygen, forming an ionic compound of the metal ion and oxide ion. For example, when calcium metal is exposed to air, the bright metallic surface of the metal tarnishes as CaO forms:

$$2\,Ca(s) + O_2(g) \longrightarrow 2\,CaO(s) \qquad [4.24]$$

As Ca is oxidized in Equation 4.24, oxygen is transformed from neutral O_2 to two O^{2-} ions (Figure 4.12 ▼). When an atom, ion, or molecule has become more negatively charged (gained electrons), we say that it is *reduced*. *Gain of electrons by a substance is called* **reduction**. When one reactant loses

▼ **Figure 4.12   Oxidation of calcium metal by molecular oxygen.** The oxidation involves transfer of electrons from the metal to O_2, eventually leading to formation of CaO.

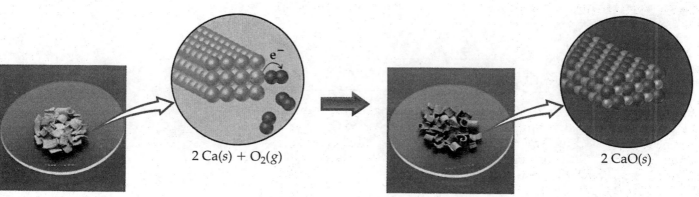

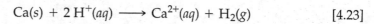

$2\,Ca(s) + O_2(g)$

$2\,CaO(s)$

Science Fundamentals Second Edition

electrons, another reactant must gain them; the oxidation of one substance is always accompanied by the reduction of another as electrons are transferred between them.

Oxidation Numbers

Before we can properly identify an oxidation-reduction reaction, we must have a kind of bookkeeping system, a way of keeping track of the electrons gained by the substance reduced and those lost by the substance oxidized. The concept of oxidation numbers (also called *oxidation states*) was devised as a way of doing this. Each atom in a neutral molecule or charged species is assigned an **oxidation number**, which is the actual charge for a monatomic ion; otherwise, the oxidation number is the hypothetical charge assigned to the atom, assuming that the electrons are *completely* held by one atom or the other. The oxidation numbers of certain atoms change in an oxidation-reduction reaction. Oxidation occurs when there is an increase in oxidation number, whereas reduction occurs when there is a decrease in oxidation number.

We use the following rules for assigning oxidation numbers:

1. *For an atom in its **elemental form**, the oxidation number is always zero.* Thus, each H atom in the H_2 molecule has an oxidation number of 0, and each P atom in the P_4 molecule has an oxidation number of 0.

2. *For any **monatomic ion** the oxidation number equals the charge on the ion.* Thus, K^+ has an oxidation number of +1, S^{2-} has an oxidation state of −2, and so forth. The alkali metal ions (group 1A) always have a 1+ charge, and therefore the alkali metals always have an oxidation number of +1 in their compounds. Similarly, the alkaline earth metals (group 2A) are always +2, and aluminum (group 3A) is always +3 in its compounds. (In writing oxidation numbers, we will write the sign before the number to distinguish them from the actual electronic charges, which we write with the number first.)

3. *Nonmetals* usually have negative oxidation numbers, although they can sometimes be positive:

   (a) *The oxidation number of **oxygen** is usually −2* in both ionic and molecular compounds. The major exception is in compounds called peroxides, which contain the O_2^{2-} ion, giving each oxygen an oxidation number of −1.

   (b) *The oxidation number of **hydrogen** is +1 when bonded to nonmetals and −1 when bonded to metals.*

   (c) *The oxidation number of **fluorine** is −1 in all compounds.* The other *halogens* have an oxidation number of −1 in most binary compounds. When combined with oxygen, as in oxyanions, however, they have positive oxidation states.

4. **The sum of the oxidation numbers** *of all atoms in a neutral compound is zero. The sum of the oxidation numbers in a polyatomic ion equals the charge of the ion.* For example, in the hydronium ion, H_3O^+, the oxidation number of each hydrogen is +1 and that of oxygen is −2. Thus, the sum of the oxidation numbers is $3(+1) + (-2) = +1$, which equals the net charge of the ion. This rule is very useful in obtaining the oxidation number of one atom in a compound or ion if you know the oxidation numbers of the other atoms, as illustrated in Sample Exercise 4.8.

ACTIVITY
Oxidation Numbers I

ACTIVITY
Oxidation Numbers II

 GIVE IT SOME THOUGHT

(a) What noble gas element has the same number of electrons as the fluoride ion?
(b) What is the oxidation number of that species?

Science Fundamentals Second Edition

SAMPLE EXERCISE 4.8 | Determining Oxidation Numbers

Determine the oxidation number of sulfur in each of the following: **(a)** H_2S, **(b)** S_8, **(c)** SCl_2, **(d)** Na_2SO_3, **(e)** SO_4^{2-}.

Solution

Analyze: We are asked to determine the oxidation number of sulfur in two molecular species, in the elemental form, and in two ionic substances.

Plan: In each species the sum of oxidation numbers of all the atoms must equal the charge on the species. We will use the rules outlined above to assign oxidation numbers.

Solve: (a) When bonded to a nonmetal, hydrogen has an oxidation number of +1 (rule 3b). Because the H_2S molecule is neutral, the sum of the oxidation numbers must equal zero (rule 4). Letting x equal the oxidation number of S, we have $2(+1) + x = 0$. Thus, S has an oxidation number of −2.

   (b) Because this is an elemental form of sulfur, the oxidation number of S is 0 (rule 1).

   (c) Because this is a binary compound, we expect chlorine to have an oxidation number of −1 (rule 3c). The sum of the oxidation numbers must equal zero (rule 4). Letting x equal the oxidation number of S, we have $x + 2(-1) = 0$. Consequently, the oxidation number of S must be +2.

   (d) Sodium, an alkali metal, always has an oxidation number of +1 in its compounds (rule 2). Oxygen has a common oxidation state of −2 (rule 3a). Letting x equal the oxidation number of S, we have $2(+1) + x + 3(-2) = 0$. Therefore, the oxidation number of S in this compound is +4.

   (e) The oxidation state of O is −2 (rule 3a). The sum of the oxidation numbers equals −2, the net charge of the SO_4^{2-} ion (rule 4). Thus, we have $x + 4(-2) = -2$. From this relation we conclude that the oxidation number of S in this ion is +6.

Comment: These examples illustrate that the oxidation number of a given element depends on the compound in which it occurs. The oxidation numbers of sulfur, as seen in these examples, range from −2 to +6.

PRACTICE EXERCISE

What is the oxidation state of the boldfaced element in each of the following: **(a)** P_2O_5, **(b)** NaH, **(c)** $Cr_2O_7^{2-}$, **(d)** $SnBr_4$, **(e)** BaO_2?
Answers: **(a)** +5, **(b)** −1, **(c)** +6, **(d)** +4, **(e)** −1

MOVIE
Oxidation-Reduction Chemistry of Tin and Zinc

Oxidation of Metals by Acids and Salts

There are many kinds of redox reactions. For example, combustion reactions are redox reactions because elemental oxygen is converted to compounds of oxygen. ⟶ (Section 3.2) In this chapter we consider the redox reactions between metals and either acids or salts. In Chapter 20 we will examine more complex kinds of redox reactions.

The reaction of a metal with either an acid or a metal salt conforms to the following general pattern:

$$A + BX \longrightarrow AX + B \qquad [4.25]$$

Examples:
$$Zn(s) + 2\,HBr(aq) \longrightarrow ZnBr_2(aq) + H_2(g)$$

$$Mn(s) + Pb(NO_3)_2(aq) \longrightarrow Mn(NO_3)_2(aq) + Pb(s)$$

These reactions are called **displacement reactions** because the ion in solution is displaced or replaced through oxidation of an element.

Many metals undergo displacement reactions with acids, producing salts and hydrogen gas. For example, magnesium metal reacts with hydrochloric acid to form magnesium chloride and hydrogen gas (Figure 4.13 ▶). To show that oxidation and reduction have occurred, the oxidation number for each atom is shown below the chemical equation for this reaction:

$$Mg(s) + 2\,HCl(aq) \longrightarrow MgCl_2(aq) + H_2(g), \qquad [4.26]$$

$$\begin{array}{cccc} 0 & +1 \;\; -1 & +2 \;\; -1 & 0 \end{array}$$

Science Fundamentals Second Edition

▲ **Figure 4.13 Reaction of magnesium with acid.** The bubbles are due to hydrogen gas.

Notice that the oxidation number of Mg changes from 0 to +2. The increase in the oxidation number indicates that the atom has lost electrons and has therefore been oxidized. The H^+ ion of the acid decreases in oxidation number from +1 to 0, indicating that this ion has gained electrons and has therefore been reduced. The oxidation number of the Cl^- ion remains −1, and it is a spectator ion in the reaction. The net ionic equation is as follows:

$$Mg(s) + 2\,H^+(aq) \longrightarrow Mg^{2+}(aq) + H_2(g) \qquad [4.27]$$

Metals can also be oxidized by aqueous solutions of various salts. Iron metal, for example, is oxidized to Fe^{2+} by aqueous solutions of Ni^{2+}, such as $Ni(NO_3)_2(aq)$:

Molecular equation: $Fe(s) + Ni(NO_3)_2(aq) \longrightarrow Fe(NO_3)_2(aq) + Ni(s) \quad [4.28]$

Net ionic equation: $Fe(s) + Ni^{2+}(aq) \longrightarrow Fe^{2+}(aq) + Ni(s) \qquad [4.29]$

The oxidation of Fe to form Fe^{2+} in this reaction is accompanied by the reduction of Ni^{2+} to Ni. Remember: *Whenever one substance is oxidized, some other substance must be reduced.*

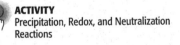

ACTIVITY
Precipitation, Redox, and Neutralization Reactions

■ **SAMPLE EXERCISE 4.9 | Writing Molecular and Net Ionic Equations for Oxidation-Reduction Reactions**

Write the balanced molecular and net ionic equations for the reaction of aluminum with hydrobromic acid.

Solution
Analyze: We must write two equations—molecular and net ionic—for the redox reaction between a metal and an acid.

Science Fundamentals Second Edition

Plan: Metals react with acids to form salts and H_2 gas. To write the balanced equations, we must write the chemical formulas for the two reactants and then determine the formula of the salt. The salt is composed of the cation formed by the metal and the anion of the acid.

Solve: The formulas of the given reactants are Al and HBr. The cation formed by Al is Al^{3+}, and the anion from hydrobromic acid is Br^-. Thus, the salt formed in the reaction is $AlBr_3$. Writing the reactants and products and then balancing the equation gives this molecular equation:

$$2\,Al(s) + 6\,HBr(aq) \longrightarrow 2\,AlBr_3(aq) + 3\,H_2(g)$$

Both HBr and $AlBr_3$ are soluble strong electrolytes. Thus, the complete ionic equation is

$$2\,Al(s) + 6\,H^+(aq) + 6\,Br^-(aq) \longrightarrow 2\,Al^{3+}(aq) + 6\,Br^-(aq) + 3\,H_2(g)$$

Because Br^- is a spectator ion, the net ionic equation is

$$2\,Al(s) + 6\,H^+(aq) \longrightarrow 2\,Al^{3+}(aq) + 3\,H_2(g)$$

Comment: The substance oxidized is the aluminum metal because its oxidation state changes from 0 in the metal to +3 in the cation, thereby increasing in oxidation number. The H^+ is reduced because its oxidation state changes from +1 in the acid to 0 in H_2.

▬▬ PRACTICE EXERCISE

(a) Write the balanced molecular and net ionic equations for the reaction between magnesium and cobalt(II) sulfate. **(b)** What is oxidized and what is reduced in the reaction?
Answers: **(a)** $Mg(s) + CoSO_4(aq) \longrightarrow MgSO_4(aq) + Co(s)$;
$Mg(s) + Co^{2+}(aq) \longrightarrow Mg^{2+}(aq) + Co(s)$; **(b)** Mg is oxidized and Co^{2+} is reduced.

The Activity Series

Can we predict whether a certain metal will be oxidized either by an acid or by a particular salt? This question is of practical importance as well as chemical interest. According to Equation 4.28, for example, it would be unwise to store a solution of nickel nitrate in an iron container because the solution would dissolve the container. When a metal is oxidized, it appears to be eaten away as it reacts to form various compounds. Extensive oxidation can lead to the failure of metal machinery parts or the deterioration of metal structures.

Different metals vary in the ease with which they are oxidized. Zn is oxidized by aqueous solutions of Cu^{2+}, for example, but Ag is not. Zn, therefore, loses electrons more readily than Ag; that is, Zn is easier to oxidize than Ag.

A list of metals arranged in order of decreasing ease of oxidation is called an **activity series**. Table 4.5 ▶ gives the activity series in aqueous solution for many of the most common metals. Hydrogen is also included in the table. The metals at the top of the table, such as the alkali metals and the alkaline earth metals, are most easily oxidized; that is, they react most readily to form compounds. They are called the *active metals*. The metals at the bottom of the activity series, such as the transition elements from groups 8B and 1B, are very stable and form compounds less readily. These metals, which are used to make coins and jewelry, are called *noble metals* because of their low reactivity.

The activity series can be used to predict the outcome of reactions between metals and either metal salts or acids. *Any metal on the list can be oxidized by the ions of elements below it.* For example, copper is above silver in the series. Thus, copper metal will be oxidized by silver ions, as pictured in Figure 4.14 ▶:

$$Cu(s) + 2\,Ag^+(aq) \longrightarrow Cu^{2+}(aq) + 2\,Ag(s) \qquad [4.30]$$

The oxidation of copper to copper ions is accompanied by the reduction of silver ions to silver metal. The silver metal is evident on the surface of the copper wires in Figure 4.14(b) and (c). The copper(II) nitrate produces a blue color in the solution, which is most evident in part (c).

TABLE 4.5   Activity Series of Metals in Aqueous Solution

Metal	Oxidation Reaction
Lithium	$Li(s) \longrightarrow Li^+(aq) + e^-$
Potassium	$K(s) \longrightarrow K^+(aq) + e^-$
Barium	$Ba(s) \longrightarrow Ba^{2+}(aq) + 2e^-$
Calcium	$Ca(s) \longrightarrow Ca^{2+}(aq) + 2e^-$
Sodium	$Na(s) \longrightarrow Na^+(aq) + e^-$
Magnesium	$Mg(s) \longrightarrow Mg^{2+}(aq) + 2e^-$
Aluminum	$Al(s) \longrightarrow Al^{3+}(aq) + 3e^-$
Manganese	$Mn(s) \longrightarrow Mn^{2+}(aq) + 2e^-$
Zinc	$Zn(s) \longrightarrow Zn^{2+}(aq) + 2e^-$
Chromium	$Cr(s) \longrightarrow Cr^{3+}(aq) + 3e^-$
Iron	$Fe(s) \longrightarrow Fe^{2+}(aq) + 2e^-$
Cobalt	$Co(s) \longrightarrow Co^{2+}(aq) + 2e^-$
Nickel	$Ni(s) \longrightarrow Ni^{2+}(aq) + 2e^-$
Tin	$Sn(s) \longrightarrow Sn^{2+}(aq) + 2e^-$
Lead	$Pb(s) \longrightarrow Pb^{2+}(aq) + 2e^-$
Hydrogen	$H_2(g) \longrightarrow 2 H^+(aq) + 2e^-$
Copper	$Cu(s) \longrightarrow Cu^{2+}(aq) + 2e^-$
Silver	$Ag(s) \longrightarrow Ag^+(aq) + e^-$
Mercury	$Hg(l) \longrightarrow Hg^{2+}(aq) + 2e^-$
Platinum	$Pt(s) \longrightarrow Pt^{2+}(aq) + 2e^-$
Gold	$Au(s) \longrightarrow Au^{3+}(aq) + 3e^-$

Ease of oxidation increases

MOVIE
Formation of Silver Crystals

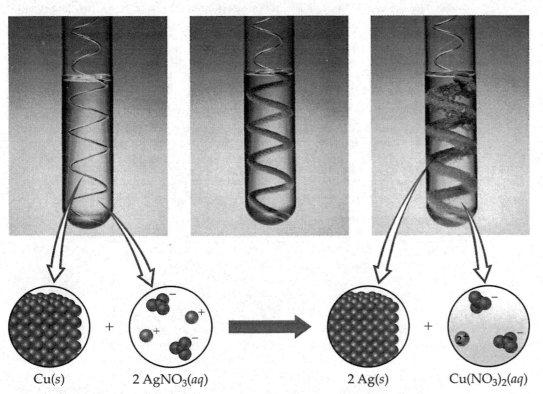

$Cu(s)$ + $2 AgNO_3(aq)$ $\longrightarrow$ $2 Ag(s)$ + $Cu(NO_3)_2(aq)$

▲ **Figure 4.14 Reaction of copper with silver ion.** When copper metal is placed in a solution of silver nitrate, a redox reaction occurs, forming silver metal and a blue solution of copper(II) nitrate.

Science Fundamentals Second Edition

GIVE IT SOME THOUGHT

Which is the more easily reduced, $Mg^{2+}(aq)$ or $Ni^{2+}(aq)$?

Only those metals above hydrogen in the activity series are able to react with acids to form H_2. For example, Ni reacts with $HCl(aq)$ to form H_2:

$$Ni(s) + 2\,HCl(aq) \longrightarrow NiCl_2(aq) + H_2(g) \qquad [4.31]$$

Because elements below hydrogen in the activity series are not oxidized by H^+, Cu does not react with $HCl(aq)$. Interestingly, copper does react with nitric acid, as shown previously in Figure 1.11. This reaction, however, is not a simple oxidation of Cu by the H^+ ions of the acid. Instead, the metal is oxidized to Cu^{2+} by the nitrate ion of the acid, accompanied by the formation of brown nitrogen dioxide, $NO_2(g)$:

$$Cu(s) + 4\,HNO_3(aq) \longrightarrow Cu(NO_3)_2(aq) + 2\,H_2O(l) + 2\,NO_2(g) \quad [4.32]$$

What substance is reduced as copper is oxidized in Equation 4.32? In this case the NO_2 results from the reduction of NO_3^-. We will examine reactions of this type in more detail in Chapter 20.

SAMPLE EXERCISE 4.10 | Determining When an Oxidation-Reduction Reaction Can Occur

Will an aqueous solution of iron(II) chloride oxidize magnesium metal? If so, write the balanced molecular and net ionic equations for the reaction.

Solution

Analyze: We are given two substances—an aqueous salt, $FeCl_2$, and a metal, Mg— and asked if they react with each other.

Plan: A reaction will occur if Mg is above Fe in the activity series, Table 4.5. If the reaction occurs, the Fe^{2+} ion in $FeCl_2$ will be reduced to Fe, and the elemental Mg will be oxidized to Mg^{2+}.

Solve: Because Mg is above Fe in the table, the reaction will occur. To write the formula for the salt that is produced in the reaction, we must remember the charges on common ions. Magnesium is always present in compounds as Mg^{2+}; the chloride ion is Cl^-. The magnesium salt formed in the reaction is $MgCl_2$, meaning the balanced molecular equation is

$$Mg(s) + FeCl_2(aq) \longrightarrow MgCl_2(aq) + Fe(s)$$

Both $FeCl_2$ and $MgCl_2$ are soluble strong electrolytes and can be written in ionic form. Cl^-, then, is a spectator ion in the reaction. The net ionic equation is

$$Mg(s) + Fe^{2+}(aq) \longrightarrow Mg^{2+}(aq) + Fe(s)$$

The net ionic equation shows that Mg is oxidized and Fe^{2+} is reduced in this reaction.

Check: Note that the net ionic equation is balanced with respect to both charge and mass.

PRACTICE EXERCISE

Which of the following metals will be oxidized by $Pb(NO_3)_2$: Zn, Cu, Fe?
Answer: Zn and Fe

4.5 | Concentrations of Solutions

The behavior of solutions often depends not only on the nature of the solutes but also on their concentrations. Scientists use the term **concentration** to designate the amount of solute dissolved in a given quantity of solvent or quantity of solution. The concept of concentration is intuitive: The greater the amount of solute dissolved in a certain amount of solvent, the more concentrated the resulting solution. In chemistry we often need to express the concentrations of solutions quantitatively.

A CLOSER LOOK | The Aura of Gold

Gold has been known since the earliest records of human existence. Throughout history people have cherished gold, have fought for it, and have died for it.

The physical and chemical properties of gold serve to make it a special metal. First, its intrinsic beauty and rarity make it precious. Second, gold is soft and can be easily formed into artistic objects, jewelry, and coins (Figure 4.15 ▶). Third, gold is one of the least active metals (Table 4.5). It is not oxidized in air and does not react with water. It is unreactive toward basic solutions and nearly all acidic solutions. As a result, gold can be found in nature as a pure element rather than combined with oxygen or other elements, which accounts for its early discovery.

Many of the early studies of the reactions of gold arose from the practice of alchemy, in which people attempted to turn cheap metals, such as lead, into gold. Alchemists discovered that gold can be dissolved in a 3:1 mixture of concentrated hydrochloric and nitric acids, known as aqua regia ("royal water"). The action of nitric acid on gold is similar to that on copper (Equation 4.32) in that the nitrate ion, rather than H^+, oxidizes the metal to Au^{3+}. The Cl^- ions interact with Au^{3+} to form highly stable $AuCl_4^-$ ions. The net ionic equation for the reaction of gold with aqua regia is

$$Au(s) + NO_3^-(aq) + 4 H^+(aq) + 4 Cl^-(aq) \longrightarrow$$

$$AuCl_4^-(aq) + 2 H_2O(l) + NO(g)$$

All the gold ever mined would easily fit in a cube 19 m on a side and weighing about 1.1×10^8 kg (125,000 tons). More than 90% of this amount has been produced since the beginning of the California gold rush of 1848. Each year, worldwide production of gold amounts to about 1.8×10^6 kg (2000 tons). By contrast, over 1.5×10^{10} kg (16 million tons) of aluminum are produced annually. Gold is used mainly in jewelry (73%), coins (10%), and electronics (9%). Its use in electronics relies on its excellent conductivity and its corrosion resistance. Gold is used, for example, to plate contacts in electrical switches, relays, and connections. A typical touch-tone telephone contains 33 gold-plated contacts. Gold is also used in computers and other microelectronic devices where fine gold wire is used to link components.

Because of its resistance to corrosion by acids and other substances found in saliva, gold is an ideal metal for dental crowns and caps, which accounts for about 3% of the annual use of the element. The pure metal is too soft to use in dentistry, so it is combined with other metals to form alloys. *Related Exercise:* 4.95

◀ **Figure 4.15 Portrait of Pharaoh Tutankhamun (1346–1337 BC) made of gold and precious stones.** This highly prized article is from the inner coffin of the tomb of Tutankhamun.

 STRATEGIES IN CHEMISTRY | Analyzing Chemical Reactions

In this chapter you have been introduced to a great number of chemical reactions. A major difficulty that students face in trying to master material of this sort is gaining a "feel" for what happens when chemicals are allowed to react. In fact, you might marvel at the ease with which your professor or teaching assistant can figure out the results of a chemical reaction. One of our goals in this textbook is to help you become more adept at predicting the outcome of reactions. The key to gaining this "chemical intuition" is understanding how to categorize reactions.

There are so many individual reactions in chemistry that memorizing them all is a futile task. It is far more fruitful to try to use pattern recognition to determine the general category of a reaction, such as metathesis or oxidation-reduction. Thus, when you are faced with the challenge of predicting the outcome of a chemical reaction, ask yourself the following pertinent questions:

• What are the reactants in the reaction?

• Are they electrolytes or nonelectrolytes?

• Are they acids and bases?

• If the reactants are electrolytes, will metathesis produce a precipitate? Water? A gas?

• If metathesis cannot occur, can the reactants possibly engage in an oxidation-reduction reaction? This requires that there be both a reactant that can be oxidized and one that can be reduced.

By asking questions such as these, you should be able to predict what might happen during the reaction. You might not always be entirely correct, but if you keep your wits about you, you will not be far off. As you gain experience with chemical reactions, you will begin to look for reactants that might not be immediately obvious, such as water from the solution or oxygen from the atmosphere.

One of the greatest tools available to us in chemistry is experimentation. If you perform an experiment in which two solutions are mixed, you can make observations that help you understand what is happening. For example, using the information in Table 4.1 to predict whether a precipitate will form is not nearly as exciting as actually seeing the precipitate form, as in Figure 4.4. Careful observations in the laboratory portion of the course will make your lecture material easier to master.

(a)

(b)

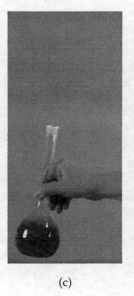
(c)

(d)

▲ **Figure 4.16 Procedure for preparation of 0.250 L of 1.00 *M* solution of CuSO₄.** (a) Weigh out 0.250 mol (39.9 g) of CuSO₄ (formula weight = 159.6 amu). (b) Put the CuSO₄ (solute) into a 250-mL volumetric flask, and add a small quantity of water. (c) Dissolve the solute by swirling the flask. (d) Add more water until the solution just reaches the calibration mark etched on the neck of the flask. Shake the stoppered flask to ensure complete mixing.

Molarity

Molarity (symbol M) expresses the concentration of a solution as the number of moles of solute in a liter of solution (soln):

$$\text{Molarity} = \frac{\text{moles solute}}{\text{volume of solution in liters}} \qquad [4.33]$$

A 1.00 molar solution (written 1.00 M) contains 1.00 mol of solute in every liter of solution. Figure 4.16 ▲ shows the preparation of 250.0 mL of a 1.00 M solution of CuSO₄ by using a volumetric flask that is calibrated to hold exactly 250.0 mL. First, 0.250 mol of CuSO₄ (39.9 g) is weighed out and placed in the volumetric flask. Water is added to dissolve the salt, and the resultant solution is diluted to a total volume of 250.0 mL. The molarity of the solution is (0.250 mol CuSO₄)/(0.250 L soln) = 1.00 M.

■ SAMPLE EXERCISE 4.11 | Calculating Molarity

Calculate the molarity of a solution made by dissolving 23.4 g of sodium sulfate (Na₂SO₄) in enough water to form 125 mL of solution.

Solution

Analyze: We are given the number of grams of solute (23.4 g), its chemical formula (Na₂SO₄), and the volume of the solution (125 mL), and we are asked to calculate the molarity of the solution.

Plan: We can calculate molarity using Equation 4.33. To do so, we must convert the number of grams of solute to moles and the volume of the solution from milliliters to liters.

Solve: The number of moles of Na₂SO₄ is obtained by using its molar mass:

$$\text{Moles Na}_2\text{SO}_4 = (23.4 \ \text{g Na}_2\text{SO}_4)\left(\frac{1 \ \text{mol Na}_2\text{SO}_4}{142 \ \text{g Na}_2\text{SO}_4}\right) = 0.165 \ \text{mol Na}_2\text{SO}_4$$

Converting the volume of the solution to liters:

$$\text{Liters soln} = (125 \ \text{mL})\left(\frac{1 \ \text{L}}{1000 \ \text{mL}}\right) = 0.125 \ \text{L}$$

Thus, the molarity is

$$\text{Molarity} = \frac{0.165 \ \text{mol Na}_2\text{SO}_4}{0.125 \ \text{L soln}} = 1.32 \frac{\text{mol Na}_2\text{SO}_4}{\text{L soln}} = 1.32 \ M$$

Check: Because the numerator is only slightly larger than the denominator, it's reasonable for the answer to be a little over 1 M. The units (mol/L) are appropriate for molarity, and three significant figures are appropriate for the answer because each of the initial pieces of data had three significant figures.

■ PRACTICE EXERCISE

Calculate the molarity of a solution made by dissolving 5.00 g of glucose ($C_6H_{12}O_6$) in sufficient water to form exactly 100 mL of solution.
Answer: 0.278 M

Expressing the Concentration of an Electrolyte

When an ionic compound dissolves, the relative concentrations of the ions introduced into the solution depend on the chemical formula of the compound. For example, a 1.0 M solution of NaCl is 1.0 M in Na^+ ions and 1.0 M in Cl^- ions. Similarly, a 1.0 M solution of Na_2SO_4 is 2.0 M in Na^+ ions and 1.0 M in SO_4^{2-} ions. Thus, the concentration of an electrolyte solution can be specified either in terms of the compound used to make the solution (1.0 M Na_2SO_4) or in terms of the ions that the solution contains (2.0 M Na^+ and 1.0 M SO_4^{2-}).

■ SAMPLE EXERCISE 4.12 | Calculating Molar Concentrations of Ions

What are the molar concentrations of each of the ions present in a 0.025 M aqueous solution of calcium nitrate?

Solution

Analyze: We are given the concentration of the ionic compound used to make the solution and asked to determine the concentrations of the ions in the solution.
Plan: We can use the subscripts in the chemical formula of the compound to determine the relative concentrations of the ions.
Solve: Calcium nitrate is composed of calcium ions (Ca^{2+}) and nitrate ions (NO_3^-), so its chemical formula is $Ca(NO_3)_2$. Because there are two NO_3^- ions for each Ca^{2+} ion in the compound, each mole of $Ca(NO_3)_2$ that dissolves dissociates into 1 mol of Ca^{2+} and 2 mol of NO_3^-. Thus, a solution that is 0.025 M in $Ca(NO_3)_2$ is 0.025 M in Ca^{2+} and 2 × 0.025 M = 0.050 M in NO_3^-.
Check: The concentration of NO_3^- ions is twice that of Ca^{2+} ions, as the subscript 2 after the NO_3^- in the chemical formula $Ca(NO_3)_2$ suggests it should be.

■ PRACTICE EXERCISE

What is the molar concentration of K^+ ions in a 0.015 M solution of potassium carbonate?
Answer: 0.030 M K^+

Interconverting Molarity, Moles, and Volume

The definition of molarity (Equation 4.33) contains three quantities—molarity, moles solute, and liters of solution. If we know any two of these, we can calculate the third. For example, if we know the molarity of a solution, we can calculate the number of moles of solute in a given volume. Molarity, therefore, is a conversion factor between volume of solution and moles of solute. Calculation of the number of moles of HNO_3 in 2.0 L of 0.200 M HNO_3 solution illustrates the conversion of volume to moles:

$$\text{Moles } HNO_3 = (2.0 \text{ L soln})\left(\frac{0.200 \text{ mol } HNO_3}{1 \text{ L soln}}\right)$$

$$= 0.40 \text{ mol } HNO_3$$

Dimensional analysis can be used in this conversion if we express molarity as moles/liter soln. To obtain moles, therefore, we multiply liters and molarity: moles = liters × molarity = liters × moles/liter.

To illustrate the conversion of moles to volume, let's calculate the volume of 0.30 M HNO_3 solution required to supply 2.0 mol of HNO_3:

$$\text{Liters soln} = (2.0 \text{ mol } HNO_3)\left(\frac{1 \text{ L soln}}{0.30 \text{ mol } HNO_3}\right) = 6.7 \text{ L soln}$$

In this case we must use the reciprocal of molarity in the conversion: liters = moles × $1/M$ = moles × liters/mole.

■■■ SAMPLE EXERCISE 4.13 | Using Molarity to Calculate Grams of Solute

How many grams of Na_2SO_4 are required to make 0.350 L of 0.500 M Na_2SO_4?

Solution

Analyze: We are given the volume of the solution (0.350 L), its concentration (0.500 M), and the identity of the solute (Na_2SO_4) and asked to calculate the number of grams of the solute in the solution.

Plan: We can use the definition of molarity (Equation 4.33) to determine the number of moles of solute, and then convert moles to grams using the molar mass of the solute.

$$M_{Na_2SO_4} = \frac{\text{moles } Na_2SO_4}{\text{liters soln}}$$

Solve: Calculating the moles of Na_2SO_4 using the molarity and volume of solution gives

$$M_{Na_2SO_4} = \frac{\text{moles } Na_2SO_4}{\text{liters soln}}$$

$$\text{Moles } Na_2SO_4 = \text{liters soln} \times M_{Na_2SO_4}$$

$$= (0.350 \text{ L soln})\left(\frac{0.500 \text{ mol } Na_2SO_4}{1 \text{ L soln}}\right)$$

$$= 0.175 \text{ mol } Na_2SO_4$$

Because each mole of Na_2SO_4 weighs 142 g, the required number of grams of Na_2SO_4 is

$$\text{Grams } Na_2SO_4 = (0.175 \text{ mol } Na_2SO_4)\left(\frac{142 \text{ g } Na_2SO_4}{1 \text{ mol } Na_2SO_4}\right) = 24.9 \text{ g } Na_2SO_4$$

Check: The magnitude of the answer, the units, and the number of significant figures are all appropriate.

■■■ PRACTICE EXERCISE

(a) How many grams of Na_2SO_4 are there in 15 mL of 0.50 M Na_2SO_4? **(b)** How many milliliters of 0.50 M Na_2SO_4 solution are needed to provide 0.038 mol of this salt?

Answers: **(a)** 1.1 g, **(b)** 76 mL

Dilution

ANIMATION
Solution Formation by Dilution

Solutions that are used routinely in the laboratory are often purchased or prepared in concentrated form (called *stock solutions*). Hydrochloric acid, for example, is purchased as a 12 M solution (concentrated HCl). Solutions of lower concentrations can then be obtained by adding water, a process called **dilution**.*

To illustrate the preparation of a dilute solution from a concentrated one, suppose we wanted to prepare 250.0 mL (that is, 0.250 L) of 0.100 M $CuSO_4$ solution by diluting a stock solution containing 1.00 M $CuSO_4$. When solvent is added to dilute a solution, the number of moles of solute remains unchanged.

$$\text{Moles solute before dilution} = \text{moles solute after dilution} \qquad [4.34]$$

---

* In diluting a concentrated acid or base, the acid or base should be added to water and then further diluted by adding more water. Adding water directly to concentrated acid or base can cause spattering because of the intense heat generated.

Because we know both the volume and concentration of the dilute solution, we can calculate the number of moles of $CuSO_4$ it contains.

$$\text{Moles } CuSO_4 \text{ in dil soln} = (0.250 \text{ L soln})\left(0.100 \frac{\text{mol } CuSO_4}{\text{L soln}}\right)$$

$$= 0.0250 \text{ mol } CuSO_4$$

Now we can calculate the volume of the concentrated solution needed to provide 0.0250 mol $CuSO_4$:

$$\text{Liters of conc soln} = (0.0250 \text{ mol } CuSO_4)\left(\frac{1 \text{ L soln}}{1.00 \text{ mol } CuSO_4}\right) = 0.0250 \text{ L}$$

Thus, this dilution is achieved by withdrawing 0.0250 L (that is, 25.0 mL) of the 1.00 M solution using a pipet, adding it to a 250-mL volumetric flask, and then diluting it to a final volume of 250.0 mL, as shown in Figure 4.18 ▶. Notice that the diluted solution is less intensely colored than the concentrated one.

In laboratory situations, calculations of this sort are often made very quickly with a simple equation that can be derived by remembering that the number of moles of solute is the same in both the concentrated and dilute solutions and that moles = molarity × liters:

$$\text{Moles solute in conc soln} = \text{moles solute in dil soln}$$

$$M_{\text{conc}} \times V_{\text{conc}} = M_{\text{dil}} \times V_{\text{dil}} \qquad [4.35]$$

Science Fundamentals Second Edition

▶ **Figure 4.18 Procedure for preparing 250 mL of 0.100 *M* CuSO₄ by dilution of 1.00 *M* CuSO₄.** (a) Draw 25.0 mL of the 1.00 *M* solution into a pipet. (b) Add this to a 250-mL volumetric flask. (c) Add water to dilute the solution to a total volume of 250 mL.

(a)   (b)   (c)

GIVE IT SOME THOUGHT

How is the molarity of a 0.50 *M* KBr solution changed when water is added to double its volume?

The molarity of the more concentrated stock solution (M_{conc}) is always larger than the molarity of the dilute solution (M_{dil}). Because the volume of the solution increases upon dilution, V_{dil} is always larger than V_{conc}. Although Equation 4.35 is derived in terms of liters, any volume unit can be used as long as that same unit is used on both sides of the equation. For example, in the calculation we did for the CuSO₄ solution, we have

$$(1.00\ M)(V_{conc}) = (0.100\ M)(250\ mL)$$

Solving for V_{conc} gives $V_{conc} = 25.0$ mL as before.

SAMPLE EXERCISE 4.14 | Preparing a Solution by Dilution

How many milliliters of 3.0 *M* H₂SO₄ are needed to make 450 mL of 0.10 *M* H₂SO₄?

Solution

Analyze: We need to dilute a concentrated solution. We are given the molarity of a more concentrated solution (3.0 *M*) and the volume and molarity of a more dilute one containing the same solute (450 mL of 0.10 *M* solution). We must calculate the volume of the concentrated solution needed to prepare the dilute solution.

Plan: We can calculate the number of moles of solute, H₂SO₄, in the dilute solution and then calculate the volume of the concentrated solution needed to supply this amount of solute. Alternatively, we can directly apply Equation 4.35. Let's compare the two methods.

Solve: Calculating the moles of H₂SO₄ in the dilute solution:

$$\text{Moles } H_2SO_4 \text{ in dilute solution} = (0.450\ \cancel{\text{L soln}})\left(\frac{0.10\ \text{mol } H_2SO_4}{1\ \cancel{\text{L soln}}}\right)$$

$$= 0.045\ \text{mol } H_2SO_4$$

Calculating the volume of the concentrated solution that contains 0.045 mol H₂SO₄:

$$\text{L conc soln} = (0.045\ \cancel{\text{mol } H_2SO_4})\left(\frac{1\ \text{L soln}}{3.0\ \cancel{\text{mol } H_2SO_4}}\right) = 0.015\ \text{L soln}$$

Converting liters to milliliters gives 15 mL.

If we apply Equation 4.35, we get the same result:

$$(3.0\ M)(V_{conc}) = (0.10\ M)(450\ mL)$$

$$V_{conc} = \frac{(0.10\ M)(450\ mL)}{3.0\ M} = 15\ mL$$

Either way, we see that if we start with 15 mL of 3.0 M H_2SO_4 and dilute it to a total volume of 450 mL, the desired 0.10 M solution will be obtained.

Check: The calculated volume seems reasonable because a small volume of concentrated solution is used to prepare a large volume of dilute solution.

■ PRACTICE EXERCISE

(a) What volume of 2.50 M lead(II) nitrate solution contains 0.0500 mol of Pb^{2+}?
(b) How many milliliters of 5.0 M $K_2Cr_2O_7$ solution must be diluted to prepare 250 mL of 0.10 M solution? **(c)** If 10.0 mL of a 10.0 M stock solution of NaOH is diluted to 250 mL, what is the concentration of the resulting stock solution?
Answers: **(a)** 0.0200 L = 20.0 mL, **(b)** 5.0 mL, **(c)** 0.40 M

4.6 | Solution Stoichiometry and Chemical Analysis

Imagine that you have to determine the concentrations of several ions in a sample of lake water. Although many instrumental methods have been developed for such analyses, chemical reactions such as those discussed in this chapter continue to be used. In Chapter 3 we learned that if you know the chemical equation and the amount of one reactant consumed in the reaction, you can calculate the quantities of other reactants and products. In this section we briefly explore such analyses of solutions.

Recall that the coefficients in a balanced equation give the relative number of moles of reactants and products. ∞ (Section 3.6) To use this information, we must convert the quantities of substances involved in a reaction into moles. When we are dealing with grams of substances, as we were in Chapter 3, we use the molar mass to achieve this conversion. When we are working with solutions of known molarity, however, we use molarity and volume to determine the number of moles (moles solute = $M \times L$). Figure 4.19 ▼ summarizes this approach to using stoichiometry.

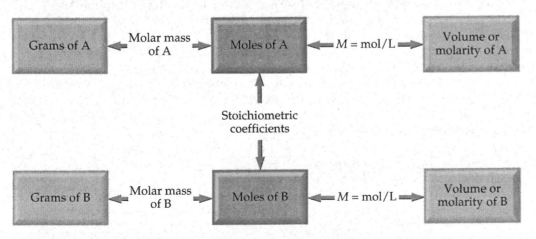

▲ **Figure 4.19 Problem-solving procedure.** Outline of the procedure used to solve stoichiometry problems that involve measured (laboratory) units of mass, solution concentration (molarity), or volume.

▅▅ **SAMPLE EXERCISE 4.15** | Using Mass Relations in a Neutralization Reaction

How many grams of $Ca(OH)_2$ are needed to neutralize 25.0 mL of 0.100 M HNO_3?

Solution

Analyze: The reactants are an acid, HNO_3, and a base, $Ca(OH)_2$. The volume and molarity of HNO_3 are given, and we are asked how many grams of $Ca(OH)_2$ are needed to neutralize this quantity of HNO_3.

Plan: We can use the molarity and volume of the HNO_3 solution to calculate the number of moles of HNO_3. We then use the balanced equation to relate the moles of HNO_3 to moles of $Ca(OH)_2$. Finally, we can convert moles of $Ca(OH)_2$ to grams. These steps can be summarized as follows:

$$L_{HNO_3} \times M_{HNO_3} \Rightarrow mol\ HNO_3 \Rightarrow mol\ Ca(OH)_2 \Rightarrow g\ Ca(OH)_2$$

Solve: The product of the molar concentration of a solution and its volume in liters gives the number of moles of solute:

$$Moles\ HNO_3 = L_{HNO_3} \times M_{HNO_3} = (0.0250\ \cancel{L})\left(0.100\frac{mol\ HNO_3}{\cancel{L}}\right)$$

$$= 2.50 \times 10^{-3}\ mol\ HNO_3$$

Because this is an acid-base neutralization reaction, HNO_3 and $Ca(OH)_2$ react to form H_2O and the salt containing Ca^{2+} and NO_3^-:

$$2\ HNO_3(aq) + Ca(OH)_2(s) \longrightarrow 2\ H_2O(l) + Ca(NO_3)_2(aq)$$

Thus, 2 mol $HNO_3 \simeq$ 1 mol $Ca(OH)_2$. Therefore,

$$Grams\ Ca(OH)_2 = (2.50 \times 10^{-3}\ \cancel{mol\ HNO_3})\left(\frac{1\ \cancel{mol\ Ca(OH)_2}}{2\ \cancel{mol\ HNO_3}}\right)\left(\frac{74.1\ g\ Ca(OH)_2}{1\ \cancel{mol\ Ca(OH)_2}}\right)$$

$$= 0.0926\ g\ Ca(OH)_2$$

Check: The size of the answer is reasonable. A small volume of dilute acid will require only a small amount of base to neutralize it.

▅▅ **PRACTICE EXERCISE**

(a) How many grams of NaOH are needed to neutralize 20.0 mL of 0.150 M H_2SO_4 solution? **(b)** How many liters of 0.500 M HCl(aq) are needed to react completely with 0.100 mol of $Pb(NO_3)_2(aq)$, forming a precipitate of $PbCl_2(s)$?

Answers: **(a)** 0.240 g, **(b)** 0.400 L

Titrations

To determine the concentration of a particular solute in a solution, chemists often carry out a **titration**, which involves combining a sample of the solution with a reagent solution of known concentration, called a **standard solution**. Titrations can be conducted using acid-base, precipitation, or oxidation-reduction reactions. Suppose we have an HCl solution of unknown concentration and an NaOH solution we know to be 0.100 M. To determine the concentration of the HCl solution, we take a specific volume of that solution, say 20.00 mL. We then slowly add the standard NaOH solution to it until the neutralization reaction between the HCl and NaOH is complete. The point at which stoichiometrically equivalent quantities are brought together is known as the **equivalence point** of the titration.

ANIMATION
Acid-Base Titration

Concepts in Acid-Base Titrations

💡 **GIVE IT SOME THOUGHT**

25.00 mL of a 0.100 M HBr solution is titrated with a 0.200 M NaOH solution. How many mL of the NaOH solution are required to reach the equivalence point?

In order to titrate an unknown with a standard solution, there must be some way to determine when the equivalence point of the titration has been

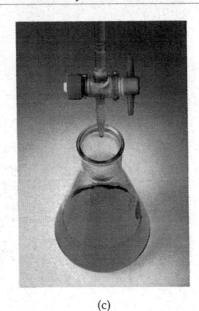

(a)   (b)   (c)

▲ **Figure 4.20 Change in appearance of a solution containing phenolphthalein indicator as base is added.** Before the end point, the solution is colorless (a). As the end point is approached, a pale pink color forms where the base is added (b). At the end point, this pale pink color extends throughout the solution after mixing. As even more base is added, the intensity of the pink color increases (c).

reached. In acid-base titrations, dyes known as acid-base **indicators** are used for this purpose. For example, the dye known as phenolphthalein is colorless in acidic solution but is pink in basic solution. If we add phenolphthalein to an unknown solution of acid, the solution will be colorless, as seen in Figure 4.20(a) ▲. We can then add standard base from a buret until the solution barely turns from colorless to pink, as seen in Figure 4.20(b). This color change indicates that the acid has been neutralized and the drop of base that caused the solution to become colored has no acid to react with. The solution therefore becomes basic, and the dye turns pink. The color change signals the *end point* of the titration, which usually coincides very nearly with the equivalence point. Care must be taken to choose indicators whose end points correspond to the equivalence point of the titration. We will consider this matter in Chapter 17. The titration procedure is summarized in Figure 4.21 ▼.

ACTIVITY
Acid-Base Titration

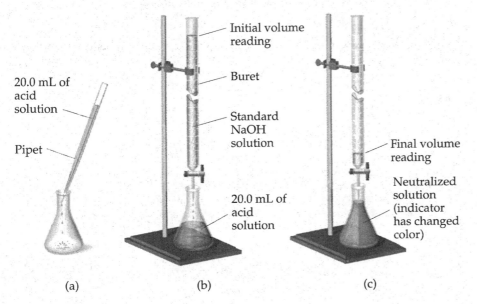

20.0 mL of acid solution

Pipet

Initial volume reading

Buret

Standard NaOH solution

20.0 mL of acid solution

Final volume reading

Neutralized solution (indicator has changed color)

(a)   (b)   (c)

◀ **Figure 4.21 Procedure for titrating an acid against a standardized solution of NaOH.** (a) A known quantity of acid is added to a flask. (b) An acid-base indicator is added, and standardized NaOH is added from a buret. (c) The equivalence point is signaled by a color change in the indicator.

SAMPLE EXERCISE 4.16 | Determining the Quantity of Solute by Titration

The quantity of Cl^- in a municipal water supply is determined by titrating the sample with Ag^+. The reaction taking place during the titration is

$$Ag^+(aq) + Cl^-(aq) \longrightarrow AgCl(s)$$

The end point in this type of titration is marked by a change in color of a special type of indicator. **(a)** How many grams of chloride ion are in a sample of the water if 20.2 mL of 0.100 M Ag^+ is needed to react with all the chloride in the sample? **(b)** If the sample has a mass of 10.0 g, what percent Cl^- does it contain?

Solution

Analyze: We are given the volume (20.2 mL) and molarity (0.100 M) of a solution of Ag^+ and the chemical equation for reaction of this ion with Cl^-. We are asked first to calculate the number of grams of Cl^- in the sample and, second, to calculate the mass percent of Cl^- in the sample.

(a) Plan: We begin by using the volume and molarity of Ag^+ to calculate the number of moles of Ag^+ used in the titration. We can then use the balanced equation to determine the moles of Cl^- in the sample and from that the grams of Cl^-.

Solve: Moles $Ag^+ = (20.2 \text{ mL soln})\left(\dfrac{1 \text{ L soln}}{1000 \text{ mL soln}}\right)\left(0.100\dfrac{\text{mol } Ag^+}{\text{L soln}}\right)$

$$= 2.02 \times 10^{-3} \text{ mol } Ag^+$$

From the balanced equation we see that 1 mol $Ag^+ \triangleq 1$ mol Cl^-. Using this information and the molar mass of Cl, we have

$$\text{Grams } Cl^- = (2.02 \times 10^{-3} \text{ mol } Ag^+)\left(\dfrac{1 \text{ mol } Cl^-}{1 \text{ mol } Ag^+}\right)\left(\dfrac{35.5 \text{ g } Cl^-}{1 \text{ mol } Cl^-}\right)$$

$$= 7.17 \times 10^{-2} \text{ g } Cl^-$$

(b) Plan: To calculate the percentage of Cl^- in the sample, we compare the number of grams of Cl^- in the sample, 7.17×10^{-2} g, with the original mass of the sample, 10.0 g.

Solve: Percent $Cl^- = \dfrac{7.17 \times 10^{-3} \text{ g}}{10.0 \text{ g}} \times 100\% = 0.717\% \text{ } Cl^-$

Comment: Chloride ion is one of the most common ions in water and sewage. Ocean water contains 1.92% Cl^-. Whether water containing Cl^- tastes salty depends on the other ions present. If the only accompanying ions are Na^+, a salty taste may be detected with as little as 0.03% Cl^-.

PRACTICE EXERCISE

A sample of an iron ore is dissolved in acid, and the iron is converted to Fe^{2+}. The sample is then titrated with 47.20 mL of 0.02240 M MnO_4^- solution. The oxidation-reduction reaction that occurs during titration is as follows:

$$MnO_4^-(aq) + 5 Fe^{2+}(aq) + 8 H^+(aq) \longrightarrow Mn^{2+}(aq) + 5 Fe^{3+}(aq) + 4 H_2O(l)$$

(a) How many moles of MnO_4^- were added to the solution? **(b)** How many moles of Fe^{2+} were in the sample? **(c)** How many grams of iron were in the sample? **(d)** If the sample had a mass of 0.8890 g, what is the percentage of iron in the sample?
Answers: **(a)** 1.057×10^{-3} mol MnO_4^-, **(b)** 5.286×10^{-3} mol Fe^{2+}, **(c)** 0.2952 g, **(d)** 33.21%

SAMPLE EXERCISE 4.17 | Determining Solution Concentration Via an Acid-Base Titration

One commercial method used to peel potatoes is to soak them in a solution of NaOH for a short time, remove them from the NaOH, and spray off the peel. The concentration of NaOH is normally in the range of 3 to 6 M. The NaOH is analyzed periodically. In one such analysis, 45.7 mL of 0.500 M H_2SO_4 is required to neutralize a 20.0-mL sample of NaOH solution. What is the concentration of the NaOH solution?

Solution

Analyze: We are given the volume (45.7 mL) and molarity (0.500 M) of an H_2SO_4 solution that reacts completely with a 20.0-mL sample of NaOH. We are asked to calculate the molarity of the NaOH solution.

Plan: We can use the volume and molarity of the H_2SO_4 to calculate the number of moles of this substance. Then, we can use this quantity and the balanced equation for the reaction to calculate the number of moles of NaOH. Finally, we can use the moles of NaOH and the volume of this solution to calculate molarity.

Solve: The number of moles of H_2SO_4 is given by the product of the volume and molarity of this solution:

$$\text{Moles } H_2SO_4 = (45.7 \text{ mL soln})\left(\frac{1 \text{ L soln}}{1000 \text{ mL soln}}\right)\left(0.500 \frac{\text{mol } H_2SO_4}{\text{L soln}}\right)$$

$$= 2.28 \times 10^{-2} \text{ mol } H_2SO_4$$

Acids react with metal hydroxides to form water and a salt. Thus, the balanced equation for the neutralization reaction is

$$H_2SO_4(aq) + 2 \text{ NaOH}(aq) \longrightarrow 2 H_2O(l) + Na_2SO_4(aq)$$

According to the balanced equation, 1 mol $H_2SO_4 \simeq 2$ mol NaOH. Therefore,

$$\text{Moles NaOH} = (2.28 \times 10^{-2} \text{ mol } H_2SO_4)\left(\frac{2 \text{ mol NaOH}}{1 \text{ mol } H_2SO_4}\right)$$

$$= 4.56 \times 10^{-2} \text{ mol NaOH}$$

Knowing the number of moles of NaOH present in 20.0 mL of solution allows us to calculate the molarity of this solution:

$$\text{Molarity NaOH} = \frac{\text{mol NaOH}}{\text{L soln}} = \left(\frac{4.56 \times 10^{-2} \text{ mol NaOH}}{20.0 \text{ mL soln}}\right)\left(\frac{1000 \text{ mL soln}}{1 \text{ L soln}}\right)$$

$$= 2.28 \frac{\text{mol NaOH}}{\text{L soln}} = 2.28 \ M$$

PRACTICE EXERCISE

What is the molarity of an NaOH solution if 48.0 mL is needed to neutralize 35.0 mL of 0.144 M H_2SO_4?

Answers: 0.210 M

SAMPLE INTEGRATIVE EXERCISE | Putting Concepts Together

Note: Integrative exercises require skills from earlier chapters as well as ones from the present chapter.

A sample of 70.5 mg of potassium phosphate is added to 15.0 mL of 0.050 M silver nitrate, resulting in the formation of a precipitate. **(a)** Write the molecular equation for the reaction. **(b)** What is the limiting reactant in the reaction? **(c)** Calculate the theoretical yield, in grams, of the precipitate that forms.

Solution (a) Potassium phosphate and silver nitrate are both ionic compounds. Potassium phosphate contains K^+ and PO_4^{3-} ions, so its chemical formula is K_3PO_4. Silver nitrate contains Ag^+ and NO_3^- ions, so its chemical formula is $AgNO_3$. Because both reactants are strong electrolytes, the solution contains K^+, PO_4^{3-}, Ag^+, and NO_3^- ions before the reaction occurs. According to the solubility guidelines in Table 4.1, Ag^+ and PO_4^{3-} form an insoluble compound, so Ag_3PO_4 will precipitate from the solution. In contrast, K^+ and NO_3^- will remain in solution because KNO_3 is water soluble. Thus, the balanced molecular equation for the reaction is

$$K_3PO_4(aq) + 3 \text{ AgNO}_3(aq) \longrightarrow Ag_3PO_4(s) + 3 \text{ KNO}_3(aq)$$

(b) To determine the limiting reactant, we must examine the number of moles of each reactant. ⟳ (Section 3.7) The number of moles of K_3PO_4 is calculated from the mass of the sample using the molar mass as a conversion factor. ⟳ (Section 3.4) The molar mass of K_3PO_4 is $3(39.1) + 31.0 + 4(16.0) = 212.3$ g/mol. Converting milligrams to grams and then to moles, we have

$$(70.5 \text{ mg } K_3PO_4)\left(\frac{10^{-3} \text{ g } K_3PO_4}{1 \text{ mg } K_3PO_4}\right)\left(\frac{1 \text{ mol } K_3PO_4}{212.3 \text{ g } K_3PO_4}\right) = 3.32 \times 10^{-4} \text{ mol } K_3PO_4$$

We determine the number of moles of $AgNO_3$ from the volume and molarity of the solution. ∞ (Section 4.5) Converting milliliters to liters and then to moles, we have

$$(15.0 \ mL)\left(\frac{10^{-3} \ L}{1 \ mL}\right)\left(\frac{0.050 \ mol \ AgNO_3}{L}\right) = 7.5 \times 10^{-4} \ mol \ AgNO_3$$

Comparing the amounts of the two reactants, we find that there are $(7.5 \times 10^{-4})/(3.32 \times 10^{-4}) = 2.3$ times as many moles of $AgNO_3$ as there are moles of K_3PO_4. According to the balanced equation, however, 1 mol K_3PO_4 requires 3 mol of $AgNO_3$. Thus, there is insufficient $AgNO_3$ to consume the K_3PO_4, and $AgNO_3$ is the limiting reactant.

(c) The precipitate is Ag_3PO_4, whose molar mass is $3(107.9) + 31.0 + 4(16.0) = 418.7$ g/mol. To calculate the number of grams of Ag_3PO_4 that could be produced in this reaction (the theoretical yield), we use the number of moles of the limiting reactant, converting mol $AgNO_3 \Rightarrow$ mol $Ag_3PO_4 \Rightarrow$ g Ag_3PO_4. We use the coefficients in the balanced equation to convert moles of $AgNO_3$ to moles Ag_3PO_4, and we use the molar mass of Ag_3PO_4 to convert the number of moles of this substance to grams.

$$(7.5 \times 10^{-4} \ mol \ AgNO_3)\left(\frac{1 \ mol \ Ag_3PO_4}{3 \ mol \ AgNO_3}\right)\left(\frac{418.7 \ g \ Ag_3PO_4}{1 \ mol \ Ag_3NO_4}\right) = 0.10 \ g \ Ag_3PO_4$$

The answer has only two significant figures because the quantity of $AgNO_3$ is given to only two significant figures.

SUMMARY AND KEY TERMS

Introduction and Section 4.1   Solutions in which water is the dissolving medium are called **aqueous solutions**. The component of the solution that is in the greater quantity is the **solvent**. The other components are **solutes**.

Any substance whose aqueous solution contains ions is called an **electrolyte**. Any substance that forms a solution containing no ions is a **nonelectrolyte**. Those electrolytes that are present in solution entirely as ions are **strong electrolytes**, whereas those that are present partly as ions and partly as molecules are **weak electrolytes**. Ionic compounds dissociate into ions when they dissolve, and they are strong electrolytes. The solubility of ionic substances is made possible by **solvation**, the interaction of ions with polar solvent molecules. Most molecular compounds are nonelectrolytes, although some are weak electrolytes and a few are strong electrolytes. When representing the ionization of a weak electrolyte in solution, a double arrow is used, indicating that the forward and reverse reactions can achieve a chemical balance called a **chemical equilibrium**.

Section 4.2   **Precipitation reactions** are those in which an insoluble product, called a **precipitate**, forms. Solubility guidelines help determine whether or not an ionic compound will be soluble in water. (The **solubility** of a substance is the amount that dissolves in a given quantity of solvent.) Reactions such as precipitation reactions, in which cations and anions appear to exchange partners, are called **exchange reactions**, or **metathesis reactions**.

Chemical equations can be written to show whether dissolved substances are present in solution predominantly as ions or molecules. When the complete chemical formulas of all reactants and products are used, the equation is called a **molecular equation**. A **complete ionic equation** shows all dissolved strong electrolytes as their component ions. In a **net ionic equation**, those ions that go through the reaction unchanged (**spectator ions**) are omitted.

Section 4.3   Acids and bases are important electrolytes. **Acids** are proton donors; they increase the concentration of $H^+(aq)$ in aqueous solutions to which they are added. **Bases** are proton acceptors; they increase the concentration of $OH^-(aq)$ in aqueous solutions. Those acids and bases that are strong electrolytes are called **strong acids** and **strong bases**, respectively. Those that are weak electrolytes are **weak acids** and **weak bases**. When solutions of acids and bases are mixed, a **neutralization reaction** results. The neutralization reaction between an acid and a metal hydroxide produces water and a **salt**. Gases can also be formed as a result of acid-base reactions. The reaction of a sulfide with an acid forms $H_2S(g)$; the reaction between a carbonate and an acid forms $CO_2(g)$.

Section 4.4   **Oxidation** is the loss of electrons by a substance, whereas **reduction** is the gain of electrons by a substance. **Oxidation numbers** help us keep track of electrons during chemical reactions and are assigned to atoms by using specific rules. The oxidation of an element results in an increase in its oxidation number, whereas reduction is accompanied by a decrease in oxidation number. Oxidation is always accompanied by reduction, giving **oxidation-reduction**, or redox, **reactions**.

Many metals are oxidized by O_2, acids, and salts. The redox reactions between metals and acids and between metals and salts are called **displacement reactions**.

The products of these displacement reactions are always an element (H_2 or a metal) and a salt. Comparing such reactions allows us to rank metals according to their ease of oxidation. A list of metals arranged in order of decreasing ease of oxidation is called an **activity series**. Any metal on the list can be oxidized by ions of metals (or H^+) below it in the series.

Section 4.5 The composition of a solution expresses the relative quantities of solvent and solutes that it contains. One of the common ways to express the **concentration** of a solute in a solution is in terms of molarity. The **molarity** of a solution is the number of moles of solute per liter of solution. Molarity makes it possible to interconvert solution volume and number of moles of solute. Solutions of known molarity can be formed either by weighing out the solute and diluting it to a known volume or by the **dilution** of a more concentrated solution of known concentration (a stock solution). Adding solvent to the solution (the process of dilution) decreases the concentration of the solute without changing the number of moles of solute in the solution ($M_{conc} \times V_{conc} = M_{dil} \times V_{dil}$).

Section 4.6 In the process called **titration**, we combine a solution of known concentration (a **standard solution**) with a solution of unknown concentration in order to determine the unknown concentration or the quantity of solute in the unknown. The point in the titration at which stoichiometrically equivalent quantities of reactants are brought together is called the **equivalence point**. An **indicator** can be used to show the end point of the titration, which coincides closely with the equivalence point.

VISUALIZING CONCEPTS

4.1 Which of the following schematic drawings best describes a solution of Li_2SO_4 in water (water molecules not shown for simplicity)? [Section 4.1]

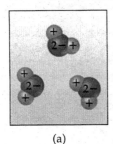

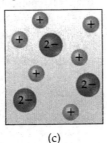

(a)   (b)   (c)

4.2 Methanol, CH_3OH, and hydrogen chloride, HCl, are both molecular substances, yet an aqueous solution of methanol does not conduct an electrical current, whereas a solution of HCl does conduct. Account for this difference. [Section 4.1]

4.3 Aqueous solutions of three different substances, AX, AY, and AZ, are represented by the three diagrams below. Identify each substance as a strong electrolyte, weak electrolyte, or nonelectrolyte. [Section 4.1]

AX   AY   AZ

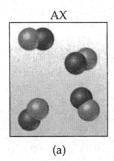

(a)   (b)   (c)

4.4 A 0.1 M solution of acetic acid, $HC_2H_3O_2$, causes the lightbulb in the apparatus of Figure 4.2 to glow about as brightly as a 0.001 M solution of HBr. How do you account for this fact? [Section 4.1]

4.5 You are presented with three white solids, A, B and C, which are glucose (a sugar substance), NaOH, and AgBr. Solid A dissolves in water to form a conducting solution. B is not soluble in water. C dissolves in water to form a nonconducting solution. Identify A, B and C. [Section 4.2]

4.6 We have seen that ions in aqueous solution are stabilized by the attractions between the ions and the water molecules. Why then do some pairs of ions in solution form precipitates? [Section 4.2]

4.7 Which of the following ions will *always* be a spectator ion in a precipitation reaction? **(a)** Cl^-, **(b)** NO_3^-, **(c)** NH_4^+, **(d)** S^{2-}, **(e)** SO_4^{2-}. Explain briefly. [Section 4.2]

4.8 The labels have fallen off two bottles, one containing $Mg(NO_3)_2$ and the other containing $Pb(NO_3)_2$. You have a bottle of dilute H_2SO_4. How could you use it to test a portion of each solution to identify which solution is which? [Section 4.2]

4.9 Which of the following chemical equations is represented schematically in the drawing below? [Section 4.2]
(a) $BaCl_2(aq) + Na_2(SO)_4(aq) \longrightarrow$
$$BaSO_4(s) + 2\,NaCl(aq)$$
(b) $SrCO_3(s) + 2\,HBr(aq) \longrightarrow$
$$SrBr_2(aq) + H_2O(l) + CO_2(g)$$
(c) $2\,NaOH(aq) + CdCl_2(aq) \longrightarrow$
$$Cd(OH)_2(s) + 2\,NaCl(aq)$$

Science Fundamentals Second Edition

4.10 Which of the three solutions shown schematically to the right corresponds to the result of each of the following reactions: (Water molecules are excluded for clarity) [Section 4.3]

(a) $Ag_2O(s) + 2\,HCl(aq) \longrightarrow 2\,AgCl(s) + H_2O(l)$
(b) $NaOH(aq) + HCl(aq) \longrightarrow NaCl(aq) + H_2O(l)$
(c) $AgNO_3(aq) + KCl(aq) \longrightarrow AgCl(s) + KCl(aq)$

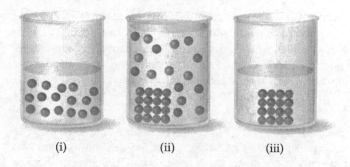

(i)   (ii)   (iii)

EXERCISES

Electrolytes

4.11 When asked what causes electrolyte solutions to conduct electricity, a student responds that it is due to the movement of electrons through the solution. Is the student correct? If not, what is the correct response?

4.12 When methanol, CH_3OH, is dissolved in water, a non-conducting solution results. When acetic acid, $HC_2H_3O_2$, dissolves in water, the solution is weakly conducting and acidic in nature. Describe what happens upon dissolution in the two cases, and account for the different results.

4.13 We have learned in this chapter that many ionic solids dissolve in water as strong electrolytes, that is, as separated ions in solution. What properties of water facilitate this process?

4.14 What does it mean to say that ions are hydrated when an ionic substance dissolves in water?

4.15 Specify what ions are present in solution upon dissolving each of the following substances in water: (a) $ZnCl_2$, (b) HNO_3, (c) $(NH_4)_2SO_4$, (d) $Ca(OH)_2$.

4.16 Specify what ions are present upon dissolving each of the following substances in water: (a) MgI_2, (b) $Al(NO_3)_3$, (c) $HClO_4$, (d) $KC_2H_3O_2$.

4.17 Formic acid, $HCHO_2$, is a weak electrolyte. What solute particles are present in an aqueous solution of this compound? Write the chemical equation for the ionization of $HCHO_2$.

4.18 Acetone, CH_3COCH_3, is a nonelectrolyte; hypochlorous acid, $HClO$, is a weak electrolyte; and ammonium chloride, NH_4Cl, is a strong electrolyte. (a) What are the solute particles present in aqueous solutions of each compound? (b) If 0.1 mol of each compound is dissolved in solution, which one contains 0.2 mol of solute particles, which contains 0.1 mol of solute particles, and which contains somewhere between 0.1 and 0.2 mol of solute particles?

Precipitation Reactions and Net Ionic Equations

4.19 Using solubility guidelines, predict whether each of the following compounds is soluble or insoluble in water: (a) $NiCl_2$, (b) Ag_2S, (c) Cs_3PO_4, (d) $SrCO_3$, (e) $PbSO_4$.

4.20 Predict whether each of the following compounds is soluble in water: (a) $Ni(OH)_2$, (b) $PbBr_2$, (c) $Ba(NO_3)_2$, (d) $AlPO_4$, (e) $AgC_2H_3O_2$.

4.21 Will precipitation occur when the following solutions are mixed? If so, write a balanced chemical equation for the reaction. (a) Na_2CO_3 and $AgNO_3$, (b) $NaNO_3$ and $NiSO_4$, (c) $FeSO_4$ and $Pb(NO_3)_2$.

4.22 Identify the precipitate (if any) that forms when the following solutions are mixed, and write a balanced equation for each reaction. (a) $Ni(NO_3)_2$ and $NaOH$, (b) $NaOH$ and K_2SO_4, (c) Na_2S and $Cu(C_2H_3O_2)_2$.

4.23 Name the spectator ions in any reactions that may be involved when each of the following pairs of solutions are mixed.
(a) $Na_2CO_3(aq)$ and $MgSO_4(aq)$
(b) $Pb(NO_3)_2(aq)$ and $Na_2S(aq)$
(c) $(NH_4)_3PO_4(aq)$ and $CaCl_2(aq)$

4.24 Write balanced net ionic equations for the reactions that occur in each of the following cases. Identify the spectator ion or ions in each reaction.

(a) $Cr_2(SO_4)_3(aq) + (NH_4)_2CO_3(aq) \longrightarrow$
(b) $Ba(NO_3)_2(aq) + K_2SO_4(aq) \longrightarrow$
(c) $Fe(NO_3)_2(aq) + KOH(aq) \longrightarrow$

4.25 Separate samples of a solution of an unknown salt are treated with dilute solutions of HBr, H_2SO_4, and NaOH. A precipitate forms in all three cases. Which of the following cations could the solution contain: K^+; Pb^{2+}; Ba^{2+}?

4.26 Separate samples of a solution of an unknown ionic compound are treated with dilute $AgNO_3$, $Pb(NO_3)_2$, and $BaCl_2$. Precipitates form in all three cases. Which of the following could be the anion of the unknown salt: Br^-; CO_3^{2-}; NO_3^-?

4.27 You know that an unlabeled bottle contains a solution of one of the following: $AgNO_3$, $CaCl_2$, or $Al_2(SO_4)_3$. A friend suggests that you test a portion of the solution with $Ba(NO_3)_2$ and then with NaCl solutions. Explain how these two tests together would be sufficient to determine which salt is present in the solution.

4.28 Three solutions are mixed together to form a single solution. One contains 0.2 mol $Pb(C_2H_3O_2)_2$, the second contains 0.1 mol Na_2S, and the third contains 0.1 mol $CaCl_2$. (a) Write the net ionic equations for the precipitation reaction or reactions that occur. (b) What are the spectator ions in the solution?

Acid-Base Reactions

4.29 Which of the following solutions has the largest concentration of solvated protons: **(a)** 0.1 M LiOH, **(b)** 0.1 M HI, **(c)** 0.5 M methyl alcohol (CH_3OH)? Explain.

4.30 Which of the following solutions is the most basic? **(a)** 0.5 M NH_3, **(b)** 0.1 M KOH, **(c)** 0.1 M $Ca(OH)_2$. Explain.

4.31 What is the difference between **(a)** a monoprotic acid and a diprotic acid, **(b)** a weak acid and a strong acid, **(c)** an acid and a base?

4.32 Explain the following observations: **(a)** NH_3 contains no OH^- ions, and yet its aqueous solutions are basic; **(b)** HF is called a weak acid, and yet it is very reactive; **(c)** although sulfuric acid is a strong electrolyte, an aqueous solution of H_2SO_4 contains more HSO_4^- ions than SO_4^{2-} ions.

4.33 It is said that $HClO_4$ is a strong acid, whereas $HClO_2$ is a weak acid. What does this mean in terms of the extent to which the two substances are ionized in solution?

4.34 What is the relationship between the solubility rules in Table 4.1 and the list of strong bases in Table 4.2? Another way of asking this question is, why is $Cd(OH)_2$, for example, not listed as a strong base in Table 4.2?

4.35 Label each of the following substances as an acid, base, salt, or none of the above. Indicate whether the substance exists in aqueous solution entirely in molecular form, entirely as ions, or as a mixture of molecules and ions. **(a)** HF; **(b)** acetonitrile, CH_3CN; **(c)** $NaClO_4$; **(d)** $Ba(OH)_2$.

4.36 An aqueous solution of an unknown solute is tested with litmus paper and found to be acidic. The solution is weakly conducting compared with a solution of NaCl of the same concentration. Which of the following substances could the unknown be: KOH, NH_3, HNO_3, $KClO_2$, H_3PO_3, CH_3COCH_3 (acetone)?

4.37 Classify each of the following substances as a nonelectrolyte, weak electrolyte, or strong electrolyte in water: **(a)** H_2SO_3, **(b)** C_2H_5OH (ethanol), **(c)** NH_3, **(d)** $KClO_3$, **(e)** $Cu(NO_3)_2$.

4.38 Classify each of the following aqueous solutions as a nonelectrolyte, weak electrolyte, or strong electrolyte: **(a)** $HClO_4$, **(b)** HNO_3, **(c)** NH_4Cl, **(d)** CH_3COCH_3 (acetone), **(e)** $CoSO_4$, **(f)** $C_{12}H_{22}O_{11}$ (sucrose).

4.39 Complete and balance the following molecular equations, and then write the net ionic equation for each:
(a) $HBr(aq) + Ca(OH)_2(aq) \longrightarrow$
(b) $Cu(OH)_2(s) + HClO_4(aq) \longrightarrow$
(c) $Al(OH)_3(s) + HNO_3(aq) \longrightarrow$

4.40 Write the balanced molecular and net ionic equations for each of the following neutralization reactions:
(a) Aqueous acetic acid is neutralized by aqueous potassium hydroxide.
(b) Solid chromium(III) hydroxide reacts with nitric acid.
(c) Aqueous hypochlorous acid and aqueous calcium hydroxide react.

4.41 Write balanced molecular and net ionic equations for the following reactions, and identify the gas formed in each: **(a)** solid cadmium sulfide reacts with an aqueous solution of sulfuric acid; **(b)** solid magnesium carbonate reacts with an aqueous solution of perchloric acid.

4.42 Because the oxide ion is basic, metal oxides react readily with acids. **(a)** Write the net ionic equation for the following reaction:

$$FeO(s) + 2\,HClO_4(aq) \longrightarrow Fe(ClO_4)_2(aq) + H_2O(l).$$

(b) Based on the equation in part (a), write the net ionic equation for the reaction that occurs between NiO(s) and an aqueous solution of nitric acid.

4.43 Write a balanced molecular equation and a net ionic equation for the reaction that occurs when **(a)** solid $CaCO_3$ reacts with an aqueous solution of nitric acid; **(b)** solid iron(II) sulfide reacts with an aqueous solution of hydrobromic acid.

4.44 As K_2O dissolves in water, the oxide ion reacts with water molecules to form hydroxide ions. Write the molecular and net ionic equations for this reaction. Based on the definitions of acid and base, what ion is the base in this reaction? What is the acid? What is the spectator ion in the reaction?

Oxidation-Reduction Reactions

4.45 Define oxidation and reduction in terms of **(a)** electron transfer and **(b)** oxidation numbers.

4.46 Can oxidation occur without accompanying reduction? Explain.

4.47 Which circled region of the periodic table shown here contains the most readily oxidized elements? Which contains the least readily oxidized?

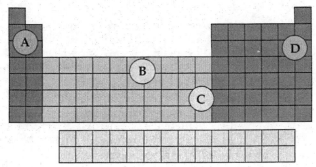

4.48 From the elements listed in Table 4.5, select an element that lies in region A of the periodic table shown to the left and an element that lies in region C. Write a balanced oxidation-reduction equation that shows the oxidation of one metal and reduction of an ion of the other. You will need to decide which element is oxidized and which is reduced.

4.49 Determine the oxidation number for the indicated element in each of the following substances: **(a)** S in SO_2, **(b)** C in $COCl_2$, **(c)** Mn in MnO_4^-, **(d)** Br in HBrO, **(e)** As in As_4, **(f)** O in K_2O_2.

4.50 Determine the oxidation number for the indicated element in each of the following compounds: **(a)** Ti in TiO_2, **(b)** Sn in $SnCl_3^-$, **(c)** C in $C_2O_4^{2-}$, **(d)** N in N_2H_4, **(e)** N in HNO_2, **(f)** Cr in $Cr_2O_7^{2-}$.

4.51 Which element is oxidized and which is reduced in the following reactions?
(a) $Ni(s) + Cl_2(g) \longrightarrow NiCl_2(s)$
(b) $3\,Fe(NO_3)_2(aq) + 2\,Al(s) \longrightarrow$
$3\,Fe(s) + 2\,Al(NO_3)_3(aq)$

(c) $Cl_2(aq) + 2\,NaI(aq) \longrightarrow I_2(aq) + 2\,NaCl(aq)$
(d) $PbS(s) + 4\,H_2O_2(aq) \longrightarrow PbSO_4(s) + 4\,H_2O(l)$

4.52 Which of the following are redox reactions? For those that are, indicate which element is oxidized and which is reduced. For those that are not, indicate whether they are precipitation or acid-base reactions.
(a) $Cu(OH)_2(s) + 2\,HNO_3(aq) \longrightarrow$
$$Cu(NO_3)_2(aq) + 2\,H_2O(l)$$
(b) $Fe_2O_3(s) + 3\,CO(g) \longrightarrow 2\,Fe(s) + 3\,CO_2(g)$
(c) $Sr(NO_3)_2(aq) + H_2SO_4(aq) \longrightarrow$
$$SrSO_4(s) + 2\,HNO_3(aq)$$
(d) $4\,Zn(s) + 10\,H^+(aq) + 2\,NO_3{}^-(aq) \longrightarrow$
$$4\,Zn^{2+}(aq) + N_2O(g) + 5\,H_2O(l)$$

4.53 Write balanced molecular and net ionic equations for the reactions of (a) manganese with dilute sulfuric acid; (b) chromium with hydrobromic acid; (c) tin with hydrochloric acid; (d) aluminum with formic acid, $HCHO_2$.

4.54 Write balanced molecular and net ionic equations for the reactions of (a) hydrochloric acid with nickel; (b) dilute sulfuric acid with iron; (c) hydrobromic acid with magnesium; (d) acetic acid, $HC_2H_3O_2$, with zinc.

4.55 Using the activity series (Table 4.5), write balanced chemical equations for the following reactions. If no reaction occurs, simply write NR. (a) Iron metal is added to a solution of copper(II) nitrate; (b) zinc metal is added to a solution of magnesium sulfate; (c) hydrobromic acid is added to tin metal; (d) hydrogen gas is bubbled through an aqueous solution of nickel(II) chloride; (e) aluminum metal is added to a solution of cobalt(II) sulfate.

4.56 Based on the activity series (Table 4.5), what is the outcome (if any) of each of the following reactions?
(a) $Mn(s) + NiCl_2(aq) \longrightarrow$
(b) $Cu(s) + Cr(C_2H_3O_2)_3(aq) \longrightarrow$
(c) $Cr(s) + NiSO_4(aq) \longrightarrow$
(d) $Pt(s) + HBr(aq) \longrightarrow$
(e) $H_2(g) + CuCl_2(aq) \longrightarrow$

4.57 The metal cadmium tends to form Cd^{2+} ions. The following observations are made: (i) When a strip of zinc metal is placed in $CdCl_2(aq)$, cadmium metal is deposited on the strip. (ii) When a strip of cadmium metal is placed in $Ni(NO_3)_2(aq)$, nickel metal is deposited on the strip. (a) Write net ionic equations to explain each of the observations made above. (b) What can you conclude about the position of cadmium in the activity series? (c) What experiments would you need to perform to locate more precisely the position of cadmium in the activity series?

4.58 (a) Use the following reactions to prepare an activity series for the halogens:

$Br_2(aq) + 2\,NaI(aq) \longrightarrow 2\,NaBr(aq) + I_2(aq);$

$Cl_2(aq) + 2\,NaBr(aq) \longrightarrow 2\,NaCl(aq) + Br_2(aq).$

(b) Relate the positions of the halogens in the periodic table with their locations in this activity series. (c) Predict whether a reaction occurs when the following reagents are mixed: $Cl_2(aq)$ and $KI(aq)$; $Br_2(aq)$ and $LiCl(aq)$.

Solution Composition; Molarity

4.59 (a) Is the concentration of a solution an intensive or an extensive property? (b) What is the difference between 0.50 mol HCl and 0.50 M HCl?

4.60 (a) Suppose you prepare 500 mL of a 0.10 M solution of some salt and then spill some of it. What happens to the concentration of the solution left in the container? (b) A certain volume of a 0.50 M solution contains 4.5 g of a salt. What mass of the salt is present in the same volume of a 2.50 M solution?

4.61 (a) Calculate the molarity of a solution that contains 0.0345 mol NH_4Cl in exactly 400 mL of solution. (b) How many moles of HNO_3 are present in 35.0 mL of a 2.20 M solution of nitric acid? (c) How many milliliters of 1.50 M KOH solution are needed to provide 0.125 mol of KOH?

4.62 (a) Calculate the molarity of a solution made by dissolving 0.145 mol Na_2SO_4 in enough water to form exactly 750 mL of solution. (b) How many moles of $KMnO_4$ are present in 125 mL of a 0.0850 M solution? (c) How many milliliters of 11.6 M HCl solution are needed to obtain 0.255 mol of HCl?

4.63 The average adult human male has a total blood volume of 5.0 L. If the concentration of sodium ion in this average individual is 0.135 M, what is the mass of sodium ion circulating in the blood?

4.64 A person suffering from hyponatremia has a sodium ion concentration in the blood of 0.118 M and a total blood volume of 4.6 L. What mass of sodium chloride would need to be added to the blood to bring the sodium ion concentration up to 0.138 M, assuming no change in blood volume?

4.65 Calculate (a) the number of grams of solute in 0.250 L of 0.150 M KBr, (b) the molar concentration of a solution containing 4.75 g of $Ca(NO_3)_2$ in 0.200 L, (c) the volume of 1.50 M Na_3PO_4 in milliliters that contains 5.00 g of solute.

4.66 (a) How many grams of solute are present in 50.0 mL of 0.360 M $K_2Cr_2O_7$? (b) If 4.28 g of $(NH_4)_2SO_4$ is dissolved in enough water to form 300 mL of solution, what is the molarity of the solution? (c) How many milliliters of 0.240 M $CuSO_4$ contain 2.25 g of solute?

4.67 (a) Which will have the highest concentration of potassium ion: 0.20 M KCl, 0.15 M K_2CrO_4, or 0.080 M K_3PO_4? (b) Which will contain the greater number of moles of potassium ion: 30.0 mL of 0.15 M K_2CrO_4 or 25.0 mL of 0.080 M K_3PO_4?

4.68 In each of the following pairs, indicate which has the higher concentration of Cl^- ion: (a) 0.10 M $CaCl_2$ or 0.15 M KCl solution, (b) 100 mL of 0.10 M KCl solution or 400 mL of 0.080 M LiCl solution, (c) 0.050 M HCl solution or 0.020 M $CdCl_2$ solution.

4.69 Indicate the concentration of each ion or molecule present in the following solutions: **(a)** 0.22 *M* NaOH, **(b)** 0.16 *M* CaBr₂, **(c)** 0.15 *M* CH₃OH, **(d)** a mixture of 40.0 mL of 0.15 *M* KClO₃ and 35.0 mL of 0.22 *M* Na₂SO₄. Assume the volumes are additive.

4.70 Indicate the concentration of each ion present in the solution formed by mixing **(a)** 16.0 mL of 0.130 *M* HCl and 12.0 mL of 0.600 *M* HCl, **(b)** 18.0 mL of 0.200 *M* Na₂SO₄ and 15.0 mL of 0.150 *M* KCl, **(c)** 2.38 g of NaCl in 50.0 mL of 0.400 *M* CaCl₂ solution. (Assume that the volumes are additive.)

4.71 **(a)** You have a stock solution of 14.8 *M* NH₃. How many milliliters of this solution should you dilute to make 100.0 mL of 0.250 *M* NH₃? **(b)** If you take a 10.0-mL portion of the stock solution and dilute it to a total volume of 0.250 L, what will be the concentration of the final solution?

4.72 **(a)** How many milliliters of a stock solution of 10.0 *M* HNO₃ would you have to use to prepare 0.350 L of 0.400 *M* HNO₃? **(b)** If you dilute 25.0 mL of the stock solution to a final volume of 0.500 L, what will be the concentration of the diluted solution?

4.73 **(a)** Starting with solid sucrose, C₁₂H₂₂O₁₁, describe how you would prepare 125 mL of 0.150 *M* sucrose solution. **(b)** Describe how you would prepare 400.0 mL of 0.100 *M* C₁₂H₂₂O₁₁ starting with 2.00 L of 1.50 *M* C₁₂H₂₂O₁₁.

4.74 **(a)** How would you prepare 250.0 mL of 0.150 *M* AgNO₃ solution starting with pure solute? **(b)** An experiment calls for you to use 100 mL of 0.50 *M* HNO₃ solution. All you have available is a bottle of 6.0 *M* HNO₃. How would you prepare the desired solution?

[4.75] Pure acetic acid, known as glacial acetic acid, is a liquid with a density of 1.049 g/mL at 25°C. Calculate the molarity of a solution of acetic acid made by dissolving 20.00 mL of glacial acetic acid at 25°C in enough water to make 250.0 mL of solution.

[4.76] Glycerol, C₃H₈O₃, is a substance used extensively in the manufacture of cosmetics, foodstuffs, antifreeze, and plastics. Glycerol is a water-soluble liquid with a density of 1.2656 g/L at 15°C. Calculate the molarity of a solution of glycerol made by dissolving 50.000 mL glycerol at 15°C in enough water to make 250.00 mL of solution.

Solution Stoichiometry; Titrations

4.77 What mass of NaCl is needed to precipitate the silver ions from 20.0 mL of 0.100 *M* AgNO₃ solution?

4.78 What mass of NaOH is needed to precipitate the Cd²⁺ ions from 25.0 mL of 0.500 *M* Cd(NO₃)₂ solution?

4.79 **(a)** What volume of 0.115 *M* HClO₄ solution is needed to neutralize 50.00 mL of 0.0875 *M* NaOH? **(b)** What volume of 0.128 *M* HCl is needed to neutralize 2.87 g of Mg(OH)₂? **(c)** If 25.8 mL of AgNO₃ is needed to precipitate all the Cl⁻ ions in a 785-mg sample of KCl (forming AgCl), what is the molarity of the AgNO₃ solution? **(d)** If 45.3 mL of 0.108 *M* HCl solution is needed to neutralize a solution of KOH, how many grams of KOH must be present in the solution?

4.80 **(a)** How many milliliters of 0.120 *M* HCl are needed to completely neutralize 50.0 mL of 0.101 *M* Ba(OH)₂ solution? **(b)** How many milliliters of 0.125 *M* H₂SO₄ are needed to neutralize 0.200 g of NaOH? **(c)** If 55.8 mL of BaCl₂ solution is needed to precipitate all the sulfate ion in a 752-mg sample of Na₂SO₄, what is the molarity of the solution? **(d)** If 42.7 mL of 0.208 *M* HCl solution is needed to neutralize a solution of Ca(OH)₂, how many grams of Ca(OH)₂ must be in the solution?

4.81 Some sulfuric acid is spilled on a lab bench. It can be neutralized by sprinkling sodium bicarbonate on it and then mopping up the resultant solution. The sodium bicarbonate reacts with sulfuric acid as follows:

$$2\,NaHCO_3(s) + H_2SO_4(aq) \longrightarrow$$
$$Na_2SO_4(aq) + 2\,H_2O(l) + 2\,CO_2(g)$$

Sodium bicarbonate is added until the fizzing due to the formation of CO₂(g) stops. If 27 mL of 6.0*M* H₂SO₄ was spilled, what is the minimum mass of NaHCO₃ that must be added to the spill to neutralize the acid?

4.82 The distinctive odor of vinegar is due to acetic acid, HC₂H₃O₂, which reacts with sodium hydroxide in the following fashion:

$$HC_2H_3O_2(aq) + NaOH(aq) \longrightarrow$$
$$H_2O(l) + NaC_2H_3O_2(aq)$$

If 3.45 mL of vinegar needs 42.5 mL of 0.115 *M* NaOH to reach the equivalence point in a titration, how many grams of acetic acid are in a 1.00-qt sample of this vinegar?

4.83 A sample of solid Ca(OH)₂ is stirred in water at 30°C until the solution contains as much dissolved Ca(OH)₂ as it can hold. A 100-mL sample of this solution is withdrawn and titrated with 5.00 × 10⁻² *M* HBr. It requires 48.8 mL of the acid solution for neutralization. What is the molarity of the Ca(OH)₂ solution? What is the solubility of Ca(OH)₂ in water, at 30°C in grams of Ca(OH)₂ per 100 mL of solution?

4.84 In the laboratory 6.82 g of Sr(NO₃)₂ is dissolved in enough water to form 0.500 L. A 0.100-L sample is withdrawn from this stock solution and titrated with a 0.0335 *M* solution of Na₂CrO₄. What volume of Na₂CrO₄ solution is needed to precipitate all the Sr²⁺(aq) as SrCrO₄?

4.85 A solution of 100.0 mL of 0.200 *M* KOH is mixed with a solution of 200.0 mL of 0.150 *M* NiSO₄. **(a)** Write the balanced chemical equation for the reaction that occurs. **(b)** What precipitate forms? **(c)** What is the limiting reactant? **(d)** How many grams of this precipitate form? **(e)** What is the concentration of each ion that remains in solution?

4.86 A solution is made by mixing 12.0 g of NaOH and 75.0 mL of 0.200 *M* HNO₃. **(a)** Write a balanced equation for the reaction that occurs between the solutes. **(b)** Calculate the concentration of each ion remaining in solution. **(c)** Is the resultant solution acidic or basic?

[4.87] A 0.5895-g sample of impure magnesium hydroxide is dissolved in 100.0 mL of 0.2050 M HCl solution. The excess acid then needs 19.85 mL of 0.1020 M NaOH for neutralization. Calculate the percent by mass of magnesium hydroxide in the sample, assuming that it is the only substance reacting with the HCl solution.

[4.88] A 1.248-g sample of limestone rock is pulverized and then treated with 30.00 mL of 1.035 M HCl solution. The excess acid then requires 11.56 mL of 1.010 M NaOH for neutralization. Calculate the percent by mass of calcium carbonate in the rock, assuming that it is the only substance reacting with the HCl solution.

Additional Exercises

[4.89] Suppose it were possible to instantaneously form a solution of uniformly dispersed K^+ and Br^- ions in a solvent such as mineral oil. What would you expect to occur? How does this compare with what would happen if the same uniform dispersion of ions were formed in water? How do you account for the difference?

4.90 The accompanying photo shows the reaction between a solution of $Cd(NO_3)_2$ and one of Na_2S. What is the identity of the precipitate? What ions remain in solution? Write the net ionic equation for the reaction.

4.91 Suppose you have a solution that might contain any or all of the following cations: Ni^{2+}, Ag^+, Sr^{2+}, and Mn^{2+}. Addition of HCl solution causes a precipitate to form. After filtering off the precipitate, H_2SO_4 solution is added to the resultant solution and another precipitate forms. This is filtered off, and a solution of NaOH is added to the resulting solution. No precipitate is observed. Which ions are present in each of the precipitates? Which of the four ions listed above must be absent from the original solution?

4.92 You choose to investigate some of the solubility guidelines for two ions not listed in Table 4.1, the chromate ion (CrO_4^{2-}) and the oxalate ion ($C_2O_4^{2-}$). You are given 0.01 M solutions (A, B, C, D) of four water-soluble salts:

Solution	Solute	Color of Solution
A	Na_2CrO_4	Yellow
B	$(NH_4)_2C_2O_4$	Colorless
C	$AgNO_3$	Colorless
D	$CaCl_2$	Colorless

When these solutions are mixed, the following observations are made:

Expt Number	Solutions Mixed	Result
1	A + B	No precipitate, yellow solution
2	A + C	Red precipitate forms
3	A + D	No precipitate, yellow solution
4	B + C	White precipitate forms
5	B + D	White precipitate forms
6	C + D	White precipitate forms

(a) Write a net ionic equation for the reaction that occurs in each of the experiments. (b) Identify the precipitate formed, if any, in each of the experiments. (c) Based on these limited observations, which ion tends to form the more soluble salts, chromate or oxalate?

4.93 Antacids are often used to relieve pain and promote healing in the treatment of mild ulcers. Write balanced net ionic equations for the reactions between the HCl(aq) in the stomach and each of the following substances used in various antacids: (a) $Al(OH)_3(s)$, (b) $Mg(OH)_2(s)$, (c) $MgCO_3(s)$, (d) $NaAl(CO_3)(OH)_2(s)$, (e) $CaCO_3(s)$.

[4.94] Salts of the sulfite ion, SO_3^{2-}, react with acids in a way similar to that of carbonates. (a) Predict the chemical formula, and name the weak acid that forms when the sulfite ion reacts with acids. (b) The acid formed in part (a) decomposes to form water and a gas. Predict the molecular formula, and name the gas formed. (c) Use a source book such as the *CRC Handbook of Chemistry and Physics* to confirm that the substance in part (b) is a gas under normal room-temperature conditions. (d) Write balanced net ionic equations of the reaction of HCl(aq) with (i) $Na_2SO_3(aq)$, (ii) $Ag_2SO_3(s)$, (iii) $KHSO_3(s)$, and (iv) $ZnSO_3(aq)$.

4.95 The commercial production of nitric acid involves the following chemical reactions:

$$4\,NH_3(g) + 5\,O_2(g) \longrightarrow 4\,NO(g) + 6\,H_2O(g)$$

$$2\,NO(g) + O_2(g) \longrightarrow 2\,NO_2(g)$$

$$3\,NO_2(g) + H_2O(l) \longrightarrow 2\,HNO_3(aq) + NO(g)$$

(a) Which of these reactions are redox reactions? (b) In each redox reaction identify the element undergoing oxidation and the element undergoing reduction.

4.96 Use Table 4.5 to predict which of the following ions can be reduced to their metal forms by reacting with zinc: **(a)** $Na^+(aq)$, **(b)** $Pb^{2+}(aq)$, **(c)** $Mg^{2+}(aq)$, **(d)** $Fe^{2+}(aq)$, **(e)** $Cu^{2+}(aq)$, **(f)** $Al^{3+}(aq)$. Write the balanced net ionic equation for each reaction that occurs.

[4.97] Lanthanum metal forms cations with a charge of 3+. Consider the following observations about the chemistry of lanthanum: When lanthanum metal is exposed to air, a white solid (compound A) is formed that contains lanthanum and one other element. When lanthanum metal is added to water, gas bubbles are observed and a different white solid (compound B) is formed. Both A and B dissolve in hydrochloric acid to give a clear solution. When either of these solution is evaporated, a soluble white solid (compound C) remains. If compound C is dissolved in water and sulfuric acid is added, a white precipitate (compound D) forms. **(a)** Propose identities for the substances A, B, C, and D. **(b)** Write net ionic equations for all the reactions described. **(c)** Based on the preceding observations, what can be said about the position of lanthanum in the activity series (Table 4.5)?

4.98 A 35.0-mL sample of 1.00 M KBr and a 60.0-mL sample of 0.600 M KBr are mixed. The solution is then heated to evaporate water until the total volume is 50.0 mL. What is the molarity of the KBr in the final solution?

4.99 Calculate the molarity of the solution produced by mixing **(a)** 40.0 mL of 0.160 M NaCl and 65.0 mL of 0.150 M NaCl, **(b)** 32.5 mL of 0.750 M NaOH and 26.8 mL of 0.750 M NaOH. (Assume that the volumes are additive.)

4.100 Using modern analytical techniques, it is possible to detect sodium ions in concentrations as low as 50 pg/mL. What is this detection limit expressed in **(a)** molarity of Na^+, **(b)** Na^+ ions per cubic centimeter?

4.101 Hard water contains Ca^{2+}, Mg^{2+}, and Fe^{2+}, which interfere with the action of soap and leave an insoluble coating on the insides of containers and pipes when heated. Water softeners replace these ions with Na^+. If 1.0×10^3 L of hard water contains 0.010 M Ca^{2+} and 0.0050 M Mg^{2+}, how many moles of Na^+ are needed to replace these ions?

4.102 Tartaric acid, $H_2C_4H_4O_6$, has two acidic hydrogens. The acid is often present in wines and precipitates from solution as the wine ages. A solution containing an unknown concentration of the acid is titrated with NaOH. It requires 22.62 mL of 0.2000 M NaOH solution to titrate both acidic protons in 40.00 mL of the tartaric acid solution. Write a balanced net ionic equation for the neutralization reaction, and calculate the molarity of the tartaric acid solution.

4.103 The concentration of hydrogen peroxide in a solution is determined by titrating a 10.0-mL sample of the solution with permanganate ion.

$$2\,MnO_4^-(aq) + 5\,H_2O_2(aq) + 6\,H^+(aq) \longrightarrow$$
$$2\,Mn^{2+}(aq) + 5\,O_2(g) + 8\,H_2O(l)$$

If it takes 16.8 mL of 0.124 M MnO_4^- solution to reach the equivalence point, what is the molarity of the hydrogen peroxide solution?

[4.104] A solid sample of $Zn(OH)_2$ is added to 0.400 L of 0.500 M aqueous HBr. The solution that remains is still acidic. It is then titrated with 0.500 M NaOH solution, and it takes 98.5 mL of the NaOH solution to reach the equivalence point. What mass of $Zn(OH)_2$ was added to the HBr solution?

Integrative Exercises

4.105 A solution of sodium chlorate is prepared by dissolving 1.28 g of the salt in water to form 1.00 L of solution. To form a solution of sodium chlorite of the same molarity and volume, what mass of sodium chlorite would be needed?

4.106 **(a)** By titration, 15.0 mL of 0.1008 M sodium hydroxide is needed to neutralize a 0.2053-g sample of an organic acid. What is the molar mass of the acid if it is monoprotic? **(b)** An elemental analysis of the acid indicates that it is composed of 5.89% H, 70.6% C, and 23.5% O by mass. What is its molecular formula?

4.107 A 3.455-g sample of a mixture was analyzed for barium ion by adding a small excess of sulfuric acid to an aqueous solution of the sample. The resultant reaction produced a precipitate of barium sulfate, which was collected by filtration, washed, dried, and weighed. If 0.2815 g of barium sulfate was obtained, what was the mass percentage of barium in the sample?

[4.108] A tanker truck carrying 5.0×10^3 kg of concentrated sulfuric acid solution tips over and spills its load. If the sulfuric acid is 95.0% H_2SO_4 by mass and has a density of 1.84 gm/L, how many kilograms of sodium carbonate must be added to neutralize the acid?

4.109 A sample of 5.53 g of $Mg(OH)_2$ is added to 25.0 mL of 0.200 M HNO_3. **(a)** Write the chemical equation for the reaction that occurs. **(b)** Which is the limiting reactant in the reaction? **(c)** How many moles of $Mg(OH)_2$, HNO_3, and $Mg(NO_3)_2$ are present after the reaction is complete?

4.110 A sample of 1.50 g of lead(II) nitrate is mixed with 125 mL of 0.100 M sodium sulfate solution. **(a)** Write the chemical equation for the reaction that occurs. **(b)** Which is the limiting reactant in the reaction? **(c)** What are the concentrations of all ions that remain in solution after the reaction is complete?

4.111 A mixture contains 76.5% NaCl, 6.5% $MgCl_2$, and 17.0% Na_2SO_4 by mass. What is the molarity of Cl^- ions in a solution formed by dissolving 7.50 g of the mixture in enough water to form 500.0 mL of solution?

[4.112] The average concentration of bromide ion in seawater is 65 mg of bromide ion per kg of seawater. What is the molarity of the bromide ion if the density of the seawater is 1.025 g/mL?

[4.113] The mass percentage of chloride ion in a 25.00-mL sample of seawater was determined by titrating the sample with silver nitrate, precipitating silver chloride. It took 42.58 mL of 0.2997 M silver nitrate solution to reach the equivalence point in the titration. What is the mass percentage of chloride ion in the seawater if its density is 1.025 g/mL?

4.114 The arsenic in a 1.22-g sample of a pesticide was converted to AsO_4^{3-} by suitable chemical treatment. It was then titrated using Ag^+ to form Ag_3AsO_4 as a precipitate. (a) What is the oxidation state of As in AsO_4^{3-}? (b) Name Ag_3AsO_4 by analogy to the corresponding compound containing phosphorus in place of arsenic. (c) If it took 25.0 mL of 0.102 M Ag^+ to reach the equivalence point in this titration, what is the mass percentage of arsenic in the pesticide?

[4.115] The new standard for arsenate in drinking water, mandated by the Safe Drinking Water Act, requires that by January, 2006, public water supplies must contain no greater than 10 parts per billion (ppb) arsenic. Assuming that this arsenic is present as arsenate, AsO_4^{3-}, what mass of sodium arsenate would be present in a 1.00-L sample of drinking water that just meets the standard?

[4.116] Federal regulations set an upper limit of 50 parts per million (ppm) of NH_3 in the air in a work environment (that is, 50 molecules of $NH_3(g)$ for every million molecules in the air). Air from a manufacturing operation was drawn through a solution containing 1.00×10^2 mL of 0.0105 M HCl. The NH_3 reacts with HCl as follows:

$$NH_3(aq) + HCl(aq) \longrightarrow NH_4Cl(aq)$$

After drawing air through the acid solution for 10.0 min at a rate of 10.0 L/min, the acid was titrated. The remaining acid needed 13.1 mL of 0.0588 M NaOH to reach the equivalence point. (a) How many grams of NH_3 were drawn into the acid solution? (b) How many ppm of NH_3 were in the air? (Air has a density of 1.20 g/L and an average molar mass of 29.0 g/mol under the conditions of the experiment.) (c) Is this manufacturer in compliance with regulations?

eMEDIA EXERCISES

These exercises make use of the interactive objects available online in OneKey or the Companion Website, and on your Accelerator CD. Access to these resources comes in your MediaPak.

4.117 The **Electrolytes and Non-Electrolytes** animation (4.1) and the **Introduction to Aqueous Acids** and **Introduction to Aqueous Bases** animations (4.3) illustrate the behavior of various substances in aqueous solution. For each of the seven substances mentioned in the animations, write the chemical equation that corresponds to dissolution in water. (The chemical formula of sugar is $C_{12}H_{22}O_{11}$.) Where appropriate, use the double arrow notation.

4.118 In the **Strong and Weak Electrolytes** movie (4.1), the lightbulb glows brightly when the beaker contains aqueous hydrochloric acid, but relatively dimly when the beaker contains aqueous acetic acid. (a) For each of the compounds in Exercise 4.3, would you expect an aqueous solution to cause the bulb to light? If so, how brightly? (b) Consider the use of aqueous solutions of each of the following compounds in the apparatus shown in the demonstration. For each compound, tell whether you would expect the lightbulb to glow brightly, dimly, or not at all: H_2CO_3, C_2H_5OH, NH_4Cl, CaF_2, and HF.

4.119 (a) Use the solubility rules to predict what precipitate, if any, will form as the result of each combination. (i) $Na_2CO_3(aq)$ and $Fe(NO_3)_2(aq)$, (ii) $NH_4NO_3(aq)$ and $K_2SO_4(aq)$, (iii) $AlBr_3(aq)$ and $Fe_2(SO_4)_3(aq)$, (iv) $H_2SO_4(aq)$ and $Pb(NO_3)_2(aq)$, (v) $Na_2S(aq)$ and $(NH_4)_2SO_4(aq)$. Use the **Ionic Compounds** activity (4.2) to check your answers. (b) For each combination that produces a precipitate, write a balanced net ionic equation. (c) When $NH_4Cl(aq)$ and $Pb(NO_3)_2(aq)$ are combined, a precipitate forms. What ions are still present in the solution in significant concentration after the precipitation? Explain.

4.120 In the **Oxidation-Reduction Chemistry of Tin and Zinc** movie (4.4), zinc is oxidized by a solution containing tin ions. (a) Write the equation corresponding to this redox reaction. (b) In addition to the reaction between zinc metal and tin ions, there is another process occurring. Write the net ionic equation corresponding to this process. (Refer to Exercise 4.54.)

4.121 After watching the **Solution Formation from a Solid** animation (4.5), answer the following questions: (a) If we neglect to account for the mass of the weighing paper, how would our calculated concentration differ from the actual concentration of the solution? (b) Describe the process of preparing an aqueous solution of known concentration, starting with a solid. (c) Why is it necessary to make the solution as described in the animation, rather than simply filling the flask up to the mark with water and then adding the solute? (d) Describe how you would prepare the solution in part (a) starting with the concentrated stock solution in the **Solution Formation by Dilution** animation (4.5).

4.122 Use the **Acid-Base Titration** activity (4.6) to determine the concentration of an unknown acid by adding 0.40 M NaOH in increments of 1.0 mL. Repeat the titration, adding increments of 0.10 mL of base near the end point. Once more, repeat the titration, adding increments of 0.05 mL of base near the end point. If your acid is dilute enough, repeat the titration three more times, using 0.10 M NaOH in 1.0-mL, 0.50-mL, and 0.05-mL increments. (a) Tabulate the acid concentrations that you calculate from your titration data. Are the values all the same? If not, why not? **(b)** Which value do you consider to be most accurate and why?

4.123 **(a)** What is the maximum concentration of monoprotic acid that could be titrated in the **Acid-Base Titration** activity *(4.6)* using 0.05 *M* NaOH? **(b)** What is the maximum concentration of a diprotic acid that could be titrated in this simulation using 0.10 *M* base? **(c)** All of the acid-base indicators available in the simulation change color within a pH range of ~4 to 10.5. What effect would the use of an indicator such as metacresol purple have on the experimentally determined value of an unknown acid's concentration? (Metacresol purple changes colors in the pH range of ~1.2 to 2.8.)

VCL eLABORATORY EXERCISES

These exercises allow students to apply the concepts and skills for this chapter in the simulated laboratory of Virtual ChemLab. Worksheets for each of these exercises are found in the Virtual ChemLab Workbook in your MediaPak.

4.124 *(VCL 4-1) Strong and Weak Electrolytes*
As discussed in the chapter, strong electrolytes are compounds that fully dissociate in water and weak electrolytes are ones that do so only to a small extent. A method for measuring the degree of dissociation is to measure the electrical conductivity of the solution. In this assignment you will measure the conductivity of several solutions and make some important conclusions.

4.125 *(VCL 4-2) Precipitation Reactions*
A precipitation reaction is defined as one in which a soluble cation and a soluble anion combine to form an insoluble combination product. In this assignment you will mix several different combinations of cations and anions and observe those that form precipitates and those that do not. You will also write full balanced equations and net ionic equations for these reactions.

4.126 *(VCL 4-3) Concepts in Acid-Base Titrations*
Titrations provide a method of quantitatively measuring the concentration of an unknown solution. In an acid-base titration this is done by delivering a titrant of known concentration into an analyte of known volume. The equivalence point of the titration, or the point where the analyte has been completely consumed by the titrant, is identified by the point where the pH changes rapidly over a small volume of titrant delivered. In this assignment you will titrate a strong acid, HCl, with a strong base, NaOH, and observe the pH of the solution as a function of the volume of titrant delivered.

4.127 *(VCL 4-4) Predicting the Equivalence Point*
To make a titration more efficient and more accurate, it is often important to be able to predict the equivalence point for the titration. In this assignment you will be given 0.3000 *M* HCl and 0.3000 *M* NaOH. You will predict the equivalence point and then perform the titration to check your prediction.

4.128 *(VCL 4-5) Predicting the Equivalence Point*
To make a titration more efficient and more accurate, it is often important to be able to predict the equivalence point for the titration. In this assignment you will be given 0.1276 *M* HCl and 0.1475 *M* NaOH. You will predict the equivalence point and then perform the titration to check your prediction.

4.129 *(VCL 4-6) Predicting the Equivalence Point*
To make a titration more efficient and more accurate, it is often important to be able to predict the equivalence point for the titration. In this assignment you will be given 0.1033 *M* CH₃COOH (acetic acid, or HAc) and 0.1104 *M* NaOH. You will predict the equivalence point and then perform the titration to check your prediction.

4.130 *(VCL 4-7) Acid-Base Titration: Practice*
Titrations provide a method of quantitatively measuring the concentration of an unknown solution. In an acid-base titration this is done by delivering a titrant of known concentration into an analyte of known volume. In this assignment you will titrate a 0.3000 *M* solution of NaOH into 25 mL of 0.3000 *M* HCl. Although in this situation you know the concentration of both NaOH and HCl, this will give you practice in performing a titration and calculating the concentration of the analyte, which in this case is HCl.

4.131 *(VCL 4-8) Acid-Base Titration: Unknown HCl*
Titrations provide a method of quantitatively measuring the concentration of an unknown solution. In an acid-base titration this is done by delivering a titrant of known concentration into an analyte of known volume. In this assignment you will titrate a 0.2564 *M* solution of NaOH into 25 mL of an unknown concentration of HCl and calculate the concentration of the HCl solution.

6.1 The Wave Nature of Light

6.2 Quantized Energy and Photons

6.3 Line Spectra and the Bohr Model

6.4 The Wave Behavior of Matter

6.5 Quantum Mechanics and Atomic Orbitals

6.6 Representations of Orbitals

6.7 Many-Electron Atoms

6.8 Electron Configurations

6.9 Electron Configurations and the Periodic Table

WHAT'S AHEAD

- Light (radiant energy, or *electromagnetic radiation*) has wavelike properties and so is characterized by *wavelength*, *frequency*, and *speed*. *(Section 6.1)*

- Studies of the radiation given off by hot objects and of the way in which light striking a metal surface can free electrons indicate that electromagnetic radiation also has particle-like properties and can be described in terms of *photons*. *(Section 6.2)*

- The fact that atoms give off characteristic colors of light (*line spectra*) provides clues about how electrons are arranged in atoms, leading to two important ideas: Electrons exist only in certain energy levels around a nucleus, and energy is involved in moving an electron from one level to another. *(Section 6.3)*

- Because matter also has wavelike properties, it is impossible to determine simultaneously the exact position and exact motion of an electron in an atom (*Heisenberg's uncertainty principle*). *(Section 6.4)*

- The arrangement of electrons in atoms is described by quantum mechanics in terms of *atomic orbitals*. *(Sections 6.5, 6.6, and 6.7)*

- Knowing the energies of orbitals as well as some fundamental characteristics of electrons described by *Hund's rule* allows us to determine how electrons are distributed among various orbitals in an atom (*electron configurations*). *(Section 6.8)*

- The electron configuration of an atom is related to the location of the element in the periodic table. *(Section 6.9)*

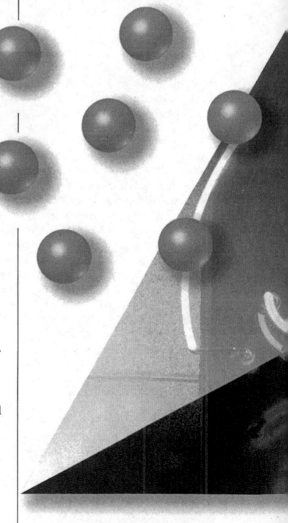

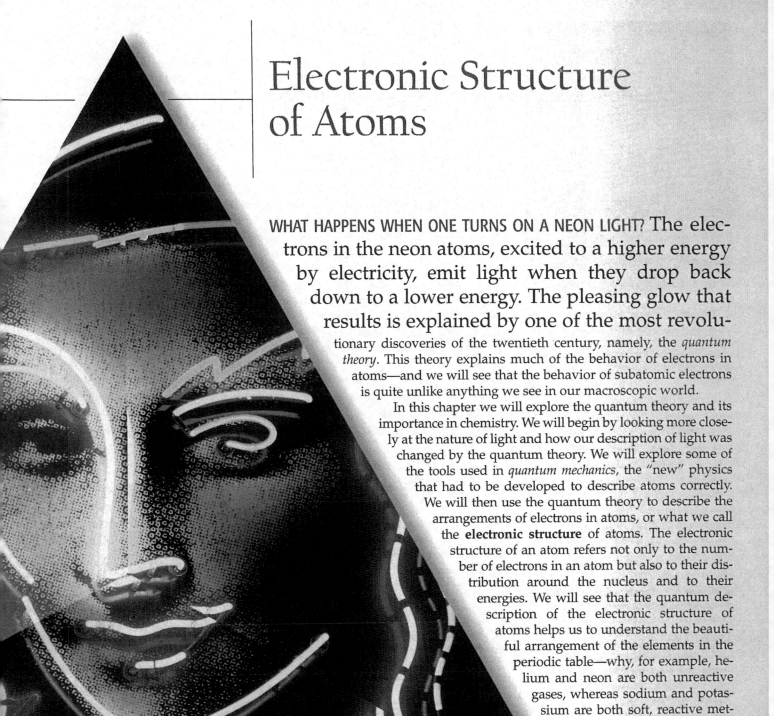

Electronic Structure of Atoms

WHAT HAPPENS WHEN ONE TURNS ON A NEON LIGHT? The electrons in the neon atoms, excited to a higher energy by electricity, emit light when they drop back down to a lower energy. The pleasing glow that results is explained by one of the most revolutionary discoveries of the twentieth century, namely, the *quantum theory*. This theory explains much of the behavior of electrons in atoms—and we will see that the behavior of subatomic electrons is quite unlike anything we see in our macroscopic world.

In this chapter we will explore the quantum theory and its importance in chemistry. We will begin by looking more closely at the nature of light and how our description of light was changed by the quantum theory. We will explore some of the tools used in *quantum mechanics*, the "new" physics that had to be developed to describe atoms correctly. We will then use the quantum theory to describe the arrangements of electrons in atoms, or what we call the **electronic structure** of atoms. The electronic structure of an atom refers not only to the number of electrons in an atom but also to their distribution around the nucleus and to their energies. We will see that the quantum description of the electronic structure of atoms helps us to understand the beautiful arrangement of the elements in the periodic table—why, for example, helium and neon are both unreactive gases, whereas sodium and potassium are both soft, reactive metals. In the chapters that follow, we will see how the concepts of quantum theory are used to explain trends in the periodic table and the formation of bonds between atoms.

THE GLASS TUBES OF NEON LIGHTS contain various gases that can be excited by electricity. Light is produced when electrically excited atoms return to their lowest-energy states.

217

▲ Figure 6.1 Water waves. The movement of the boat through the water forms waves. The regular variation of the peaks and troughs enables us to sense the motion, or *propagation*, of the waves.

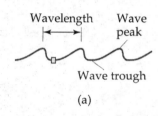

Wavelength   Wave peak

Wave trough

(a)

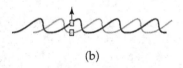

(b)

▲ Figure 6.2 Characteristics of water waves. (a) The distance between corresponding points on each wave is called the *wavelength*. In this drawing, the two corresponding points are two peaks, but they could be any other two corresponding points, such as two adjacent troughs. (b) The number of times per second that the cork bobs up and down is called the *frequency* of the wave.

6.1 | The Wave Nature of Light

Much of our present understanding of the electronic structure of atoms has come from analysis of the light either emitted or absorbed by substances. To understand electronic structure, therefore, we must first learn more about light. The light that we can see with our eyes, *visible light*, is an example of **electromagnetic radiation**. Because electromagnetic radiation carries energy through space, it is also known as *radiant energy*. There are many types of electromagnetic radiation in addition to visible light. These different forms—such as the radio waves that carry music to our radios, the infrared radiation (heat) from a glowing fireplace, and the X rays used by a dentist—may *seem* very different from one another, but they all share certain fundamental characteristics.

All types of electromagnetic radiation move through a vacuum at a speed of 3.00×10^8 m/s, the *speed of light*. Furthermore, all have wavelike characteristics similar to those of waves that move through water. Water waves are the result of energy imparted to the water, perhaps by the dropping of a stone or the movement of a boat on the water surface (Figure 6.1 ◀). This energy is expressed as the up-and-down movements of the water.

A cross section of a water wave (Figure 6.2 ◀) shows that it is periodic, which means that the pattern of peaks and troughs repeats itself at regular intervals. The distance between two adjacent peaks (or between two adjacent troughs) is called the **wavelength**. The number of complete wavelengths, or *cycles*, that pass a given point each second is the **frequency** of the wave. We can measure the frequency of a water wave by counting the number of times per second that a cork bobbing on the water moves through a complete cycle of upward and downward motion.

GIVE IT SOME THOUGHT

What is the difference between visible light and electromagnetic radiation?

Just as with water waves, we can assign a frequency and wavelength to electromagnetic waves, as illustrated in Figure 6.3 ▼. These and all other wave characteristics of electromagnetic radiation are due to the periodic oscillations in the intensities of the electric and magnetic fields associated with the radiation.

▼ Figure 6.3 Characteristics of electromagnetic waves. Radiant energy has wave characteristics; it consists of electromagnetic waves. Notice that the shorter the wavelength, λ, the higher the frequency, ν. The wavelength in (b) is half as long as that in (a), and the frequency of the wave in (b) is therefore twice as great as the frequency in (a). The *amplitude* of the wave relates to the intensity of the radiation. It is the maximum extent of the oscillation of the wave. In these diagrams amplitude is measured as the vertical distance from the midline of the wave to its peak. The waves in (a) and (b) have the same amplitude. The wave in (c) has the same frequency as that in (b), but its amplitude is lower.

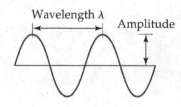

(a) Two complete cycles of wavelength λ

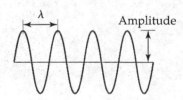

(b) Wavelength half of that in (a); frequency twice as great as in (a)

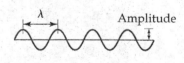

(c) Same frequency as (b), smaller amplitude

Science Fundamentals Second Edition

The speed of water waves can vary depending on how they are created—for example, the waves produced by a speedboat travel faster than those produced by a rowboat. In contrast, all electromagnetic radiation moves at the same speed, namely the speed of light. As a result, the wavelength and frequency of electromagnetic radiation are always related in a straightforward way. If the wavelength is long, there will be fewer cycles of the wave passing a point per second; thus, the frequency will be low. Conversely, for a wave to have a high frequency, the distance between the peaks of the wave must be small (short wavelength). This inverse relationship between the frequency and the wavelength of electromagnetic radiation can be expressed by the equation

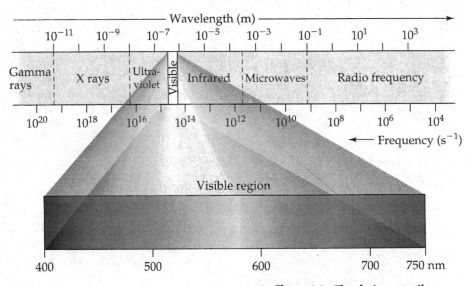

$$\nu\lambda = c \qquad [6.1]$$

where ν (nu) is the frequency, λ (lambda) is the wavelength, and c is the speed of light.

▲ **Figure 6.4 The electromagnetic spectrum.** Wavelengths in the spectrum range from very short gamma rays to very long radio waves. Notice that the color of visible light can be expressed quantitatively by wavelength.

Why do different forms of electromagnetic radiation have different properties? Their differences are due to their different wavelengths, which are expressed in units of length. Figure 6.4 ▲ shows the various types of electromagnetic radiation arranged in order of increasing wavelength, a display called the *electromagnetic spectrum*. Notice that the wavelengths span an enormous range. The wavelengths of gamma rays are similar to the diameters of atomic nuclei, whereas the wavelengths of radio waves can be longer than a football field. Notice also that visible light, which corresponds to wavelengths of about 400 to 700 nm (4×10^{-9} m to 7×10^{-9} m), is an extremely small portion of the electromagnetic spectrum. We can see visible light because of the chemical reactions it triggers in our eyes. The unit of length normally chosen to express wavelength depends on the type of radiation, as shown in Table 6.1 ▼.

ACTIVITY
Electromagnetic Spectrum

Frequency is expressed in cycles per second, a unit also called a *hertz* (Hz). Because it is understood that cycles are involved, the units of frequency are normally given simply as "per second," which is denoted by s^{-1} or /s. For example, a frequency of 820 kilohertz (kHz), a typical frequency for an AM radio station, could be written either as 820,000 s^{-1} or as 820,000/s.

TABLE 6.1	Common Wavelength Units for Electromagnetic Radiation		
Unit	Symbol	Length (m)	Type of Radiation
Angstrom	Å	10^{-10}	X ray
Nanometer	nm	10^{-9}	Ultraviolet, visible
Micrometer	μm	10^{-6}	Infrared
Millimeter	mm	10^{-3}	Infrared
Centimeter	cm	10^{-2}	Microwave
Meter	m	1	TV, radio

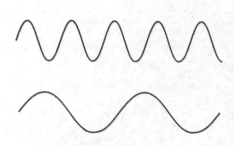

SAMPLE EXERCISE 6.1 | Concepts of Wavelength and Frequency

Two electromagnetic waves are represented in the margin. **(a)** Which wave has the higher frequency? **(b)** If one wave represents visible light and the other represents infrared radiation, which wave is which?

Solution (a) The lower wave has a longer wavelength (greater distance between peaks). The longer the wavelength, the lower the frequency ($\nu = c/\lambda$). Thus, the lower wave has the lower frequency, and the upper one has the higher frequency.

    (b) The electromagnetic spectrum (Figure 6.4) indicates that infrared radiation has a longer wavelength than visible light. Thus, the lower wave would be the infrared radiation.

PRACTICE EXERCISE

If one of the waves in the margin represents blue light and the other red light, which is which?

Answer: The expanded visible-light portion of Figure 6.4 tells you that red light has a longer wavelength than blue light. The lower wave has the longer wavelength (lower frequency) and would be the red light.

SAMPLE EXERCISE 6.2 | Calculating Frequency from Wavelength

The yellow light given off by a sodium vapor lamp used for public lighting has a wavelength of 589 nm. What is the frequency of this radiation?

Solution

Analyze: We are given the wavelength, λ, of the radiation and asked to calculate its frequency, ν.

Plan: The relationship between the wavelength (which is given) and the frequency (which is the unknown) is given by Equation 6.1. We can solve this equation for ν and then use the values of λ and c to obtain a numerical answer. (The speed of light, c, is a fundamental constant whose value is given in the text or in the table of fundamental constants on the back inside cover.)

Solve: Solving Equation 6.1 for frequency gives $\nu = c/\lambda$. When we insert the values for c and λ, we note that the units of length in these two quantities are different. We can convert the wavelength from nanometers to meters, so the units cancel:

$$\nu = \frac{c}{\lambda} = \left(\frac{3.00 \times 10^{8}\,\text{m/s}}{589\,\text{nm}} \right)\left(\frac{1\,\text{nm}}{10^{-9}\,\text{m}} \right) = 5.09 \times 10^{14}\,\text{s}^{-1}$$

Check: The high frequency is reasonable because of the short wavelength. The units are proper because frequency has units of "per second," or s^{-1}.

PRACTICE EXERCISE

(a) A laser used in eye surgery to fuse detached retinas produces radiation with a wavelength of 640.0 nm. Calculate the frequency of this radiation. **(b)** An FM radio station broadcasts electromagnetic radiation at a frequency of 103.4 MHz (megahertz; MHz = $10^{6}\,s^{-1}$). Calculate the wavelength of this radiation.

Answers: **(a)** $4.688 \times 10^{14}\,s^{-1}$, **(b)** 2.901 m

 GIVE IT SOME THOUGHT

Human skin is not penetrated by visible light but is penetrated by X rays. Which travels faster, visible light or X rays?

6.2 | Quantized Energy and Photons

Although the wave model of light explains many aspects of its behavior, there are several phenomena this model can't explain. Three of these are particularly pertinent to our understanding of how electromagnetic radiation and atoms interact: (1) the emission of light from hot objects (referred to as *blackbody radiation* because the objects studied appear black before heating), (2) the emission of electrons from metal surfaces on which light shines (the *photoelectric effect*), and (3) the emission of light from electronically excited gas atoms (*emission spectra*). We examine the first two here and the third in Section 6.3.

Hot Objects and the Quantization of Energy

When solids are heated, they emit radiation, as seen in the red glow of an electric stove burner and the bright white light of a tungsten lightbulb. The wavelength distribution of the radiation depends on temperature, a red-hot object being cooler than a white-hot one (Figure 6.5 ▶). In the late 1800s a number of physicists were studying this phenomenon, trying to understand the relationship between the temperature and the intensity and wavelengths of the emitted radiation. The prevailing laws of physics could not account for the observations.

In 1900 a German physicist named Max Planck (1858–1947) solved the problem by making a daring assumption: He assumed that energy can be either released or absorbed by atoms only in discrete "chunks" of some minimum size. Planck gave the name **quantum** (meaning "fixed amount") to the smallest quantity of energy that can be emitted or absorbed as electromagnetic radiation. He proposed that the energy, E, of a single quantum equals a constant times the frequency of the radiation:

$$E = h\nu \qquad [6.2]$$

The constant h is called **Planck's constant** and has a value of 6.626×10^{-34} joule-seconds (J-s). According to Planck's theory, matter is allowed to emit and absorb energy only in whole-number multiples of $h\nu$, such as $h\nu$, $2h\nu$, $3h\nu$, and so forth. If the quantity of energy emitted by an atom is $3h\nu$, for example, we say that three quanta of energy have been emitted (quanta being the plural of quantum). Because the energy can be released only in specific amounts, we say that the allowed energies are *quantized*—their values are restricted to certain quantities. Planck's revolutionary proposal that energy is quantized was proved correct, and he was awarded the 1918 Nobel Prize in Physics for his work on the quantum theory.

If the notion of quantized energies seems strange, it might be helpful to draw an analogy by comparing a ramp and a staircase (Figure 6.6 ▼). As you walk up a ramp, your potential energy increases in a uniform, continuous manner. When you climb a staircase, you can step only *on* individual stairs, not *between* them, so that your potential energy is restricted to certain values and is therefore quantized.

If Planck's quantum theory is correct, why aren't its effects more obvious in our daily lives? Why do energy changes seem continuous rather than quantized, or "jagged"? Notice that Planck's constant is an extremely small number. Thus, a quantum of energy, $h\nu$, is an extremely small amount. Planck's rules regarding the gain or loss of energy are always the same, whether we are concerned with objects on the size scale of our ordinary experience or with microscopic objects. With everyday macroscopic objects, however, the gain or loss of a single quantum of energy goes completely unnoticed. In contrast, when dealing with matter at the atomic level, the impact of quantized energies is far more significant.

▲ **Figure 6.5 Color as a function of temperature.** The color and intensity of the light emitted by a hot object depend on the temperature of the object. The temperature is highest at the center of this pour of molten steel. As a result, the light emitted from the center is most intense and of shortest wavelength.

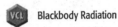

Blackbody Radiation

▲ **Figure 6.6 A model for quantized energy.** The potential energy of a person walking up a ramp (a) increases in a uniform, continuous manner, whereas that of a person walking up steps (b) increases in a stepwise, quantized manner.

Science Fundamentals Second Edition

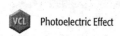

> **GIVE IT SOME THOUGHT**
>
> The temperature of stars is gauged by their colors. For example, red stars have a lower temperature than blue-white stars. How is this temperature scale consistent with Planck's assumption?

The Photoelectric Effect and Photons

A few years after Planck presented his theory, scientists began to see its applicability to a great many experimental observations. It soon became apparent that Planck's theory had within it the seeds of a revolution in the way the physical world is viewed. In 1905, Albert Einstein (1879–1955) used Planck's quantum theory to explain the **photoelectric effect**, which is illustrated in Figure 6.7 ▼. Experiments had shown that light shining on a clean metal surface causes the surface to emit electrons. For each metal, there is a minimum frequency of light below which no electrons are emitted. For example, light with a frequency of $4.60 \times 10^{14}\ \text{s}^{-1}$ or greater will cause cesium metal to emit electrons, but light of lower frequency has no effect.

To explain the photoelectric effect, Einstein assumed that the radiant energy striking the metal surface is behaving not like a wave but rather as if it were a stream of tiny energy packets. Each energy packet, called a **photon**, behaves like a tiny particle. Extending Planck's quantum theory, Einstein deduced that each photon must have an energy equal to Planck's constant times the frequency of the light:

$$\text{Energy of photon} = E = h\nu \qquad [6.3]$$

Thus, radiant energy itself is quantized.

Under the right conditions, a photon can strike a metal surface and be absorbed. When this happens, the photon can transfer its energy to an electron in the metal. A certain amount of energy—called the *work function*—is required for an electron to overcome the attractive forces that hold it in the metal. If the photons of the radiation impinging on the metal have less energy than the work function, electrons do not acquire sufficient energy to escape from the metal surface, even if the light beam is intense. If the photons of radiation have sufficient energy, electrons are emitted from the metal. If the photons have more than the minimum energy required to free electrons, the excess energy appears as the kinetic energy of the emitted electrons.

To better understand what a photon is, imagine that you have a light source that produces radiation with a single wavelength. Further suppose that you could switch the light on and off faster and faster to provide ever-smaller bursts of energy. Einstein's photon theory tells us that you would eventually come to a smallest energy burst, given by $E = h\nu$. This smallest burst of energy consists of a single photon of light.

▼ **Figure 6.7 The photoelectric effect.** When photons of sufficiently high energy strike a metal surface, electrons are emitted from the metal, as in (a). The photoelectric effect is the basis of the photocell shown in (b). The emitted electrons are drawn toward the positive terminal. As a result, current flows in the circuit. Photocells are used in photographic light meters as well as in numerous other electronic devices.

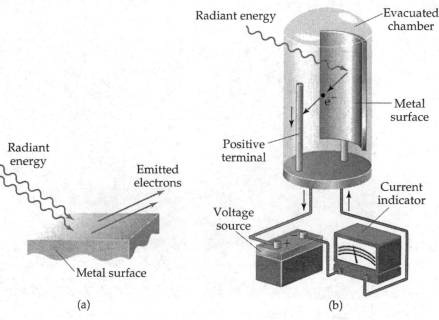

◼ SAMPLE EXERCISE 6.3 | Energy of a Photon

Calculate the energy of one photon of yellow light whose wavelength is 589 nm.

Solution

Analyze: Our task is to calculate the energy, E, of a photon, given $\lambda = 589$ nm.

Plan: We can use Equation 6.1 to convert the wavelength to frequency:

$$\nu = c/\lambda$$

We can then use Equation 6.3 to calculate energy:

$$E = h\nu$$

Solve: The frequency, ν, is calculated from the given wavelength, as shown in Sample Exercise 6.2:

$$\nu = c/\lambda = 5.09 \times 10^{14}\ \text{s}^{-1}$$

The value of Planck's constant, h, is given both in the text and in the table of physical constants on the inside front cover of the text, and so we can easily calculate E:

$$E = (6.626 \times 10^{-34}\ \text{J-s})(5.09 \times 10^{14}\ \text{s}^{-1}) = 3.37 \times 10^{-19}\ \text{J}$$

Comment: If one photon of radiant energy supplies 3.37×10^{-19} J, then one mole of these photons will supply

$$(6.02 \times 10^{23}\ \text{photons/mol})(3.37 \times 10^{-19}\ \text{J/photon}) = 2.03 \times 10^5\ \text{J/mol}$$

This is the magnitude of enthalpies of reactions (Section 5.4), so radiation can break chemical bonds, producing what are called *photochemical reactions.*

◼ PRACTICE EXERCISE

(a) A laser emits light with a frequency of $4.69 \times 10^{14}\ \text{s}^{-1}$. What is the energy of one photon of the radiation from this laser? (b) If the laser emits a pulse of energy containing 5.0×10^{17} photons of this radiation, what is the total energy of that pulse? (c) If the laser emits 1.3×10^{-2} J of energy during a pulse, how many photons are emitted during the pulse?
Answers: (a) 3.11×10^{-19} J, (b) 0.16 J, (c) 4.2×10^{16} photons

The idea that the energy of light depends on its frequency helps us understand the diverse effects that different kinds of electromagnetic radiation have on matter. For example, the high frequency (short wavelength) of X rays (Figure 6.4) causes X-ray photons to have high energy, sufficient to cause tissue damage and even cancer. Thus, signs are normally posted around X-ray equipment warning us of high-energy radiation.

Although Einstein's theory of light as a stream of particles rather than a wave explains the photoelectric effect and a great many other observations, it does pose a dilemma. Is light a wave, or does it consist of particles? The only way to resolve this dilemma is to adopt what might seem to be a bizarre position: We must consider that light possesses both wavelike and particle-like characteristics and, depending on the situation, will behave more like a wave or more like particles. We will soon see that this dual nature is also characteristic of matter.

♀ GIVE IT SOME THOUGHT

Suppose that yellow visible light can be used to eject electrons from a certain metal surface. What would happen if ultraviolet light were used instead?

▲ **Figure 6.8 Quantum giants.** Niels Bohr (right) with Albert Einstein. Bohr (1885–1962) made major contributions to the quantum theory. From 1911 to 1913 Bohr studied in England, working first with J. J. Thomson at Cambridge University and then with Ernest Rutherford at the University of Manchester. He published his quantum theory of the atom in 1914 and was awarded the Nobel Prize in Physics in 1922.

▲ **Figure 6.9 Monochromatic radiation.** Lasers produce light of one wavelenght, which we call *monocromatic light*. Different lasers produce light of different wavelenght. The photo shows beams from a variety of lasers that produce visible light of different colors. Other lasers produce light that is not visible, including infrared and ultraviolet light.

▶ **Figure 6.10 Creating a spectrum.** A continuous visible spectrum is produced when a narrow beam of white light is passed through a prism. The white light could be sunlight or light from an incandescent lamp.

6.3 | Line Spectra and the Bohr Model

The work of Planck and Einstein paved the way for understanding how electrons are arranged in atoms. In 1913 the Danish physicist Niels Bohr (Figure 6.8 ◀) offered a theoretical explanation of *line spectra*, another phenomenon that had puzzled scientists in the nineteenth century. Let's first examine this phenomenon and then consider how Bohr used the ideas of Planck and Einstein.

Line Spectra

A particular source of radiant energy may emit a single wavelength, as in the light from a laser (Figure 6.9 ◀). Radiation composed of a single wavelength is said to be *monochromatic*. However, most common radiation sources, including lightbulbs and stars, produce radiation containing many different wavelengths. When radiation from such sources is separated into its different wavelength components, a **spectrum** is produced. Figure 6.10 ▼ shows how a prism spreads light from a lightbulb into its component wavelengths. The spectrum so produced consists of a continuous range of colors: Violet merges into blue, blue into green, and so forth, with no blank spots. This rainbow of colors, containing light of all wavelengths, is called a **continuous spectrum**. The most familiar example of a continuous spectrum is the rainbow produced when raindrops or mist acts as a prism for sunlight.

Not all radiation sources produce a continuous spectrum. When different gases are placed under reduced pressure in a tube and a high voltage is applied, the gases emit different colors of light (Figure 6.11 ▶). The light emitted by neon gas is the familiar red-orange glow of many "neon" lights, whereas sodium vapor emits the yellow light characteristic of some modern streetlights. When light coming from such tubes is passed through a prism, only a few wavelengths are present in the resultant spectra, as shown in Figure 6.12 ▶. Each wavelength is represented by a colored line in one of these spectra. The

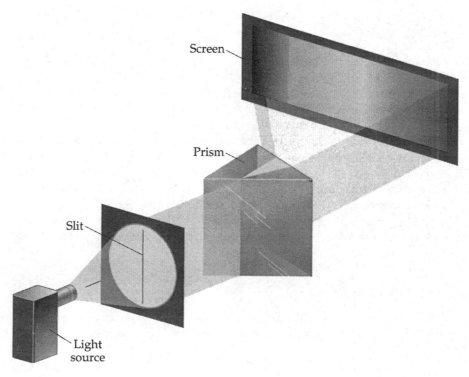

Screen

Prism

Slit

Light source

colored lines are separated by black regions, which correspond to wavelengths that are absent from the light. A spectrum containing radiation of only specific wavelengths is called a **line spectrum**.

When scientists first detected the line spectrum of hydrogen in the mid-1800s, they were fascinated by its simplicity. At that time, only the four lines in the visible portion of the spectrum were observed, as shown in Figure 6.12. In 1885 a Swiss schoolteacher named Johann Balmer showed that the wavelengths of these four visible lines of hydrogen fit an intriguingly simple formula. Later, additional lines were found to occur in the ultraviolet and infrared regions of the hydrogen spectrum. Soon Balmer's equation was extended to a more general one, called the *Rydberg equation*, which allowed the calculation of the wavelengths of all the spectral lines of hydrogen:

$$\frac{1}{\lambda} = (R_H)\left(\frac{1}{n_1^2} - \frac{1}{n_2^2}\right) \qquad [6.4]$$

In this formula λ is the wavelength of a spectral line, R_H is the *Rydberg constant* (1.096776×10^7 m^{-1}), and n_1 and n_2 are positive integers, with n_2 being larger than n_1. How could the remarkable simplicity of this equation be explained? It took nearly 30 more years to answer this question.

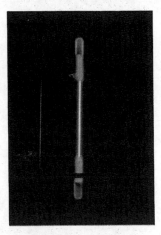

▲ **Figure 6.11 Atomic emission.** Different gases emit light of different characteristic colors upon excitation by an electrical discharge: (a) hydrogen, (b) neon.

 Atomic Emission Spectra

 The Rydberg Equation

 MOVIE Flame Tests for Metals

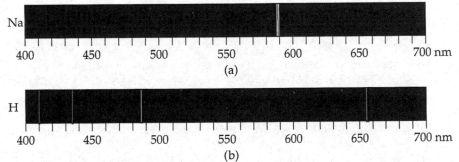

(a)

(b)

◄ **Figure 6.12 Line spectra.** Spectra obtained from the electrical discharge from (a) Na, (b) H. Light of only a few specific wavelenghts are produced, as shown by colored lines in the spectra.

Bohr's Model

After Rutherford discovered the nuclear nature of the atom (Section 2.2), scientists thought of the atom as a "microscopic solar system" in which electrons orbited the nucleus. To explain the line spectrum of hydrogen, Bohr started by assuming that electrons move in circular orbits around the nucleus. According to classical physics, however, an electrically charged particle (such as an electron) that moves in a circular path should continuously lose energy by emitting electromagnetic radiation. As the electron loses energy, it should spiral into the nucleus. This spiraling obviously does not happen since hydrogen atoms are stable, and so what could explain how these atoms seem to violate the laws of physics? Bohr approached this problem in much the same way that Planck had approached the problem of the nature of the radiation emitted by hot objects: He assumed that the prevailing laws of physics were inadequate to describe all aspects of atoms. Furthermore, he adopted Planck's idea that energies are quantized.

Bohr based his model on three postulates:

1. Only orbits of certain radii, corresponding to certain definite energies, are permitted for the electron in a hydrogen atom.
2. An electron in a permitted orbit has a specific energy and is in an "allowed" energy state. An electron in an allowed energy state will not radiate energy and therefore will not spiral into the nucleus.
3. Energy is emitted or absorbed by the electron only as the electron changes from one allowed energy state to another. This energy is emitted or absorbed as a photon, $E = h\nu$.

 GIVE IT SOME THOUGHT

Before reading further about the details of Bohr's model, speculate as to how they explain the fact that hydrogen gas emits a line spectrum (Figure 6.12) rather than a continuous spectrum.

The Energy States of the Hydrogen Atom

Starting with his three postulates and using classical equations for motion and for interacting electrical charges, Bohr calculated the energies corresponding to each allowed orbit for the electron in the hydrogen atom. These energies fit the formula

$$E = (-hcR_H)\left(\frac{1}{n^2}\right) = (-2.18 \times 10^{-18} \text{ J})\left(\frac{1}{n^2}\right) \qquad [6.5]$$

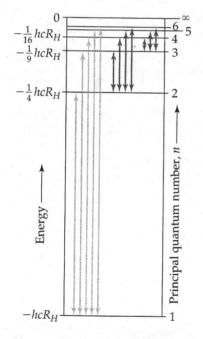

▲ **Figure 6.13 Energy levels in the hydrogen atom from the Bohr model.** The arrows refer to the transitions of the electron from one allowed energy state to another. The states shown are those for which $n = 1$ through $n = 6$ and the state for $n = \infty$, for which the energy, E, equals zero.

In this equation, h, c, and R_H are Planck's constant, the speed of light, and the Rydberg constant, respectively. The product of these three constants equals 2.18×10^{-18} J. The integer n, which can have values from 1 to infinity, is called the *principal quantum number*. Each orbit corresponds to a different value of n, and the radius of the orbit gets larger as n increases. Thus, the first allowed orbit (the one closest to the nucleus) has $n = 1$, the next allowed orbit (the one second closest to the nucleus) has $n = 2$, and so forth. The electron in the hydrogen atom can be in any allowed orbit, and Equation 6.5 tells us the energy that the electron will have, depending on which orbit it is in.

The energies of the electron of a hydrogen atom given by Equation 6.5 are negative for all values of n. The lower (more negative) the energy is, the more stable the atom will be. The energy is lowest (most negative) for $n = 1$. As n gets larger, the energy becomes successively less negative and therefore increases. We can liken the situation to a ladder in which the rungs are numbered from the bottom rung on up. The higher one climbs the ladder (the greater the value of n), the higher the energy. The lowest energy state ($n = 1$, analogous to the bottom rung) is called the **ground state** of the atom. When the electron is in a higher energy (less negative) orbit—$n = 2$ or higher—the atom is said to be in an **excited state**. Figure 6.13 ◀ shows the energy of the electron in a hydrogen atom for several values of n.

What happens to the orbit radius and the energy as n becomes infinitely large? The radius increases as n^2, so we reach a point at which the electron is completely separated from the nucleus. When $n = \infty$, the energy is zero:

$$E = (-2.18 \times 10^{-18} \text{ J})\left(\frac{1}{\infty^2}\right) = 0$$

Thus, the state in which the electron is removed from the nucleus is the reference, or zero-energy, state of the hydrogen atom. This zero-energy state is *higher* in energy than the states with negative energies.

In his third postulate, Bohr assumed that the electron could "jump" from one allowed energy state to another by either absorbing or emitting photons whose radiant energy corresponds exactly to the energy difference between the two states. Energy must be absorbed for an electron to move to a higher energy state (one with a higher value of n). Conversely, radiant energy is emitted when the electron jumps to a lower energy state (one with a lower value of n). Thus, if the electron jumps from an initial state that has energy E_i to a final state of energy E_f, the change in energy is

$$\Delta E = E_f - E_i = E_{photon} = h\nu \qquad [6.6]$$

Bohr's model of the hydrogen atom states, therefore, that only the specific frequencies of light that satisfy Equation 6.6 can be absorbed or emitted by the atom.

Substituting the energy expression in Equation 6.5 into Equation 6.6 and recalling that $\nu = c/\lambda$, we have

$$\Delta E = h\nu = \frac{hc}{\lambda} = (-2.18 \times 10^{-18}\ \mathrm{J})\left(\frac{1}{n_f^2} - \frac{1}{n_i^2}\right) \qquad [6.7]$$

In this equation n_i and n_f are the principal quantum numbers of the initial and final states of the atom, respectively. If n_f is smaller than n_i, the electron moves closer to the nucleus and ΔE is a negative number, indicating that the atom releases energy. For example, if the electron moves from $n_i = 3$ to $n_f = 1$, we have

$$\Delta E = (-2.18 \times 10^{-18}\ \mathrm{J})\left(\frac{1}{1^2} - \frac{1}{3^2}\right) = (-2.18 \times 10^{-18}\ \mathrm{J})\left(\frac{8}{9}\right) = -1.94 \times 10^{-18}\ \mathrm{J}$$

Knowing the energy for the emitted photon, we can calculate either its frequency or its wavelength. For the wavelength, we have

$$\lambda = \frac{c}{\nu} = \frac{hc}{\Delta E} = \frac{(6.63 \times 10^{-34}\ \mathrm{J\text{-}s})(3.00 \times 10^8\ \mathrm{m/s})}{1.94 \times 10^{-18}\ \mathrm{J}} = 1.03 \times 10^{-7}\ \mathrm{m}$$

We have not included the negative sign of the energy in this calculation because wavelength and frequency are always reported as positive quantities. The direction of energy flow is indicated by saying that a photon of wavelength 1.03×10^{-7} has been *emitted*.

If we solve Equation 6.7 for $1/\lambda$, we find that this equation derived from Bohr's theory corresponds to the Rydberg equation, Equation 6.4, which was obtained using experimental data:

$$\frac{1}{\lambda} = \frac{-hcR_H}{hc}\left(\frac{1}{n_f^2} - \frac{1}{n_i^2}\right) = R_H\left(\frac{1}{n_i^2} - \frac{1}{n_f^2}\right)$$

Thus, the existence of discrete spectral lines can be attributed to the quantized jumps of electrons between energy levels.

 GIVE IT SOME THOUGHT

As the electron in a hydrogen atom jumps from the $n = 3$ orbit to the $n = 7$ orbit, does it absorb energy or emit energy?

> ### ▇ SAMPLE EXERCISE 6.4 | Electronic Transitions in the Hydrogen Atom
>
> Using Figure 6.13, predict which of the following electronic transitions produces the spectral line having the longest wavelength: $n = 2$ to $n = 1$, $n = 3$ to $n = 2$, or $n = 4$ to $n = 3$.
>
> **Solution** The wavelength increases as frequency decreases ($\lambda = c/\nu$). Hence the longest wavelength will be associated with the lowest frequency. According to Planck's equation, $E = h\nu$, the lowest frequency is associated with the lowest energy. In Figure 6.13 the shortest vertical line represents the smallest energy change. Thus, the $n = 4$ to $n = 3$ transition produces the longest wavelength (lowest frequency) line.
>
> ### ▇ PRACTICE EXERCISE
>
> Indicate whether each of the following electronic transitions emits energy or requires the absorption of energy: **(a)** $n = 3$ to $n = 1$; **(b)** $n = 2$ to $n = 4$.
> *Answers:* **(a)** emits energy, **(b)** requires absorption of energy

Limitations of the Bohr Model

While the Bohr model offers an explanation for the line spectrum of the hydrogen atom, it cannot explain the spectra of other atoms, except in a rather crude way. Furthermore, there is a problem with describing an electron merely as a small particle circling about the nucleus. As we will see in Section 6.4, the electron exhibits wavelike properties, a fact that any acceptable model of electronic structure must accommodate. As it turns out, the Bohr model was only an important step along the way toward the development of a more comprehensive model. What is most significant about Bohr's model is that it introduces two important ideas that are also incorporated into our current model: (1) Electrons exist only in certain discrete energy levels, which are described by quantum numbers, and (2) energy is involved in moving an electron from one level to another. We will now start to develop the successor to the Bohr model, which requires that we take a closer look at the behavior of matter.

6.4 | The Wave Behavior of Matter

In the years following the development of Bohr's model for the hydrogen atom, the dual nature of radiant energy became a familiar concept. Depending on the experimental circumstances, radiation appears to have either a wavelike or a particle-like (photon) character. Louis de Broglie (1892–1987), who was working on his Ph.D. thesis in physics at the Sorbonne in Paris, boldly extended this idea. If radiant energy could, under appropriate conditions, behave as though it were a stream of particles, could matter, under appropriate conditions, possibly show the properties of a wave? Suppose that the electron orbiting the nucleus of a hydrogen atom could be thought of not as a particle but rather as a wave, with a characteristic wavelength. De Broglie suggested that, in its movement about the nucleus, the electron has associated with it a particular wavelength. He went on to propose that the characteristic wavelength of the electron or of any other particle depends on its mass, m, and on its velocity, v:

$$\lambda = \frac{h}{mv} \qquad [6.8]$$

(h is Planck's constant.) The quantity mv for any object is called its **momentum**. De Broglie used the term **matter waves** to describe the wave characteristics of material particles.

Because de Broglie's hypothesis is applicable to all matter, any object of mass m and velocity v would give rise to a characteristic matter wave. However, Equation 6.8 indicates that the wavelength associated with an object of ordinary size, such as a golf ball, is so tiny as to be completely out of the range of any possible observation. This is not so for an electron because its mass is so small, as we see in Sample Exercise 6.5.

SAMPLE EXERCISE 6.5 | Matter Waves

What is the wavelength of an electron moving with a speed of 5.97×10^6 m/s? (The mass of the electron is 9.11×10^{-28} g.)

Solution

Analyze: We are given the mass, m, and velocity, v, of the electron, and we must calculate its de Broglie wavelength, λ.

Plan: The wavelength of a moving particle is given by Equation 6.8, so λ is calculated by inserting the known quantities h, m, and v. In doing so, however, we must pay attention to units.

Solve: Using the value of Planck's constant,

$$h = 6.63 \times 10^{-34} \text{ J-s}$$

and recalling that

$$1\,\text{J} = 1 \text{ kg-m}^2/\text{s}^2$$

we have the following:

$$\lambda = \frac{h}{mv}$$

$$= \frac{(6.63 \times 10^{-34} \text{ J-s})}{(9.11 \times 10^{-28} \text{ g})(5.97 \times 10^6 \text{ m/s})} \left(\frac{1 \text{ kg-m}^2/\text{s}^2}{1 \text{ J}} \right) \left(\frac{10^3 \text{ g}}{1 \text{ kg}} \right)$$

$$= 1.22 \times 10^{-10} \text{ m} = 0.122 \text{ nm}$$

Comment: By comparing this value with the wavelengths of electromagnetic radiation shown in Figure 6.4, we see that the wavelength of this electron is about the same as that of X rays.

PRACTICE EXERCISE

Calculate the velocity of a neutron whose de Broglie wavelength is 500 pm. The mass of a neutron is given in the table on the back inside cover of the text.

Answer: 7.92×10^2 m/s

Within a few years after de Broglie published his theory, the wave properties of the electron were demonstrated experimentally. Electrons passed through a crystal were diffracted by the crystal, just as X rays are diffracted. Thus, a stream of moving electrons exhibits the same kinds of wave behavior as electromagnetic radiation.

The technique of electron diffraction has been highly developed. In the electron microscope, for instance, the wave characteristics of electrons are used to obtain pictures of tiny objects. This microscope is an important tool for studying surface phenomena at very high magnifications. Figure 6.14 ▶ is a photograph of an electron microscope image, which demonstrates that tiny particles of matter can behave as waves.

 GIVE IT SOME THOUGHT

A baseball pitcher throws a fastball that moves at 95 miles per hour. Does that moving baseball generate matter waves? If so, can we observe them?

The Uncertainty Principle

The discovery of the wave properties of matter raised some new and interesting questions about classical physics. Consider, for example, a ball rolling down a ramp. Using the equations of classical physics, we can calculate its position, direction of motion, and speed at any time, with great accuracy. Can we do the same for an electron, which exhibits wave properties? A wave extends in space, and therefore its location is not precisely defined. We might therefore anticipate that it is impossible to determine exactly where an electron is located at a specific time.

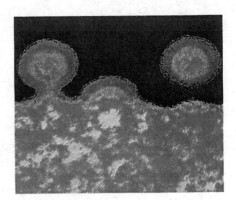

▲ **Figure 6.14 Electrons as waves.** Color-enhanced electron microscope image of human immunodeficiency viruses (HIV) budding from an infected T-lymphocyte human blood cell. In an electron microscope the wave behavior of a stream of electrons is utilized in analogy to the way that a conventional microscope uses the wave behavior of a beam of light.

 Heisenberg Uncertainty Principle

▲ Figure 6.15   Werner Heisenberg (1901–1976). During his postdoctoral assistantship with Niels Bohr, Heisenberg formulated his famous uncertainty principle. At the age of 25, he became the chair in theoretical physics at the University of Leipzig. At 32 he was one of the youngest scientists to receive the Nobel Prize.

The German physicist Werner Heisenberg (Figure 6.15 ◄) proposed that the dual nature of matter places a fundamental limitation on how precisely we can know both the location and the momentum of any object. The limitation becomes important only when we deal with matter at the subatomic level (that is, with masses as small as that of an electron). Heisenberg's principle is called the **uncertainty principle**. When applied to the electrons in an atom, this principle states that it is inherently impossible for us to know simultaneously both the exact momentum of the electron and its exact location in space.

Heisenberg mathematically related the uncertainty of the position (Δx) and the uncertainty in momentum $\Delta(mv)$ to a quantity involving Planck's constant:

$$\Delta x \cdot \Delta(mv) \geq \frac{h}{4\pi} \tag{6.9}$$

A brief calculation illustrates the dramatic implications of the uncertainty principle. The electron has a mass of 9.11×10^{-31} kg and moves at an average speed of about 5×10^6 m/s in a hydrogen atom. Let's assume that we know the speed to an uncertainty of 1% [that is, an uncertainty of $(0.01)(5 \times 10^6 \text{ m/s}) = 5 \times 10^4$ m/s] and that this is the only important source of uncertainty in the momentum, so that $\Delta(mv) = m\Delta v$. We can then use Equation 6.9 to calculate the uncertainty in the position of the electron:

$$\Delta x \geq \frac{h}{4\pi m \Delta v} = \frac{(6.63 \times 10^{-34} \text{ J-s})}{4\pi(9.11 \times 10^{-31} \text{ kg})(5 \times 10^4 \text{ m/s})} = 1 \times 10^{-9} \text{ m}$$

Because the diameter of a hydrogen atom is only about 1×10^{-10} m, the uncertainty is an order of magnitude greater than the size of the atom. Thus, we have essentially no idea of where the electron is located within the atom. On the other hand, if we were to repeat the calculation with an object of ordinary mass

---

▲ A CLOSER LOOK | Measurement and the Uncertainty Principle

Whenever any measurement is made, some uncertainty exists. Our experience with objects of ordinary dimensions, like balls or trains or laboratory equipment, indicates that the uncertainty of a measurement can be decreased by using more precise instruments. In fact, we might expect that the uncertainty in a measurement can be made indefinitely small. However, the uncertainty principle states that there is an actual limit to the accuracy of measurements. This limit is not a restriction on how well instruments can be made; rather, it is inherent in nature. This limit has no practical consequences when dealing with ordinary-sized objects, but its implications are enormous when dealing with subatomic particles, such as electrons.

To measure an object, we must disturb it, at least a little, with our measuring device. Imagine using a flashlight to locate a large rubber ball in a dark room. You see the ball when the light from the flashlight bounces off the ball and strikes your eyes. When a beam of photons strikes an object of this size, it does not alter its position or momentum to any practical extent. Imagine, however, that you wish to locate an electron by similarly bouncing light off it into some detector. Objects can be located to an accuracy no greater than the wavelength of the radiation used. Thus, if we want an accurate position measurement for an electron, we must

use a short wavelength. This means that photons of high energy must be employed. The more energy the photons have, the more momentum they impart to the electron when they strike it, which changes the electron's motion in an unpredictable way. The attempt to measure accurately the electron's position introduces considerable uncertainty in its momentum; the act of measuring the electron's position at one moment makes our knowledge of its future position inaccurate.

Suppose, then, that we use photons of longer wavelength. Because these photons have lower energy, the momentum of the electron is not so appreciably changed during measurement, but its position will be correspondingly less accurately known. This is the essence of the uncertainty principle: *There is an uncertainty in simultaneously knowing either the position or the momentum of the electron that cannot be reduced beyond a certain minimum level.* The more accurately one is known, the less accurately the other is known. Although we can never know the exact position and momentum of the electron, we can talk about the probability of its being at certain locations in space. In Section 6.5 we introduce a model of the atom that provides the probability of finding electrons of specific energies at certain positions in atoms.
Related Exercises: 6.45 and 6.46

---

such as a tennis ball, the uncertainty would be so small that it would be inconsequential. In that case, m is large and Δx is out of the realm of measurement and therefore of no practical consequence.

De Broglie's hypothesis and Heisenberg's uncertainty principle set the stage for a new and more broadly applicable theory of atomic structure. In this new approach, any attempt to define precisely the instantaneous location and momentum of the electron is abandoned. The wave nature of the electron is recognized, and its behavior is described in terms appropriate to waves. The result is a model that precisely describes the energy of the electron while describing its location not precisely, but in terms of probabilities.

 GIVE IT SOME THOUGHT

What is the principal reason that the uncertainty principle seems very important when discussing electrons and other subatomic particles, but seems rather unimportant in our macroscopic world?

6.5 | Quantum Mechanics and Atomic Orbitals

In 1926 the Austrian physicist Erwin Schrödinger (1887–1961) proposed an equation, now known as Schrödinger's wave equation, that incorporates both the wavelike behavior and the particle-like behavior of the electron. His work opened a new way of dealing with subatomic particles, known as either *quantum mechanics* or *wave mechanics*. The application of Schrödinger's equation requires advanced calculus, and we will not be concerned with the details of his approach. We will, however, qualitatively consider the results he obtained, because they give us a powerful new way to view electronic structure. Let's begin by examining the electronic structure of the simplest atom, hydrogen.

Solving Schrödinger's equation leads to a series of mathematical functions called **wave functions** that describe the electron. These wave functions are usually represented by the symbol ψ (the Greek lowercase letter *psi*). Although the wave function itself has no direct physical meaning, the square of the wave function, ψ^2, provides information about an electron's location when the electron is in an allowed energy state.

For the hydrogen atom, the allowed energies are the same as those predicted by the Bohr model. However, the Bohr model assumes that the electron is in a circular orbit of some particular radius about the nucleus. In the quantum mechanical model, the electron's location cannot be described so simply. According to the uncertainty principle, if we know the momentum of the electron with high accuracy, our simultaneous knowledge of its location is very uncertain. Thus, we cannot hope to specify the exact location of an individual electron around the nucleus. Rather, we must be content with a kind of statistical knowledge. In the quantum mechanical model, we therefore speak of the *probability* that the electron will be in a certain region of space at a given instant. As it turns out, the square of the wave function, ψ^2, at a given point in space represents the probability that the electron will be found at that location. For this reason, ψ^2 is called either the **probability density** or the **electron density**.

One way of representing the probability of finding the electron in various regions of an atom is shown in Figure 6.16 ▶. In this figure the density of the dots represents the probability of finding the electron. The regions with a high density of dots correspond to relatively large values for ψ^2 and are therefore regions where there is a high probability of finding the electron. In Section 6.6 we will say more about the ways in which we can represent electron density.

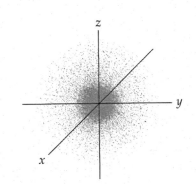

▲ **Figure 6.16 Electron-density distribution.** This rendering represents the probability of where in the space surrounding the nucleus the electron is to be found in a hydrogen atom in its ground state.

Orbitals and Quantum Numbers

The solution to Schrödinger's equation for the hydrogen atom yields a set of wave functions and corresponding energies. These wave functions are called **orbitals**. Each orbital describes a specific distribution of electron density in space, as given by the orbital's probability density. Each orbital therefore has a characteristic energy and shape. For example, the lowest-energy orbital in the hydrogen atom has an energy of -2.18×10^{-18} J and the shape illustrated in Figure 6.16. Note that an *orbital* (quantum mechanical model) is not the same as an *orbit* (Bohr model). The quantum mechanical model doesn't refer to orbits because the motion of the electron in an atom cannot be precisely measured or tracked (Heisenberg uncertainty principle).

The Bohr model introduced a single quantum number, n, to describe an orbit. The quantum mechanical model uses three quantum numbers, n, l, and m_l, to describe an orbital. Let's consider what information we obtain from each of these and how they are interrelated.

ACTIVITY
Quantum Numbers

1. The *principal quantum number*, n, can have positive integral values of 1, 2, 3, and so forth. As n increases, the orbital becomes larger, and the electron spends more time farther from the nucleus. An increase in n also means that the electron has a higher energy and is therefore less tightly bound to the nucleus. For the hydrogen atom, $E_n = -(2.18 \times 10^{-18} \text{ J})(1/n^2)$, as in the Bohr model.

2. The second quantum number—the *azimuthal quantum number*, l—can have integral values from 0 to $n - 1$ for each value of n. This quantum number defines the shape of the orbital. (We will consider these shapes in Section 6.6.) The value of l for a particular orbital is generally designated by the letters s, p, d, and f,* corresponding to l values of 0, 1, 2, and 3, respectively, as summarized here:

Value of l	0	1	2	3
Letter used	s	p	d	f

3. The *magnetic quantum number*, m_l, can have integral values between $-l$ and l, including zero. This quantum number describes the orientation of the orbital in space, as we will discuss in Section 6.6.

Notice that because the value of n can be any positive integer, there is an infinite number of orbitals for the hydrogen atom. The electron in a hydrogen atom is described by only one of these orbitals at any given time—we say that the electron *occupies* a certain orbital. The remaining orbitals are *unoccupied* for that particular state of the hydrogen atom. We will see that we are mainly interested in the orbitals of the hydrogen atom with small values of n.

---

* The letters s, p, d, and f come from the words sharp, principal, diffuse, and fundamental, which were used to describe certain features of spectra before quantum mechanics was developed.

TABLE 6.2 Relationship Among Values of n, l, and m_l Through $n = 4$

n	Possible Values of l	Subshell Designation	Possible Values of m_l	Number of Orbitals in Subshell	Total Number of Orbitals in Shell
1	0	1s	0	1	1
2	0	2s	0	1	
	1	2p	1, 0, −1	3	4
3	0	3s	0	1	
	1	3p	1, 0, −1	3	
	2	3d	2, 1, 0, −1, −2	5	9
4	0	4s	0	1	
	1	4p	1, 0, −1	3	
	2	4d	2, 1, 0, −1, −2	5	
	3	4f	3, 2, 1, 0, −1, −2, −3	7	16

The collection of orbitals with the same value of n is called an **electron shell**. For example, all the orbitals that have $n = 3$ are said to be in the third shell. Further, the set of orbitals that have the same n and l values is called a **subshell**. Each subshell is designated by a number (the value of n) and a letter (s, p, d, or f, corresponding to the value of l). For example, the orbitals that have $n = 3$ and $l = 2$ are called $3d$ orbitals and are in the $3d$ subshell.

Table 6.2 ▲ summarizes the possible values of the quantum numbers l and m_l for values of n through $n = 4$. The restrictions on the possible values of the quantum numbers give rise to the following very important observations:

1. The shell with principal quantum number n will consist of exactly n subshells. Each subshell corresponds to a different allowed value of l from 0 to $n − 1$. Thus, the first shell ($n = 1$) consists of only one subshell, the $1s$ ($l = 0$); the second shell ($n = 2$) consists of two subshells, the $2s$ ($l = 0$) and $2p$ ($l = 1$); the third shell consists of three subshells, $3s$, $3p$, and $3d$, and so forth.

2. Each subshell consists of a specific number of orbitals. Each orbital corresponds to a different allowed value of m_l. For a given value of l, there are $2l + 1$ allowed values of m_l, ranging from $−l$ to $+l$. Thus, each s ($l = 0$) subshell consists of one orbital; each p ($l = 1$) subshell consists of three orbitals; each d ($l = 2$) subshell consists of five orbitals, and so forth.

3. The total number of orbitals in a shell is n^2, where n is the principal quantum number of the shell. The resulting number of orbitals for the shells—1, 4, 9, 16—is related to a pattern seen in the periodic table: We see that the number of elements in the rows of the periodic table—2, 8, 18, and 32—equal twice these numbers. We will discuss this relationship further in Section 6.9.

Figure 6.17 ▶ shows the relative energies of the hydrogen atom orbitals through $n = 3$. Each box represents an orbital; orbitals of the same subshell, such as the $2p$, are grouped together. When the electron occupies the lowest-energy orbital ($1s$), the hydrogen atom is said to be in its *ground state*. When the electron occupies any other orbital, the atom is in an *excited state*. At ordinary temperatures, essentially all hydrogen atoms are in the ground state. The electron can be excited to a higher-energy orbital by absorption of a photon of appropriate energy.

GIVE IT SOME THOUGHT

In Figure 6.17, why is the energy difference between the $n = 1$ and $n = 2$ levels so much greater than the energy difference between the $n = 2$ and $n = 3$ levels?

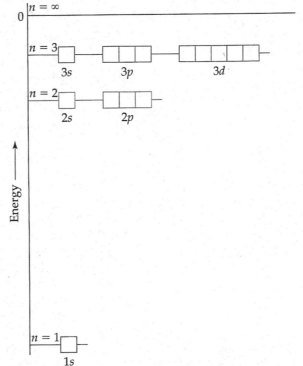

▼ **Figure 6.17 Orbital energy levels in the hydrogen atom.** Each box represents an orbital. Note that all orbitals with the same value for the principal quantum number, n, have the same energy. This is true only in one-electron systems, such as the hydrogen atom.

SAMPLE EXERCISE 6.6 | Subshells of the Hydrogen Atom

(a) Without referring to Table 6.2, predict the number of subshells in the fourth shell, that is, for $n = 4$. **(b)** Give the label for each of these subshells. **(c)** How many orbitals are in each of these subshells?

Analyze and Plan: We are given the value of the principal quantum number, n. We need to determine the allowed values of l and m_l for this given value of n and then count the number of orbitals in each subshell.

Solution (a) There are four subshells in the fourth shell, corresponding to the four possible values of l (0, 1, 2, and 3).

(b) These subshells are labeled $4s$, $4p$, $4d$, and $4f$. The number given in the designation of a subshell is the principal quantum number, n; the letter designates the value of the azimuthal quantum number, l: for $l = 0$, s; for $l = 1$, p; for $l = 2$, d; for $l = 3$, f.

(c) There is one $4s$ orbital (when $l = 0$, there is only one possible value of m_l: 0). There are three $4p$ orbitals (when $l = 1$, there are three possible values of m_l: 1, 0, and −1). There are five $4d$ orbitals (when $l = 2$, there are five allowed values of m_l: 2, 1, 0, −1, −2). There are seven $4f$ orbitals (when $l = 3$, there are seven permitted values of m_l: 3, 2, 1, 0, −1, −2, −3).

PRACTICE EXERCISE

(a) What is the designation for the subshell with $n = 5$ and $l = 1$? **(b)** How many orbitals are in this subshell? **(c)** Indicate the values of m_l for each of these orbitals.
Answers: **(a)** $5p$; **(b)** 3; **(c)** 1, 0, −1

6.6 | Representations of Orbitals

In our discussion of orbitals so far, we have emphasized their energies. But the wave function also provides information about the electron's location in space when it occupies an orbital. Let's examine the ways that we can picture the orbitals. In doing so, we will examine some important aspects of the electron-density distributions of the orbitals. First, we will look at the three-dimensional shape of the orbital—is it spherical, for example, or does it have directionality? Second, we will examine how the probability density changes as we move on a straight line farther and farther from the nucleus. Finally, we will look at the typical three-dimensional sketches that chemists use in describing the orbitals.

The *s* Orbitals

One representation of the lowest-energy orbital of the hydrogen atom, the $1s$, is shown in Figure 6.16. This type of drawing, which shows the distribution of electron density around the nucleus, is one of the several ways we use to help us visualize orbitals. The first thing that we notice about the electron density for the $1s$ orbital is that it is *spherically symmetric*—in other words, the electron density at a given distance from the nucleus is the same regardless of the direction in which we proceed from the nucleus. All of the other s orbitals ($2s$, $3s$, $4s$, and so forth) are spherically symmetric as well.

So what is different about the s orbitals having different n quantum numbers? For example, how does the electron-density distribution of the hydrogen atom change when the electron is excited from the $1s$ orbital to the $2s$ orbital? To address questions like this, we must take a look at the *radial probability density*, that is, the probability that we will find the electron at a specific distance from the nucleus. In Figure 6.18 ▶ we have plotted the radial probability density for the $1s$ orbital as a function of r, the distance from the nucleus—the resulting curve is the **radial probability function** for the $1s$ orbital. (Radial probability functions are described more fully in the "A Closer Look" box in this section.) We see that the probability of finding the electron rises rapidly as we move away from the nucleus, maximizing at a distance of 0.529 Å from the nucleus, and then falls off rapidly. Thus, when the electron occupies the $1s$ orbital, it is *most likely* to be found

ANIMATION
Radial Electron Distribution

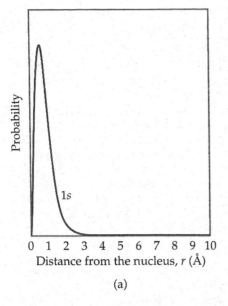

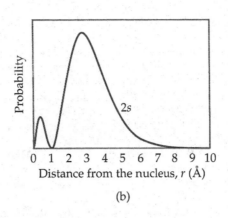

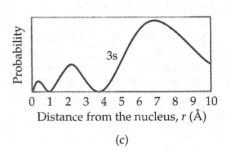

| (a) | (b) | (c) |

▲ **Figure 6.18   Radial probability functions for the 1s, 2s, and 3s orbitals.** These plots show the probability of finding the electron as a function of distance from the nucleus. As *n* increases, the most likely distance at which to find the electron moves farther from the nucleus, similar to the Bohr model. In the 2s and 3s orbitals the radial probability function drops to zero at certain distances from the nucleus but then rises again. The points at which the probability is zero are called *nodes*.

0.529 Å from the nucleus*—we still use the probabilistic description, consistent with the uncertainty principle. Notice also that the probability of finding the electron at a distance greater than 3 Å from the nucleus is essentially zero.

Figure 6.18(b) shows the radial probability function for the 2s orbital of the hydrogen atom. We can see three significant differences between this plot and that for the 1s orbital: (1) There are two separate maxima in the radial probability function for the 2s orbital, namely a small peak at about $r = 0.5$ Å and a much larger peak at about $r = 3$ Å; (2) Between these two peaks is a point at which the function goes to zero (at about $r = 1$ Å). An intermediate point at which a probability function goes to zero is called a **node**. There is a zero probability of finding the electron at a distance corresponding to a node, even though the electron might be found at shorter or longer distances; (3) The radial probability function for the 2s orbital is significantly broader (more spread out) than that for the 1s orbital. Thus, for the 2s orbital, there is a larger range of distances from the nucleus, at which there is a high probability of finding the electron than for the 1s orbital. This trend continues for the 3s orbital, as shown in Figure 6.18(c). The radial probability function for the 3s orbital has three peaks of increasing size, with the largest peak maximizing even farther from the nucleus (at about $r = 7$ Å) at which it has two nodes and is even more spread out.

The radial probability functions in Figure 6.18 tell us that as *n* increases, there is also an increase in the most likely distance from the nucleus to find the electron. In other words, the size of the orbital increases with increasing *n*, just as it did in the Bohr model.

One widely used method of representing orbitals is to display a boundary surface that encloses some substantial portion, say 90%, of the total electron density for the orbital. For the s orbitals, these contour representations are spheres. The contour representations of the 1s, 2s, and 3s orbitals are shown in Figure 6.19 ▶. They all have the same shape, but they differ in size. Although

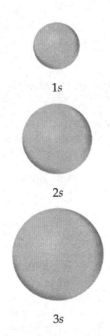

▲ **Figure 6.19   Contour representations of the 1s, 2s, and 3s orbitals.** The relative radii of the spheres correspond to a 90% probability of finding the electron within each sphere.

---

* In the quantum mechanical model, the most probable distance at which to find the electron in the 1s orbital—0.529 Å—is identical to the radius of the orbit predicted by Bohr for $n = 1$. The distance 0.529 Å is often called the *Bohr radius*.

A CLOSER LOOK | Probability Density and Radial Probability Functions

The quantum mechanical description of the hydrogen atom requires that we talk about the position of the electron in the atom in a somewhat unfamiliar way. In classical physics, we can exactly pinpoint the position and velocity of an orbiting object, such as a planet orbiting a star. Under quantum mechanics, however, we must describe the position of the electron in the hydrogen atom in terms of probabilities rather than an exact location—an exact answer would violate the uncertainty principle, which we have seen becomes important when considering subatomic particles. The information we need about the probability of finding the electron is contained in the wave functions, ψ, that are obtained when Schrödinger's equation is solved. Remember that there are an infinite number of wave functions (orbitals) for the hydrogen atom, but the electron can occupy only one of them at any given time. Here we will discuss briefly how we can use the orbitals to obtain radial probability functions, such as those in Figure 6.18.

In Section 6.5 we stated that the square of the wave function, ψ^2, gives the probability that the electron is at any one given point in space—recall that this quantity is called the *probability density* for the point. For a spherically symmetric *s* orbital, the value of ψ depends only on the distance from the nucleus, r. Let's consider a straight line outward from the nucleus, as shown in Figure 6.20 ▼. The probability of finding the electron at distance r from the nucleus along that line is

$[\psi(r)]^2$ where $\psi(r)$ is the value of ψ at distance r. Figure 6.21 ▼ shows plots of $[\psi(r)]^2$ as a function of r for the 1s, 2s, and 3s orbitals of the hydrogen atom.

You will notice that the plots in Figure 6.21 look distinctly different from the radial probability functions plotted in Figure 6.18. These two types of plots for the *s* orbitals are very closely related, but they provide somewhat different information. The probability density, $[\psi(r)]^2$, tells us the probability of finding the electron at *a specific* point in space that is at distance r from the nucleus. The radial probability function, which we will denote $P(r)$, tells us the probability of finding the electron at *any* point that is distance r from the nucleus—in other words, to get $P(r)$ we need to "add up" the probabilities of finding the electron over all the points at distance r from the nucleus. The difference between these descriptions may seem rather subtle, but mathematics provides us with a precise way to connect them.

As shown in Figure 6.20, the collection of points at distance r from the nucleus is simply a sphere of radius r. The probability density at every point on that sphere is $[\psi(r)]^2$. To add up all of the individual probability densities requires the use of calculus and is beyond the scope of this text (in the language of calculus "we integrate the probability density over the surface of the sphere"). The result we obtain is easy to describe, however. The radial probability function at distance r, $P(r)$, is simply the probability density at distance r, $[\psi(r)]^2$, multiplied by the surface area of the sphere, which is given by the formula $4\pi r^2$:

$$P(r) = 4\pi r^2 [\psi(r)]^2$$

Thus, the plots of $P(r)$ in Figure 6.18 are equal to the plots of $[\psi(r)]^2$ in Figure 6.21 multiplied by $4\pi r^2$. The fact that $4\pi r^2$ increases rapidly as we move away from the nucleus makes the two sets of plots look very different. For example, the plot of $[\psi(r)]^2$ for the 3s orbital (Figure 6.21) shows that the function generally gets smaller the farther we go from the nucleus. But when we multiply by $4\pi r^2$, we see peaks that get larger and larger as we move away from the nucleus (Figure 6.18). We will see that the radial probability functions in Figure 6.18 provide us with the more useful information because they tell us the probability for finding the electron at *all* points distance r from the nucleus, not just one particular point.

Related Exercises: 6.48, 6.57, 6.58, and 6.91

A point at distance r from the nucleus

A sphere of radius r around the nucleus

▲ **Figure 6.20 Probability at a point.** The probability density, $\psi(r)^2$, gives the probability that the electron will be found at *a specific point* at distance r from the nucleus. The radial probability function, $4\pi r^2\psi(r)^2$, gives the probability that the electron will be found at *any* point distance r from the nucleus—in other words, at any point on the sphere of radius r.

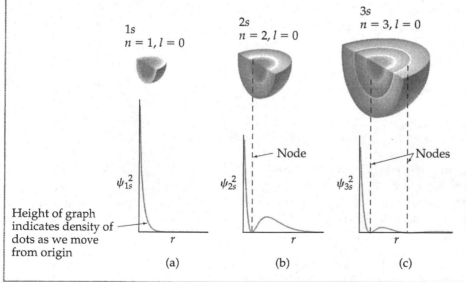

1s
$n = 1, l = 0$

2s
$n = 2, l = 0$

3s
$n = 3, l = 0$

Node

Nodes

ψ_{1s}^2 ψ_{2s}^2 ψ_{3s}^2

Height of graph indicates density of dots as we move from origin

r r r

(a)   (b)   (c)

◀ **Figure 6.21 Probability density distribution in 1s, 2s, and 3s orbitals.** The lower part of the figure shows how the probability density, $\psi(r)^2$, varies as a function of distance r from the nucleus. The upper part of the figure shows a cutaway of the spherical electron density in each of the *s* orbitals.

the details of how the electron density varies within the contour representation are lost in these representations, this is not a serious disadvantage. For more qualitative discussions, the most important features of orbitals are their relative sizes and their shapes, which are adequately displayed by contour representations.

GIVE IT SOME THOUGHT

How many maxima would you expected to find in the radial probability function for the 4s orbital of the hydrogen atom? How many nodes would you expect in the 4s radial probability function?

▼ **Figure 6.22 The *p* orbitals.** (a) Electron-density distribution of a 2*p* orbital. (b) Contour representations of the three *p* orbitals. Note that the subscript on the orbital label indicates the axis along which the orbital lies.

The *p* Orbitals

The distribution of electron density for a 2*p* orbital is shown in Figure 6.22(a) ▶. As we can see from this figure, the electron density is not distributed in a spherically symmetric fashion as in an *s* orbital. Instead, the electron density is concentrated in two regions on either side of the nucleus, separated by a node at the nucleus. We say that this dumbbell-shaped orbital has two *lobes*. It is useful to recall that we are making no statement of how the electron is moving within the orbital; the only thing Figure 6.22(a) portrays is the *averaged* distribution of the electron density in a 2*p* orbital.

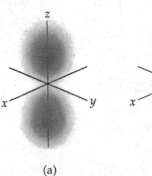

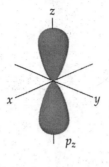

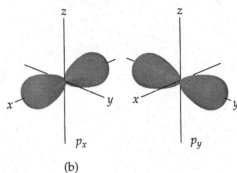

(a)   (b)

Beginning with the $n = 2$ shell, each shell has three *p* orbitals. Thus, there are three 2*p* orbitals, three 3*p* orbitals, and so forth. Each set of *p* orbitals has the dumbbell shapes shown in Figure 6.22(a) for the 2*p* orbitals. For each value of *n*, the three *p* orbitals have the same size and shape but differ from one another in spatial orientation. We usually represent *p* orbitals by drawing the shape and orientation of their wave functions, as shown in Figure 6.22(b). It is convenient to label these as the p_x, p_y, and p_z orbitals. The letter subscript indicates the Cartesian axis along which the orbital is oriented.* Like *s* orbitals, *p* orbitals increase in size as we move from 2*p* to 3*p* to 4*p*, and so forth.

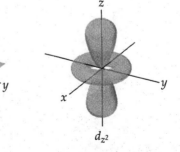

The *d* and *f* Orbitals

When *n* is 3 or greater, we encounter the *d* orbitals (for which $l = 2$). There are five 3*d* orbitals, five 4*d* orbitals, and so forth. The different *d* orbitals in a given shell have different shapes and orientations in space, as shown in Figure 6.23 ▶. Four of the *d*-orbital contour representations have a "four-leaf clover" shape, and each lies primarily in a plane. The d_{xy}, d_{xz}, and d_{yz} lie in the *xy*, *xz*, and *yz* planes,

▲ **Figure 6.23 Contour representations of the five *d* orbitals.**

---

* We cannot make a simple correspondence between the subscripts (*x*, *y*, and *z*) and the allowed m_l values (1, 0, and −1). To explain why this is so is beyond the scope of an introductory text.

respectively, with the lobes oriented *between* the axes. The lobes of the $d_{x^2-y^2}$ orbital also lie in the xy plane, but the lobes lie *along* the x and y axes. The d_{z^2} orbital looks very different from the other four: It has two lobes along the z axis and a "doughnut" in the xy plane. Even though the d_{z^2} orbital looks different from the other d orbitals, it has the same energy as the other four d orbitals. The representations in Figure 6.23 are commonly used for all d orbitals, regardless of principal quantum number.

When n is 4 or greater, there are seven equivalent f orbitals (for which $l = 3$). The shapes of the f orbitals are even more complicated than those of the d orbitals and are not presented here. As you will see in the next section, however, you must be aware of f orbitals as we consider the electronic structure of atoms in the lower part of the periodic table.

In many instances later in the text you will find that knowing the number and shapes of atomic orbitals will help you understand chemistry at the molecular level. You will therefore find it useful to memorize the shapes of the orbitals shown in Figures 6.19, 6.22, and 6.23.

 GIVE IT SOME THOUGHT

Note in Figure 6.22(a) that the color is deep pink in the interior of each lobe but fades to pale pink at the edges. What does this change in color represent?

6.7 | Many-Electron Atoms

One of our goals in this chapter has been to determine the electronic structures of atoms. So far, we have seen that quantum mechanics leads to a very elegant description of the hydrogen atom. This atom, however, has only one electron. How must our description of the electronic structure of atoms change when we consider atoms with two or more electrons (a *many-electron* atom)? To describe these atoms, we must consider not only the nature of orbitals and their relative energies but also how the electrons populate the available orbitals.

Orbitals and Their Energies

The quantum mechanical model would not be very useful if we could not extend what we have learned about hydrogen to other atoms. Fortunately, we can describe the electronic structure of a many-electron atom in terms of orbitals like those of the hydrogen atom. Thus, we can continue to designate orbitals as $1s$, $2p_x$, and so forth. Further, these orbitals have the same general shapes as the corresponding hydrogen orbitals.

Although the shapes of the orbitals for many-electron atoms are the same as those for hydrogen, the presence of more than one electron greatly changes the energies of the orbitals. In hydrogen the energy of an orbital depends only on its principal quantum number, n (Figure 6.17); the $3s$, $3p$, and $3d$ subshells all have the same energy, for instance. In a many-electron atom, however, the electron-electron repulsions cause the different subshells to be at different energies, as shown in Figure 6.24 ◀. To understand why this is so, we must consider the forces between the electrons and how these forces are affected by the shapes of the orbitals. We will, however, forgo this analysis until Chapter 7.

The important idea is this: *In a many-electron atom, for a given value of n, the energy of an orbital increases with increasing value of l.* You can see this illustrated in Figure 6.24. Notice, for example, that the $n = 3$ orbitals (red) increase in energy in the order $3s < 3p < 3d$. Figure 6.24 is a *qualitative* energy-level diagram; the exact energies of the orbitals and their spacings differ from one atom

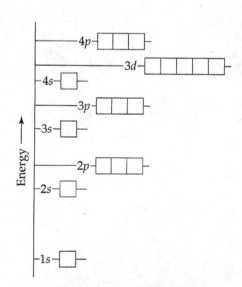

▲ **Figure 6.24 Orbital energy levels in many-electron atoms.** In a many-electron atom, the energies of the subshells in each shell follow the order $ns < np < nd < nf$. As in Figure 6.17, each box represents an orbital.

to another. Notice that all orbitals of a given subshell (such as the five 3*d* orbitals) still have the same energy as one another, just as they do in the hydrogen atom. Orbitals with the same energy are said to be **degenerate**.

 GIVE IT SOME THOUGHT

For a many-electron atom, can we predict unambiguously whether the 4*s* orbital is lower in energy or higher in energy than the 3*d* orbitals?

Electron Spin and the Pauli Exclusion Principle

We have now seen that we can use hydrogen-like orbitals to describe many-electron atoms. What, however, determines which orbitals the electrons reside in? That is, how do the electrons of a many-electron atom populate the available orbitals? To answer this question, we must consider an additional property of the electron.

When scientists studied the line spectra of many-electron atoms in great detail, they noticed a very puzzling feature: Lines that were originally thought to be single were actually closely spaced pairs. This meant, in essence, that there were twice as many energy levels as there were "supposed" to be. In 1925 the Dutch physicists George Uhlenbeck and Samuel Goudsmit proposed a solution to this dilemma. They postulated that electrons have an intrinsic property, called **electron spin**, that causes each electron to behave as if it were a tiny sphere spinning on its own axis.

By now it probably does not surprise you to learn that electron spin is quantized. This observation led to the assignment of a new quantum number for the electron, in addition to n, l, and m_l that we have already discussed. This new quantum number, the **spin magnetic quantum number**, is denoted m_s (the subscript s stands for *spin*). Two possible values are allowed for m_s, $+\frac{1}{2}$ or $-\frac{1}{2}$, which was first interpreted as indicating the two opposite directions in which the electron can spin. A spinning charge produces a magnetic field. The two opposite directions of spin therefore produce oppositely directed magnetic fields, as shown in Figure 6.25 ▶.* These two opposite magnetic fields lead to the splitting of spectral lines into closely spaced pairs.

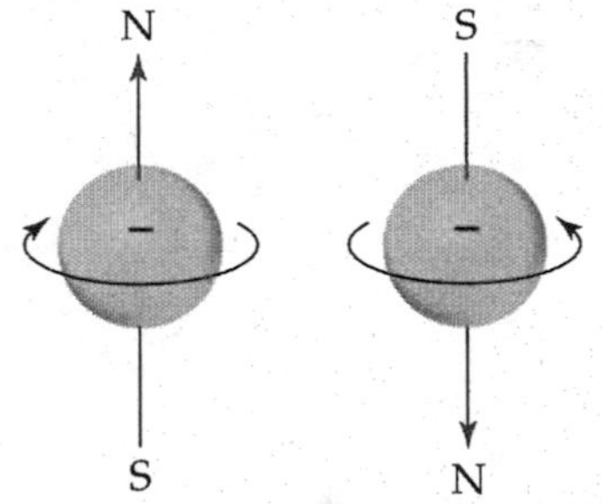

Electron spin is crucial for understanding the electronic structures of atoms. In 1925 the Austrian-born physicist Wolfgang Pauli (1900–1958) discovered the principle that governs the arrangements of electrons in many-electron atoms. The **Pauli exclusion principle** states that *no two electrons in an atom can have the same set of four quantum numbers n, l, m_l, and m_s.* For a given orbital (1*s*, 2*p_z*, and so forth), the values of n, l, and m_l are fixed. Thus, if we want to put more than one electron in an orbital *and* satisfy the Pauli exclusion principle, our only choice is to assign different m_s values to the electrons. Because there are only two such values, we conclude that *an orbital can hold a maximum of two electrons and they must have opposite spins.* This restriction allows us to index the electrons in an atom, giving their quantum numbers and thereby defining the region in space where each electron is most likely to be found. It also provides the key to one of the great problems in chemistry—understanding the structure of the periodic table of the elements. We will discuss these issues in the next two sections.

▲ **Figure 6.25 Electron spin.** The electron behaves as if it were spinning about an axis, thereby generating a magnetic field whose direction depends on the direction of spin. The two directions for the magnetic field correspond to the two possible values for the spin quantum number, m_S.

---

* As we discussed earlier, the electron has both particle-like and wavelike properties. Thus, the picture of an electron as a spinning charged sphere is, strictly speaking, just a useful pictorial representation that helps us understand the two directions of magnetic field that an electron can possess.

| Experimental Evidence for Electron Spin

Even before electron spin had been proposed, there was experimental evidence that electrons had an additional property that needed explanation. In 1921, Otto Stern and Walter Gerlach succeeded in separating a beam of neutral atoms into two groups by passing them through a nonhomogeneous magnetic field. Their experiment is diagrammed in Figure 6.26 ▶. Let's assume that they used a beam of hydrogen atoms (in actuality, they used silver atoms, which contain just one unpaired electron). We would normally expect that neutral atoms would not be affected by a magnetic field. However, the magnetic field arising from the electron's spin interacts with the magnet's field, deflecting the atom from its straight-line path. As shown in Figure 6.26, the magnetic field splits the beam in two, suggesting that there are two (and only two) equivalent values for the electron's own magnetic field. The Stern–Gerlach experiment could be readily interpreted once it was realized that there are exactly two values for the spin of the electron. These values will produce equal magnetic fields that are opposite in direction.
Related Exercise: 6.94

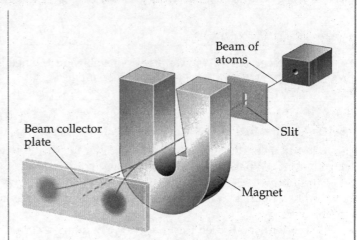

▲ **Figure 6.26   The Stern–Gerlach experiment.** Atoms in which the electron spin quantum number (m_S) of the unpaired electron is $+\frac{1}{2}$ are deflected in one direction, and those in which m_S is $-\frac{1}{2}$ are deflected in the other.

6.8 | Electron Configurations

Armed with a knowledge of the relative energies of orbitals and the Pauli exclusion principle, we are now in a position to consider the arrangements of electrons in atoms. The way in which the electrons are distributed among the various orbitals of an atom is called the **electron configuration** of the atom. The most stable electron configuration of an atom—the ground state—is that in which the electrons are in the lowest possible energy states. If there were no restrictions on the possible values for the quantum numbers of the electrons, all the electrons would crowd into the 1s orbital because it is the lowest in energy (Figure 6.24). The Pauli exclusion principle tells us, however, that there can be at most two electrons in any single orbital. Thus, *the orbitals are filled in order of increasing energy, with no more than two electrons per orbital.* For example, consider the lithium atom, which has three electrons. (Recall that the number of electrons in a neutral atom equals its atomic number.) The 1s orbital can accommodate two of the electrons. The third one goes into the next lowest energy orbital, the 2s.

We can represent any electron configuration by writing the symbol for the occupied subshell and adding a superscript to indicate the number of electrons in that subshell. For example, for lithium we write $1s^2 2s^1$ (read "1s two, 2s one"). We can also show the arrangement of the electrons as

Li   [↑↓]   [↑]

1s   2s

In this kind of representation, which we call an *orbital diagram*, each orbital is denoted by a box and each electron by a half arrow. A half arrow pointing up (↑) represents an electron with a positive spin magnetic quantum number $\left(m_s = +\frac{1}{2}\right)$, and a half arrow pointing down (↓) represents an electron with a negative spin magnetic quantum number $\left(m_s = -\frac{1}{2}\right)$. This pictorial representation of electron spin is quite convenient. In fact, chemists and physicists often

CHEMISTRY AND LIFE | Nuclear Spin and Magnetic Resonance Imaging

A major challenge facing medical diagnosis is seeing inside the human body from the outside. Until recently, this was accomplished primarily by using X rays to image human bones, muscles, and organs. However, there are several drawbacks to using X rays for medical imaging. First, X rays do not give well-resolved images of overlapping physiological structures. Moreover, because damaged or diseased tissue often yields the same image as healthy tissue, X rays frequently fail to detect illness or injuries. Finally, X rays are high-energy radiation that can cause physiological harm, even in low doses.

In the 1980s a new technique called *magnetic resonance imaging* (MRI) moved to the forefront of medical imaging technology. The foundation of MRI is a phenomenon called nuclear magnetic resonance (NMR), which was discovered in the mid-1940s. Today NMR has become one of the most important spectroscopic methods used in chemistry. It is based on the observation that, like electrons, the nuclei of many elements possess an intrinsic spin. Like electron spin, nuclear spin is quantized. For example, the nucleus of ^{1}H (a proton) has two possible magnetic nuclear spin quantum numbers, $+\frac{1}{2}$ and $-\frac{1}{2}$. The hydrogen nucleus is the most common one studied by NMR.

A spinning hydrogen nucleus acts like a tiny magnet. In the absence of external effects, the two spin states have the same energy. However, when the nuclei are placed in an external magnetic field, they can align either parallel or opposed (antiparallel) to the field, depending on their spin. The parallel alignment is lower in energy than the antiparallel one by a certain amount, ΔE (Figure 6.27 ▼). If the nuclei are irradiated with photons with energy equal to ΔE, the spin of the nuclei can be "flipped," that is, excited from the parallel to the antiparallel alignment. Detection of the flipping of nuclei between the two spin states leads to an NMR spectrum. The radiation used in an NMR experiment is in the radiofrequency range, typically 100 to 900 MHz.

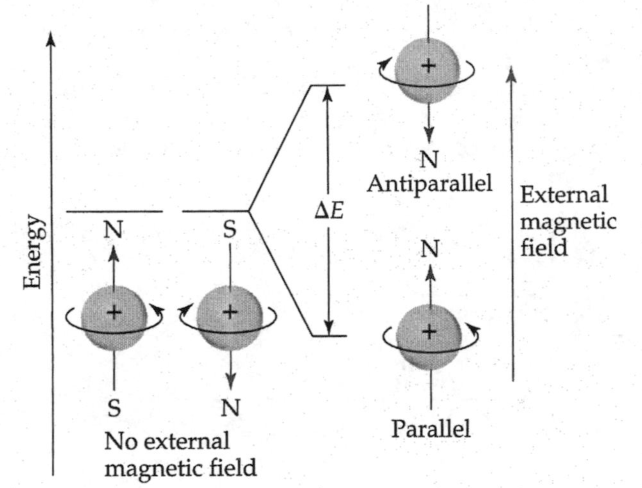

Because hydrogen is a major constituent of aqueous body fluids and fatty tissue, the hydrogen nucleus is the most convenient one for study by MRI. In MRI a person's body is placed in a strong magnetic field. By irradiating the body with pulses of radiofrequency radiation and using sophisticated detection techniques, tissue can be imaged at specific depths within the body, giving pictures with spectacular detail (Figure 6.28 ▼). The ability to sample at different depths allows medical technicians to construct a three-dimensional picture of the body.

MRI has none of the disadvantages of X rays. Diseased tissue appears very different from healthy tissue, resolving overlapping structures at different depths in the body is much easier, and the radiofrequency radiation is not harmful to humans in the doses used. The technique has had such a profound influence on the modern practice of medicine that Paul Lauterbur, a chemist, and Peter Mansfield, a physicist, were awarded the 2003 Nobel Prize in Physiology or Medicine for their discoveries concerning MRI. The major drawback of this technique is expense: The current cost of a new MRI instrument for clinical applications is over $1.5 million.

Related Exercises: 6.94 and 6.95

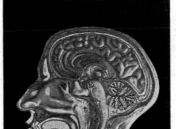

◀ **Figure 6.28 MRI image.** This image of a human head, obtained using MRI, shows the structures of a normal brain, airways, and facial tissues.

▲ **Figure 6.27 Nuclear spin.** Like electron spin, nuclear spin generates a small magnetic field and has two allowed values. In the absence of an external magnetic field (left), the two spin states have the same energy. If an external magnetic field is applied (right), the parallel alignment of the nuclear magnetic field is lower in energy than the antiparallel alignment. The energy difference, ΔE, is in the radio frequency portion of the electromagnetic spectrum.

refer to electrons as "spin-up" and "spin-down" rather than specifying the value for m_s.

Electrons having opposite spins are said to be *paired* when they are in the same orbital (↑↓). An *unpaired electron* is one not accompanied by a partner of opposite spin. In the lithium atom the two electrons in the 1s orbital are paired and the electron in the 2s orbital is unpaired.

Hund's Rule

Consider now how the electron configurations of the elements change as we move from element to element across the periodic table. Hydrogen has one electron, which occupies the 1s orbital in its ground state.

ANIMATION
Electron Configurations

$$\text{H} \quad \boxed{\uparrow} \quad : 1s^1$$
$$ \quad 1s$$

The choice of a spin-up electron here is arbitrary; we could equally well show the ground state with one spin-down electron in the 1s orbital. It is customary, however, to show unpaired electrons with their spins up.

The next element, helium, has two electrons. Because two electrons with opposite spins can occupy an orbital, both of helium's electrons are in the 1s orbital.

$$\text{He} \quad \boxed{\uparrow\downarrow} \quad : 1s^2$$
$$ \quad 1s$$

The two electrons present in helium complete the filling of the first shell. This arrangement represents a very stable configuration, as is evidenced by the chemical inertness of helium.

The electron configurations of lithium and several elements that follow it in the periodic table are shown in Table 6.3 ▼. For the third electron of lithium, the change in principal quantum number represents a large jump in energy and a corresponding jump in the average distance of the electron from the nucleus. It represents the start of a new shell occupied with electrons. As you can see by examining the periodic table, lithium starts a new row of the table. It is the first member of the alkali metals (group 1A).

The element that follows lithium is beryllium; its electron configuration is $1s^2 2s^2$ (Table 6.3). Boron, atomic number 5, has the electron configuration $1s^2 2s^2 2p^1$. The fifth electron must be placed in a 2p orbital because the 2s orbital

ACTIVITY
Electron Configuration

TABLE 6.3	**Electron Configurations of Several Lighter Elements**			
Element	Total Electrons	Orbital Diagram		Electron Configuration

Orbital Diagram columns: 1s 2s 2p 3s

Element	Total Electrons	1s	2s	2p	3s	Electron Configuration
Li	3	↑↓	↑	□ □ □	□	$1s^2 2s^1$
Be	4	↑↓	↑↓	□ □ □	□	$1s^2 2s^2$
B	5	↑↓	↑↓	↑ □ □	□	$1s^2 2s^2 2p^1$
C	6	↑↓	↑↓	↑ ↑ □	□	$1s^2 2s^2 2p^2$
N	7	↑↓	↑↓	↑ ↑ ↑	□	$1s^2 2s^2 2p^3$
Ne	10	↑↓	↑↓	↑↓ ↑↓ ↑↓	□	$1s^2 2s^2 2p^6$
Na	11	↑↓	↑↓	↑↓ ↑↓ ↑↓	↑	$1s^2 2s^2 2p^6 3s^1$

is filled. Because all the three $2p$ orbitals are of equal energy, it doesn't matter which $2p$ orbital is occupied.

With the next element, carbon, we encounter a new situation. We know that the sixth electron must go into a $2p$ orbital. However, does this new electron go into the $2p$ orbital that already has one electron, or into one of the other two $2p$ orbitals? This question is answered by **Hund's rule**, which states that *for degenerate orbitals, the lowest energy is attained when the number of electrons with the same spin is maximized*. This means that electrons will occupy orbitals singly to the maximum extent possible and that these single electrons in a given subshell will all have the same spin magnetic quantum number. Electrons arranged in this way are said to have *parallel spins*. For a carbon atom to achieve its lowest energy, therefore, the two $2p$ electrons will have the same spin. In order for this to happen, the electrons must be in different $2p$ orbitals, as shown in Table 6.3. Thus, a carbon atom in its ground state has two unpaired electrons. Similarly, for nitrogen in its ground state, Hund's rule requires that the three $2p$ electrons singly occupy each of the three $2p$ orbitals. This is the only way that all three electrons can have the same spin. For oxygen and fluorine, we place four and five electrons, respectively, in the $2p$ orbitals. To achieve this, we pair up electrons in the $2p$ orbitals, as we will see in Sample Exercise 6.7.

Hund's rule is based in part on the fact that electrons repel one another. By occupying different orbitals, the electrons remain as far as possible from one another, thus minimizing electron-electron repulsions.

■■ SAMPLE EXERCISE 6.7 | Orbital Diagrams and Electron Configurations

Draw the orbital diagram for the electron configuration of oxygen, atomic number 8. How many unpaired electrons does an oxygen atom possess?

Solution

Analyze and Plan: Because oxygen has an atomic number of 8, each oxygen atom has 8 electrons. Figure 6.24 shows the ordering of orbitals. The electrons (represented as arrows) are placed in the orbitals (represented as boxes) beginning with the lowest-energy orbital, the $1s$. Each orbital can hold a maximum of two electrons (the Pauli exclusion principle). Because the $2p$ orbitals are degenerate, we place one electron in each of these orbitals (spin-up) before pairing any electrons (Hund's rule).
Solve: Two electrons each go into the $1s$ and $2s$ orbitals with their spins paired. This leaves four electrons for the three degenerate $2p$ orbitals. Following Hund's rule, we put one electron into each $2p$ orbital until all three orbitals have one electron each. The fourth electron is then paired up with one of the three electrons already in a $2p$ orbital, so that the representation is

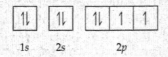

The corresponding electron configuration is written $1s^2 2s^2 2p^4$. The atom has two unpaired electrons.

■■ PRACTICE EXERCISE

(a) Write the electron configuration for phosphorus, element 15. (b) How many unpaired electrons does a phosphorus atom possess?
Answers: **(a)** $1s^2 2s^2 2p^6 3s^2 3p^3$, **(b)** three

Condensed Electron Configurations

The filling of the $2p$ subshell is complete at neon (Table 6.3), which has a stable configuration with eight electrons (an *octet*) in the outermost occupied shell. The next element, sodium, atomic number 11, marks the beginning of a new row of the periodic table. Sodium has a single $3s$ electron beyond the stable configuration of neon. We can therefore abbreviate the electron configuration of sodium as

$$\text{Na:} \quad [\text{Ne}]3s^1$$

The symbol [Ne] represents the electron configuration of the ten electrons of neon, $1s^2 2s^2 2p^6$. Writing the electron configuration as $[\text{Ne}]3s^1$ helps focus attention on the outermost electrons of the atom, which are the ones largely responsible for the chemical behavior of an element.

We can generalize what we have just done for the electron configuration of sodium: In writing the *condensed electron configuration* of an element, the electron configuration of the nearest noble-gas element of lower atomic number is represented by its chemical symbol in brackets. For example, we can write the electron configuration of lithium as

$$\text{Li:} \quad [\text{He}]2s^1$$

We refer to the electrons represented by the symbol for a noble gas as the *noble-gas core* of the atom. More usually, these inner-shell electrons are referred to merely as the **core electrons**. The electrons given after the noble-gas core are called the *outer-shell electrons*. The outer-shell electrons include the electrons involved in chemical bonding, which are called the **valence electrons.** For ligher elements (those with atomic number of 30 or less), all of the outer-shell electrons are valence electrons. As we will discuss later, many of the heavier elements have completely filled subshells in their outer-shell electrons that are not involved in bonding and are therefore not considered valence electrons.

By comparing the condensed electron configuration of lithium with that of sodium, we can appreciate why these two elements are so similar chemically: They have the same type of electron configuration in the outermost occupied shell. Indeed, all the members of the alkali metal group (1A) have a single *s* valence electron beyond a noble-gas configuration.

Transition Metals

The noble-gas element argon marks the end of the row started by sodium. The configuration for argon is $1s^2 2s^2 2p^6 3s^2 3p^6$. The element following argon in the periodic table is potassium (K), atomic number 19. In all its chemical properties, potassium is clearly a member of the alkali metal group. The experimental facts about the properties of potassium leave no doubt that the outermost electron of this element occupies an *s* orbital. But this means that the electron that has the highest energy has *not* gone into a 3*d* orbital, which we might have expected it to do. Here the ordering of energy levels is such that the 4*s* orbital is lower in energy than the 3*d* (Figure 6.24). Hence, the condensed electron configuration of potassium is

$$\text{K:} \quad [\text{Ar}]4s^1$$

Following complete filling of the 4*s* orbital (this occurs in the calcium atom), the next set of orbitals to be filled is the 3*d*. (You will find it helpful as we go along to refer often to the periodic table on the front inside cover.) Beginning with scandium and extending through zinc, electrons are added to the five 3*d* orbitals until they are completely filled. Thus, the fourth row of the periodic table is ten elements wider than the two previous rows. These ten elements are known as either **transition elements** or **transition metals**. Note the position of these elements in the periodic table.

In deriving the electron configurations of the transition elements, the orbitals are filled in accordance with Hund's rule—electrons are added to the 3*d* orbitals singly until all five orbitals have one electron each. Additional electrons are then placed in the 3*d* orbitals with spin pairing until the shell is completely filled. The condensed electron configurations and the corresponding orbital diagram representations of two transition elements are as follows:

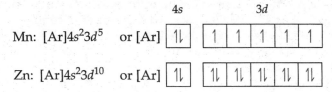

Once all the 3d orbitals have been filled with two electrons each, the 4p orbitals begin to be occupied until the completed octet of outer electrons $(4s^2 4p^6)$ is reached with krypton (Kr), atomic number 36, another of the noble gases. Rubidium (Rb) marks the beginning of the fifth row. Refer again to the periodic table on the front inside cover. Notice that this row is in every respect like the preceding one, except that the value for n is greater by 1.

 GIVE IT SOME THOUGHT

Based on the structure of the periodic table, which becomes occupied first, the 6s orbital or the 5d orbitals?

The Lanthanides and Actinides

The sixth row of the periodic table begins similarly to the preceding one: one electron in the 6s orbital of cesium (Cs) and two electrons in the 6s orbital of barium (Ba). Notice, however, that the periodic table then has a break, and the subsequent set of elements (elements 57–70) is placed below the main portion of the table. It is at this place that we begin to encounter a new set of orbitals, the 4f.

There are seven degenerate 4f orbitals, corresponding to the seven allowed values of m_l, ranging from 3 to −3. Thus, it takes 14 electrons to fill the 4f orbitals completely. The 14 elements corresponding to the filling of the 4f orbitals are known as either the **lanthanide elements** or the **rare earth elements**. They are set below the other elements to avoid making the periodic table unduly wide. The properties of the lanthanide elements are all quite similar, and these elements occur together in nature. For many years it was virtually impossible to separate them from one another.

Because the energies of the 4f and 5d orbitals are very close to each other, the electron configurations of some of the lanthanides involve 5d electrons. For example, the elements lanthanum (La), cerium (Ce), and praseodymium (Pr) have the following electron configurations:

$$[Xe]6s^2 5d^1 \qquad [Xe]6s^2 5d^1 4f^1 \qquad [Xe]6s^2 4f^3$$
Lanthanum   Cerium   Praseodymium

Because La has a single 5d electron, it is sometimes placed below yttrium (Y) as the first member of the third series of transition elements, and Ce is then placed as the first member of the lanthanides. Based on their chemistry, however, La can be considered the first element in the lanthanide series. Arranged this way, there are fewer apparent exceptions to the regular filling of the 4f orbitals among the subsequent members of the series.

After the lanthanide series, the third transition element series is completed by the filling of the 5d orbitals, followed by the filling of the 6p orbitals. This brings us to radon (Rn), heaviest of the known noble-gas elements.

The final row of the periodic table begins by filling the 7s orbitals. The **actinide elements**, of which uranium (U, element 92) and plutonium (Pu, element 94) are the best known, are then built up by completing the 5f orbitals. The actinide elements are radioactive, and most of them are not found in nature.

6.9 | Electron Configurations and the Periodic Table

Our rather brief survey of electron configurations of the elements has taken us through the periodic table. We have seen that the electron configurations of the elements are related to their locations in the periodic table. The periodic table is structured so that elements with the same pattern of outer-shell (valence) electron configuration are arranged in columns. For example, the electron configurations for the elements in groups 2A and 3A are given in Table 6.4 ◀. We see that the 2A elements all have ns^2 outer configurations, while the 3A elements all have ns^2np^1 configurations.

Earlier, in Table 6.2, we saw that the total number of orbitals in each shell is equal to n^2: 1, 4, 9, or 16. Because each orbital can hold two electrons, each shell can accommodate up to $2n^2$ electrons: 2, 8, 18, or 32. The structure of the periodic table reflects this orbital structure. The first row has two elements, the second and third rows have eight elements, the fourth and fifth rows have 18 elements, and the sixth row has 32 elements (including the lanthanide metals). Some of the numbers repeat because we reach the end of a row of the periodic table before a shell completely fills. For example, the third row has eight elements, which corresponds to filling the 3s and 3p orbitals. The remaining orbitals of the third shell, the 3d orbitals, do not begin to fill until the fourth row of the periodic table (and after the 4s orbital is filled). Likewise, the 4d orbitals don't begin to fill until the fifth row of the table, and the 4f orbitals don't begin filling until the sixth row.

All these observations are evident in the structure of the periodic table. For this reason, we will emphasize that *the periodic table is your best guide to the order in which orbitals are filled*. You can easily write the electron configuration of an element based on its location in the periodic table. The pattern is summarized in Figure 6.29 ◀. Notice that the elements can be grouped by the *type* of orbital into which the electrons are placed. On the left are *two* columns of elements, depicted in blue. These elements, known as the alkali metals (group 1A) and alkaline earth metals (group 2A), are those in which the valence s orbitals are being filled. On the right is a pink block of *six* columns. These are the elements in which the valence p orbitals are being filled. The s block and the p block of the periodic table together are the **representative elements**, which are sometimes called the **main-group elements**.

In the middle of Figure 6.29 is a gold block of *ten* columns containing the transition metals. These are the elements in which the valence d orbitals are being filled. Below the main portion of the table are two tan rows containing 14 columns. These elements are often referred to as the **f-block metals** because they are the ones in which the valence f orbitals are being filled. Recall that the numbers 2, 6, 10, and 14 are precisely the number of electrons that can fill the s, p, d, and f subshells, respectively. Recall also that the 1s subshell is the first s subshell, the 2p is the first p subshell, the 3d is the first d subshell, and the 4f is the first f subshell.

TABLE 6.4 Electron Configurations of the Group 2A and 3A Elements

Group 2A

Be	$[\text{He}]2s^2$
Mg	$[\text{Ne}]3s^2$
Ca	$[\text{Ar}]4s^2$
Sr	$[\text{Kr}]5s^2$
Ba	$[\text{Xe}]6s^2$
Ra	$[\text{Rn}]7s^2$

Group 3A

B	$[\text{He}]2s^22p^1$
Al	$[\text{Ne}]3s^23p^1$
Ga	$[\text{Ar}]3d^{10}4s^24p^1$
In	$[\text{Kr}]4d^{10}5s^25p^1$
Tl	$[\text{Xe}]4f^{14}5d^{10}6s^26p^1$

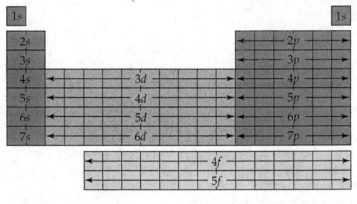

☐ Representative s-block elements

☐ Transition metals

☐ Representative p-block elements

☐ f-Block metals

▲ **Figure 6.29 Regions of the periodic table.** This block diagram of the periodic table shows the order in which electrons are added to orbitals as we move through the table from beginning to end.

▌ **SAMPLE EXERCISE 6.8** | Electron Configurations for a Group

What is the characteristic valence electron configuration of the group 7A elements, the halogens?

Solution

Analyze and Plan: We first locate the halogens in the periodic table, write the electron configurations for the first two elements, and then determine the general similarity between them.

Solve: The first member of the halogen group is fluorine, atomic number 9. The condensed electron configuration for fluorine is

$$\text{F:} \quad [\text{He}]2s^2 2p^5$$

Similarly, that for chlorine, the second halogen, is

$$\text{Cl:} \quad [\text{Ne}]3s^2 3p^5$$

From these two examples, we see that the characteristic valence electron configuration of a halogen is $ns^2 np^5$, where n ranges from 2 in the case of fluorine to 6 in the case of astatine.

■ PRACTICE EXERCISE
Which family of elements is characterized by an $ns^2 np^2$ electron configuration in the outermost occupied shell?
Answer: group 4A

■ SAMPLE EXERCISE 6.9 | Electron Configurations from the Periodic Table
(a) Write the electron configuration for bismuth, element number 83. **(b)** Write the condensed electron configuration for this element. **(c)** How many unpaired electrons does each atom of bismuth possess?

Solution (a) We write the electron configuration by moving across the periodic table one row at a time and writing the occupancies of the orbital corresponding to each row (refer to Figure 6.29).

First row	$1s^2$
Second row	$2s^2 2p^6$
Third row	$3s^2 3p^6$
Fourth row	$4s^2 3d^{10} 4p^6$
Fifth row	$5s^2 4d^{10} 5p^6$
Sixth row	$6s^2 4f^{14} 5d^{10} 6p^3$
Total:	$1s^2 2s^2 2p^6 3s^2 3p^6 3d^{10} 4s^2 4p^6 4d^{10} 4f^{14} 5s^2 5p^6 5d^{10} 6s^2 6p^3$

Note that 3 is the lowest possible value that n may have for a d orbital and that 4 is the lowest possible value of n for an f orbital.

The total of the superscripted numbers should equal the atomic number of bismuth, 83. The electrons may be listed, as shown above in the "Total" row, in the order of increasing principal quantum number. However, it is equally correct to list the orbitals in the order in which they are read from Figure 6.29: $1s^2 2s^2 2p^6 3s^2 3p^6 4s^2 3d^{10} 4p^6 5s^2 4d^{10} 5p^6 6s^2 4f^{14} 5d^{10} 6p^3$.

(b) We write the condensed electron configuration by locating bismuth on the periodic table and then moving *backward* to the nearest noble gas, which is Xe, element 54. Thus, the noble-gas core is [Xe]. The outer electrons are then read from the periodic table as before. Moving from Xe to Cs, element 55, we find ourselves in the sixth row. Moving across this row to Bi gives us the outer electrons. Thus, the abbreviated electron configuration is $[\text{Xe}]6s^2 4f^{14} 5d^{10} 6p^3$ or $[\text{Xe}]4f^{14} 5d^{10} 6s^2 6p^3$.

(c) We can see from the abbreviated electron configuration that the only partially occupied subshell is the $6p$. The orbital diagram representation for this subshell is

In accordance with Hund's rule, the three $6p$ electrons occupy the three $6p$ orbitals singly, with their spins parallel. Thus, there are three unpaired electrons in each atom of bismuth.

■ PRACTICE EXERCISE
Use the periodic table to write the condensed electron configurations for **(a)** Co (atomic number 27), **(b)** Te (atomic number 52).
Answers: **(a)** $[\text{Ar}]4s^2 3d^7$ or $[\text{Ar}]3d^7 4s^2$, **(b)** $[\text{Kr}]5s^2 4d^{10} 5p^4$ or $[\text{Kr}]4d^{10} 5s^2 5p^4$

Figure 6.30 — Valence electron configurations of the elements

Group	1A 1	2A 2	3B 3	4B 4	5B 5	6B 6	7B 7	8	8B 9	10	1B 11	2B 12	3A 13	4A 14	5A 15	6A 16	7A 17	8A 18
Core	1 H $1s^1$																	2 He $1s^2$
[He]	3 Li $2s^1$	4 Be $2s^2$											5 B $2s^2 2p^1$	6 C $2s^2 2p^2$	7 N $2s^2 2p^3$	8 O $2s^2 2p^4$	9 F $2s^2 2p^5$	10 Ne $2s^2 2p^6$
[Ne]	11 Na $3s^1$	12 Mg $3s^2$											13 Al $3s^2 3p^1$	14 Si $3s^2 3p^2$	15 P $3s^2 3p^3$	16 S $3s^2 3p^4$	17 Cl $3s^2 3p^5$	18 Ar $3s^2 3p^6$
[Ar]	19 K $4s^1$	20 Ca $4s^2$	21 Sc $3d^1 4s^2$	22 Ti $3d^2 4s^2$	23 V $3d^3 4s^2$	24 Cr $3d^5 4s^1$	25 Mn $3d^5 4s^2$	26 Fe $3d^6 4s^2$	27 Co $3d^7 4s^2$	28 Ni $3d^8 4s^2$	29 Cu $3d^{10} 4s^1$	30 Zn $3d^{10} 4s^2$	31 Ga $3d^{10} 4s^2 4p^1$	32 Ge $3d^{10} 4s^2 4p^2$	33 As $3d^{10} 4s^2 4p^3$	34 Se $3d^{10} 4s^2 4p^4$	35 Br $3d^{10} 4s^2 4p^5$	36 Kr $3d^{10} 4s^2 4p^6$
[Kr]	37 Rb $5s^1$	38 Sr $5s^2$	39 Y $4d^1 5s^2$	40 Zr $4d^2 5s^2$	41 Nb $4d^3 5s^2$	42 Mo $4d^5 5s^1$	43 Tc $4d^5 5s^2$	44 Ru $4d^7 5s^1$	45 Rh $4d^8 5s^1$	46 Pd $4d^{10}$	47 Ag $4d^{10} 5s^1$	48 Cd $4d^{10} 5s^2$	49 In $4d^{10} 5s^2 5p^1$	50 Sn $4d^{10} 5s^2 5p^2$	51 Sb $4d^{10} 5s^2 5p^3$	52 Te $4d^{10} 5s^2 5p^4$	53 I $4d^{10} 5s^2 5p^5$	54 Xe $4d^{10} 5s^2 5p^6$
[Xe]	55 Cs $6s^1$	56 Ba $6s^2$	71 Lu $4f^{14} 5d^1 6s^2$	72 Hf $4f^{14} 5d^2 6s^2$	73 Ta $4f^{14} 5d^3 6s^2$	74 W $4f^{14} 5d^4 6s^2$	75 Re $4f^{14} 5d^5 6s^2$	76 Os $4f^{14} 5d^6 6s^2$	77 Ir $4f^{14} 5d^7 6s^2$	78 Pt $4f^{14} 5d^9 6s^1$	79 Au $4f^{14} 5d^{10} 6s^1$	80 Hg $4f^{14} 5d^{10} 6s^2$	81 Tl $4f^{14} 5d^{10} 6s^2 6p^1$	82 Pb $4f^{14} 5d^{10} 6s^2 6p^2$	83 Bi $4f^{14} 5d^{10} 6s^2 6p^3$	84 Po $4f^{14} 5d^{10} 6s^2 6p^4$	85 At $4f^{14} 5d^{10} 6s^2 6p^5$	86 Rn $4f^{14} 5d^{10} 6s^2 6p^6$
[Rn]	87 Fr $7s^1$	88 Ra $7s^2$	103 Lr $5f^{14} 6d^1 7s^2$	104 Rf $5f^{14} 6d^2 7s^2$	105 Db $5f^{14} 6d^3 7s^2$	106 Sg $5f^{14} 6d^4 7s^2$	107 Bh $5f^{14} 6d^5 7s^2$	108 Hs $5f^{14} 6d^6 7s^2$	109 Mt $5f^{14} 6d^7 7s^2$	110	111	112	113	114	115	116		

Lanthanide series [Xe]

57 La $5d^1 6s^2$	58 Ce $4f^1 5d^1 6s^2$	59 Pr $4f^3 6s^2$	60 Nd $4f^4 6s^2$	61 Pm $4f^5 6s^2$	62 Sm $4f^6 6s^2$	63 Eu $4f^7 6s^2$	64 Gd $4f^7 5d^1 6s^2$	65 Tb $4f^9 6s^2$	66 Dy $4f^{10} 6s^2$	67 Ho $4f^{11} 6s^2$	68 Er $4f^{12} 6s^2$	69 Tm $4f^{13} 6s^2$	70 Yb $4f^{14} 6s^2$

Actinide series [Rn]

89 Ac $6d^1 7s^2$	90 Th $6d^2 7s^2$	91 Pa $5f^2 6d^1 7s^2$	92 U $5f^3 6d^1 7s^2$	93 Np $5f^4 6d^1 7s^2$	94 Pu $5f^6 7s^2$	95 Am $5f^7 7s^2$	96 Cm $5f^7 6d^1 7s^2$	97 Bk $5f^9 7s^2$	98 Cf $5f^{10} 7s^2$	99 Es $5f^{11} 7s^2$	100 Fm $5f^{12} 7s^2$	101 Md $5f^{13} 7s^2$	102 No $5f^{14} 7s^2$

☐ Metals   ▩ Metalloids   ☐ Nonmetals

▲ **Figure 6.30   Valence electron configurations of the elements.**

ACTIVITY
Periodic Table

Figure 6.30 ▲ gives the valence ground-state electron configurations for all the elements. You can use this figure to check your answers as you practice writing electron configurations. We have written these configurations with orbitals listed in order of increasing principal quantum number. As we saw in Sample Exercise 6.9, the orbitals can also be listed in order of filling, as they would be read off the periodic table.

The electron configurations in Figure 6.30 allow us to reexamine the concept of *valence electrons*. Notice, for example, that as we proceed from Cl ($[Ne]3s^2 3p^5$) to Br ($[Ar]3d^{10}4s^2 4p^5$) we have added a complete subshell of $3d$ electrons to the outer-shell electrons beyond the noble-gas core of Ar. Although the $3d$ electrons are outer-shell electrons, they are not involved in chemical bonding and are therefore not considered valence electrons. Thus, we consider only the $4s$ and $4p$ electrons of Br to be valence electrons. Similarly, if we compare the electron configuration of Ag and Au, Au has a completely full $4f^{14}$ subshell beyond its noble-gas core, but those $4f$ electrons are not involved in bonding. In general, *for representative elements we do not consider completely full* d *or* f *subshells to be among the valence electrons*, and *for transition elements we likewise do not consider a completely full* f *subshell to be among the valence electrons*.

Science Fundamentals Second Edition

Anomalous Electron Configurations

If you inspect Figure 6.30 closely, you will see that the electron configurations of certain elements appear to violate the rules we have just discussed. For example, the electron configuration of chromium is $[Ar]3d^54s^1$ rather than the $[Ar]3d^44s^2$ configuration we might have expected. Similarly, the configuration of copper is $[Ar]3d^{10}4s^1$ instead of $[Ar]3d^94s^2$. This anomalous behavior is largely a consequence of the closeness of the $3d$ and $4s$ orbital energies. It frequently occurs when there are enough electrons to lead to precisely half-filled sets of degenerate orbitals (as in chromium) or to completely fill a d subshell (as in copper). There are a few similar cases among the heavier transition metals (those with partially filled $4d$ or $5d$ orbitals) and among the f-block metals. Although these minor departures from the expected are interesting, they are not of great chemical significance.

 GIVE IT SOME THOUGHT

The elements Ni, Pd, and Pt are all in the same group. By examining the electron configurations for these elements in Figure 6.30, what can you conclude about the relative energies of the nd and $(n + 1)s$ orbitals for this group?

SAMPLE INTEGRATIVE EXERCISE | Putting Concepts Together

Boron, atomic number 5, occurs naturally as two isotopes, ^{10}B and ^{11}B, with natural abundances of 19.9% and 80.1%, respectively. **(a)** In what ways do the two isotopes differ from each other? Does the electronic configuration of ^{10}B differ from that of ^{11}B? **(b)** Draw the orbital diagram for an atom of ^{11}B. Which electrons are the valence electrons? **(c)** Indicate three major ways in which the $1s$ electrons in boron differ from the $2s$ electrons in the atom. **(d)** Elemental boron reacts with fluorine to form BF_3, a gas. Write a balanced chemical equation for the reaction of solid boron with fluorine gas. **(e)** $\Delta H_f°$ for $BF_3(g)$ is -1135.6 kJ mol^{-1}. Calculate the standard enthalpy change in the reaction of boron with fluorine. **(f)** When BCl_3, also a gas at room temperature, comes into contact with water, the two react to form hydrochloric acid and boric acid, H_3BO_3, a very weak acid in water. Write a balanced net ionic equation for this reaction.

Solution (a) The two nuclides of boron differ in the number of neutrons in the nucleus. ∞ (Sections 2.3 and 2.4) Each of the nuclides contains five protons, but ^{10}B contains five neutrons, whereas ^{11}B contains six neutrons. The two isotopes of boron have identical electron configurations, $1s^22s^22p^1$, because each has five electrons.

(b) The complete orbital diagram is

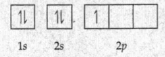

The valence electrons are the ones in the outermost occupied shell, the $2s^2$ and $2p^1$ electrons. The $1s^2$ electrons constitute the core electrons, which we represent as [He] when we write the condensed electron configuration, $[He]2s^22p^1$.

(c) The $1s$ and $2s$ orbitals are both spherical, but they differ in three important respects: First, the $1s$ orbital is lower in energy than the $2s$ orbital. Second, the average distance of the $2s$ electrons from the nucleus is greater than that of the $1s$ electrons, so the $1s$ orbital is smaller than the $2s$. Third, the $2s$ orbital has one node, whereas the $1s$ orbital has no nodes (Figure 6.18).

(d) The balanced chemical equation is

$$2\,B(s) + 3\,F_2(g) \longrightarrow 2\,BF_3(g)$$

(e) $\Delta H° = 2(-1135.6) - [0 + 0] = -2271.2$ kJ. The reaction is strongly exothermic.

(f) $BCl_3(g) + 3\,H_2O(l) \longrightarrow H_3BO_3(aq) + 3\,H^+(aq) + 3\,Cl^-(aq)$. Note that because H_3BO_3 is a very weak acid, its chemical formula is written in molecular form, as discussed in Section 4.3.

Science Fundamentals Second Edition

SUMMARY AND KEY TERMS

Introduction and Section 6.1   The **electronic structure** of an atom describes the energies and arrangement of electrons around the atom. Much of what is known about the electronic structure of atoms was obtained by observing the interaction of light with matter. Visible light and other forms of **electromagnetic radiation** (also known as radiant energy) move through a vacuum at the speed of light, $c = 3.00 \times 10^8$ m/s. Electromagnetic radiation has both electric and magnetic components that vary periodically in wavelike fashion. The wave characteristics of radiant energy allow it to be described in terms of **wavelength**, λ, and **frequency**, ν, which are interrelated: $\lambda\nu = c$.

Section 6.2   Planck proposed that the minimum amount of radiant energy that an object can gain or lose is related to the frequency of the radiation: $E = h\nu$. This smallest quantity is called a **quantum** of energy. The constant h is called **Planck's constant**: $h = 6.626 \times 10^{-34}$ J-s. In the quantum theory, energy is quantized, meaning that it can have only certain allowed values. Einstein used the quantum theory to explain the **photoelectric effect**, the emission of electrons from metal surfaces by light. He proposed that light behaves as if it consists of quantized energy packets called **photons**. Each photon carries energy $E = h\nu$.

Section 6.3   Dispersion of radiation into its component wavelengths produces a **spectrum**. If the spectrum contains all wavelengths, it is called a **continuous spectrum**; if it contains only certain specific wavelengths, the spectrum is called a **line spectrum**. The radiation emitted by excited hydrogen atoms forms a line spectrum; the frequencies observed in the spectrum follow a simple mathematical relationship that involves small integers.

Bohr proposed a model of the hydrogen atom that explains its line spectrum. In this model the energy of the hydrogen atom depends on the value of a number n, called the quantum number. The value of n must be a positive integer $(1, 2, 3, \ldots)$, and each value of n corresponds to a different specific energy, E_n. The energy of the atom increases as n increases. The lowest energy is achieved for $n = 1$; this is called the **ground state** of the hydrogen atom. Other values of n correspond to **excited states** of the atom. Light is emitted when the electron drops from a higher energy state to a lower energy state; light must be absorbed to excite the electron from a lower energy state to a higher one. The frequency of light emitted or absorbed must be such that $h\nu$ equals the difference in energy between two allowed states of the atom.

Section 6.4   De Broglie proposed that matter, such as electrons, should exhibit wavelike properties; this hypothesis of **matter waves** was proved experimentally by observing the diffraction of electrons. An object has a characteristic wavelength that depends on its **momentum**, mv: $\lambda = h/mv$. Discovery of the wave properties of the electron led to Heisenberg's **uncertainty**

principle, which states that there is an inherent limit to the accuracy with which the position and momentum of a particle can be measured simultaneously.

Section 6.5   In the quantum mechanical model of the hydrogen atom, the behavior of the electron is described by mathematical functions called **wave functions**, denoted with the Greek letter ψ. Each allowed wave function has a precisely known energy, but the location of the electron cannot be determined exactly; rather, the probability of it being at a particular point in space is given by the **probability density**, ψ^2. The **electron density** distribution is a map of the probability of finding the electron at all points in space.

The allowed wave functions of the hydrogen atom are called **orbitals**. An orbital is described by a combination of an integer and a letter, corresponding to values of three quantum numbers for the orbital. The principal quantum number, n, is indicated by the integers 1, 2, 3, ... This quantum number relates most directly to the size and energy of the orbital. The azimuthal quantum number, l, is indicated by the letters s, p, d, f, and so on, corresponding to the values of 0, 1, 2, 3, ... The l quantum number defines the shape of the orbital. For a given value of n, l can have integer values ranging from 0 to $n - 1$. The magnetic quantum number, m_l, relates to the orientation of the orbital in space. For a given value of l, m_l can have integral values ranging from $-l$ to l. Cartesian labels can be used to label the orientations of the orbitals. For example, the three $3p$ orbitals are designated $3p_x, 3p_y$, and $3p_z$, with the subscripts indicating the axis along which the orbital is oriented.

An **electron shell** is the set of all orbitals with the same value of n, such as $3s, 3p$, and $3d$. In the hydrogen atom all the orbitals in an electron shell have the same energy. A **subshell** is the set of one or more orbitals with the same n and l values; for example, $3s, 3p$, and $3d$ are each subshells of the $n = 3$ shell. There is one orbital in an s subshell, three in a p subshell, five in a d subshell, and seven in an f subshell.

Section 6.6   Contour representations are useful for visualizing the spatial characteristics (shapes) of the orbitals. Represented this way, s orbitals appear as spheres that increase in size as n increases. The **radial probability function** tells us the probability that the electron will be found at a certain distance from the nucleus. The wave function for each p orbital has two lobes on opposite sides of the nucleus. They are oriented along the x-, y-, and z-axes. Four of the d orbitals appear as shapes with four lobes around the nucleus; the fifth one, the d_{z^2} orbital, is represented as two lobes along the z-axis and a "doughnut" in the xy plane. Regions in which the wave function is zero are called **nodes**. There is zero probability that the electron will be found at a node.

Section 6.7 In many-electron atoms, different subshells of the same electron shell have different energies. For a given value of n, the energy of the subshells increases as the value of l increases: $ns < np < nd < nf$. Orbitals within the same subshell are **degenerate**, meaning they have the same energy.

Electrons have an intrinsic property called **electron spin**, which is quantized. The **spin magnetic quantum number**, m_s, can have two possible values, $+\frac{1}{2}$ and $-\frac{1}{2}$, which can be envisioned as the two directions of an electron spinning about an axis. The **Pauli exclusion principle** states that no two electrons in an atom can have the same values for n, l, m_l, and m_s. This principle places a limit of two on the number of electrons that can occupy any one atomic orbital. These two electrons differ in their value of m_s.

Sections 6.8 and 6.9 The **electron configuration** of an atom describes how the electrons are distributed among the orbitals of the atom. The ground-state electron configurations are generally obtained by placing the electrons in the atomic orbitals of lowest possible energy with the restriction that each orbital can hold no more than two electrons. When electrons occupy a subshell with more than one degenerate orbital, such as the $2p$ subshell, **Hund's rule** states that the lowest energy is attained by maximizing the number of electrons with the same electron spin. For example, in the ground-state electron configuration of carbon, the two $2p$ electrons have the same spin and must occupy two different $2p$ orbitals.

Elements in any given group in the periodic table have the same type of electron arrangements in their outermost shells. For example, the electron configurations of the halogens fluorine and chlorine are $[\text{He}]2s^2 2p^5$ and $[\text{Ne}]3s^2 3p^5$, respectively. The outer-shell electrons are those that lie outside the orbitals occupied in the next lowest noble-gas element. The outer-shell electrons that are involved in chemical bonding are the **valence electrons** of an atom; for the elements with atomic number 30 or less, all the outer-shell electrons are valence electrons. The electrons that are not valence electrons are called **core electrons**.

The periodic table is partitioned into different types of elements, based on their electron configurations. Those elements in which the outermost subshell is an s or p subshell are called the **representative** (or **main-group**) **elements**. The alkali metals (group 1A), halogens (group 7A), and noble gases (group 8A) are representative elements. Those elements in which a d subshell is being filled are called the **transition elements** (or **transition metals**). The elements in which the $4f$ subshell is being filled are called the **lanthanide** (or **rare earth**) **elements**. The **actinide elements** are those in which the $5f$ subshell is being filled. The lanthanide and actinide elements are collectively referred to as the **f-block metals**. These elements are shown as two rows of 14 elements below the main part of the periodic table. The structure of the periodic table, summarized in Figure 6.29, allows us to write the electron configuration of an element from its position in the periodic table.

VISUALIZING CONCEPTS

6.1 Consider the water wave shown here. **(a)** How could you measure the speed of this wave? **(b)** How would you determine the wavelength of the wave? **(c)** Given the speed and wavelength of the wave, how could you determine the frequency of the wave? **(d)** Suggest an independent experiment to determine the frequency of the wave. [Section 6.1]

6.2 A popular kitchen appliance produces electromagnetic radiation with a wavelength of 1 cm. With reference to Figure 6.4, answer the following: **(a)** Would the radiation produced by the appliance be visible by the human eye? **(b)** If the radiation is not visible, do photons of this radiation have more or less energy than photons of visible light? **(c)** Propose an identity to the kitchen appliance. [Section 6.1]

6.3 As shown in the photograph below, an electric stove burner on its highest setting exhibits an orange glow. **(a)** When the burner setting is changed to low, the burner continues to produce heat but the orange glow disappears. How can this observation be explained with reference to one of the fundamental observations that led to the notion of quanta? **(b)** Suppose that the energy provided to the burner could be increased beyond the highest setting of the stove. What would we expect to observe with regard to visible light emitted by the burner? [Section 6.2]

Science Fundamentals Second Edition

6.4 The familiar phenomenon of a rainbow results from the diffraction of sunlight through raindrops. **(a)** Does the wavelength of light increase or decrease as we proceed outward from the innermost band of the rainbow? **(b)** Does the frequency of light increase or decrease as we proceed outward? **(c)** Suppose that instead of sunlight, the visible light from a hydrogen discharge tube (Figure 6.11) was used as the light source. What do you think the resulting "hydrogen discharge rainbow" would look like? [Section 6.3]

6.5 A certain quantum mechanical system has the energy levels shown in the diagram below. The energy levels are indexed by a single quantum number n that is an integer. **(a)** As drawn, which quantum numbers are involved in the transition that requires the most energy? **(b)** Which quantum numbers are involved in the transition that requires the least energy? **(c)** Based on the drawing, put the following in order of increasing wavelength of the light absorbed or emitted during the transition: (i) $n = 1$ to $n = 2$; (ii) $n = 3$ to $n = 2$; (iii) $n = 2$ to $n = 4$; (iv) $n = 3$ to $n = 1$. [Section 6.3]

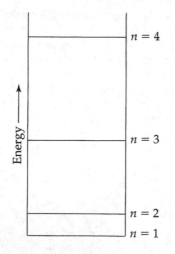

6.6 Consider a fictitious one-dimensional system with one electron. The wave function for the electron, drawn below, is $\psi(x) = \sin x$ from $x = 0$ to $x = 2\pi$. **(a)** Sketch the probability density, $\psi^2(x)$, from $x = 0$ to $x = 2\pi$. **(b)** At what value or values of x will there be the greatest probability of finding the electron? **(c)** What is the probability that the electron will be found at $x = \pi$? What is such a point in a wave function called? [Section 6.5]

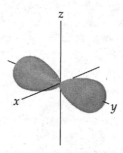

6.7 The contour representation of one of the orbitals for the $n = 3$ shell of a hydrogen atom is shown below. **(a)** What is the quantum number l for this orbital? **(b)** How do we label this orbital? **(c)** How would you modify this sketch to show the analogous orbital for the $n = 4$ shell? [Section 6.6]

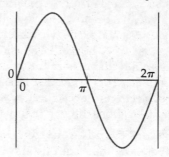

6.8 The drawing below shows part of the orbital diagram for an element. **(a)** As drawn, the drawing is *incorrect*. Why? **(b)** How would you correct the drawing without changing the number of electrons? **(c)** To which group in the periodic table does the element belong? [Section 6.8]

EXERCISES

Radiant Energy

6.9 What are the basic SI units for **(a)** the wavelength of light, **(b)** the frequency of light, **(c)** the speed of light?

6.10 (a) What is the relationship between the wavelength and the frequency of radiant energy? **(b)** Ozone in the upper atmosphere absorbs energy in the 210–230-nm range of the spectrum. In what region of the electromagnetic spectrum does this radiation occur?

6.11 Label each of the following statements as true or false. For those that are false, correct the statement. **(a)** Visible light is a form of electromagnetic radiation. **(b)** The frequency of radiation increases as the wavelength increases. **(c)** Ultraviolet light has longer wavelengths than visible light. **(d)** Electromagnetic radiation and sound waves travel at the same speed.

6.12 Determine which of the following statements are false, and correct them. **(a)** Electromagnetic radiation is incapable of passing through water. **(b)** Electromagnetic radiation travels through a vacuum at a constant speed, regardless of wavelength. **(c)** Infrared light has higher frequencies than visible light. **(d)** The glow from a fireplace, the energy within a microwave oven, and a foghorn blast are all forms of electromagnetic radiation.

6.13 Arrange the following kinds of electromagnetic radiation in order of increasing wavelength: infrared, green light, red light, radio waves, X rays, ultraviolet light.

6.14 List the following types of electromagnetic radiation in order of increasing wavelength: **(a)** the gamma rays produced by a radioactive nuclide used in medical imaging; **(b)** radiation from an FM radio station at 93.1 MHz on the dial; **(c)** a radio signal from an AM radio station at 680 kHz on the dial; **(d)** the yellow light from sodium vapor streetlights; **(e)** the red light of a light-emitting diode, such as in a calculator display.

6.15 **(a)** What is the frequency of radiation that has a wavelength of 955 μm? **(b)** What is the wavelength of radiation that has a frequency of 5.50×10^{14} s^{-1}? **(c)** Would the radiations in part (a) or part (b) be visible to the human eye? **(d)** What distance does electromagnetic radiation travel in 50.0 μs?

6.16 **(a)** What is the frequency of radiation whose wavelength is 10.0 Å? **(b)** What is the wavelength of radiation that has a frequency of 7.6×10^{10} s^{-1}? **(c)** Would the radiations in part (a) or part (b) be detected by an X-ray detector? **(d)** What distance does electromagnetic radiation travel in 25.5 fs?

6.17 Excited mercury atoms emit light strongly at a wavelength of 436 nm. What is the frequency of this radiation? Using Figure 6.4, predict the color associated with this wavelength.

6.18 An argon ion laser emits light at 489 nm. What is the frequency of this radiation? Is this emission in the visible spectrum? If yes, what color is it?

Quantized Energy and Photons

6.19 **(a)** What does it mean when we say energy is quantized? **(b)** Why don't we notice the quantization of energy in everyday activities?

6.20 Einstein's 1905 paper on the photoelectric effect was the first important application of Planck's quantum hypothesis. Describe Planck's original hypothesis, and explain how Einstein made use of it in his theory of the photoelectric effect.

6.21 **(a)** Calculate the smallest increment of energy (a quantum) that can be emitted or absorbed at a wavelength of 438 nm. **(b)** Calculate the energy of a photon of frequency 6.75×10^{12} s^{-1}. **(c)** What wavelength of radiation has photons of energy 2.87×10^{-18} J? In what portion of the electromagnetic spectrum would this radiation be found?

6.22 **(a)** Calculate the smallest increment of energy that can be emitted or absorbed at a wavelength of 10.8 mm. **(b)** Calculate the energy of a photon from an FM radio station at a frequency of 101.1 MHz. **(c)** For what frequency of radiation will a mole of photons have energy 24.7 kJ? In what region of the electromagnetic spectrum would this radiation be found?

6.23 **(a)** Calculate and compare the energy of a photon of wavelength 3.3 μm with that of wavelength 0.154 nm. **(b)** Use Figure 6.4 to identify the region of the electromagnetic spectrum to which each belongs.

6.24 An AM radio station broadcasts at 1010 kHz, and its FM partner broadcasts at 98.3 MHz. Calculate and compare the energy of the photons emitted by these two radio stations.

6.25 One type of sunburn occurs on exposure to UV light of wavelength in the vicinity of 325 nm. **(a)** What is the energy of a photon of this wavelength? **(b)** What is the energy of a mole of these photons? **(c)** How many photons are in a 1.00 mJ burst of this radiation?

6.26 The energy from radiation can be used to cause the rupture of chemical bonds. A minimum energy of 941 kJ/mol is required to break the nitrogen-nitrogen bond in N_2. What is the longest wavelength of radiation that possesses the necessary energy to break the bond? What type of electromagnetic radiation is this?

6.27 A diode laser emits at a wavelength of 987 nm. **(a)** In what portion of the electromagnetic spectrum is this radiation found? **(b)** All of its output energy is absorbed in a detector that measures a total energy of 0.52 J over a period of 32 s. How many photons per second are being emitted by the laser?

6.28 A stellar object is emitting radiation at 3.55 mm. **(a)** What type of electromagnetic spectrum is this radiation? **(b)** If the detector is capturing 3.2×10^8 photons per second at this wavelength, what is the total energy of the photons detected in one hour?

6.29 Molybdenum metal must absorb radiation with a minimum frequency of 1.09×10^{15} s^{-1} before it can emit an electron from its surface via the photoelectric effect. **(a)** What is the minimum energy needed to produce this effect? **(b)** What wavelength radiation will provide a photon of this energy? **(c)** If molybdenum is irradiated with light of wavelength of 120 nm, what is the maximum possible kinetic energy of the emitted electrons?

6.30 It requires a photon with a minimum energy of 4.41×10^{-19} J to emit electrons from sodium metal. **(a)** What is the minimum frequency of light necessary to emit electrons from sodium via the photoelectric effect? **(b)** What is the wavelength of this light? **(c)** If sodium is irradiated with light of 439 nm, what is the maximum possible kinetic energy of the emitted electrons? **(d)** What is the maximum number of electrons that can be freed by a burst of light whose total energy is 1.00 μJ?

Bohr's Model; Matter Waves

6.31 Explain how the existence of line spectra is consistent with Bohr's theory of quantized energies for the electron in the hydrogen atom.

6.32 (a) In terms of the Bohr theory of the hydrogen atom, what process is occurring when excited hydrogen atoms emit radiant energy of certain wavelengths and only those wavelengths? (b) Does a hydrogen atom "expand" or "contract" as it moves from its ground state to an excited state?

6.33 Is energy emitted or absorbed when the following electronic transitions occur in hydrogen? (a) from $n = 4$ to $n = 2$, (b) from an orbit of radius 2.12 Å to one of radius 8.46 Å, (c) an electron adds to the H^+ ion and ends up in the $n = 3$ shell.

6.34 Indicate whether energy is emitted or absorbed when the following electronic transitions occur in hydrogen: (a) from $n = 2$ to $n = 6$, (b) from an orbit of radius 4.76 Å to one of radius 0.529 Å, (c) from the $n = 6$ to the $n = 9$ state.

6.35 Using Equation 6.5, calculate the energy of an electron in the hydrogen atom when $n = 2$ and when $n = 6$. Calculate the wavelength of the radiation released when an electron moves from $n = 6$ to $n = 2$. Is this line in the visible region of the electromagnetic spectrum? If so, what color is it?

6.36 For each of the following electronic transitions in the hydrogen atom, calculate the energy, frequency, and wavelength of the associated radiation, and determine whether the radiation is emitted or absorbed during the transition: (a) from $n = 4$ to $n = 1$, (b) from $n = 5$ to $n = 2$, (c) from $n = 3$ to $n = 6$. Does any of these transitions emit or absorb visible light?

6.37 The visible emission lines observed by Balmer all involved $n_f = 2$. (a) Explain why only the lines with $n_f = 2$ were observed in the visible region of the electromagnetic spectrum. (b) Calculate the wavelengths of the first three lines in the Balmer series—those for which $n_i = 3, 4,$ and 5—and identify these lines in the emission spectrum shown in Figure 6.12.

6.38 The Lyman series of emission lines of the hydrogen atom are those for which $n_f = 1$. (a) Determine the region of the electromagnetic spectrum in which the lines of the Lyman series are observed. (b) Calculate the wavelengths of the first three lines in the Lyman series—those for which $n_i = 2, 3,$ and 4.

[6.39] One of the emission lines of the hydrogen atom has a wavelength of 93.8 nm. (a) In what region of the electromagnetic spectrum is this emission found? (b) Determine the initial and final values of n associated with this emission.

[6.40] The hydrogen atom can absorb light of wavelength 2626 nm. (a) In what region of the electromagnetic spectrum is this absorption found? (b) Determine the initial and final values of n associated with this absorption.

6.41 Use the de Broglie relationship to determine the wavelengths of the following objects: (a) an 85-kg person skiing at 50 km/hr, (b) a 10.0-g bullet fired at 250 m/s, (c) a lithium atom moving at 2.5×10^5 m/s.

6.42 Among the elementary subatomic particles of physics is the muon, which decays within a few nanoseconds after formation. The muon has a rest mass 206.8 times that of an electron. Calculate the de Broglie wavelength associated with a muon traveling at a velocity of 8.85×10^5 cm/s.

6.43 Neutron diffraction is an important technique for determining the structures of molecules. Calculate the velocity of a neutron that has a characteristic wavelength of 0.955 Å. (Refer to the inside cover for the mass of the neutron.)

6.44 The electron microscope has been widely used to obtain highly magnified images of biological and other types of materials. When an electron is accelerated through a particular potential field, it attains a speed of 9.38×10^6 m/s. What is the characteristic wavelength of this electron? Is the wavelength comparable to the size of atoms?

6.45 Using Heisenberg's uncertainty principle, calculate the uncertainty in the position of (a) a 1.50-mg mosquito moving at a speed of 1.40 m/s if the speed is known to within ±0.01 m/s; (b) a proton moving at a speed of $(5.00 \pm 0.01) \times 10^4$ m/s. (The mass of a proton is given in the table of fundamental constants in the inside cover of the text.)

6.46 Calculate the uncertainty in the position of (a) an electron moving at a speed of $(3.00 \pm 0.01) \times 10^5$ m/s, (b) a neutron moving at this same speed. (The masses of an electron and a neutron are given in the table of fundamental constants in the inside cover of the text.) (c) What are the implications of these calculations to our model of the atom?

Quantum Mechanics and Atomic Orbitals

6.47 (a) Why does the Bohr model of the hydrogen atom violate the uncertainty principle? (b) In what way is the description of the electron using a wave function consistent with de Broglie's hypothesis? (c) What is meant by the term *probability density*? Given the wave function, how do we find the probability density at a certain point in space?

6.48 (a) According to the Bohr model, an electron in the ground state of a hydrogen atom orbits the nucleus at a specific radius of 0.53 Å. In the quantum mechanical description of the hydrogen atom, the most probable dis-

tance of the electron from the nucleus is 0.53 Å. Why are these two statements different? (b) Why is the use of Schrödinger's wave equation to describe the location of a particle very different from the description obtained from classical physics? (c) In the quantum mechanical description of an electron, what is the physical significance of the square of the wave function, ψ^2?

6.49 (a) For $n = 4$, what are the possible values of l? (b) For $l = 2$, what are the possible values of m_l?

6.50 How many possible values for l and m_l are there when (a) $n = 3$; (b) $n = 5$?

6.51 Give the numerical values of n and l corresponding to each of the following designations: **(a)** $3p$, **(b)** $2s$, **(c)** $4f$, **(d)** $5d$.

6.52 Give the values for n, l, and m_l for **(a)** each orbital in the $2p$ subshell, **(b)** each orbital in the $5d$ subshell.

6.53 Which of the following represent impossible combinations of n and l: **(a)** $1p$, **(b)** $4s$, **(c)** $5f$, **(d)** $2d$?

6.54 Which of the following are permissible sets of quantum numbers for an electron in a hydrogen atom: **(a)** $n = 2$, $l = 1$, $m_l = 1$; **(b)** $n = 1$, $l = 0$, $m_l = -1$; **(c)** $n = 4$, $l = 2$, $m_l = -2$; **(d)** $n = 3$, $l = 3$, $m_l = 0$? For those combinations that are permissible, write the appropriate designation for the subshell to which the orbital belongs (that is, $1s$, and so on).

6.55 Sketch the shape and orientation of the following types of orbitals: **(a)** s, **(b)** p_z, **(c)** d_{xy}.

6.56 Sketch the shape and orientation of the following types of orbitals: **(a)** p_x, **(b)** d_{z^2}, **(c)** $d_{x^2-y^2}$.

6.57 **(a)** What are the similarities and differences between the $1s$ and $2s$ orbitals of the hydrogen atom? **(b)** In what sense does a $2p$ orbital have directional character? Compare the "directional" characteristics of the p_x and $d_{x^2-y^2}$ orbitals (that is, in what direction or region of space is the electron density concentrated?). **(c)** What can you say about the average distance from the nucleus of an electron in a $2s$ orbital as compared with a $3s$ orbital? **(d)** For the hydrogen atom, list the following orbitals in order of increasing energy (that is, most stable ones first): $4f$, $6s$, $3d$, $1s$, $2p$.

6.58 **(a)** With reference to Figure 6.18, what is the relationship between the number of nodes in an s orbital and the value of the principal quantum number? **(b)** Identify the number of nodes; that is, identify places where the electron density is zero, in the $2p_x$ orbital; in the $3s$ orbital. **(c)** What information is obtained from the radial probability functions in Figure 6.18? **(d)** For the hydrogen atom, list the following orbitals in order of increasing energy: $3s$, $2s$, $2p$, $5s$, $4d$.

Many-Electron Atoms and Electron Configurations

6.59 For a given value of the principal quantum number, n, how do the energies of the s, p, d, and f subshells vary for **(a)** hydrogen, **(b)** a many-electron atom?

6.60 **(a)** The average distance from the nucleus of a $3s$ electron in a chlorine atom is smaller than that for a $3p$ electron. In light of this fact, which orbital is higher in energy? **(b)** Would you expect it to require more or less energy to remove a $3s$ electron from the chlorine atom, as compared with a $2p$ electron? Explain.

6.61 **(a)** What are the possible values of the electron spin quantum number? **(b)** What piece of experimental equipment can be used to distinguish electrons that have different values of the electron spin quantum number? **(c)** Two electrons in an atom both occupy the $1s$ orbital. What quantity must be different for the two electrons? What principle governs the answer to this question?

6.62 **(a)** State the Pauli exclusion principle in your own words. **(b)** The Pauli exclusion principle is, in an important sense, the key to understanding the periodic table. Explain why.

6.63 What is the maximum number of electrons that can occupy each of the following subshells: **(a)** $3p$, **(b)** $5d$, **(c)** $2s$, **(d)** $4f$?

6.64 What is the maximum number of electrons in an atom that can have the following quantum numbers: **(a)** $n = 2$, $m_s = -\frac{1}{2}$; **(b)** $n = 5$, $l = 3$; **(c)** $n = 4$, $l = 3$, $m_l = -3$; **(d)** $n = 4$, $l = 1$, $m_l = 1$.

6.65 **(a)** What does each box in an orbital diagram represent? **(b)** What quantity is represented by the direction (either up or down) of the half arrows in an orbital diagram? **(c)** Is Hund's rule needed to write the electron configuration of beryllium? Explain.

6.66 **(a)** What are "valence electrons"? **(b)** What are "unpaired electrons"? **(c)** How many valence electrons does a P atom possess? How many of these are unpaired?

6.67 Write the condensed electron configurations for the following atoms, using the appropriate noble-gas core abbreviations: **(a)** Cs, **(b)** Ni, **(c)** Se, **(d)** Cd, **(e)** Ac, **(f)** Pb.

6.68 Write the condensed electron configurations for the following atoms, and indicate how many unpaired electrons each has: **(a)** Ga, **(b)** Ca, **(c)** V, **(d)** I, **(e)** Y, **(f)** Pt, **(g)** Lu.

6.69 Meitnerium, Mt, element 109, named after Lisa Meitner, is a transition metal expected to have the same outer-electron configuration as iridium. By using this observation (and without looking at Figure 6.30), write the electron configuration of meitnerium. Use [Rn] to represent the first 86 electrons of the electron configuration.

6.70 In 1999 it was reported that element 118 had been made artificially. This report was retracted in 2001, and since then there have been no other claims that element 118 can be made. **(a)** Write the electron configuration for element 118. **(b)** How many unpaired electrons would you expect an atom of element 118 to have? **(c)** To which group of elements in the periodic table would you expect element 118 to belong?

6.71 Identify the specific element that corresponds to each of the following electron configurations: **(a)** $1s^2 2s^2 2p^6 3s^2$, **(b)** [Ne]$3s^2 3p^1$, **(c)** [Ar]$4s^1 3d^5$, **(d)** [Kr]$5s^2 4d^{10} 5p^4$.

6.72 Identify the group of elements that corresponds to each of the following generalized electron configurations:
(a) [noble gas] $ns^2 np^5$
(b) [noble gas] $ns^2 (n-1)d^2$
(c) [noble gas] $ns^2 (n-1)d^{10} np^1$
(d) [noble gas] $ns^2 (n-2)f^6$

6.73 What is wrong with the following electron configurations for atoms in their ground states? **(a)** $1s^2 2s^2 3s^1$, **(b)** [Ne]$2s^2 2p^3$, **(c)** [Ne]$3s^2 3d^5$.

6.74 The following electron configurations represent excited states. Identify the element, and write its ground-state condensed electron configuration. **(a)** $1s^2 2s^2 3p^2 4p^1$, **(b)** [Ar]$3d^{10} 4s^1 4p^4 5s^1$, **(c)** [Kr]$4d^6 5s^2 5p^1$.

Additional Exercises

6.75 Consider the two waves shown here, which we will consider to represent two electromagnetic radiations:
(a) What is the wavelength of wave A? Of wave B?
(b) What is the frequency of wave A? Of wave B?
(c) Identify the regions of the electromagnetic spectrum to which waves A and B belong.

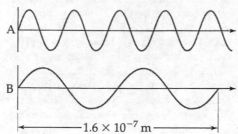

6.76 Certain elements emit light of a specific wavelength when they are burned. Historically, chemists used such emission wavelengths to determine whether specific elements were present in a sample. Some characteristic wavelengths for some of the elements are

Ag	328.1 nm	Fe	372.0 nm
Au	267.6 nm	K	404.7 nm
Ba	455.4 nm	Mg	285.2 nm
Ca	422.7 nm	Na	589.6 nm
Cu	324.8 nm	Ni	341.5 nm

(a) Determine which elements emit radiation in the visible part of the spectrum. (b) Which element emits photons of highest energy? Of lowest energy? (c) When burned, a sample of an unknown substance is found to emit light of frequency $6.59 \times 10^{14}\ s^{-1}$. Which of these elements is probably in the sample?

6.77 In June 2004, the Cassini–Huygens spacecraft began orbiting Saturn and transmitting images to Earth. The closest distance between Saturn and Earth is 746 million miles. What is the minimum amount of time it takes for the transmitted signals to travel from the spacecraft to Earth?

6.78 The rays of the Sun that cause tanning and burning are in the ultraviolet portion of the electromagnetic spectrum. These rays are categorized by wavelength: So-called UV-A radiation has wavelengths in the range of 320–380 nm, whereas UV-B radiation has wavelengths in the range of 290–320 nm. (a) Calculate the frequency of light that has a wavelength of 320 nm. (b) Calculate the energy of a mole of 320-nm photons. (c) Which are more energetic, photons of UV-A radiation or photons of UV-B radiation? (d) The UV-B radiation from the Sun is considered a greater cause of sunburn in humans than is UV-A radiation. Is this observation consistent with your answer to part (c)?

6.79 The watt is the derived SI unit of power, the measure of energy per unit time: 1 W = 1 J/s. A semiconductor laser in a CD player has an output wavelength of 780 nm and a power level of 0.10 mW. How many photons strike the CD surface during the playing of a CD 69 minutes in length?

6.80 Carotenoids, present in all organisms capable of photosynthesis, extend the range of light absorbed by the organism. They exhibit maximal capacity for absorption of light in the range of 440–470 nm. Calculate the energy in kilojoules represented by absorption of an Avogadro's number of photons of wavelength 455 nm.

[6.81] A photocell, such as the one illustrated in Figure 6.7(b), is a device used to measure the intensity of light. In a certain experiment, when light of wavelength 630 nm is directed onto the photocell, electrons are emitted at the rate of 2.6×10^{-12} C/s. Assume that each photon that impinges on the photocell emits one electron. How many photons per second are striking the photocell? How much energy per second is the photocell absorbing?

6.82 The light-sensitive substance in black-and-white photographic film is AgBr. Photons provide the energy necessary to transfer an electron from Br^- to Ag^+ to produce Ag and Br and thereby darken the film. (a) If a minimum energy of 2.00×10^5 J/mol is needed for this process, what is the minimum energy needed by each photon? (b) Calculate the wavelength of the light necessary to provide photons of this energy. (c) Explain why this film can be handled in a darkroom under red light.

[6.83] In an experiment to study the photoelectric effect, a scientist measures the kinetic energy of ejected electrons as a function of the frequency of radiation hitting a metal surface. She obtains the following plot:

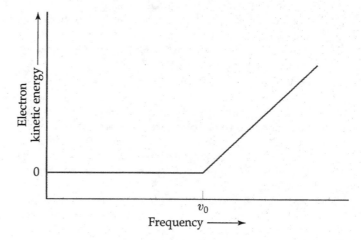

The point labeled "ν_0" corresponds to light with a wavelength of 680 nm. (a) What is the value of ν_0 in s^{-1}? (b) What is the value of the work function of the metal in units of kJ/mol of ejected electrons? (c) What happens when the metal is irradiated with light of frequency less than ν_0? (d) Note that when the frequency of the light is greater than ν_0, the plot shows a straight line with a nonzero slope. Why is this the case? (e) Can you determine the slope of the line segment discussed in part (d)? Explain.

6.84 The series of emission lines of the hydrogen atom for which $n_f = 3$ is called the *Paschen series.* (a) Determine the region of the electromagnetic spectrum in which the lines of the Paschen series are observed. (b) Calculate the wavelengths of the first three lines in the Paschen series—those for which $n_i = 4, 5,$ and 6.

6.85 When the spectrum of light from the Sun is examined in high resolution in an experiment similar to that illustrated in Figure 6.10, dark lines are evident. These are called Fraunhofer lines, after the scientist who studied them extensively in the early nineteenth century. Altogether, about 25,000 lines have been identified in the solar spectrum between 2950 Å and 10,000 Å. The Fraunhofer lines are attributed to absorption of certain wavelengths of the Sun's "white" light by gaseous elements in the Sun's atmosphere. (a) Describe the process that causes absorption of specific wavelengths of light from the solar spectrum. (b) If a scientist wanted to know which Fraunhofer lines belonged to a given element, say neon, what experiments could she conduct here on Earth to provide data?

[6.86] Bohr's model can be used for hydrogen-like ions—ions that have only one electron, such as He^+ and Li^{2+}. (a) Why is the Bohr model applicable to He^+ ions but not to neutral He atoms? (b) The ground-state energies of H, He^+, and Li^{2+} are tabulated as follows:

Atom or ion	H	He^+	Li^{2+}
Ground-state energy	-2.18×10^{-18} J	-8.72×10^{-18} J	-1.96×10^{-17} J

By examining these numbers, propose a relationship between the ground-state energy of hydrogen-like systems and the nuclear charge, Z. (c) Use the relationship you derive in part (b) to predict the ground-state energy of the C^{5+} ion.

6.87 Under appropriate conditions, molybdenum emits X rays that have a characteristic wavelength of 0.711 Å. These X rays are used in diffraction experiments to determine the structures of molecules. How fast would an electron have to be moving in order to have the same wavelength as these X rays?

[6.88] An electron is accelerated through an electric potential to a kinetic energy of 18.6 keV. What is its characteristic wavelength? [Hint: Recall that the kinetic energy of a moving object is $E = \frac{1}{2}mv^2$, where m is the mass of the object and v is the speed of the object.]

6.89 What is the difference between an *orbit* (Bohr model of the hydrogen atom) and an *orbital* (quantum mechanical model of the hydrogen atom)?

6.90 Which of the quantum numbers governs (a) the shape of an orbital, (b) the energy of an orbital, (c) the spin properties of the electron, (d) the spatial orientation of the orbital?

[6.91] Consider the discussion of radial probability functions in the "A Closer Look" box in Section 6.6. (a) What is the difference between the probability density as a function of r and the radial probability function as a function of r? (b) What is the significance of the term $4\pi r^2$ in the radial probability functions for the s orbitals? (c) Based on Figures 6.18 and 6.21, make sketches of what you think the probability density as a function of r and the radial probability function would look like for the $4s$ orbital of the hydrogen atom.

6.92 The "magic numbers" in the periodic table are the atomic numbers of elements with high stability (the noble gases): 2, 10, 18, 36, 54, and 86. In terms of allowed values of orbitals and spin quantum numbers, explain why these electron arrangements correspond to special stability.

[6.93] For non-spherically symmetric orbitals, the contour representations (as in Figures 6.22 and 6.23) suggest where nodal planes exist (that is, where the electron density is zero). For example, the p_x orbital has a node wherever $x = 0$; this equation is satisfied by all points on the yz plane, so this plane is called a nodal plane of the p_x orbital. (a) Determine the nodal plane of the p_z orbital. (b) What are the two nodal planes of the d_{xy} orbital? (c) What are the two nodal planes of the $d_{x^2-y^2}$ orbital?

[6.94] As noted in Figure 6.25, the spin of an electron generates a magnetic field, with spin-up and spin-down electrons having opposite fields. In the absence of a magnetic field, a spin-up and a spin-down electron have the same energy. (a) Why do you think that the use of a magnet was important in the discovery of electron spin (see the "A Closer Look" box in Section 6.7)? (b) Imagine that the two spinning electrons in Figure 6.25 were placed between the poles of a horseshoe magnet, with the north pole of the magnet at the top of the figure. Based on what you know about magnets, would you expect the left or right electron in the figure to have the lower energy? (c) A phenomenon called *electron spin resonance* (ESR) is closely related to nuclear magnetic resonance. In ESR a compound with an unpaired electron is placed in a magnetic field, which causes the unpaired electron to have two different energy states analogous to Figure 6.27. ESR uses microwave radiation to excite the unpaired electron from one state to the other. Based on your reading of the "Chemistry and Life" box in Section 6.7, does an ESR experiment require photons of greater or lesser energy than an NMR experiment?

[6.95] The "Chemistry and Life" box in Section 6.7 described the techniques called NMR and MRI. (a) Instruments for obtaining MRI data are typically labeled with a frequency, such as 600 MHz. Why do you suppose this label is relevant to the experiment? (b) What is the value of ΔE in Figure 6.27 that would correspond to the absorption of a photon of radiation with frequency 450 MHz? (c) In general, the stronger the magnetic field, the greater the information obtained from an NMR or MRI experiment. Why do you suppose this is the case?

[6.96] Suppose that the spin quantum number, m_s, could have *three* allowed values instead of two. How would this affect the number of elements in the first four rows of the periodic table?

6.97 Using only a periodic table as a guide, write the condensed electron configurations for the following atoms: (a) Se, (b) Rh, (c) Si, (d) Hg, (e) Hf.

6.98 Scientists have speculated that element 126 might have a moderate stability, allowing it to be synthesized and characterized. Predict what the condensed electron configuration of this element might be.

Integrative Exercises

[6.99] Microwave ovens use microwave radiation to heat food. The microwaves are absorbed by moisture in the food, which is transferred to other components of the food. As the water becomes hotter, so does the food. Suppose that the microwave radiation has a wavelength of 11.2 cm. How many photons are required to heat 200 mL of coffee from 23°C to 60°C?

6.100 The stratospheric ozone (O_3) layer helps to protect us from harmful ultraviolet radiation. It does so by absorbing ultraviolet light and falling apart into an O_2 molecule and an oxygen atom, a process known as photodissociation.

$$O_3(g) \longrightarrow O_2(g) + O(g)$$

Use the data in Appendix C to calculate the enthalpy change for this reaction. What is the maximum wavelength a photon can have if it is to possess sufficient energy to cause this dissociation? In what portion of the spectrum does this wavelength occur?

6.101 The discovery of hafnium, element number 72, provided a controversial episode in chemistry. G. Urbain, a French chemist, claimed in 1911 to have isolated an element number 72 from a sample of rare earth (elements 58–71) compounds. However, Niels Bohr believed that hafnium was more likely to be found along with zirconium than with the rare earths. D. Coster and G. von Hevesy, working in Bohr's laboratory in Copenhagen, showed in 1922 that element 72 was present in a sample of Norwegian zircon, an ore of zirconium. (The name hafnium comes from the Latin name for Copenhagen, *Hafnia*). (a) How would you use electron configuration arguments to justify Bohr's prediction? (b) Zirconium, hafnium's neighbor in group 4B, can be produced as a metal by reduction of solid $ZrCl_4$ with molten sodium metal. Write a balanced chemical equation for the reaction. Is this an oxidation-reduction reaction? If yes, what is reduced and what is oxidized? (c) Solid zirconium dioxide, ZrO_2, is reacted with chlorine gas in the presence of carbon. The products of the reaction are $ZrCl_4$ and two gases, CO_2 and CO in the ratio 1:2. Write a balanced chemical equation for the reaction. Starting with a 55.4-g sample of ZrO_2, calculate the mass of $ZrCl_4$ formed, assuming that ZrO_2, is the limiting reagent and

assuming 100% yield. (d) Using their electron configurations, account for the fact that Zr and Hf form chlorides MCl_4 and oxides MO_2.

6.102 (a) Account for formation of the following series of oxides in terms of the electron configurations of the elements and the discussion of ionic compounds in Section 2.7: K_2O, CaO, Sc_2O_3, TiO_2, V_2O_5, CrO_3.   (b) Name these oxides. (c) Consider the metal oxides whose enthalpies of formation (in kJ mol^{-1}) are listed here.

Oxide	$K_2O(s)$	$CaO(s)$	$TiO_2(s)$	$V_2O_5(s)$
ΔH_f°	−363.2	−635.1	−938.7	−1550.6

Calculate the enthalpy changes in the following general reaction for each case:

$$M_nO_m(s) + H_2(g) \longrightarrow nM(s) + mH_2O(g)$$

(You will need to write the balanced equation for each case, then compute $\Delta H°$.) (d) Based on the data given, estimate a value of ΔH_f° for $Sc_2O_3(s)$.

6.103 The first 25 years of the twentieth century were momentous for the rapid pace of change in scientists' understanding of the nature of matter. (a) How did Rutherford's experiments on the scattering of α particles by a gold foil set the stage for Bohr's theory of the hydrogen atom? (b) In what ways is de Broglie's hypothesis, as it applies to electrons, consistent with J. J. Thomson's conclusion that the electron has mass? In what sense is it consistent with proposals that preceded Thomson's work, that the cathode rays are a wave phenomenon?

[6.104] The two most common isotopes of uranium are ^{235}U and ^{238}U. (a) Compare the number of protons, the number of electrons, and the number of neutrons in atoms of these two isotopes. (b) Using the periodic table in the front inside cover, write the electron configuration for a U atom. (c) Compare your answer to part (b) to the electron configuration given in Figure 6.30. How can you explain any differences between these two electron configurations? (d) ^{238}U undergoes radioactive decay to ^{234}Th. How many protons, electrons, and neutrons are gained or lost by the ^{238}U atom during this process? (e) Examine the electron configuration for Th in Figure 6.30. Are you surprised by what you find? Explain.

e MEDIA EXERCISES

These exercises make use of the interactive objects available online in OneKey or the Companion Website, and on your Accelerator CD. Access to these resources comes in your MediaPak.

6.105 The **Electromagnetic Spectrum** activity (*6.1*) allows you to choose a color in the visible spectrum and see its wavelength, frequency, and energy per photon. (a) What is the wavelength range of blue light? (b) What are the ranges of its frequency and energy per photon? (c) Exercise 6.25 indicates that a type of sunburn is caused by light with wavelength ~325 nm. Would you expect any of the visible wavelengths to cause sunburn? Explain.

6.106 In the **Flame Tests for Metals** movie (*6.3*) the characteristic color of the flame is produced by emissions at several visible wavelengths, with the most intense spectral lines dominating the color. For instance, the most intense visible lines in the spectrum of lithium occur at ~671 nm. (a) What color is light of this wavelength? (b) At what approximate wavelength would you expect to find the most intense lines in the visible spectrum of potassium? (c) Based on the movie, how would you expect the intensity of visible lines in the spectrum of potassium to compare to those in the spectrum of lithium? (d) Would it be possible to verify the presence of individual metals using flame color if several metal salts were mixed together? If not, explain why not.

6.107 In the **Radial Electron Distribution** animation (6.6) the radial electron density plots of helium, neon, and argon are all placed on the same graph. **(a)** Explain why the maximum for the helium plot and the first maximum for each of the other two occur at significantly different distances from the nucleus. **(b)** Based on how far the *outermost* maximum for each plot is from the nucleus, predict which pair would have the greater difference between their first ionization energies (the energy required to remove completely an electron from the outermost

shell): helium and neon, or neon and argon. Explain your reasoning.

6.108 The electron configuration given in Exercise 6.71(c) is one of a handful of examples of an *s* electron being "stolen" in order to fill or half-fill a *d* subshell. (As seen in the **Electron Configurations** animation (6.8), there is special stability associated with filled and half-filled subshells.) **(a)** Using the **Electron Configuration** activity (6.8), identify at least three more examples like this. **(b)** Are there any instances of *both s* electrons being stolen in order to fill a *d* subshell? If so, name the element(s). **(c)** Why is this phenomenon not observed in *p*-block elements? That is, why is chlorine's electron configuration $[Ne]3s^23p^5$ rather than $[Ne]3s^13p^6$?

⬢ eLABORATORY EXERCISES

These exercises allow students to apply the concepts and skills for this chapter in the simulated laboratory of Virtual ChemLab. Worksheets for each of these exercises are found in the Virtual ChemLab Workbook in your MediaPak.

6.109 *(VCL 6-1) Blackbody Radiation*
In the early 1900s several experimental results appeared to be in conflict with classical physics. One of these experiments was the study of blackbody radiation. A blackbody is a solid (such as a piece of iron) that does not emit light at low temperatures, but when heated, the "blackbody" begins to emit first red and then orange light and at higher temperatures eventually becomes white-hot. The intensity of the emitted light is also a function of temperature. In this problem you will make observations similar to those of Max Planck (1858–1947), who, through his study of blackbody radiation, found an explanation that revolutionized how scientists think about radiated energy.

6.110 *(VCL 6-2) Photoelectric Effect*
Though Albert Einstein is most famous for $E = mc^2$ and his work in describing relativity in mechanics, his Nobel Prize was for understanding a very simple experiment. It was long understood that if you directed light of a certain wavelength at a piece of metal, it would emit electrons. In classical theory the energy of the light was thought to be based on its intensity and not its frequency. However, the results of the photoelectric effect contradicted classical theory. These inconsistencies led Einstein to suggest that we need to think of light as being composed of particles (photons) and not just as waves. In this experiment you will reproduce a photoelectric experiment and show that the energy (E) of a photon of light is related to its frequency and not its intensity.

6.111 *(VCL 6-3) The Rydberg Equation*
When a sample of gas is excited by applying a large alternating electric field, the gas emits light at certain discrete wavelengths, but the classical picture of atoms would allow electrons to be at any energy level and thus the energy would be continuous over all wavelengths. In the late 1800s two scientists, Johann Balmer and Johannes Rydberg, developed a mathematical equation that correlated the wavelength of the emitted light for certain gases such as H_2. Later, Niels Bohr's concept of quantized "jumps" by electrons between orbits was shown to be consistent with the Rydberg equation. In this assignment you will measure the wavelengths of the lines in the hydrogen emission spectra and graphically determine the value of the Rydberg constant, R_H.

6.112 *(VCL 6-4) Atomic Emission Spectra*
When a sample of gas is excited by applying a large alternating electric field, the gas emits light at certain discrete wavelengths. The intensity and wavelength of the light that is emitted is called the atomic emission spectrum and is unique for each gas. In this assignment you will measure the emission spectra for several gases and make some observations about the differences in their spectra.

6.113 *(VCL 6-5) Heisenberg Uncertainty Principle*
It has long been known that if you shine light through narrow slits that are spaced at small intervals, the light will form a diffraction pattern. A diffraction pattern is a series of light and dark patterns caused by wave interference. The wave interference can be either constructive (light) or destructive (dark). In this experiment you will shine a laser through a device with two slits where the spacing can be adjusted, and you will investigate the patterns that will be made at a distance from the slits. From this you will be able to study the effect of the Heisenberg uncertainty principle on the diffraction of light.

7.1 Development of the Periodic Table

7.2 Effective Nuclear Charge

7.3 Sizes of Atoms and Ions

7.4 Ionization Energy

7.5 Electron Affinities

7.6 Metals, Nonmetals, and Metalloids

7.7 Group Trends for the Active Metals

7.8 Group Trends for Selected Nonmetals

WHAT'S AHEAD

- Our discussion begins with a brief history of the periodic table. (*Section 7.1*)

- We will see that many properties of atoms depend both on the net attraction of the outer electrons to the nucleus (an attraction that is due to the *effective nuclear charge*) and on the average distance of those electrons from the nucleus. (*Sections 7.2 and 7.3*)

- We will examine periodic trends in the *atomic size*, *ionization energy*, and *electron affinity* of atoms. (*Sections 7.3, 7.4, and 7.5*)

- We will also examine the sizes of ions and their electron configurations. (*Sections 7.3 and 7.4*)

- We will explore some of the differences in the physical and chemical properties of metals, nonmetals, and metalloids. (*Section 7.6*)

- Finally, we will discuss some periodic trends in the chemistry of the active metals (groups 1A and 2A), of hydrogen, and of several other nonmetals (groups 6A to 8A). (*Sections 7.7 and 7.8*)

Periodic Properties of the Elements

THE BEAUTY OF AN IMPRESSIONIST OIL PAINTING, such as the Monet masterpiece shown here, begins with chemistry. Colorful inorganic salts are suspended in various organic media that contain hydrocarbons and other molecular substances. Indeed, the great painters had a gift for using compounds of elements that span nearly the entire periodic table.

Today the periodic table is still the most significant tool chemists have for organizing and remembering chemical facts. As we saw in Chapter 6, the periodic nature of the table arises from the repeating patterns in the electron configurations of the elements. Elements in the same column of the table contain the same number of electrons in their **valence orbitals**, the occupied orbitals that hold the electrons involved in bonding. For example, O ([He]$2s^2 2p^4$) and S ([Ne]$3s^2 3p^4$) are both members of group 6A; the similarity of the electron distribution in their valence s and p orbitals leads to similarities in the properties of these two elements. When we compare O and S, however, it is apparent that they exhibit differences as well, not the least of which is that oxygen is a colorless gas at room temperature, whereas sulfur is a yellow solid (Figure 7.1 ▶)! One of the major differences between atoms of these two elements is their electron configurations: The outermost electrons of O are in the second shell, whereas those of S are in the third shell. We will see that electron configurations can be used to explain differences as well as similarities in the properties of elements.

OIL PAINTS CONTAIN PIGMENTS, which are usually highly colored salts, suspended in an organic carrier composed of a variety of heavy hydrocarbon molecules. This painting, by the famous French Impressionist Claude Monet (1840–1926), is entitled *La rue Montorgueil, fête du 30 juin 1878*. Claude Monet (1840–1926) "Rue Montorgueil in Paris, Festival of 30 June 1878" 1878. Herve Lewandowski/Reunion des Musees Nationaux/Art Resource, NY.

261

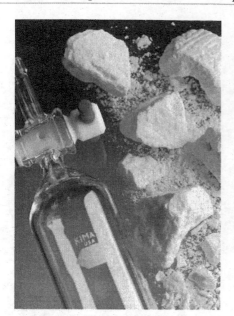

▲ **Figure 7.1   Oxygen and sulfur.** Because they are both group 6A elements, oxygen and sulfur have many chemical similarities. They also have many differences, however, including the forms they take at room temperature. Oxygen consists of O_2 molecules that appear as a colorless gas (shown here enclosed in a glass container on the left). In contrast, sulfur consists of S_8 molecules that form a yellow solid.

In this chapter we explore how some of the important properties of elements change as we move across a row or down a column of the periodic table. In many cases the trends within a row or column allow us to make predictions about the physical and chemical properties of the elements.

7.1 | Development of the Periodic Table

The discovery of the chemical elements has been an ongoing process since ancient times (Figure 7.2 ▼). Certain elements, such as gold, appear in nature in elemental form and were thus discovered thousands of years ago. In contrast, some elements are radioactive and intrinsically unstable. We know about them only because of technology developed in the twentieth century.

The majority of the elements, although stable, are dispersed widely in nature and are incorporated into numerous compounds. For centuries, therefore, scientists were unaware of their existence. In the early nineteenth century, advances in chemistry made it easier to isolate elements from their compounds. As a result, the number of known elements more than doubled from 31 in 1800 to 63 by 1865.

As the number of known elements increased, scientists began to investigate the possibilities of classifying them in useful ways. In 1869, Dmitri Mendeleev in Russia and Lothar Meyer in Germany published nearly identical classification schemes. Both scientists noted that similar chemical and physical properties recur periodically when the elements are arranged in order of increasing atomic weight. Scientists at that time had no knowledge of atomic numbers. Atomic weights, however, generally increase with increasing atomic number, so both Mendeleev and Meyer fortuitously arranged the elements in proper sequence. The tables of elements advanced by Mendeleev and Meyer were the forerunners of the modern periodic table.

Although Mendeleev and Meyer came to essentially the same conclusion about the periodicity of elemental properties, Mendeleev is given credit for advancing his ideas more vigorously and stimulating much new work in chemistry. His insistence that elements with similar characteristics be listed in the same family forced him to leave several blank spaces in his table. For example,

▶ **Figure 7.2   Discovering the elements.** Periodic table showing the dates of discovery of the elements.

ANIMATION
Periodic Properties

ACTIVITY
Periodic Table

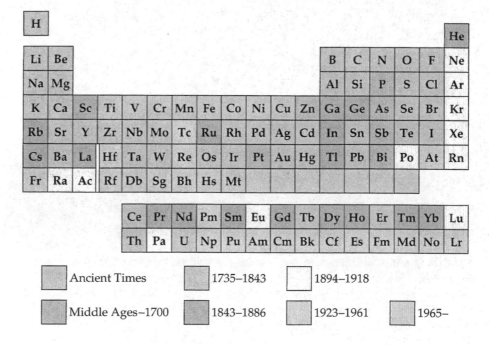

TABLE 7.1 Comparison of the Properties of Eka-Silicon Predicted by Mendeleev with the Observed Properties of Germanium

Property	Mendeleev's Predictions for Eka-Silicon (made in 1871)	Observed Properties of Germanium (discovered in 1886)
Atomic weight	72	72.59
Density (g/cm^3)	5.5	5.35
Specific heat (J/g-k)	0.305	0.309
Melting point (°C)	High	947
Color	Dark gray	Grayish white
Formula of oxide	XO_2	GeO_2
Density of oxide (g/cm^3)	4.7	4.70
Formula of chloride	XCl_4	$GeCl_4$
Boiling point of chloride (°C)	A little under 100	84

both gallium (Ga) and germanium (Ge) were unknown at that time. Mendeleev boldly predicted their existence and properties, referring to them as *eka-aluminum* ("under" aluminum) and *eka-silicon* ("under" silicon), respectively, after the elements under which they appear in the periodic table. When these elements were discovered, their properties closely matched those predicted by Mendeleev, as shown in Table 7.1 ▲.

In 1913, two years after Rutherford proposed the nuclear model of the atom ∞ (Section 2.2), an English physicist named Henry Moseley (1887–1915) developed the concept of atomic numbers. Moseley determined that the frequencies of X rays emitted as different elements were bombarded with high-energy electrons. He found that each element produces X rays of a unique frequency; furthermore, he found that the frequency generally increased as the atomic mass increased. He arranged the X-ray frequencies in order by assigning a unique whole number, called an *atomic number*, to each element. Moseley correctly identified the atomic number as the number of protons in the nucleus of the atom and the number of electrons in the atom. ∞ (Section 2.3)

The concept of atomic number clarified some problems in the early version of the periodic table, which was based on atomic weights. For example, the atomic weight of Ar (atomic number 18) is greater than that of K (atomic number 19). However, when the elements are arranged in order of increasing atomic number, rather than increasing atomic weight, Ar and K appear in their correct places in the table. Moseley's studies also made it possible to identify "holes" in the periodic table, which led to the discovery of other previously unknown elements.

 GIVE IT SOME THOUGHT

Arranging the elements by atomic weight leads to a slightly different order than arranging them by atomic number. How can this happen?

7.2 | Effective Nuclear Charge

Because electrons are negatively charged, they are attracted to nuclei, which are positively charged. Many of the properties of atoms depend not only on their electron configurations but also on how strongly their outer electrons are attracted to the nucleus. Coulomb's law tells us that the strength of the interaction between two electrical charges depends on the signs and magnitudes of the charges and on the distance between them. ∞ (Section 2.3) Thus, the force of attraction between an electron and the nucleus depends on the magnitude of the net nuclear charge acting on the electron and on the average distance between the nucleus and the electron. The force of attraction increases as the nuclear charge increases and decreases as the electron moves farther from the nucleus.

In a many-electron atom, each electron is simultaneously attracted to the nucleus and repelled by the other electrons. In general, there are so many electron-electron repulsions that we cannot analyze the situation exactly. We can, however, estimate the net attraction of each electron to the nucleus by considering how it interacts with the *average* environment created by the nucleus and the other electrons in the atom. This approach allows us to treat each electron individually as though it were moving in the net electric field created by the nucleus and the electron density of the other electrons. We can view this net electric field as if it results from a single positive charge located at the nucleus, called the **effective nuclear charge**, Z_{eff}. It is important to realize that the effective nuclear charge acting on an electron in an atom is smaller than the *actual* nuclear charge because the effective nuclear charge also accounts for the repulsion of the electron by the other electrons in the atom—in other words, $Z_{eff} < Z$. Let's consider how we can get a sense of the magnitude of Z_{eff} for an electron in an atom.

A valence electron in an atom is attracted to the nucleus of the atom and is repelled by the other electrons in the atom. In particular, the electron density that is due to the inner (core) electrons is particularly effective at partially canceling the attraction of the valence electron to the nucleus—we say that the inner electrons partially *shield* or *screen* the outer electrons from the attraction of the nucleus. We can therefore write a simple relationship between the effective nuclear charge, Z_{eff}, and the number of protons in the nucleus, Z:

$$Z_{eff} = Z - S \qquad [7.1]$$

The factor S is a positive number called the *screening constant*, and it represents the portion of the nuclear charge that is screened from the valence electron by the other electrons in the atom. Because the core electrons are most effective at screening a valence electron from the nucleus, *the value of S is usually close to the number of core electrons in an atom.* Electrons in the same valence shell hardly screen one another but do affect the value of S slightly.

Let's take a look at an Na atom to see what we would expect for the magnitude of Z_{eff}. Sodium (atomic number 11) has a condensed electron configuration of [Ne]$3s^1$. The nuclear charge of the atom is 11+, and the Ne inner core consists of 10 electrons ($1s^2 2s^2 2p^6$). Very roughly then, we would expect the $3s$ valence electron of the Na atom to experience an effective nuclear charge of about $11 - 10 = 1+$, as pictured in a simplified way in Figure 7.3(a) ◀. The situation is a bit more complicated because of the electron distributions of atomic orbitals. ∞ (Section 6.6) Recall that a $3s$ electron has a small probability of being found close to the nucleus and inside the core electrons, as shown in Figure 7.3(b). Thus, there is a probability that the $3s$ electron will experience a greater attraction than our simple model suggests, which will increase the value of Z_{eff} somewhat. Indeed, more detailed calculations (which are beyond the scope of our discussion) indicate that the effective nuclear charge acting on the $3s$ electron in Na is 2.5+.

The notion of effective nuclear charge also explains an important effect we noted in Section 6.7, namely, that for a many-electron atom the energies of orbitals with

ANIMATION
Effective Nuclear Charge

▼ **Figure 7.3   Effective nuclear charge.**
(a) The effective nuclear charge experienced by the valence electron in sodium depends mostly on the 11+ charge of the nucleus and the 10− charge of the neon core. If the neon core were totally effective in shielding the valence electron from the nucleus, then the valence electron would experience an effective nuclear charge of 1+.
(b) The 3s electron has some probability of being inside the Ne core. As a consequence of this "penetration," the core is not totally effective in screening the 3s electron from the nucleus. Thus, the effective nuclear charge experienced by the 3s electron is somewhat greater than 1+.

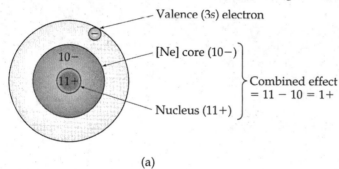

(a)

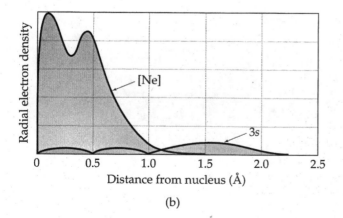

(b)

the same n value increase with increasing l value. For example, consider a carbon atom, for which the electron configuration is $1s^2 2s^2 2p^2$. The energy of the $2p$ orbital ($l = 1$) is slightly higher than that of the $2s$ orbital ($l = 0$) even though both of these orbitals are in the $n = 2$ shell (Figure 6.24). The reason that these orbitals have different energy in a many-electron atom is due to the radial probability functions for the orbitals, shown in Figure 7.4 ▶. Notice that the $2s$ probability function has a small peak fairly close to the nucleus, whereas the $2p$ probability function does not. As a result, an electron in the $2s$ orbital is less effectively screened by the core orbitals than is an electron in the $2p$ orbital. In other words, the electron in the $2s$ orbital has a higher effective nuclear charge than one in the $2p$ orbital. The greater attraction between the 2s electron and the nucleus leads to a lower energy for the $2s$ orbital than for the $2p$ orbital. The same reasoning explains the general trend in orbital energies ($ns < np < nd$) in many-electron atoms.

Finally, let's examine the trends in Z_{eff} for valence electrons as we move from one element to another in the periodic table. The effective nuclear charge increases as we move across any row (period) of the table. Although the number of core electrons stays the same as we move across the row, the actual nuclear charge increases. The valence electrons added to counterbalance the increasing nuclear charge shield one another very ineffectively. Thus, the effective nuclear charge increases steadily. For example, the $1s^2$ core electrons of lithium ($1s^2 2s^1$) shield the $2s$ valence electron from the 3+ nucleus fairly efficiently. Consequently, the outer electron experiences an effective nuclear charge of roughly $3 - 2 = 1+$. For beryllium ($1s^2 2s^2$) the effective nuclear charge experienced by each $2s$ valence electron is larger; in this case, the inner $1s^2$ electrons are shielding a 4+ nucleus, and each $2s$ electron only partially shields the other from the nucleus. Consequently, the effective nuclear charge experienced by each $2s$ electron is about $4 - 2 = 2+$.

Going down a column, the effective nuclear charge experienced by valence electrons changes far less than it does across a row. For example, we would expect the effective nuclear charge for the outer electrons in lithium and sodium to be about the same, roughly $3 - 2 = 1+$ for lithium and $11 - 10 = 1+$ for sodium. In fact, however, the effective nuclear charge increases slightly as we go down a family because larger electron cores are less able to screen the outer electrons from the nuclear charge. We saw earlier, for example, that the value for sodium is 2.5+. Nevertheless, the small change in effective nuclear charge that occurs moving down a column is generally of less importance than the increase that occurs when moving across a row.

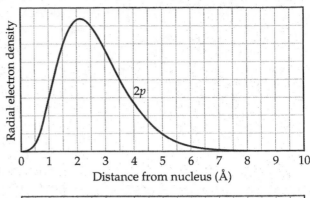

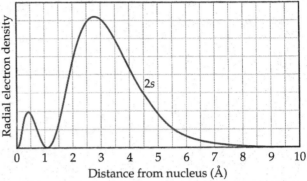

▲ Figure 7.4 2s and 2p radial functions. The radial probability function for the 2s orbital of the hydrogen atom (red curve) shows a "bump" of probability close to the nucleus, whereas that for the 2p orbital (blue curve) does not. As a result, an electron in the 2s orbital for a many-electron atom "sees" more of the nuclear charge than does an electron in the 2p orbital—the effective nuclear charge experienced by the 2s electron is greater than that for the 2p electron. This difference leads to our observation that in a many-electron atom the orbitals for a given n value increase in energy with increasing l value, that is, ns is lower in energy than np, which is lower in energy than nd (Figure 6.24).

 GIVE IT SOME THOUGHT

Which would you expect to experience a greater effective nuclear charge, a 2p electron of an Ne atom or a 3s electron of an Na atom?

7.3 | Sizes of Atoms and Ions

One of the important properties of an atom or an ion is its size. We often think of atoms and ions as hard, spherical objects. According to the quantum mechanical model, however, atoms and ions do not have sharply defined boundaries at which the electron distribution becomes zero. ∞∞ (Section 6.5)

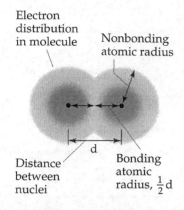

Electron distribution in molecule

Nonbonding atomic radius

Distance between nuclei

d

Bonding atomic radius, $\frac{1}{2}$ d

▲ **Figure 7.5   Distinction between nonbonding and bonding atomic radii.** The nonbonding atomic radius is the effective radius of an atom when it is not involved in bonding to another atom. Values of bonding atomic radii are obtained from measurements of interatomic distances in chemical compounds.

▼ **Figure 7.6   Trends in atomic radii.** Bonding atomic radii for the first 54 elements of the periodic table. The height of the bar for each element is proportional to its radius, giving a "relief map" view of the radii.

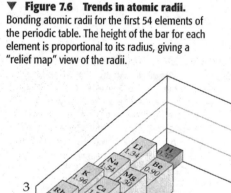
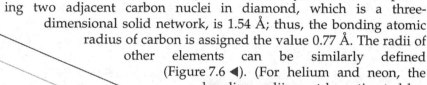

Nevertheless, we can define atomic size in several ways, based on the distances between atoms in various situations.

Imagine a collection of argon atoms in the gas phase. When two atoms collide with each other in the course of their motions, they ricochet apart—somewhat like billiard balls. This happens because the electron clouds of the colliding atoms cannot penetrate each other to any significant extent. The closest distances separating the nuclei during such collisions determine the *apparent* radii of the argon atoms. We might call this radius the *nonbonding atomic radius* of an atom.

When two atoms are chemically bonded to each other, as in the Cl_2 molecule, there is an attractive interaction between the two atoms leading to a chemical bond. We will discuss the nature of such bonding in Chapter 8. For now, the only thing we need to realize is that this attractive interaction brings the two atoms closer together than they would be in a nonbonding collision. We can define an atomic radius based on the distances separating the nuclei of atoms when they are chemically bonded to each other. This distance, called the **bonding atomic radius**, is shorter than the nonbonding atomic radius, as illustrated in Figure 7.5 ◄.

Space-filling models, such as those in Figures 1.1 and 2.20, use nonbonding atomic radii (also called *van der Waals radii*) to determine the size of the spheres used to represent atoms of different elements. When a space-filling model of a molecule is being built, the bonding atomic radii (also called *covalent radii*) are used to determine how much the spheres interpenetrate each other to represent the correct distance between the centers of two adjacent atoms in the molecule.

Scientists have developed a variety of methods for measuring the distances separating nuclei in molecules. From observations of these distances in many molecules, each element can be assigned a bonding atomic radius. For example, in the I_2 molecule, the distance separating the iodine nuclei is observed to be 2.66 Å.* We can define the bonding atomic radius of iodine on this basis to be one-half of the bond distance, namely 1.33 Å. Similarly, the distance separating two adjacent carbon nuclei in diamond, which is a three-dimensional solid network, is 1.54 Å; thus, the bonding atomic radius of carbon is assigned the value 0.77 Å. The radii of other elements can be similarly defined (Figure 7.6 ◄). (For helium and neon, the bonding radii must be estimated because there are no known compounds of these elements.)

Knowing atomic radii allows us to estimate the bond lengths between different elements in molecules. For example, the Cl—Cl bond length in Cl_2 is 1.99 Å, so a radius of 0.99 Å is assigned to Cl. In the compound CCl_4 the measured length of the C—Cl bond is 1.77 Å, very close to the sum (0.77 + 0.99 Å) of the atomic radii of C and Cl.

---

* *Remember:* The angstrom (1 Å = 10^{-10} m) is a convenient metric unit for atomic measurements of length. The angstrom is *not* an SI unit. The most commonly used SI unit for such measurements is the picometer (1 pm = 10^{-12} m; 1 Å = 100 pm).

Science Fundamentals Second Edition

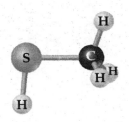

SAMPLE EXERCISE 7.1 | Bond Lengths in a Molecule

Natural gas used in home heating and cooking is odorless. Because natural gas leaks pose the danger of explosion or suffocation, various smelly substances are added to the gas to allow detection of a leak. One such substance is methyl mercaptan, CH_3SH, whose structure is shown in the margin. Use Figure 7.6 to predict the lengths of the C—S, C—H, and S—H bonds in this molecule.

Solution

Analyze and Plan: We are given three bonds and the list of bonding atomic radii. We will assume that each bond length is the sum of the radii of the two atoms involved.

Solve: Using radii for C, S, and H from Figure 7.6, we predict

$$C—S \text{ bond length} = \text{radius of C} + \text{radius of S}$$

$$= 0.77 \text{ Å} + 1.02 \text{ Å} = 1.79 \text{ Å}$$

$$C—H \text{ bond length} = 0.77 \text{ Å} + 0.37 \text{ Å} = 1.14 \text{ Å}$$

$$S—H \text{ bond length} = 1.02 \text{ Å} + 0.37 \text{ Å} = 1.39 \text{ Å}$$

Check: The experimentally determined bond lengths in methyl mercaptan are C—S = 1.82 Å, C—H = 1.10 Å, and S—H = 1.33 Å. (In general, the lengths of bonds involving hydrogen show larger deviations from the values predicted by the sum of the atomic radii than do those bonds involving larger atoms.)

Comment: Notice that the estimated bond lengths using bonding atomic radii are close to, but not exact matches of, the experimental bond lengths. Atomic radii must be used with some caution in estimating bond lengths. In Chapter 8 we will examine some of the average lengths of common types of bonds.

PRACTICE EXERCISE

Using Figure 7.6, predict which will be greater, the P—Br bond length in PBr_3 or the As—Cl bond length in $AsCl_3$.

Answer: P—Br

ANIMATION
Periodic Trends: Atomic Radii

Periodic Trends in Atomic Radii

If we examine the "relief map" of atomic radii shown in Figure 7.6, we observe two interesting trends in the data:

1. Within each column (group), atomic radius tends to increase from top to bottom. This trend results primarily from the increase in the principal quantum number (n) of the outer electrons. As we go down a column, the outer electrons have a greater probability of being farther from the nucleus, causing the atom to increase in size.

2. Within each row (period), atomic radius tends to decrease from left to right. The major factor influencing this trend is the increase in the effective nuclear charge (Z_{eff}) as we move across a row. The increasing effective nuclear charge steadily draws the valence electrons closer to the nucleus, causing the atomic radius to decrease.

GIVE IT SOME THOUGHT

As we proceed across a row of the periodic table, atomic weight increases but atomic radius decreases. Are these trends a contradiction?

SAMPLE EXERCISE 7.2 | Atomic Radii

Referring to a periodic table, arrange (as much as possible) the following atoms in order of increasing size: $_{15}P$, $_{16}S$, $_{33}As$, $_{34}Se$. (Atomic numbers are given for the elements to help you locate them quickly in the periodic table.)

Science Fundamentals Second Edition

491

Solution

Analyze and Plan: We are given the chemical symbols for four elements. We can use their relative positions in the periodic table and the two periodic trends just described to predict the relative order of their atomic radii.

Solve: Notice that P and S are in the same row of the periodic table, with S to the right of P. Therefore, we expect the radius of S to be smaller than that of P. (Radii decrease as we move from left to right.) Likewise, the radius of Se is expected to be smaller than that of As. We also notice that As is directly below P and that Se is directly below S. We expect, therefore, that the radius of As is greater than that of P and the radius of Se is greater than that of S. From these observations, we predict $S < P$, $P < As$, $S < Se$, and $Se < As$. We can therefore conclude that S has the smallest radius of the four elements and that As has the largest radius.

Using just the two trends described above, we cannot determine whether P or Se has the larger radius; to go from P to Se in the periodic table, we must move down (radius tends to increase) and to the right (radius tends to decrease). In Figure 7.6 we see that the radius of Se (1.16 Å) is greater than that of P (1.06 Å). If you examine the figure carefully, you will discover that for the representative elements the increase in radius moving down a column tends to be the greater effect. There are exceptions, however.

Check: From Figure 7.6, we have S (1.02 Å) $<$ P (1.06 Å) $<$ Se (1.16 Å) $<$ As (1.19 Å).

Comment: Note that the trends we have just discussed are for the representative elements. You will see in Figure 7.6 that the transition elements do not show a regular decrease from left to right in a row.

▪ PRACTICE EXERCISE

Arrange the following atoms in order of increasing atomic radius: Na, Be, Mg.
Answer: Be $<$ Mg $<$ Na

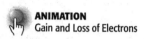
ANIMATION
Gain and Loss of Electrons

Periodic Trends in Ionic Radii

The radii of ions are based on the distances between ions in ionic compounds. Like the size of an atom, the size of an ion depends on its nuclear charge, on the number of electrons it possesses, and on the orbitals in which the valence electrons reside. The formation of a cation vacates the most spatially extended occupied orbitals in an atom and also decreases the number of electron-electron repulsions. As a consequence, *cations are smaller than their parent atoms*, as illustrated in Figure 7.7 ▶. The opposite is true of anions. When electrons are added to a neutral atom to form an anion, the increased electron-electron repulsions cause the electrons to spread out more in space. Thus, *anions are larger than their parent atoms.*

For ions carrying the same charge, size increases as we go down a column in the periodic table. This trend is also seen in Figure 7.7. As the principal quantum number of the outermost occupied orbital of an ion increases, the radius of the ion increases.

▪ SAMPLE EXERCISE 7.3 | Atomic and Ionic Radii

Arrange these atoms and ions in order of decreasing size: Mg^{2+}, Ca^{2+}, and Ca.

Solution Cations are smaller than their parent atoms, and so the Ca^{2+} ion is smaller than the Ca atom. Because Ca is below Mg in group 2A of the periodic table, Ca^{2+} is larger than Mg^{2+}. Consequently, $Ca > Ca^{2+} > Mg^{2+}$.

▪ PRACTICE EXERCISE

Which of the following atoms and ions is largest: S^{2-}, S, O^{2-}?
Answer: S^{2-}

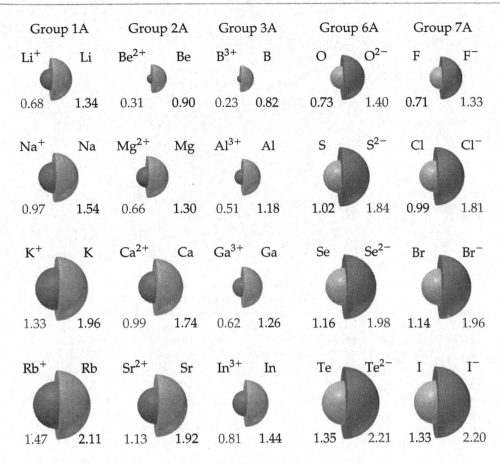

Group 1A		Group 2A		Group 3A		Group 6A		Group 7A	
Li^+	Li	Be^{2+}	Be	B^{3+}	B	O	O^{2-}	F	F^-
0.68	1.34	0.31	0.90	0.23	0.82	0.73	1.40	0.71	1.33
Na^+	Na	Mg^{2+}	Mg	Al^{3+}	Al	S	S^{2-}	Cl	Cl^-
0.97	1.54	0.66	1.30	0.51	1.18	1.02	1.84	0.99	1.81
K^+	K	Ca^{2+}	Ca	Ga^{3+}	Ga	Se	Se^{2-}	Br	Br^-
1.33	1.96	0.99	1.74	0.62	1.26	1.16	1.98	1.14	1.96
Rb^+	Rb	Sr^{2+}	Sr	In^{3+}	In	Te	Te^{2-}	I	I^-
1.47	2.11	1.13	1.92	0.81	1.44	1.35	2.21	1.33	2.20

An **isoelectronic series** is a group of ions all containing the same number of electrons. For example, each ion in the isoelectronic series O^{2-}, F^-, Na^+, Mg^{2+}, Al^{3+} has 10 electrons. In any isoelectronic series we can list the members in order of increasing atomic number, and therefore nuclear charge increases as we move through the series. (Recall that the charge on the nucleus of an atom or monatomic ion is given by the atomic number of the element.) Because the number of electrons remains constant, the radius of the ion decreases with increasing nuclear charge, as the electrons are more strongly attracted to the nucleus:

$$\text{—— Increasing nuclear charge} \longrightarrow$$

O^{2-}	F^-	Na^+	Mg^{2+}	Al^{3+}
1.40 Å	1.33 Å	0.97 Å	0.66 Å	0.51 Å

$$\text{—— Decreasing ionic radius} \longrightarrow$$

Notice the positions of these elements in the periodic table and also their atomic numbers. The nonmetal anions precede the noble gas Ne in the table. The metal cations follow Ne. Oxygen, the largest ion in this isoelectronic series, has the lowest atomic number, 8. Aluminum, the smallest of these ions, has the highest atomic number, 13.

CHEMISTRY AND LIFE | Ionic Size Makes a BIG Difference

Ionic size plays a major role in determining the properties of ions in solution. For example, a small difference in ionic size is often sufficient for one metal ion to be biologically important and another not to be. To illustrate, let's examine some of the biological chemistry of the zinc ion (Zn^{2+}) and compare it with the cadmium ion (Cd^{2+}).

Recall from the "Chemistry and Life" box in Section 2.7 that zinc is needed in our diets in trace amounts. Zinc is an essential part of several enzymes, the proteins that facilitate or regulate the speeds of key biological reactions. For example, one of the most important zinc-containing enzymes is *carbonic anhydrase*. This enzyme is found in red blood cells. Its job is to facilitate the reaction of carbon dioxide (CO_2) with water to form the bicarbonate ion (HCO_3^-):

$$CO_2(aq) + H_2O(l) \longrightarrow HCO_3^-(aq) + H^+(aq) \qquad [7.2]$$

You might be surprised to know that our bodies need an enzyme for such a simple reaction. In the absence of carbonic anhydrase, however, the CO_2 produced in cells when they are oxidizing glucose or other fuels in vigorous exercise would be cleared out much too slowly. About 20% of the CO_2 produced by cell metabolism binds to hemoglobin and is carried to the lungs, where it is expelled. About 70% of the CO_2 produced is converted to bicarbonate ion through the action of carbonic anhydrase. When the CO_2 has been converted into bicarbonate ion, it diffuses into the blood plasma and eventually is passed into the lungs in the reverse of Equation 7.2. These processes are illustrated in Figure 7.8 ▶. In the absence of zinc, the carbonic anhydrase would be inactive and serious imbalances would result in the amount of CO_2 present in blood.

Zinc is also found in several other enzymes, including some found in the liver and kidneys. It is obviously essential to life. By contrast, cadmium, zinc's neighbor in group 2B, is extremely toxic to humans. But why are two elements so different?

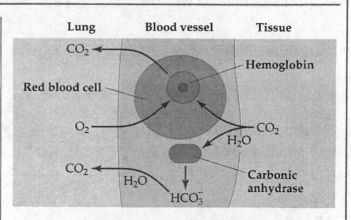

▲ **Figure 7.8 Ridding the body of carbon dioxide.** Illustration of the flow of CO_2 from tissues into blood vessels and eventually into the lungs. About 20% of the CO_2 binds to hemoglobin and is released in the lungs. About 70% is converted by carbonic anhydrase into HCO_3^- ion, which remains in the blood plasma until the reverse reaction releases CO_2 into the lungs. Small amounts of CO_2 simply dissolve in the blood plasma and are released in the lungs.

Both occur as 2+ ions, but Zn^{2+} is smaller than Cd^{2+}. The radius of Zn^{2+} is 0.74 Å; that of Cd^{2+} is 0.95 Å. Can this difference be the cause of such a dramatic reversal of biological properties? The answer is that while size is not the only factor, it is very important. In the carbonic anhydrase enzyme the Zn^{2+} ion is found electrostatically bonded to atoms on the protein, as shown in Figure 7.9 ▼. It turns out that Cd^{2+} binds in this same place preferentially over Zn^{2+}, thus displacing it. When Cd^{2+} is present instead of Zn^{2+}, however, the reaction of CO_2 with water is not facilitated. More seriously, Cd^{2+} inhibits reactions that are essential to the kidneys' functioning.
Related Exercises: 7.28, 7.88, 7.89, and 7.92

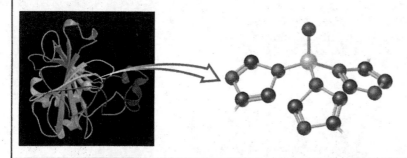

◀ **Figure 7.9 A zinc-containing enzyme.** The enzyme called carbonic anhydrase (left) catalyzes the reaction between CO_2 and water to form HCO_3^-. The ribbon represents the folding of the protein chain. The "active site" of the enzyme (represented by the ball-and-stick model) is where the reaction occurs. (H atoms have been excluded from this model for clarity.) The red sphere represents the oxygen of a water molecule that is bound to the zinc ion (gold sphere) at the center of the active site. The water molecule is replaced by CO_2 in the reaction. The bonds coming off the five-member rings attach the active site to the protein.

■ SAMPLE EXERCISE 7.4 | Ionic Radii in an Isoelectronic Series

Arrange the ions K^+, Cl^-, Ca^{2+}, and S^{2-} in order of decreasing size.

Solution First, we note that this is an isoelectronic series of ions, with all ions having 18 electrons. In such a series, size decreases as the nuclear charge (atomic number) of the ion increases. The atomic numbers of the ions are S (16), Cl (17), K (19), and Ca (20). Thus, the ions decrease in size in the order $S^{2-} > Cl^- > K^+ > Ca^{2+}$.

■ PRACTICE EXERCISE

Which of the following ions is largest, Rb^+, Sr^{2+}, or Y^{3+}?
Answer: Rb^+

Science Fundamentals Second Edition

7.4 | Ionization Energy

The ease with which electrons can be removed from an atom or ion has a major impact on chemical behavior. The **ionization energy** of an atom or ion is the minimum energy required to remove an electron from the ground state of the isolated gaseous atom or ion. The *first ionization energy*, I_1, is the energy needed to remove the first electron from a neutral atom. For example, the first ionization energy for the sodium atom is the energy required for the process

ANIMATION
Ionization Energy

$$Na(g) \longrightarrow Na^+(g) + e^- \qquad [7.3]$$

The *second ionization energy*, I_2, is the energy needed to remove the second electron, and so forth, for successive removals of additional electrons. Thus, I_2 for the sodium atom is the energy associated with the process

$$Na^+(g) \longrightarrow Na^{2+}(g) + e^- \qquad [7.4]$$

The greater the ionization energy, the more difficult it is to remove an electron.

 GIVE IT SOME THOUGHT

Light can be used to ionize atoms and ions, as in Equations 7.3 and 7.4. What concept discussed in Chapter 6 can be related to the ionization of atoms and molecules?

Variations in Successive Ionization Energies

Ionization energies for the elements sodium through argon are listed in Table 7.2 ▼. Notice that the values for a given element increase as successive electrons are removed: $I_1 < I_2 < I_3$, and so forth. This trend exists because with each successive removal, an electron is being pulled away from an increasingly more positive ion, requiring increasingly more energy.

ACTIVITY
Ionization Energies

A second important feature shown in Table 7.2 is the sharp increase in ionization energy that occurs when an inner-shell electron is removed. For example, consider silicon, whose electron configuration is $1s^2 2s^2 2p^6 3s^2 3p^2$ or $[Ne]3s^2 3p^2$. The ionization energies increase steadily from 786 kJ/mol to 4360 kJ/mol for the loss of the four electrons in the outer 3s and 3p subshells. Removal of the fifth electron, which comes from the 2p subshell, requires a great deal more energy: 16,100 kJ/mol. The large increase occurs because the 2p electron is much more likely to be found close to the nucleus than are the four $n = 3$ electrons, and therefore the 2p electron experiences a much greater effective nuclear charge than do the 3s and 3p electrons.

Element	I_1	I_2	I_3	I_4	I_5	I_6	I_7
TABLE 7.2 Successive Values of Ionization Energies, *I*, for the Elements Sodium Through Argon (kJ/mol)							
Na	495	4562			(inner-shell electrons)		
Mg	738	1451	7733				
Al	578	1817	2745	11,577			
Si	786	1577	3232	4356	16,091		
P	1012	1907	2914	4964	6274	21,267	
S	1000	2252	3357	4556	7004	8496	27,107
Cl	1251	2298	3822	5159	6542	9362	11,018
Ar	1521	2666	3931	5771	7238	8781	11,995

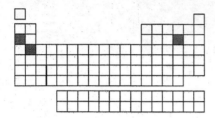

GIVE IT SOME THOUGHT

Which would you expect to be greater, I_1 for a boron atom or I_2 for a carbon atom?

Every element exhibits a large increase in ionization energy when electrons are removed from its noble-gas core. This observation supports the idea that only the outermost electrons, those beyond the noble-gas core, are involved in the sharing and transfer of electrons that give rise to chemical bonding and reactions. The inner electrons are too tightly bound to the nucleus to be lost from the atom or even shared with another atom.

▪ SAMPLE EXERCISE 7.5 | Trends in Ionization Energy

Three elements are indicated in the periodic table in the margin. Based on their locations, predict the one with the largest second ionization energy.

Solution

Analyze and Plan: The locations of the elements in the periodic table allow us to predict the electron configurations. The greatest ionization energies involve removal of core electrons. Thus, we should look first for an element with only one electron in the outermost occupied shell.

Solve: The element in group 1A (Na), indicated by the red box, has only one valence electron. The second ionization energy of this element is associated, therefore, with the removal of a core electron. The other elements indicated, S (green box) and Ca (blue box), have two or more valence electrons. Thus, Na should have the largest second ionization energy.

Check: If we consult a chemistry handbook, we find the following values for the second ionization energies (I_2) of the respective elements: Ca (1,145 kJ/mol) < S (2,252 kJ/mol) < Na (4,562 kJ/mol).

▪ PRACTICE EXERCISE

Which will have the greater third ionization energy, Ca or S?
Answer: Ca

Periodic Trends in First Ionization Energies

We have seen that the ionization energy for a given element increases as we remove successive electrons. What trends do we observe in ionization energy as we move from one element to another in the periodic table? Figure 7.10 ◄ shows a graph of I_1 versus atomic number for the first 54 elements. The important trends are as follows:

1. Within each row (period) of the table, I_1 generally increases with increasing atomic number. The alkali metals show the lowest ionization energy in each row, and the noble gases the highest. There are slight irregularities in this trend that we will discuss shortly.

2. Within each column (group) of the table, the ionization energy generally decreases with increasing atomic number. For example, the ionization energies of the noble gases follow the order He > Ne > Ar > Kr > Xe.

3. The representative elements show a larger range of values of I_1 than do the transition-metal elements. Generally,

▼ **Figure 7.10 First ionization energy versus atomic number.** The red dots mark the beginning of a period (alkali metals), the blue dots mark the end of a period (noble gases), and the black dots indicate other representative elements. Green dots are used for the transition metals.

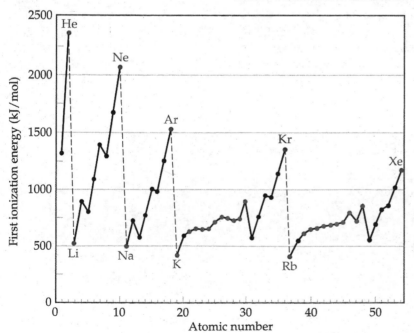

the ionization energies of the transition metals increase slowly as we proceed from left to right in a period. The *f*-block metals, which are not shown in Figure 7.10, also show only a small variation in the values of I_1.

The periodic trends in the first ionization energies of the representative elements are further illustrated in Figure 7.11 ▶.

In general, smaller atoms have higher ionization energies. The same factors that influence atomic size also influence ionization energies. The energy needed to remove an electron from the outermost occupied shell depends on both the effective nuclear charge and the average distance of the electron from the nucleus. Either increasing the effective nuclear charge or decreasing the distance from the nucleus increases the attraction between the electron and the nucleus. As this attraction increases, it becomes harder to remove the electron and, thus, the ionization energy increases. As we move across a period, there is both an increase in effective nuclear charge and a decrease in atomic radius, causing the ionization energy to increase. As we move down a column, however, the atomic radius increases, while the effective nuclear charge changes little. Thus, the attraction between the nucleus and the electron decreases, causing the ionization energy to decrease.

The irregularities within a given row are somewhat more subtle but still readily explained. For example, the decrease in ionization energy from beryllium ($[He]2s^2$) to boron ($[He]2s^22p^1$), shown in Figures 7.10 and 7.11, occurs because the third valence electron of B must occupy the 2p subshell, which is empty for Be. Recall that, as we discussed earlier, the 2p subshell is at a higher energy than the 2s (Figure 6.22). The decrease in ionization energy on going from nitrogen ($[He]2s^22p^3$) to oxygen ($[He]2s^22p^4$) is because of repulsion of paired electrons in the p^4 configuration. Remember that according to Hund's rule, each electron in the p^3 configuration resides in a different p orbital, which minimizes the electron-electron repulsion among the three 2p electrons. ∞∞ (Section 6.8)

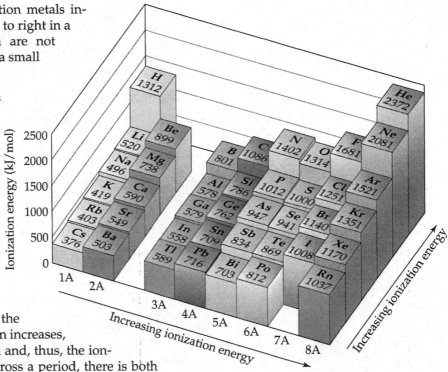

▲ **Figure 7.11 Trends in first ionization energy.** First ionization energies for the representative elements in the first six periods. The ionization energy generally increases from left to right and decreases from top to bottom. The ionization energy of astatine has not been determined.

ANIMATION
Periodic Trends: Ionization Energies

SAMPLE EXERCISE 7.6 | Periodic Trends in Ionization Energy

Referring to a periodic table, arrange the following atoms in order of increasing first ionization energy: Ne, Na, P, Ar, K.

Solution
Analyze and Plan: We are given the chemical symbols for five elements. In order to rank them according to increasing first ionization energy, we need to locate each element in the periodic table. We can then use their relative positions and the trends in first ionization energies to predict their order.
Solve: Ionization energy increases as we move left to right across a row. It decreases as we move from the top of a group to the bottom. Because Na, P, and Ar are in the same row of the periodic table, we expect I_1 to vary in the order Na < P < Ar.

Because Ne is above Ar in group 8A, we expect Ne to have the greater first ionization energy: Ar < Ne. Similarly, K is the alkali metal directly below Na in group 1A, and so we expect I_1 for K to be less than that of Na: K < Na.

From these observations, we conclude that the ionization energies follow the order

$$K < Na < P < Ar < Ne$$

Check: The values shown in Figure 7.11 confirm this prediction.

■ PRACTICE EXERCISE

Which has the lowest first ionization energy, B, Al, C, or Si? Which has the highest first ionization energy?
Answer: Al lowest, C highest

Electron Configurations of Ions

When electrons are removed from an atom to form a cation, they are always removed first from the occupied orbitals having the largest principal quantum number, n. For example, when one electron is removed from a lithium atom ($1s^2 2s^1$), it is the $2s^1$ electron that is removed:

$$Li\ (1s^2 2s^1) \Rightarrow Li^+\ (1s^2)$$

Likewise, when two electrons are removed from Fe ($[Ar]3d^6 4s^2$), the $4s^2$ electrons are the ones removed:

$$Fe\ ([Ar]3d^6 4s^2) \Rightarrow Fe^{2+}\ ([Ar]3d^6)$$

If an additional electron is removed, forming Fe^{3+}, it now comes from a $3d$ orbital because all the orbitals with $n = 4$ are empty:

$$Fe^{2+}\ ([Ar]3d^6) \Rightarrow Fe^{3+}\ ([Ar]3d^5)$$

It may seem odd that the $4s$ electrons are removed before the $3d$ electrons in forming transition-metal cations. After all, in writing electron configurations, we added the $4s$ electrons before the $3d$ ones. In writing electron configurations for atoms, however, we are going through an imaginary process in which we move through the periodic table from one element to another. In doing so, we are adding not only an electron to an orbital but also a proton to the nucleus, in order to change the identity of the element. In ionization, we do not reverse this process because no protons are being removed.

When electrons are added to an atom to form an anion, they are added to the empty or partially filled orbital having the lowest value of n. For example, when an electron is added to a fluorine atom to form the F^- ion, the electron goes into the one remaining vacancy in the $2p$ subshell:

$$F\ (1s^2 2s^2 2p^5) \Rightarrow F^-\ (1s^2 2s^2 2p^6)$$

 GIVE IT SOME THOUGHT

Would Cr^{3+} and V^{2+} have the same or different electron configurations?

■ SAMPLE EXERCISE 7.7 | Electron Configurations of Ions

Write the electron configuration for **(a)** Ca^{2+}, **(b)** Co^{3+}, and **(c)** S^{2-}.

Solution

Analyze and Plan: We are asked to write electron configurations for three ions. To do so, we first write the electron configuration of the parent atom. We then remove electrons to form cations or add electrons to form anions. Electrons are first removed from the orbitals having the highest value of n. They are added to the empty or partially filled orbitals having the lowest value of n.

Solve: (a) Calcium (atomic number 20) has the electron configuration

$$Ca:\ [Ar]4s^2$$

To form a 2+ ion, the two outer electrons must be removed, giving an ion that is iso-electronic with Ar:

$$Ca^{2+}: [Ar]$$

(b) Cobalt (atomic number 27) has the electron configuration

$$Co: [Ar]3d^7 4s^2$$

To form a 3+ ion, three electrons must be removed. As discussed in the text preceding this Sample Exercise, the 4s electrons are removed before the 3d electrons. Consequently, the electron configuration for Co^{3+} is

$$Co^{3+}: [Ar]3d^6$$

(c) Sulfur (atomic number 16) has the electron configuration

$$S: [Ne]3s^2 3p^4$$

To form a 2− ion, two electrons must be added. There is room for two additional electrons in the 3p orbitals. Thus, the S^{2-} electron configuration is

$$S^{2-}: [Ne]3s^2 3p^6 = [Ar]$$

Comment: Remember that many of the common ions of the representative elements, such as Ca^{2+} and S^{2-}, have the same number of electrons as the closest noble gas. ⟨∞⟩ (Section 2.7)

■ PRACTICE EXERCISE

Write the electron configuration for **(a)** Ga^{3+}, **(b)** Cr^{3+}, and **(c)** Br^-.
Answers: **(a)** $[Ar]3d^{10}$, **(b)** $[Ar]3d^3$, **(c)** $[Ar]3d^{10}4s^2 4p^6 = [Kr]$

7.5 | Electron Affinities

The first ionization energy of an atom is a measure of the energy change associated with removing an electron from the atom to form a positively charged ion. For example, the first ionization energy of $Cl(g)$, 1251 kJ/mol, is the energy change associated with the process

$$Ionization\ energy:\quad Cl(g) \longrightarrow Cl^+(g) + e^- \qquad \Delta E = 1251\ kJ/mol \quad [7.5]$$
$$[Ne]3s^2 3p^5 \quad\ [Ne]3s^2 3p^4$$

The positive value of the ionization energy means that energy must be put into the atom in order to remove the electron.

In addition, most atoms can gain electrons to form negatively charged ions. The energy change that occurs when an electron is added to a gaseous atom is called the **electron affinity** because it measures the attraction, or *affinity*, of the atom for the added electron. For most atoms, energy is released when an electron is added. For example, the addition of an electron to a chlorine atom is accompanied by an energy change of −349 kJ/mol, the negative sign indicating that energy is released during the process. We therefore say that the electron affinity of Cl is −349 kJ/mol:*

ANIMATION
Electron Affinity

$$Electron\ affinity:\quad Cl(g) + e^- \longrightarrow Cl^-(g) \qquad \Delta E = -349\ kJ/mol \quad [7.6]$$
$$[Ne]3s^2 3p^5 \qquad\qquad [Ne]3s^2 3p^6$$

It is important to understand the difference between ionization energy and electron affinity: Ionization energy measures the ease with which an atom *loses*

---

* Two sign conventions are used for electron affinity. In most introductory texts, including this one, the thermodynamic sign convention is used: A negative sign indicates that the addition of an electron is an exothermic process, as in the electron affinity given for chlorine, −349 kJ/mol. Historically, however, electron affinity has been defined as the energy released when an electron is added to a gaseous atom or ion. Because 349 kJ/mol is *released* when an electron is added to $Cl(g)$, the electron affinity by this convention would be +349 kJ/mol.

an electron, whereas electron affinity measures the ease with which an atom *gains* an electron.

The greater the attraction between a given atom and an added electron, the more negative the atom's electron affinity. For some elements, such as the noble gases, the electron affinity has a positive value, meaning that the anion is higher in energy than are the separated atom and electron:

$$\text{Ar}(g) + e^- \longrightarrow \text{Ar}^-(g) \qquad \Delta E > 0 \qquad\qquad [7.7]$$

$$\underset{[\text{Ne}]3s^23p^6}{} \qquad\qquad \underset{[\text{Ne}]3s^23p^64s^1}{}$$

The fact that the electron affinity is a positive number means that an electron will not attach itself to an Ar atom; the Ar⁻ ion is unstable and does not form.

Figure 7.12 ◀ shows the electron affinities for the representative elements in the first five rows of the periodic table. Notice that the trends in electron affinity as we proceed through the periodic table are not as evident as they were for ionization energy. The halogens, which are one electron shy of a filled *p* subshell, have the most-negative electron affinities. By gaining an electron, a halogen atom forms a stable negative ion that has a noble-gas configuration (Equation 7.6). The addition of an electron to a noble gas, however, would require that the electron reside in a higher-energy subshell that is empty in the neutral atom (Equation 7.7). Because occupying a higher-energy subshell is energetically very unfavorable, the electron affinity is highly positive. The electron affinities of Be and Mg are positive for the same reason; the added electron would reside in a previously empty *p* subshell that is higher in energy.

The electron affinities of the group 5A elements (N, P, As, Sb) are also interesting. Because these elements have half-filled *p* subshells, the added electron must be put in an orbital that is already occupied, resulting in larger electron-electron repulsions. Consequently, these elements have electron affinities that are either positive (N) or less negative than their neighbors to the left (P, As, Sb).

Electron affinities do not change greatly as we move down a group. For example, consider the electron affinities of the halogens (Figure 7.12). For F, the added electron goes into a 2*p* orbital, for Cl a 3*p* orbital, for Br a 4*p* orbital, and so forth. As we proceed from F to I, therefore, the average distance between the added electron and the nucleus steadily increases, causing the electron-nucleus attraction to decrease. The orbital that holds the outermost electron is increasingly spread out, however, as we proceed from F to I, thereby reducing the electron-electron repulsions. A lower electron-nucleus attraction is thus counterbalanced by lower electron-electron repulsions.

ANIMATION
Periodic Trends: Electron Affinity

H −73								He >0
Li −60	Be >0	B −27	C −122	N >0	O −141	F −328	Ne >0	
Na −53	Mg >0	Al −43	Si −134	P −72	S −200	Cl −349	Ar >0	
K −48	Ca −2	Ga −30	Ge −119	As −78	Se −195	Br −325	Kr >0	
Rb −47	Sr −5	In −30	Sn −107	Sb −103	Te −190	I −295	Xe >0	
1A	2A	3A	4A	5A	6A	7A	8A	

▲ **Figure 7.12   Electron affinity.** Electron affinities in kJ/mol for the representative elements in the first five rows of the periodic table. The more negative the electron affinity, the greater the attraction of the atom for an electron. An electron affinity > 0 indicates that the negative ion is higher in energy than the separated atom and electron.

> 💡 **GIVE IT SOME THOUGHT**
>
> Suppose you were asked for a value for the first ionization energy of a Cl⁻(g) ion. What is the relationship between this quantity and the electron affinity of Cl(g) ?

7.6 | Metals, Nonmetals, and Metalloids

Atomic radii, ionization energies, and electron affinities are properties of individual atoms. With the exception of the noble gases, however, none of the elements exists in nature as individual atoms. To get a broader understanding of the properties of elements, we must also examine periodic trends in properties that involve large collections of atoms.

The elements can be broadly grouped into the categories of metals, nonmetals, and metalloids. ∞ (Section 2.5) This classification is shown in

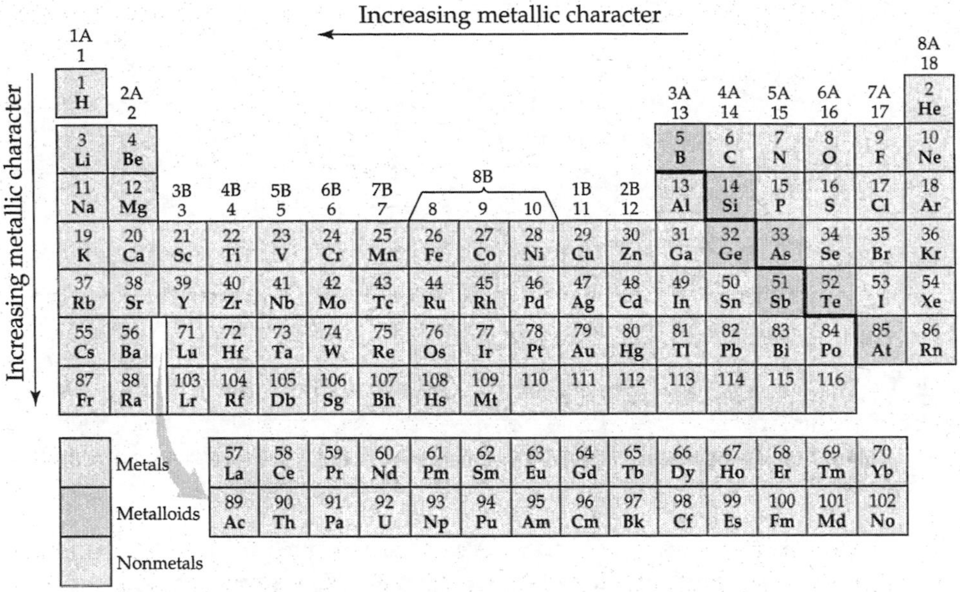

Increasing metallic character

Increasing metallic character

1A 1												8A 18

Metals

57 La	58 Ce	59 Pr	60 Nd	61 Pm	62 Sm	63 Eu	64 Gd	65 Tb	66 Dy	67 Ho	68 Er	69 Tm	70 Yb

Metalloids

89 Ac	90 Th	91 Pa	92 U	93 Np	94 Pu	95 Am	96 Cm	97 Bk	98 Cf	99 Es	100 Fm	101 Md	102 No

Nonmetals

▲ **Figure 7.13 Metals, metalloids, and nonmetals.** The majority of elements are metals. Metallic character increases from right to left across a period and also increases from top to bottom in a group.

Figure 7.13 ▲. Roughly three-quarters of the elements are metals, situated in the left and middle portions of the table. The nonmetals are located at the top right corner, and the metalloids lie between the metals and nonmetals. Hydrogen, which is located at the top left corner, is a nonmetal. This is why we set off hydrogen from the remaining group 1A elements in Figure 7.13 by inserting a space between the H box and the Li box. Some of the distinguishing properties of metals and nonmetals are summarized in Table 7.3 ▼.

The more an element exhibits the physical and chemical properties of metals, the greater its **metallic character**. As indicated in Figure 7.13, metallic character generally increases as we proceed down a column of the periodic table and increases as we proceed from right to left in a row. Let's now examine the close relationships that exist between electron configurations and the properties of metals, nonmetals, and metalloids.

Metals

Most metallic elements exhibit the shiny luster that we associate with metals (Figure 7.14 ▶). Metals conduct heat and electricity. They are malleable (can be pounded into thin sheets) and ductile (can be drawn into wires). All are solids at room temperature except mercury (melting point = −39°C), which is a liquid. Two melt at slightly above room temperature, cesium at 28.4°C and gallium at 29.8°C. At the other extreme, many metals melt at very high temperatures. For example, chromium melts at 1900°C.

▲ **Figure 7.14 The luster of metals.** Metallic objects are readily recognized by their characteristic shiny luster.

TABLE 7.3 Characteristic Properties of Metals and Nonmetals	
Metals	**Nonmetals**
Have a shiny luster; various colors, although most are silvery	Do not have a luster; various colors
Solids are malleable and ductile	Solids are usually brittle; some are hard, some are soft
Good conductors of heat and electricity	Poor conductors of heat and electricity
Most metal oxides are ionic solids that are basic	Most nonmetal oxides are molecular substances that form acidic solutions
Tend to form cations in aqueous solution	Tend to form anions or oxyanions in aqueous solution

Science Fundamentals Second Edition

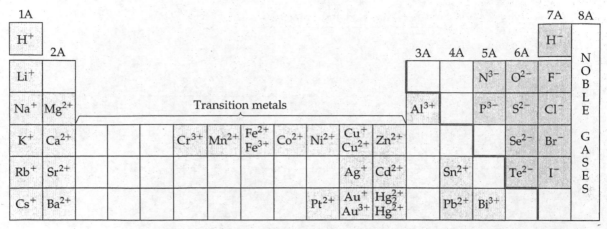

▲ **Figure 7.15   Common ions.** Charges of some common ions found in ionic compounds. Notice that the steplike line that divides metals from nonmetals also separates cations from anions.

Metals tend to have low ionization energies and therefore tend to form positive ions relatively easily. As a result, metals are oxidized (lose electrons) when they undergo chemical reactions. The relative ease of oxidation of common metals was discussed earlier, in Section 4.6. As we noted there, many metals are oxidized by a variety of common substances, including O_2 and acids.

Figure 7.15 ▲ shows the charges of some common ions of both metals and nonmetals. As we noted in Section 2.7, the charge on any alkali metal ion is always 1+, and that on any alkaline earth metal is always 2+ in their compounds. In atoms in both these groups, the outer *s* electrons are easily lost, yielding a noble-gas electron configuration. The charge on transition-metal ions does not follow an obvious pattern. Many transition-metal ions carry a charge of 2+, but 1+ and 3+ are also encountered. One of the characteristic features of the transition metals is their ability to form more than one positive ion. For example, iron may be 2+ in some compounds and 3+ in others.

⏻ GIVE IT SOME THOUGHT

Based on periodic trends discussed in this chapter, can you see a general relationship between the trends in metallic character and those for ionization energy?

Compounds of metals with nonmetals tend to be ionic substances. For example, most metal oxides and halides are ionic solids. To illustrate, the reaction between nickel metal and oxygen produces nickel oxide, an ionic solid containing Ni^{2+} and O^{2-} ions:

$$2\,Ni(s) + O_2(g) \longrightarrow 2\,NiO(s) \qquad [7.8]$$

The oxides are particularly important because of the great abundance of oxygen in our environment.

Most metal oxides are basic. Those that dissolve in water react to form metal hydroxides, as in the following examples:

$$\text{Metal oxide} + \text{water} \longrightarrow \text{metal hydroxide}$$

$$Na_2O(s) + H_2O(l) \longrightarrow 2\,NaOH(aq) \qquad [7.9]$$

$$CaO(s) + H_2O(l) \longrightarrow Ca(OH)_2(aq) \qquad [7.10]$$

The basicity of metal oxides is due to the oxide ion, which reacts with water according to the net ionic equation

$$O^{2-}(aq) + H_2O(l) \longrightarrow 2\,OH^-(aq) \qquad [7.11]$$

Science Fundamentals Second Edition

NiO

(a)   (b)

◀ **Figure 7.16 Metal oxides react with acids.** (a) Nickel oxide (NiO), nitric acid (HNO₃), and water. (b) NiO is insoluble in water, but reacts with HNO₃ to give a green solution of the salt Ni(NO₃)₂.

ANIMATION
Periodic Trends: Acid-Base Behavior of Oxides

Metal oxides also demonstrate their basicity by reacting with acids to form a salt plus water, as illustrated in Figure 7.16 ▲:

$$\text{Metal oxide} + \text{acid} \longrightarrow \text{salt} + \text{water}$$

$$NiO(s) + 2\,HCl(aq) \longrightarrow NiCl_2(aq) + H_2O(l) \qquad [7.12]$$

In contrast, we will soon see that nonmetal oxides are acidic, dissolving in water to form acidic solutions and reacting with bases to form salts.

SAMPLE EXERCISE 7.8 | Metal Oxides

(a) Would you expect aluminum oxide to be a solid, liquid, or gas at room temperature? **(b)** Write the balanced chemical equation for the reaction of aluminum oxide with nitric acid.

Solution
Analyze and Plan: We are asked about one physical property of aluminum oxide—its state at room temperature—and one chemical property—how it reacts with nitric acid.
Solve: (a) Because aluminum oxide is the oxide of a metal, we would expect it to be an ionic solid. Indeed it is, with the very high melting point of 2072°C.
   (b) In its compounds, aluminum has a 3+ charge, Al^{3+}; the oxide ion is O^{2-}. Consequently, the formula of aluminum oxide is Al_2O_3. Metal oxides tend to be basic and therefore to react with acids to form a salt plus water. In this case the salt is aluminum nitrate, $Al(NO_3)_3$. The balanced chemical equation is

$$Al_2O_3(s) + 6\,HNO_3(aq) \longrightarrow 2\,Al(NO_3)_3(aq) + 3\,H_2O(l)$$

PRACTICE EXERCISE
Write the balanced chemical equation for the reaction between copper(II) oxide and sulfuric acid.
Answer: $CuO(s) + H_2SO_4(aq) \longrightarrow CuSO_4(aq) + H_2O(l)$

Nonmetals

Nonmetals vary greatly in appearance (Figure 7.17 ▶). They are not lustrous and generally are poor conductors of heat and electricity. Their melting points are generally lower than those of metals (although diamond, a form of carbon, melts at 3570°C). Under ordinary conditions, seven nonmetals exist as diatomic molecules. Five of these are gases (H_2, N_2, O_2, F_2, and Cl_2), one is a liquid (Br_2), and one is a volatile solid (I_2). The remaining nonmetals are solids that can be either hard, such as diamond, or soft, such as sulfur.

   Because of their electron affinities, nonmetals tend to gain electrons when they react with metals. For example, the reaction of aluminum

▼ **Figure 7.17 The diversity of nonmetals.** Nonmetallic elements are diverse in their appearances. Shown here are (clockwise from left) carbon in the form of graphite, sulfur, white phosphorus (stored under water), and iodine.

(a)   (b)

▲ **Figure 7.18   The reaction of CO_2 with water.** (a) The water has been made slightly basic and contains a few drops of bromthymol blue, an acid-base indicator that is blue in basic solution. (b) Upon the addition of a piece of solid carbon dioxide, $CO_2(s)$, the color changes to yellow, indicating an acidic solution. The mist is due to water droplets condensed from the air by the cold CO_2 gas.

with bromine produces aluminum bromide, an ionic compound containing the aluminum ion, Al^{3+}, and the bromide ion, Br^-:

$$2\,Al(s) + 3\,Br_2(l) \longrightarrow 2\,AlBr_3(s) \qquad [7.13]$$

A nonmetal typically will gain enough electrons to fill its outermost occupied p subshell, giving a noble-gas electron configuration. For example, the bromine atom gains one electron to fill its $4p$ subshell:

$$Br\ ([Ar]4s^23d^{10}4p^5) \Rightarrow Br^-\ ([Ar]4s^23d^{10}4p^6)$$

Compounds composed entirely of nonmetals are molecular substances. For example, the oxides, halides, and hydrides of the nonmetals are molecular substances that tend to be gases, liquids, or low-melting solids at room temperature.

Most nonmetal oxides are acidic; those that dissolve in water react to form acids, as in the following examples:

$$\text{Nonmetal oxide} + \text{water} \longrightarrow \text{acid}$$
$$CO_2(g) + H_2O(l) \longrightarrow H_2CO_3(aq) \qquad [7.14]$$
$$P_4O_{10}(s) + 6\,H_2O(l) \longrightarrow 4\,H_3PO_4(aq) \qquad [7.15]$$

The reaction of carbon dioxide with water (Figure 7.18 ◄) accounts for the acidity of carbonated water and, to some extent, rainwater. Because sulfur is present in oil and coal, combustion of these common fuels produces sulfur dioxide and sulfur trioxide. These substances dissolve in water to produce *acid rain*, a major pollution problem in many parts of the world. Like acids, most nonmetal oxides dissolve in basic solutions to form a salt plus water:

$$\text{Nonmetal oxide} + \text{base} \longrightarrow \text{salt} + \text{water}$$
$$CO_2(g) + 2\,NaOH(aq) \longrightarrow Na_2CO_3(aq) + H_2O(l) \qquad [7.16]$$

 GIVE IT SOME THOUGHT

A compound ACl_3 (A is an element) has a melting point of $-112\,°C$. Would you expect the compound to be a molecular or ionic substance? Is element A more likely to be scandium (Sc) or phosphorus (P)?

SAMPLE EXERCISE 7.9 | Nonmetal Oxides

Write the balanced chemical equations for the reactions of solid selenium dioxide with **(a)** water, **(b)** aqueous sodium hydroxide.

Solution

Analyze and Plan: We first note that selenium (Se) is a nonmetal. We therefore need to write chemical equations for the reaction of a nonmetal oxide, first with water and then with a base, NaOH. Nonmetal oxides are acidic, reacting with water to form an acid and with bases to form a salt and water.

Solve: (a) Selenium dioxide is SeO_2. Its reaction with water is like that of carbon dioxide (Equation 7.14):

$$SeO_2(s) + H_2O(l) \longrightarrow H_2SeO_3(aq)$$

(It doesn't matter that SeO_2 is a solid and CO_2 is a gas; the point is that both are water-soluble nonmetal oxides.)

(b) The reaction with sodium hydroxide is like the reaction summarized by Equation 7.16:

$$SeO_2(s) + 2\,NaOH(aq) \longrightarrow Na_2SeO_3(aq) + H_2O(l)$$

Write the balanced chemical equation for the reaction of solid tetraphosphorus hexoxide with water.
Answer: $P_4O_6(s) + 6 H_2O(l) \longrightarrow 4 H_3PO_3(aq)$

Metalloids

Metalloids have properties intermediate between those of metals and those of nonmetals. They may have *some* characteristic metallic properties but lack others. For example, silicon *looks* like a metal (Figure 7.19 ▶), but it is brittle rather than malleable and is a much poorer conductor of heat and electricity than are metals. Compounds of metalloids can have characteristics of the compounds of metals or nonmetals, depending on the specific compound.

Several of the metalloids, most notably silicon, are electrical semiconductors and are the principal elements used in the manufacture of integrated circuits and computer chips.

▲ **Figure 7.19 Elemental silicon.** Silicon is an example of a metalloid. Although it looks metallic, silicon is brittle and is a poor thermal and electrical conductor as compared to metals. Large crystals of silicon are sliced into thin wafers for use in integrated circuits.

7.7 | Group Trends for the Active Metals

Our discussion of atomic radius, ionization energy, electron affinity, and metallic character gives some idea of the way the periodic table can be used to organize and remember facts. Not only do elements in a group possess general similarities, but there are also trends as we move through a group or from one group to another. In this section we will use the periodic table and our knowledge of electron configurations to examine the chemistry of the **alkali metals** (group 1A) and the **alkaline earth metals** (group 2A).

Group 1A: The Alkali Metals

The alkali metals are soft metallic solids (Figure 7.20 ▶). All have characteristic metallic properties such as a silvery, metallic luster and high thermal and electrical conductivities. The name *alkali* comes from an Arabic word meaning "ashes." Many compounds of sodium and potassium, two alkali metals, were isolated from wood ashes by early chemists.

Sodium and potassium are among the most abundant elements in Earth's crust, in seawater, and in biological systems. We all have sodium ions in our bodies. If we ingest too much, however, it can raise our blood pressure. Potassium is also prevalent in our bodies; a 140-pound person contains about 130 g of potassium, as K^+ ions in intracellular fluids. Plants require potassium for growth and development (Figure 7.21 ▶).

Some of the physical and chemical properties of the alkali metals are given in Table 7.4 ▼. The elements have low densities and melting points, and these properties vary in a fairly regular way with increasing atomic number. We can

▲ **Figure 7.20 Alkali metals.** Sodium and the other alkali metals are soft enough to be cut with a knife. The shiny metallic surface quickly tarnishes as the metal reacts with oxygen in the air.

TABLE 7.4 Some Properties of the Alkali Metals					
Element	Electron Configuration	Melting Point (°C)	Density (g/cm³)	Atomic Radius (Å)	I_1 (kJ/mol)
Lithium	[He]$2s^1$	181	0.53	1.34	520
Sodium	[Ne]$3s^1$	98	0.97	1.54	496
Potassium	[Ar]$4s^1$	63	0.86	1.96	419
Rubidium	[Kr]$5s^1$	39	1.53	2.11	403
Cesium	[Xe]$6s^1$	28	1.88	2.25	376

▲ **Figure 7.21 Elements in fertilizers.** Fertilizers contain large quantities of potassium, phosphorus, and nitrogen to meet the needs of growing plants.

Science Fundamentals Second Edition

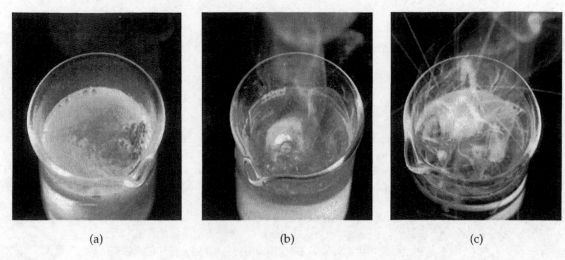

(a)   (b)   (c)

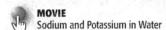

MOVIE
Sodium and Potassium in Water

also see some of the usual trends as we move down the group, such as increasing atomic radius and decreasing first ionization energy. For each row of the periodic table, the alkali metal has the lowest I_1 value (Figure 7.10), which reflects the relative ease with which its outer s electron can be removed. As a result, the alkali metals are all very reactive, readily losing one electron to form ions carrying a 1+ charge. ∞∞ (Section 4.4)

The alkali metals exist in nature only as compounds. The metals combine directly with most nonmetals. For example, they react with hydrogen to form hydrides and with sulfur to form sulfides:

$$2\,M(s) + H_2(g) \longrightarrow 2\,MH(s) \qquad [7.17]$$

$$2\,M(s) + S(s) \longrightarrow M_2S(s) \qquad [7.18]$$

(The symbol M in Equations 7.17 and 7.18 represents any one of the alkali metals.) In hydrides of the alkali metals (LiH, NaH, and so forth), hydrogen is present as H^-, called the **hydride ion**. The hydride ion, which is a hydrogen atom that has *gained* an electron, is distinct from the hydrogen ion, H^+, formed when a hydrogen atom *loses* its electron.

The alkali metals react vigorously with water, producing hydrogen gas and a solution of an alkali metal hydroxide:

$$2\,M(s) + 2\,H_2O(l) \longrightarrow 2\,MOH(aq) + H_2(g) \qquad [7.19]$$

These reactions are very exothermic. In many cases enough heat is generated to ignite the H_2, producing a fire or sometimes even an explosion (Figure 7.22 ▲). This reaction is most violent for the heavier members of the group, in keeping with their weaker hold on the single valence electron.

The reactions between the alkali metals and oxygen are more complex. When oxygen reacts with metals, metal oxides, which contain the O^{2-} ion, are usually formed. Indeed, lithium shows this reactivity:

$$4\,Li(s) + O_2(g) \longrightarrow 2\,Li_2O(s) \qquad [7.20]$$
$$\text{lithium oxide}$$

When dissolved in water, Li_2O and other soluble metal oxides react with water to form hydroxide ions from the reaction of O^{2-} ions with H_2O (Equation 7.11).

In contrast, the other alkali metals all react with oxygen to form metal *per-oxides*, which contain the O_2^{2-} ion. For example, sodium forms sodium peroxide, Na_2O_2:

$$2\,Na(s) + O_2(g) \longrightarrow Na_2O_2(s) \qquad [7.21]$$
$$\text{sodium peroxide}$$

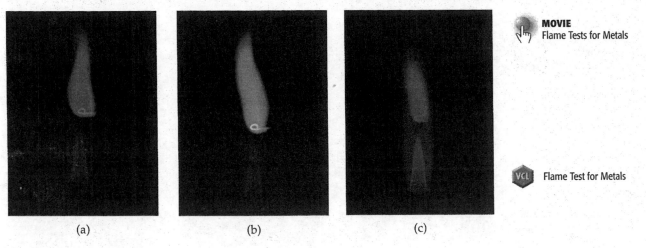

(a)   (b)   (c)

▲ **Figure 7.23   Flame tests.** (a) Li (crimson red), (b) Na (yellow), and (c) K (lilac).

Potassium, rubidium, and cesium also form compounds that contain the O_2^- ion, which we call the *superoxide ion*. For example, potassium forms potassium superoxide, KO_2:

$$K(s) + O_2(g) \longrightarrow KO_2(s) \qquad [7.22]$$
potassium superoxide

You should realize that the reactions shown in Equations 7.21 and 7.22 are somewhat surprising; in most cases, the reaction of oxygen with a metal forms the metal oxide.

As is evident from Equations 7.19 through 7.22, the alkali metals are extremely reactive toward water and oxygen. Because of this, the metals are usually stored submerged in a liquid hydrocarbon, such as mineral oil or kerosene.

Although alkali metal ions are colorless, each emits a characteristic color when placed in a flame (Figure 7.23 ▲). The ions are reduced to gaseous metal atoms in the central region of the flame. The high temperature of the flame then excites the valence electron to a higher-energy orbital, causing the atom to be in an excited state. The atom then emits energy in the form of visible light as the electron falls back into the lower-energy orbital and the atom returns to its ground state. Sodium, for instance, gives a yellow flame because of emission at 589 nm. This wavelength is produced when the excited valence electron drops from the $3p$ subshell to the lower-energy $3s$ subshell. The characteristic yellow emission of sodium is the basis for sodium vapor lamps (Figure 7.24 ▶).

▲ **Figure 7.24   Light from sodium.** Sodium vapor lamps, which are used for commercial and highway lighting, have a yellow glow because of the emission from excited sodium atoms.

 Emission Spectra of Sodium and Mercury

 GIVE IT SOME THOUGHT

Cesium metal tends to be the most reactive of the stable alkali metals (francium, element number 87, is radioactive and has not been extensively studied). What *atomic* property of Cs is most responsible for its high reactivity?

■ **SAMPLE EXERCISE 7.10 | Reactions of an Alkali Metal**

Write a balanced equation that predicts the reaction of cesium metal with **(a)** $Cl_2(g)$, **(b)** $H_2O(l)$, **(c)** $H_2(g)$.

Solution

Analyze and Plan: Cesium is an alkali metal (atomic number 55). We therefore expect that its chemistry will be dominated by oxidation of the metal to Cs^+ ions. Further, we recognize that Cs is far down the periodic table, which means it will be among the most active of all metals and will probably react with all three of the substances listed.

Science Fundamentals Second Edition

Solve: The reaction between Cs and Cl_2 is a simple combination reaction between two elements, one a metal and the other a nonmetal, forming the ionic compound CsCl:

$$2\,Cs(s) + Cl_2(g) \longrightarrow 2\,CsCl(s)$$

By analogy to Equations 7.19 and 7.17, respectively, we predict the reactions of cesium with water and hydrogen to proceed as follows:

$$2\,Cs(s) + 2\,H_2O(l) \longrightarrow 2\,CsOH(aq) + H_2(g)$$
$$2\,Cs(s) + H_2(g) \longrightarrow 2\,CsH(s)$$

In each case cesium forms a Cs^+ ion in its compounds. The chloride (Cl^-), hydroxide (OH^-), and hydride (H^-) ions are all 1− ions, which means the final products have 1:1 stoichiometry with Cs^+.

■ **PRACTICE EXERCISE**

Write a balanced equation for the reaction between potassium metal and elemental sulfur.
Answer: $2\,K(s) + S(s) \longrightarrow K_2S(s)$

 CHEMISTRY AND LIFE | The Improbable Development of Lithium Drugs

The alkali metal ions tend to play a rather unexciting role in most chemical reactions in general chemistry. As noted in Section 4.2, all salts of the alkali metal ions are soluble, and the ions are spectators in most aqueous reactions (except for those involving the alkali metals in their elemental form, such as in Equations 7.17 through 7.22).

The alkali metal ions play an important role in human physiology, however. Sodium and potassium ions are major components of blood plasma and intracellular fluid, respectively, with average concentrations on the order of 0.1 *M*. These electrolytes serve as vital charge carriers in normal cellular function, and, as we will discuss further in Chapter 20, they are two of the principal ions involved in regulation of the heart.

In contrast, the lithium ion (Li^+) has no known function in normal human physiology. Since the discovery of lithium in 1817, however, salts of the element were thought to possess almost mystical healing powers; there were claims that it was an ingredient in ancient "fountain of youth" formulas. In 1927, Mr. C. L. Grigg began marketing a lithium-containing soft drink with the unwieldy name "Bib-Label Lithiated Lemon-Lime Soda." Grigg soon gave his lithiated beverage a much simpler name: Seven-Up® (Figure 7.25 ▶).

Because of concerns of the Food and Drug Administration, lithium was removed from Seven-Up® in the early 1950s. At nearly the same time, it was found that the lithium ion has a remarkable therapeutic effect on the mental disorder called *bipolar affective disorder*, or *manic-depressive illness*. Over 1 million Americans suffer from this psychosis, undergoing severe mood swings from deep depression to a manic euphoria. The lithium ion smooths out these mood swings, allowing the bipolar patient to function more effectively in daily life.

The antipsychotic action of Li^+ was discovered by accident in the late 1940s by Australian psychiatrist John Cade as he was researching the use of uric acid—a component of urine—to treat manic-depressive illness. He administered the acid to manic laboratory animals in the form of its most soluble salt, lithium urate, and found that many of the manic symptoms seemed to disappear. Later studies showed that uric acid has no role in the therapeutic effects observed; rather, the seemingly innocuous Li^+ ions were responsible. Because lithium overdose can cause severe side effects in humans, including kidney failure and death, lithium salts were not approved as antipsychotic drugs for humans until 1970. Today Li^+ is usually administered orally in the form of Li_2CO_3, which is the active ingredient in prescription drugs such as Eskalith®. Lithium drugs are effective for about 70% of the bipolar patients who take it.

In this age of sophisticated drug design and biotechnology, the simple lithium ion is still the most effective treatment of a destructive psychological disorder. Remarkably, in spite of intensive research, scientists still don't fully understand the biochemical action of lithium that leads to its therapeutic effects. Because of its similarity to the Na^+ ion, the Li+ ion is incorporated into blood plasma, where it can affect the behavior of both nerve cells and muscle cells. The Li^+ ion has a smaller radius than the Na^+ ion (Figure 7.7), so its interaction with molecules in cells is somewhat different. Other studies indicate that Li^+ alters the function of certain neurotransmitters, which might lead to its effectiveness as an antipsychotic drug.

▲ **Figure 7.25 Lithium no more.** The soft drink Seven-Up® originally contained lithium citrate, the lithium salt of citric acid. The lithium was claimed to give the beverage healthful benefits, including "an abundance of energy, enthusiasm, a clear complexion, lustrous hair, and shining eyes!" The lithium was removed from the beverage in the early 1950s, about the same time that the antipsychotic action of Li^+ was discovered.

Element	Electron Configuration	Melting Point (°C)	Density (g/cm³)	Atomic Radius (Å)	I_1 (kJ/mol)
Beryllium	[He]$2s^2$	1287	1.85	0.90	899
Magnesium	[Ne]$3s^2$	650	1.74	1.30	738
Calcium	[Ar]$4s^2$	842	1.55	1.74	590
Strontium	[Kr]$5s^2$	777	2.63	1.92	549
Barium	[Xe]$6s^2$	727	3.51	1.98	503

TABLE 7.5   Some Properties of the Alkaline Earth Metals

Group 2A: The Alkaline Earth Metals

Like the alkali metals, the group 2A elements are all solids at room temperature and have typical metallic properties, some of which are listed in Table 7.5 ▲. Compared with the alkali metals, the alkaline earth metals are harder and more dense, and they melt at higher temperatures.

The first ionization energies of the alkaline earth elements are low, but not as low as those of the alkali metals. Consequently, the alkaline earths are less reactive than their alkali metal neighbors. As we noted in Section 7.4, the ease with which the elements lose electrons decreases as we move across the periodic table from left to right and increases as we move down a group. Thus, beryllium and magnesium, the lightest members of the alkaline earth metals, are the least reactive.

The trend of increasing reactivity within the group is shown by the way the alkaline earths behave in the presence of water. Beryllium does not react with water or steam, even when heated red-hot. Magnesium does not react with liquid water but does react with steam to form magnesium oxide and hydrogen:

$$Mg(s) + H_2O(g) \longrightarrow MgO(s) + H_2(g) \qquad [7.23]$$

Calcium and the elements below it react readily with water at room temperature (although more slowly than the alkali metals adjacent to them in the periodic table), as shown in Figure 7.26 ▶. The reaction between calcium and water, for example, is

$$Ca(s) + 2 H_2O(l) \longrightarrow Ca(OH)_2(aq) + H_2(g) \qquad [7.24]$$

The reactions represented in Equations 7.23 and 7.24 illustrate the dominant pattern in the reactivity of the alkaline earth elements—the tendency to lose their two outer s electrons and form 2+ ions. For example, magnesium reacts with chlorine at room temperature to form $MgCl_2$ and burns with dazzling brilliance in air to give MgO (Figure 3.5):

$$Mg(s) + Cl_2(g) \longrightarrow MgCl_2(s) \qquad [7.25]$$

$$2 Mg(s) + O_2(g) \longrightarrow 2 MgO(s) \qquad [7.26]$$

In the presence of O_2, magnesium metal is protected from many chemicals by a thin surface coating of water-insoluble MgO. Thus, even though it is high in the activity series (Section 4.4), Mg can be incorporated into lightweight structural alloys used in, for example, automobile wheels. The heavier alkaline earth metals (Ca, Sr, and Ba) are even more reactive toward nonmetals than is magnesium.

The heavier alkaline earth ions give off characteristic colors when strongly heated in a flame. The colored flame produced by calcium is brick red, that of strontium is crimson red, and that of barium is green. Strontium salts produce the brilliant red color in fireworks, and barium salts produce the green color.

Both magnesium and calcium are essential for living organisms (Figure 2.24). Calcium is particularly important for growth and maintenance of

▲ **Figure 7.26   Elemental calcium solution.** Calcium metal reacts with water to form hydrogen gas and aqueous calcium hydroxide, $Ca(OH)_2(aq)$.

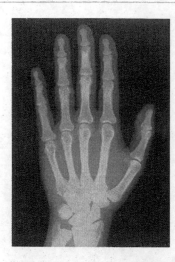

▲ **Figure 7.27 Calcium in the body.** This X-ray photograph shows the bone structure of the human hand. The primary mineral in bone and teeth is hydroxyapatite, $Ca_5(PO_4)_3OH$, in which calcium is present as Ca^{2+}.

▲ **Figure 7.28 Exploring Saturn.** The Cassini–Huygens spacecraft entered orbit around Saturn in June 2004. The probe will use advanced scientific instruments to explore several aspects of Saturn and its largest moon, Titan, including the metallic hydrogen composition of the planet. This photograph of Saturn was taken by Cassini–Huygens in May 2004 at a distance of 28.2 million kilometers (17.6 million miles) from the planet.

bones and teeth (Figure 7.27 ◄). In humans 99% of the calcium is found in the skeletal system.

 GIVE IT SOME THOUGHT

Calcium carbonate, $CaCO_3$, is often used as a dietary calcium supplement for bone health. Although $CaCO_3(s)$ is insoluble in water (Table 4.1), it can be taken orally to allow for the delivery of $Ca^{2+}(aq)$ ions to the musculoskeletal system. Why is this the case? [*Hint:* Recall the reactions of metal carbonates that were discussed in Section 4.3]

7.8 | Group Trends for Selected Nonmetals

Hydrogen

Hydrogen, the first element in the periodic table, has a $1s^1$ electron configuration, and for this reason its usual position in the table is above the alkali metals. However, hydrogen does not truly belong to any particular group. Unlike the alkali metals, hydrogen is a nonmetal that occurs as a colorless diatomic gas, $H_2(g)$, under most conditions. Nevertheless, hydrogen can be metallic under tremendous pressures. The interiors of the planets Jupiter and Saturn, for example, are believed to consist of a rocky core surrounded by a thick shell of metallic hydrogen. The metallic hydrogen is in turn surrounded by a layer of liquid molecular hydrogen with gaseous hydrogen occurring above that near the surface. The Cassini–Huygens satellite mission, launched in 1997, is designed to explore Saturn and its largest moon, Titan, including their chemical compositions. The spacecraft successfully entered orbit around Saturn in June 2004 and is already using telescopy and spectroscopy to provide spectacular images and chemical analysis (Figure 7.28 ◄).

Owing to the complete absence of nuclear shielding of its sole electron, the ionization energy of hydrogen, 1312 kJ/mol, is markedly higher than that of any of the alkali metals (Figure 7.10). In fact, it is comparable to the I_1 values of other nonmetals, such as oxygen and chlorine. As a result, hydrogen has less tendency to lose an electron than do the alkali metals. Whereas the alkali metals readily lose their valence electron to nonmetals to form ionic compounds, hydrogen shares its electron with nonmetals and thereby forms molecular compounds. The reactions between hydrogen and nonmetals can be quite exothermic, as evidenced by the combustion reaction between hydrogen and oxygen to form water (Figure 5.14):

$$2\,H_2(g) + O_2(g) \longrightarrow 2\,H_2O(l) \qquad \Delta H^\circ = -571.7 \text{ kJ} \qquad [7.27]$$

We have also seen (Equation 7.17) that hydrogen reacts with active metals to form solid metal hydrides, which contain the hydride ion, H^-. The fact that hydrogen can gain an electron further illustrates that it is not truly a member of the alkali metal family. In fact, this property of hydrogen suggests a slight resemblance between hydrogen and the halogens.

In addition to its ability to form covalent bonds and metal hydrides, probably the most important characteristic of hydrogen is its ability to lose its electron to form a cation. Indeed, the aqueous chemistry of hydrogen is dominated by the $H^+(aq)$ ion, which we first encountered in Chapter 4. ∞ (Section 4.1) We will study this important ion in greater detail in Chapter 16.

Group 6A: The Oxygen Group

As we proceed down group 6A, there is a change from nonmetallic to metallic character (Figure 7.13). Oxygen, sulfur, and selenium are typical nonmetals. Tellurium has some metallic properties and is classified as a metalloid. Polonium, which is radioactive and quite rare, is a metal.

	TABLE 7.6 Some Properties of the Group 6A Elements				
Element	Electron Configuration	Melting Point (°C)	Density	Atomic Radius (Å)	I_1 (kJ/mol)
Oxygen	$[He]2s^2 2p^4$	−218	1.43 g/L	0.73	1314
Sulfur	$[Ne]3s^2 3p^4$	115	1.96 g/cm^3	1.02	1000
Selenium	$[Ar]3d^{10}4s^2 4p^4$	221	4.82 g/cm^3	1.16	941
Tellurium	$[Kr]4d^{10}5s^2 5p^4$	450	6.24 g/cm^3	1.35	869
Polonium	$[Xe]4f^{14}5d^{10}6s^2 6p^4$	254	9.20 g/cm^3	—	812

Oxygen is a colorless gas at room temperature; all of the other members of group 6A are solids. Some of the physical properties of the group 6A elements are given in Table 7.6 ▲.

As we saw in Section 2.6, oxygen is encountered in two molecular forms, O_2 and O_3. The O_2 form is the common one. People generally mean O_2 when they say "oxygen," although the name *dioxygen* is more descriptive. The O_3 form is called **ozone**. The two forms of oxygen are examples of *allotropes*. Allotropes are different forms of the same element in the same state. (In this case both forms are gases.) About 21% of dry air consists of O_2 molecules. Ozone, which is toxic and has a pungent odor, is present in very small amounts in the upper atmosphere and in polluted air. It is also formed from O_2 in electrical discharges, such as in lightning storms:

$$3 O_2(g) \longrightarrow 2 O_3(g) \qquad \Delta H° = 284.6 \text{ kJ} \qquad [7.28]$$

This reaction is endothermic, telling us that O_3 is less stable than O_2.

Oxygen has a great tendency to attract electrons from other elements (to *oxidize* them). Oxygen in combination with a metal is almost always present as the oxide ion, O^{2-}. This ion has a noble-gas configuration and is particularly stable. As shown in Equation 7.27, the formation of nonmetal oxides is also often very exothermic and thus energetically favorable.

In our discussion of the alkali metals, we noted two less common oxygen anions—the peroxide (O_2^{2-}) ion and the superoxide (O_2^-) ion. Compounds of these ions often react with themselves to produce an oxide and O_2. For example, aqueous hydrogen peroxide, H_2O_2, slowly decomposes into water and O_2 at room temperature:

$$2 H_2O_2(aq) \longrightarrow 2 H_2O(l) + O_2(g) \qquad \Delta H° = -196.1 \text{ kJ} \qquad [7.29]$$

For this reason, bottles of aqueous hydrogen peroxide are topped with caps that are able to release the $O_2(g)$ produced before the pressure inside becomes too great (Figure 7.29 ▶).

After oxygen, the most important member of group 6A is sulfur. This element also exists in several allotropic forms, the most common and stable of which is the yellow solid having the molecular formula S_8. This molecule consists of an eight-membered ring of sulfur atoms, as shown in Figure 7.30 ▶. Even though solid sulfur consists of S_8 rings, we usually write it simply as $S(s)$ in chemical equations to simplify the stoichiometric coefficients.

Like oxygen, sulfur has a tendency to gain electrons from other elements to form sulfides, which contain the S^{2-} ion. In fact, most sulfur in nature is present as metal sulfides. Sulfur is below oxygen in the periodic table, and the tendency of sulfur to form sulfide anions is not as great as that of oxygen to form oxide ions. As a result, the chemistry of sulfur is more complex than that of oxygen. In fact, sulfur and its compounds (including those in coal and petroleum) can be burned in oxygen. The main product is sulfur dioxide, a major pollutant:

$$S(s) + O_2(g) \longrightarrow SO_2(g) \qquad [7.30]$$

We will discuss the environmental aspects of sulfur oxide chemistry in greater depth in Chapter 18.

▲ **Figure 7.29 Hydrogen peroxide solution.** Bottles of this common antiseptic are topped with a cap that allows any excess pressure created by $O_2(g)$ to be released from the bottle. Hydrogen peroxide is often stored in dark-colored or opaque bottles to minimize exposure to light, which accelerates its decomposition.

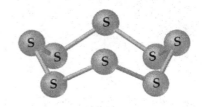

▲ **Figure 7.30 Elemental sulfur.** At room temperature, the most common allotropic form of sulfur is an eight-member ring, S_8.

TABLE 7.7	Some Properties of the Halogens				
Element	Electron Configuration	Melting Point (°C)	Density	Atomic Radius (Å)	I_1 (kJ/mol)
Fluorine	$[He]2s^2 2p^5$	−220	1.69 g/L	0.71	1681
Chlorine	$[Ne]3s^2 3p^5$	−102	3.21 g/L	0.99	1251
Bromine	$[Ar]3d^{10}4s^2 4p^5$	−7.3	3.12 g/cm^3	1.14	1140
Iodine	$[Kr]4d^{10}5s^2 5p^5$	114	4.94 g/cm^3	1.33	1008

MOVIE
Physical Properties of the Halogens

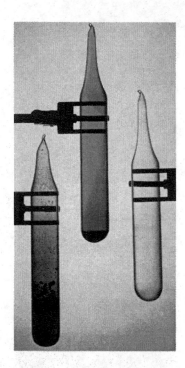

▲ **Figure 7.31   Elemental halogens.** All three of these elements—from left to right, iodine (I_2), bromine (Br_2), and chlorine (Cl_2)—exist as diatomic molecules.

Group 7A: The Halogens

The group 7A elements are known as the **halogens**, after the Greek words *halos* and *gennao*, meaning "salt formers." Some of the properties of these elements are given in Table 7.7 ▲. Astatine, which is both extremely rare and radioactive, is omitted because many of its properties are not yet known.

Unlike the group 6A elements, all the halogens are typical nonmetals. Their melting and boiling points increase with increasing atomic number. Fluorine and chlorine are gases at room temperature, bromine is a liquid, and iodine is a solid. Each element consists of diatomic molecules: F_2, Cl_2, Br_2, and I_2. Fluorine gas is pale yellow; chlorine gas is yellow-green; bromine liquid is reddish brown and readily forms a reddish brown vapor; and solid iodine is grayish black and readily forms a violet vapor (Figure 7.31 ◄).

The halogens have highly negative electron affinities (Figure 7.12). Thus, it is not surprising that the chemistry of the halogens is dominated by their tendency to gain electrons from other elements to form halide ions, X^-. (In many equations X is used to indicate any one of the halogen elements.) Fluorine and chlorine are more reactive than bromine and iodine. In fact, fluorine removes electrons from almost any substance with which it comes into contact, including water, and usually does so very exothermically, as in the following examples:

$$2\,H_2O(l) + 2\,F_2(g) \longrightarrow 4\,HF(aq) + O_2(g) \qquad \Delta H = -758.9\ \text{kJ} \qquad [7.31]$$

$$SiO_2(s) + 2\,F_2(g) \longrightarrow SiF_4(g) + O_2(g) \qquad \Delta H = -704.0\ \text{kJ} \qquad [7.32]$$

As a result, fluorine gas is difficult and dangerous to use in the laboratory, requiring specialized equipment.

Chlorine is the most industrially useful of the halogens. In 2003 total production was 26 billion pounds, making it the eighth most produced chemical in the United States. Unlike fluorine, chlorine reacts slowly with water to form relatively stable aqueous solutions of HCl and HOCl (hypochlorous acid):

$$Cl_2(g) + H_2O(l) \longrightarrow HCl(aq) + HOCl(aq) \qquad [7.33]$$

Chlorine is often added to drinking water and swimming pools, where the HOCl(*aq*) that is generated serves as a disinfectant.

The .halogens react directly with most metals to form ionic halides. The halogens also react with hydrogen to form gaseous hydrogen halide compounds:

$$H_2(g) + X_2 \longrightarrow 2\,HX(g) \qquad [7.34]$$

These compounds are all very soluble in water and dissolve to form the hydrohalic acids. As we discussed in Section 4.3, HCl(*aq*), HBr(*aq*), and HI(*aq*) are strong acids, whereas HF(*aq*) is a weak acid.

 GIVE IT SOME THOUGHT

Can you use data in Table 7.7 to provide estimates for the atomic radius and first ionization energy of an astatine atom?

TABLE 7.8 Some Properties of the Noble Gases

Element	Electron Configuration	Boiling Point (K)	Density (g/L)	Atomic Radius* (Å)	I_1 (kJ/mol)
Helium	$1s^2$	4.2	0.18	0.32	2372
Neon	$[He]2s^22p^6$	27.1	0.90	0.69	2081
Argon	$[Ne]3s^23p^6$	87.3	1.78	0.97	1521
Krypton	$[Ar]3d^{10}4s^24p^6$	120	3.75	1.10	1351
Xenon	$[Kr]4d^{10}5s^25p^6$	165	5.90	1.30	1170
Radon	$[Xe]4f^{14}5d^{10}6s^26p^6$	211	9.73	1.45	1037

*Only the heaviest of the noble-gas elements form chemical compounds. Thus, the atomic radii for the lighter noble-gas elements are estimated values.

Group 8A: The Noble Gases

The group 8A elements, known as the **noble gases**, are all nonmetals that are gases at room temperature. They are all *monatomic* (that is, they consist of single atoms rather than molecules). Some physical properties of the noble-gas elements are listed in Table 7.8 ▲. The high radioactivity of radon (Rn, atomic number 86) has limited the study of its reaction chemistry and some of its properties.

The noble gases have completely filled s and p subshells. All elements of group 8A have large first ionization energies, and we see the expected decrease as we move down the column. Because the noble gases possess such stable electron configurations, they are exceptionally unreactive. In fact, until the early 1960s the elements were called the *inert gases* because they were thought to be incapable of forming chemical compounds. In 1962, Neil Bartlett at the University of British Columbia reasoned that the ionization energy of Xe might be low enough to allow it to form compounds. In order for this to happen, Xe would have to react with a substance with an extremely high ability to remove electrons from other substances, such as fluorine. Bartlett synthesized the first noble-gas compound by combining Xe with the fluorine-containing compound PtF_6. Xenon also reacts directly with $F_2(g)$ to form the molecular compounds XeF_2, XeF_4, and XeF_6 (Figure 7.32 ▶). Krypton has a higher I_1 value than xenon and is therefore less reactive. In fact, only a single stable compound of krypton is known, KrF_2. In 2000, Finnish scientists reported the first neutral molecule that contains argon, the HArF molecule, which is stable only at low temperatures.

▲ **Figure 7.32 A compound of xenon.** Crystals of XeF_4, which is one of the very few compounds that contain a group 8A element.

■ SAMPLE INTEGRATIVE EXERCISE | Putting Concepts Together

The element bismuth (Bi, atomic number 83) is the heaviest member of group 5A. A salt of the element, bismuth subsalicylate, is the active ingredient in Pepto-Bismol®, an over-the-counter medication for gastric distress.

(a) The covalent atomic radii of thallium (Tl) and lead (Pb) are 1.48 Å and 1.47 Å, respectively. Using these values and those in Figure 7.6, predict the covalent atomic radius of the element bismuth (Bi). Explain your answer.

(b) What accounts for the general increase in atomic radius going down the group 5A elements?

(c) Another major use of bismuth has been as an ingredient in low-melting metal alloys, such as those used in fire sprinkler systems and in typesetting. The element itself is a brittle white crystalline solid. How do these characteristics fit with the fact that bismuth is in the same periodic group with such nonmetallic elements as nitrogen and phosphorus?

(d) Bi_2O_3 is a basic oxide. Write a balanced chemical equation for its reaction with dilute nitric acid. If 6.77 g of Bi_2O_3 is dissolved in dilute acidic solution to make up 500 mL of solution, what is the molarity of the solution of Bi^{3+} ion?

(e) ^{209}Bi is the heaviest stable isotope of any element. How many protons and neutrons are present in this nucleus?

(f) The density of Bi at 25°C is 9.808 g/cm^3. How many Bi atoms are present in a cube of the element that is 5.00 cm on each edge? How many moles of the element are present?

Solution (a) Note that there is a rather steady decrease in radius for the elements in the row preceding the one we are considering, that is, in the series In–Sn–Sb. It is reasonable to expect a decrease of about 0.02 Å in moving from Pb to Bi, leading to an estimate of 1.45 Å. The tabulated value is 1.46 Å.

(b) The general increase in radius with increasing atomic number in the group 5A elements occurs because additional shells of electrons are being added, with corresponding increases in nuclear charge. The core electrons in each case largely shield the outermost electrons from the nucleus, so the effective nuclear charge does not vary greatly as we go to higher atomic numbers. However, the principal quantum number, n, of the outermost electrons steadily increases, with a corresponding increase in orbital radius.

(c) The contrast between the properties of bismuth and those of nitrogen and phosphorus illustrates the general rule that there is a trend toward increased metallic character as we move down in a given group. Bismuth, in fact, is a metal. The increased metallic character occurs because the outermost electrons are more readily lost in bonding, a trend that is consistent with lower ionization energy.

(d) Following the procedures described in Section 4.2 for writing molecular and net ionic equations, we have the following:

Molecular equation: $Bi_2O_3(s) + 6\,HNO_3(aq) \longrightarrow 2\,Bi(NO_3)_3(aq) + 3\,H_2O(l)$

Net ionic equation: $Bi_2O_3(s) + 6\,H^+(aq) \longrightarrow 2\,Bi^{3+}(aq) + 3\,H_2O(l)$

In the net ionic equation, nitric acid is a strong acid and $Bi(NO_3)_3$ is a soluble salt, so we need show only the reaction of the solid with the hydrogen ion forming the $Bi^{3+}(aq)$ ion and water.

To calculate the concentration of the solution, we proceed as follows (Section 4.5):

$$\frac{6.77\ g\ Bi_2O_3}{0.500\ L\ soln} \times \frac{1\ mol\ Bi_2O_3}{466.0\ g\ Bi_2O_3} \times \frac{2\ mol\ Bi^{3+}}{1\ mol\ Bi_2O_3} = \frac{0.0581\ mol\ Bi^{3+}}{L\ soln} = 0.0581\ M$$

(e) We can proceed as in Section 2.3. Bismuth is element 83; there are therefore 83 protons in the nucleus. Because the atomic mass number is 209, there are $209 - 83 = 126$ neutrons in the nucleus.

(f) We proceed as in Sections 1.4 and 3.4: The volume of the cube is $(5.00)^3$ $cm^3 = 125\ cm^3$. Then we have

$$125\ cm^3\ Bi \times \frac{9.780\ g\ Bi}{1\ cm^3} \times \frac{1\ mol\ Bi}{209.0\ g\ Bi} = 5.87\ mol\ Bi$$

$$5.87\ mol\ Bi \times \frac{6.022 \times 10^{23}\ atom\ Bi}{1\ mol\ Bi} = 3.54 \times 10^{24}\ atoms\ Bi$$

SUMMARY AND KEY TERMS

Introduction and Section 7.1 The periodic table was first developed by Mendeleev and Meyer on the basis of the similarity in chemical and physical properties exhibited by certain elements. Moseley established that each element has a unique atomic number, which added more order to the periodic table. We now recognize that elements in the same column of the periodic table have the same number of electrons in their **valence orbitals**. This similarity in valence electronic structure leads to the similarities among elements in the same group. The differences among elements in the same group arise because their valence orbitals are in different shells.

Section 7.2 Many properties of atoms are due to the average distance of the outer electrons from the nucleus and to the **effective nuclear charge** experienced by these electrons. The core electrons are very effective in screening the outer electrons from the full charge of the nucleus, whereas electrons in the same shell do not screen each other very effectively at all. As a result, the effective nu-

clear charge experienced by valence electrons increases as we move left to right across a period.

Section 7.3 The size of an atom can be gauged by its **bonding atomic radius**, based on measurements of the distances separating atoms in their chemical compounds. In general, atomic radii increase as we go down a column in the periodic table and decrease as we proceed left to right across a row.

Cations are smaller than their parent atoms; anions are larger than their parent atoms. For ions of the same charge, size increases going down a column of the periodic table. An **isoelectronic series** is a series of ions that has the same number of electrons. For such a series, size decreases with increasing nuclear charge as the electrons are attracted more strongly to the nucleus.

Section 7.4 The first **ionization energy** of an atom is the minimum energy needed to remove an electron from the atom in the gas phase, forming a cation. The second ionization energy is the energy needed to remove a second electron, and so forth. Ionization energies show a sharp increase after all the valence electrons have been removed, because of the much higher effective nuclear charge experienced by the core electrons. The first ionization energies of the elements show periodic trends that are opposite those seen for atomic radii, with smaller atoms having higher first ionization energies. Thus, first ionization energies decrease as we go down a column and increase as we proceed left to right across a row.

We can write electron configurations for ions by first writing the electron configuration of the neutral atom and then removing or adding the appropriate number of electrons. Electrons are removed first from the orbitals with the largest value of n. Electrons are added to orbitals with the lowest value of n.

Section 7.5 The **electron affinity** of an element is the energy change upon adding an electron to an atom in the gas phase, forming an anion. A negative electron affinity means that the anion is stable; a positive electron affinity means that the anion is not stable relative to the separated atom and electron. In general, electron affinities become more negative as we proceed from left to right across the periodic table. The halogens have the most-negative electron affinities. The electron affinities of the noble gases are all positive because the added electron would have to occupy a new, higher-energy subshell.

Section 7.6 The elements can be categorized as metals, nonmetals, and metalloids. Most elements are metals; they occupy the left side and the middle of the periodic table. Nonmetals appear in the upper-right section of the table. Metalloids occupy a narrow band between the metals and nonmetals. The tendency of an element to exhibit the properties of metals, called the **metallic character**, increases as we proceed down a column and decreases as we proceed from left to right across a row.

Metals have a characteristic luster, and they are good conductors of heat and electricity. When metals react with nonmetals, the metal atoms are oxidized to cations and ionic substances are generally formed. Most metal oxides are basic; they react with acids to form salts and water.

Nonmetals lack metallic luster and are poor conductors of heat and electricity. Several are gases at room temperature. Compounds composed entirely of nonmetals are generally molecular. Nonmetals usually form anions in their reactions with metals. Nonmetal oxides are acidic; they react with bases to form salts and water. Metalloids have properties that are intermediate between those of metals and nonmetals.

Section 7.7 The periodic properties of the elements can help us understand the properties of groups of the representative elements. The **alkali metals** (group 1A) are soft metals with low densities and low melting points. They have the lowest ionization energies of the elements. As a result, they are very reactive toward nonmetals, easily losing their outer s electron to form 1+ ions. The **alkaline earth metals** (group 2A) are harder and more dense and have higher melting points than the alkali metals. They are also very reactive toward nonmetals, although not as reactive as the alkali metals. The alkaline earth metals readily lose their two outer s electrons to form 2+ ions. Both alkali and alkaline earth metals react with hydrogen to form ionic substances that contain the **hydride ion**, H^-.

Section 7.8 Hydrogen is a nonmetal with properties that are distinct from any of the groups of the periodic table. It forms molecular compounds with other nonmetals, such as oxygen and the halogens.

Oxygen and sulfur are the most important elements in group 6A. Oxygen is usually found as a diatomic molecule, O_2. **Ozone**, O_3, is an important allotrope of oxygen. Oxygen has a strong tendency to gain electrons from other elements, thus oxidizing them. In combination with metals, oxygen is usually found as the oxide ion, O^{2-}, although salts of the peroxide ion, O_2^{2-}, and superoxide ion, O_2^-, are sometimes formed. Elemental sulfur is most commonly found as S_8 molecules. In combination with metals, it is most often found as the sulfide ion, S^{2-}.

The **halogens** (group 7A) are nonmetals that exist as diatomic molecules. The halogens have the most negative electron affinities of the elements. Thus their chemistry is dominated by a tendency to form 1− ions, especially in reactions with metals.

The **noble gases** (group 8A) are nonmetals that exist as monoatomic gases. They are very unreactive because they have completely filled s and p subshells. Only the heaviest noble gases are known to form compounds, and they do so only with very active nonmetals, such as fluorine.

VISUALIZING CONCEPTS

7.1 We can draw an analogy between the attraction of an electron to a nucleus and seeing a lightbulb—in essence, the more nuclear charge the electron "sees," the greater the attraction. **(a)** Within this analogy, discuss how the shielding by core electrons is analogous to putting a frosted-glass lampshade between the lightbulb and your eyes, as shown in the illustration. **(b)** Explain how we could mimic moving to the right in a row of the periodic table by changing the wattage of the lightbulb. **(c)** How would you change the wattage of the bulb and/or the frosted glass to mimic the effect of moving down a column of the periodic table? [Section 7.2]

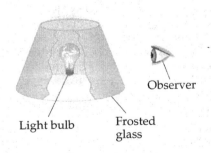

Observer

Light bulb   Frosted glass

Science Fundamentals Second Edition

7.2 Neon has atomic number 10. What are the similarities and differences in describing the radius of a neon atom and the radius of the billiard ball illustrated here? Could you use billiard balls to illustrate the concept of bonding atomic radius? Explain. [Section 7.3]

7.3 Consider the A_2X_4 molecule depicted below, where A and X are elements. The A—A bond length in this molecule is d_1, and the four A—X bond lengths are each d_2. (a) In terms of d_1 and d_2, how could you define the bonding atomic radii of atoms A and X? (b) In terms of d_1 and d_2, what would you predict for the X—X bond length of an X_2 molecule? [Section 7.3]

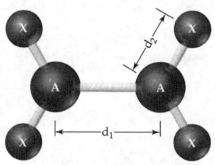

7.4 Make a simple sketch of the shape of the main part of the periodic table, as shown. (a) Ignoring H and He, write a single straight arrow from the element with the smallest bonding atomic radius to the element with the largest. (b) Ignoring H and He, write a single straight arrow from the element with the smallest first ionization energy to the element with the largest. (c) What significant observation can you make from the arrows you drew in parts (a) and (b)? [Sections 7.3 and 7.4]

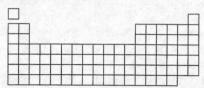

7.5 In the chemical process called *electron transfer*, an electron is transferred from one atom or molecule to another (we will talk about electron transfer extensively in Chapter 20). A simple electron transfer reaction is

$$A(g) + A(g) \longrightarrow A^+(g) + A^-(g)$$

In terms of the ionization energy and electron affinity of atom A, what is the energy change for this reaction? [Sections 7.4 and 7.5]

7.6 An element X reacts with $F_2(g)$ to form the molecular product shown below. (a) Write a balanced equation for this reaction (do not worry about the phases for X and the product). (b) Do you think that X is a metal or non-metal? Explain. [Section 7.6]

EXERCISES

Periodic Table; Effective Nuclear Charge

7.7 Why did Mendeleev leave blanks in his early version of the periodic table? How did he predict the properties of the elements that belonged in those blanks?

7.8 (a) In the period from about 1800 to about 1865, the atomic weights of many elements were accurately measured. Why was this important to Mendeleev's formulation of the periodic table? (b) What property of the atom did Moseley associate with the wavelength of X rays emitted from an element in his experiments? In what ways did this affect the meaning of the periodic table?

7.9 (a) What is meant by the term *effective nuclear charge*? (b) How does the effective nuclear charge experienced by the valence electrons of an atom vary going from left to right across a period of the periodic table?

7.10 (a) How is the concept of effective nuclear charge used to simplify the numerous electron-electron repulsions in a many-electron atom? (b) Which experiences a greater effective nuclear charge in a Be atom, the $1s$ electrons or the $2s$ electrons? Explain.

7.11 (a) If each core electron were totally effective in screening the valence electrons from the full charge of the nucleus and the valence electrons provided no screening for each other, what would be the values of the screening constant, S, and the effective nuclear charge, Z_{eff}, for the $4s$ electron in a potassium atom? (b) Detailed calculations show that the value of Z_{eff} for a K atom is 3.49+. Explain the difference between this number and the one you obtained in part (a).

7.12 (a) If the core electrons were totally effective at shielding the valence electrons from the full charge of the nucleus and the valence electrons provided no shielding for each other, what would be the values of S and Z_{eff} for a $3p$ electron in a sulfur atom? (b) Detailed calculations indicate that the value of S for a $3p$ electron in a sulfur atom is 10.52. Can you explain any difference between this number and the one you obtained in part (a)?

7.13 Which will experience the greater effective nuclear charge, the electrons in the $n = 3$ shell in Ar or the $n = 3$ shell in Kr? Which will be closer to the nucleus? Explain.

7.14 Arrange the following atoms in order of increasing effective nuclear charge experienced by the electrons in the $n = 3$ electron shell: K, Mg, P, Rh, and Ti. Explain the basis for your order.

Atomic and Ionic Radii

7.15 Because an exact outer boundary cannot be measured or even calculated for an atom, how are atomic radii determined? What is the difference between a bonding radius and a nonbonding radius?

7.16 (a) Why does the quantum mechanical description of many-electron atoms make it difficult to define a precise atomic radius? (b) When nonbonded atoms come up against one another, what determines how closely the nuclear centers can approach?

7.17 The distance between W atoms in tungsten metal is 2.74 Å. What is the atomic radius of a tungsten atom in this environment? (This radius is called the *metallic radius*.)

7.18 Based on the radii presented in Figure 7.6, predict the distance between Ge atoms in solid germanium.

7.19 Estimate the As—I bond length from the data in Figure 7.6, and compare your value to the experimental As—I bond length in arsenic triiodide, AsI_3, 2.55 Å.

7.20 The experimental Bi—I bond length in bismuth triiodide, BiI_3, is 2.81 Å. Based on this value and data in Figure 7.6, predict the atomic radius of Bi.

7.21 How do the sizes of atoms change as we move (a) from left to right across a row in the periodic table, (b) from top to bottom in a group in the periodic table? (c) Arrange the following atoms in order of increasing atomic radius: F, P, S, As.

7.22 (a) Among the nonmetallic elements, the change in atomic radius in moving one place left or right in a row is smaller than the change in moving one row up or down. Explain these observations. (b) Arrange the following atoms in order of increasing atomic radius: Si, S, Ge, Se.

7.23 Using only the periodic table, arrange each set of atoms in order of increasing radius: (a) Ca, Mg, Be; (b) Ga, Br, Ge; (c) Al, Tl, Si.

7.24 Using only the periodic table, arrange each set of atoms in order of increasing radius: (a) Cs, K, Rb; (b) In, Te, Sn; (c) P, Cl, Sr.

7.25 (a) Why are monatomic cations smaller than their corresponding neutral atoms? (b) Why are monatomic anions larger than their corresponding neutral atoms? (c) Why does the size of ions increase as one proceeds down a column in the periodic table?

7.26 Explain the following variations in atomic or ionic radii: (a) $I^- > I > I^+$, (b) $Ca^{2+} > Mg^{2+} > Be^{2+}$, (c) $Fe > Fe^{2+} > Fe^{3+}$.

7.27 Consider a reaction represented by the following spheres:

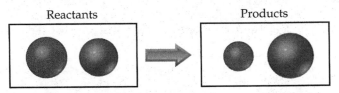

Reactants   Products

Which sphere represents a metal and which a nonmetal? Explain.

7.28 Consider the following spheres:

Which one represents Ca, which Ca^{2+}, and which Mg^{2+}?

7.29 (a) What is an isoelectronic series? (b) Which neutral atom is isoelectronic with each of the following ions: (*i*) N^{3-}, (*ii*) Ba^{2+}, (*iii*) Se^{2-}, (*iv*) Bi^{3+}?

7.30 Select the ions or atoms from the following sets that are isoelectronic with each other: (a) Na^+, Sr^{2+}, Br^-; (b) Y^{3+}, Br^-, Kr; (c) N^{3-}, P^{3-}, Ti^{4+}; (d) Fe^{3+}, Co^{3+}, Mn^{2+}.

7.31 (a) Why do the radii of isoelectronic ions decrease with increasing nuclear charge? (b) Which experiences the greatest effective nuclear charge, a 2p electron in F^-, a 2p electron in Ne, or a 2p electron in Na^+?

7.32 Consider S, Cl, and K and their most common ions. (a) List the atoms in order of increasing size. (b) List the ions in order of increasing size. (c) Explain any differences in the orders of the atomic and ionic sizes.

7.33 For each of the following sets of atoms and ions, arrange the members in order of increasing size: (a) Se^{2-}, Te^{2-}, Se; (b) Co^{3+}, Fe^{2+}, Fe^{3+}; (c) Ca, Ti^{4+}, Sc^{3+}; (d) Be^{2+}, Na^+, Ne.

7.34 For each of the following statements, provide an explanation: (a) Cl^- is larger than Cl; (b) S^{2-} is larger than O^{2-}; (c) K^+ is larger than Ca^{2+}.

Ionization Energies; Electron Affinities

7.35 Write equations that show the processes that describe the first, second, and third ionization energies of a boron atom.

7.36 Write equations that show the process for (a) the first two ionization energies of tin and (b) the fourth ionization energy of titanium.

7.37 (a) Why are ionization energies always positive quantities? (b) Why does F have a larger first ionization energy than O? (c) Why is the second ionization energy of an atom always greater than its first ionization energy?

7.38 (a) Why does Li have a larger first ionization energy than Na? (b) The difference between the third and

fourth ionization energies of scandium is much larger than the difference between the third and fourth ionization energies of titanium. Why? (c) Why does Li have a much larger second ionization energy than Be?

7.39 (a) What is the general relationship between the size of an atom and its first ionization energy? (b) Which element in the periodic table has the largest ionization energy? Which has the smallest?

7.40 (a) What is the trend in first ionization energies as one proceeds down the group 7A elements? Explain how this trend relates to the variation in atomic radii. (b) What is the trend in first ionization energies as one moves across the fourth period from K to Kr? How does this trend compare with the trend in atomic sizes?

7.41 Based on their positions in the periodic table, predict which atom of the following pairs will have the larger first ionization energy: **(a)** Cl, Ar; **(b)** Be, Ca; **(c)** K, Co; **(d)** S, Ge; **(e)** Sn, Te.

7.42 For each of the following pairs, indicate which element has the larger first ionization energy: **(a)** Rb, Mo; **(b)** N, P; **(c)** Ga, Cl; **(d)** Pb, Rn. (In each case use electron configuration and effective nuclear charge to explain your answer.)

7.43 Write the electron configurations for the following ions: **(a)** Si^{2+}, **(b)** Bi^{3+}, **(c)** Te^{2-}, **(d)** V^{3+}, **(e)** Hg^{2+}, **(f)** Ni^{2+}.

7.44 Write electron configurations for the following ions, and determine which have noble-gas configurations: **(a)** Mn^{3+}, **(b)** Se^{2-}, **(c)** Sc^{3+}, **(d)** Ru^{2+}, **(e)** Tl^{+}, **(f)** Au^{+}.

7.45 Write the electron configuration for **(a)** the Mn^{2+} ion and **(b)** the Si^{2-} ion. How many unpaired electrons does each contain?

7.46 Identify the element whose ions have the following electron configurations: **(a)** a 2+ ion with $[Ar]3d^9$, **(b)** a 1+ ion with $[Xe]4f^{14}5d^{10}6s^2$. How many unpaired electrons does each ion contain?

7.47 Write equations, including electron configurations beneath the species involved, that explain the difference between the first ionization energy of $Se(g)$ and the electron affinity of $Se(g)$.

7.48 The first ionization energy of Ar and the electron affinity of Ar are both positive values. What is the significance of the positive value in each case?

7.49 The electron affinity of lithium is a negative value, whereas the electron affinity of beryllium is a positive value. Use electron configurations to account for this observation.

7.50 While the electron affinity of bromine is a negative quantity, it is positive for Kr. Use the electron configurations of the two elements to explain the difference.

7.51 What is the relationship between the ionization energy of an anion with a 1− charge such as F^- and the electron affinity of the neutral atom, F?

7.52 Write an equation for the process that corresponds to the electron affinity of the Mg^+ ion. Also write the electron configurations of the species involved. What process does this electron affinity equation correspond to? What is the magnitude of the energy change in the process? [*Hint:* The answer is in Table 7.2.]

Properties of Metals and Nonmetals

7.53 How are metallic character and first ionization energy related?

7.54 Arrange the following pure solid elements in order of increasing electrical conductivity: Ge, Ca, S, and Si. Explain the reasoning you used.

7.55 For each of the following pairs, which element will have the greater metallic character: **(a)** Li or Be, **(b)** Li or Na, **(c)** Sn or P, **(d)** Al or B?

7.56 **(a)** What data can you cite from this chapter to support a prediction that the metallic character of the group 5A elements will increase with increasing atomic number? **(b)** *Nonmetallic character* is the opposite of metallic character—nonmetallic character decreases as metallic character increases. Arrange the following elements in order of increasing nonmetallic character: Se, Ag, Sn, F, and C.

7.57 Predict whether each of the following oxides is ionic or molecular: SO_2, MgO, Li_2O, P_2O_5, Y_2O_3, N_2O, and XeO_3. Explain the reasons for your choices.

7.58 When metal oxides react with water, the oxygen generally ends up as the hydroxide ion, separate from the metal. In contrast, when nonmetallic oxides react with water, the oxygen ends up as part of the nonmetal species. (For example, upon reaction of CO_2 with water, the oxygen remains on the carbon in H_2CO_3.) **(a)** Give two examples each from metals and nonmetals to support these generalizations. **(b)** What connection is there between this contrasting behavior of metal and nonmetal oxides and ionization energies?

7.59 **(a)** What is meant by the terms acidic oxide and basic oxide? **(b)** How can we predict whether an oxide will be acidic or basic, based on its composition?

7.60 Arrange the following oxides in order of increasing acidity: CO_2, CaO, Al_2O_3, SO_3, SiO_2, and P_2O_5.

7.61 Chlorine reacts with oxygen to form Cl_2O_7. **(a)** What is the name of this product (see Table 2.6)? **(b)** Write a balanced equation for the formation $Cl_2O_7(l)$ from the elements. **(c)** Under usual conditions, Cl_2O_7 is a colorless liquid with a boiling point of 81°C. Is this boiling point expected or surprising? **(d)** Would you expect Cl_2O_7 to be more reactive toward $H^+(aq)$ or $OH^-(aq)$? Explain.

[7.62] An element X reacts with oxygen to form XO_2 and with chlorine to form XCl_4. XO_2 is a white solid that melts at high temperatures (above 1000°C). Under usual conditions, XCl_4 is a colorless liquid with a boiling point of 58°C. **(a)** XCl_4 reacts with water to form XO_2 and another product. What is the likely identity of the other product? **(b)** Do you think that element X is a metal, nonmetal, or metalloid? Explain. **(c)** By using a sourcebook such as the *CRC Handbook of Chemistry and Physics*, try to determine the identity of element X.

[7.63] Write balanced equations for the following reactions: **(a)** barium oxide with water, **(b)** iron(II) oxide with perchloric acid, **(c)** sulfur trioxide with water, **(d)** carbon dioxide with aqueous sodium hydroxide.

7.64 Write balanced equations for the following reactions: **(a)** potassium oxide with water, **(b)** diphosphorus trioxide with water, **(c)** chromium(III) oxide with dilute hydrochloric acid, **(d)** selenium dioxide with aqueous potassium hydroxide.

Group Trends in Metals and Nonmetals

7.65 Compare the elements sodium and magnesium with respect to the following properties: **(a)** electron configuration, **(b)** most common ionic charge, **(c)** first ionization energy, **(d)** reactivity toward water, **(e)** atomic radius. Account for the differences between the two elements.

7.66 (a) Compare the electron configurations and atomic radii (see Figure 7.6) of rubidium and silver. In what respects are their electronic configurations similar? Account for the difference in radii of the two elements. (b) As with rubidium, silver is most commonly found as the 1+ ion, Ag^+. However, silver is far less reactive. Explain these observations.

7.67 (a) Why is calcium generally more reactive than magnesium? (b) Why is calcium generally less reactive than potassium?

7.68 (a) Why is cesium more reactive toward water than is lithium? (b) One of the alkali metals reacts with oxygen to form a solid white substance. When this substance is dissolved in water, the solution gives a positive test for hydrogen peroxide, H_2O_2. When the solution is tested in a burner flame, a lilac-purple flame is produced. What is the likely identity of the metal? (c) Write a balanced chemical equation for reaction of the white substance with water.

7.69 Write a balanced equation for the reaction that occurs in each of the following cases: (a) Potassium metal burns in an atmosphere of chlorine gas. (b) Strontium oxide is added to water. (c) A fresh surface of lithium metal is exposed to oxygen gas. (d) Sodium metal is reacted with molten sulfur.

7.70 Write a balanced equation for the reaction that occurs in each of the following cases: (a) Potassium is added to water. (b) Barium is added to water. (c) Lithium is heated in nitrogen, forming lithium nitride. (d) Magnesium burns in oxygen.

7.71 Use electron configurations to explain why hydrogen exhibits properties similar to those of both Li and F.

7.72 (a) As described in Section 7.7, the alkali metals react with hydrogen to form hydrides and react with halogens—for example, fluorine—to form halides.

Compare the roles of hydrogen and the halogen in these reactions. In what sense are the forms of hydrogen and halogen in the products alike? (b) Write balanced equations for the reaction of fluorine with calcium and for the reaction of hydrogen with calcium. What are the similarities among the products of these reactions?

7.73 Compare the elements fluorine and chlorine with respect to the following properties: (a) electron configuration, (b) most common ionic charge, (c) first ionization energy, (d) reactivity toward water, (e) electron affinity, (f) atomic radius. Account for the differences between the two elements.

7.74 Little is known about the properties of astatine, At, because of its rarity and high radioactivity. Nevertheless, it is possible for us to make many predictions about its properties. (a) Do you expect the element to be a gas, liquid, or solid at room temperature? Explain. (b) What is the chemical formula of the compound it forms with Na?

7.75 Until the early 1960s the group 8A elements were called the inert gases. Why was this name given? Why is it inappropriate?

7.76 Why does xenon react with fluorine whereas neon does not?

7.77 Write a balanced equation for the reaction that occurs in each of the following cases: (a) Ozone decomposes to dioxygen. (b) Xenon reacts with fluorine. (Write three different equations.) (c) Sulfur reacts with hydrogen gas. (d) Fluorine reacts with water.

7.78 Write a balanced equation for the reaction that occurs in each of the following cases: (a) Chlorine reacts with water. (b) Barium metal is heated in an atmosphere of hydrogen gas. (c) Lithium reacts with sulfur. (d) Fluorine reacts with magnesium metal.

Additional Exercises

7.79 Consider the stable elements through lead ($Z = 82$). In how many instances are the atomic weights of the elements in the reverse order relative to the atomic numbers of the elements? What is the explanation for these cases?

7.80 In 1871, Mendeleev predicted the existence of an element that he called eka-aluminum, which would have the following properties: atomic weight of about 68 amu, density of about 5.9 g/cm^3, low melting point, high boiling point, and an oxide with stoichiometry M_2O_3. (a) In 1875 the element predicted by Mendeleev was discovered. By what name is the element known? (b) Use a reference such as the *CRC Handbook of Chemistry and Physics* or WebElements.com to check the accuracy of Mendeleev's predictions.

7.81 (a) Which will have the lower energy, a $4s$ or a $4p$ electron in an As atom? (b) How can we use the concept of effective nuclear charge to explain your answer to part (a)?

7.82 (a) If the core electrons were totally effective at shielding the valence electrons and the valence electrons provided no shielding for each other, what would be the effective nuclear charge acting on the valence electron in P? (b) Detailed calculations indicate that the effective nu-

clear charge is 5.6+ for the $3s$ electrons and 4.9+ for the $3p$ electrons. Why are the values for the $3s$ and $3p$ electrons different? (c) If you remove a single electron from a P atom, which orbital will it come from? Explain.

7.83 Nearly all the mass of an atom is in the nucleus, which has a very small radius. When atoms bond together (for example, two fluorine atoms in F_2), why is the distance separating the nuclei so much larger than the radii of the nuclei?

[7.84] Consider the change in effective nuclear charge experienced by a $2p$ electron as we proceed from C to N. (a) Based on a simple model in which core electrons screen the valence electrons completely and valence electrons do not screen other valence electrons, what do you predict for the change in Z_{eff} from C to N? (b) The actual calculated change in Z_{eff} from C to N is 0.70+. How can we explain the difference between this number and the one obtained in part (a)? (c) The calculated change in Z_{eff} from N to O is smaller than that from C to N. Can you provide an explanation for this observation?

7.85 As we move across a period of the periodic table, why do the sizes of the transition elements change more gradually than those of the representative elements?

7.86 In the series of group 5A hydrides, of general formula MH_3, the measured bond distances are P—H, 1.419 Å; As—H, 1.519 Å; Sb—H, 1.707 Å. **(a)** Compare these values with those estimated by use of the atomic radii in Figure 7.6. **(b)** Explain the steady increase in M—H bond distance in this series in terms of the electronic configurations of the M atoms.

7.87 It is possible to produce compounds of the form $GeClH_3$, $GeCl_2H_2$, and $GeCl_3H$. What values do you predict for the Ge—H and Ge—Cl bond lengths in these compounds?

7.88 Note from the following table that the increase in atomic radius in moving from Zr to Hf is smaller than in moving from Y to La. Suggest an explanation for this effect.

Atomic Radii (Å)

Sc	1.44	Ti	1.36
Y	1.62	Zr	1.48
La	1.69	Hf	1.50

7.89 The "Chemistry and Life" box on ionic size in Section 7.3 compares the ionic radii of Zn^{2+} and Cd^{2+}. **(a)** The 2+ ion of which other element seems the most obvious one to compare to Zn^{2+} and Cd^{2+}? **(b)** With reference to Figure 2.24, is the element in part (a) essential for life? **(c)** Estimate the ionic radius of the 2+ ion of the element in part (a). Explain any assumptions you have made. **(d)** Would you expect the 2+ ion of the element in part (a) to be physiologically more similar to Zn^{2+} or to Cd^{2+}? **(e)** Use a sourcebook or a Web search to determine whether the element in part (a) is toxic to humans.

[7.90] The ionic substance strontium oxide, SrO, forms from the direct reaction of strontium metal with molecular oxygen. The arrangement of the ions in solid SrO is analogous to that in solid NaCl (see Figure 2.23) and is shown below. **(a)** Write a balanced equation for the formation of SrO(*s*) from the elements. **(b)** In the figure, do the large spheres represent Sr^{2+} ions or O^{2-} ions? Explain. **(c)** Based on the ionic radii in Figure 7.7, predict the length of the side of the cube in the figure. **(d)** The experimental density of SrO is 5.10 g/cm^3. Given your answer to part (c), what is the number of formula units of SrO that are contained in the cube in the figure? (We will examine structures like those in the figure more closely in Chapter 11.)

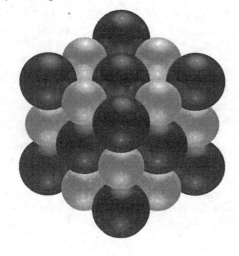

7.91 Explain the variation in ionization energies of carbon, as displayed in the following graph:

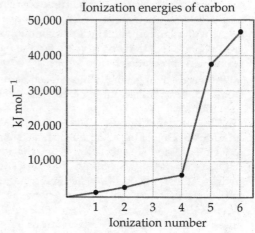

[7.92] Listed here are the atomic and ionic (2+) radii for calcium and zinc:

Radii (Å)

Ca 1.74	Ca^{2+} 0.99
Zn 1.31	Zn^{2+} 0.74

(a) Explain why the ionic radius in each case is smaller than the atomic radius. **(b)** Why is the atomic radius of calcium larger than that of zinc? **(c)** Suggest a reason why the difference in the ionic radii is much less than the difference in the atomic radii.

7.93 Do you agree with the following statement? "A negative value for the electron affinity of an atom occurs when the outermost electrons only incompletely shield one another from the nucleus." If not, change it to make it more nearly correct in your view. Apply either the statement as given or your revised statement to explain why the electron affinity of bromine is -325 kJ/mol and that for its neighbor Kr is > 0.

7.94 Use orbital diagrams to illustrate what happens when an oxygen atom gains two electrons. Why is it extremely difficult to add a third electron to the atom?

[7.95] Use electron configurations to explain the following observations: **(a)** The first ionization energy of phosphorus is greater than that of sulfur. **(b)** The electron affinity of nitrogen is lower (less negative) than those of both carbon and oxygen. **(c)** The second ionization energy of oxygen is greater than that of fluorine. **(d)** The third ionization energy of manganese is greater than those of both chromium and iron.

7.96 The following table gives the electron affinities, in kJ/mol, for the group 1B and group 2B metals:

Cu	Zn
−119	> 0
Ag	Cd
−126	> 0
Au	Hg
−223	> 0

(a) Why are the electron affinities of the group 2B elements greater than zero? (b) Why do the electron affinities of the group 1B elements become more negative as we move down the group? [*Hint:* Examine the trends in the electron affinity of other groups as we proceed down the periodic table.]

7.97 Hydrogen is an unusual element because it behaves in some ways like the alkali metal elements and in other ways like a nonmetal. Its properties can be explained in part by its electron configuration and by the values for its ionization energy and electron affinity. (a) Explain why the electron affinity of hydrogen is much closer to the values for the alkali elements than for the halogens. (b) Is the following statement true? "Hydrogen has the smallest bonding atomic radius of any element that forms chemical compounds." If not, correct it. If it is, explain in terms of electron configurations. (c) Explain why the ionization energy of hydrogen is closer to the values for the halogens than for the alkali metals.

[7.98] The first ionization energy of the oxygen molecule is the energy required for the following process:

$$O_2(g) \longrightarrow O_2^+(g) + e^-$$

The energy needed for this process is 1175 kJ/mol, very similar to the first ionization energy of Xe. Would you expect O_2 to react with F_2? If so, suggest a product or products of this reaction.

7.99 Based on your reading of this chapter, arrange the following in order of increasing melting point: K, Br_2, Mg, and O_2. Explain the factors that determine the order.

[7.100] There are certain similarities in properties that exist between the first member of any periodic family and the element located below it and to the right in the periodic table. For example, in some ways Li resembles Mg, Be resembles Al, and so forth. This observation is called the diagonal relationship. Using what we have learned in this chapter, offer a possible explanation for this relationship.

[7.101] The elements at the bottom of groups 1A, 2A, 6A, 7A, and 8A—Fr, Ra, Po, At, and Rn—are all radioactive. As a result, much less is known about their physical and chemical properties than those of the elements above them. Based on what we have learned in this chapter, which of these five elements would you expect (a) to have the most metallic character, (b) to have the least metallic (that is, the most nonmetallic) character, (c) to have the largest first ionization energy, (d) to have the smallest first ionization energy, (e) to have the greatest (most negative) electron affinity, (f) to have the largest atomic radius, (g) to resemble least in appearance the element immediately above it, (h) to have the highest melting point, (i) to react most exothermically with water?

[7.102] A historian discovers a nineteenth-century notebook in which some observations, dated 1822, on a substance thought to be a new element, were recorded. Here are some of the data recorded in the notebook: Ductile, silver-white, metallic looking. Softer than lead. Unaffected by water. Stable in air. Melting point: 153°C. Density: 7.3 g/cm^3. Electrical conductivity: 20% that of copper. Hardness: About 1% as hard as iron. When 4.20 g of the unknown is heated in an excess of oxygen, 5.08 g of a white solid is formed. The solid could be sublimed by heating to over 800°C. (a) Using information in the text and a handbook of chemistry, and making allowances for possible variations in numbers from current values, identify the element reported. (b) Write a balanced chemical equation for the reaction with oxygen. (c) Judging from Figure 7.2, might this nineteenth-century investigator have been the first to discover a new element?

[7.103] It has been discovered in recent years that many organic compounds that contain chlorine, including dioxins, which had been thought to be entirely of man-made origin, are formed in natural processes. More than 3000 natural organohalogen compounds, most involving chlorine and bromine, are known. These compounds, in which the halogen is attached to carbon, are nearly all nonionic materials. Why are these materials typically not ionic, as are the more abundant inorganic halogen compounds found in nature?

Integrative Exercises

[7.104] Moseley established the concept of atomic number by studying X rays emitted by the elements. The X rays emitted by some of the elements have the following wavelengths:

Element	Wavelength (Å)
Ne	14.610
Ca	3.358
Zn	1.435
Zr	0.786
Sn	0.491

(a) Calculate the frequency, ν, of the X rays emitted by each of the elements, in Hz. (b) Using graph paper (or suitable computer software), plot the square root of ν versus the atomic number of the element. What do you observe about the plot? (c) Explain how the plot in part (b) allowed Moseley to predict the existence of undiscovered elements. (d) Use the result from part (b) to predict the X-ray wavelength emitted by iron. (e) A particular element emits X rays with a wavelength of 0.980 Å. What element do you think it is?

[7.105] (a) Write the electron configuration for Li, and estimate the effective nuclear charge experienced by the valence electron. (b) The energy of an electron in a one-electron atom or ion equals $(-2.18 \times 10^{-18} \text{ J})\left(\dfrac{Z^2}{n^2}\right)$, where Z is the nuclear charge and n is the principal quantum number of the electron. Estimate the first ionization energy of Li. (c) Compare the result of your calculation with the value reported in Table 7.4, and explain the difference. (d) What value of the effective nuclear charge gives the proper value for the ionization energy? Does this agree with your explanation in (c)?

[7.106] One way to measure ionization energies is photoelectron spectroscopy (PES), a technique based on the photoelectric effect. ∞∞ (Section 6.2) In PES, monochromatic light is directed onto a sample, causing electrons to be emitted. The kinetic energy of the emitted electrons is measured. The difference between the energy of the photons and the kinetic energy of the electrons corresponds to the energy needed to remove the electrons (that is, the ionization energy). Suppose that a PES experiment is performed in which mercury vapor is irradiated with ultraviolet light of wavelength 58.4 nm. **(a)** What is the energy of a photon of this light, in eV? **(b)** Write an equation that shows the process corresponding to the first ionization energy of Hg. **(c)** The kinetic energy of the emitted electrons is measured to be 10.75 eV. What is the first ionization energy of Hg, in kJ/mol? **(d)** With reference to Figure 7.11, determine which of the halogen elements has a first ionization energy closest to that of mercury.

7.107 Consider the gas-phase transfer of an electron from a sodium atom to a chlorine atom:

$$Na(g) + Cl(g) \longrightarrow Na^+(g) + Cl^-(g)$$

(a) Write this reaction as the sum of two reactions, one that relates to an ionization energy and one that relates to an electron affinity. **(b)** Use the result from part (a), data in this chapter, and Hess's law to calculate the enthalpy of the above reaction. Is the reaction exothermic or endothermic? **(c)** The reaction between sodium metal and chlorine gas is highly exothermic and produces NaCl(s), whose structure was discussed in Section 2.6. Comment on this observation relative to the calculated enthalpy for the aforementioned gas-phase reaction.

[7.108] When magnesium metal is burned in air (Figure 3.5), two products are produced. One is magnesium oxide, MgO. The other is the product of the reaction of Mg with molecular nitrogen, magnesium nitride. When water is added to magnesium nitride, it reacts to form magnesium oxide and ammonia gas. **(a)** Based on the charge of the nitride ion (Table 2.5), predict the formula of magnesium nitride. **(b)** Write a balanced equation for the reaction of magnesium nitride with water. What is the driving force for this reaction? **(c)** In an experiment a piece of magnesium ribbon is burned in air in a crucible. The mass of the mixture of MgO and magnesium nitride after burning is 0.470 g. Water is added to the crucible,

further reaction occurs, and the crucible is heated to dryness until the final product is 0.486 g of MgO. What was the mass percentage of magnesium nitride in the mixture obtained after the initial burning? **(d)** Magnesium nitride can also be formed by reaction of the metal with ammonia at high temperature. Write a balanced equation for this reaction. If a 6.3-g Mg ribbon reacts with 2.57 g $NH_3(g)$ and the reaction goes to completion, which component is the limiting reactant? What mass of $H_2(g)$ is formed in the reaction? **(e)** The standard enthalpy of formation of solid magnesium nitride is -461.08 kJ mol^{-1}. Calculate the standard enthalpy change for the reaction between magnesium metal and ammonia gas.

7.109 **(a)** The experimental Bi—Br bond length in bismuth tribromide, $BiBr_3$, is 2.63 Å. Based on this value and the data in Figure 7.6, predict the atomic radius of Bi. **(b)** Bismuth tribromide is soluble in acidic solution. It is formed by treating solid bismuth(III) oxide with aqueous hydrobromic acid. Write a balanced chemical equation for this reaction. **(c)** While bismuth(III) oxide is soluble in acidic solutions, it is insoluble in basic solutions such as NaOH(aq). On the basis of these properties, is bismuth characterized as a metallic, metalloid, or nonmetallic element? **(d)** Treating bismuth with fluorine gas forms BiF_5. Use the electron configuration of Bi to explain the formation of a compound with this formulation. **(e)** While it is possible to form BiF_5 in the manner just described, pentahalides of bismuth are not known for the other halogens. Explain why the pentahalide might form with fluorine, but not with the other halogens. How does the behavior of bismuth relate to the fact that xenon reacts with fluorine to form compounds, but not with the other halogens?

7.110 Potassium superoxide, KO_2, is often used in oxygen masks (such as those used by firefighters) because KO_2 reacts with CO_2 to release molecular oxygen. Experiments indicate that 2 mol of $KO_2(s)$ react with each mole of $CO_2(g)$. **(a)** The products of the reaction are $K_2CO_3(s)$ and $O_2(g)$. Write a balanced equation for the reaction between $KO_2(s)$ and $CO_2(g)$. **(b)** Indicate the oxidation number for each atom involved in the reaction in part (a). What elements are being oxidized and reduced? **(c)** What mass of $KO_2(s)$ is needed to consume 18.0 g $CO_2(g)$? What mass of $O_2(g)$ is produced during this reaction?

eMEDIA EXERCISES

These exercises make use of the interactive objects available online in OneKey or the Companion Website, and on your Accelerator CD. Access to these resources comes in your MediaPak.

7.111 The **Periodic Trends: Atomic Radii** animation (7.3) describes the trends in the sizes of atoms on the periodic table—from left to right and from top to bottom. **(a)** What factors influence atomic radius? **(b)** Based on the factors that influence the atomic radius, explain why the radius of gallium is smaller than that of aluminum.

7.112 The **Gain and Loss of Electrons** animation (7.3) illustrates how addition or subtraction of an electron affects

the size of an atom. The first ionization of aluminum produces the Al^+ ion, which is smaller than the neutral Al atom. The second ionization of aluminum produces the Al^{2+} ion, which is smaller still. The third ionization of aluminum produces the Al^{3+} ion, and the 3+ cation is even smaller than the 2+ cation. Of the first, second, and third ionizations, which would you expect to cause the biggest change in size? Explain your reasoning.

7.113 According to the information given in the **Periodic Trends: Ionization Energy** animation (7.4), you might expect fluorine and chlorine to have two of the highest ionization energies among the representative elements. Explain why those two elements are almost always found in nature as ions.

7.114 Although the **Periodic Trends: Ionization Energy** animation (7.4) depicts clear trends in the magnitudes of first ionization energies, the movie shows that the trend from left to right across the periodic table is not smooth. **(a)** Based on electron configurations, explain why this is so. **(b)** For each pair, predict which one will have the higher first ionization energy: N, O; Be, B; Ca, Ga; P, S.

7.115 **(a)** What happens to the size of the chlorine atom in the **Ionization Energy** animation (7.4) when the first electron is removed? **(b)** How do you account for this change in size? **(c)** Based on your answer to part (b),

how would you expect the size of the chlorine atom to change if an electron were *added* rather than removed?

7.116 **(a)** Based on the information in the **Periodic Trends: Acid-Base Behavior of Oxides** animation (7.6), which of the following compounds would you expect to form a basic solution with water: NaO, NO, N_2O, K_2O, CO_2? **(b)** Which oxide in each pair would produce the most acidic solution, and why? CO_2, CO; NO, N_2O; N_2O_5, N_2O_4.

7.117 Watch the **Sodium and Potassium in Water** movie (7.7), and note the differences between the two reactions shown. **(a)** What property of the elements involved is responsible for the observed differences? **(b)** How would you expect the reaction of Rb and water to differ from the reactions in the demonstration? Describe what you would expect to happen.

eLABORATORY EXERCISES

These exercises allow students to apply the concepts and skills for this chapter in the simulated laboratory of Virtual ChemLab. Worksheets for each of these exercises are found in the Virtual ChemLab Workbook in your MediaPak.

7.119 *(VCL 7-1) Flame Tests for Metals*

Have you ever wondered why a candle flame is yellow? The characteristic yellow of the flame comes from the glow of burning carbon fragments. The carbon fragments are produced by the incomplete combustion reaction of the wick and candle wax. When elements, such as carbon, are heated to high temperatures, some of their electrons are excited to higher energy levels. When these excited electrons fall back to lower energy levels, they release excess energy in packages of light called photons. The color of the emitted light depends on the individual energy level spacing in the atom. When heated, each element emits a characteristic pattern of photons, which is useful for identifying the element. The characteristic colors of light produced when substances are heated in the flame of a gas burner are the basis for flame tests of several

elements. In this assignment you will perform flame tests that are used to identify several metallic elements.

7.120 *(VCL 7-2) Emission Spectra of Sodium and Mercury*

In the 1800s scientists found that when a sample of gas is excited by an alternating electric field, light with only certain discrete wavelengths is emitted. This property allowed for the development of spectroscopic techniques that can be used in the identification and analysis of elements and compounds. Even though scientists found spectroscopy very useful, they could not explain why the spectrum was not continuous. The explanation of this was left to Niels Bohr, a Danish physicist, who first proposed that energy levels of electrons are quantized and excited electrons can fall only to discrete energy levels. This assignment illustrates the measurements that helped Bohr develop his original quantum model and also illustrates some practical uses for this science by measuring the emission spectra for mercury and sodium. Mercury vapor is used in fluorescent lights, and sodium vapor in street lighting.

8.1 Chemical Bonds, Lewis Symbols, and the Octet Rule

8.2 Ionic Bonding

8.3 Covalent Bonding

8.4 Bond Polarity and Electronegativity

8.5 Drawing Lewis Structures

8.6 Resonance Structures

8.7 Exceptions to the Octet Rule

8.8 Strengths of Covalent Bonds

WHAT'S AHEAD

- We begin with a brief discussion of chemical bond types and introduce *Lewis symbols*, a way of showing the valence electrons in atoms and ions. *(Section 8.1)*

- *Ionic bonding* results from the essentially complete transfer of one or more electrons from one atom to another. We will study the energetics of formation of ionic substances and describe the *lattice energy* of these substances. *(Section 8.2)*

- *Covalent bonding* involves the sharing of one or more electron pairs between atoms, as needed to attain an *octet* of electrons about each atom. *(Section 8.3)*

- We then see that covalent bonds can be represented by diagrams called *Lewis structures* and that covalent bonds can be *single*, *double*, or *triple*. *(Section 8.3)*

- *Electronegativity* is defined as the ability of an atom to attract electrons to itself in a bonding situation. Electron pairs will in general be shared unequally between atoms of differing electronegativity, leading to *polar covalent bonds*. *(Section 8.4)*

- We will examine more closely some of the rules we use for drawing Lewis structures, including the assignment of *formal charges* to atoms in molecules. *(Section 8.5)*

- It may occur that more than one equivalent Lewis structure can be drawn for a molecule or polyatomic ion. The actual structure in such cases is a blend of two or more contributing Lewis structures, called *resonance structures*. *(Section 8.6)*

- *Exceptions to the octet rule* include a relatively few cases in which there are fewer than 8 electrons in the valence-

shell orbitals. By contrast, the structures of many compounds of third-period and heavier elements can best be described by assuming that the valence-shell orbitals hold more than an octet of electrons. *(Section 8.7)*

- The strengths of covalent bonds vary with the number of shared electron pairs as well as other factors. We can use *average bond enthalpy* values, which are average values of the energy needed to break a specific type of bond, to estimate the enthalpies of reaction in cases where thermodynamic data such as heats of formation are unavailable. *(Section 8.8)*

Basic Concepts of Chemical Bonding

ON THE TABLE IN MOST DINERS, YOU CAN EXPECT TO FIND THE TWO WHITE crystalline substances shown in the photograph: table salt and granulated sugar. In spite of their similarities in appearance, salt and sugar are vastly different kinds of substances. Table salt is sodium chloride, NaCl, which consists of sodium ions, Na^+, and chloride ions, Cl^-. The structure is held together by the attractions between the oppositely charged ions, which we call *ionic bonds*. Granulated sugar, in contrast, does not contain ions. Instead, it consists of molecules of sucrose, $C_{12}H_{22}O_{11}$, in which attractions called *covalent bonds* hold the atoms together. One consequence of the difference in bonding in salt and sugar is their different behaviors in water: NaCl dissolves in water to yield ions in solution (NaCl is an *electrolyte*), whereas sucrose dissolves in water to yield aqueous $C_{12}H_{22}O_{11}$ molecules (sucrose is a *nonelectrolyte*). ∞∞ (Section 4.1)

The properties of substances are determined in large part by the *chemical bonds* that hold their atoms together. What determines the type of bonding in each substance, and just how do the characteristics of these bonds give rise to different physical and chemical properties? The keys to answering the first question are found in the electronic structures of the atoms involved, which we discussed in Chapters 6 and 7. In this chapter and the next, we will examine the relationships among electronic structure, chemical bonding forces, and chemical bond type. We'll also see how the properties of ionic and covalent substances arise from the distributions of electronic charge within atoms, ions, and molecules.

ALTHOUGH TABLE SALT AND SUGAR are both white crystalline substances, they involve distinctly different chemical bonds. Table salt has ionic bonds between Na^+ and Cl^- ions, whereas table sugar (sucrose, $C_{12}H_{22}O_{11}$) is a molecular substance with covalent bonds.

301

8.1 | Chemical Bonds, Lewis Symbols, and the Octet Rule

Whenever two atoms or ions are strongly attached to each other, we say there is a **chemical bond** between them. There are three general types of chemical bonds: ionic, covalent, and metallic. Figure 8.1 ◀ shows examples of substances in which we find each of these types of attractive forces.

The term **ionic bond** refers to electrostatic forces that exist between ions of opposite charge. Ions may be formed from atoms by the transfer of one or more electrons from one atom to another. Ionic substances generally result from the interaction of metals on the far left side of the periodic table with nonmetals on the far right side (excluding the noble gases, group 8A). Ionic bonding will be discussed in Section 8.2.

A **covalent bond** results from the sharing of electrons between two atoms. The most familiar examples of covalent bonding are seen in the interactions of nonmetallic elements with one another. We devote much of this chapter and the next to describing and understanding covalent bonds.

Metallic bonds are found in metals, such as copper, iron, and aluminum. Each atom in a metal is bonded to several neighboring atoms. The bonding electrons are relatively free to move throughout the three-dimensional structure of the metal. Metallic bonds give rise to such typical metallic properties as high electrical conductivity and luster. We will examine these bonds in Chapter 23.

Lewis Symbols

The electrons involved in chemical bonding are the *valence electrons*, which, for most atoms, are those residing in the outermost occupied shell of an atom. ⚬⚬⚬ (Section 6.8) The American chemist G. N. Lewis (1875–1946) suggested a simple way of showing the valence electrons in an atom and tracking them in the course of bond formation, using what are now known as *Lewis electron-dot symbols* or merely Lewis symbols.

The **Lewis symbol** for an element consists of the chemical symbol for the element plus a dot for each valence electron. Sulfur, for example, has the electron configuration $[Ne]3s^2 3p^4$; its Lewis symbol therefore shows six valence electrons:

$$\cdot \ddot{S} \cdot$$

The dots are placed on the four sides of the atomic symbol: the top, the bottom, and the left and right sides. Each side can accommodate up to two electrons. All four sides of the symbol are equivalent, which means that the choice of which side to place two electrons versus one electron is arbitrary.

The electron configurations and Lewis symbols for the representative elements of the second and third rows of the periodic table are shown in Table 8.1 ▶. Notice that the number of valence electrons in any representative element is the same as the group number of the element. For example, the Lewis symbols for oxygen and sulfur, members of group 6A, both show six dots.

  GIVE IT SOME THOUGHT

Which of the following three possible Lewis symbols for Cl is correct?

$$:\ddot{C}l \cdot \quad :\ddot{C}l: \quad :\ddot{C}l \cdot$$

Magnesium oxide

Potassium dichromate   Nickel(II) oxide

(a)

Sulfur

Bromine   Sucrose

(b)

Magnesium

Gold   Copper

(c)

▲ **Figure 8.1 Chemical bonds.** Examples of substances in which (a) ionic, (b) covalent, and (c) metallic bonds are found.

TABLE 8.1	Lewis Symbols				
Element	Electron Configuration	Lewis Symbol	Element	Electron Configuration	Lewis Symbol
Li	[He]$2s^1$	Li·	Na	[Ne]$3s^1$	Na·
Be	[He]$2s^2$	·Be·	Mg	[Ne]$3s^2$	·Mg·
B	[He]$2s^22p^1$	·Ḃ·	Al	[Ne]$3s^23p^1$	·Ȧl·
C	[He]$2s^22p^2$	·Ċ·	Si	[Ne]$3s^23p^2$	·Ṡi·
N	[He]$2s^22p^3$	·N̈:	P	[Ne]$3s^23p^3$	·P̈:
O	[He]$2s^22p^4$	:Ö:	S	[Ne]$3s^23p^4$	:S̈:
F	[He]$2s^22p^5$	·F̈:	Cl	[Ne]$3s^23p^5$	·C̈l:
Ne	[He]$2s^22p^6$	:N̈e:	Ar	[Ne]$3s^23p^6$	: Är:

The Octet Rule

Atoms often gain, lose, or share electrons to achieve the same number of electrons as the noble gas closest to them in the periodic table. The noble gases have very stable electron arrangements, as evidenced by their high ionization energies, low affinity for additional electrons, and general lack of chemical reactivity. ∞ (Section 7.8) Because all noble gases (except He) have eight valence electrons, many atoms undergoing reactions also end up with eight valence electrons. This observation has led to a guideline known as the **octet rule**: *Atoms tend to gain, lose, or share electrons until they are surrounded by eight valence electrons.*

An octet of electrons consists of full *s* and *p* subshells in an atom. In terms of Lewis symbols, an octet can be thought of as four pairs of valence electrons arranged around the atom, as in the Lewis symbol for Ne in Table 8.1. There are many exceptions to the octet rule, but it provides a useful framework for introducing many important concepts of bonding.

ACTIVITY
Octet Rule

8.2 | Ionic Bonding

When sodium metal, Na(s), is brought into contact with chlorine gas, $Cl_2(g)$, a violent reaction ensues (Figure 8.2 ▶). The product of this very exothermic reaction is sodium chloride, NaCl(s):

$$Na(s) + \tfrac{1}{2}Cl_2(g) \longrightarrow NaCl(s) \qquad \Delta H^\circ_f = -410.9 \text{ kJ} \qquad [8.1]$$

Sodium chloride is composed of Na^+ and Cl^- ions, which are arranged in a regular three-dimensional array, as shown in Figure 8.3 ▶.

The formation of Na^+ from Na and Cl^- from Cl_2 indicates that an electron has been lost by a sodium atom and gained by a chlorine atom—we can envision an *electron transfer* from the Na atom to the Cl atom. Two of the atomic properties we discussed in Chapter 7 give us an indication of how readily electron transfer occurs: the ionization energy, which indicates how easily an electron can be removed from an atom, and the electron affinity, which measures how much an atom wants to gain an electron. ∞ (Sections 7.4 and 7.5) Electron transfer to form oppositely charged ions occurs when one of the atoms readily gives up an electron (low ionization energy) and the other atom readily gains an electron (high electron affinity). Thus, NaCl is a typical ionic compound because it consists of a metal of low ionization energy and a nonmetal of high electron affinity. Using Lewis electron-dot symbols (and showing a chlorine atom rather than the Cl_2 molecule), we can represent this reaction as follows:

$$Na· + ·C̈l: \longrightarrow Na^+ + [:C̈l:]^- \qquad [8.2]$$

MOVIE
Formation of Sodium Chloride

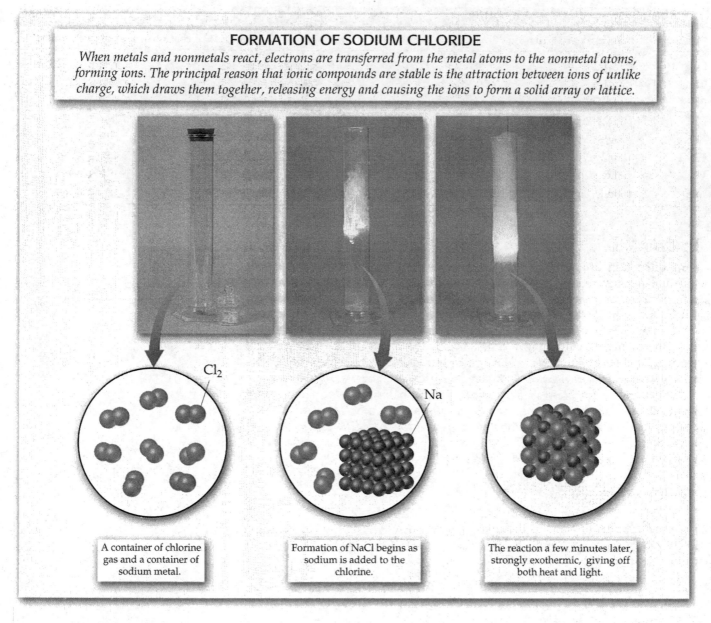

FORMATION OF SODIUM CHLORIDE

When metals and nonmetals react, electrons are transferred from the metal atoms to the nonmetal atoms, forming ions. The principal reason that ionic compounds are stable is the attraction between ions of unlike charge, which draws them together, releasing energy and causing the ions to form a solid array or lattice.

Cl₂

Na

| A container of chlorine gas and a container of sodium metal. | Formation of NaCl begins as sodium is added to the chlorine. | The reaction a few minutes later, strongly exothermic, giving off both heat and light. |

▲ **Figure 8.2 Formation of sodium chloride.**

Na⁺ Cl⁻

▲ **Figure 8.3 The crystal structure of sodium chloride.** In this three-dimensional array of ions, each Na⁺ ion is surrounded by six Cl⁻ ions, and each Cl⁻ ion is surrounded by six Na⁺ ions.

The arrow indicates the transfer of an electron from the Na atom to the Cl atom. Each ion has an octet of electrons, the octet on Na^+ being the $2s^2 2p^6$ electrons that lie below the single $3s$ valence electron of the Na atom. We've put a bracket around the chloride ion to emphasize that all eight electrons are located exclusively on the Cl^- ion.

 GIVE IT SOME THOUGHT

Describe the electron transfers that occur in the formation of magnesium fluoride from elemental magnesium and fluorine.

Science Fundamentals Second Edition

Energetics of Ionic Bond Formation

As seen in Figure 8.2, the reaction of sodium with chlorine is *very* exothermic. In fact, Equation 8.1 is the reaction for the formation of NaCl(s) from its elements, so that the enthalpy change for the reaction is ΔH_f° for NaCl(s). In Appendix C we see that the heat of formation of other ionic substances is also quite negative. What factors make the formation of ionic compounds so exothermic?

In Equation 8.2 we represented the formation of NaCl as the transfer of an electron from Na to Cl. Recall from our discussion of ionization energies, however, that the loss of electrons from an atom is always an endothermic process. ∞∞ (Section 7.4) Removing an electron from Na(g) to form Na$^+$(g), for instance, requires 496 kJ/mol. Conversely, when a nonmetal gains an electron, the process is generally exothermic, as seen from the negative electron affinities of the elements. ∞∞ (Section 7.5) Adding an electron to Cl(g), for example, releases 349 kJ/mol. If the transfer of an electron from one atom to another were the only factor in forming an ionic bond, the overall process would rarely be exothermic. For example, removing an electron from Na(g) and adding it to Cl(g) is an endothermic process that requires 496 − 349 = 147 kJ/mol. This endothermic process corresponds to the formation of sodium and chloride ions that are infinitely far apart—in other words, the positive energy change assumes that the ions are not interacting with one another, which is quite different from the situation in ionic solids.

The principal reason that ionic compounds are stable is the attraction between ions of unlike charge. This attraction draws the ions together, releasing energy and causing the ions to form a solid array, or lattice, such as that shown for NaCl in Figure 8.3. A measure of just how much stabilization results from arranging oppositely charged ions in an ionic solid is given by the **lattice energy**, which is *the energy required to completely separate a mole of a solid ionic compound into its gaseous ions.*

To get a picture of this process for NaCl, imagine that the structure shown in Figure 8.3 expands from within, so that the distances between the ions increase until the ions are very far apart. This process requires 788 kJ/mol, which is the value of the lattice energy:

$$NaCl(s) \longrightarrow Na^+(g) + Cl^-(g) \qquad \Delta H_{lattice} = +788 \text{ kJ/mol} \qquad [8.3]$$

Notice that this process is highly endothermic. The reverse process—the coming together of Na(g)$^+$ and Cl(g)$^-$ to form NaCl(s)—is therefore highly exothermic ($\Delta H = -788$ kJ/mol).

Table 8.2 ▶ lists the lattice energies of NaCl and other ionic compounds. All are large positive values, indicating that the ions are strongly attracted to one another in these solids. The energy released by the attraction between ions of unlike charge more than makes up for the endothermic nature of ionization energies, making the formation of ionic compounds an exothermic process. The strong attractions also cause most ionic materials to be hard and brittle, with high melting points—for example, NaCl melts at 801°C.

The magnitude of the lattice energy of a solid depends on the charges of the ions, their sizes, and their arrangement in the solid. We saw in Chapter 5 that the potential energy of two interacting charged particles is given by

$$E_{el} = \frac{\kappa Q_1 Q_2}{d} \qquad [8.4]$$

ACTIVITY
Bond Enthalpy

ACTIVITY
Coulomb's Law

TABLE 8.2   Lattice Energies for Some Ionic Compounds

Compound	Lattice Energy (kJ/mol)	Compound	Lattice Energy (kJ/mol)
LiF	1030	MgCl$_2$	2326
LiCl	834	SrCl$_2$	2127
LiI	730		
NaF	910	MgO	3795
NaCl	788	CaO	3414
NaBr	732	SrO	3217
NaI	682		
KF	808	ScN	7547
KCl	701		
KBr	671		
CsCl	657		
CsI	600		

In this equation Q_1 and Q_2 are the charges on the particles, d is the distance between their centers, and κ is a constant, 8.99×10^9 J-m/C^2. ∞ (Section 5.1) Equation 8.4 indicates that the attractive interaction between two oppositely charged ions increases as the magnitudes of their charges increase and as the distance between their centers decreases. Thus, *for a given arrangement of ions, the lattice energy increases as the charges on the ions increase and as their radii decrease*. The magnitude of lattice energies depends primarily on the ionic charges because ionic radii do not vary over a very wide range.

■■ SAMPLE EXERCISE 8.1 | Magnitudes of Lattice Energies

Without consulting Table 8.2, arrange the following ionic compounds in order of increasing lattice energy: NaF, CsI, and CaO.

Solution

Analyze: From the formulas for three ionic compounds, we must determine their relative lattice energies.

Plan: We need to determine the charges and relative sizes of the ions in the compounds. We can then use Equation 8.4 qualitatively to determine the relative energies, knowing that the larger the ionic charges, the greater the energy and the farther apart the ions are, the lower the energy.

Solve: NaF consists of Na$^+$ and F$^-$ ions, CsI of Cs$^+$ and I$^-$ ions, and CaO of Ca^{2+} and O^{2-} ions. Because the product of the charges, Q_1Q_2, appears in the numerator of Equation 8.4, the lattice energy will increase dramatically when the charges of the ions increase. Thus, we expect the lattice energy of CaO, which has 2+ and 2− ions, to be the greatest of the three.

The ionic charges in NaF and CsI are the same. As a result, the difference in their lattice energies will depend on the difference in the distance between the centers of the ions in their lattice. Because ionic size increases as we go down a group in the periodic table (Section 7.3), we know that Cs$^+$ is larger than Na$^+$ and I$^-$ is larger than F$^-$. Therefore the distance between the Na$^+$ and F$^-$ ions in NaF will be less than the distance between the Cs$^+$ and I$^-$ ions in CsI. As a result, the lattice energy of NaF should be greater than that of CsI. In order of increasing energy, therefore, we have CsI < NaF < CaO.

Check: Table 8.2 confirms our predicted order is correct.

■■ PRACTICE EXERCISE

Which substance would you expect to have the greatest lattice energy, AgCl, CuO, or CrN?
Answer: CrN

Electron Configurations of Ions of the Representative Elements

We began considering the electron configurations of ions in Section 7.4. In light of our examination of ionic bonding, we will continue with that discussion here. The energetics of ionic bond formation helps explain why many ions tend to have noble-gas electron configurations. For example, sodium readily loses one electron to form Na$^+$, which has the same electron configuration as Ne:

$$\text{Na} \qquad 1s^2 2s^2 2p^6 3s^1 = [\text{Ne}]3s^1$$

$$\text{Na}^+ \qquad 1s^2 2s^2 2p^6 \quad = [\text{Ne}]$$

Even though lattice energy increases with increasing ionic charge, we never find ionic compounds that contain Na^{2+} ions. The second electron removed would have to come from an inner shell of the sodium atom, and removing electrons from an inner shell requires a very large amount of energy. ∞ (Section 7.4) The increase in lattice energy is not enough to compensate for the energy needed to remove an inner-shell electron. Thus, sodium and the other group 1A metals are found in ionic substances only as 1+ ions.

Similarly, the addition of electrons to nonmetals is either exothermic or only slightly endothermic as long as the electrons are being added to the valence shell. Thus, a Cl atom easily adds an electron to form Cl^-, which has the same electron configuration as Ar:

$$Cl \qquad 1s^2 2s^2 2p^6 3s^2 3p^5 = [Ne]3s^2 3p^5$$

$$Cl^- \qquad 1s^2 2s^2 2p^6 3s^2 3p^6 = [Ne]3s^2 3p^6 = [Ar]$$

ACTIVITY
Ion Electron Configurations

In order to form a Cl^{2-} ion, the second electron would have to be added to the next higher shell of the Cl atom, which is energetically very unfavorable. Therefore, we never observe Cl^{2-} ions in ionic compounds.

Based on these concepts, we expect that ionic compounds of the representative metals from groups 1A, 2A, and 3A will contain cations with charges of 1+, 2+, and 3+, respectively. Likewise, ionic compounds of the representative nonmetals of groups 5A, 6A, and 7A usually contain anions of charge 3−, 2−, and 1−, respectively. Although we rarely find ionic compounds of the nonmetals from group 4A (C, Si, and Ge), the heaviest elements in group 4A (Sn and Pb) are metals and are usually found as 2+ cations in ionic compounds: Sn^{2+} and Pb^{2+}. This behavior is consistent with the increasing metallic character found as one proceeds down a column in the periodic table. ⟶ (Section 7.6)

SAMPLE EXERCISE 8.2 | Charges on Ions

Predict the ion generally formed by **(a)** Sr, **(b)** S, **(c)** Al.

Solution

Analyze: We must decide how many electrons are most likely to be gained or lost by atoms of Sr, S, and Al.

Plan: In each case we can use the element's position in the periodic table to predict whether it will form a cation or an anion. We can then use its electron configuration to determine the ion that is likely to be formed.

Solve: (a) Strontium is a metal in group 2A and will therefore form a cation. Its electron configuration is $[Kr]5s^2$, and so we expect that the two valence electrons can be lost easily to give an Sr^{2+} ion. **(b)** Sulfur is a nonmetal in group 6A and will thus tend to be found as an anion. Its electron configuration ($[Ne]3s^2 3p^4$) is two electrons short of a noble-gas configuration. Thus, we expect that sulfur tends to form S^{2-} ions. **(c)** Aluminum is a metal in group 3A. We therefore expect it to form Al^{3+} ions.

Check: The ionic charges we predict here are confirmed in Tables 2.4 and 2.5.

PRACTICE EXERCISE

Predict the charges on the ions formed when magnesium reacts with nitrogen.

Answer: Mg^{2+} and N^{3-}

Transition-Metal Ions

Because ionization energies increase rapidly for each successive electron removed, the lattice energies of ionic compounds are generally large enough to compensate for the loss of up to only three electrons from atoms. Thus, we find cations with charges of 1+, 2+, or 3+ in ionic compounds. Most transition metals, however, have more than three electrons beyond a noble-gas core. Silver, for example, has a $[Kr]4d^{10}5s^1$ electron configuration. Metals of group 1B (Cu, Ag, Au) often occur as 1+ ions (as in CuBr and AgCl). In forming Ag^+, the $5s$ electron is lost, leaving a completely filled $4d$ subshell. As in this example, transition metals generally do not form ions that have a noble-gas configuration. The octet rule, although useful, is clearly limited in scope.

Recall from our discussion in Section 7.4 that when a positive ion is formed from an atom, electrons are always lost first from the subshell having the largest value of n. Thus, *in forming ions, transition metals lose the valence-shell s electrons first, then as many d electrons as are required to reach the charge of the ion.* Let's consider Fe, which has the electron configuration $[Ar]3d^6 4s^2$. In forming the Fe^{2+} ion, the two $4s$ electrons are lost, leading to an $[Ar]3d^6$ configuration. Removal of an additional electron gives the Fe^{3+} ion, whose electron configuration is $[Ar]3d^5$.

A CLOSER LOOK | Calculation of Lattice Energies: The Born–Haber Cycle

Lattice energy is a useful concept because it relates directly to the stability of an ionic solid. Unfortunately, the lattice energy cannot be determined directly by experiment. It can, however, be calculated by envisioning the formation of an ionic compound as occurring in a series of well-defined steps. We can then use Hess's law (Section 5.6) to put these steps together in a way that gives us the lattice energy for the compound. By so doing, we construct a **Born–Haber cycle**, a thermochemical cycle named after the German scientists Max Born (1882–1970) and Fritz Haber (1868–1934), who introduced it to analyze the factors contributing to the stability of ionic compounds.

In the Born–Haber cycle for NaCl, we consider the formation of NaCl(s) from the elements Na(s) and $Cl_2(g)$ by two different routes, as shown in Figure 8.4 ▶. The enthalpy change for the direct route (red arrow) is the heat of formation of NaCl(s):

$$Na(s) + \tfrac{1}{2}Cl_2(g) \longrightarrow NaCl(s)$$
$$\Delta H_f^\circ[NaCl(s)] = -411 \text{ kJ} \quad [8.5]$$

The indirect route consists of five steps, shown by the green arrows in Figure 8.4. First, we generate gaseous atoms of sodium by vaporizing sodium metal. Then we form gaseous atoms of chlorine by breaking the bonds in the Cl_2 molecules. The enthalpy changes for these processes are available to us as enthalpies of formation (Appendix C):

$$Na(s) \longrightarrow Na(g) \quad \Delta H_f^\circ[Na(g)] = 108 \text{ kJ} \quad [8.6]$$

$$\tfrac{1}{2}Cl_2(g) \longrightarrow Cl(g) \quad \Delta H_f^\circ[Cl(g)] = 122 \text{ kJ} \quad [8.7]$$

Both of these processes are endothermic; energy is required to generate gaseous sodium and chlorine atoms.

In the next two steps we remove the electron from Na(g) to form $Na^+(g)$ and then add the electron to Cl(g) to form $Cl^-(g)$. The enthalpy changes for these processes equal the first ionization energy of Na, $I_1(Na)$, and the electron affinity of Cl, denoted E(Cl), respectively: ∞ (Sections 7.4, 7.5)

$$Na(g) \longrightarrow Na^+(g) + e^- \quad \Delta H = I_1(Na) = 496 \text{ kJ} \quad [8.8]$$

$$Cl(g) + e^- \longrightarrow Cl^-(g) \quad \Delta H = E(Cl) = -349 \text{ kJ} \quad [8.9]$$

Finally, we combine the gaseous sodium and chloride ions to form solid sodium chloride. Because this process is just the reverse of the lattice energy (breaking a solid into gaseous ions), the enthalpy change is the negative of the lattice energy, the quantity that we want to determine:

$$Na^+(g) + Cl^-(g) \longrightarrow NaCl(s)$$
$$\Delta H = -\Delta H_{lattice} = ? \quad [8.10]$$

The sum of the five steps in the indirect path gives us NaCl(s) from Na(s) and $\tfrac{1}{2}Cl_2(g)$. Thus, from Hess's law we know that the sum of the enthalpy changes for these five steps equals that for the direct path, indicated by the red arrow, Equation 8.5:

$$\Delta H_f^\circ[NaCl(s)] = \Delta H_f^\circ[Na(g)] + \Delta H_f^\circ[Cl(g)]$$
$$+ I_1(Na) + E(Cl) - \Delta H_{lattice}$$
$$-411 \text{ kJ} = 108 \text{ kJ} + 122 \text{ kJ} + 496 \text{ kJ} - 349 \text{ kJ} - \Delta H_{lattice}$$

Solving for $\Delta H_{lattice}$:

$$\Delta H_{lattice} = 108 \text{ kJ} + 122 \text{ kJ} + 496 \text{ kJ} - 349 \text{ kJ} + 411 \text{ kJ}$$
$$= 788 \text{ kJ}$$

Thus, the lattice energy of NaCl is 788 kJ/mol.
Related Exercises: 8.26, 8.27, and 8.28

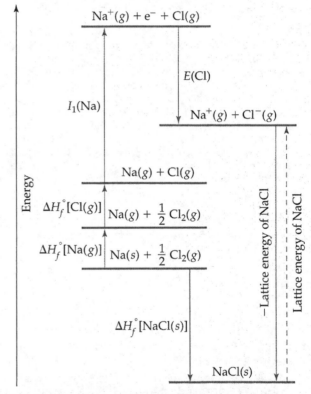

▲ **Figure 8.4 The Born-Haber cycle.** This representation shows the energetic relationships in the formation of ionic solids from the elements. By Hess's law, the enthalpy of formation of NaCl(s) from elemental sodium and chlorine (Equation 8.5) is equal to the sum of the energies of several individual steps (Equations 8.6 through 8.10).

GIVE IT SOME THOUGHT

Which element forms a 1+ ion that has the electron configuration $[Kr]4d^8$?

Polyatomic Ions

Let's now briefly reconsider Tables 2.4 and 2.5, which list the common ions. ∞∞ (Section 2.8) Several cations and many common anions are polyatomic. Examples include the ammonium ion, NH_4^+, and the carbonate ion, CO_3^{2-}. In polyatomic ions, two or more atoms are bound together by predominantly covalent bonds. They form a stable grouping that carries a charge, either positive or negative. We will examine the covalent bonding forces in these ions in Chapter 9. For now, the only thing you need to understand about any polyatomic ion is that the group of atoms as a whole acts as a charged species when the ion forms an ionic compound with an ion of opposite charge.

8.3 | Covalent Bonding

Ionic substances possess several characteristic properties. They are usually brittle substances with high melting points. They are usually crystalline, meaning that the solids have flat surfaces that make characteristic angles with one another. Ionic crystals often can be cleaved; that is, they break apart along smooth, flat surfaces. These characteristics result from electrostatic forces that maintain the ions in a rigid, well-defined, three-dimensional arrangement such as that shown in Figure 8.3.

The vast majority of chemical substances do not have the characteristics of ionic materials. Most of the substances with which we come into daily contact—such as water—tend to be gases, liquids, or solids with low melting points. Many, such as gasoline, vaporize readily. Many are pliable in their solid forms—for example, plastic bags and paraffin.

For the very large class of substances that do not behave like ionic substances, we need a different model for the bonding between atoms. G. N. Lewis reasoned that atoms might acquire a noble-gas electron configuration by sharing electrons with other atoms. As we noted in Section 8.1, a chemical bond formed by sharing a pair of electrons is called a *covalent bond*.

The hydrogen molecule, H_2, provides the simplest example of a covalent bond. When two hydrogen atoms are close to each other, electrostatic interactions occur between them. The two positively charged nuclei repel each other, the two negatively charged electrons repel each other, and the nuclei and electrons attract each other, as shown in Figure 8.5 ▶. Because the H_2 molecule exists as a stable entity, the attractive forces must exceed the repulsive ones. Why is this so?

By using quantum mechanical methods analogous to those employed for atoms ∞∞ (Section 6.5), it is possible to calculate the distribution of electron density in molecules. Such a calculation for H_2 shows that the attractions between the nuclei and the electrons cause electron density to concentrate between the nuclei, as shown in Figure 8.5(b). As a result, the overall electrostatic interactions are attractive. Thus, the atoms in H_2 are held together principally because the two nuclei are electrostatically attracted to the concentration of negative charge between them. In essence, the shared pair of electrons in any covalent bond acts as a kind of "glue" to bind atoms together.

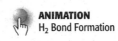

ANIMATION
H_2 Bond Formation

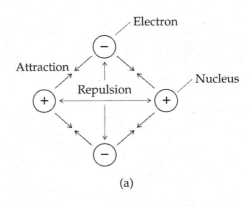

(a)

(b)

▲ **Figure 8.5 The covalent bond in H_2.**
(a) The attractions and repulsions among electrons and nuclei in the hydrogen molecule. (b) Electron distribution in the H_2 molecule. The concentration of electron density between the nuclei leads to a net attractive force that constitutes the covalent bond holding the molecule together.

Science Fundamentals Second Edition

Lewis Structures

The formation of covalent bonds can be represented using Lewis symbols for the constituent atoms. The formation of the H_2 molecule from two H atoms, for example, can be represented as

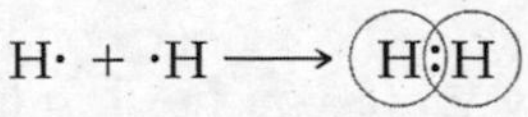

$$H\cdot + \cdot H \longrightarrow (H\!:\!H)$$

In this way, each hydrogen atom acquires a second electron, achieving the stable, two-electron, noble-gas electron configuration of helium.

The formation of a bond between two Cl atoms to give a Cl_2 molecule can be represented in a similar way:

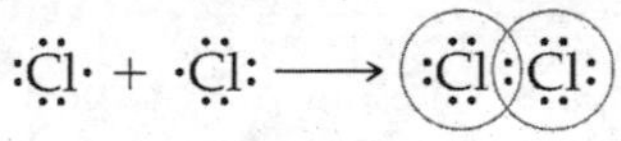

$$:\!\ddot{C}l\cdot + \cdot\ddot{C}l\!: \longrightarrow (:\!\ddot{C}l\!:\!\ddot{C}l\!:)$$

By sharing the bonding electron pair, each chlorine atom has eight electrons (an octet) in its valence shell. It thus achieves the noble-gas electron configuration of argon.

The structures shown here for H_2 and Cl_2 are called **Lewis structures** (or Lewis electron-dot structures). In writing Lewis structures, we usually show each electron pair shared between atoms as a line and the unshared electron pairs as dots. Written this way, the Lewis structures for H_2 and Cl_2 are

$$H\!-\!H \qquad :\!\ddot{C}l\!-\!\ddot{C}l\!:$$

For the nonmetals, the number of valence electrons in a neutral atom is the same as the group number. Therefore, one might predict that 7A elements, such as F, would form one covalent bond to achieve an octet; 6A elements, such as O, would form two covalent bonds; 5A elements, such as N, would form three covalent bonds; and 4A elements, such as C, would form four covalent bonds. These predictions are borne out in many compounds. For example, consider the simple hydrogen compounds of the nonmetals of the second row of the periodic table:

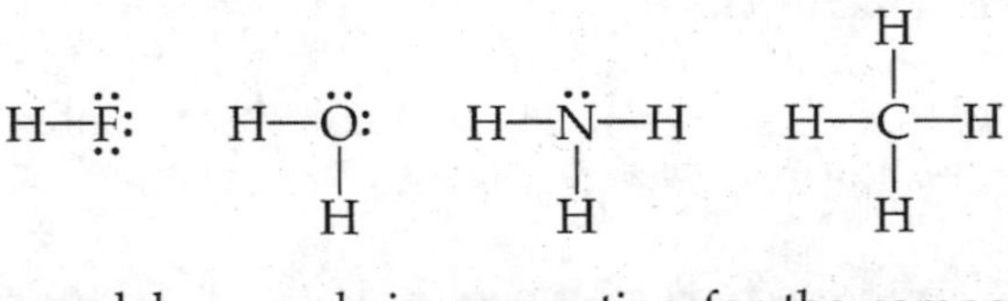

$$H\!-\!\ddot{F}\!: \qquad H\!-\!\overset{..}{O}\!: \qquad H\!-\!\overset{..}{N}\!-\!H \qquad H\!-\!\overset{\displaystyle H}{\underset{\displaystyle H}{\overset{|}{\underset{|}{C}}}}\!-\!H$$

Thus, the Lewis model succeeds in accounting for the compositions of many compounds of nonmetals, in which covalent bonding predominates.

■ **SAMPLE EXERCISE 8.3** | Lewis Structure of a Compound

Given the Lewis symbols for the elements nitrogen and fluorine shown in Table 8.1, predict the formula of the stable binary compound (a compound composed of two elements) formed when nitrogen reacts with fluorine, and draw its Lewis structure.

Solution

Analyze: The Lewis symbols for nitrogen and fluorine reveal that nitrogen has five valence electrons and fluorine has seven.

Plan: We need to find a combination of the two elements that results in an octet of electrons around each atom in the compound. Nitrogen requires three additional electrons to complete its octet, whereas fluorine requires but one. Sharing a pair of electrons between one N atom and one F atom will result in an octet of electrons for fluorine but not for nitrogen. We therefore need to figure out a way to get two more electrons for the N atom.

Solve: Nitrogen must share a pair of electrons with three fluorine atoms to complete its octet. Thus, the Lewis structure for the resulting compound, NF_3, is

$$:\!\ddot{F}\!:\!\ddot{N}\!:\!\ddot{F}\!: \longrightarrow :\!\ddot{F}\!-\!\ddot{N}\!-\!\ddot{F}\!:$$
$$:\!\ddot{F}\!: \qquad\qquad |$$
$$:\!\ddot{F}\!:$$

Check: The Lewis structure on the left shows that each atom is surrounded by an octet of electrons. Once you are accustomed to thinking of each line in a Lewis structure as representing *two* electrons, you can just as easily use the structure on the right to check for octets.

■ PRACTICE EXERCISE

Compare the Lewis symbol for neon with the Lewis structure for methane, CH_4. In what important way are the electron arrangements about neon and carbon alike? In what important respect are they different?
Answer: Both atoms have an octet of electrons about them. However, the electrons about neon are unshared electron pairs, whereas those about carbon are shared with four hydrogen atoms.

Multiple Bonds

The sharing of a pair of electrons constitutes a single covalent bond, generally referred to simply as a **single bond**. In many molecules, atoms attain complete octets by sharing more than one pair of electrons. When two electron pairs are shared, two lines are drawn, representing a **double bond**. In carbon dioxide, for example, bonding occurs between carbon, with four valence electrons, and oxygen, with six:

$$:\!\ddot{O}\!: + \cdot\dot{C}\cdot + :\!\ddot{O}\!: \longrightarrow \ddot{O}\!:\!:\!C\!:\!:\!\ddot{O} \quad (\text{or } \ddot{O}\!=\!C\!=\!\ddot{O})$$

As the diagram shows, each oxygen acquires an octet of electrons by sharing two electron pairs with carbon. Carbon, on the other hand, acquires an octet of electrons by sharing two pairs with two oxygen atoms.

A **triple bond** corresponds to the sharing of three pairs of electrons, such as in the N_2 molecule:

$$:\!\dot{N}\!\cdot + \cdot\dot{N}\!: \longrightarrow :\!N\!:\!:\!:\!N\!: \quad (\text{or } :\!N\!\equiv\!N\!:)$$

Because each nitrogen atom possesses five electrons in its valence shell, three electron pairs must be shared to achieve the octet configuration.

The properties of N_2 are in complete accord with its Lewis structure. Nitrogen is a diatomic gas with exceptionally low reactivity that results from the very stable nitrogen–nitrogen bond. Study of the structure of N_2 reveals that the nitrogen atoms are separated by only 1.10 Å. The short N—N bond distance is a result of the triple bond between the atoms. From structure studies of many different substances in which nitrogen atoms share one or two electron pairs, we have learned that the average distance between bonded nitrogen atoms varies with the number of shared electron pairs:

$$\begin{array}{ccc} \text{N—N} & \text{N=N} & \text{N} \equiv \text{N} \\ 1.47\text{ Å} & 1.24\text{ Å} & 1.10\text{ Å} \end{array}$$

As a general rule, the distance between bonded atoms decreases as the number of shared electron pairs increases. The distance between the nuclei of the atoms involved in a bond is called the **bond length** for the bond. We first encountered bond lengths in Section 7.3 in our discussion of atomic radii, and we will discuss them further in Section 8.8.

 GIVE IT SOME THOUGHT

The C—O bond length in carbon monoxide, CO, is 1.13 Å, whereas the C—O bond length in CO_2 is 1.24 Å. Without drawing a Lewis structure, do you think that carbon monoxide has a single, double, or triple bond between the C and O atoms?

8.4 | Bond Polarity and Electronegativity

When two identical atoms bond, as in Cl_2 or N_2, the electron pairs must be shared equally. In ionic compounds, on the other hand, such as NaCl, there is essentially no sharing of electrons, which means that NaCl is best described as composed of Na^+ and Cl^- ions. The 3s electron of the Na atom is, in effect, transferred completely to chlorine. The bonds occurring in most covalent substances fall somewhere between these extremes.

The concept of **bond polarity** helps describe the sharing of electrons between atoms. A **nonpolar covalent bond** is one in which the electrons are shared equally between two atoms, as in the Cl_2 and N_2 examples we just cited. In a **polar covalent bond**, one of the atoms exerts a greater attraction for the bonding electrons than the other. If the difference in relative ability to attract electrons is large enough, an ionic bond is formed.

Electronegativity

 **ANIMATION**
Periodic Trends: Electronegativity

We use a quantity called electronegativity to estimate whether a given bond will be nonpolar covalent, polar covalent, or ionic. **Electronegativity** is defined as the ability of an atom *in a molecule* to attract electrons to itself. The greater an atom's electronegativity, the greater is its ability to attract electrons to itself. The electronegativity of an atom in a molecule is related to its ionization energy and electron affinity, which are properties of isolated atoms. The *ionization energy* measures how strongly an atom holds on to its electrons. ⚭ (Section 7.4) Likewise, the *electron affinity* is a measure of how strongly an atom attracts additional electrons. ⚭ (Section 7.5) An atom with a very negative electron affinity and high ionization energy will both attract electrons from other atoms and resist having its electrons attracted away; it will be highly electronegative. Numerical estimates of electronegativity can be based on a variety of properties, not just ionization energy and electron affinity. The first and most widely used electronegativity scale was developed by the American chemist Linus Pauling (1901–1994), who based his scale on thermochemical data. Figure 8.6 ◄ shows Pauling's electronegativity values for many of the elements. The values are unitless. Fluorine, the most electronegative element, has an electronegativity of 4.0. The least electronegative element, cesium, has an electronegativity of 0.7. The values for all other elements lie between these two extremes.

▼ **Figure 8.6   Electronegativities of the elements.** Electronegativity generally increases from left to right across a period and decreases from top to bottom down a group.

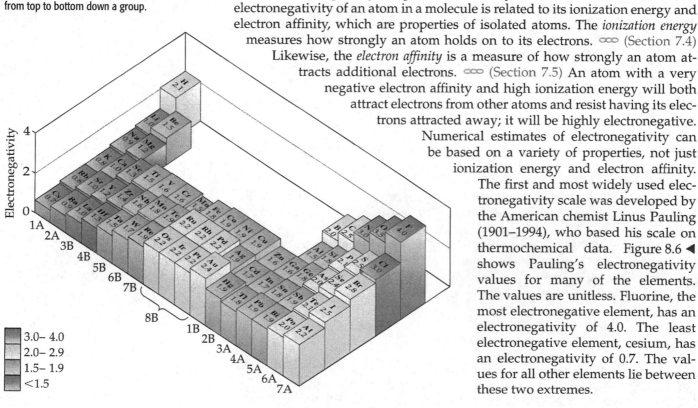

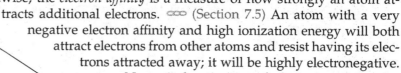

Within each period there is generally a steady increase in electronegativity from left to right; that is, from the most metallic to the most nonmetallic elements. With some exceptions (especially within the transition metals), electronegativity decreases with increasing atomic number in any one group. This is what we might expect because we know that ionization energies tend to decrease with increasing atomic number in a group and electron affinities don't change very much. You do not need to memorize numerical values for electronegativity. Instead, you should know the periodic trends so that you can predict which of two elements is more electronegative.

GIVE IT SOME THOUGHT

How does the *electronegativity* of an element differ from its *electron affinity*?

Electronegativity and Bond Polarity

We can use the difference in electronegativity between two atoms to gauge the polarity of the bonding between them. Consider these three fluorine-containing compounds:

Compound	F_2	HF	LiF
Electronegativity difference	$4.0 - 4.0 = 0$	$4.0 - 2.1 = 1.9$	$4.0 - 1.0 = 3.0$
Type of bond	Nonpolar covalent	Polar covalent	Ionic

In F_2 the electrons are shared equally between the fluorine atoms, and thus the covalent bond is *nonpolar*. In general, a nonpolar covalent bond results when the electronegativities of the bonded atoms are equal.

In HF the fluorine atom has a greater electronegativity than the hydrogen atom, with the result that the sharing of electrons is unequal—the bond is polar. In general, a polar covalent bond results when the atoms differ in electronegativity. In HF the more electronegative fluorine atom attracts electron density away from the less electronegative hydrogen atom, leaving a partial positive charge on the hydrogen atom and a partial negative charge on the fluorine atom. We can represent this charge distribution as

$$\overset{\delta+}{H}\text{---}\overset{\delta-}{F}$$

The $\delta+$ and $\delta-$ (read "delta plus" and "delta minus") symbolize the partial positive and negative charges, respectively.

In LiF the electronegativity difference is very large, meaning that the electron density is shifted far toward F. In the three-dimensional structure of LiF, analogous to that shown for NaCl in Figure 8.3, the transfer of electronic charge from Li to F is essentially complete. The resultant bond is therefore *ionic*. This shift of electron density toward the more electronegative atom can be seen in the results of calculations of electron density distributions. For the three species in our example, the calculated electron density distributions are shown in Figure 8.7 ▶. The regions of space that have relatively higher electron density are shown in red, and those with a relatively lower electron density are shown in blue. You can see that in F_2 the distribution is symmetrical, in HF it is clearly shifted

ACTIVITY
Electronegativity Differences and Bond Types

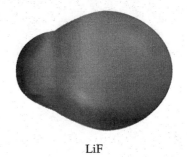
▼ **Figure 8.7 Electron density distribution.** This computer-generated rendering shows the calculated electron-density distribution on the surface of the F_2, HF, and LiF molecules. The regions of relatively low electron density (net positive charge) appear blue, those of relatively high electron density (net negative charge) appear red, and regions that are close to electrically neutral appear green.

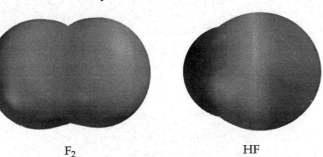

| F_2 | HF | LiF |

toward fluorine, and in LiF the shift is even greater.* These examples illustrate, therefore, that *the greater the difference in electronegativity between two atoms, the more polar their bond*. The nonpolar covalent bond lies at one end of a continuum of bond types, and the ionic bond lies at the other end. In between is a broad range of polar covalent bonds, differing in the extent to which there is unequal sharing of electrons.

GIVE IT SOME THOUGHT

The difference in the electronegativity of two elements is 0.7. Would you expect a bond between these elements to be nonpolar, polar covalent, or ionic?

SAMPLE EXERCISE 8.4 | Bond Polarity

In each case, which bond is more polar: (a) B—Cl or C—Cl, (b) P—F or P—Cl? Indicate in each case which atom has the partial negative charge.

Solution

Analyze: We are asked to determine relative bond polarities, given nothing but the atoms involved in the bonds.

Plan: We need to know electronegativity values for all the atoms involved, which we can get from Figure 8.6. Alternatively, because we are not asked for quantitative answers, we can use the periodic table and our knowledge of electron-affinity trends to answer the question.

Solve: (a) Using Figure 8.6: The difference in the electronegativities of chlorine and boron is $3.0 - 2.0 = 1.0$; the difference between chlorine and carbon is $3.0 - 2.5 = 0.5$. Consequently, the B—Cl bond is more polar; the chlorine atom carries the partial negative charge because it has a higher electronegativity.

Using the periodic table: Because boron is to the left of carbon in the periodic table, we predict that boron has the lower electronegativity. Chlorine, being on the right side of the table, has a higher electronegativity. The more polar bond will be the one between the atoms having the lowest electronegativity (boron) and the highest electronegativity (chlorine).

(b) The electronegativities are P = 2.1, F = 4.0, Cl = 3.0. Consequently, the P—F bond will be more polar than the P—Cl bond. You should compare the electronegativity differences for the two bonds to verify this prediction. The fluorine atom carries the partial negative charge. We reach the same conclusion by noting that fluorine is above chlorine in the periodic table, and so fluorine should be more electronegative and will form the more polar bond with P.

PRACTICE EXERCISE

Which of the following bonds is most polar: S—Cl, S—Br, Se—Cl, Se—Br?
Answer: Se—Cl

Dipole Moments

The difference in electronegativity between H and F leads to a polar covalent bond in the HF molecule. As a consequence, there is a concentration of negative charge on the more electronegative F atom, leaving the less electronegative H atom at the positive end of the molecule. A molecule such as HF, in which the centers of positive and negative charge do not coincide, is said to be a **polar molecule**. Thus, we describe not only bonds as being polar and nonpolar but also entire molecules.

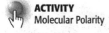

ACTIVITY
Molecular Polarity

We can indicate the polarity of the HF molecule in two ways:

$$\overset{\delta+}{H} - \overset{\delta-}{F} \quad \text{or} \quad \overset{\longrightarrow}{H - F}$$

---

* The calculated electron density distribution for LiF is for an isolated LiF "molecule," not the ionic solid. While the bond in this isolated diatomic system is very polar, it is not 100% ionic, as is the bonding in solid lithium fluoride. The solid state promotes a more complete electron transfer from Li to F because of the stabilizing effects of the ionic lattice.

Recall from the preceding subsection that "δ+" and "δ−" indicate the partial positive and negative charges on the H and F atoms. In the notation on the right, the arrow denotes the shift in electron density toward the fluorine atom. The crossed end of the arrow can be thought of as a plus sign that designates the positive end of the molecule.

Polarity helps determine many of the properties of substances that we observe at the macroscopic level, in the laboratory and in everyday life. Polar molecules align themselves with respect to one another, with the negative end of one molecule and the positive end of another attracting each other. Polar molecules are likewise attracted to ions. The negative end of a polar molecule is attracted to a positive ion, and the positive end is attracted to a negative ion. These interactions account for many properties of liquids, solids, and solutions, as you will see in Chapters 11, 12, and 13.

How can we quantify the polarity of a molecule? Whenever two electrical charges of equal magnitude but opposite sign are separated by a distance, a **dipole** is established. The quantitative measure of the magnitude of a dipole is called its **dipole moment**, denoted μ. If two equal and opposite charges $Q+$ and $Q−$ are separated by a distance r, the magnitude of the dipole moment is the product of Q and r (Figure 8.8 ▶):

$$\mu = Qr \qquad [8.11]$$

The dipole moment increases as the magnitude of charge that is separated increases and as the distance between the charges increases. For a nonpolar molecule, such as F_2, the dipole moment is zero because there is no charge separation.

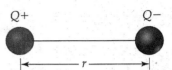

▲ **Figure 8.8 Dipole and dipole moment.** When charges of equal magnitude and opposite sign $Q+$ and $Q−$ are separated by a distance r, a dipole is produced. The size of the dipole is given by the dipole moment, μ, which is the product of the charge separated and the distance of separation between the charge centers: $\mu = Qr$.

 GIVE IT SOME THOUGHT

The molecules chlorine monofluoride, ClF, and iodine monofluoride, IF, are examples of *interhalogen* compounds—compounds that contain bonds between different halogen elements. Which of these molecules will have the larger dipole moment?

Dipole moments are usually reported in *debyes* (D), a unit that equals 3.34×10^{-30} coulomb-meters (C-m). For molecules, we usually measure charge in units of the electronic charge e, 1.60×10^{-19} C, and distance in units of angstroms. Suppose that two charges 1+ and 1− (in units of e) are separated by a distance of 1.00 Å. The dipole moment produced is

$$\mu = Qr = (1.60 \times 10^{-19} \text{ C})(1.00 \text{ Å})\left(\frac{10^{-10} \text{ m}}{1 \text{ Å}}\right)\left(\frac{1 \text{ D}}{3.34 \times 10^{-30} \text{ C-m}}\right) = 4.79 \text{ D}$$

Measurement of the dipole moments can provide us with valuable information about the charge distributions in molecules, as illustrated in Sample Exercise 8.5.

SAMPLE EXERCISE 8.5 | Dipole Moments of Diatomic Molecules

The bond length in the HCl molecule is 1.27 Å. **(a)** Calculate the dipole moment, in debyes, that would result if the charges on the H and Cl atoms were 1+ and 1−, respectively. **(b)** The experimentally measured dipole moment of HCl(g) is 1.08 D. What magnitude of charge, in units of e, on the H and Cl atoms would lead to this dipole moment?

Solution
Analyze and Plan: We are asked in (a) to calculate the dipole moment of HCl that would result if there was a full charge transferred from H to Cl. We can use Equation 8.11 to obtain this result. In (b), we are given the actual dipole moment for the molecule and will use that value to calculate the actual partial charges on the H and Cl atoms.

Solve: (a) The charge on each atom is the electronic charge, $e =$ 1.60×10^{-19} C. The separation is 1.27 Å. The dipole moment is therefore

$$\mu = Qr = (1.60 \times 10^{-19} \text{ C})(1.27 \text{ Å})\left(\frac{10^{-10} \text{ m}}{1 \text{ Å}}\right)\left(\frac{1 \text{ D}}{3.34 \times 10^{-30} \text{ C-m}}\right) = 6.08 \text{ D}$$

(b) We know the value of μ, 1.08 D, and the value of r, 1.27 Å, and we want to calculate the value of Q:

$$Q = \frac{\mu}{r} = \frac{(1.08\ \text{D})\left(\dfrac{3.34 \times 10^{-30}\ \text{C-m}}{1\ \text{D}}\right)}{(1.27\ \text{Å})\left(\dfrac{10^{-10}\ \text{m}}{1\ \text{Å}}\right)} = 2.84 \times 10^{-20}\ \text{C}$$

We can readily convert this charge to units of e:

$$\text{Charge in } e = (2.84 \times 10^{-20}\ \text{C})\left(\frac{1\ e}{1.60 \times 10^{-19}\ \text{C}}\right) = 0.178e$$

Thus, the experimental dipole moment indicates that the charge separation in the HCl molecule is

$$\overset{0.178+}{\text{H}} - \overset{0.178-}{\text{Cl}}$$

Because the experimental dipole moment is less than that calculated in part (a), the charges on the atoms are less than a full electronic charge. We could have anticipated this because the H—Cl bond is polar covalent rather than ionic.

■ PRACTICE EXERCISE

The dipole moment of chlorine monofluoride, ClF(g), is 0.88 D. The bond length of the molecule is 1.63 Å. **(a)** Which atom is expected to have the partial negative charge? **(b)** What is the charge on that atom, in units of e?
Answers: **(a)** F, **(b)** 0.11−

TABLE 8.3 Bond Lengths, Electronegativity Differences, and Dipole Moments of the Hydrogen Halides			
Compound	Bond Length (Å)	Electronegativity Difference	Dipole Moment (D)
HF	0.92	1.9	1.82
HCl	1.27	0.9	1.08
HBr	1.41	0.7	0.82
HI	1.61	0.4	0.44

Table 8.3 ◀ presents the bond lengths and dipole moments of the hydrogen halides. Notice that as we proceed from HF to HI, the electronegativity difference decreases and the bond length increases. The first effect decreases the amount of charge separated and causes the dipole moment to decrease from HF to HI, even though the bond length is increasing. We can "observe" the varying degree of electronic charge shift in these substances from computer-generated renderings based on calculations of electron distribution, as shown in Figure 8.9 ▼. For these molecules, the change in the electronegativity difference has a greater effect on the dipole moment than does the change in bond length.

  GIVE IT SOME THOUGHT

How do you interpret the fact that there is no red in the HBr and HI representations in Figure 8.9?

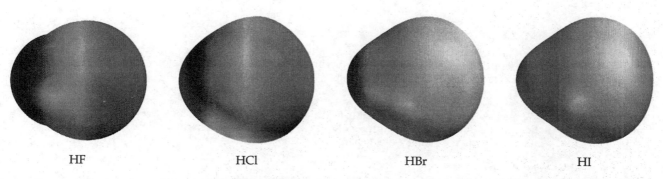

HF   HCl   HBr   HI

▲ **Figure 8.9   Charge separation in the hydrogen halides.** Blue represents regions of lowest electron density, red regions of highest electron density. In HF the strongly electronegative F pulls much of the electron density away from H. In HI the I, being much less electronegative than F, does not attract the shared electrons as strongly, and consequently there is far less polarization of the bond.

Bond Types and Nomenclature

This is a good point for a brief interlude about nomenclature. We saw in Section 2.8 that there are two general approaches to naming binary compounds: one used for ionic compounds and the other for molecular ones. In both approaches, the name of the less electronegative element is given first. The name of the more electronegative element then follows, modified to have an -*ide* ending. Compounds that are ionic are given names based on their component ions, including the charge of the cation if that charge is variable. Those that are molecular are named using the prefixes listed in Table 2.6 to indicate the number of atoms of each kind in the substance (except when there is only one atom, in which case the prefix *mono*- is frequently not used):

Ionic		*Molecular*	
MgH_2	Magnesium hydride	H_2S	Dihydrogen sulfide
FeF_2	Iron(II) fluoride	OF_2	Oxygen difluoride
Mn_2O_3	Manganese(III) oxide	Cl_2O_3	Dichlorine trioxide

The dividing line between the two approaches, however, is not always clear, and both approaches are often applied to the same substances. The compound TiO_2, for example, which is a commercially important white paint pigment, is sometimes referred to as titanium(IV) oxide but is more commonly called titanium dioxide. The roman numeral in the first name is the oxidation number of the titanium. ∞ (Section 4.4)

One reason for the overlap in the two approaches to nomenclature is that many compounds of metals with higher oxidation numbers have properties more similar to molecular compounds (which contain covalent bonds) than to ionic compounds (which contain ionic bonds). Historically, these metal compounds have been named using both conventions even though naming them as molecular compounds is more correct based on their properties. For example, ionic compounds are solids with very high melting points, but $SnCl_4$, which is called either tin tetrachloride or tin(IV) chloride, is a colorless liquid that freezes at $-33°C$ and boils at $114°C$. As another example, the compound Mn_2O_7, which is called either dimanganese heptoxide or manganese(VII) oxide, is a green liquid that freezes at $5.9°C$. In short, whenever you see the formula of a compound containing a metal in a high oxidation state (usually above $+3$), you should not be surprised if it exhibits the general properties of molecular, rather than ionic, compounds.

 GIVE IT SOME THOUGHT

The compounds MoO_3 and OsO_4 are more properly named molybdenum(VI) oxide and osmium tetroxide, respectively. Which of these compounds do you think has the higher melting point?

8.5 | Drawing Lewis Structures

Lewis structures can help us understand the bonding in many compounds and are frequently used when discussing the properties of molecules. For this reason, drawing Lewis structures is an important skill that you should practice. To do so, you should follow a regular procedure. First we'll outline the procedure, and then we'll go through several examples.

1. *Sum the valence electrons from all atoms.* (Use the periodic table as necessary to help you determine the number of valence electrons in each atom.) For an anion, add one electron to the total for each negative charge. For a cation, subtract one electron from the total for each positive charge. Don't worry about keeping track of which electrons come from which atoms. Only the total number is important.

2. *Write the symbols for the atoms to show which atoms are attached to which, and connect them with a single bond* (a dash, representing *two* electrons). Chemical formulas are often written in the order in which the atoms are connected in the molecule or ion; the formula HCN, for example, tells you that the carbon atom is bonded to the H and to the N. When a central atom has a group of other atoms bonded to it, the central atom is usually written first, as in $CO_3{}^{2-}$ and SF_4. It also helps to remember that the central atom is generally less electronegative than the atoms surrounding it. In other cases you may need more information before you can draw the Lewis structure.

3. *Complete the octets around all the atoms bonded to the central atom.* (Remember, however, that you use only a single pair of electrons around hydrogen.)

4. *Place any leftover electrons on the central atom,* even if doing so results in more than an octet of electrons around the atom. In Section 8.7 we will discuss molecules that don't adhere to the octet rule.

5. *If there are not enough electrons to give the central atom an octet, try multiple bonds.* Use one or more of the unshared pairs of electrons on the atoms bonded to the central atom to form double or triple bonds.

ACTIVITIES
Writing Lewis Structures I, Writing Lewis Structures II

SAMPLE EXERCISE 8.6 | Drawing Lewis Structures

Draw the Lewis structure for phosphorus trichloride, PCl_3.

Solution

Analyze and Plan We are asked to draw a Lewis structure from a molecular formula. Our plan is to follow the five-step procedure just described.

Solve: First, we sum the valence electrons. Phosphorus (group 5A) has five valence electrons, and each chlorine (group 7A) has seven. The total number of valence electrons is therefore

$$5 + (3 \times 7) = 26$$

Second, we arrange the atoms to show which atom is connected to which, and we draw a single bond between them. There are various ways the atoms might be arranged. In binary (two-element) compounds, however, the first element listed in the chemical formula is generally surrounded by the remaining atoms. Thus, we begin with a skeleton structure that shows a single bond between the phosphorus atom and each chlorine atom:

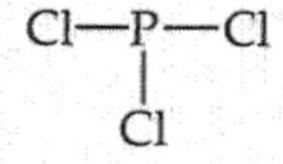

Cl—P—Cl
    |
   Cl

(It is not crucial to place the atoms in exactly this arrangement.)

Third, we complete the octets on the atoms bonded to the central atom. Placing octets around each Cl atom accounts for 24 electrons (remember, each line in our structure represents *two* electrons):

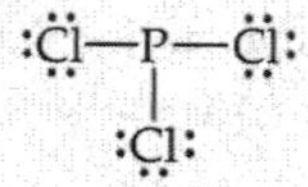

:Cl—P—Cl:
    |
   :Cl:

Fourth, we place the remaining two electrons on the central atom, completing the octet around it:

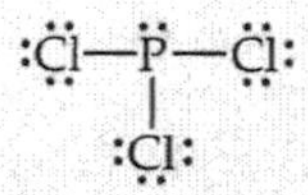

:Cl—P—Cl:
    |
   :Cl:

This structure gives each atom an octet, so we stop at this point. (Remember that in achieving an octet, the bonding electrons are counted for both atoms.)

PRACTICE EXERCISE

(a) How many valence electrons should appear in the Lewis structure for CH_2Cl_2?
(b) Draw the Lewis structure.

Answers: (a) 20, (b)

$$:\ddot{C}l-\underset{\underset{H}{|}}{\overset{\overset{H}{|}}{C}}-\ddot{C}l:$$

SAMPLE EXERCISE 8.7 | Lewis Structures with Multiple Bonds

Draw the Lewis structure for HCN.

Solution Hydrogen has one valence electron, carbon (group 4A) has four, and nitrogen (group 5A) has five. The total number of valence electrons is therefore $1 + 4 + 5 = 10$. In principle, there are different ways in which we might choose to arrange the atoms. Because hydrogen can accommodate only one electron pair, it always has only one single bond associated with it in any compound. Therefore, C—H—N is an impossible arrangement. The remaining two possibilities are H—C—N and H—N—C. The first is the arrangement found experimentally. You might have guessed this to be the atomic arrangement because the formula is written with the atoms in this order. Thus, we begin with a skeleton structure that shows single bonds between hydrogen, carbon, and nitrogen:

$$H-C-N$$

These two bonds account for four electrons. If we then place the remaining six electrons around N to give it an octet, we do not achieve an octet on C:

$$H-C-\ddot{N}:$$

We therefore try a double bond between C and N, using one of the unshared pairs of electrons we placed on N. Again, there are fewer than eight electrons on C, and so we next try a triple bond. This structure gives an octet around both C and N:

$$H-C\overset{\frown}{-}\ddot{N}: \longrightarrow H-C\equiv N:$$

We see that the octet rule is satisfied for the C and N atoms, and the H atom has two electrons around it, so this appears to be a correct Lewis structure.

PRACTICE EXERCISE

Draw the Lewis structure for (a) NO^+ ion, (b) C_2H_4.

Answers: (a) $[:N\equiv O:]^+$, (b)

$$\underset{H}{\overset{H}{>}}C=C\underset{H}{\overset{H}{<}}$$

SAMPLE EXERCISE 8.8 | Lewis Structure for a Polyatomic Ion

Draw the Lewis structure for the BrO_3^- ion.

Solution Bromine (group 7A) has seven valence electrons, and oxygen (group 6A) has six. We must now add one more electron to our sum to account for the 1− charge of the ion. The total number of valence electrons is therefore $7 + (3 \times 6) + 1 = 26$. For oxyanions—$BrO_3^-$, SO_4^{2-}, NO_3^-, CO_3^{2-}, and so forth—the oxygen atoms surround the central nonmetal atoms. After following this format and then putting in the single bonds and distributing the unshared electron pairs, we have

$$\left[:\ddot{O}-\underset{\underset{:\ddot{O}:}{|}}{\ddot{B}r}-\ddot{O}:\right]^-$$

Notice here and elsewhere that the Lewis structure for an ion is written in brackets with the charge shown outside the brackets at the upper right.

■ **PRACTICE EXERCISE**

Draw the Lewis structure for **(a)** ClO_2^- ion, **(b)** PO_4^{3-} ion.

Answers: **(a)** $\left[:\ddot{O}-\ddot{C}l-\ddot{O}:\right]^-$ **(b)** $\begin{bmatrix} :\ddot{O}: \\ | \\ :\ddot{O}-P-\ddot{O}: \\ | \\ :\ddot{O}: \end{bmatrix}^{3-}$

ANIMATION
Formal Charges

Formal Charge

When we draw a Lewis structure, we are describing how the electrons are distributed in a molecule (or polyatomic ion). In some instances we can draw several different Lewis structures that all obey the octet rule. How do we decide which one is the most reasonable? One approach is to do some "bookkeeping" of the valence electrons to determine the formal charge of each atom in each Lewis structure. The **formal charge** of any atom in a molecule is the charge the atom would have if all the atoms in the molecule had the same electronegativity (that is, if each bonding electron pair in the molecule were shared equally between its two atoms).

To calculate the formal charge on any atom in a Lewis structure, we assign the electrons to the atom as follows:

1. *All* unshared (nonbonding) electrons are assigned to the atom on which they are found.
2. For any bond—single, double, or triple—*half* of the bonding electrons are assigned to each atom in the bond.

The formal charge of each atom is then calculated *by subtracting the number of electrons assigned to the atom from the number of valence electrons in the isolated atom.*

Let's illustrate this procedure by calculating the formal charges on the C and N atoms in the cyanide ion, CN^-, which has the Lewis structure

$$[:C\equiv N:]^-$$

For the C atom, there are 2 nonbonding electrons and 3 electrons from the 6 in the triple bond $\left(\frac{1}{2} \times 6 = 3\right)$, for a total of 5. The number of valence electrons on a neutral C atom is 4. Thus, the formal charge on C is $4 - 5 = -1$. For N, there are 2 nonbonding electrons and 3 electrons from the triple bond. Because the number of valence electrons on a neutral N atom is 5, its formal charge is $5 - 5 = 0$. Thus, the formal charges on the atoms in the Lewis structure of CN^- are

$$[:\overset{-1}{C}\equiv\overset{0}{N}:]^-$$

Notice that the sum of the formal charges equals the overall charge on the ion, 1−. In general, the formal charges on a neutral molecule add to zero, whereas those on an ion add to give the overall charge on the ion.

The concept of formal charge can help us choose between alternative Lewis structures. We will see how this is done by considering the CO_2 molecule. As shown in Section 8.3, CO_2 is represented as having two double bonds. The octet rule is also obeyed, however, in a Lewis structure having one single bond and one triple bond. Calculating the formal charge for each atom in these structures, we have

	$\ddot{O}=C=\ddot{O}$			$:\ddot{O}-C\equiv O:$		
Valence electrons:	6	4	6	6	4	6
−(Electrons assigned to atom):	6	4	6	7	4	5
Formal charge:	0	0	0	−1	0	+1

Note that in both cases the formal charges add up to zero, as they must because CO_2 is a neutral molecule. So, which is the correct structure? With both choices following all our rules, how do we decide? As a general rule, when several Lewis structures are possible, we will use the following guidelines to choose the most correct one:

1. *We generally choose the Lewis structure in which the atoms bear formal charges closest to zero.*

2. *We generally choose the Lewis structure in which any negative charges reside on the more electronegative atoms.*

Thus, the first Lewis structure of CO_2 is preferred because the atoms carry no formal charges and so satisfy the first guideline.

Although the concept of formal charge helps us choose between alternative Lewis structures, it is very important that you remember that *formal charges do not represent real charges on atoms.* These charges are just a bookkeeping convention. The actual charge distributions in molecules and ions are determined not by formal charges but by a number of factors, including the electronegativity differences between atoms.

GIVE IT SOME THOUGHT

Suppose that a Lewis structure for a neutral fluorine-containing molecule results in a formal charge on the fluorine atom of $+1$. What conclusion would you draw?

SAMPLE EXERCISE 8.9 | Lewis Structures and Formal Charges

The following are three possible Lewis structures for the thiocyanate ion, NCS^-:

$$[:\ddot{N}-C\equiv S:]^- \qquad [\ddot{N}=C=\ddot{S}]^- \qquad [:N\equiv C-\ddot{S}:]^-$$

(a) Determine the formal charges of the atoms in each structure. **(b)** Which Lewis structure is the preferred one?

Solution (a) Neutral N, C, and S atoms have five, four, and six valence electrons, respectively. We can determine the following formal charges in the three structures by using the rules we just discussed:

$$\begin{matrix} -2 & 0 & +1 \\ [:\ddot{N}-C\equiv S:]^- \end{matrix} \qquad \begin{matrix} -1 & 0 & 0 \\ [\ddot{N}=C=\ddot{S}]^- \end{matrix} \qquad \begin{matrix} 0 & 0 & -1 \\ [:N\equiv C-\ddot{S}:]^- \end{matrix}$$

As they must, the formal charges in all three structures sum to $1-$, the overall charge of the ion.

(b) We will use the guidelines for the best Lewis structure to determine which of the three structures is likely the most correct. As discussed in Section 8.4, N is more electronegative than C or S. Therefore, we expect that any negative formal charge will reside on the N atom (guideline 2). Further, we usually choose the Lewis structure that produces the formal charges of smallest magnitude (guideline 1). For these two reasons, the middle structure is the preferred Lewis structure of the NCS^- ion.

PRACTICE EXERCISE

The cyanate ion (NCO^-), like the thiocyanate ion, has three possible Lewis structures. **(a)** Draw these three Lewis structures, and assign formal charges to the atoms in each structure. **(b)** Which Lewis structure is the preferred one?

$$\text{Answers: (a)} \begin{matrix} -2 & 0 & +1 \\ [:\ddot{N}-C\equiv O:]^- \\ \text{(i)} \end{matrix} \qquad \begin{matrix} -1 & 0 & 0 \\ [\ddot{N}=C=\ddot{O}]^- \\ \text{(ii)} \end{matrix} \qquad \begin{matrix} 0 & 0 & -1 \\ [:N\equiv C-\ddot{O}:]^- \\ \text{(iii)} \end{matrix}$$

(b) Structure (iii), which places a negative charge on oxygen, the most electronegative of the three elements, is the preferred Lewis structure.

A CLOSER LOOK | Oxidation Numbers, Formal Charges, and Actual Partial Charges

In Chapter 4 we introduced the rules for assigning *oxidation numbers* to atoms. The concept of electronegativity is the basis of these numbers. The oxidation number of an atom is the charge it would have if its bonds were completely ionic. That is, in determining the oxidation number, all shared electrons are counted with the more electronegative atom. For example, consider the Lewis structure of HCl shown in Figure 8.10(a) ▼. To assign oxidation numbers, the pair of electrons in the covalent bond between the atoms is assigned to the more electronegative Cl atom. This procedure gives Cl eight valence-shell electrons, one more than the neutral atom. Thus, it is assigned an oxidation number of −1. Hydrogen has no valence electrons when they are counted this way, giving it an oxidation number of +1.

In this section we have just considered another way of counting electrons that gives rise to *formal charges*. The formal charge is assigned by completely ignoring electronegativity and assigning the electrons in bonds equally between the bonded atoms. Consider again the HCl molecule, but this time divide the bonding pair of electrons equally between H and Cl as shown in Figure 8.10(b). In this case Cl has seven assigned electrons, the same as that of the neutral Cl atom. Thus, the formal charge of Cl in this compound is 0. Likewise, the formal charge of H is also 0.

Neither the oxidation number nor the formal charge gives an accurate depiction of the actual charges on atoms. Oxidation numbers overstate the role of electronegativity, and formal charges ignore it completely. It seems reasonable that

electrons in covalent bonds should be apportioned according to the relative electronegativities of the bonded atoms. From Figure 8.6 we see that Cl has an electronegativity of 3.0 while that of H is 2.1. The more electronegative Cl atom might therefore be expected to have roughly $3.0/(3.0 + 2.1) = 0.59$ of the electrical charge in the bonding pair, whereas the H atom has $2.1/(3.0 + 2.1) = 0.41$ of the charge. Because the bond consists of two electrons, the Cl atom's share is $0.59 \times 2e = 1.18e$, or $0.18e$ more than the neutral Cl atom. This gives rise to a partial charge of 0.18− on Cl and 0.18+ on H (notice again that we place the + and − signs before the magnitude when speaking about oxidation numbers and formal charges but after the magnitude when talking about actual charges).

The dipole moment of HCl gives an experimental measure of the partial charges on each atom. In Sample Exercise 8.5 we saw that the dipole moment of HCl indicates a charge separation with a partial charge of 0.178+ on H and 0.178− on Cl, in remarkably good agreement with our simple approximation based on electronegativities. Although that type of calculation provides "ballpark" numbers for the magnitude of charge on atoms, the relationship between electronegativities and charge separation is generally more complicated. As we have already seen, computer programs employing quantum mechanical principles have been developed to calculate the partial charges on atoms, even in complex molecules. Figure 8.10(c) shows a graphical representation of the charge distribution in HCl.

Related Exercises: 8.47, 8.48, 8.49, 8.50, and 8.85

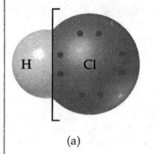

(a)

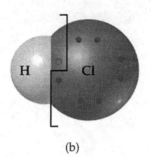

(b)

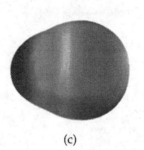

(c)

◀ **Figure 8.10 Oxidation number and formal charge.** (a) The oxidation number for any atom in a molecule is determined by assigning all shared electrons to the more electronegative atom (in this case Cl). (b) Formal charges are derived by dividing all shared electron pairs equally between the bonded atoms. (c) The calculated distribution of electron density on an HCl molecule. Regions of relatively more negative charge are red; those of more positive charge are blue. Negative charge is clearly localized on the chlorine atom.

8.6 | Resonance Structures

We sometimes encounter molecules and ions in which the experimentally determined arrangement of atoms is not adequately described by a single Lewis structure. Consider a molecule of ozone, O_3, which is a bent molecule with two equal O—O bond lengths (Figure 8.11 ▶). Because each oxygen atom contributes 6 valence electrons, the ozone molecule has 18 valence electrons. In writing the Lewis structure, we find that we must have one O—O single bond and one O—O double bond to attain an octet of electrons about each atom:

$$\ddot{\underset{..}{O}} \diagdown \overset{\overset{..}{O}}{\diagup} \diagdown \ddot{\underset{..}{O}}$$

However, this structure cannot by itself be correct because it requires that one O—O bond be different from the other, contrary to the observed structure—we would expect the O=O double bond to be shorter than the O—O single bond. ∞∞ (Section 8.3) In drawing the Lewis structure, however, we could just as easily have put the O=O bond on the left:

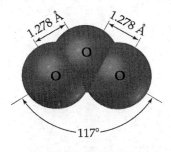

The placement of the atoms in these two alternative but completely equivalent Lewis structures for ozone is the same, but the placement of the electrons is different. Lewis structures of this sort are called **resonance structures**. To describe the structure of ozone properly, we write both Lewis structures and use a double-headed arrow to indicate that the real molecule is described by an average of the two resonance structures:

▲ Figure 8.11 Ozone. Molecular structure (top) and electron-distribution diagram (bottom) for the ozone molecule, O_3.

To understand why certain molecules require more than one resonance structure, we can draw an analogy to the mixing of paint (Figure 8.12 ▶). Blue and yellow are both primary colors of paint pigment. An equal blend of blue and yellow pigments produces green pigment. We can't describe green paint in terms of a single primary color, yet it still has its own identity. Green paint does not oscillate between its two primary colors: It is not blue part of the time and yellow the rest of the time. Similarly, molecules such as ozone cannot be described by a single Lewis structure in which the electrons are "locked into" a particular arrangement.

The true arrangement of the electrons in molecules such as O_3 must be considered as a blend of two (or more) Lewis structures. By analogy to the green paint, the molecule has its own identity separate from the individual resonance structures. For example, the ozone molecule always has two equivalent O—O bonds whose lengths are intermediate between the lengths of an oxygen–oxygen single bond and an oxygen–oxygen double bond. Another way of looking at it is to say that the rules for drawing Lewis structures don't allow us to have a single structure that adequately represents the ozone molecule. For example, there are no rules for drawing half-bonds. We can get around this limitation by drawing two equivalent Lewis structures that, when averaged, amount to something very much like what is observed experimentally.

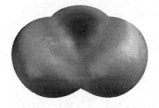

Primary color   Primary color

(a)

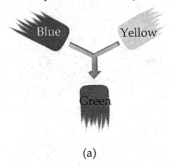

Resonance structure   Resonance structure

Ozone molecule

(b)

▲ Figure 8.12 Resonance. Describing a molecule as a blend of different resonance structures is similar to describing a paint color as a blend of primary colors. (a) Green paint is a blend of blue and yellow. We cannot describe green as a single primary color. (b) The ozone molecule is a blend of two resonance structures. We cannot describe the ozone molecule in terms of a single Lewis structure.

 GIVE IT SOME THOUGHT

The O—O bonds in ozone are often described as "one-and-a-half" bonds. Is this description consistent with the idea of resonance?

As an additional example of resonance structures, consider the nitrate ion, NO_3^-, for which three equivalent Lewis structures can be drawn:

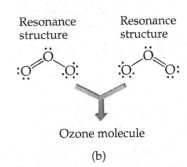

Notice that the arrangement of atoms is the same in each structure; only the placement of electrons differs. In writing resonance structures, the same atoms must be bonded to each other in all structures, so that the only differences are in the arrangements of electrons. All three Lewis structures taken together adequately describe the nitrate ion, in which all three N—O bond lengths are the same.

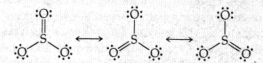

GIVE IT SOME THOUGHT

In the same sense that we describe the O—O bonds in O_3 as "one-and-a-half" bonds, how would you describe the N—O bonds in NO_3^-?

In some instances all the possible Lewis structures for a species may not be equivalent to one another; instead, one or more may represent a more stable arrangement than other possibilities. We will encounter examples of this as we proceed.

SAMPLE EXERCISE 8.10 | Resonance Structures

Which is predicted to have the shorter sulfur–oxygen bonds, SO_3 or SO_3^{2-}?

Solution The sulfur atom has six valence electrons, as does oxygen. Thus, SO_3 contains 24 valence electrons. In writing the Lewis structure, we see that three equivalent resonance structures can be drawn:

As was the case for NO_3^-, the actual structure of SO_3 is an equal blend of all three. Thus, each S—O bond distance should be about one-third of the way between that of a single and that of a double bond (see the immediately preceding Give It Some Thought exercise). That is, they should be shorter than single bonds but not as short as double bonds.

The SO_3^{2-} ion has 26 electrons, which leads to a Lewis structure in which all the S—O bonds are single bonds:

There are no other reasonable Lewis structures for this ion—it can be described quite well by a single Lewis structure rather than by multiple resonance structures.

Our analysis of the Lewis structures leads us to conclude that SO_3 should have the shorter S—O bonds and SO_3^{2-} the longer ones. This conclusion is correct: The experimentally measured S—O bond lengths are 1.42 Å in SO_3 and 1.51 Å in SO_3^{2-}.

PRACTICE EXERCISE

Draw two equivalent resonance structures for the formate ion, HCO_2^-.

Answer:

Resonance in Benzene

Resonance is an extremely important concept in describing the bonding in organic molecules, particularly in the ones called *aromatic* molecules. Aromatic organic molecules include the hydrocarbon called *benzene*, which has the molecular formula C_6H_6 (Figure 8.13 ◄). The six C atoms of benzene are bonded in a hexagonal ring, and one H atom is bonded to each C atom.

(a)

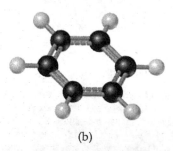

(b)

▲ **Figure 8.13 Benzene, an "aromatic" organic compound.** (a) Benzene is obtained from the distillation of fossil fuels. More than 4 billion pounds of benzene is produced annually in the United States. Because benzene is a carcinogen, its use is closely regulated. (b) The benzene molecule is a regular hexagon of carbon atoms with a hydrogen atom bonded to each one.

We can write two equivalent Lewis structures for benzene, each of which satisfies the octet rule. These two structures are in resonance:

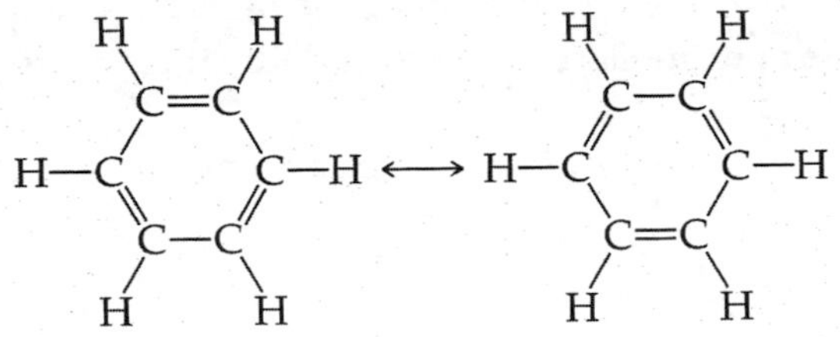

Each resonance structure shows three C—C single bonds and three C=C double bonds, but the double bonds are in different places in the two structures. The experimental structure of benzene shows that all six C—C bonds are of equal length, 1.40 Å, intermediate between the typical bond lengths for a C—C single bond (1.54 Å) and a C=C double bond (1.34 Å).

Benzene is commonly represented by omitting the hydrogen atoms attached to carbon and showing only the carbon–carbon framework with the vertices unlabeled. In this convention, the resonance in the benzene molecule is represented either by two structures separated by a double-headed arrow, as with our other examples, or by a shorthand notation in which we draw a hexagon with a circle in it:

The shorthand notation on the right reminds us that benzene is a blend of two resonance structures—it emphasizes that the C=C double bonds cannot be assigned to specific edges of the hexagon. Chemists use both representations of benzene interchangeably.

The bonding arrangement in benzene confers special stability to the molecule. As a result, literally millions of organic compounds contain the six-membered rings characteristic of benzene. Many of these compounds are important in biochemistry, in pharmaceuticals, and in the production of modern materials. We will say more about the bonding in benzene in Chapter 9 and about its unusual stability in Chapter 25.

GIVE IT SOME THOUGHT

Each Lewis structure of benzene has three C=C double bonds. Another hydrocarbon containing three C=C double bonds is *hexatriene*, C_6H_8. A Lewis structure of hexatriene is

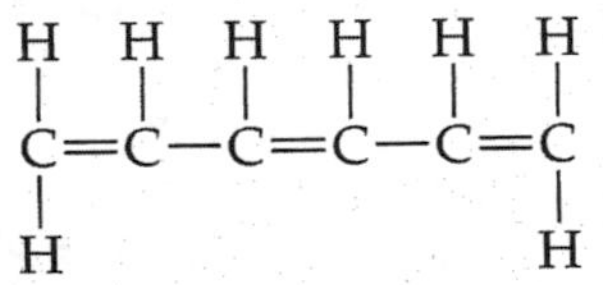

Would you expect hexatriene to have multiple resonance structures like benzene? If not, why is this molecule different from benzene with respect to resonance?

8.7 | Exceptions to the Octet Rule

The octet rule is so simple and useful in introducing the basic concepts of bonding that you might assume that it is always obeyed. In Section 8.2, however, we noted its limitation in dealing with ionic compounds of the transition metals.

The octet rule also fails in many situations involving covalent bonding. These exceptions to the octet rule are of three main types:

1. Molecules and polyatomic ions containing an odd number of electrons
2. Molecules and polyatomic ions in which an atom has fewer than an octet of valence electrons
3. Molecules and polyatomic ions in which an atom has more than an octet of valence electrons

Odd Number of Electrons

In the vast majority of molecules and polyatomic ions, the total number of valence electrons is even, and complete pairing of electrons occurs. In a few molecules and polyatomic ions, however, such as ClO_2, NO, NO_2, and O_2^-, the number of valence electrons is odd. Complete pairing of these electrons is impossible, and an octet around each atom cannot be achieved. For example, NO contains $5 + 6 = 11$ valence electrons. The two most important Lewis structures for this molecule are

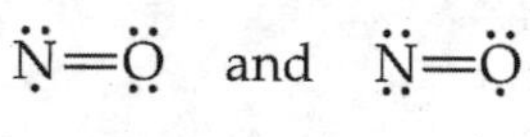

$$\ddot{N}=\ddot{O} \quad \text{and} \quad \ddot{N}=\ddot{O}$$

Less than an Octet of Valence Electrons

A second type of exception occurs when there are fewer than eight valence electrons around an atom in a molecule or polyatomic ion. This situation is also relatively rare, most often encountered in compounds of boron and beryllium. As an example, let's consider boron trifluoride, BF_3. If we follow the first four steps of the procedure at the beginning of Section 8.5 for drawing Lewis structures, we obtain the structure

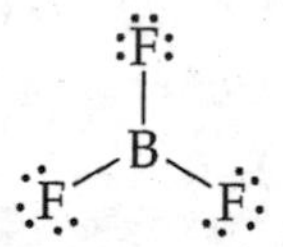

$$:\ddot{F}: \\ | \\ :\ddot{F}\!\!-\!\!B\!\!-\!\!\ddot{F}:$$

There are only six electrons around the boron atom. In this Lewis structure the formal charges on both the B and the F atoms are zero. We could complete the octet around boron by forming a double bond (step 5). In so doing, we see that there are three equivalent resonance structures (the formal charges on each atom are shown in red):

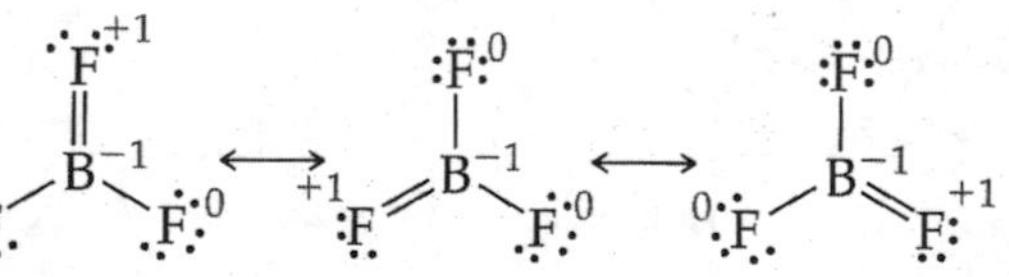

These Lewis structures force a fluorine atom to share additional electrons with the boron atom, which is inconsistent with the high electronegativity of fluorine. In fact, the formal charges tell us that this is an unfavorable situation: In each of the Lewis structures, the F atom involved in the B=F double bond has a formal charge of +1, while the less electronegative B atom has a formal charge of −1. Thus, the Lewis structures in which there is a B=F double bond are less important than the one in which there are fewer than an octet of valence electrons around boron:

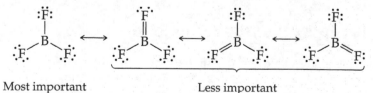

| Most important | Less important |

We usually represent BF$_3$ solely by the leftmost resonance structure, in which there are only six valence electrons around boron. The chemical behavior of BF$_3$ is consistent with this representation. In particular, BF$_3$ reacts very energetically with molecules having an unshared pair of electrons that can be used to form a bond with boron. For example, it reacts with ammonia, NH$_3$, to form the compound NH$_3$BF$_3$:

$$
\begin{array}{ccc}
\underset{\underset{\displaystyle H}{|}}{\overset{\overset{\displaystyle H}{|}}{H-\ddot{N}:}} + \underset{\underset{\displaystyle F}{|}}{\overset{\overset{\displaystyle F}{|}}{B-F}} & \longrightarrow & \underset{\underset{\displaystyle H\ \ F}{|\ \ |}}{\overset{\overset{\displaystyle H\ \ F}{|\ \ |}}{H-N-B-F}}
\end{array}
$$

In this stable compound, boron has an octet of valence electrons.

More than an Octet of Valence Electrons

The third and largest class of exceptions consists of molecules or polyatomic ions in which there are more than eight electrons in the valence shell of an atom. When we draw the Lewis structure for PCl$_5$, for example, we are forced to "expand" the valence shell and place ten electrons around the central phosphorus atom:

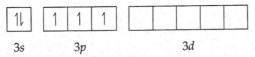

Other examples of molecules and ions with "expanded" valence shells are SF$_4$, AsF$_6^-$, and ICl$_4^-$. The corresponding molecules with a second-period atom bonded to the halogen atom, such as NCl$_5$ and OF$_4$, do *not* exist. Let's take a look at why expanded valence shells are observed only for elements in period 3 and beyond in the periodic table.

Elements of the second period have only the 2s and 2p valence orbitals available for bonding. Because these orbitals can hold a maximum of eight electrons, we never find more than an octet of electrons around elements from the second period. Elements from the third period and beyond, however, have *ns*, *np*, and unfilled *nd* orbitals that can be used in bonding. For example, the orbital diagram for the valence shell of a phosphorus atom is

$\uparrow\downarrow$	$\uparrow$	$\uparrow$	$\uparrow$					

   3s   3p   3d

Although third-period elements often satisfy the octet rule, as in PCl$_3$, they also often exceed an octet by seeming to use their empty *d* orbitals to accommodate additional electrons.*

Size also plays an important role in determining whether an atom in a molecule or polyatomic ion can accommodate more than eight electrons in its valence shell. The larger the central atom, the larger the number of atoms that can surround it. The number of molecules and ions with expanded valence shells therefore increases with increasing size of the central atom. The size of the surrounding atoms is also important. Expanded valence shells occur most often when the central atom is bonded to the smallest and most electronegative atoms, such as F, Cl, and O.

---

* On the basis of theoretical calculations, some chemists have questioned whether valence *d* orbitals are actually used in the bonding of molecules and ions with expanded valence shells. Nevertheless, the presence of valence *d* orbitals in period 3 and beyond provides the simplest explanation of this phenomenon, especially within the scope of a general chemistry textbook.

■ **SAMPLE EXERCISE 8.11** | Lewis Structure for an Ion with an Expanded Valence Shell

Draw the Lewis structure for ICl_4^-.

Solution Iodine (group 7A) has seven valence electrons; each chlorine (group 7A) also has seven; an extra electron is added to account for the 1− charge of the ion. Therefore, the total number of valence electrons is

$$7 + 4(7) + 1 = 36$$

The I atom is the central atom in the ion. Putting eight electrons around each Cl atom (including a pair of electrons between I and each Cl to represent the single bond between these atoms) requires $8 \times 4 = 32$ electrons.

We are thus left with $36 - 32 = 4$ electrons to be placed on the larger iodine:

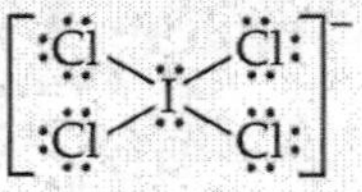

Iodine has 12 valence electrons around it, four more than needed for an octet.

■ **PRACTICE EXERCISE**

(a) Which of the following atoms is never found with more than an octet of valence electrons around it: S, C, P, Br? **(b)** Draw the Lewis structure for XeF_2.

Answers: **(a)** C, **(b)** :F̈—Xë—F̈:

At times you may see Lewis structures written with an expanded valence shell even though structures can be written with an octet. For example, consider these Lewis structures for the phosphate ion, PO_4^{3-}:

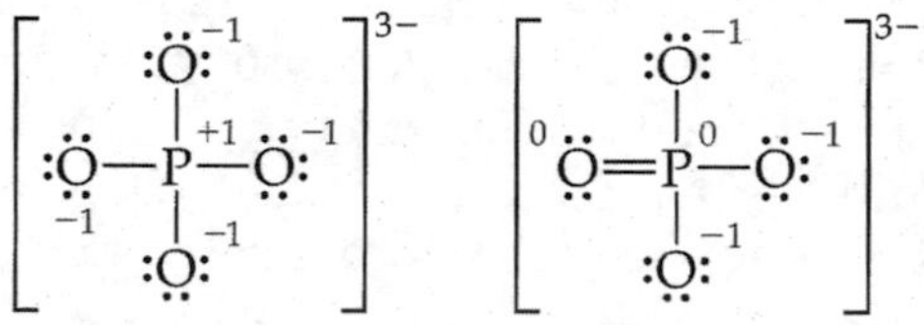

The formal charges on the atoms are shown in red. On the left, the P atom has an octet; on the right, the P atom has an expanded valence shell of five electron pairs. The structure on the right is often used for PO_4^{3-} because it has smaller formal charges on the atoms. The best representation of PO_4^{3-} is a series of such Lewis structures in resonance with one another. However, theoretical calculations based on quantum mechanics suggest that the structure on the left is the best single Lewis structure for the phosphate ion. In general, when choosing between alternative Lewis structures, you should choose one that satisfies the octet rule if it is possible to do so.

8.8 | Strengths of Covalent Bonds

The stability of a molecule is related to the strengths of the covalent bonds it contains. The strength of a covalent bond between two atoms is determined by the energy required to break that bond. It is easiest to relate bond strength to the enthalpy change in reactions in which bonds are broken. ⟳ (Section 5.4)

The **bond enthalpy** is the enthalpy change, ΔH, for the breaking of a particular bond in one mole of a gaseous substance. For example, the bond enthalpy for the bond between chlorine atoms in the Cl_2 molecule is the enthalpy change when 1 mol of Cl_2 is dissociated into chlorine atoms:

$$:\ddot{Cl}-\ddot{Cl}:(g) \longrightarrow 2 :\ddot{Cl}\cdot(g)$$

We use the designation D(bond type) to represent bond enthalpies.

It is relatively simple to assign bond enthalpies to bonds that are found in diatomic molecules, such as the $Cl-Cl$ bond in Cl_2 or the $H-Br$ bond in HBr: The bond enthalpy is just the energy required to break the diatomic molecule into its component atoms. Many important bonds, such as the $C-H$ bond, exist only in polyatomic molecules. For these types of bonds, we usually utilize *average* bond enthalpies. For example, the enthalpy change for the following process in which a methane molecule is decomposed to its five atoms (a process called *atomization*) can be used to define an average bond enthalpy for the $C-H$ bond:

$$\begin{array}{c} H \\ | \\ H-C-H(g) \\ | \\ H \end{array} \longrightarrow \cdot\ddot{C}\cdot(g) + 4 H\cdot(g) \qquad \Delta H = 1660 \text{ kJ}$$

Because there are four equivalent $C-H$ bonds in methane, the heat of atomization is equal to the sum of the bond enthalpies of the four $C-H$ bonds. Therefore, the average $C-H$ bond enthalpy for CH_4 is $D(C-H) = (1660/4)$ kJ/mol = 415 kJ/mol.

The bond enthalpy for a given set of atoms, say $C-H$, depends on the rest of the molecule of which the atom pair is a part. However, the variation from one molecule to another is generally small, which supports the idea that bonding electron pairs are localized between atoms. If we consider $C-H$ bond enthalpies in many different compounds, we find that the average bond enthalpy is 413 kJ/mol, which compares closely with the 415 kJ/mol value calculated from CH_4.

GIVE IT SOME THOUGHT

The hydrocarbon *ethane*, C_2H_6, was first introduced in Section 2.9. How could you use the enthalpy of atomization of $C_2H_6(g)$ along with the value of $D(C-H)$ to provide an estimate for $D(C-C)$?

Table 8.4 ▶ lists several average bond enthalpies. *The bond enthalpy is always a positive quantity*; energy is always required to break chemical bonds. Conversely, energy is always released when a bond forms between two gaseous atoms or molecular fragments. The greater the bond enthalpy, the stronger the bond.

A molecule with strong chemical bonds generally has less tendency to undergo chemical change than does one with weak bonds. This relationship between strong bonding and chemical stability helps explain the chemical form in which many elements are found in nature. For example, $Si-O$ bonds are among the strongest ones that silicon forms. It should not be surprising, therefore, that SiO_2 and other substances containing $Si-O$ bonds (silicates) are so common; it is estimated that over 90% of Earth's crust is composed of SiO_2 and silicates.

TABLE 8.4 Average Bond Enthalpies (kJ/mol)							
Single Bonds							
C—H	413	N—H	391	O—H	463	F—F	155
C—C	348	N—N	163	O—O	146		
C—N	293	N—O	201	O—F	190	Cl—F	253
C—O	358	N—F	272	O—Cl	203	Cl—Cl	242
C—F	485	N—Cl	200	O—I	234		
C—Cl	328	N—Br	243			Br—F	237
C—Br	276			S—H	339	Br—Cl	218
C—I	240			S—F	327	Br—Br	193
C—S	259	H—H	436	S—Cl	253		
		H—F	567	S—Br	218	I—Cl	208
Si—H	323	H—Cl	431	S—S	266	I—Br	175
Si—Si	226	H—Br	366			I—I	151
Si—C	301	H—I	299				
Si—O	368						
Si—Cl	464						
Multiple Bonds							
C=C	614	N=N	418	O_2	495		
C≡C	839	N≡N	941				
C=N	615	N=O	607	S=O	523		
C≡N	891			S=S	418		
C=O	799						
C≡O	1072						

Bond Enthalpies and the Enthalpies of Reactions

We can use average bond enthalpies to estimate the enthalpies of reactions in which bonds are broken and new bonds are formed. This procedure allows us to estimate quickly whether a given reaction will be endothermic ($\Delta H > 0$) or exothermic ($\Delta H < 0$) even if we do not know ΔH_f° for all the chemical species involved.

Our strategy for estimating reaction enthalpies is a straightforward application of Hess's law. ∞ (Section 5.6) We use the fact that breaking bonds is always an endothermic process and bond formation is always exothermic. We therefore imagine that the reaction occurs in two steps: (1) We supply enough energy to break those bonds in the reactants that are not present in the products. In this step the enthalpy of the system is increased by the sum of the bond enthalpies of the bonds that are broken. (2) We form the bonds in the products that were not present in the reactants. This step releases energy and therefore lowers the enthalpy of the system by the sum of the bond enthalpies of the bonds that are formed. The enthalpy of the reaction, ΔH_{rxn}, is estimated as the sum of the bond enthalpies of the bonds broken minus the sum of the bond enthalpies of the bonds formed:

$$\Delta H_{rxn} = \Sigma(\text{bond enthalpies of bonds broken})$$
$$- \Sigma(\text{bond enthalpies of bonds formed}) \quad [8.12]$$

Consider, for example, the gas-phase reaction between methane, CH_4, and chlorine to produce methyl chloride, CH_3Cl, and hydrogen chloride, HCl:

$$H—CH_3(g) + Cl—Cl(g) \longrightarrow Cl—CH_3(g) + H—Cl(g) \quad \Delta H_{rxn} = ? \quad [8.13]$$

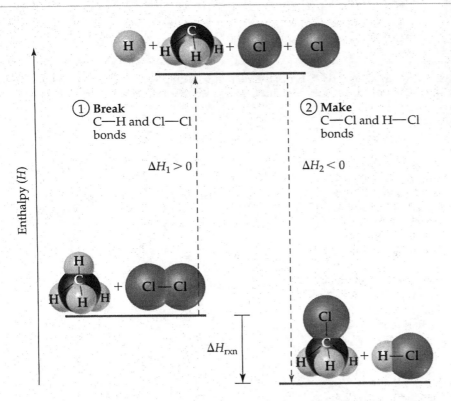

▲ **Figure 8.14 Using bond enthalpies to calculate** ΔH_{rxn}. Average bond enthalpies are used to estimate ΔH_{rxn} for the reaction in Equation 8.13. Breaking the C—H and Cl—Cl bonds produces a positive enthalpy change (ΔH_1), whereas making the C—Cl and H—Cl bonds causes a negative enthalpy change (ΔH_2). The values of ΔH_1 and ΔH_2 are estimated from the values in Table 8.4. From Hess's law, $\Delta H_{rxn} = \Delta H_1 + \Delta H_2$.

ACTIVITY
Bond Enthalpy

Our two-step procedure is outlined in Figure 8.14 ▲. We note that in the course of this reaction the following bonds are broken and made:

Bonds broken: 1 mol C—H, 1 mol Cl—Cl

Bonds made: 1 mol C—Cl, 1 mol H—Cl

We first supply enough energy to break the C—H and Cl—Cl bonds, which will raise the enthalpy of the system. We then form the C—Cl and H—Cl bonds, which will release energy and lower the enthalpy of the system. By using Equation 8.12 and the data in Table 8.4, we estimate the enthalpy of the reaction as

$$\Delta H_{rxn} = [D(C—H) + D(Cl—Cl)] - [D(C—Cl) + D(H—Cl)]$$
$$= (413 \text{ kJ} + 242 \text{ kJ}) - (328 \text{ kJ} + 431 \text{ kJ}) = -104 \text{ kJ}$$

The reaction is exothermic because the bonds in the products (especially the H—Cl bond) are stronger than the bonds in the reactants (especially the Cl—Cl bond).

We usually use bond enthalpies to estimate ΔH_{rxn} only if we do not have the needed ΔH_f° values readily at hand. For the above reaction, we cannot calculate ΔH_{rxn} from ΔH_f° values and Hess's law because the value of ΔH_f° for $CH_3Cl(g)$ is not given in Appendix C. If we obtain the value of ΔH_f° for $CH_3Cl(g)$ from another source (such as the *CRC Handbook of Chemistry and Physics*) and use Equation 5.31, we find that $\Delta H_{rxn} = -99.8$ kJ for the reaction in Equation 8.13. Thus, the use of average bond enthalpies provides a reasonably accurate estimate of the actual reaction enthalpy change.

It is important to remember that bond enthalpies are derived for *gaseous* molecules and that they are often *averaged* values. Nonetheless, average bond enthalpies are useful for estimating reaction enthalpies quickly, especially for gas-phase reactions.

CHEMISTRY AT WORK | Explosives and Alfred Nobel

Enormous amounts of energy can be stored in chemical bonds. Perhaps the most graphic illustration of this fact is seen in certain molecular substances that are used as explosives. Our discussion of bond enthalpies allows us to examine more closely some of the properties of such explosive substances.

An explosive must have the following characteristics: (1) It must decompose very exothermically; (2) the products of its decomposition must be gaseous, so that a tremendous gas pressure accompanies the decomposition; (3) its decomposition must occur very rapidly; and (4) it must be stable enough so that it can be detonated predictably. The combination of the first three effects leads to the violent evolution of heat and gases.

To give the most exothermic reaction, an explosive should have weak chemical bonds and should decompose into molecules with very strong bonds. Looking at bond enthalpies (Table 8.4), the $N\equiv N$, $C\equiv O$, and $C=O$ bonds are among the strongest. Not surprisingly, explosives are usually designed to produce the gaseous products $N_2(g)$, $CO(g)$, and $CO_2(g)$. Water vapor is nearly always produced as well.

Many common explosives are organic molecules that contain nitro (NO_2) or nitrate (NO_3) groups attached to a carbon skeleton. The structures of two of the most familiar explosives, nitroglycerin and trinitrotoluene (TNT), are shown here. TNT contains the six-membered ring characteristic of benzene.

Nitroglycerin

TNT

SAMPLE EXERCISE 8.12 | Using Average Bond Enthalpies

Using Table 8.4, estimate ΔH for the following reaction (where we explicitly show the bonds involved in the reactants and products):

$$H-\underset{\underset{H}{|}}{\overset{\overset{H}{|}}{C}}-\underset{\underset{H}{|}}{\overset{\overset{H}{|}}{C}}-H(g) + \tfrac{7}{2}O_2(g) \longrightarrow 2\,O=C=O(g) + 3\,H-O-H(g)$$

Solution

Analyze: We are asked to estimate the enthalpy change for a chemical process by using average bond enthalpies for the bonds that are broken in the reactants and formed in the products.

Plan: Among the reactants, we must break six C—H bonds and a C—C bond in C_2H_6; we also break $\tfrac{7}{2}O_2$ bonds. Among the products, we form four C=O bonds (two in each CO_2) and six O—H bonds (two in each H_2O).

Solve: Using Equation 8.12 and data from Table 8.4, we have

$$\Delta H = 6D(C-H) + D(C-C) + \tfrac{7}{2}D(O_2) - 4D(C=O) - 6D(O-H)$$

$$= 6(413\text{ kJ}) + 348\text{ kJ} + \tfrac{7}{2}(495\text{ kJ}) - 4(799\text{ kJ}) - 6(463\text{ kJ})$$

$$= 4558\text{ kJ} - 5974\text{ kJ}$$

$$= -1416\text{ kJ}$$

Check: This estimate can be compared with the value of -1428 kJ calculated from more accurate thermochemical data; the agreement is good.

PRACTICE EXERCISE

Using Table 8.4, estimate ΔH for the reaction

$$H-\underset{\underset{H}{|}}{N}-\underset{\underset{H}{|}}{N}-H(g) \longrightarrow N\equiv N(g) + 2\,H-H(g)$$

Answer: -86 kJ

Nitroglycerin is a pale yellow, oily liquid. It is highly *shock-sensitive*: Merely shaking the liquid can cause its explosive decomposition into nitrogen, carbon dioxide, water, and oxygen gases:

$$4\ C_3H_5N_3O_9(l) \longrightarrow 6\ N_2(g) + 12\ CO_2(g) + 10\ H_2O(g) + O_2(g)$$

The large bond enthalpies of the N_2 molecules (941 kJ/mol), CO_2 molecules (2×799 kJ/mol), and water molecules (2×463 kJ/mol) make this reaction enormously exothermic. Nitroglycerin is an exceptionally unstable explosive because it is in nearly perfect *explosive balance*: With the exception of a small amount of $O_2(g)$ produced, the only products are N_2, CO_2, and H_2O. Note also that, unlike combustion reactions (Section 3.2), explosions are entirely self-contained: No other reagent, such as $O_2(g)$, is needed for the explosive decomposition.

Because nitroglycerin is so unstable, it is difficult to use as a controllable explosive. The Swedish inventor Alfred Nobel (Figure 8.15 ▶) found that mixing nitroglycerin with an absorbent solid material such as diatomaceous earth or cellulose gives a solid explosive (*dynamite*) that is much safer than liquid nitroglycerin.

Related Exercises 8.89 and 8.90

▲ **Figure 8.15 Alfred Nobel (1833–1896), the Swedish inventor of dynamite.** By many accounts Nobel's discovery that nitroglycerin could be made more stable by absorbing it onto cellulose was an accident. This discovery made Nobel a very wealthy man. He was also a complex and lonely man, however, who never married, was frequently ill, and suffered from chronic depression. He had invented the most powerful military explosive to date, but he strongly supported international peace movements. His will stated that his fortune be used to establish prizes awarding those who "have conferred the greatest benefit on mankind," including the promotion of peace and "fraternity between nations." The Nobel Prize is probably the most coveted award that a scientist, economist, writer, or peace advocate can receive.

Bond Enthalpy and Bond Length

Just as we can define an average bond enthalpy, we can also define an average bond length for a number of common bond types. Some of these are listed in Table 8.5 ▼. Of particular interest is the relationship among bond enthalpy, bond length, and the number of bonds between the atoms. For example, we can use data in Tables 8.4 and 8.5 to compare the bond lengths and bond enthalpies of carbon–carbon single, double, and triple bonds:

C—C	C=C	C≡C
1.54 Å	1.34 Å	1.20 Å
348 kJ/mol	614 kJ/mol	839 kJ/mol

As the number of bonds between the carbon atoms increases, the bond enthalpy increases and the bond length decreases; that is, the carbon atoms are held more closely and more tightly together. In general, *as the number of bonds between two atoms increases, the bond grows shorter and stronger.*

TABLE 8.5 Average Bond Lengths for Some Single, Double, and Triple Bonds

Bond	Bond Length (Å)	Bond	Bond Length (Å)
C—C	1.54	N—N	1.47
C=C	1.34	N=N	1.24
C≡C	1.20	N≡N	1.10
C—N	1.43	N—O	1.36
C=N	1.38	N=O	1.22
C≡N	1.16		
		O—O	1.48
C—O	1.43	O=O	1.21
C=O	1.23		
C≡O	1.13		

■ **SAMPLE INTEGRATIVE EXERCISE** | Putting Concepts Together

Phosgene, a substance used in poisonous gas warfare in World War I, is so named because it was first prepared by the action of sunlight on a mixture of carbon monoxide and chlorine gases. Its name comes from the Greek words *phos* (light) and *genes* (born of). Phosgene has the following elemental composition: 12.14% C, 16.17% O, and 71.69% Cl by mass. Its molar mass is 98.9 g/mol. **(a)** Determine the molecular formula of this compound. **(b)** Draw three Lewis structures for the molecule that satisfy the octet rule for each atom. (The Cl and O atoms bond to C.) **(c)** Using formal charges, determine which Lewis structure is the most important one. **(d)** Using average bond enthalpies, estimate ΔH for the formation of gaseous phosgene from $CO(g)$ and $Cl_2(g)$.

Solution **(a)** The empirical formula of phosgene can be determined from its elemental composition. ⚬⚬⚬ (Section 3.5) Assuming 100 g of the compound and calculating the number of moles of C, O, and Cl in this sample, we have

$$(12.14 \text{ g C})\left(\frac{1 \text{ mol C}}{12.01 \text{ g C}}\right) = 1.011 \text{ mol C}$$

$$(16.17 \text{ g O})\left(\frac{1 \text{ mol O}}{16.00 \text{ g O}}\right) = 1.011 \text{ mol O}$$

$$(71.69 \text{ g Cl})\left(\frac{1 \text{ mol Cl}}{35.45 \text{ g Cl}}\right) = 2.022 \text{ mol Cl}$$

The ratio of the number of moles of each element, obtained by dividing each number of moles by the smallest quantity, indicates that there is one C and one O for each two Cl in the empirical formula, $COCl_2$.

The molar mass of the empirical formula is $12.01 + 16.00 + 2(35.45) = 98.91$ g/mol, the same as the molar mass of the molecule. Thus, $COCl_2$ is the molecular formula.

(b) Carbon has four valence electrons, oxygen has six, and chlorine has seven, giving $4 + 6 + 2(7) = 24$ electrons for the Lewis structures. Drawing a Lewis structure with all single bonds does not give the central carbon atom an octet. Using multiple bonds, three structures satisfy the octet rule:

(c) Calculating the formal charges on each atom gives

The first structure is expected to be the most important one because it has the lowest formal charges on each atom. Indeed, the molecule is usually represented by this Lewis structure.

(d) Writing the chemical equation in terms of the Lewis structures of the molecules, we have

Thus, the reaction involves breaking a $C{\equiv}O$ bond and a Cl—Cl bond and forming a $C{=}O$ bond and two C—Cl bonds. Using bond enthalpies from Table 8.4, we have

$$\Delta H = D(C{\equiv}O) + D(Cl—Cl) - D(C{=}O) - 2D(C—Cl)$$
$$= 1072 \text{ kJ} + 242 \text{ kJ} - 799 \text{ kJ} - 2(328 \text{ kJ}) = -141 \text{ kJ}$$

SUMMARY AND KEY TERMS

Introduction and Section 8.1 In this chapter we have focused on the interactions that lead to the formation of **chemical bonds**. We classify these bonds into three broad groups: **ionic bonds**, which are the electrostatic forces that exist between ions of opposite charge; **covalent bonds**, which result from the sharing of electrons by two atoms; and **metallic bonds**, which bind together the atoms in metals. The formation of bonds involves interactions of the outermost electrons of atoms, their valence electrons. The valence electrons of an atom can be represented by electron-dot symbols, called **Lewis symbols**. The tendencies of atoms to gain, lose, or share their valence electrons often follow the **octet rule**, which can be viewed as an attempt by atoms to achieve a noble-gas electron configuration.

Section 8.2 Ionic bonding results from the complete transfer of electrons from one atom to another, with formation of a three-dimensional lattice of charged particles. The stabilities of ionic substances result from the strong electrostatic attractions between an ion and the surrounding ions of opposite charge. The magnitude of these interactions is measured by the **lattice energy**, which is the energy needed to separate an ionic lattice into gaseous ions. Lattice energy increases with increasing charge on the ions and with decreasing distance between the ions. The **Born–Haber** cycle is a useful thermochemical cycle in which we use Hess's law to calculate the lattice energy as the sum of several steps in the formation of an ionic compound.

An element's position in the periodic table allows us to predict the ion it will tend to form. Metals tend to form cations; nonmetals tend to form anions. We can write electron configurations for ions by first writing the electron configuration of the neutral atom and then removing or adding the appropriate number of electrons.

Section 8.3 A covalent bond results from the sharing of electrons. We can represent the electron distribution in molecules by means of **Lewis structures**, which indicate how many valence electrons are involved in forming bonds and how many remain as unshared electron pairs. The octet rule helps determine how many bonds will be formed between two atoms. The sharing of one pair of electrons produces a **single bond**; the sharing of two or three pairs of electrons between two atoms produces **double** or **triple bonds**, respectively. Double and triple bonds are examples of multiple bonding between atoms. The **bond length** between two bonded atoms is the distance between the two nuclei. The bond length decreases as the number of bonds between the atoms increases.

Section 8.4 In covalent bonds, the electrons may not necessarily be shared equally between two atoms. **Bond polarity** helps describe unequal sharing of electrons in a bond. In a **nonpolar covalent bond** the electrons in the bond are shared equally by the two atoms; in a **polar covalent bond** one of the atoms exerts a greater attraction for the electrons than the other.

Electronegativity is a numerical measure of the ability of an atom to compete with other atoms for the electrons shared between them. Fluorine is the most electronegative element, meaning it has the greatest ability to attract electrons from other atoms. Electronegativity values range from 0.7 for Cs to 4.0 for F. Electronegativity generally increases from left to right in a row of the periodic table, and decreases going down a column. The difference in the electronegativities of bonded atoms can be used to determine the polarity of a bond. The greater the difference, the more polar the bond.

A **polar molecule** is one whose centers of positive and negative charge do not coincide. Thus, a polar molecule has a positive side and a negative side. This separation of charge produces a **dipole**, the magnitude of which is given by the **dipole moment**, which is measured in debyes (D). Dipole moments increase with increasing amount of charge separated and increasing distance of separation. Any diatomic molecule $X—Y$ in which X and Y have different electronegativities is a polar molecule.

Sections 8.5 and 8.6 If we know which atoms are connected to one another, we can draw Lewis structures for molecules and ions by a simple procedure. Once we do so, we can determine the **formal charge** of each atom in a Lewis structure, which is the charge that the atom would have if all atoms had the same electronegativity. Most acceptable Lewis structures will have low formal charges with any negative formal charges residing on more electronegative atoms.

Sometimes a single Lewis structure is inadequate to represent a particular molecule (or ion). In such situations, we describe the molecule by using two or more **resonance structures** for the molecule. The molecule is envisioned as a blend of these multiple resonance structures. Resonance structures are important in describing the bonding in ozone, O_3, and the organic molecule benzene, C_6H_6.

Section 8.7 The octet rule is not obeyed in all cases. The exceptions occur when (a) a molecule has an odd number of electrons, (b) it is not possible to complete an octet around an atom without forcing an unfavorable distribution of electrons, or (c) a large atom is surrounded by so many small electronegative atoms that it has more than an octet of electrons around it. In this last case we envision using the unfilled d orbitals of the large atom to "expand" the valence shell of the atom. Expanded valence shells are observed for atoms in the third row and beyond in the periodic table, for which low-energy d orbitals are available.

Section 8.8 The strength of a covalent bond is measured by its **bond enthalpy**, which is the molar enthalpy

Science Fundamentals Second Edition

change upon breaking a particular bond. Average bond enthalpies can be determined for a wide variety of covalent bonds. The strengths of covalent bonds increase with the number of electron pairs shared between two atoms. We can use bond enthalpies to estimate the enthalpy

change during chemical reactions in which bonds are broken and new bonds formed. The average bond length between two atoms decreases as the number of bonds between the atoms increases, consistent with the bond being stronger as the number of bonds increases.

VISUALIZING CONCEPTS

8.1 For each of these Lewis symbols, indicate the group in the periodic table in which the element X belongs: (a) $\cdot \overset{\cdot}{X} \cdot$ (b) $\cdot X \cdot$ (c) $: \overset{\cdot}{X} \cdot$ [Section 8.1]

8.2 Illustrated below are four ions—A_1, A_2, Z_1, and Z_2—showing their relative ionic radii. The ions shown in red carry a 1+ charge, and those shown in blue carry a 1− charge. (a) Would you expect to find an ionic compound of formula A_1A_2? Explain. (b) Which combination of ions leads to the ionic compound having the largest lattice energy? (c) Which combination of ions leads to the ionic compound having the smallest lattice energy? [Section 8.2]

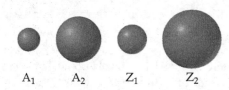

A₁   A₂   Z₁   Z₂

8.3 The orbital diagram below shows the valence electrons for a 2+ ion of an element. (a) What is the element? (b) What is the electron configuration of an atom of this element? [Section 8.2]

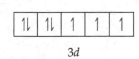

3d

8.4 In the Lewis structure shown below, A, D, E, Q, X, and Z represent elements in the first two rows of the periodic table. Identify all six elements. [Section 8.3]

$$\overset{\ddot{:}E:}{\underset{\ddot{:}\ddot{A}}{\parallel}}\!-\!\overset{X}{\underset{}{\mid}}\!-\!\overset{}{\underset{\ddot{:}}{Q}}\!-\!Z$$

8.5 The partial Lewis structure below is for a hydrocarbon molecule. In the full Lewis structure, each carbon atom satisfies the octet rule, and there are no unshared electron pairs in the molecule. The carbon–carbon bonds are labeled 1, 2, and 3. (a) Determine where the hydrogen atoms are in the molecule. (b) Rank the carbon–carbon bonds in order of increasing bond length. (c) Rank the carbon–carbon bonds in order of increasing bond enthalpy. [Section 8.3 and 8.8]

$$C\overset{1}{=}C\overset{2}{-}C\overset{3}{\equiv}C$$

8.6 One possible Lewis structure for the compound xenon trioxide, XeO_3, is shown below. (a) Prior to the 1960s, this compound was thought to be impossible. Why? (b) How many other equivalent resonant structures are there for this Lewis structure? (c) Does this Lewis structure satisfy the octet rule? Explain why or why not. (d) Do you think this is the best choice of Lewis structure for XeO_3? [Sections 8.5, 8.6, and 8.7]

$$\overset{\overset{\ddot{:}O:}{\parallel}}{\ddot{O}\!=\!\overset{}{\underset{\ddot{}}{Xe}}\!-\!\ddot{O}:}$$

EXERCISES

Lewis Symbols

8.7 (a) What are valence electrons? (b) How many valence electrons does a nitrogen atom possess? (c) An atom has the electron configuration $1s^22s^22p^63s^23p^2$. How many valence electrons does the atom have?

8.8 (a) What is the octet rule? (b) How many electrons must a sulfur atom gain to achieve an octet in its valence shell? (c) If an atom has the electron configuration $1s^22s^22p^3$, how many electrons must it gain to achieve an octet?

8.9 Write the electron configuration for phosphorus. Identify a valence electron in this configuration and a nonvalence

electron. From the standpoint of chemical reactivity, what is the important difference between them?

8.10 Write the electron configuration for the element scandium, Sc. How many valence electrons does this atom possess? What distinguishes these valence electrons from the other electrons in the atom?

8.11 Write the Lewis symbol for atoms of each of the following elements: (a) Al, (b) Br, (c) Ar, (d) Sr.

8.12 What is the Lewis symbol for each of the following atoms or ions: (a) K, (b) Si, (c) Mg^{2+}, (d) P^{3-}?

Ionic Bonding

8.13 Using Lewis symbols, diagram the reaction between magnesium and oxygen atoms to give the ionic substance MgO.

8.14 Use Lewis symbols to represent the reaction that occurs between Mg and Br atoms.

8.15 Predict the chemical formula of the ionic compound formed between the following pairs of elements: **(a)** Al and F, **(b)** K and S, **(c)** Y and O, **(d)** Mg and N.

8.16 Which ionic compound is expected to form from combination of the following pairs of elements: **(a)** barium and oxygen, **(b)** rubidium and iodine, **(c)** lithium and sulfur, **(d)** bromine and magnesium?

8.17 Write the electron configuration for each of the following ions, and determine which ones possess noble-gas configurations: **(a)** Sr^{2+}, **(b)** Ti^{2+}, **(c)** Se^{2-}, **(d)** Ni^{2+}, **(e)** Br^-, **(f)** Mn^{3+}.

8.18 Write electron configurations for the following ions, and determine which have noble-gas configurations: **(a)** Zn^{2+}, **(b)** Te^{2-}, **(c)** Se^{3+}, **(d)** Ru^{2+}, **(e)** Tl^+, **(f)** Au^+.

8.19 **(a)** Define the term *lattice energy*. **(b)** Which factors govern the magnitude of the lattice energy of an ionic compound?

8.20 **(a)** The lattice energies of NaF and MgO are given in Table 8.2. Account for the difference in these two quantities. **(b)** Account for the difference in the lattice energies of $MgCl_2$ and $SrCl_2$, which are also listed in that table.

8.21 The ionic substances KF, CaO, and ScN are isoelectronic (they have the same number of electrons). Examine the lattice energies for these substances in Table 8.2, and account for the trends you observe.

8.22 **(a)** Does the lattice energy of an ionic solid increase or decrease (i) as the charges of the ions increase, (ii) as the sizes of the ions increase? **(b)** Using a periodic table, arrange the following substances according to their expected lattice energies, listing them from lowest lattice energy to the highest: LiCl, NaBr, RbBr, MgO. Compare your list with the data in Table 8.2.

8.23 The lattice energies of KBr and CsCl are nearly equal (Table 8.2). What can you conclude from this observation?

8.24 Explain the following trends in lattice energy: **(a)** $MgO > MgCl_2$; **(b)** $NaCl > RbBr > CsBr$; **(c)** $BaO > KF$.

8.25 Energy is required to remove two electrons from Ca to form Ca^{2+} and is also required to add two electrons to O to form O^{2-}. Why, then, is CaO stable relative to the free elements?

8.26 List the individual steps used in constructing a Born–Haber cycle for the formation of $CaBr_2$ from the elements. Which of these steps would you expect to be exothermic?

[8.27] Use data from Appendix C, Figure 7.11, and Table 7.4 to calculate the lattice energy of RbCl. Is this value greater than or less than the lattice energy of NaCl? Explain.

[8.28] By using data from Appendix C, Figure 7.11, Table 7.5, and the value of the second ionization energy for Ca, 1145 kJ/mol, calculate the lattice energy of $CaCl_2$. Is this value greater than or less than the lattice energy of NaCl? Explain.

Covalent Bonding, Electronegativity, and Bond Polarity

8.29 **(a)** What is meant by the term *covalent bond*? **(b)** Give three examples of covalent bonding. **(c)** A substance XY, formed from two different elements, boils at −33°C. Is XY likely to be a covalent or an ionic substance? Explain.

8.30 Which of these elements is unlikely to form covalent bonds: S, H, K, Ar, Si? Explain your choices.

8.31 Using Lewis symbols and Lewis structures, diagram the formation of $SiCl_4$ from Si and Cl atoms.

8.32 Use Lewis symbols and Lewis structures to diagram the formation of PF_3 from P and F atoms.

8.33 **(a)** Construct a Lewis structure for O_2 in which each atom achieves an octet of electrons. **(b)** Explain why it is necessary to form a double bond in the Lewis structure. **(c)** The bond in O_2 is shorter than the O—O bond in compounds that contain an O—O single bond. Explain this observation.

8.34 The C—S bond lengths in carbon disulfide, CS_2, are shorter than would be expected for C—S single bonds. Use a Lewis structure to rationalize this observation.

8.35 **(a)** What is meant by the term electronegativity? **(b)** On the Pauling scale what is the range of electronegativity values for the elements? **(c)** Which element has the greatest electronegativity? **(d)** Which element has the smallest electronegativity?

8.36 **(a)** What is the trend in electronegativity going from left to right in a row of the periodic table? **(b)** How do electronegativity values generally vary going down a column in the periodic table? **(c)** How do periodic trends in electronegativity relate to those for ionization energy and electron affinity?

8.37 Using only the periodic table as your guide, select the most electronegative atom in each of the following sets: **(a)** As, Se, Br, I; **(b)** Al, B, C, Si; **(c)** Ge, As, P, Sn; **(d)** Li, Rb, Be, Sr.

8.38 By referring only to the periodic table, select **(a)** the most electronegative element in group 6A; **(b)** the least electronegative element in the group Al, Si, P; **(c)** the most electronegative element in the group Ga, P, Cl, Na; **(d)** the element in the group K, C, Zn, F, that is most likely to form an ionic compound with Ba.

8.39 Which of the following bonds are polar: **(a)** B—F, **(b)** Cl—Cl, **(c)** Se—O, **(d)** H—I? Which is the more electronegative atom in each polar bond?

8.40 Arrange the bonds in each of the following sets in order of increasing polarity: **(a)** C—F, O—F, Be—F; **(b)** O—Cl, S—Br, C—P; **(c)** C—S, B—F, N—O.

8.41 From the data in Table 8.3, calculate the effective charges on the H and F atoms of the HF molecule in units of the electronic charge *e*.

8.42 The iodine monobromide molecule, IBr, has a bond length of 2.49 Å and a dipole moment of 1.21 D. **(a)** Which atom of the molecule is expected to have a negative charge? Explain. **(b)** Calculate the effective charges on the I and Br atoms in IBr, in units of the electronic charge *e*.

8.43 Give the name or chemical formula, as appropriate, for each of the following substances, and in each case predict whether the bonding is better described by the ionic-bonding or covalent-bonding model: **(a)** manganese(IV) oxide, **(b)** phosphorus(III) sulfide, **(c)** cobalt(II) oxide, **(d)** Cu_2S, **(e)** ClF_3, **(f)** VF_5.

8.44 Give the name or chemical formula, as appropriate, for each of the following substances, and in each case predict whether the bonding is better described by the ionic-bonding or covalent-bonding model: **(a)** manganese(III) fluoride, **(b)** chromium(VI) oxide, **(c)** arsenic(V) bromide, **(d)** SF_4, **(e)** $MoCl_4$, **(f)** $ScCl_3$.

Lewis Structures; Resonance Structures

8.45 Draw Lewis structures for the following: **(a)** SiH_4, **(b)** CO, **(c)** SF_2, **(d)** H_2SO_4 (H is bonded to O), **(e)** ClO_2^-, **(f)** NH_2OH.

8.46 Write Lewis structures for the following: **(a)** H_2CO (both H atoms are bonded to C), **(b)** H_2O_2, **(c)** C_2F_6 (contains a C—C bond), **(d)** AsO_3^{3-}, **(e)** H_2SO_3 (H is bonded to O), **(f)** C_2H_2.

8.47 **(a)** When talking about atoms in a Lewis structure, what is meant by the term *formal charge*? **(b)** Does the formal charge of an atom represent the actual charge on that atom? Explain. **(c)** How does the formal charge of an atom in a Lewis structure differ from the oxidation number of the atom?

8.48 **(a)** Write a Lewis structure for the phosphorus trifluoride molecule, PF_3. Is the octet rule satisfied for all the atoms in your structure? **(b)** Determine the oxidation numbers of the P and F atoms. **(c)** Determine the formal charges of the P and F atoms. **(d)** Is the oxidation number for the P atom the same as its formal charge? Explain why or why not.

8.49 Write Lewis structures that obey the octet rule for each of the following, and assign oxidation numbers and formal charges to each atom: **(a)** NO^+, **(b)** $POCl_3$ (P is bonded to the three Cl atoms and to the O), **(c)** ClO_4^-, **(d)** $HClO_3$ (H is bonded to O).

8.50 For each of the following molecules or ions of sulfur and oxygen, write a single Lewis structure that obeys the octet rule, and calculate the oxidation numbers and formal charges on all the atoms: **(a)** SO_2, **(b)** SO_3, **(c)** SO_3^{2-}, **(d)** SO_4^{2-}.

8.51 **(a)** Write one or more appropriate Lewis structures for the nitrite ion, NO_2^-. **(b)** With what compound of oxygen is it isoelectronic? **(c)** What would you predict for the lengths of the bonds in this species relative to N—O single bonds?

8.52 Consider the nitryl cation, NO_2^+. **(a)** Write one or more appropriate Lewis structures for this species. **(b)** Are resonance structures needed to describe the structure? **(c)** With what familiar species is it isoelectronic?

8.53 Predict the ordering of the C—O bond lengths in CO, CO_2, and CO_3^{2-}.

8.54 Based on Lewis structures, predict the ordering of N—O bond lengths in NO^+, NO_2^-, and NO_3^-.

8.55 **(a)** Use the concept of resonance to explain why all six C—C bonds in benzene are equal in length. **(b)** The C—C bond lengths in benzene are shorter than C—C single bonds but longer than C=C double bonds. Use the resonance model to explain this observation.

8.56 Mothballs are composed of naphthalene, $C_{10}H_8$, a molecule of which consists of two six-membered rings of carbon fused along an edge, as shown in this incomplete Lewis structure:

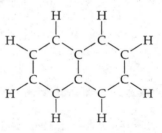

(a) Write two complete Lewis structures for naphthalene. **(b)** The observed C—C bond lengths in the molecule are intermediate between C—C single and C=C double bonds. Explain. **(c)** Represent the resonance in naphthalene in a way analogous to that used to represent it in benzene.

Exceptions to the Octet Rule

8.57 **(a)** State the octet rule. **(b)** Does the octet rule apply to ionic as well as to covalent compounds? Explain, using examples as appropriate.

8.58 Considering the representative nonmetals, what is the relationship between the group number for an element (carbon, for example, belongs to group 14; see the periodic table on the inside front cover) and the number of single covalent bonds that element needs to form to conform to the octet rule?

8.59 What is the most common exception to the octet rule? Give two examples.

8.60 For elements in the third row of the periodic table and beyond, the octet rule is often not obeyed. What factors are usually cited to explain this fact?

8.61 Draw the Lewis structures for each of the following ions or molecules. Identify those that do not obey the octet rule, and explain why they do not. **(a)** SO_3^{2-}, **(b)** AlH_3, **(c)** N_3^-, **(d)** CH_2Cl_2, **(e)** SbF_5.

8.62 Draw the Lewis structures for each of the following molecules or ions. Which do not obey the octet rule? **(a)** CO_2, **(b)** IO_3^-, **(c)** BH_3, **(d)** BF_4^-, **(e)** XeF_2.

8.63 In the vapor phase, $BeCl_2$ exists as a discrete molecule. **(a)** Draw the Lewis structure of this molecule, using only single bonds. Does this Lewis structure satisfy the octet rule? **(b)** What other resonance forms are possible that satisfy the octet rule? **(c)** Using formal charges, select the resonance form from among all the Lewis structures that is most important in describing $BeCl_2$.

8.64 **(a)** Describe the molecule chlorine dioxide, ClO_2, using three possible resonance structures. **(b)** Do any of these resonance structures satisfy the octet rule for every atom in the molecule? Why or why not? **(c)** Using formal charges, select the resonance structure(s) that is (are) most important.

Bond Enthalpies

8.65 Using the bond enthalpies tabulated in Table 8.4, estimate ΔH for each of the following gas-phase reactions:

(a)

$$H_2C=CH_2 \ + \ H{-}O{-}O{-}H \longrightarrow$$

$$H{-}O{-}\underset{\underset{H}{|}}{\overset{\overset{H}{|}}{C}}{-}\underset{\underset{H}{|}}{\overset{\overset{H}{|}}{C}}{-}O{-}H$$

(b)

$$H_2C=CH_2 \ + \ H{-}C\equiv N \longrightarrow$$

$$H{-}\underset{\underset{H}{|}}{\overset{\overset{H}{|}}{C}}{-}\underset{\underset{H}{|}}{\overset{\overset{H}{|}}{C}}{-}C\equiv N$$

(c) $2\,Cl{-}\underset{\underset{Cl}{|}}{N}{-}Cl \longrightarrow N\equiv N + 3\,Cl{-}Cl$

8.66 Using bond enthalpies (Table 8.4), estimate ΔH for the following gas-phase reactions:

(a) $Br{-}\underset{\underset{Br}{|}}{\overset{\overset{Br}{|}}{C}}{-}H + Cl{-}Cl \longrightarrow Br{-}\underset{\underset{Br}{|}}{\overset{\overset{Br}{|}}{C}}{-}Cl + H{-}Cl$

(b) $H{-}S{-}\underset{\underset{H}{|}}{\overset{\overset{H}{|}}{C}}{-}\underset{\underset{H}{|}}{\overset{\overset{H}{|}}{C}}{-}S{-}H + 2\,H{-}Br \longrightarrow$

$$Br{-}\underset{\underset{H}{|}}{\overset{\overset{H}{|}}{C}}{-}\underset{\underset{H}{|}}{\overset{\overset{H}{|}}{C}}{-}Br + 2\,H{-}S{-}H$$

(c) $H{-}\underset{\underset{H}{|}}{N}{-}\underset{\underset{H}{|}}{N}{-}H + Cl{-}Cl \longrightarrow 2\,H{-}\underset{\underset{H}{|}}{N}{-}Cl$

8.67 Using bond enthalpies (Table 8.4), estimate ΔH for each of the following reactions:

(a) $2\,CH_4(g) + O_2(g) \longrightarrow 2\,CH_3OH(g)$
(b) $H_2(g) + Br_2(g) \longrightarrow 2\,HBr(g)$
(c) $2\,H_2O_2(g) \longrightarrow 2\,H_2O(g) + O_2(g)$

[8.68] Use bond enthalpies (Table 8.4) to estimate the enthalpy change for each of the following reactions:
(a) $3\,H_2C=CH_2(g) \longrightarrow C_6H_{12}(g)$ (the six carbon atoms from a six-membered ring with two hydrogen atoms on each carbon atom)
(b) $SiClH_3(g) + 3\,Cl_2(g) \longrightarrow SiCl_4(g) + 3\,HCl(g)$
(c) $8\,H_2S(g) \longrightarrow 8\,H_2(g) + S_8(s)$
(See Figure 7.28. Strictly speaking, the average bond enthalpy values apply to species in the gas phase. The heat of formation of $S_8(g)$ is 102.3 kJ/mol. Apply the needed correction in order to estimate the enthalpy change for the reaction as shown.)

8.69 Ammonia is produced directly from nitrogen and hydrogen by using the Haber process. The chemical reaction is

$$N_2(g) + 3\,H_2(g) \longrightarrow 2\,NH_3(g)$$

(a) Use bond enthalpies (Table 8.4) to estimate the enthalpy change for the reaction, and tell whether this reaction is exothermic or endothermic. **(b)** Compare the enthalpy change you calculate in (a) to the true enthalpy change as obtained using ΔH_f° values.

8.70 **(a)** Use bond enthalpies to estimate the enthalpy change for the reaction of hydrogen with ethene:

$$H_2(g) + C_2H_4(g) \longrightarrow C_2H_6(g)$$

(b) Calculate the standard enthalpy change for this reaction, using heats of formation. Why does this value differ from that calculated in (a)?

8.71 Given the following bond-dissociation energies, calculate the average bond enthalpy for the Ti—Cl bond.

	ΔH(kJ/mol)
$TiCl_4(g) \longrightarrow TiCl_3(g) + Cl(g)$	335
$TiCl_3(g) \longrightarrow TiCl_2(g) + Cl(g)$	423
$TiCl_2(g) \longrightarrow TiCl(g) + Cl(g)$	444
$TiCl(g) \longrightarrow Ti(g) + Cl(g)$	519

[8.72] **(a)** Using average bond enthalpies, predict which of the following reactions will be most exothermic:
(i) $C(g) + 2\,F_2(g) \longrightarrow CF_4(g)$
(ii) $CO(g) + 3\,F_2 \longrightarrow CF_4(g) + OF_2(g)$
(iii) $CO_2(g) + 4\,F_2 \longrightarrow CF_4(g) + 2\,OF_2(g)$
(b) Explain the trend, if any, that exists between reaction exothermicity and the extent to which the carbon atom is bonded to oxygen.

Additional Exercises

8.73 How many elements in the periodic table are represented by a Lewis symbol with a single dot? Are all these elements in the same group? Explain.

8.74 **(a)** Explain the following trend in lattice energy: BeH_2, 3205 kJ/mol; MgH_2, 2791 kJ/mol; CaH_2, 2410 kJ/mol; SrH_2, 2250 kJ/mol; BaH_2, 2121 kJ/mol. **(b)** The lattice energy of ZnH_2 is 2870 kJ/mol. Based on the data given in part (a), the radius of the Zn^{2+} ion is expected to be closest to that of which group 2A element?

8.75 Based on data in Table 8.2, estimate (within 30 kJ/mol) the lattice energy for **(a)** LiBr, **(b)** CsBr, **(c)** $CaCl_2$.

[8.76] From the ionic radii given in Figure 7.7, calculate the potential energy of a Ca^{2+} and O^{2-} ion pair that are just touching (the magnitude of the electronic charge is given on the back inside cover). Calculate the energy of a mole of such pairs. How does this value compare with the lattice energy of CaO (Table 8.2)? Explain the difference.

[8.77] From Equation 8.4 and the ionic radii given in Figure 7.7, calculate the potential energy of the following pairs of ions. Assume that the ions are separated by a distance equal to the sum of their ionic radii: (a) Na^+, Br^-; (b) Rb^+, Br^-; (c) Sr^{2+}, S^{2-}.

8.78 (a) How does a polar molecule differ from a nonpolar one? (b) Atoms X and Y have different electronegativities. Will the diatomic molecule X—Y necessarily be polar? Explain. (c) What factors affect the size of the dipole moment of a diatomic molecule?

8.79 Which of the following molecules or ions contain polar bonds: (a) P_4, (b) H_2S, (c) NO_2^-, (d) S_2^{2-}?

8.80 For the following collection of nonmetallic elements, O, P, Te, I, B, (a) which two would form the most polar single bond? (b) Which two would form the longest single bond? (c) Which two would be likely to form a compound of formula XY_2? (d) Which combinations of elements would likely yield a compound of empirical formula X_2Y_3? In each case explain your answer.

[8.81] (a) Triazine, $C_3H_3N_3$, is like benzene except that in triazine every other C—H group is replaced by a nitrogen atom. Draw the Lewis structure(s) for the triazine molecule. (b) Estimate the carbon–nitrogen bond distances in the ring.

[8.82] Using the electronegativities of Br and Cl, estimate the partial charges on the atoms in the Br—Cl molecule. Using these partial charges and the atomic radii given in Figure 7.7, estimate the dipole moment of the molecule. The measured dipole moment is 0.57 D.

8.83 Although I_3^- is known, F_3^- is not. Using Lewis structures, explain why F_3^- does not form.

8.84 Calculate the formal charge on the indicated atom in each of the following molecules or ions: (a) the central oxygen atom in O_3, (b) phosphorus in PF_6^-, (c) nitrogen in NO_2, (d) iodine in ICl_3, (e) chlorine in $HClO_4$ (hydrogen is bonded to O).

8.85 (a) Determine the formal charge on the chlorine atom in the hypochlorite ion, ClO^-, and the perchlorate ion, ClO_4^-, if the Cl atom has an octet. (b) What are the oxidation numbers of chlorine in ClO^- and in ClO_4^-? (c) What are the essential differences in the definitions of formal charge and oxidation number that lead to the differences in your answers to parts (a) and (b)?

8.86 The following three Lewis structures can be drawn for N_2O:

$$:N\equiv N-\ddot{O}: \longleftrightarrow :\ddot{N}-N\equiv O: \longleftrightarrow :\ddot{N}=N=\ddot{O}:$$

(a) Using formal charges, which of these three resonance forms is likely to be the most important? (b) The N—N bond length in N_2O is 1.12 Å, slightly longer than a typical $N\equiv N$ bond, and the N—O bond length is 1.19 Å, slightly shorter than a typical $N=O$ bond. (See Table 8.5.) Rationalize these observations in terms of the resonance structures shown previously and your conclusion for (a).

8.87 An important reaction for the conversion of natural gas to other useful hydrocarbons is the conversion of methane to ethane.

$$2\,CH_4(g) \longrightarrow C_2H_6(g) + H_2(g)$$

In practice, this reaction is carried out in the presence of oxygen, which converts the hydrogen produced to water.

$$2\,CH_4(g) + \tfrac{1}{2}O_2(g) \longrightarrow C_2H_6(g) + H_2O(g)$$

Use bond enthalpies (Table 8.4) to estimate ΔH for these two reactions. Why is the conversion of methane to ethane more favorable when oxygen is used?

8.88 Two compounds are isomers if they have the same chemical formula but a different arrangement of atoms. Use bond enthalpies (Table 8.4) to estimate ΔH for each of the following gas-phase isomerization reactions, and indicate which isomer has the lower enthalpy:

(a)   Ethanol   Dimethyl ether

(b)   Ethylene oxide   Acetaldehyde

(c)   Cyclopentene   Pentadiene

(d)   Methyl isocyanide   Acetonitrile

[8.89] With reference to the "Chemistry at Work" box on explosives, (a) use bond enthalpies to estimate the enthalpy change for the explosion of 1.00 g of nitroglycerin. (b) Write a balanced equation for the decomposition of TNT. Assume that, upon explosion, TNT decomposes into $N_2(g)$, $CO_2(g)$, $H_2O(g)$, and $C(s)$.

[8.90] The "plastic" explosive C-4, often used in action movies, contains the molecule *cyclotrimethylenetrinitramine*, which is often called RDX (for Royal Demolition eXplosive):

Cyclotrimethylenetrinitramine (RDX)

(a) Complete the Lewis structure for the molecule by adding unshared electron pairs where they are needed. (b) Does the Lewis structure you drew in part (a) have any resonance structures? If so, how many? (c) The molecule causes an explosion by decomposing into $CO(g)$, $N_2(g)$, and $H_2O(g)$. Write a balanced equation for the decomposition reaction. (d) With reference to Table 8.4, which is the weakest type of bond in the molecule? (e) Use average bond enthalpies to estimate the enthalpy change when 5.0 g of RDX decomposes.

[8.91] Consider this reaction involving the hypothetical molecule A=A, which contains a double bond:

$$\begin{array}{ccc} \text{A} & \text{A} & \text{A---A} \\ \| & + \| & \longrightarrow \quad | \quad | \\ \text{A} & \text{A} & \text{A---A} \end{array}$$

(a) In terms of $D(A{=}A)$ and $D(A{-}A)$, write a general expression for the enthalpy change for this reaction. (b) What must be the relationship between $D(A{=}A)$ and $D(A{-}A)$ for the reaction to be exothermic? (c) If the reaction is exothermic, what can you say about the strength of the second bond between the A atoms in A=A relative to the strength of the first bond?

[8.92] The bond lengths of carbon–carbon, carbon–nitrogen, carbon–oxygen, and nitrogen–nitrogen single, double, and triple bonds are listed in Table 8.5. Plot bond enthalpy (Table 8.4) versus bond length for these bonds. What do you conclude about the relationship between bond length and bond enthalpy? What do you conclude about the relative strengths of C—C, C—N, C—O, and N—N bonds?

[8.93] Use the data in Table 8.5 and the following data: S—S distance in $S_8 = 2.05$ Å; S—O distance in $SO_2 = 1.43$ Å, to answer the following questions: (a) Predict the bond length in an S—N single bond. (b) Predict the bond length in an S—O single bond. (c) Why is the S—O bond length in SO_2 considerably shorter than your predicted value for the S—O single bond? (d) When elemental sulfur, S_8, is carefully oxidized, a compound S_8O is formed, in which one of the sulfur atoms in the S_8 ring is bonded to an oxygen atom. The S—O bond length in this compound is 1.48 Å. In light of this information, write Lewis structures that can account for the observed S—O bond length. Does the sulfur bearing the oxygen in this compound obey the octet rule?

Integrative Exercises

8.94 The Ti^{2+} ion is isoelectronic with the Ca atom. (a) Are there any differences in the electron configurations of Ti^{2+} and Ca? (b) With reference to Figure 6.24, comment on the changes in the ordering of the $4s$ and $3d$ subshells in Ca and Ti^{2+}. (c) Will Ca and Ti^{2+} have the same number of unpaired electrons? Explain.

[8.95] (a) Write the chemical equations that are used in calculating the lattice energy of $SrCl_2(s)$ via a Born–Haber cycle. (b) The second ionization energy of $Sr(g)$ is 1064 kJ/mol. Use this fact along with data in Appendix C, Figure 7.11, Figure 7.12, and Table 8.2 to calculate ΔH_f° for $SrCl_2(s)$.

[8.96] The electron affinity of oxygen is −141 kJ/mol, corresponding to the reaction

$$O(g) + e^- \longrightarrow O^-(g)$$

The lattice energy of $K_2O(s)$ is 2238 kJ/mol. Use these data along with data in Appendix C and Figure 7.11 to calculate the "second electron affinity" of oxygen, corresponding to the reaction

$$O^-(g) + e^- \longrightarrow O^{2-}(g)$$

8.97 The reaction of indium, In, with sulfur leads to three binary compounds, which we will assume to be purely ionic. The three compounds have the following properties:

Compound	Mass % In	Melting Point (°C)
A	87.7	653
B	78.2	692
C	70.5	1050

(a) Determine the empirical formulas of compounds A, B, and C. (b) Give the oxidation state of In in each of the three compounds. (c) Write the electron configuration for the In ion in each compound. Do any of these

configurations correspond to a noble-gas configuration? (d) In which compound is the ionic radius of In expected to be smallest? Explain. (e) The melting point of ionic compounds often correlates with the lattice energy. Explain the trends in the melting points of compounds A, B, and C in these terms.

[8.98] One scale for electronegativity is based on the concept that the electronegativity of any atom is proportional to the ionization energy of the atom minus its electron affinity: electronegativity = $k(IE - EA)$, where k is a proportionality constant. (a) How does this definition explain why the electronegativity of F is greater than that of Cl even though Cl has the greater electron affinity? (b) Why are both ionization energy and electron affinity relevant to the notion of electronegativity? (c) By using data in Chapter 7, determine the value of k that would lead to an electronegativity of 4.0 for F under this definition. (d) Use your result from part (c) to determine the electronegativities of Cl and O using this scale. Do these values follow the trend shown in Figure 8.6?

8.99 The compound chloral hydrate, known in detective stories as knockout drops, is composed of 14.52% C, 1.83% H, 64.30% Cl, and 19.35% O by mass and has a molar mass of 165.4 g/mol. (a) What is the empirical formula of this substance? (b) What is the molecular formula of this substance? (c) Draw the Lewis structure of the molecule, assuming that the Cl atoms bond to a single C atom and that there is a C—C bond and two C—O bonds in the compound.

8.100 Barium azide is 62.04% Ba and 37.96% N. Each azide ion has a net charge of 1−. (a) Determine the chemical formula of the azide ion. (b) Write three resonance structures for the azide ion. (c) Which structure is most important? (d) Predict the bond lengths in the ion.

[8.101] Acetylene (C_2H_2) and nitrogen (N_2) both contain a triple bond, but they differ greatly in their chemical properties. (a) Write the Lewis structures for the two substances. (b) By referring to the index, look up the chemical properties of acetylene and nitrogen and compare their reactivities. (c) Write balanced chemical equations for the complete oxidation of N_2 to form $N_2O_5(g)$ and of acetylene to form $CO_2(g)$ and $H_2O(g)$. (d) Calculate the enthalpy of oxidation per mole of N_2 and C_2H_2 (the enthalpy of formation of $N_2O_5(g)$ is 11.30 kJ/mol). How do these comparative values relate to your response to part (b)? Both N_2 and C_2H_2 possess triple bonds with quite high bond enthalpies (Table 8.4). What aspect of chemical bonding in these molecules or in the oxidation products seems to account for the difference in chemical reactivities?

[8.102] Under special conditions, sulfur reacts with anhydrous liquid ammonia to form a binary compound of sulfur and nitrogen. The compound is found to consist of 69.6% S and 30.4% N. Measurements of its molecular mass yield a value of 184.3 g mol^{-1}. The compound occasionally detonates on being struck or when heated rapidly. The sulfur and nitrogen atoms of the molecule are joined in a ring. All the bonds in the ring are of the same length. (a) Calculate the empirical and molecular formulas for the substance. (b) Write Lewis structures for the molecule, based on the information you are given. [Hint: You should find a relatively small number of dominant Lewis structures.] (c) Predict the bond distances between the atoms in the ring. (Note: The S—S distance in the S_8 ring is 2.05Å.) (d) The enthalpy of formation of the compound is estimated to be 480 kJ mol^{-1}. ΔH_f° of S(g) is 222.8 kJ mol^{-1}. Estimate the average bond enthalpy in the compound.

[8.103] A common form of elemental phosphorus is the tetrahedral P_4 molecule:

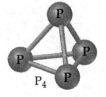

P_4

At room temperature phosphorus is a solid. (a) Do you think there are any unshared pairs of electrons in the P_4 molecule? (b) How many P—P bonds are there in the molecule? (c) Use data in Appendix C to determine the enthalpy of atomization of $P_4(g)$. (d) Based on these results, what value would you give for $D(P—P)$? (e) Is the P—P bond stronger or weaker than an N—N single bond?

8.104 Use bond enthalpies (Table 8.4), electron affinities (Figure 7.12), and the ionization energy of hydrogen (1312 kJ/mol) to estimate ΔH for the following gas-phase ionization reactions:
(a) $HF(g) \longrightarrow H^+(g) + F^-(g)$
(b) $HCl(g) \longrightarrow H^+(g) + Cl^-(g)$
(c) $HBr(g) \longrightarrow H^+(g) + Br^-(g)$

[8.105] Consider benzene (C_6H_6) in the gas phase. (a) Write the reaction for breaking all the bonds in $C_6H_6(g)$, and use data in Appendix C to determine the enthalpy change for this reaction. (b) Write a reaction that corresponds to breaking all the carbon–carbon bonds in $C_6H_6(g)$. (c) By combining your answers to parts (a) and (b) and using the average bond enthalpy for C—H from Table 8.4, calculate the average bond enthalpy for the carbon-carbon bonds in $C_6H_6(g)$. (d) Comment on your answer from part (c) as compared to the values for C—C single bonds and C=C double bonds in Table 8.4.

8.106 Average bond enthalpies are generally defined for gas-phase molecules. Many substances are liquids in their standard state. ∞∞ (Section 5.7) By using appropriate thermochemical data from Appendix C, calculate average bond enthalpies in the liquid state for the following bonds, and compare these values to the gas-phase values given in Table 8.4: (a) Br—Br, from $Br_2(l)$; (b) C—Cl, from $CCl_4(l)$; (c) O—O, from $H_2O_2(l)$ (assume that the O—H bond enthalpy is the same as in the gas phase). (d) What can you conclude about the process of breaking bonds in the liquid as compared to the gas phase? Explain the difference in the ΔH values between the two phases.

eMEDIA EXERCISES

These exercises make use of the interactive objects available online in OneKey or the Companion Website, and on your Accelerator CD. Access to these resources comes in your MediaPak.

8.107 The principle that oppositely charged particles attract one another and like charges repel one another is summarized in Coulomb's law. Try some experiments using the **Coulomb's Law** activity (8.2) to get a feel for the magnitudes of attractive and repulsive forces between charged particles. **(a)** Between which particles is the attractive force the stronger: a particle with a charge of -2 at a distance of 3 Å from a particle with a charge of $+1$; or a particle with a charge of -1 at a distance of 2 Å from a particle with a charge of $+1$? **(b)** Consider a particle with a charge of $+3$ at a distance of 5 Å from a particle with a charge of -3. If there were another negatively charged particle in between the two, what would you expect to happen to the magnitude of the attractive force between them?

8.108 In Exercise 8.22(a) you assessed the effects of *ionic size* and *ionic charge* on lattice energy separately. When size and charge are *both* significantly different, a more quantitative approach is required to compare lattice energies. Use the ionic radii in Figure 7.7 and the **Coulomb's Law** activity (8.2) to determine which would have the greater lattice energy: CaSe or LiF.

8.109 Covalent bonding can occur when atoms are close enough to share electrons. The **H₂ Bond Formation** animation (8.3) describes this process for the formation of a single bond between two hydrogen atoms. Bonds can also form this way between nitrogen atoms. Unlike hydrogen atoms, though, nitrogen atoms can form more than one bond. $N-N$, $N=N$, and $N\equiv N$ bonds are all possible. Section 8.3 explained that bond length decreases with increasing number of shared electron pairs between atoms. Thus, the $N\equiv N$ bond is the shortest of the three. Explain why this is so in terms of the information provided in the movie.

8.110 The **Molecular Polarity** activity (8.4) allows you to determine the polarity of bonds and of molecules. **(a)** How is it possible for a molecule that contains polar bonds to be nonpolar? **(b)** Is it possible for a molecule containing only nonpolar bonds to be polar? Explain.

8.111 One of the elements that can violate the octet rule is boron. An example of a compound in which boron has fewer than eight electrons around it is BF_3. The **BF₃** 3-D model (8.7) illustrates the molecule's most important resonance structure. **(a)** What characteristics of boron allow it to exist with less than a full octet? **(b)** Boron *can* obey the octet rule in substances such as the adduct displayed in **BF₃—NH₃** 3-D model (8.7). Are the formal charges on boron and nitrogen *completely* consistent with the electronegativities of the two elements? (Is it possible to draw a resonance structure in which you think they are *more* consistent?)

Science Fundamentals Second Edition

14.1 Factors that Affect Reaction Rates

14.2 Reaction Rates

14.3 Concentration and Rate

14.4 The Change of Concentration with Time

14.5 Temperature and Rate

14.6 Reaction Mechanisms

14.7 Catalysis

WHAT'S AHEAD

- There are four experimental variables that affect reaction rates: concentration, physical states of reactants, temperature, and catalysts. These factors can be understood in terms of the collisions among reactant molecules that lead to reaction. *(Section 14.1)*

- We consider how to express *reaction rates* and how the rates of disappearance of reactants and the rates of appearance of products are related to the stoichiometry of the reaction. *(Section 14.2)*

- We then examine how the effect of concentration on rate is expressed quantitatively by *rate laws* and how rate laws can be determined experimentally. *(Section 14.3)*

- Rate equations can be written to express how concentrations change with time. We will look at two simple kinds of such rate equations. *(Section 14.4)*

- We next consider the effect of temperature on rate and the fact that reactions require a minimum input of energy called the *activation energy* in order to occur. *(Section 14.5)*

- We then examine the *mechanisms* of reactions, the step-by-step molecular pathways leading from reactants to products. *(Section 14.6)*

- The chapter ends with a discussion of how *catalysts* speed reaction rates, including a discussion of biological catalysts, called *enzymes*. *(Section 14.7)*

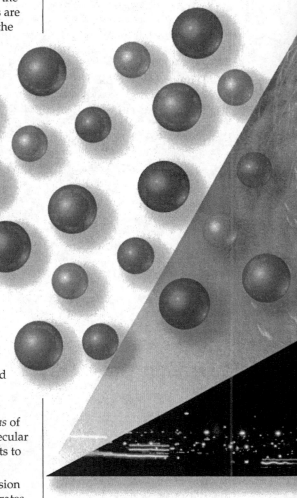

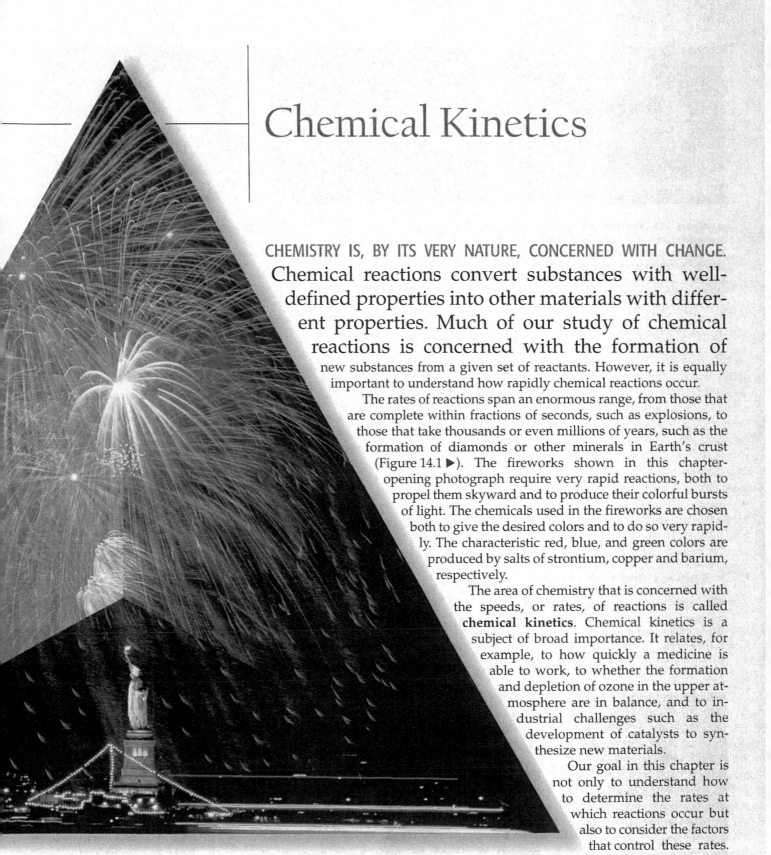

Chemical Kinetics

CHEMISTRY IS, BY ITS VERY NATURE, CONCERNED WITH CHANGE. Chemical reactions convert substances with well-defined properties into other materials with different properties. Much of our study of chemical reactions is concerned with the formation of new substances from a given set of reactants. However, it is equally important to understand how rapidly chemical reactions occur.

The rates of reactions span an enormous range, from those that are complete within fractions of seconds, such as explosions, to those that take thousands or even millions of years, such as the formation of diamonds or other minerals in Earth's crust (Figure 14.1 ▶). The fireworks shown in this chapter-opening photograph require very rapid reactions, both to propel them skyward and to produce their colorful bursts of light. The chemicals used in the fireworks are chosen both to give the desired colors and to do so very rapidly. The characteristic red, blue, and green colors are produced by salts of strontium, copper and barium, respectively.

The area of chemistry that is concerned with the speeds, or rates, of reactions is called **chemical kinetics**. Chemical kinetics is a subject of broad importance. It relates, for example, to how quickly a medicine is able to work, to whether the formation and depletion of ozone in the upper atmosphere are in balance, and to industrial challenges such as the development of catalysts to synthesize new materials.

Our goal in this chapter is not only to understand how to determine the rates at which reactions occur but also to consider the factors that control these rates.

FIREWORKS RELY ON RAPID CHEMICAL reactions both to propel them skyward and to produce their colorful bursts of light.

▲ **Figure 14.1 Reaction rates.** The rates of chemical reactions span a range of time scales. For example, explosions are rapid, occurring in seconds or fractions of seconds; corrosion can take years; and the weathering of rocks takes place over thousands or even millions of years.

For example, what factors determine how rapidly food spoils? How does one design a fast-setting material for dental fillings? What determines the rate at which steel rusts? What controls the rate at which fuel burns in an automobile engine? Although we won't address these specific questions directly, we will see that the rates of all chemical reactions are subject to the same basic principles.

14.1 | Factors that Affect Reaction Rates

Before we examine the quantitative aspects of chemical kinetics, such as how rates are measured, let's examine the key factors that influence the rates of reactions. Because reactions involve the breaking and forming of bonds, their speeds depend on the nature of the reactants themselves. There are, however, four factors that allow us to change the rates at which particular reactions occur:

1. *The physical state of the reactants.* Reactants must come together in order to react. The more readily molecules collide with each other, the more rapidly they react. Most of the reactions we consider are homogeneous, involving either gases or liquid solutions. When reactants are in different phases, such as when one is a gas and another a solid, the reaction is limited to their area of contact. Thus, reactions that involve solids tend to proceed faster if the surface area of the solid is increased. For example, a medicine in the form of a tablet will dissolve in the stomach and enter the bloodstream more slowly than the same medicine in the form of a fine powder.

2. *The concentrations of the reactants.* Most chemical reactions proceed faster if the concentration of one or more of the reactants is increased. For example, steel wool burns with difficulty in air, which contains 20% O_2, but bursts into a brilliant white flame in pure oxygen (Figure 14.2 ◄). As concentration increases, the frequency with which the reactant molecules collide increases, leading to increased rates.

▼ **Figure 14.2 Effect of concentration on rate.** (a) When heated in air, steel wool glows red-hot but oxidizes slowly. (b) When the red-hot steel wool is placed in an atmosphere of pure oxygen, it burns vigorously, forming Fe_2O_3 at a much faster rate. The difference in behavior is due to the different concentrations of O_2 in the two environments.

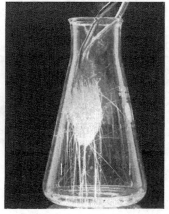

(a)   (b)

3. *The temperature at which the reaction occurs.* The rates of chemical reactions increase as temperature is increased. It is for this reason that we refrigerate perishable foods such as milk. The bacterial reactions that lead to the spoiling of milk proceed much more rapidly at room temperature than they do at the lower temperature of a refrigerator. Increasing temperature increases the kinetic energies of molecules. ⚮ (Section 10.7) As molecules move more rapidly, they collide more frequently and also with higher energy, leading to increased reaction rates.

4. *The presence of a catalyst.* Catalysts are agents that increase reaction rates without being used up. They affect the kinds of collisions (the mechanism) that lead to reaction. Catalysts play a crucial role in our lives. The physiology of most living species depends on *enzymes*, protein molecules that act as catalysts, increasing the rates of selected biochemical reactions.

On a molecular level, reaction rates depend on the frequency of collisions between molecules. The greater the frequency of collisions, the greater the rate of reaction. In order for a collision to lead to reaction, however, it must occur with sufficient energy to stretch bonds to a critical length and with suitable orientation for new bonds to form in the proper locations. We will consider these factors as we proceed through this chapter.

GIVE IT SOME THOUGHT

How does increasing the partial pressures of the reactive components of a gaseous mixture affect the rate at which the components react with one another?

14.2 | Reaction Rates

The *speed* of an event is defined as the *change* that occurs in a given interval of *time*: Whenever we talk about speed, we necessarily bring in the notion of time. For example, the speed of a car is expressed as the change in the car's position over a certain period of time. The units of this speed are usually miles per hour (mi/hr)—that is, the quantity that is changing (position, measured in miles) divided by a time interval (hours).

Similarly, the speed of a chemical reaction—its **reaction rate**—is the change in the concentration of reactants or products per unit time. Thus, the units for reaction rate are usually molarity per second (M/s)—that is, the change in concentration (measured in molarity) divided by a time interval (seconds).

Let's consider a simple hypothetical reaction, A $\longrightarrow$ B, depicted in Figure 14.3 ▼. Each red sphere represents 0.01 mol of A, and each blue sphere represents 0.01 mol of B. Let's assume that the container has a volume of 1.00 L. At the beginning of the reaction there is 1.00 mol A, so the concentration is 1.00 mol/L = 1.00 M. After 20 s the concentration of A has fallen to 0.54 M, whereas that of B has risen to 0.46 M. The sum of the concentrations is still 1.00 M because 1 mol of B is produced for each mole of A that reacts. After 40 s the concentration of A is 0.30 M and that of B is 0.70 M.

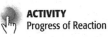
ACTIVITY
Progress of Reaction

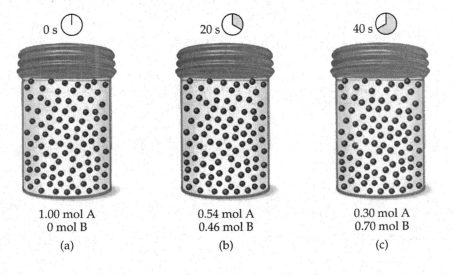

1.00 mol A
0 mol B
(a)

0.54 mol A
0.46 mol B
(b)

0.30 mol A
0.70 mol B
(c)

◀ **Figure 14.3 Progress of a hypothetical reaction A → B.** Each red sphere represents 0.01 mol A, each blue sphere represents 0.01 mol B, and the vessel has a volume of 1.00 L. (a) At time zero the vessel contains 1.00 mol A (100 red spheres) and 0 mol B (no blue spheres). (b) After 20 s the vessel contains 0.54 mol A and 0.46 mol B. (c) After 40 s the vessel contains 0.30 mol A and 0.70 mol B.

The rate of this reaction can be expressed either as the rate of disappearance of reactant A or as the rate of appearance of product B. The *average* rate of appearance of B over a particular time interval is given by the change in concentration of B divided by the change in time:

$$\text{Average rate of appearance of B} = \frac{\text{change in concentration of B}}{\text{change in time}}$$

$$= \frac{[B] \text{ at } t_2 - [B] \text{ at } t_1}{t_2 - t_1} = \frac{\Delta[B]}{\Delta t} \quad [14.1]$$

We use brackets around a chemical formula, as in [B], to indicate the concentration of the substance in molarity. The Greek letter delta, Δ, is read "change in," and it is always equal to the final quantity minus the initial quantity. ∞ (Section 5.2) The average rate of appearance of B over the 20-s interval from the beginning of the reaction ($t_1 = 0$ s to $t_2 = 20$ s) is given by

$$\text{Average rate} = \frac{0.46\ M - 0.00\ M}{20\ s - 0\ s} = 2.3 \times 10^{-2}\ M/s$$

We could equally well express the rate of the reaction with respect to the change of concentration of the reactant, A. In this case we would be describing the rate of disappearance of A, which we express as

$$\text{Average rate of disappearance of A} = -\frac{\Delta[A]}{\Delta t} \quad [14.2]$$

Notice the minus sign in this equation. By convention, *rates are always expressed as positive quantities*. Because [A] is decreasing with time, $\Delta[A]$ is a negative number. We use the negative sign to convert the negative $\Delta[A]$ to a positive rate. Because one molecule of A is consumed for every molecule of B that forms, the average rate of disappearance of A equals the average rate of appearance of B, as the following calculation shows:

$$\text{Average rate} = -\frac{\Delta[A]}{\Delta t} = -\frac{0.54\ M - 1.00\ M}{20\ s - 0\ s} = 2.3 \times 10^{-2}\ M/s$$

■ SAMPLE EXERCISE 14.1 | Calculating an Average Rate of Reaction

From the data given in the caption of Figure 14.3, calculate the average rate at which A disappears over the time interval from 20 s to 40 s.

Solution
Analyze: We are given the concentration of A at 20 s (0.54 M) and at 40 s (0.30 M) and asked to calculate the average rate of reaction over this time interval.
Plan: The average rate is given by the change in concentration, $\Delta[A]$, divided by the corresponding change in time, Δt. Because A is a reactant, a minus sign is used in the calculation to make the rate a positive quantity.
Solve:

$$\text{Average rate} = -\frac{\Delta[A]}{\Delta t} = -\frac{0.30\ M - 0.54\ M}{40\ s - 20\ s} = 1.2 \times 10^{-2}\ M/s$$

■ PRACTICE EXERCISE

For the reaction pictured in Figure 14.3, calculate the average rate of appearance of B over the time interval from 0 to 40 s. (The necessary data are given in the figure caption.)
Answer: $1.8 \times 10^{-2}\ M/s$

Time, t(s)	[C_4H_9Cl] (M)	Average Rate (M/s)
0.0	0.1000	
50.0	0.0905	1.9×10^{-4}
100.0	0.0820	1.7×10^{-4}
150.0	0.0741	1.6×10^{-4}
200.0	0.0671	1.4×10^{-4}
300.0	0.0549	1.22×10^{-4}
400.0	0.0448	1.01×10^{-4}
500.0	0.0368	0.80×10^{-4}
800.0	0.0200	0.560×10^{-4}
10,000	0	

TABLE 14.1 Rate Data for Reaction of C_4H_9Cl with Water

Change of Rate with Time

Now, let's consider an actual chemical reaction, one that occurs when butyl chloride (C_4H_9Cl) is placed in water. The products formed are butyl alcohol (C_4H_9OH) and hydrochloric acid:

$$C_4H_9Cl(aq) + H_2O(l) \longrightarrow C_4H_9OH(aq) + HCl(aq) \qquad [14.3]$$

Suppose that we prepare a 0.1000 M aqueous solution of C_4H_9Cl and then measure the concentration of C_4H_9Cl at various times after time zero, collecting the data shown in the first two columns of Table 14.1 ▲. We can use these data to calculate the average rate of disappearance of C_4H_9Cl over the intervals between measurements, and these rates are given in the third column. Notice that the average rate decreases over each 50-s interval for the first several measurements and continues to decrease over even larger intervals through the remaining measurements. It is typical for rates to decrease as a reaction proceeds, because the concentration of reactants decreases. The change in rate as the reaction proceeds is also seen in a graph of the concentration of C_4H_9Cl versus time (Figure 14.4 ▶). Notice how the steepness of the curve decreases with time, indicating a decreasing rate of reaction.

The graph shown in Figure 14.4 is particularly useful because it allows us to evaluate the **instantaneous rate**, the rate at a particular moment in the reaction. The instantaneous rate is determined from the slope (or tangent) of this curve at the point of interest. We have drawn two tangents in Figure 14.4, one at $t = 0$ and the other at $t = 600$ s. The slopes of these tangents give the instantaneous rates at these times.* For example, to determine the instantaneous rate at 600 s, we draw the tangent to the curve at this time, then construct horizontal and vertical lines to form the right triangle shown. The slope is the ratio of the height of the vertical side to the length of the horizontal side:

$$\text{Instantaneous rate} = \frac{\Delta[C_4H_9Cl]}{\Delta t} = -\frac{(0.017 - 0.042)\,M}{(800 - 400)\,s}$$

$$= 6.2 \times 10^{-5}\,M/s$$

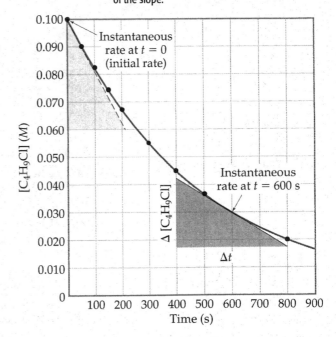

▼ **Figure 14.4 Concentration of butyl chloride (C_4H_9Cl) as a function of time.** The dots represent the experimental data from the first two columns of Table 14.1, and the red curve is drawn to connect the data points smoothly. Lines are drawn that are tangent to the curve at $t = 0$ and $t = 600$ s. The slope of each tangent is defined as the vertical change divided by the horizontal change: $\Delta[C_4H_9Cl]/\Delta t$. The reaction rate at any time is related to the slope of the tangent to the curve at that time. Because C_4H_9Cl is disappearing, the rate is equal to the negative of the slope.

---

*You may wish to review briefly the idea of graphical determination of slopes by referring to Appendix A. If you are familiar with calculus, you may recognize that the average rate approaches the instantaneous rate as the time interval approaches zero. This limit, in the notation of calculus, is represented as $-d[C_4H_9Cl]/dt$.

In what follows, the term "rate" means "instantaneous rate," unless indicated otherwise. The instantaneous rate at $t = 0$ is called the *initial rate* of the reaction.

To understand better the difference between average rate and instantaneous rate, imagine that you have just driven 98 mi in 2.0 hr. Your average speed is 49 mi/hr, whereas your instantaneous speed at any moment is the speedometer reading at that time.

 SAMPLE EXERCISE 14.2 | Calculating an Instantaneous Rate of Reaction

Using Figure 14.4, calculate the instantaneous rate of disappearance of C_4H_9Cl at $t = 0$ (the initial rate).

Solution

Analyze: We are asked to determine an instantaneous rate from a graph of concentration versus time.

Plan: To obtain the instantaneous rate at $t = 0$, we must determine the slope of the curve at $t = 0$. The tangent is drawn on the graph. The slope of this straight line equals the change in the vertical axis divided by the corresponding change in the horizontal axis (that is, change in molarity over change in time).

Solve: The straight line falls from $[C_4H_9Cl] = 0.100\ M$ to $0.060\ M$ in the time change from 0 s to 200 s, as indicated by the tan triangle shown in Figure 14.4. Thus, the initial rate is

$$\text{Rate} = -\frac{\Delta[C_4H_9Cl]}{\Delta t} = -\frac{(0.060 - 0.100)\ M}{(200 - 0)\ s} = 2.0 \times 10^{-4}\ M/s$$

PRACTICE EXERCISE

Using Figure 14.4, determine the instantaneous rate of disappearance of C_4H_9Cl at $t = 300$ s.
Answer: $1.1 \times 10^{-4}\ M/s$

GIVE IT SOME THOUGHT

Figure 14.4 shows two triangles that are used to determine the slope of the curve at two different times. How do you determine how large a triangle to draw when determining the slope of a curve at a particular point?

Reaction Rates and Stoichiometry

During our earlier discussion of the hypothetical reaction A ⟶ B, we saw that the stoichiometry requires that the rate of disappearance of A equals the rate of appearance of B. Likewise, the stoichiometry of Equation 14.3 indicates that 1 mol of C_4H_9OH is produced for each mole of C_4H_9Cl consumed. Therefore, the rate of appearance of C_4H_9OH equals the rate of disappearance of C_4H_9Cl:

$$\text{Rate} = -\frac{\Delta[C_4H_9Cl]}{\Delta t} = \frac{\Delta[C_4H_9OH]}{\Delta t}$$

What happens when the stoichiometric relationships are not one to one? For example, consider the following reaction:

$$2\ HI(g) \longrightarrow H_2(g) + I_2(g)$$

We can measure the rate of disappearance of HI or the rate of appearance of either H_2 or I_2. Because 2 mol of HI disappear for each mole of H_2 or I_2 that forms, the rate of disappearance of HI is twice the rate of appearance of either H_2 or I_2. To equate the rates, we must therefore divide the rate of disappearance of HI by 2 (its coefficient in the balanced chemical equation):

$$\text{Rate} = -\frac{1}{2}\frac{\Delta[HI]}{\Delta t} = \frac{\Delta[H_2]}{\Delta t} = \frac{\Delta[I_2]}{\Delta t}$$

Science Fundamentals Second Edition

A CLOSER LOOK | Using Spectroscopic Methods to Measure Reaction Rates

A variety of techniques can be used to monitor the concentration of a reactant or product during a reaction. Spectroscopic methods, which rely on the ability of substances to absorb (or emit) electromagnetic radiation, are some of the most useful. Spectroscopic kinetic studies are often performed with the reaction mixture in the sample compartment of the spectrometer. The spectrometer is set to measure the light absorbed at a wavelength characteristic of one of the reactants or products. In the decomposition of $HI(g)$ into $H_2(g)$ and $I_2(g)$, for example, both HI and H_2 are colorless, whereas I_2 is violet. During the course of the reaction, the color increases in intensity as I_2 forms. Thus, visible light of appropriate wavelength can be used to monitor the reaction.

Figure 14.5 ▼ shows the basic components of a spectrometer. The spectrometer measures the amount of light absorbed by the sample by comparing the intensity of the light emitted from the light source with the intensity of the light that emerges from the sample. As the concentration of I_2 increases and its color becomes more intense, the amount of light absorbed by the reaction mixture increases, causing less light to reach the detector.

Beer's law relates the amount of light being absorbed to the concentration of the substance absorbing the light:

$$A = abc \qquad [14.5]$$

In this equation, A is the measured absorbance, a is the molar absorptivity constant (a characteristic of the substance being monitored), b is the path length through which the radiation must pass, and c is the molar concentration of the absorbing substance. Thus, the concentration is directly proportional to absorbance.

Related Exercise: 14.88

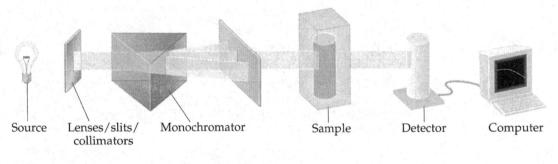

Source   Lenses/slits/   Monochromator   Sample   Detector   Computer
          collimators

▲ **Figure 14.5   Basic components of a spectrometer.**

In general, for the reaction

$$a\,A + b\,B \longrightarrow c\,C + d\,D$$

the rate is given by

$$\text{Rate} = -\frac{1}{a}\frac{\Delta[A]}{\Delta t} = -\frac{1}{b}\frac{\Delta[B]}{\Delta t} = \frac{1}{c}\frac{\Delta[C]}{\Delta t} = \frac{1}{d}\frac{\Delta[D]}{\Delta t} \qquad [14.4]$$

When we speak of the rate of a reaction without specifying a particular reactant or product, we will mean it in this sense.*

SAMPLE EXERCISE 14.3 | Relating Rates at Which Products Appear and Reactants Disappear

(a) How is the rate at which ozone disappears related to the rate at which oxygen appears in the reaction $2\,O_3(g) \longrightarrow 3\,O_2(g)$?
(b) If the rate at which O_2 appears, $\Delta[O_2]/\Delta t$, is 6.0×10^{-5} M/s at a particular instant, at what rate is O_3 disappearing at this same time, $-\Delta[O_3]/\Delta t$?

Solution
Analyze: We are given a balanced chemical equation and asked to relate the rate of appearance of the product to the rate of disappearance of the reactant.
Plan: We can use the coefficients in the chemical equation as shown in Equation 14.4 to express the relative rates of reactions.

---

* Equation 14.4 does not hold true if substances other than C and D are formed in significant amounts during the course of the reaction. For example, sometimes intermediate substances build in concentration before forming the final products. In that case the relationship between the rate of disappearance of reactants and the rate of appearance of products will not be given by Equation 14.4. All reactions whose rates we consider in this chapter obey Equation 14.4.

Solve: (a) Using the coefficients in the balanced equation and the relationship given by Equation 14.4, we have:

$$\text{Rate} = -\frac{1}{2}\frac{\Delta[O_3]}{\Delta t} = \frac{1}{3}\frac{\Delta[O_2]}{\Delta t}$$

(b) Solving the equation from part (a) for the rate at which O_3 disappears, $-\Delta[O_3]/\Delta t$, we have:

$$-\frac{\Delta[O_3]}{\Delta t} = \frac{2}{3}\frac{\Delta[O_2]}{\Delta t} = \frac{2}{3}(6.0 \times 10^{-5}\,M/s) = 4.0 \times 10^{-5}\,M/s$$

Check: We can directly apply a stoichiometric factor to convert the O_2 formation rate to the rate at which the O_3 disappears:

$$-\frac{\Delta[O_3]}{\Delta t} = \left(6.0 \times 10^{-5}\,\frac{\text{mol }O_2/L}{s}\right)\left(\frac{2\,\text{mol }O_3}{3\,\text{mol }O_2}\right) = 4.0 \times 10^{-5}\,\frac{\text{mol }O_3/L}{s}$$

$$= 4.0 \times 10^{-5}\,M/s$$

▬ PRACTICE EXERCISE

The decomposition of N_2O_5 proceeds according to the following equation:

$$2\,N_2O_5(g) \longrightarrow 4\,NO_2(g) + O_2(g)$$

If the rate of decomposition of N_2O_5 at a particular instant in a reaction vessel is $4.2 \times 10^{-7}\,M/s$, what is the rate of appearance of (a) NO_2, (b) O_2?
Answers: **(a)** $8.4 \times 10^{-7}\,M/s$, **(b)** $2.1 \times 10^{-7}\,M/s$

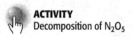

ACTIVITY
Decomposition of N_2O_5

14.3 | Concentration and Rate

One way of studying the effect of concentration on reaction rate is to determine the way in which the rate at the beginning of a reaction (the initial rate) depends on the starting concentrations. To illustrate this approach, consider the following reaction:

$$NH_4^+(aq) + NO_2^-(aq) \longrightarrow N_2(g) + 2\,H_2O(l)$$

We might study the rate of this reaction by measuring the concentration of NH_4^+ or NO_2^- as a function of time or by measuring the volume of N_2 collected. Because the stoichiometric coefficients on NH_4^+, NO_2^-, and N_2 are all the same, all of these rates will be equal.

Table 14.2 ▼ shows the initial reaction rate for various starting concentrations of NH_4^+ and NO_2^-. These data indicate that changing either $[NH_4^+]$ or $[NO_2^-]$ changes the reaction rate. Notice that if we double $[NH_4^+]$ while holding $[NO_2^-]$ constant, the rate doubles (compare experiments 1 and 2). If $[NH_4^+]$ is increased by a factor of 4 with $[NO_2^-]$ left unchanged (compare experiments 1 and 3), the rate changes by a factor of 4, and so forth. These results indicate that the rate is proportional to $[NH_4^+]$. When $[NO_2^-]$ is similarly varied while $[NH_4^+]$ is held constant, the rate is affected in the same manner. Thus, the rate is also directly proportional to the concentration of NO_2^-. We can express the

ACTIVITY
Rates of Reaction

Experiment Number	Initial NH₄⁺ Concentration (M)	Initial NO₂⁻ Concentration (M)	Observed Initial Rate (M/s)
	TABLE 14.2 Rate Data for the Reaction of Ammonium and Nitrite Ions in Water at 25°C		
1	0.0100	0.200	5.4×10^{-7}
2	0.0200	0.200	10.8×10^{-7}
3	0.0400	0.200	21.5×10^{-7}
4	0.0600	0.200	32.3×10^{-7}
5	0.200	0.0202	10.8×10^{-7}
6	0.200	0.0404	21.6×10^{-7}
7	0.200	0.0606	32.4×10^{-7}
8	0.200	0.0808	43.3×10^{-7}

way in which the rate depends on the concentrations of the reactants, NH_4^+ and NO_2^-, in terms of the following equation:

$$\text{Rate} = k[NH_4^+][NO_2^-] \qquad [14.6]$$

An equation such as Equation 14.6, which shows how the rate depends on the concentrations of reactants, is called a **rate law**. For a general reaction,

$$a\,A + b\,B \longrightarrow c\,C + d\,D$$

the rate law generally has the form

$$\text{Rate} = k[A]^m[B]^n \qquad [14.7]$$

The constant k in the rate law is called the **rate constant**. The magnitude of k changes with temperature and therefore determines how temperature affects rate, as we will see in Section 14.5. The exponents m and n are typically small whole numbers (usually 0, 1, or 2). We will consider these exponents more closely very shortly.

If we know the rate law for a reaction and its rate for a set of reactant concentrations, we can calculate the value of the rate constant, k. For example, using the data in Table 14.2 and the results from experiment 1, we can substitute into Equation 14.6

$$5.4 \times 10^{-7} \; M/s = k(0.0100 \; M)(0.200 \; M)$$

Solving for k gives

$$k = \frac{5.4 \times 10^{-7} \; M/s}{(0.0100 \; M)(0.200 \; M)} = 2.7 \times 10^{-4} \; M^{-1}\,s^{-1}$$

You may wish to verify that this same value of k is obtained using any of the other experimental results given in Table 14.2.

Once we have both the rate law and the value of the rate constant for a reaction, we can calculate the rate of reaction for any set of concentrations. For example, using Equation 14.6 and $k = 2.7 \times 10^{-4} \; M^{-1}\,s^{-1}$, we can calculate the rate for $[NH_4^+] = 0.100 \; M$ and $[NO_2^-] = 0.100 \; M$:

$$\text{Rate} = (2.7 \times 10^{-4} \; M^{-1}\,s^{-1})(0.100 \; M)(0.100 \; M) = 2.7 \times 10^{-6} \; M/s$$

 GIVE IT SOME THOUGHT

(a) What is a rate law? (b) What is the name of the quantity k in any rate law?

Exponents in the Rate Law

The rate laws for most reactions have the general form

$$\text{Rate} = k[\text{reactant 1}]^m[\text{reactant 2}]^n \ldots \qquad [14.8]$$

The exponents m and n in a rate law are called **reaction orders**. For example, consider again the rate law for the reaction of NH_4^+ with NO_2^-:

$$\text{Rate} = k[NH_4^+][NO_2^-]$$

Because the exponent of $[NH_4^+]$ is 1, the rate is *first order* in NH_4^+. The rate is also first order in NO_2^-. (The exponent "1" is not shown explicitly in rate laws.) The **overall reaction order** is the sum of the orders with respect to each reactant in the rate law. Thus, the rate law has an overall reaction order of $1 + 1 = 2$, and the reaction is *second order overall*.

The exponents in a rate law indicate how the rate is affected by the concentration of each reactant. Because the rate at which NH_4^+ reacts with NO_2^- depends on $[NH_4^+]$ raised to the first power, the rate doubles when $[NH_4^+]$ doubles, triples when $[NH_4^+]$ triples, and so forth. Doubling or tripling $[NO_2^-]$ likewise doubles or triples the rate. If a rate law is second order with respect to a reactant, $[A]^2$, then doubling the concentration of that substance causes the reaction rate to quadruple ($[2]^2 = 4$), whereas tripling the concentration causes the rate to increase ninefold ($[3]^2 = 9$).

The following are some additional examples of rate laws:

$$2 N_2O_5(g) \longrightarrow 4 NO_2(g) + O_2(g) \qquad Rate = k[N_2O_5] \qquad [14.9]$$

$$CHCl_3(g) + Cl_2(g) \longrightarrow CCl_4(g) + HCl(g) \qquad Rate = k[CHCl_3][Cl_2]^{1/2} \quad [14.10]$$

$$H_2(g) + I_2(g) \longrightarrow 2 HI(g) \qquad Rate = k[H_2][I_2] \qquad [14.11]$$

Although the exponents in a rate law are sometimes the same as the coefficients in the balanced equation, this is not necessarily the case, as seen in Equations 14.9 and 14.10. *The values of these exponents must be determined experimentally.* In most rate laws, reaction orders are 0, 1, or 2. However, we also occasionally encounter rate laws in which the reaction order is fractional (such as Equation 14.10) or even negative.

 GIVE IT SOME THOUGHT

The experimentally determined rate law for the reaction $2 NO(g) + 2 H_2(g) \longrightarrow N_2(g) + 2 H_2O(g)$ is rate $= k[NO]^2[H_2]$. (a) What are the reaction orders in this rate law? (b) Does doubling the concentration of NO have the same effect on rate as doubling the concentration of H_2?

■■■ **SAMPLE EXERCISE 14.4** | Relating a Rate Law to the Effect of Concentration on Rate

Consider a reaction $A + B \longrightarrow C$ for which rate $= k[A][B]^2$. Each of the following boxes represents a reaction mixture in which A is shown as red spheres and B as purple ones. Rank these mixtures in order of increasing rate of reaction.

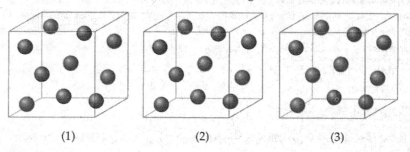

(1)   (2)   (3)

Solution

Analyze: We are given three boxes containing different numbers of spheres representing mixtures containing different reactant concentrations. We are asked to use the given rate law and the compositions of the boxes to rank the mixtures in order of increasing reaction rates.

Plan: Because all three boxes have the same volume, we can put the number of spheres of each kind into the rate law and calculate the rate for each box.

Solve: Box 1 contains 5 red spheres and 5 purple spheres, giving the following rate:

$$Box\ 1: Rate = k(5)(5)^2 = 125k$$

Box 2 contains 7 red spheres and 3 purple spheres:

$$Box\ 2: Rate = k(7)(3)^2 = 63k$$

Box 3 contains 3 red spheres and 7 purple spheres:

$$Box\ 3: Rate = k(3)(7)^2 = 147k$$

The slowest rate is $63k$ (box 2), and the highest is $147k$ (box 3). Thus, the rates vary in the order $2 < 1 < 3$.

Check: Each box contains 10 spheres. The rate law indicates that in this case [B] has a greater influence on rate than [A] because B has a higher reaction order. Hence, the mixture with the highest concentration of B (most purple spheres) should react fastest. This analysis confirms the order $2 < 1 < 3$.

PRACTICE EXERCISE
Assuming that rate $= k[A][B]$, rank the mixtures represented in this Sample Exercise in order of increasing rate.
Answer: $2 = 3 < 1$

Units of Rate Constants

The units of the rate constant depend on the overall reaction order of the rate law. In a reaction that is second order overall, for example, the units of the rate constant must satisfy the equation:

$$\text{Units of rate} = (\text{units of rate constant})(\text{units of concentration})^2$$

Hence, in our usual units of concentration and time

$$\text{Units of rate constant} = \frac{\text{units of rate}}{(\text{units of concentration})^2} = \frac{M/s}{M^2} = M^{-1}s^{-1}$$

SAMPLE EXERCISE 14.5 | Determining Reaction Orders and Units for Rate Constants

(a) What are the overall reaction orders for the reactions described in Equations 14.9 and 14.10? (b) What are the units of the rate constant for the rate law for Equation 14.9?

Solution
Analyze: We are given two rate laws and asked to express (a) the overall reaction order for each and (b) the units for the rate constant for the first reaction.
Plan: The overall reaction order is the sum of the exponents in the rate law. The units for the rate constant, k, are found by using the normal units for rate (M/s) and concentration (M) in the rate law and applying algebra to solve for k.
Solve: (a) The rate of the reaction in Equation 14.9 is first order in N_2O_5 and first order overall. The reaction in Equation 14.10 is first order in $CHCl_3$ and one-half order in Cl_2. The overall reaction order is three halves.
   (b) For the rate law for Equation 14.9, we have

$$\text{Units of rate} = (\text{units of rate constant})(\text{units of concentration})$$

So

$$\text{Units of rate constant} = \frac{\text{units of rate}}{\text{units of concentration}} = \frac{M/s}{M} = s^{-1}$$

Notice that the units of the rate constant change as the overall order of the reaction changes.

PRACTICE EXERCISE
(a) What is the reaction order of the reactant H_2 in Equation 14.11? (b) What are the units of the rate constant for Equation 14.11?
Answers: (a) 1, (b) $M^{-1}s^{-1}$

Using Initial Rates to Determine Rate Laws

The rate law for any chemical reaction must be determined experimentally; it cannot be predicted by merely looking at the chemical equation. We often determine the rate law for a reaction by the same method we applied to the data in Table 14.2: We observe the effect of changing the initial concentrations of the reactants on the initial rate of the reaction.

In most reactions the exponents in the rate law are 0, 1, or 2. If a reaction is zero order in a particular reactant, changing its concentration will have no effect on rate (as long as some of the reactant is present) because any concentration raised to the zero power equals 1. On the other hand, we have seen that when a reaction is first order in a reactant, changes in the concentration of that reactant will produce proportional changes in the rate. Thus, doubling the concentration will double the rate, and so forth. Finally, when the rate law is second order in a particular reactant, doubling its concentration increases the rate by a factor of $2^2 = 4$, tripling its concentration causes the rate to increase by a factor of $3^2 = 9$, and so forth.

In working with rate laws, it is important to realize that the *rate* of a reaction depends on concentration, but the *rate constant* does not. As we will see later in this chapter, the rate constant (and hence the reaction rate) is affected by temperature and by the presence of a catalyst.

■ SAMPLE EXERCISE 14.6 | Determining a Rate Law from Initial Rate Data

The initial rate of a reaction A + B $\longrightarrow$ C was measured for several different starting concentrations of A and B, and the results are as follows:

Experiment Number	[A] (M)	[B] (M)	Initial Rate (M/s)
1	0.100	0.100	4.0×10^{-5}
2	0.100	0.200	4.0×10^{-5}
3	0.200	0.100	16.0×10^{-5}

Using these data, determine **(a)** the rate law for the reaction, **(b)** the magnitude of the rate constant, **(c)** the rate of the reaction when [A] = 0.050 M and [B] = 0.100 M.

Solution

Analyze: We are given a table of data that relates concentrations of reactants with initial rates of reaction and asked to determine **(a)** the rate law, **(b)** the rate constant, and **(c)** the rate of reaction for a set of concentrations not listed in the table.

Plan: (a) We assume that the rate law has the following form: Rate = $k[A]^m[B]^n$, so we must use the given data to deduce the reaction orders m and n. We do so by determining how changes in the concentration change the rate. **(b)** Once we know m and n, we can use the rate law and one of the sets of data to determine the rate constant k. **(c)** Now that we know both the rate constant and the reaction orders, we can use the rate law with the given concentrations to calculate rate.

Solve: (a) As we move from experiment 1 to experiment 2, [A] is held constant and [B] is doubled. Thus, this pair of experiments shows how [B] affects the rate, allowing us to deduce the order of the rate law with respect to B. Because the rate remains the same when [B] is doubled, the concentration of B has no effect on the reaction rate. The rate law is therefore zero order in B (that is, $n = 0$).

In experiments 1 and 3, [B] is held constant so these data show how [A] affects rate. Holding [B] constant while doubling [A] increases the rate fourfold. This result indicates that rate is proportional to $[A]^2$ (that is, the reaction is second order in A). Hence, the rate law is

$$\text{Rate} = k[A]^2[B]^0 = k[A]^2$$

This rate law could be reached in a more formal way by taking the ratio of the rates from two experiments:

$$\frac{\text{Rate } 2}{\text{Rate } 1} = \frac{4.0 \times 10^{-5} \, M/s}{4.0 \times 10^{-5} \, M/s} = 1$$

Using the rate law, we have

$$1 = \frac{\text{rate } 2}{\text{rate } 1} = \frac{k[0.100 \, M]^m[0.200 \, M]^n}{k[0.100 \, M]^m[0.100 \, M]^n} = \frac{[0.200]^n}{[0.100]^n} = 2^n$$

2^n equals 1 under only one condition:

$$n = 0$$

We can deduce the value of m in a similar fashion:

$$\frac{\text{Rate } 3}{\text{Rate } 1} = \frac{16.0 \times 10^{-5} \, M/s}{4.0 \times 10^{-5} \, M/s} = 4$$

Using the rate law gives

$$4 = \frac{\text{rate } 3}{\text{rate } 1} = \frac{k[0.200 \, M]^m[0.100 \, M]^n}{k[0.100 \, M]^m[0.100 \, M]^n} = \frac{[0.200]^m}{[0.100]^m} = 2^m$$

Because $2^m = 4$, we conclude that

$$m = 2$$

(b) Using the rate law and the data from experiment 1, we have

$$k = \frac{\text{rate}}{[A]^2} = \frac{4.0 \times 10^{-5} \ M/s}{(0.100 \ M)^2} = 4.0 \times 10^{-3} \ M^{-1} s^{-1}$$

(c) Using the rate law from part (a) and the rate constant from part (b), we have

$$\text{Rate} = k[A]^2 = (4.0 \times 10^{-3} \ M^{-1} s^{-1})(0.050 \ M)^2 = 1.0 \times 10^{-5} \ M/s$$

Because [B] is not part of the rate law, it is irrelevant to the rate, provided that there is at least some B present to react with A.
Check: A good way to check our rate law is to use the concentrations in experiment 2 or 3 and see if we can correctly calculate the rate. Using data from experiment 3, we have

$$\text{Rate} = k[A]^2 = (4.0 \times 10^{-3} \ M^{-1} s^{-1})(0.200 \ M)^2 = 1.60 \times 10^{-4} \ M/s$$

Thus, the rate law correctly reproduces the data, giving both the correct number and the correct units for the rate.

■ PRACTICE EXERCISE

The following data were measured for the reaction of nitric oxide with hydrogen:

$$2 \ NO(g) + 2 \ H_2(g) \longrightarrow N_2(g) + 2 \ H_2O(g)$$

Experiment Number	[NO] (M)	[H$_2$] (M)	Initial Rate (M/s)
1	0.10	0.10	1.23×10^{-3}
2	0.10	0.20	2.46×10^{-3}
3	0.20	0.10	4.92×10^{-3}

(a) Determine the rate law for this reaction. **(b)** Calculate the rate constant. **(c)** Calculate the rate when [NO] = 0.050 M and [H$_2$] = 0.150 M.
Answers: **(a)** rate = $k[NO]^2[H_2]$; **(b)** $k = 1.2 \ M^{-2} s^{-1}$; **(c)** rate = $4.5 \times 10^{-4} \ M/s$

14.4 | The Change of Concentration with Time

Rate laws enable us to calculate the rate of a reaction from the rate constant and reactant concentrations. Rate laws can also be converted into equations that tell us what the concentrations of the reactants or products are at any time during the course of a reaction. The mathematics required involves calculus. We don't expect you to be able to perform the calculus operations; however, you should be able to use the resulting equations. We will apply this conversion to two of the simplest rate laws: those that are first order overall and those that are second order overall.

First-Order Reactions

ANIMATION
First-Order Process

A **first-order reaction** is one whose rate depends on the concentration of a single reactant raised to the first power. For a reaction of the type A $\longrightarrow$ products, the rate law may be first order:

$$\text{Rate} = -\frac{\Delta[A]}{\Delta t} = k[A]$$

This form of a rate law, which expresses how rate depends on concentration, is called the *differential rate law*. Using an operation from calculus called integration, this relationship can be transformed into an equation that relates the concentration of A at the start of the reaction, [A]$_0$, to its concentration at any other time t, [A]$_t$:

$$\ln[A]_t - \ln[A]_0 = -kt \quad \text{or} \quad \ln \frac{[A]_t}{[A]_0} = -kt \qquad [14.12]$$

This form of the rate law is called the *integrated rate law*. The function "ln" in Equation 14.12 is the natural logarithm (Appendix A.2). Equation 14.12 can also be rearranged and written as follows:

$$\ln[A]_t = -kt + \ln[A]_0 \qquad [14.13]$$

Equations 14.12 and 14.13 can be used with any concentration units, as long as the units are the same for both $[A]_t$ and $[A]_0$.

For a first-order reaction, Equation 14.12 or 14.13 can be used in several ways. Given any three of the following quantities, we can solve for the fourth: k, t, $[A]_0$, and $[A]_t$. Thus, these equations can be used, for example, to determine (1) the concentration of a reactant remaining at any time after the reaction has started, (2) the time required for a given fraction of a sample to react, or (3) the time required for a reactant concentration to fall to a certain level.

■ SAMPLE EXERCISE 14.7 | Using the Integrated First-Order Rate Law

The decomposition of a certain insecticide in water follows first-order kinetics with a rate constant of 1.45 yr^{-1} at 12°C. A quantity of this insecticide is washed into a lake on June 1, leading to a concentration of $5.0 \times 10^{-7} \text{ g/cm}^3$. Assume that the average temperature of the lake is 12°C. **(a)** What is the concentration of the insecticide on June 1 of the following year? **(b)** How long will it take for the concentration of the insecticide to drop to $3.0 \times 10^{-7} \text{ g/cm}^3$?

Solution

Analyze: We are given the rate constant for a reaction that obeys first-order kinetics, as well as information about concentrations and times, and asked to calculate how much reactant (insecticide) remains after one year. We must also determine the time interval needed to reach a particular insecticide concentration. Because the exercise gives time in (a) and asks for time in (b), we know that the integrated rate law, Equation 14.13, is required.

Plan: (a) We are given $k = 1.45 \text{ yr}^{-1}$, $t = 1.00 \text{ yr}$, and $[\text{insecticide}]_0 = 5.0 \times 10^{-7} \text{g/cm}^3$, and so Equation 14.13 can be solved for $\ln[\text{insecticide}]_t$. **(b)** We have $k = 1.45 \text{ yr}^{-1}$, $[\text{insecticide}]_0 = 5.0 \times 10^{-7} \text{ g/cm}^3$, and $[\text{insecticide}]_t = 3.0 \times 10^{-7} \text{ g/cm}^3$, and so we can solve Equation 14.13 for t.

Solve: (a) Substituting the known quantities into Equation 14.13, we have

$$\ln[\text{insecticide}]_{t=1\text{ yr}} = -(1.45 \text{ yr}^{-1})(1.00 \text{ yr}) + \ln(5.0 \times 10^{-7})$$

We use the ln function on a calculator to evaluate the second term on the right, giving

$$\ln[\text{insecticide}]_{t=1\text{ yr}} = -1.45 + (-14.51) = -15.96$$

To obtain $[\text{insecticide}]_{t=1\text{ yr}}$, we use the inverse natural logarithm, or e^x, function on the calculator:

$$[\text{insecticide}]_{t=1\text{ yr}} = e^{-15.96} = 1.2 \times 10^{-7} \text{ g/cm}^3$$

Note that the concentration units for $[A]_t$ and $[A]_0$ must be the same.

(b) Again substituting into Equation 14.13, with $[\text{insecticide}]_t = 3.0 \times 10^{-7} \text{g/cm}^3$, gives

$$\ln(3.0 \times 10^{-7}) = -(1.45 \text{ yr}^{-1})(t) + \ln(5.0 \times 10^{-7})$$

Solving for t gives

$$t = -[\ln(3.0 \times 10^{-7}) - \ln(5.0 \times 10^{-7})]/1.45 \text{ yr}^{-1}$$
$$= -(-15.02 + 14.51)/1.45 \text{ yr}^{-1} = 0.35 \text{ yr}$$

Check: In part (a) the concentration remaining after 1.00 yr (that is, $1.2 \times 10^{-7} \text{ g/cm}^3$) is less than the original concentration ($5.0 \times 10^{-7} \text{ g/cm}^3$), as it should be. In (b) the given concentration ($3.0 \times 10^{-7} \text{ g/cm}^3$) is greater than that remaining after 1.00 yr, indicating that the time must be less than a year. Thus, $t = 0.35 \text{ yr}$ is a reasonable answer.

■ PRACTICE EXERCISE

The decomposition of dimethyl ether, $(CH_3)_2O$, at 510°C is a first-order process with a rate constant of $6.8 \times 10^{-4} \text{ s}^{-1}$:

$$(CH_3)_2O(g) \longrightarrow CH_4(g) + H_2(g) + CO(g)$$

If the initial pressure of $(CH_3)_2O$ is 135 torr, what is its partial pressure after 1420 s?
Answer: 51 torr

Equation 14.13 can be used to verify whether a reaction is first order and to determine its rate constant. This equation has the form of the general equation for a straight line, $y = mx + b$, in which m is the slope and b is the y-intercept of the line (Appendix A.4):

$$\ln[A]_t = -k \cdot t + \ln[A]_0$$

$$y = m \cdot x + b$$

For a first-order reaction, therefore, a graph of $\ln[A]_t$ versus time gives a straight line with a slope of $-k$ and a y-intercept of $\ln[A]_0$. A reaction that is not first order will not yield a straight line.

As an example, consider the conversion of methyl isonitrile (CH_3NC) to acetonitrile (CH_3CN) (Figure 14.6 ▶). Because experiments show that the reaction is first order, we can write the rate equation:

$$\ln[CH_3NC]_t = -kt + \ln[CH_3NC]_0$$

Figure 14.7(a) ▼ shows how the partial pressure of methyl isonitrile varies with time as it rearranges in the gas phase at 198.9°C. We can use pressure as a unit of concentration for a gas because from the ideal-gas law the pressure is directly proportional to the number of moles per unit volume. Figure 14.7(b) shows a plot of the natural logarithm of the pressure versus time, a plot that yields a straight line. The slope of this line is $-5.1 \times 10^{-5} \text{ s}^{-1}$. (You should verify this for yourself, remembering that your result may vary slightly from ours because of inaccuracies associated with reading the graph.) Because the slope of the line equals $-k$, the rate constant for this reaction equals $5.1 \times 10^{-5} \text{ s}^{-1}$.

 GIVE IT SOME THOUGHT

What do the y-intercepts in Figure 14.7(a) and (b) represent?

Second-Order Reactions

A **second-order reaction** is one whose rate depends on the reactant concentration raised to the second power or on the concentrations of two different reactants, each raised to the first power. For simplicity, let's consider reactions of the

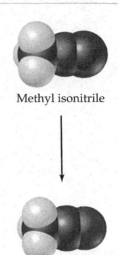

Methyl isonitrile

Acetonitrile

▲ **Figure 14.6 A first-order reaction.** The transformation of methyl isonitrile (CH_3NC) to acetonitrile (CH_3CN) is a first-order process. Methyl isonitrile and acetonitrile are isomers, molecules that have the same atoms arranged differently. This reaction is called an isomerization reaction.

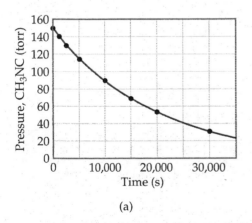

(a)

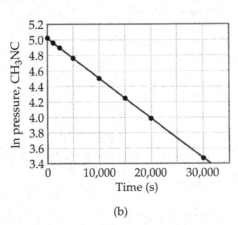

(b)

▲ **Figure 14.7 Kinetic data for conversion of methyl isonitrile.** (a) Variation in the partial pressure of methyl isonitrile (CH_3NC) with time during the reaction $CH_3NC \longrightarrow CH_3CN$ at 198.9°C. (b) A plot of the natural logarithm of the CH_3NC pressure as a function of time. The fact that a straight line fits the data confirms that the rate law is first order.

type A $\longrightarrow$ products or A + B $\longrightarrow$ products that are second order in just one reactant, A:

$$\text{Rate} = -\frac{\Delta[A]}{\Delta t} = k[A]^2$$

With the use of calculus, this differential rate law can be used to derive the following integrated rate law:

$$\frac{1}{[A]_t} = kt + \frac{1}{[A]_0} \qquad [14.14]$$

This equation, like Equation 14.13, has four variables, k, t, $[A]_0$, and $[A]_t$, and any one of these can be calculated knowing the other three. Equation 14.14 also has the form of a straight line ($y = mx + b$). If the reaction is second order, a plot of $1/[A]_t$ versus t will yield a straight line with a slope equal to k and a y-intercept equal to $1/[A]_0$. One way to distinguish between first- and second-order rate laws is to graph both $\ln[A]_t$ and $1/[A]_t$ against t. If the $\ln[A]_t$ plot is linear, the reaction is first order; if the $1/[A]_t$ plot is linear, the reaction is second order.

SAMPLE EXERCISE 14.8 | Determining Reaction Order from the Integrated Rate Law

The following data were obtained for the gas-phase decomposition of nitrogen dioxide at 300°C, $NO_2(g) \longrightarrow NO(g) + \frac{1}{2}O_2(g)$:

Time (s)	$[NO_2]$ (M)
0.0	0.01000
50.0	0.00787
100.0	0.00649
200.0	0.00481
300.0	0.00380

Is the reaction first or second order in NO_2?

Solution

Analyze: We are given the concentrations of a reactant at various times during a reaction and asked to determine whether the reaction is first or second order.

Plan: We can plot $\ln[NO_2]$ and $1/[NO_2]$ against time. One or the other will be linear, indicating whether the reaction is first or second order.

Solve: In order to graph $\ln[NO_2]$ and $1/[NO_2]$ against time, we will first prepare the following table from the data given:

Time (s)	$[NO_2]$ (M)	$\ln[NO_2]$	$1/[NO_2]$
0.0	0.01000	−4.610	100
50.0	0.00787	−4.845	127
100.0	0.00649	−5.038	154
200.0	0.00481	−5.337	208
300.0	0.00380	−5.573	263

As Figure 14.8 ▶ shows, only the plot of $1/[NO_2]$ versus time is linear. Thus, the reaction obeys a second-order rate law: Rate = $k[NO_2]^2$. From the slope of this straight-line graph, we determine that $k = 0.543\ M^{-1}\ s^{-1}$ for the disappearance of NO_2.

PRACTICE EXERCISE

Consider again the decomposition of NO_2 discussed in the Sample Exercise. The reaction is second order in NO_2 with $k = 0.543\ M^{-1}\ s^{-1}$. If the initial concentration of NO_2 in a closed vessel is 0.0500 M, what is the remaining concentration after 0.500 h? *Answer:* Using Equation 14.14, we find $[NO_2] = 1.00 \times 10^{-3}\ M$

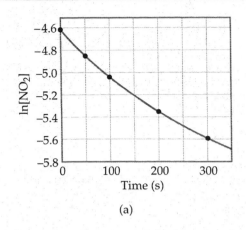

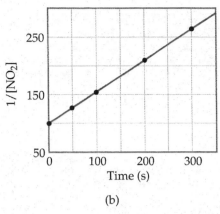

(a)

(b)

◀ **Figure 14.8 Kinetic data for decomposition of NO₂.** The reaction is $NO_2(g) \longrightarrow NO(g) + \frac{1}{2}O_2(g)$, and the data were collected at 300°C. (a) A plot of $\ln[NO_2]$ versus time is not linear, indicating that the reaction is not first order in NO_2. (b) A plot of $1/[NO_2]$ versus time is linear, indicating that the reaction is second order in NO_2.

Half-life

The **half-life** of a reaction, $t_{1/2}$, is the time required for the concentration of a reactant to reach one-half of its initial value, $[A]_{t_{1/2}} = \frac{1}{2}[A]_0$. The half-life is a convenient way to describe how fast a reaction occurs, especially if it is a first-order process. A fast reaction will have a short half-life.

We can determine the half-life of a first-order reaction by substituting $[A]_{t_{1/2}}$ into Equation 14.12:

$$\ln \frac{\frac{1}{2}[A]_0}{[A]_0} = -kt_{1/2}$$

$$\ln \frac{1}{2} = -kt_{1/2}$$

$$t_{1/2} = -\frac{\ln \frac{1}{2}}{k} = \frac{0.693}{k} \qquad [14.15]$$

From Equation 14.15, we see that $t_{1/2}$ for a first-order rate law does not depend on the starting concentration. Consequently, the half-life remains constant throughout the reaction. If, for example, the concentration of the reactant is 0.120 M at some moment in the reaction, it will be $\frac{1}{2}(0.120\ M) = 0.060\ M$ after one half-life. After one more half-life passes, the concentration will drop to 0.030 M, and so on. Equation 14.15 also indicates that we can calculate $t_{1/2}$ for a first-order reaction if k is known, or k if $t_{1/2}$ is known.

The change in concentration over time for the first-order rearrangement of methyl isonitrile at 198.9°C is graphed in Figure 14.9 ▶. The first half-life is shown at 13,600 s (that is, 3.78 h). At a time 13,600 s later, the isonitrile concentration has decreased to one-half of one-half, or one-fourth the original concentration. *In a first-order reaction, the concentration of the reactant decreases by $\frac{1}{2}$ in each of a series of regularly spaced time intervals, namely, $t_{1/2}$*. The concept of half-life is widely used in describing radioactive decay, a first-order process that we will discuss in detail in Section 21.4.

ACTIVITY
Rates of Reaction

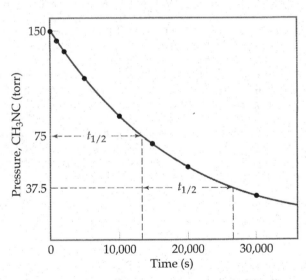

▲ **Figure 14.9 Half-life of a first-order reaction.** Pressure of methyl isonitrile as a function of time showing two successive half-lives of the isomerization reaction depicted in Figure 14.6.

SAMPLE EXERCISE 14.9 | Determining the Half-life of a First-Order Reaction

The reaction of C_4H_9Cl with water is a first-order reaction. Figure 14.4 shows how the concentration of C_4H_9Cl changes with time at a particular temperature. **(a)** From that graph, estimate the half-life for this reaction. **(b)** Use the half-life from (a) to calculate the rate constant.

Solution
Analyze: We are asked to estimate the half-life of a reaction from a graph of concentration versus time and then to use the half-life to calculate the rate constant for the reaction.

Plan: (a) To estimate a half-life, we can select a concentration and then determine the time required for the concentration to decrease to half of that value. (b) Equation 14.15 is used to calculate the rate constant from the half-life.

Solve: (a) From the graph, we see that the initial value of $[C_4H_9Cl]$ is 0.100 M. The half-life for this first-order reaction is the time required for $[C_4H_9Cl]$ to decrease to 0.050 M, which we can read off the graph. This point occurs at approximately 340 s.

(b) Solving Equation 14.15 for k, we have

$$k = \frac{0.693}{t_{1/2}} = \frac{0.693}{340 \text{ s}} = 2.0 \times 10^{-3} \text{ s}^{-1}$$

Check: At the end of the second half-life, which should occur at 680 s, the concentration should have decreased by yet another factor of 2, to 0.025 M. Inspection of the graph shows that this is indeed the case.

◼ PRACTICE EXERCISE

(a) Using Equation 14.15, calculate $t_{1/2}$ for the decomposition of the insecticide described in Sample Exercise 14.7. (b) How long does it take for the concentration of the insecticide to reach one-quarter of the initial value?
Answers: (a) 0.478 yr = 1.51×10^7 s; (b) it takes two half-lives, 2(0.478 yr) = 0.956 yr

---

 CHEMISTRY AT WORK | Methyl Bromide in the Atmosphere

Several small molecules containing carbon–chlorine or carbon–bromine bonds, when present in the stratosphere, are capable of reacting with ozone (O_3) and thus contributing to the destruction of Earth's ozone layer. Whether a halogen-containing molecule contributes significantly to destruction of the ozone layer depends in part on the molecule's average lifetime in the atmosphere. It takes quite a long time for molecules formed at Earth's surface to diffuse through the lower atmosphere (called the troposphere) and move into the stratosphere, where the ozone layer is located (Figure 14.10 ▶). Decomposition in the lower atmosphere competes with diffusion into the stratosphere.

The much-discussed chlorofluorocarbons, or CFCs, contribute to the destruction of the ozone layer because they have long lifetimes in the troposphere. Thus, they persist long enough for a substantial fraction of the molecules to find their way to the stratosphere.

Another simple molecule that has the potential to destroy the stratospheric ozone layer is methyl bromide (CH_3Br). This substance has a wide range of uses, including antifungal treatment of plant seeds, and has therefore been produced in large quantities (about 150 million pounds per year). In the stratosphere, the C—Br bond is broken through absorption of short-wavelength radiation. The resultant Br atoms then catalyze decomposition of O_3.

Methyl bromide is removed from the lower atmosphere by a variety of mechanisms, including a slow reaction with ocean water:

$$CH_3Br(g) + H_2O(l) \longrightarrow CH_3OH(aq) + HBr(aq) \quad [14.16]$$

To determine the potential importance of CH_3Br in destruction of the ozone layer, it is important to know how rapidly Equation 14.16 and all other mechanisms together remove CH_3Br from the atmosphere before it can diffuse into the stratosphere.

Scientists have carried out research to estimate the average lifetime of CH_3Br in Earth's atmosphere. Such an estimate is difficult to make. It cannot be done in laboratory-based

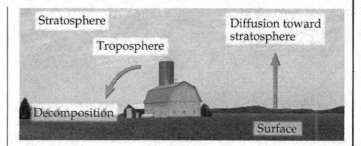

▲ **Figure 14.10 Distribution and fate of methyl bromide in the atmosphere.** Some CH_3Br is removed from the atmosphere by decomposition, and some diffuses upward into the stratosphere, where it contributes to destruction of the ozone layer. The relative rates of decomposition and diffusion determine how extensively methyl bromide is involved in destruction of the ozone layer.

experiments because the conditions that exist in the atmosphere above the planet are too complex to be simulated in the laboratory. Instead, scientists gathered nearly 4000 samples of the atmosphere during aircraft flights all over the Pacific Ocean and analyzed them for the presence of several trace organic substances, including methyl bromide. From a detailed analysis of the concentrations, it was possible to estimate that the *atmospheric residence time* for CH_3Br is 0.8 ± 0.1 yr.

The atmospheric residence time equals the half-life for CH_3Br in the lower atmosphere, assuming that it decomposes by a first-order process. That is, a collection of CH_3Br molecules present at any given time will, on average, be 50% decomposed after 0.8 years, 75% decomposed after 1.6 years, and so on. A residence time of 0.8 years, while comparatively short, is still sufficiently long so that CH_3Br contributes significantly to the destruction of the ozone layer. In 1997 an international agreement was reached to phase out use of methyl bromide in developed countries by 2005. However, in recent years exemptions for critical agricultural use have been requested and granted.
Related Exercise: 14.105

In contrast to the behavior of first-order reactions, the half-life for second-order and other reactions depends on reactant concentrations and therefore changes as the reaction progresses. Using Equation 14.14, we find that the half-life of a second-order reaction is

$$t_{1/2} = \frac{1}{k[A]_0} \qquad [14.17]$$

In this case the half-life depends on the initial concentration of reactant—the lower the initial concentration, the greater the half-life.

 GIVE IT SOME THOUGHT

How does the half-life of a second-order reaction change as the reaction proceeds?

14.5 | Temperature and Rate

The rates of most chemical reactions increase as the temperature rises. For example, dough rises faster at room temperature than when refrigerated, and plants grow more rapidly in warm weather than in cold. We can literally see the effect of temperature on reaction rate by observing a chemiluminescent reaction (one that produces light). The characteristic glow of fireflies is a familiar example of chemiluminescence. Another is the light produced by Cyalume® light sticks, which contain chemicals that produce chemiluminescence when mixed. As seen in Figure 14.11 ▼, these light sticks produce a brighter light at higher temperature. The amount of light produced is greater because the rate of the reaction is faster at the higher temperature. Although the light stick glows more brightly initially, its luminescence also dies out more rapidly.

How is this experimentally observed temperature effect reflected in the rate expression? The faster rate at higher temperature is due to an increase in the rate constant with increasing temperature. For example, let's reconsider the first-order reaction $CH_3NC \longrightarrow CH_3CN$ (Figure 14.6). Figure 14.12 ▼ shows the rate constant for this reaction as a function of temperature. The rate constant, and hence the rate of the reaction, increases rapidly with temperature, approximately doubling for each 10°C rise.

Higher temperature   Lower temperature

▲ **Figure 14.11 Temperature affects the rate of the chemiluminescence reaction in Cyalume® light sticks.** The light stick in hot water (left) glows more brightly than the one in cold water (right); at the higher temperature, the reaction is initially faster and produces a brighter light.

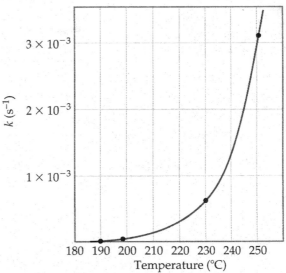

▲ **Figure 14.12 Dependence of rate constant on temperature.** The data show the variation in the first-order rate constant for the rearrangement of methyl isonitrile as a function of temperature. The four points indicated are used in connection with Sample Exercise 14.11.

The Collision Model

We have seen that reaction rates are affected both by the concentrations of reactants and by temperature. The **collision model**, which is based on the kinetic-molecular theory (Section 10.7), accounts for both of these effects at the molecular level. The central idea of the collision model is that molecules must collide to react. The greater the number of collisions occurring per second, the greater the reaction rate. As the concentration of reactant molecules increases, therefore, the number of collisions increases, leading to an increase in reaction rate. According to the kinetic-molecular theory of gases, increasing the temperature increases molecular speeds. As molecules move faster, they collide more forcefully (with more energy) and more frequently, increasing reaction rates.

For reaction to occur, though, more is required than simply a collision. For most reactions, only a tiny fraction of the collisions leads to reaction. For example, in a mixture of H_2 and I_2 at ordinary temperatures and pressures, each molecule undergoes about 10^{10} collisions per second. If every collision between H_2 and I_2 resulted in the formation of HI, the reaction would be over in much less than a second. Instead, at room temperature the reaction proceeds very slowly. Only about one in every 10^{13} collisions produces a reaction. What keeps the reaction from occurring more rapidly?

 GIVE IT SOME THOUGHT

What is the central idea of the collision model?

The Orientation Factor

In most reactions, molecules must be oriented in a certain way during collisions in order for a reaction to occur. The relative orientations of the molecules during their collisions determine whether the atoms are suitably positioned to form new bonds. For example, consider the reaction of Cl atoms with NOCl:

$$Cl + NOCl \longrightarrow NO + Cl_2$$

The reaction will take place if the collision brings Cl atoms together to form Cl_2, as shown in Figure 14.13(a) ▼. In contrast, the collision shown in Figure 14.13(b) will be ineffective and will not yield products. Indeed, a great many collisions do not lead to reaction, merely because the molecules are not suitably oriented. There is, however, another factor that is usually even more important in determining whether particular collisions result in reaction.

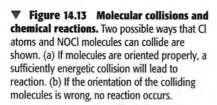

▼ **Figure 14.13 Molecular collisions and chemical reactions.** Two possible ways that Cl atoms and NOCl molecules can collide are shown. (a) If molecules are oriented properly, a sufficiently energetic collision will lead to reaction. (b) If the orientation of the colliding molecules is wrong, no reaction occurs.

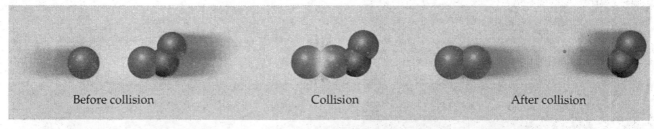

Before collision   Collision   After collision

(a) Effective collision

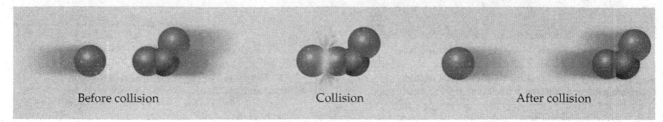

Before collision   Collision   After collision

(b) Ineffective collision

Activation Energy

In 1888 the Swedish chemist Svante Arrhenius suggested that molecules must possess a certain minimum amount of energy in order to react. According to the collision model, this energy comes from the kinetic energies of the colliding molecules. Upon collision, the kinetic energy of the molecules can be used to stretch, bend, and ultimately break bonds, leading to chemical reactions. That is, the kinetic energy is used to change the potential energy of the molecule. If molecules are moving too slowly, with too little kinetic energy, they merely bounce off one another without changing. In order to react, colliding molecules must have a total kinetic energy equal to or greater than some minimum value. The minimum energy required to initiate a chemical reaction is called the **activation energy**, E_a. The value of E_a varies from reaction to reaction.

The situation during reactions is rather like that shown in Figure 14.14 ▲. The player on the putting green needs to move her ball over the hill to the vicinity of the cup. To do this, she must impart enough kinetic energy with the putter to move the ball to the top of the hill. If she doesn't impart enough energy, the ball will roll partway up the hill and then back down. In the same way, molecules may require a certain minimum energy to break existing bonds during a chemical reaction. In the rearrangement of methyl isonitrile to acetonitrile, for example, we might imagine the reaction passing through an intermediate state in which the N≡C portion of the molecule is sitting sideways:

$$H_3C-N\equiv C: \longrightarrow \left[H_3C\cdots \underset{\underset{..}{N}}{\overset{\overset{..}{C}}{|||}} \right] \longrightarrow H_3C-C\equiv N:$$

The change in the potential energy of the molecule during the reaction is shown in Figure 14.15 ▼. The diagram shows that energy must be supplied to stretch the bond between the H_3C group and the N≡C group so as to allow

▲ **Figure 14.14 An energy barrier.** To move the golf ball to the vicinity of the cup, the player must impart enough kinetic energy to the ball to enable it to surmount the barrier represented by the hill. This situation is analogous to a chemical reaction, in which molecules must gain enough energy through collisions to enable them to overcome the barrier to chemical reaction.

◀ **Figure 14.15 Energy profile for methyl isonitrile isomerization.** The methyl isonitrile molecule must surmount the activation-energy barrier before it can form the product, acetonitrile. The horizontal axis is variously labeled "reaction pathway," as here, or "progress of reaction."

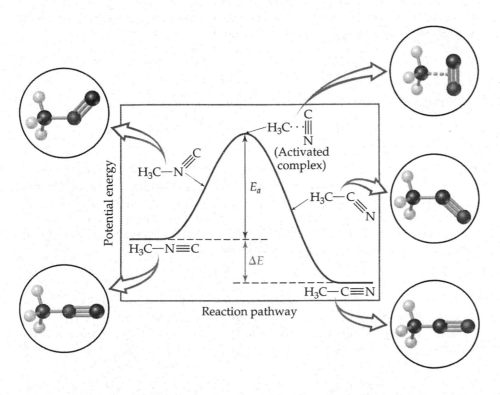

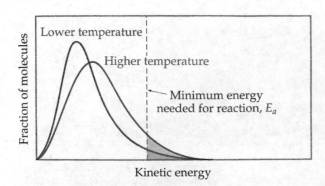

▲ Figure 14.16 The effect of temperature on the distribution of kinetic energies. At the higher temperature, a larger number of molecules have higher kinetic energies. Thus, a larger fraction at any one instant will have more than the minimum energy required for reaction.

the $N \equiv C$ group to rotate. After the $N \equiv C$ group has twisted sufficiently, the $C-C$ bond begins to form and the energy of the molecule drops. Thus, the barrier represents the energy necessary to force the molecule through the relatively unstable intermediate state to the final product. The energy difference between that of the starting molecule and the highest energy along the reaction pathway is the activation energy, E_a. The particular arrangement of atoms at the top of the barrier is called the **activated complex**, or **transition state**.

The conversion of $H_3C-N \equiv C$ to $H_3C-C \equiv N$ is exothermic. Figure 14.15 therefore shows the product as having a lower energy than the reactant. The energy change for the reaction, ΔE, has no effect on the rate of the reaction. The rate depends on the magnitude of E_a; generally, the lower E_a is, the faster the reaction. Notice that the reverse reaction is endothermic. The activation barrier for the reverse reaction is equal to the sum of ΔE and E_a for the forward reaction.

How does any particular methyl isonitrile molecule acquire sufficient energy to overcome the activation barrier? It does so through collisions with other molecules. Recall from the kinetic-molecular theory of gases that, at any given instant, gas molecules are distributed in energy over a wide range. ∞ (Section 10.7) Figure 14.16 ▲ shows the distribution of kinetic energies for two different temperatures, comparing them with the minimum energy needed for reaction, E_a. At the higher temperature a much greater fraction of the molecules has kinetic energy greater than E_a, which leads to a much greater rate of reaction.

The fraction of molecules that has an energy equal to or greater than E_a is given by the expression

$$f = e^{-E_a/RT} \qquad [14.18]$$

In this equation R is the gas constant (8.314 J/mol-K) and T is absolute temperature. To get an idea of the magnitude of f, let's suppose that E_a is 100 kJ/mol, a value typical of many reactions, and that T is 300 K, around room temperature. The calculated value of f is 3.8×10^{-18}, an extremely small number! At 310 K the fraction is $f = 1.4 \times 10^{-17}$. Thus, a 10-degree increase in temperature produces a 3.7-fold increase in the fraction of molecules possessing at least 100 kJ/mol of energy.

💡 GIVE IT SOME THOUGHT

Why isn't collision frequency the only factor affecting a reaction rate?

The Arrhenius Equation

Arrhenius noted that for most reactions the increase in rate with increasing temperature is nonlinear, as shown in Figure 14.12. He found that most reaction-rate data obeyed an equation based on three factors: (a) the fraction of molecules possessing an energy of E_a or greater, (b) the number of collisions occurring per second, and (c) the fraction of collisions that have the appropriate orientation. These three factors are incorporated into the **Arrhenius equation**:

$$k = Ae^{-E_a/RT} \qquad [14.19]$$

In this equation k is the rate constant, E_a is the activation energy, R is the gas constant (8.314 J/mol-K), and T is the absolute temperature. The **frequency factor**, A, is constant, or nearly so, as temperature is varied. It is related to the frequency of collisions and the probability that the collisions are favorably oriented for reaction.* As the magnitude of E_a increases, k decreases because the fraction of molecules that possess the required energy is smaller. Thus, *reaction rates decrease as E_a increases*.

▬ **SAMPLE EXERCISE 14.10** | Relating Energy Profiles to Activation Energies and Speeds of Reaction

Consider a series of reactions having the following energy profiles:

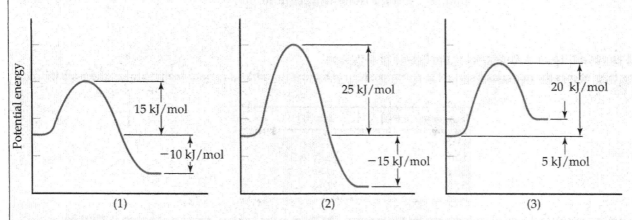

(1)   (2)   (3)

Assuming that all three reactions have nearly the same frequency factors, rank the reactions from slowest to fastest.

Solution The lower the activation energy, the faster the reaction. The value of ΔE does not affect the rate. Hence the order is (2) < (3) < (1).

▬ **PRACTICE EXERCISE**

Imagine that these reactions are reversed. Rank these reverse reactions from slowest to fastest.

Answer: (2) < (1) < (3) because E_a values are 40, 25, and 15 kJ/mol, respectively

Determining the Activation Energy

Taking the natural log of both sides of Equation 14.19, we have

$$\ln k = -\frac{E_a}{RT} + \ln A \qquad [14.20]$$

Equation 14.20 has the form of a straight line; it predicts that a graph of $\ln k$ versus $1/T$ will be a line with a slope equal to $-E_a/R$ and a y-intercept equal to $\ln A$. Thus, the activation energy can be determined by measuring k at a series of temperatures, graphing $\ln k$ versus $1/T$, and then calculating E_a from the slope of the resultant line.

We can also use Equation 14.20 to evaluate E_a in a nongraphical way if we know the rate constant of a reaction at two or more temperatures. For example, suppose that at two different temperatures, T_1 and T_2, a reaction has rate constants k_1 and k_2. For each condition, we have

ACTIVITY
Rates of Reaction

$$\ln k_1 = -\frac{E_a}{RT_1} + \ln A \quad \text{and} \quad \ln k_2 = -\frac{E_a}{RT_2} + \ln A$$

Subtracting $\ln k_2$ from $\ln k_1$ gives

$$\ln k_1 - \ln k_2 = \left(-\frac{E_a}{RT_1} + \ln A\right) - \left(-\frac{E_a}{RT_2} + \ln A\right)$$

---

* Because the frequency of collisions increases with temperature, A also has some temperature dependence, but it is small compared to the exponential term. Therefore, A is considered approximately constant.

Simplifying this equation and rearranging it gives

$$\ln\frac{k_1}{k_2} = \frac{E_a}{R}\left(\frac{1}{T_2} - \frac{1}{T_1}\right)$$ [14.21]

Equation 14.21 provides a convenient way to calculate the rate constant, k_1, at some temperature, T_1, when we know the activation energy and the rate constant, k_2, at some other temperature, T_2.

■ SAMPLE EXERCISE 14.11 | Determining the Energy of Activation

The following table shows the rate constants for the rearrangement of methyl isonitrile at various temperatures (these are the data in Figure 14.12):

Temperature (°C)	$k(s^{-1})$
189.7	2.52×10^{-5}
198.9	5.25×10^{-5}
230.3	6.30×10^{-4}
251.2	3.16×10^{-3}

(a) From these data, calculate the activation energy for the reaction. (b) What is the value of the rate constant at 430.0 K?

Solution

Analyze: We are given rate constants, k, measured at several temperatures and asked to determine the activation energy, E_a, and the rate constant, k, at a particular temperature.

Plan: We can obtain E_a from the slope of a graph of $\ln k$ versus $1/T$. Once we know E_a, we can use Equation 14.21 together with the given rate data to calculate the rate constant at 430.0 K.

Solve: (a) We must first convert the temperatures from degrees Celsius to kelvins. We then take the inverse of each temperature, $1/T$, and the natural log of each rate constant, $\ln k$. This gives us the table shown at the right:

T(K)	$1/T$ (K^{-1})	$\ln k$
462.9	2.160×10^{-3}	-10.589
472.1	2.118×10^{-3}	-9.855
503.5	1.986×10^{-3}	-7.370
524.4	1.907×10^{-3}	-5.757

A graph of $\ln k$ versus $1/T$ results in a straight line, as shown in Figure 14.17 ▶.

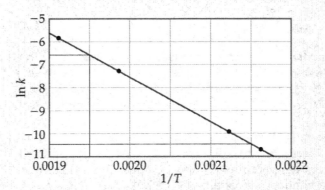

◀ **Figure 14.17 Graphical determination of activation energy.** The natural logarithm of the rate constant for the rearrangement of methyl isonitrile is plotted as a function of $1/T$. The linear relationship is predicted by the Arrhenius equation giving a slope equal to $-E_a/R$.

The slope of the line is obtained by choosing two well-separated points, as shown, and using the coordinates of each:

$$\text{Slope} = \frac{\Delta y}{\Delta x} = \frac{-6.6 - (-10.4)}{0.00195 - 0.00215} = -1.9 \times 10^4$$

Because logarithms have no units, the numerator in this equation is dimensionless. The denominator has the units of $1/T$, namely, K^{-1}. Thus, the overall units for the slope are K. The slope equals $-E_a/R$. We use the value for the molar gas constant R in units of J/mol-K (Table 10.2). We thus obtain

$$\text{Slope} = -\frac{E_a}{R}$$

$$E_a = -(\text{slope})(R) = -(-1.9 \times 10^4\,K)\left(8.314\frac{J}{\text{mol-K}}\right)\left(\frac{1\,kJ}{1000\,J}\right)$$

$$= 1.6 \times 10^2\,kJ/mol = 160\,kJ/mol$$

We report the activation energy to only two significant figures because we are limited by the precision with which we can read the graph in Figure 14.17.

(b) To determine the rate constant, k_1, at $T_1 = 430.0$ K, we can use Equation 14.21 with $E_a = 160$ kJ/mol, and one of the rate constants and temperatures from the given data, such as $k_2 = 2.52 \times 10^{-5}\,s^{-1}$ and $T_2 = 462.9$ K:

$$\ln\left(\frac{k_1}{2.52 \times 10^{-5}\,s^{-1}}\right) = \left(\frac{160\text{ kJ/mol}}{8.314\text{ J/mol-K}}\right)\left(\frac{1}{462.9\text{ K}} - \frac{1}{430.0\text{ K}}\right)\left(\frac{1000\text{ J}}{1\text{ kJ}}\right) = -3.18$$

Thus,

$$\frac{k_1}{2.52 \times 10^{-5}\,s^{-1}} = e^{-3.18} = 4.15 \times 10^{-2}$$

$$k_1 = (4.15 \times 10^{-2})(2.52 \times 10^{-5}\,s^{-1}) = 1.0 \times 10^{-6}\,s^{-1}$$

Note that the units of k_1 are the same as those of k_2.

■ PRACTICE EXERCISE

Using the data in Sample Exercise 14.11, calculate the rate constant for the rearrangement of methyl isonitrile at 280°C.
Answer: $2.2 \times 10^{-2}\,s^{-1}$

14.6 | Reaction Mechanisms

A balanced equation for a chemical reaction indicates the substances present at the start of the reaction and those produced as the reaction proceeds. It provides no information, however, about how the reaction occurs. The process by which a reaction occurs is called the **reaction mechanism**. At the most sophisticated level, a reaction mechanism will describe in great detail the order in which bonds are broken and formed and the changes in relative positions of the atoms in the course of the reaction. We will begin with more rudimentary descriptions of how reactions occur, considering further the nature of the collisions leading to reaction.

Elementary Reactions

We have seen that reactions take place as a result of collisions between reacting molecules. For example, the collisions between molecules of methyl isonitrile (CH_3NC) can provide the energy to allow the CH_3NC to rearrange:

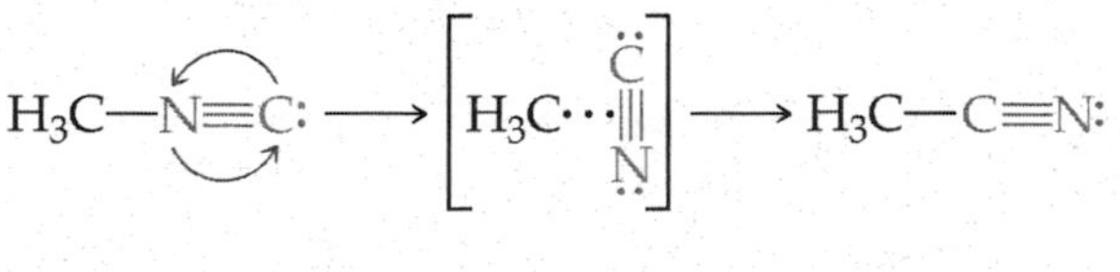

Similarly, the reaction of NO and O_3 to form NO_2 and O_2 appears to occur as a result of a single collision involving suitably oriented and sufficiently energetic NO and O_3 molecules:

$$NO(g) + O_3(g) \longrightarrow NO_2(g) + O_2(g) \qquad [14.22]$$

Both of these processes occur in a single event or step and are called **elementary reactions** (or elementary processes).

The number of molecules that participate as reactants in an elementary reaction defines the **molecularity** of the reaction. If a single molecule is involved, the reaction is **unimolecular**. The rearrangement of methyl isonitrile is a unimolecular process. Elementary reactions involving the collision of two

ANIMATION
Bimolecular Reaction

reactant molecules are **bimolecular**. The reaction between NO and O_3 (Equation 14.22) is bimolecular. Elementary reactions involving the simultaneous collision of three molecules are **termolecular**. Termolecular reactions are far less probable than unimolecular or bimolecular processes and are rarely encountered. The chance that four or more molecules will collide simultaneously with any regularity is even more remote; consequently, such collisions are never proposed as part of a reaction mechanism.

 GIVE IT SOME THOUGHT

What is the molecularity of this elementary reaction?

$$NO(g) + Cl_2(g) \longrightarrow NOCl(g) + Cl(g)$$

Multistep Mechanisms

The net change represented by a balanced chemical equation often occurs by a *multistep mechanism*, which consists of a sequence of elementary reactions. For example, consider the reaction of NO_2 and CO:

$$NO_2(g) + CO(g) \longrightarrow NO(g) + CO_2(g) \qquad [14.23]$$

Below 225°C, this reaction appears to proceed in two elementary reactions (or two *elementary steps*), each of which is bimolecular. First, two NO_2 molecules collide, and an oxygen atom is transferred from one to the other. The resultant NO_3 then collides with a CO molecule and transfers an oxygen atom to it:

$$NO_2(g) + NO_2(g) \longrightarrow NO_3(g) + NO(g)$$

$$NO_3(g) + CO(g) \longrightarrow NO_2(g) + CO_2(g)$$

Thus, we say that the reaction occurs by a two-step mechanism.

The chemical equations for the elementary reactions in a multistep mechanism must always add to give the chemical equation of the overall process. In the present example the sum of the two elementary reactions is

$$2\,NO_2(g) + NO_3(g) + CO(g) \longrightarrow NO_2(g) + NO_3(g) + NO(g) + CO_2(g)$$

Simplifying this equation by eliminating substances that appear on both sides of the arrow gives Equation 14.23, the net equation for the process. Because NO_3 is neither a reactant nor a product in the overall reaction—it is formed in one elementary reaction and consumed in the next—it is called an **intermediate**. Multistep mechanisms involve one or more intermediates.

SAMPLE EXERCISE 14.12 | Determining Molecularity and Identifying Intermediates

It has been proposed that the conversion of ozone into O_2 proceeds by a two-step mechanism:

$$O_3(g) \longrightarrow O_2(g) + O(g)$$

$$O_3(g) + O(g) \longrightarrow 2\,O_2(g)$$

(a) Describe the molecularity of each elementary reaction in this mechanism. **(b)** Write the equation for the overall reaction. **(c)** Identify the intermediate(s).

Solution
Analyze: We are given a two-step mechanism and asked for **(a)** the molecularities of each of the two elementary reactions, **(b)** the equation for the overall process, and **(c)** the intermediate.
Plan: The molecularity of each elementary reaction depends on the number of reactant molecules in the equation for that reaction. The overall equation is the sum of the

equations for the elementary reactions. The intermediate is a substance formed in one step of the mechanism and used in another and therefore not part of the equation for the overall reaction.

Solve: (a) The first elementary reaction involves a single reactant and is consequently unimolecular. The second reaction, which involves two reactant molecules, is bimolecular.

(b) Adding the two elementary reactions gives

$$2 O_3(g) + O(g) \longrightarrow 3 O_2(g) + O(g)$$

Because $O(g)$ appears in equal amounts on both sides of the equation, it can be eliminated to give the net equation for the chemical process:

$$2 O_3(g) \longrightarrow 3 O_2(g)$$

(c) The intermediate is $O(g)$. It is neither an original reactant nor a final product, but is formed in the first step of the mechanism and consumed in the second.

■ PRACTICE EXERCISE

For the reaction

$$Mo(CO)_6 + P(CH_3)_3 \longrightarrow Mo(CO)_5P(CH_3)_3 + CO$$

the proposed mechanism is

$$Mo(CO)_6 \longrightarrow Mo(CO)_5 + CO$$

$$Mo(CO)_5 + P(CH_3)_3 \longrightarrow Mo(CO)_5P(CH_3)_3$$

(a) Is the proposed mechanism consistent with the equation for the overall reaction? (b) What is the molecularity of each step of the mechanism? (c) Identify the intermediate(s).

Answers: (a) Yes, the two equations add to yield the equation for the reaction. (b) The first elementary reaction is unimolecular, and the second one is bimolecular. (c) $Mo(CO)_5$

Rate Laws for Elementary Reactions

In Section 14.3 we stressed that rate laws must be determined experimentally; they cannot be predicted from the coefficients of balanced chemical equations. We are now in a position to understand why this is so: Every reaction is made up of a series of one or more elementary steps, and the rate laws and relative speeds of these steps will dictate the overall rate law. Indeed, the rate law for a reaction can be determined from its mechanism, as we will see shortly. Thus, our next challenge in kinetics is to arrive at reaction mechanisms that lead to rate laws that are consistent with those observed experimentally. We will start by examining the rate laws of elementary reactions.

Elementary reactions are significant in a very important way: *If we know that a reaction is an elementary reaction, then we know its rate law.* The rate law of any elementary reaction is based directly on its molecularity. For example, consider the general unimolecular process.

$$A \longrightarrow \text{products}$$

As the number of A molecules increases, the number that decompose in a given interval of time will increase proportionally. Thus, the rate of a unimolecular process will be first order:

$$\text{Rate} = k[A]$$

In the case of bimolecular elementary steps, the rate law is second order, as in the following example:

$$A + B \longrightarrow \text{products} \qquad \text{Rate} = k[A][B]$$

The second-order rate law follows directly from the collision theory. If we double the concentration of A, the number of collisions between molecules of A and B will double; likewise, if we double [B], the number of collisions will double.

TABLE 14.3	Elementary Reactions and Their Rate Laws	
Molecularity	Elementary Reaction	Rate Law
Unimolecular	A $\longrightarrow$ products	Rate = $k[A]$
Bimolecular	A + A $\longrightarrow$ products	Rate = $k[A]^2$
Bimolecular	A + B $\longrightarrow$ products	Rate = $k[A][B]$
Termolecular	A + A + A $\longrightarrow$ products	Rate = $k[A]^3$
Termolecular	A + A + B $\longrightarrow$ products	Rate = $k[A]^2[B]$
Termolecular	A + B + C $\longrightarrow$ products	Rate = $k[A][B][C]$

Therefore, the rate law will be first order in both [A] and [B], and second order overall.

The rate laws for all feasible elementary reactions are given in Table 14.3 ▲. Notice how the rate law for each kind of elementary reaction follows directly from the molecularity of that reaction. It is important to remember, however, that we cannot tell by merely looking at a balanced chemical equation whether the reaction involves one or several elementary steps.

SAMPLE EXERCISE 14.13 | Predicting the Rate Law for an Elementary Reaction

If the following reaction occurs in a single elementary reaction, predict the rate law:

$$H_2(g) + Br_2(g) \longrightarrow 2\,HBr(g)$$

Solution
Analyze: We are given the equation and asked for its rate law, assuming that it is an elementary process.
Plan: Because we are assuming that the reaction occurs as a single elementary reaction, we are able to write the rate law using the coefficients for the reactants in the equation as the reaction orders.
Solve: The reaction is bimolecular, involving one molecule of H_2 with one molecule of Br_2. Thus, the rate law is first order in each reactant and second order overall:

$$\text{Rate} = k[H_2][Br_2]$$

Comment: Experimental studies of this reaction show that the reaction actually has a very different rate law:

$$\text{Rate} = k[H_2][Br_2]^{1/2}$$

Because the experimental rate law differs from the one obtained by assuming a single elementary reaction, we can conclude that the mechanism must involve two or more elementary steps.

PRACTICE EXERCISE

Consider the following reaction: $2\,NO(g) + Br_2(g) \longrightarrow 2\,NOBr(g)$. **(a)** Write the rate law for the reaction, assuming it involves a single elementary reaction. **(b)** Is a single-step mechanism likely for this reaction?
Answers: **(a)** Rate = $k[NO]^2[Br_2]$ **(b)** No, because termolecular reactions are very rare

The Rate-Determining Step for a Multistep Mechanism

As with the reaction in Sample Exercise 14.13, most chemical reactions occur by mechanisms that involve two or more elementary reactions. Each of these steps of the mechanism has its own rate constant and activation energy. Often one of the steps is much slower than the others. The overall rate of a reaction cannot exceed the rate of the slowest elementary step of its mechanism. Because the slow step limits the overall reaction rate, it is called the **rate-determining step** (or *rate-limiting step*).

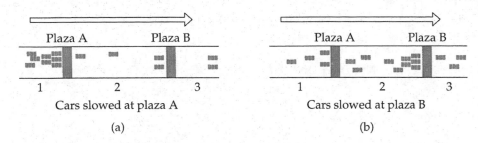

Cars slowed at plaza A (a)

Cars slowed at plaza B (b)

▲ **Figure 14.18 Rate-determining step.** The flow of traffic on a toll road illustrates how a rate-determining step controls reaction rate. The flow is limited by the flow of traffic through the slower toll plaza. In (a) the rate at which cars can reach point 3 is limited by how quickly they can get through plaza A. In this case, getting from point 1 to point 2 is the rate-determining step. In (b), getting from point 2 to point 3 is the rate-determining step.

To understand the concept of a rate-determining step, consider a toll road with two toll plazas (Figure 14.18 ▲). We will measure the rate at which cars exit the toll road. Cars enter the toll road at point 1 and pass through toll plaza A. They then pass an intermediate point 2 before passing through toll plaza B. Upon exiting, they pass point 3. We can therefore envision this trip along the toll road as occurring in two elementary steps:

$$\text{Step 1:} \quad \text{Point 1} \longrightarrow \text{point 2} \quad (\text{through plaza A})$$

$$\text{Step 2:} \quad \underline{\text{Point 2} \longrightarrow \text{point 3} \quad (\text{through plaza B})}$$

$$\text{Overall:} \quad \text{Point 1} \longrightarrow \text{point 3} \quad (\text{through plaza A and B})$$

Now suppose that several of the gates at toll plaza A are malfunctioning, so that traffic backs up behind it [Figure 14.18(a)]. The rate at which cars can get to point 3 is limited by the rate at which they can get through the traffic jam at plaza A. Thus, step 1 is the rate-determining step of the journey along the toll road. If, however, traffic flows quickly through plaza A, but gets backed up at plaza B [Figure 14.18(b)], there will be a buildup of cars in the intermediate region between the plazas. In this case step 2 is rate determining: The rate at which cars can travel the toll road is limited by the rate at which they can pass through plaza B.

In the same way, *the slowest step in a multistep reaction limits the overall rate.* By analogy to Figure 14.18(a), the rate of a faster step following the rate-determining step does not speed up the overall rate. If the slow step is not the first one, as in Figure 14.18(b), the faster preceding steps produce intermediate products that accumulate before being consumed in the slow step. In either case *the rate-determining step governs the rate law for the overall reaction.*

 GIVE IT SOME THOUGHT

Why can't the rate law for a reaction generally be deduced from the balanced equation for the reaction?

Mechanisms with a Slow Initial Step

The relationship between the slow step in a mechanism and the rate law for the overall reaction is most easily seen by considering an example in which the first step in a multistep mechanism is the slow, rate-determining step. As an example, consider the reaction of NO_2 and CO to produce NO and CO_2 (Equation 14.23). Below 225°C, it is found experimentally that the rate law for this reaction is second order in NO_2 and zero order in CO: Rate $= k[NO_2]^2$. Can we propose a reaction mechanism that is consistent with this rate law? Consider the following two-step mechanism:*

$$\text{Step 1:} \quad NO_2(g) + NO_2(g) \xrightarrow{k_1} NO_3(g) + NO(g) \quad \text{(slow)}$$

$$\text{Step 2:} \quad NO_3(g) + CO(g) \xrightarrow{k_2} NO_2(g) + CO_2(g) \quad \text{(fast)}$$

$$\text{Overall:} \quad NO_2(g) + CO(g) \longrightarrow NO(g) + CO_2(g)$$

Step 2 is much faster than step 1; that is, $k_2 \gg k_1$. The intermediate $NO_3(g)$ is slowly produced in step 1 and is immediately consumed in step 2.

Because step 1 is slow and step 2 is fast, step 1 is rate determining. Thus, the rate of the overall reaction equals the rate of step 1, and the rate law of the overall reaction equals the rate law of step 1. Step 1 is a bimolecular process that has the rate law

$$\text{Rate} = k_1[NO_2]^2$$

Thus, the rate law predicted by this mechanism agrees with the one observed experimentally.

Could we propose a one-step mechanism for the preceding reaction? We might suppose that the overall reaction is a single bimolecular elementary process that involves the collision of a molecule of NO_2 with one of CO. However, the rate law predicted by this mechanism would be

$$\text{Rate} = k[NO_2][CO]$$

Because this mechanism predicts a rate law different from that observed experimentally, we can rule it out.

■ **SAMPLE EXERCISE 14.14** | Determining the Rate Law for a Multistep Mechanism

The decomposition of nitrous oxide, N_2O, is believed to occur by a two-step mechanism:

$$N_2O(g) \longrightarrow N_2(g) + O(g) \quad \text{(slow)}$$

$$N_2O(g) + O(g) \longrightarrow N_2(g) + O_2(g) \quad \text{(fast)}$$

(a) Write the equation for the overall reaction. **(b)** Write the rate law for the overall reaction.

Solution

Analyze: Given a multistep mechanism with the relative speeds of the steps, we are asked to write the overall reaction and the rate law for that overall reaction.

Plan: (a) The overall reaction is found by adding the elementary steps and eliminating the intermediates. **(b)** The rate law for the overall reaction will be that of the slow, rate-determining step.

Solve: (a) Adding the two elementary reactions gives

$$2 N_2O(g) + O(g) \longrightarrow 2 N_2(g) + O_2(g) + O(g)$$

Omitting the intermediate, O(g), which occurs on both sides of the equation, gives the overall reaction:

$$2 N_2O(g) \longrightarrow 2 N_2(g) + O_2(g)$$

(b) The rate law for the overall reaction is just the rate law for the slow, rate-determining elementary reaction. Because that slow step is a unimolecular elementary reaction, the rate law is first order:

$$\text{Rate} = k[N_2O]$$

---

* The subscript on the rate constant identifies the elementary step involved. Thus, k_1 is the rate constant for step 1, k_2 is the rate constant for step 2, and so forth. A negative subscript refers to the rate constant for the reverse of an elementary step. For example, k_{-1} is the rate constant for the reverse of the first step.

Ozone reacts with nitrogen dioxide to produce dinitrogen pentoxide and oxygen:

$$O_3(g) + 2\,NO_2(g) \longrightarrow N_2O_5(g) + O_2(g)$$

The reaction is believed to occur in two steps:

$$O_3(g) + NO_2(g) \longrightarrow NO_3(g) + O_2(g)$$

$$NO_3(g) + NO_2(g) \longrightarrow N_2O_5(g)$$

The experimental rate law is rate $= k[O_3][NO_2]$. What can you say about the relative rates of the two steps of the mechanism?
Answer: Because the rate law conforms to the molecularity of the first step, that must be the rate-determining step. The second step must be much faster than the first one.

Mechanisms with a Fast Initial Step

It is difficult to derive the rate law for a mechanism in which an intermediate is a reactant in the rate-determining step. This situation arises in multistep mechanisms when the first step is *not* rate determining. Let's consider one example: the gas-phase reaction of nitric oxide (NO) with bromine (Br_2).

$$2\,NO(g) + Br_2(g) \longrightarrow 2\,NOBr(g) \qquad [14.24]$$

The experimentally determined rate law for this reaction is second order in NO and first order in Br_2:

$$Rate = k[NO]^2[Br_2] \qquad [14.25]$$

We seek a reaction mechanism that is consistent with this rate law. One possibility is that the reaction occurs in a single termolecular step:

$$NO(g) + NO(g) + Br_2(g) \longrightarrow 2\,NOBr(g) \qquad Rate = k[NO]^2[Br_2] \qquad [14.26]$$

As noted in Practice Exercise 14.13, this does not seem likely because termolecular processes are so rare.

Let's consider an alternative mechanism that does not invoke termolecular steps:

Step 1: $NO(g) + Br_2(g) \underset{k_{-1}}{\overset{k_1}{\rightleftharpoons}} NOBr_2(g)$ (fast)

Step 2: $NOBr_2(g) + NO(g) \xrightarrow{k_2} 2\,NOBr(g)$ (slow)

In this mechanism, step 1 actually involves two processes: a forward reaction and its reverse.

Because step 2 is the slow, rate-determining step, the rate of the overall reaction is governed by the rate law for that step:

$$Rate = k[NOBr_2][NO] \qquad [14.27]$$

However, $NOBr_2$ is an intermediate generated in step 1. Intermediates are usually unstable molecules that have a low, unknown concentration. Thus, our rate law depends on the unknown concentration of an intermediate.

Fortunately, with the aid of some assumptions, we can express the concentration of the intermediate ($NOBr_2$) in terms of the concentrations of the starting reactants (NO and Br_2). We first assume that $NOBr_2$ is intrinsically unstable and that it does not accumulate to a significant extent in the reaction mixture. There are two ways for $NOBr_2$ to be consumed once it is formed: It can either react with NO to form NOBr or fall back apart into NO and Br_2. The first of these possibilities is step 2, a slow process. The second is the reverse of step 1, a unimolecular process:

$$NOBr_2(g) \xrightarrow{k_{-1}} NO(g) + Br_2(g) \qquad [14.28]$$

Because step 2 is slow, we assume that most of the $NOBr_2$ falls apart according to Equation 14.28. Thus, we have both the forward and reverse reactions of step 1 occurring much faster than step 2. Because they occur rapidly with respect to the reaction in step 2, the forward and reverse processes of step 1 establish an equilibrium. We have seen examples of dynamic equilibrium before, in the equilibrium between a liquid and its vapor ∞ (Section 11.5) and between a solid solute and its solution. ∞ (Section 13.3) As in any dynamic equilibrium, the rates of the forward and reverse reactions are equal. Thus, we can equate the rate expression for the forward reaction in step 1 with the rate expression for the reverse reaction:

$$\underset{\text{Rate of forward reaction}}{k_1[NO][Br_2]} \quad = \quad \underset{\text{Rate of reverse reaction}}{k_{-1}[NOBr_2]}$$

Solving for $[NOBr_2]$, we have

$$[NOBr_2] = \frac{k_1}{k_{-1}}[NO][Br_2]$$

Substituting this relationship into the rate law for the rate-determining step (Equation 14.27), we have

$$\text{Rate} = k_2 \frac{k_1}{k_{-1}}[NO][Br_2][NO] = k[NO]^2[Br_2]$$

This is consistent with the experimental rate law (Equation 14.25). The experimental rate constant, k, equals $k_2 k_1/k_{-1}$. This mechanism, which involves only unimolecular and bimolecular processes, is far more probable than the single termolecular step (Equation 14.26).

In general, *whenever a fast step precedes a slow one, we can solve for the concentration of an intermediate by assuming that an equilibrium is established in the fast step.*

■ SAMPLE EXERCISE 14.15 | Deriving the Rate Law for a Mechanism with a Fast Initial Step

Show that the following mechanism for Equation 14.24 also produces a rate law consistent with the experimentally observed one:

Step 1: $NO(g) + NO(g) \underset{k_{-1}}{\overset{k_1}{\rightleftharpoons}} N_2O_2(g)$ (fast equilibrium)

Step 2: $N_2O_2(g) + Br_2(g) \xrightarrow{k_2} 2\,NOBr(g)$ (slow)

Solution
Analyze: We are given a mechanism with a fast initial step and asked to write the rate law for the overall reaction.
Plan: The rate law of the slow elementary step in a mechanism determines the rate law for the overall reaction. Thus, we first write the rate law based on the molecularity of the slow step. In this case the slow step involves the intermediate N_2O_2 as a reactant. Experimental rate laws, however, do not contain the concentrations of intermediates, but are expressed in terms of the concentrations of starting substances. Thus, we must relate the concentration of N_2O_2 to the concentration of NO by assuming that an equilibrium is established in the first step.
Solve: The second step is rate determining, so the overall rate is

$$\text{Rate} = k_2[N_2O_2][Br_2]$$

We solve for the concentration of the intermediate N_2O_2 by assuming that an equilibrium is established in step 1; thus, the rates of the forward and reverse reactions in step 1 are equal:

$$k_1[NO]^2 = k_{-1}[N_2O_2]$$

$$[N_2O_2] = \frac{k_1}{k_{-1}}[NO]^2$$

Substituting this expression into the rate expression gives

$$\text{Rate} = k_2\frac{k_1}{k_{-1}}[NO]^2[Br_2] = k[NO]^2[Br_2]$$

Thus, this mechanism also yields a rate law consistent with the experimental one.

■ PRACTICE EXERCISE

The first step of a mechanism involving the reaction of bromine is

$$Br_2(g) \underset{k_{-1}}{\overset{k_1}{\rightleftharpoons}} 2\,Br(g) \quad \text{(fast, equilibrium)}$$

What is the expression relating the concentration of Br(g) to that of $Br_2(g)$?

Answer: $[Br] = \left(\frac{k_1}{k_{-1}}[Br_2]\right)^{1/2}$

14.7 | Catalysis

A **catalyst** is a substance that changes the speed of a chemical reaction without undergoing a permanent chemical change itself in the process. Catalysts are very common; most reactions in the body, the atmosphere, and the oceans occur with the help of catalysts. Much industrial chemical research is devoted to the search for new and more effective catalysts for reactions of commercial importance. Extensive research efforts also are devoted to finding means of inhibiting or removing certain catalysts that promote undesirable reactions, such as those that corrode metals, age our bodies, and cause tooth decay.

MOVIE
Catalysis

Homogeneous Catalysis

A catalyst that is present in the same phase as the reacting molecules is called a **homogeneous catalyst**. Examples abound both in solution and in the gas phase. Consider, for example, the decomposition of aqueous hydrogen peroxide, $H_2O_2(aq)$, into water and oxygen:

$$2\,H_2O_2(aq) \longrightarrow 2\,H_2O(l) + O_2(g) \qquad [14.29]$$

In the absence of a catalyst, this reaction occurs extremely slowly.

Many different substances are capable of catalyzing the reaction represented by Equation 14.29, including bromide ion, $Br^-(aq)$, as shown in Figure 14.19 ▶. The bromide ion reacts with hydrogen peroxide in acidic solution, forming aqueous bromine and water:

$$2\,Br^-(aq) + H_2O_2(aq) + 2\,H^+ \longrightarrow Br_2(aq) + 2\,H_2O(l) \qquad [14.30]$$

The brown color observed in the middle photograph of Figure 14.19 indicates the formation of $Br_2(aq)$. If this were the complete reaction, bromide ion would not be a catalyst because it undergoes chemical change during the reaction. However, hydrogen peroxide also reacts with the $Br_2(aq)$ generated in Equation 14.30:

$$Br_2(aq) + H_2O_2(aq) \longrightarrow 2\,Br^-(aq) + 2\,H^+(aq) + O_2(g) \qquad [14.31]$$

The bubbling evident in Figure 14.19(b) is due to the formation of $O_2(g)$.

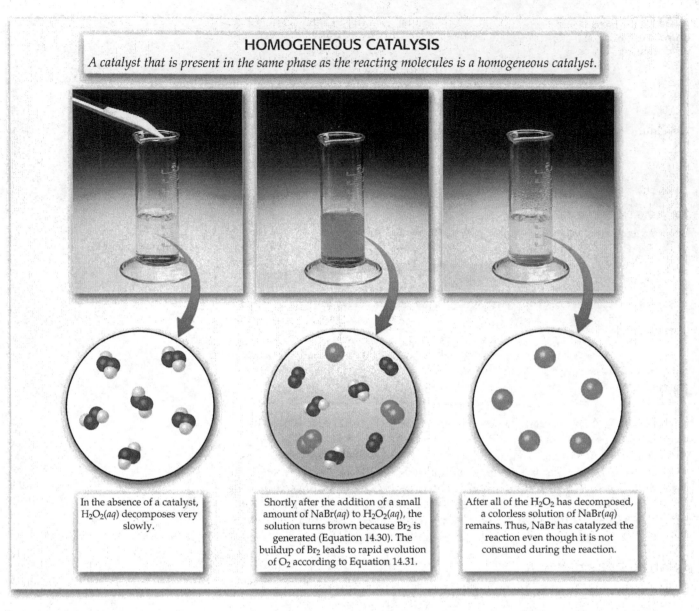

HOMOGENEOUS CATALYSIS

A catalyst that is present in the same phase as the reacting molecules is a homogeneous catalyst.

In the absence of a catalyst, $H_2O_2(aq)$ decomposes very slowly.

Shortly after the addition of a small amount of NaBr(aq) to $H_2O_2(aq)$, the solution turns brown because Br_2 is generated (Equation 14.30). The buildup of Br_2 leads to rapid evolution of O_2 according to Equation 14.31.

After all of the H_2O_2 has decomposed, a colorless solution of NaBr(aq) remains. Thus, NaBr has catalyzed the reaction even though it is not consumed during the reaction.

▲ **Figure 14.19 Effect of catalyst. (H_2O molecules and Na^+ ions are omitted from the molecular art for clarity.)**

The sum of Equations 14.30 and 14.31 is just Equation 14.29:

$$2\,H_2O_2(aq) \longrightarrow 2\,H_2O(l) + O_2(g)$$

When H_2O_2 has been totally decomposed, we are left with a colorless solution of $Br^-(aq)$, as seen in the photograph on the right in Figure 14.19. Bromide ion, therefore, is indeed a catalyst of the reaction because it speeds the overall reaction without itself undergoing any net change. In contrast, Br_2 is an intermediate because it is first formed (Equation 14.30) and then consumed (Equation 14.31). Neither the catalyst nor the intermediate appears in the chemical equation for the overall reaction. Notice, however, that the catalyst is there at the start of the reaction, whereas the intermediate is formed during the course of the reaction.

On the basis of the Arrhenius equation (Equation 14.19), the rate constant (k) is determined by the activation energy (E_a) and the frequency factor (A). A catalyst may affect the rate of reaction by altering the value of either E_a or A. The most dramatic catalytic effects come from lowering E_a. As a general rule, *a catalyst lowers the overall activation energy for a chemical reaction.*

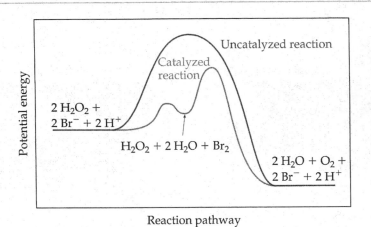

◄ Figure 14.20 Energy profiles for uncatalyzed and catalyzed reactions. The energy profiles for the uncatalyzed decomposition of hydrogen peroxide and for the reaction as catalyzed by Br$^-$ are compared. The catalyzed reaction involves two successive steps, each of which has a lower activation energy than the uncatalyzed reaction. Notice that the energies of reactants and products are unchanged by the catalyst.

A catalyst usually lowers the overall activation energy for a reaction by providing a completely different mechanism for the reaction. The examples given previously involve a reversible, cyclic reaction of the catalyst with the reactants. In the decomposition of hydrogen peroxide, for example, two successive reactions of H_2O_2, with bromide and then with bromine, take place. Because these two reactions together serve as a catalytic pathway for hydrogen peroxide decomposition, *both* of them must have significantly lower activation energies than the uncatalyzed decomposition, as shown schematically in Figure 14.20 ▲.

 GIVE IT SOME THOUGHT

How does a catalyst increase the rate of a reaction?

Heterogeneous Catalysis

A **heterogeneous catalyst** exists in a different phase from the reactant molecules, usually as a solid in contact with either gaseous reactants or with reactants in a liquid solution. Many industrially important reactions are catalyzed by the surfaces of solids. For example, hydrocarbon molecules are rearranged to form gasoline with the aid of what are called "cracking" catalysts (see the "Chemistry at Work" box in Section 25.3). Heterogeneous catalysts are often composed of metals or metal oxides. Because the catalyzed reaction occurs on the surface, special methods are often used to prepare catalysts so that they have very large surface areas.

The initial step in heterogeneous catalysis is usually **adsorption** of reactants. *Adsorption* refers to the binding of molecules to a surface, whereas *absorption* refers to the uptake of molecules into the interior of another substance. ∞ (Section 13.6) Adsorption occurs because the atoms or ions at the surface of a solid are extremely reactive. Unlike their counterparts in the interior of the substance, surface atoms and ions have unused bonding capacity. This unused bonding capability may be used to bond molecules from the gas or solution phase to the surface of the solid.

The reaction of hydrogen gas with ethylene gas to form ethane gas provides an example of heterogeneous catalysis:

$$C_2H_4(g) + H_2(g) \longrightarrow C_2H_6(g) \qquad \Delta H° = -137 \text{ kJ/mol} \qquad [14.32]$$

Ethylene   Ethane

Even though this reaction is exothermic, it occurs very slowly in the absence of a catalyst. In the presence of a finely powdered metal, however, such as nickel, palladium, or platinum, the reaction occurs rather easily at room temperature.

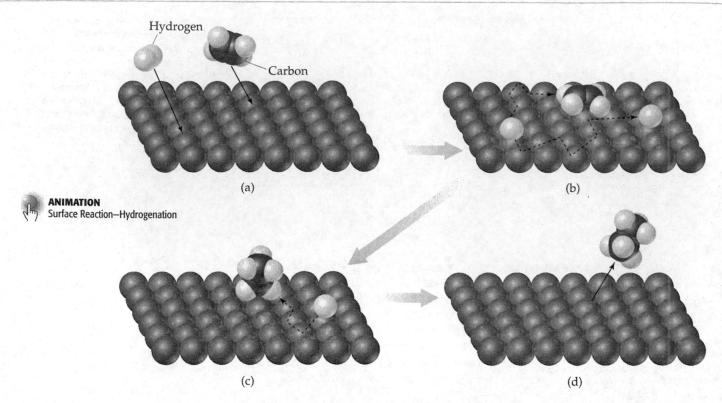

ANIMATION
Surface Reaction–Hydrogenation

▲ **Figure 14.21   Mechanism for reaction of ethylene with hydrogen on a catalytic surface.**
(a) The hydrogen and ethylene are adsorbed at the metal surface. (b) The H — H bond is broken to give adsorbed hydrogen atoms. (c) These migrate to the adsorbed ethylene and bond to the carbon atoms. (d) As C — H bonds are formed, the adsorption of the molecule to the metal surface is decreased and ethane is released.

The mechanism by which the reaction occurs is diagrammed in Figure 14.21 ▲. Both ethylene and hydrogen are adsorbed on the metal surface [Figure 14.21(a)]. Upon adsorption the H—H bond of H_2 breaks, leaving two H atoms that are bonded to the metal surface, as shown in Figure 14.21(b). The hydrogen atoms are relatively free to move about the surface. When a hydrogen encounters an adsorbed ethylene molecule, it can form a σ bond to one of the carbon atoms, effectively destroying the C—C π bond and leaving an *ethyl group* (C_2H_5) bonded to the surface via a metal-to-carbon σ bond [Figure 14.21(c)]. This σ bond is relatively weak, so when the other carbon atom also encounters a hydrogen atom, a sixth C—H σ bond is readily formed and an ethane molecule is released from the metal surface [Figure 14.21(d)]. The site is ready to adsorb another ethylene molecule and thus begin the cycle again.

We can understand the role of the catalyst in this process by considering the bond enthalpies involved. ∞ (Section 8.8) In the course of the reaction, the H—H σ bond and the C—C π bond must be broken, and to do so requires the input of energy, which we can liken to the activation energy of the reaction. The formation of the new C—H σ bonds *releases* an even greater amount of energy, making the reaction exothermic. When H_2 and C_2H_4 are bonded to the surface of the catalyst, less energy is required to break the bonds, lowering the activation energy of the reaction.

Enzymes

Many of the most interesting and important examples of catalysis involve reactions within living systems. The human body is characterized by an extremely complex system of interrelated chemical reactions. All these reactions must

CHEMISTRY AT WORK | Catalytic Converters

Heterogeneous catalysis plays a major role in the fight against urban air pollution. Two components of automobile exhausts that help form photochemical smog are nitrogen oxides and unburned hydrocarbons of various types (Section 18.4). In addition, automobile exhausts may contain considerable quantities of carbon monoxide. Even with the most careful attention to engine design, it is impossible under normal driving conditions to reduce the quantity of these pollutants to an acceptable level in the exhaust gases. It is therefore necessary to remove them from the exhaust before they are vented to the air. This removal is accomplished in the *catalytic converter*.

The catalytic converter, which is part of the exhaust system, must perform two distinct functions: (1) oxidation of CO and unburned hydrocarbons (C_xH_y) to carbon dioxide and water, and (2) reduction of nitrogen oxides to nitrogen gas:

$$CO, C_xH_y \xrightarrow{O_2} CO_2 + H_2O$$

$$NO, NO_2 \longrightarrow N_2$$

These two functions require two distinctly different catalysts, so the development of a successful catalyst system is a difficult challenge. The catalysts must be effective over a wide range of operating temperatures. They must continue to be active in spite of the fact that various components of the exhaust can block the active sites of the catalyst. They must be sufficiently rugged to withstand exhaust gas turbulence and the mechanical shocks of driving under various conditions for thousands of miles.

Catalysts that promote the combustion of CO and hydrocarbons are, in general, the transition-metal oxides and the noble metals, such as platinum. A mixture of two different metal oxides, CuO and Cr_2O_3, might be used, for example. These materials are supported on a structure (Figure 14.22 ▶) that allows the best possible contact between the flowing exhaust gas and the catalyst surface. Either bead or honeycomb structures made from alumina (Al_2O_3) and impregnated with the catalyst may be employed. Such catalysts operate by first adsorbing oxygen gas, also present in the exhaust gas. This adsorption weakens the O—O bond in O_2, so that oxygen atoms are available for reaction with adsorbed CO to form

CO_2. Hydrocarbon oxidation probably proceeds somewhat similarly, with the hydrocarbons first being adsorbed followed by rupture of a C—H bond.

The most effective catalysts for reduction of NO to yield N_2 and O_2 are transition-metal oxides and noble metals, the same kinds of materials that catalyze the oxidation of CO and hydrocarbons. The catalysts that are most effective in one reaction, however, are usually much less effective in the other. It is therefore necessary to have two different catalytic components.

Catalytic converters are remarkably efficient heterogeneous catalysts. The automotive exhaust gases are in contact with the catalyst for only 100 to 400 ms. In this very short time, 96% of the hydrocarbons and CO are converted to CO_2 and H_2O, and the emission of nitrogen oxides is reduced by 76%.

There are costs as well as benefits associated with the use of catalytic converters. Some of the metals used in the converters are very expensive. Catalytic converters currently account for about 35% of the platinum, 65% of the palladium, and 95% of the rhodium used annually. All of these metals, which come mainly from Russia and South Africa, are far more expensive than gold. *Related Exercises:* 14.54, 14.73, and 14.74

▲ **Figure 14.22 Cross section of a catalytic converter.** Automobiles are equipped with catalytic converters, which are part of their exhaust systems. The exhaust gases contain CO, NO, NO_2, and unburned hydrocarbons which pass over surfaces impregnated with catalysts. The catalysts promote the conversion of the exhaust gases into CO_2, H_2O, and N_2.

occur at carefully controlled rates in order to maintain life. A large number of marvelously efficient biological catalysts known as **enzymes** are necessary for many of these reactions to occur at suitable rates. Most enzymes are large protein molecules with molecular weights ranging from about 10,000 to about 1 million amu. They are very selective in the reactions that they catalyze, and some are absolutely specific, operating for only one substance in only one reaction. The decomposition of hydrogen peroxide, for example, is an important biological process. Because hydrogen peroxide is strongly oxidizing, it can be physiologically harmful. For this reason, the blood and livers of mammals contain an enzyme, *catalase*, which catalyzes the decomposition of hydrogen peroxide into water and oxygen (Equation 14.29). Figure 14.23 ▶ shows the dramatic acceleration of this chemical reaction by the catalase in beef liver.

▶ **Figure 14.23 Effect of an enzyme.**
Ground-up beef liver causes hydrogen peroxide
to decompose rapidly into water and oxygen.
The decomposition is catalyzed by the enzyme
catalase. Grinding the liver breaks open the cells,
so that the reaction takes place more rapidly.
The frothing is due to escape of oxygen gas from
the reaction mixture.

▶ **Figure 14.24 The lock-and-key model
for enzyme action.** The correct substrate is
recognized by its ability to fit the active site of the
enzyme, forming the enzyme-substrate complex.
After the reaction of the substrate is complete, the
products separate from the enzyme.

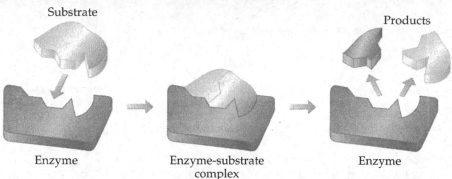

Substrate

Products

Enzyme

Enzyme-substrate
complex

Enzyme

(a)

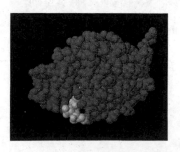

(b)

▲ **Figure 14.25 Molecular model of an
enzyme.** (a) A molecular model of the enzyme
lysozyme. Note the characteristic cleft, which is
the location of the active site. (b) Lysozyme with
a bound substrate molecule.

Although an enzyme is a large molecule, the reaction is catalyzed at a very
specific location in the enzyme, called the **active site**. The substances that undergo reaction at this site are called **substrates**. A simple explanation for the
specificity of enzymes is provided by the **lock-and-key model**, illustrated in
Figure 14.24 ▲. The substrate is pictured as fitting neatly into a special place on
the enzyme (the active site), much like a specific key fitting into a lock. The active site is created by coiling and folding of the long protein molecule to form a
space, something like a pocket, into which the substrate molecule fits.
Figure 14.25 ◀ shows a model of the enzyme *lysozyme* with and without a
bound substrate molecule.

The combination of the enzyme and the substrate is called the *enzyme-
substrate complex.* Although Figure 14.24 shows both the active site and its complementary substrate as having rigid shapes, there is often a fair amount of
flexibility in the active site. Thus, the active site may change shape as it binds
the substrate. The binding between the substrate and the active site involves intermolecular forces such as dipole-dipole attractions, hydrogen bonds, and
London dispersion forces. ∞ (Section 11.2)

As the substrate molecules enter the active site, they are somehow activated,
so that they are capable of extremely rapid reaction. This activation may result
from the withdrawal or donation of electron density at a particular bond by the
enzyme. In addition, in the process of fitting into the active site, the substrate
molecule may be distorted and thus made more reactive. Once the reaction occurs, the products then depart, allowing another substrate molecule to enter.

The activity of an enzyme is destroyed if some molecule in the solution is
able to bind strongly to the active site and block the entry of the substrate. Such
substances are called *enzyme inhibitors.* Nerve poisons and certain toxic metal
ions such as lead and mercury are believed to act in this way to inhibit enzyme

activity. Some other poisons act by attaching elsewhere on the enzyme, thereby distorting the active site so that the substrate no longer fits.

Enzymes are enormously more efficient than ordinary nonbiochemical catalysts. The number of individual catalyzed reaction events occurring at a particular active site, called the *turnover number*, is generally in the range of 10^3 to 10^7 per second. Such large turnover numbers correspond to very low activation energies.

 GIVE IT SOME THOUGHT

What names are given to the following aspects of enzymes and enzyme catalysis: (a) the place on the enzyme where catalysis occurs, (b) the substances that undergo catalysis?

 CHEMISTRY AND LIFE | Nitrogen Fixation and Nitrogenase

Nitrogen is one of the most essential elements in living organisms. It is found in many compounds that are vital to life, including proteins, nucleic acids, vitamins, and hormones. Plants use very simple nitrogen-containing compounds, especially NH_3, NH_4^+, and NO_3^-, as starting materials from which such complex, biologically necessary compounds are formed. Animals are unable to synthesize the complex nitrogen compounds they require from the simple substances used by plants. Instead, they rely on more complicated precursors present in vitamin- and protein-rich foods.

Nitrogen is continually cycling through this biological arena in various forms, as shown in the simplified nitrogen cycle in Figure 14.26 ▼. For example, certain microorganisms convert the nitrogen in animal waste and dead plants and animals into molecular nitrogen, $N_2(g)$, which returns to the atmosphere. In order for the food chain to be sustained, there must be a means of reincorporating this atmospheric N_2 in a form that plants can utilize. The process of converting N_2 into compounds that plants can use is called *nitrogen fixation*. Fixing nitrogen is difficult; N_2 is an exceptionally unreactive molecule, in large part because of its very strong $N \equiv N$ triple bond. ∞ (Section 8.3) Some fixed nitrogen results from the action of lightning on the atmosphere, and some is produced industrially using a process we will discuss in Chapter 15. About 60% of fixed nitrogen, however, is a consequence of the action of a remarkable and complex enzyme called *nitrogenase*. This enzyme is *not* present in humans or other animals; rather, it is found in bacteria that live in the root nodules of certain plants such as the legumes clover and alfalfa.

Nitrogenase converts N_2 into NH_3, a process that, in the absence of a catalyst, has a very large activation energy. This process is a *reduction* of nitrogen—during the reaction, its oxidation state is reduced from 0 in N_2 to -3 in NH_3. The mechanism by which nitrogenase reduces N_2 is not fully understood. Like many other enzymes, including catalase, the active site of nitrogenase contains transition-metal atoms;

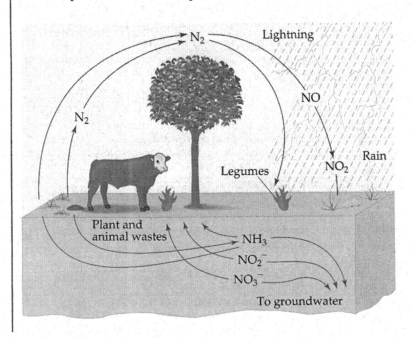

◀ **Figure 14.26 Simplified picture of the nitrogen cycle.** The compounds of nitrogen in the soil are water-soluble species, such as NH_3, NO_2^-, and NO_3^-, which can be washed out of the soil by groundwater. These nitrogen compounds are converted into biomolecules by plants and are incorporated into animals that eat the plants. Animal waste and dead plants and animals are attacked by certain bacteria that release N_2 to the atmosphere. Atmospheric N_2 is fixed in the soil predominantly by the action of certain plants that contain the enzyme nitrogenase, thereby completing the cycle.

continues on next page

continued

such enzymes are called *metalloenzymes*. Because transition metals can readily change oxidation state, metalloenzymes are especially useful for effecting transformations in which substrates are either oxidized or reduced.

It has been known for nearly 20 years that a portion of nitrogenase contains iron and molybdenum atoms. This portion, called the *FeMo-cofactor*, is thought to serve as the active site of the enzyme. The FeMo-cofactor of nitrogenase is a striking cluster of seven Fe atoms and one Mo atom, all linked by sulfur atoms (Figure 14.27 ▼). In 2002, scientists using higher resolution X-ray crystallography discovered a single light atom at the center of the FeMo-cofactor. The specific identity of the atom is not yet known, but it is thought to be a nitrogen atom. The role of this atom in the reduction of N_2 by the cofactor is an area of intense current research.

It is one of the wonders of life that simple bacteria can contain beautifully complex and vitally important enzymes such as nitrogenase. Because of this enzyme, nitrogen is continually cycled between its comparatively inert role in the atmosphere and its critical role in living organisms; without it, life as we know it could not exist on Earth.
Related Exercises: 14.77, 14.103

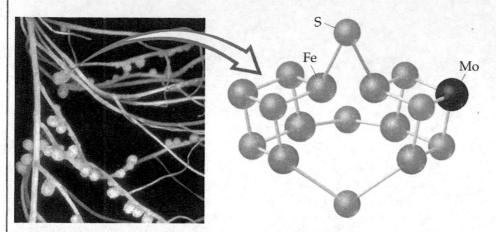

◀ **Figure 14.27　The FeMo-cofactor of nitrogenase.** Nitrogenase is found in nodules in the roots of certain plants, such as the white clover roots shown at the left. The cofactor, which is thought to be the active site of the enzyme, contains seven Fe atoms and one Mo atom, linked by sulfur atoms. The molecules on the outside of the cofactor connect it to the rest of the protein.

SAMPLE INTEGRATIVE EXERCISE | Putting Concepts Together

Formic acid (HCOOH) decomposes in the gas phase at elevated temperatures as follows:

$$HCOOH(g) \longrightarrow CO_2(g) + H_2(g)$$

The decomposition reaction is determined to be first order. A graph of the partial pressure of HCOOH versus time for decomposition at 838 K is shown as the red curve in Figure 14.28 ◀. When a small amount of solid ZnO is added to the reaction chamber, the partial pressure of acid versus time varies as shown by the blue curve in Figure 14.28.

  (a) Estimate the half-life and first-order rate constant for formic acid decomposition.

  (b) What can you conclude from the effect of added ZnO on the decomposition of formic acid?

  (c) The progress of the reaction was followed by measuring the partial pressure of formic acid vapor at selected times. Suppose that, instead, we had plotted the concentration of formic acid in units of mol/L. What effect would this have had on the calculated value of k?

  (d) The pressure of formic acid vapor at the start of the reaction is 3.00×10^2 torr. Assuming constant temperature and ideal-gas behavior, what is the pressure in the system at the end of the reaction? If the volume of the reaction chamber is 436 cm³, how many moles of gas occupy the reaction chamber at the end of the reaction?

  (e) The standard heat of formation of formic acid vapor is $\Delta H_f^\circ = -378.6$ kJ/mol. Calculate ΔH° for the overall reaction. Assuming that the activation energy (E_a) for the reaction is 184 kJ/mol, sketch an approximate energy profile for the reaction, and label E_a, ΔH°, and the transition state.

Solution **(a)** The initial pressure of HCOOH is 3.00×10^2 torr. On the graph we move to the level at which the partial pressure of HCOOH is 150 torr, half the initial value. This corresponds to a time of about 6.60×10^2 s, which is therefore the half-life. The first-order rate constant is given by Equation 14.15: $k = 0.693/t_{1/2} = 0.693/660$ s $= 1.05 \times 10^{-3}$ s^{-1}.

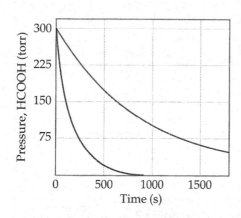

▲ **Figure 14.28　Variation in pressure of HCOOH(*g*) as a function of time at 838 K.** The red line corresponds to decomposition when only gaseous HCOOH is present. The blue line corresponds to decomposition in the presence of added ZnO(*s*).

(b) The reaction proceeds much more rapidly in the presence of solid ZnO, so the surface of the oxide must be acting as a catalyst for the decomposition of the acid. This is an example of heterogeneous catalysis.

(c) If we had graphed the concentration of formic acid in units of moles per liter, we would still have determined that the half-life for decomposition is 660 seconds, and we would have computed the same value for k. Because the units for k are s^{-1}, the value for k is independent of the units used for concentration.

(d) According to the stoichiometry of the reaction, two moles of product are formed for each mole of reactant. When reaction is completed, therefore, the pressure will be 600 torr, just twice the initial pressure, assuming ideal-gas behavior. (Because we are working at quite high temperature and fairly low gas pressure, assuming ideal-gas behavior is reasonable.) The number of moles of gas present can be calculated using the ideal-gas equation (Section 10.4):

$$n = \frac{PV}{RT} = \frac{(600/760\ atm)\ (0.436\ L)}{(0.0821\ L\text{-}atm/mol\text{-}K)(838\ K)} = 5.00 \times 10^{-3}\ moles$$

(e) We first calculate the overall change in energy, $\Delta H°$ (Section 5.7 and Appendix C), as in

$$\Delta H° = \Delta H_f°(CO_2(g)) + \Delta H_f°(H_2(g)) - \Delta H_f°(HCOOH(g))$$

$$= -393.5\ kJ/mol + 0 - (-378.6\ kJ/mol)$$

$$= -14.9\ kJ/mol$$

From this and the given value for E_a, we can draw an approximate energy profile for the reaction, in analogy to Figure 14.15.

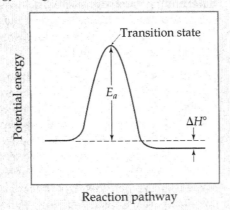

Reaction pathway

SUMMARY AND KEY TERMS

Introduction and Section 14.1   In this chapter we explored **chemical kinetics**, the area of chemistry that studies the rates of chemical reactions and the factors that affect them, namely, concentration, temperature, and catalysts.

Section 14.2   **Reaction rates** are usually expressed as changes in concentration per unit time: Typically, for reactions in solution, rates are given in units of molarity per second (M/s). For most reactions, a plot of molarity versus time shows that the rate slows down as the reaction proceeds. The **instantaneous rate** is the slope of a line drawn tangent to the concentration-versus-time curve at a specific time. Rates can be written in terms of the appearance of products or the disappearance of reactants; the stoichiometry of the reaction dictates the relationship between rates of appearance and disappearance. Spectroscopy is one technique that can be used to monitor the course of a reaction. According to **Beer's law**, the absorption of electromagnetic radiation by a substance at a particular wavelength is directly proportional to its concentration.

Section 14.3   The quantitative relationship between rate and concentration is expressed by a **rate law**, which usually has the following form:

$$Rate = k[\text{reactant 1}]^m[\text{reactant 2}]^n \dots$$

The constant k in the rate law is called the **rate constant**; the exponents m, n, and so forth are called **reaction orders** for the reactants. The sum of the reaction orders gives the **overall reaction order**. Reaction orders must be determined experimentally. The units of the rate constant depend on the overall reaction order. For a reaction in which the overall reaction order is 1, k has units of s^{-1}; for one in which the overall reaction order is 2, k has units of $M^{-1}\ s^{-1}$.

Section 14.4   Rate laws can be used to determine the concentrations of reactants or products at any time during a reaction. In a **first-order reaction** the rate is proportional to the concentration of a single reactant raised to the first power: Rate = $k[A]$. In such cases the integrated form of the rate law is $\ln[A]_t = -kt + \ln[A]_0$, where $[A]_t$ is the concentration of reactant A at time t, k is the rate constant, and $[A]_0$ is the initial concentration of A. Thus, for a first-order reaction, a graph of $\ln[A]$ versus time yields a straight line of slope $-k$.

A **second-order reaction** is one for which the overall reaction order is 2. If a second-order rate law depends on the concentration of only one reactant, then rate = $k[A]^2$, and the time dependence of [A] is given by the integrated form of the rate law: $1/[A]_t = 1/[A]_0 + kt$. In this case a graph of $1/[A]_t$ versus time yields a straight line.

The **half-life** of a reaction, $t_{1/2}$, is the time required for the concentration of a reactant to drop to one-half of its original value. For a first-order reaction, the half-life depends only on the rate constant and not on the initial concentration: $t_{1/2} = 0.693/k$. The half-life of a second-order reaction depends on both the rate constant and the initial concentration of A: $t_{1/2} = 1/k[A]_0$.

Section 14.5   The **collision model**, which assumes that reactions occur as a result of collisions between molecules, helps explain why the magnitudes of rate constants increase with increasing temperature. The greater the kinetic energy of the colliding molecules, the greater the energy of collision. The minimum energy required for a reaction to occur is called the **activation energy**, E_a. A collision with energy E_a or greater can cause the atoms of the colliding molecules to reach the **activated complex** (or **transition state**), which is the highest energy arrangement in the pathway from reactants to products. Even if a collision is energetic enough, it may not lead to reaction; the reactants must also be correctly oriented relative to one another in order for a collision to be effective.

Because the kinetic energy of molecules depends on temperature, the rate constant of a reaction is very dependent on temperature. The relationship between k and temperature is given by the **Arrhenius equation**: $k = Ae^{-E_a/RT}$. The term A is called the **frequency factor**; it relates to the number of collisions that are favorably oriented for reaction. The Arrhenius equation is often used in logarithmic form: $k = \ln A - E_a/RT$. Thus, a graph of $\ln k$ versus $1/T$ yields a straight line with slope $-E_a/R$.

Section 14.6   A **reaction mechanism** details the individual steps that occur in the course of a reaction. Each of these steps, called **elementary reactions**, has a well-defined rate law that depends on the number of molecules (the **molecularity**) of the step. Elementary reactions are defined as either **unimolecular**, **bimolecular**, or **termolecular**, depending on whether one, two, or three reactant molecules are involved, respectively. Termolecular elementary reactions are very rare. Unimolecular, bimolecular, and termolecular reactions follow rate laws that are first order overall, second order overall, and third order overall, respectively.

Many reactions occur by a multistep mechanism, involving two or more elementary reactions, or steps. An **intermediate** is produced in one elementary step and is consumed in a later elementary step and therefore does not appear in the overall equation for the reaction. When a mechanism has several elementary steps, the overall rate is limited by the slowest elementary step, called the **rate-determining step**. A fast elementary step that follows the rate-determining step will have no effect on the rate law of the reaction. A fast step that precedes the rate-determining step often creates an equilibrium that involves an intermediate. For a mechanism to be valid, the rate law predicted by the mechanism must be the same as that observed experimentally.

Section 14.7   A **catalyst** is a substance that increases the rate of a reaction without undergoing a net chemical change itself. It does so by providing a different mechanism for the reaction, one that has a lower activation energy. A **homogeneous catalyst** is one that is in the same phase as the reactants. A **heterogeneous catalyst** has a different phase from the reactants. Finely divided metals are often used as heterogeneous catalysts for solution- and gas-phase reactions. Reacting molecules can undergo binding, or **adsorption**, at the surface of the catalyst. The adsorption of a reactant at specific sites on the surface makes bond breaking easier, lowering the activation energy. Catalysis in living organisms is achieved by **enzymes**, large protein molecules that usually catalyze a very specific reaction. The specific reactant molecules involved in an enzymatic reaction are called **substrates**. The site of the enzyme where the catalysis occurs is called the **active site**. In the **lock-and-key model** for enzyme catalysis, substrate molecules bind very specifically to the active site of the enzyme, after which they can undergo reaction.

VISUALIZING CONCEPTS

14.1 Consider the following graph of the concentration of a substance over time. **(a)** Is X a reactant or product of the reaction? **(b)** Why is the average rate of the reaction greater between points 1 and 2 than between points 2 and 3? [Section 14.2]

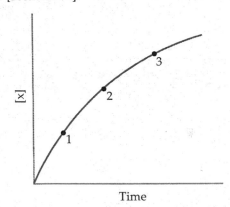

14.2 You study the rate of a reaction, measuring both the concentration of the reactant and the concentration of the product as a function of time, and obtain the following results:

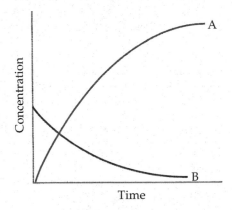

What chemical equation is consistent with this data:
(a) A $\longrightarrow$ B,   **(b)** B $\longrightarrow$ A,   **(c)** A $\longrightarrow$ 2 B,
(d) B $\longrightarrow$ 2 A. Explain your choice. [Section 14.2]

14.3 You perform a series of experiments for the reaction A $\longrightarrow$ B + C and find that the rate law has the form rate = $k[A]^x$. Determine the value of x in each of the following cases: **(a)** There is no rate change when [A] is tripled. **(b)** The rate increases by a factor of 9 when [A] is tripled. **(c)** When [A] is doubled, the rate increases by a factor of 8. [Section 14.3]

14.4 A friend studies a first-order reaction and obtains the following three graphs for experiments done at two different temperatures. **(a)** Which two lines represent experiments done at the same temperature? What accounts for the difference in these two lines? In what way are they the same? **(b)** Which two lines represent experiments done with the same starting concentration but at different temperatures? Which line probably represents the lower temperature? How do you know? [Section 14.4]

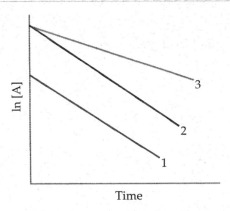

14.5 **(a)** Given the following diagrams at $t = 0$ and $t = 30$ min, what is the half-life of the reaction if it follows first-order kinetics?

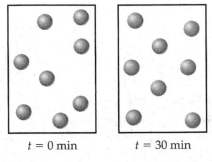

$t = 0$ min $t = 30$ min

(b) After four half-life periods for a first-order reaction, what fraction of reactant remains? [Section 14.4]

14.6 You study the effect of temperature on the rate of two reactions and graph the natural logarithm of the rate constant for each reaction as a function of $1/T$. How do the two graphs compare **(a)** if the activation energy of the second reaction is higher than the activation energy of the first reaction but the two reactions have the same frequency factor, and **(b)** if the frequency factor of the second reaction is higher than the frequency factor of the first reaction but the two reactions have the same activation energy? [Section 14.5]

14.7 Consider the diagram below, which represents two steps in an overall reaction. The red spheres are oxygen, the blue ones nitrogen, and the green ones fluorine. **(a)** Write the chemical equation for each step in the reaction. **(b)** Write the equation for the overall reaction. **(c)** Identify the intermediate in the mechanism. **(d)** Write the rate law for the overall reaction if the first step is the slow, rate-determining step. [Section 14.6]

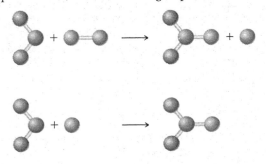

14.8 Based on the following reaction profile, how many intermediates are formed in the reaction A $\longrightarrow$ C? How many transition states are there? Which step is the fastest? Is the reaction A $\longrightarrow$ C exothermic or endothermic? [Section 14.6]

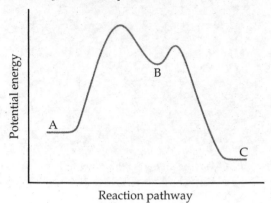

Reaction pathway

14.9 Draw a possible transition state for the bimolecular reaction depicted below. (The blue spheres are nitrogen atoms, and the red ones are oxygen atoms.) Use dashed lines to represent the bonds that are in the process of being broken or made in the transition state. [Section 14.6]

14.10 The following diagram represents an imaginary two-step mechanism. Let the orange spheres represent element A, the green ones element B, and the blue ones element C. **(a)** Write the equation for the net reaction that is occurring. **(b)** Identify the intermediate. **(c)** Identify the catalyst. [Sections 14.6 and 14.7]

EXERCISES

Reaction Rates

14.11 **(a)** What is meant by the term *reaction rate*? **(b)** Name three factors that can affect the rate of a chemical reaction. **(c)** What information is necessary to relate the rate of disappearance of reactants to the rate of appearance of products?

14.12 **(a)** What are the units usually used to express the rates of reactions occurring in solution? **(b)** From your everyday experience, give two examples of the effects of temperature on the rates of reactions. **(c)** What is the difference between average rate and instantaneous rate?

14.13 Consider the following hypothetical aqueous reaction: A(aq) $\longrightarrow$ B(aq). A flask is charged with 0.065 mol of A in a total volume of 100.0 mL. The following data are collected:

Time (min)	0	10	20	30	40
Moles of A	0.065	0.051	0.042	0.036	0.031

(a) Calculate the number of moles of B at each time in the table, assuming that there are no molecules of B at time zero. **(b)** Calculate the average rate of disappearance of A for each 10-min interval, in units of M/s. **(c)** Between t = 10 min and t = 30 min, what is the average rate of appearance of B in units of M/s? Assume that the volume of the solution is constant.

14.14 A flask is charged with 0.100 mol of A and allowed to react to form B according to the hypothetical gas-phase reaction A(g) $\longrightarrow$ B(g). The following data are collected:

Time (s)	0	40	80	120	160
Moles of A	0.100	0.067	0.045	0.030	0.020

(a) Calculate the number of moles of B at each time in the table. **(b)** Calculate the average rate of disappearance of A for each 40-s interval, in units of mol/s. **(c)** What additional information would be needed to calculate the rate in units of concentration per time?

14.15 The isomerization of methyl isonitrile (CH_3NC) to acetonitrile (CH_3CN) was studied in the gas phase at 215°C, and the following data were obtained:

Time (s)	[CH₃NC] (M)
0	0.0165
2,000	0.0110
5,000	0.00591
8,000	0.00314
12,000	0.00137
15,000	0.00074

(a) Calculate the average rate of reaction, in M/s, for the time interval between each measurement. **(b)** Graph [CH₃NC] versus time, and determine the instantaneous rates in M/s at t = 5000 s and t = 8000 s.

14.16 The rate of disappearance of HCl was measured for the following reaction:

$$CH_3OH(aq) + HCl(aq) \longrightarrow CH_3Cl(aq) + H_2O(l)$$

The following data were collected:

Time (min)	[HCl] (M)
0.0	1.85
54.0	1.58
107.0	1.36
215.0	1.02
430.0	0.580

(a) Calculate the average rate of reaction, in M/s, for the time interval between each measurement.

(b) Graph [HCl] versus time, and determine the instantaneous rates in M/min and M/s at $t = 75.0$ min and $t = 250$ min.

14.17 For each of the following gas-phase reactions, indicate how the rate of disappearance of each reactant is related to the rate of appearance of each product:

(a) $H_2O_2(g) \longrightarrow H_2(g) + O_2(g)$

(b) $2 N_2O(g) \longrightarrow 2 N_2(g) + O_2(g)$

(c) $N_2(g) + 3 H_2(g) \longrightarrow 2 NH_3(g)$

14.18 For each of the following gas-phase reactions, write the rate expression in terms of the appearance of each product or disappearance of each reactant:

(a) $2 HBr(g) \longrightarrow H_2(g) + Br_2(g)$

(b) $2 SO_2(g) + O_2(g) \longrightarrow 2 SO_3(g)$

(c) $2 NO(g) + 2 H_2(g) \longrightarrow N_2(g) + 2 H_2O(g)$

14.19 (a) Consider the combustion of $H_2(g)$: $2 H_2(g) + O_2(g) \longrightarrow 2 H_2O(g)$. If hydrogen is burning at the rate of 0.85 mol/s, what is the rate of consumption of oxygen? What is the rate of formation of water vapor? (b) The reaction $2 NO(g) + Cl_2(g) \longrightarrow 2 NOCl(g)$ is carried out in a closed vessel. If the partial pressure of NO is decreasing at the rate of 23 torr/min, what is the rate of change of the total pressure of the vessel?

14.20 (a) Consider the combustion of ethylene, $C_2H_4(g) + 3 O_2(g) \longrightarrow 2 CO_2(g) + 2 H_2O(g)$. If the concentration of C_2H_4 is decreasing at the rate of 0.37 M/s, what are the rates of change in the concentrations of CO_2 and H_2O? (b) The rate of decrease in N_2H_4 partial pressure in a closed reaction vessel from the reaction $N_2H_4(g) + H_2(g) \longrightarrow 2 NH_3(g)$ is 63 torr/h. What are the rates of change of NH_3 partial pressure and total pressure in the vessel?

Rate Laws

14.21 A reaction $A + B \longrightarrow C$ obeys the following rate law: Rate $= k[B]^2$. (a) If [A] is doubled, how will the rate change? Will the rate constant change? Explain. (b) What are the reaction orders for A and B? What is the overall reaction order? (c) What are the units of the rate constant?

14.22 A reaction $A + B \longrightarrow C$ obeys the following rate law: Rate $= k[A]^2[B]$. (a) If [A] is doubled, how will the rate change? Will the rate constant change? Explain. (b) What are the reaction orders for A and B? What is the overall reaction order? (c) What are the units of the rate constant?

14.23 The decomposition of N_2O_5 in carbon tetrachloride proceeds as follows: $2 N_2O_5 \longrightarrow 4 NO_2 + O_2$. The rate law is first order in N_2O_5. At 64°C the rate constant is $4.82 \times 10^{-3} s^{-1}$. (a) Write the rate law for the reaction. (b) What is the rate of reaction when $[N_2O_5] = 0.0240 M$? (c) What happens to the rate when the concentration of N_2O_5 is doubled to 0.0480 M?

14.24 Consider the following reaction:

$$2 NO(g) + 2 H_2(g) \longrightarrow N_2(g) + 2 H_2O(g)$$

(a) The rate law for this reaction is first order in H_2 and second order in NO. Write the rate law. (b) If the rate constant for this reaction at 1000 K is $6.0 \times 10^4 M^{-2} s^{-1}$, what is the reaction rate when $[NO] = 0.025 M$ and $[H_2] = 0.015 M$? (c) What is the reaction rate at 1000 K when the concentration of NO is increased to 0.10 M, while the concentration of H_2 is 0.010 M?

14.25 Consider the following reaction:

$$CH_3Br(aq) + OH^-(aq) \longrightarrow CH_3OH(aq) + Br^-(aq)$$

The rate law for this reaction is first order in CH_3Br and first order in OH^-. When $[CH_3Br]$ is $5.0 \times 10^{-3} M$ and $[OH^-]$ is 0.050 M, the reaction rate at 298 K is 0.0432 M/s. (a) What is the value of the rate constant? (b) What are the units of the rate constant? (c) What would happen to the rate if the concentration of OH^- were tripled?

14.26 The reaction between ethyl bromide (C_2H_5Br) and hydroxide ion in ethyl alcohol at 330 K, $C_2H_5Br(alc) + OH^-(alc) \longrightarrow C_2H_5OH(l) + Br^-(alc)$, is first order each in ethyl bromide and hydroxide ion. When $[C_2H_5Br]$ is 0.0477 M and $[OH^-]$ is 0.100 M, the rate of disappearance of ethyl bromide is $1.7 \times 10^{-7} M/s$. (a) What is the value of the rate constant? (b) What are the units of the rate constant? (c) How would the rate of disappearance of ethyl bromide change if the solution were diluted by adding an equal volume of pure ethyl alcohol to the solution?

14.27 The iodide ion reacts with hypochlorite ion (the active ingredient in chlorine bleaches) in the following way: $OCl^- + I^- \longrightarrow OI^- + Cl^-$. This rapid reaction gives the following rate data:

$[OCl^-]$, M	I^-, M	Rate, M/s
1.5×10^{-3}	1.5×10^{-3}	1.36×10^{-4}
3.0×10^{-3}	1.5×10^{-3}	2.72×10^{-4}
1.5×10^{-3}	3.0×10^{-3}	2.72×10^{-4}

(a) Write the rate law for this reaction. (b) Calculate the rate constant. (c) Calculate the rate when $[OCl^-] = 2.0 \times 10^{-3} M$ and $[I^-] = 5.0 \times 10^{-4} M$.

14.28 The reaction $2 ClO_2(aq) + 2 OH^-(aq) \longrightarrow ClO_3^-(aq) + ClO_2^-(aq) + H_2O(l)$ was studied with the following results:

Experiment	$[ClO_2]$, M	$[OH^-]$, M	Rate, M/s
1	0.060	0.030	0.0248
2	0.020	0.030	0.00276
3	0.020	0.090	0.00828

(a) Determine the rate law for the reaction. (b) Calculate the rate constant. (c) Calculate the rate when $[ClO_2] = 0.010 M$ and $[OH^-] = 0.025 M$.

14.29 The following data were measured for the reaction $BF_3(g) + NH_3(g) \longrightarrow F_3BNH_3(g)$:

Experiment	$[BF_3]$ (M)	$[NH_3]$ (M)	Initial Rate (M/s)
1	0.250	0.250	0.2130
2	0.250	0.125	0.1065
3	0.200	0.100	0.0682
4	0.350	0.100	0.1193
5	0.175	0.100	0.0596

(a) What is the rate law for the reaction? (b) What is the overall order of the reaction? (c) What is the value of the rate constant for the reaction? (d) What is the rate when $[BF_3] = 0.100\ M$ and $[NH_3] = 0.500\ M$?

14.30 The following data were collected for the rate of disappearance of NO in the reaction $2\ NO(g) + O_2(g) \longrightarrow 2\ NO_2(g)$:

Experiment	[NO] (M)	[O₂] (M)	Initial Rate (M/s)
1	0.0126	0.0125	1.41×10^{-2}
2	0.0252	0.0250	1.13×10^{-1}
3	0.0252	0.0125	5.64×10^{-2}

(a) What is the rate law for the reaction? (b) What are the units of the rate constant? (c) What is the average value of the rate constant calculated from the three data sets? (d) What is the rate of disappearance of NO when $[NO] = 0.100\ M$ and $[O_2] = 0.0200\ M$? (e) What is the rate of disappearance of O_2 at the concentrations given in part (d)?

[14.31] Consider the gas-phase reaction between nitric oxide and bromine at $273°C$: $2\ NO(g) + Br_2(g) \longrightarrow 2\ NOBr(g)$. The following data for the initial rate of appearance of NOBr were obtained:

Experiment	[NO] (M)	[Br₂] (M)	Initial Rate (M/s)
1	0.10	0.20	24
2	0.25	0.20	150
3	0.10	0.50	60
4	0.35	0.50	735

(a) Determine the rate law. (b) Calculate the average value of the rate constant for the appearance of NOBr from the four data sets. (c) How is the rate of appearance of NOBr related to the rate of disappearance of Br_2? (d) What is the rate of disappearance of Br_2 when $[NO] = 0.075\ M$ and $[Br_2] = 0.25\ M$?

[14.32] Consider the reaction of peroxydisulfate ion ($S_2O_8^{2-}$) with iodide ion (I^-) in aqueous solution:

$$S_2O_8^{2-}(aq) + 3\ I^-(aq) \longrightarrow 2\ SO_4^{2-}(aq) + I_3^-(aq)$$

At a particular temperature the rate of disappearance of $S_2O_8^{2-}$ varies with reactant concentrations in the following manner:

Experiment	[S₂O₈²⁻] (M)	[I⁻] (M)	Initial Rate (M/s)
1	0.018	0.036	2.6×10^{-6}
2	0.027	0.036	3.9×10^{-6}
3	0.036	0.054	7.8×10^{-6}
4	0.050	0.072	1.4×10^{-5}

(a) Determine the rate law for the reaction. (b) What is the average value of the rate constant for the disappearance of $S_2O_8^{2-}$ based on the four sets of data? (c) How is the rate of disappearance of $S_2O_8^{2-}$ related to the rate of disappearance of I^-? (d) What is the rate of disappearance of I^- when $[S_2O_8^{2-}] = 0.015\ M$ and $[I^-] = 0.040\ M$?

Change of Concentration with Time

14.33 (a) Define the following symbols that are encountered in rate equations: $[A]_0, t_{1/2}, [A]_t, k$. (b) What quantity, when graphed versus time, will yield a straight line for a first-order reaction?

14.34 (a) For a second-order reaction, what quantity, when graphed versus time, will yield a straight line? (b) How do the half-lives of first-order and second-order reactions differ?

14.35 (a) The gas-phase decomposition of SO_2Cl_2, $SO_2Cl_2(g) \longrightarrow SO_2(g) + Cl_2(g)$, is first order in SO_2Cl_2. At 600 K the half-life for this process is 2.3×10^5 s. What is the rate constant at this temperature? (b) At 320°C the rate constant is 2.2×10^{-5} s^{-1}. What is the half-life at this temperature?

14.36 Americium-241 is used in smoke detectors. It has a rate constant for radioactive decay of $k = 1.6 \times 10^{-3}$ yr^{-1}. By contrast, iodine-125, which is used to test for thyroid functioning, has a rate constant for radioactive decay of $k = 0.011$ day^{-1}. (a) What are the half-lives of these two isotopes? (b) Which one decays at a faster rate? (c) How much of a 1.00-mg sample of either isotope remains after three half-lives?

14.37 As described in Exercise 14.35, the decomposition of sulfuryl chloride (SO_2Cl_2) is a first-order process. The rate constant for the decomposition at 660 K is 4.5×10^{-2} s^{-1}. (a) If we begin with an initial SO_2Cl_2 pressure of 375 torr, what is the pressure of this substance after 65 s? (b) At what time will the pressure of SO_2Cl_2 decline to one-tenth its initial value?

14.38 The first-order rate constant for the decomposition of N_2O_5, $N_2O_5(g) \longrightarrow 2\ NO_2(g) + O_2(g)$, at 70°C is 6.82×10^{-3} s^{-1}. Suppose we start with 0.0250 mol of $N_2O_5(g)$ in a volume of 2.0 L. (a) How many moles of N_2O_5 will remain after 2.5 min? (b) How many minutes will it take for the quantity of N_2O_5 to drop to 0.010 mol? (c) What is the half-life of N_2O_5 at 70°C?

14.39 The reaction

$$SO_2Cl_2(g) \longrightarrow SO_2(g) + Cl_2(g)$$

is first order in SO_2Cl_2. Using the following kinetic data, determine the magnitude of the first-order rate constant:

Time (s)	Pressure SO₂Cl₂ (atm)
0	1.000
2,500	0.947
5,000	0.895
7,500	0.848
10,000	0.803

14.40 From the following data for the first-order gas-phase isomerization of CH_3NC at 215°C, calculate the first-order rate constant and half-life for the reaction:

Time (s)	Pressure CH₃NC (torr)
0	502
2,000	335
5,000	180
8,000	95.5
12,000	41.7
15,000	22.4

14.41 Consider the data presented in Exercise 14.13. **(a)** By using appropriate graphs, determine whether the reaction is first order or second order. **(b)** What is the value of the rate constant for the reaction? **(c)** What is the half-life for the reaction?

14.42 Consider the data presented in Exercise 14.14. **(a)** Determine whether the reaction is first order or second order. **(b)** What is the value of the rate constant? **(c)** What is the half-life?

14.43 The gas-phase decomposition of NO_2, $NO_2(g) \longrightarrow NO(g) + O_2(g)$, is studied at 383°C, giving the following data:

Time (s)	[NO₂] (M)
0.0	0.100
5.0	0.017
10.0	0.0090
15.0	0.0062
20.0	0.0047

(a) Is the reaction first order or second order with respect to the concentration of NO_2? **(b)** What is the value of the rate constant?

14.44 Sucrose ($C_{12}H_{22}O_{11}$), which is commonly known as table sugar, reacts in dilute acid solutions to form two simpler sugars, glucose and fructose, both of which have the formula $C_6H_{12}O_6$: At 23°C and in 0.5 M HCl, the following data were obtained for the disappearance of sucrose:

Time (min)	[C₁₂H₂₂O₁₁] (M)
0	0.316
39	0.274
80	0.238
140	0.190
210	0.146

(a) Is the reaction first order or second order with respect to $[C_{12}H_{22}O_{11}]$? **(b)** What is the value of the rate constant?

Temperature and Rate

14.45 **(a)** What factors determine whether a collision between two molecules will lead to a chemical reaction? **(b)** According to the collision model, why does temperature affect the value of the rate constant?

14.46 **(a)** Explain the rate of a unimolecular (that is, one-molecule) reaction, such as the isomerization of methyl isonitrile (Figure 14.6), in terms of the collision model. **(b)** In a reaction of the form $A(g) + B(g) \longrightarrow$ products, are all collisions of A with B that are sufficiently energetic likely to lead to reaction? Explain. **(c)** How does the kinetic-molecular theory help us understand the temperature dependence of chemical reactions?

14.47 Calculate the fraction of atoms in a sample of argon gas at 400 K that have an energy of 10.0 kJ or greater.

14.48 **(a)** The activation energy for the isomerization of methyl isonitrile (Figure 14.6) is 160 kJ/mol. Calculate the fraction of methyl isonitrile molecules that have an energy of 160.0 kJ or greater at 500 K. **(b)** Calculate this fraction for a temperature of 510 K. What is the ratio of the fraction at 510 K to that at 500 K?

14.49 The gas-phase reaction $Cl(g) + HBr(g) \longrightarrow HCl(g) + Br(g)$ has an overall enthalpy change of -66 kJ. The activation energy for the reaction is 7 kJ. **(a)** Sketch the energy profile for the reaction, and label E_a and ΔE. **(b)** What is the activation energy for the reverse reaction?

14.50 For the elementary process $N_2O_5(g) \longrightarrow NO_2(g) + NO_3(g)$ the activation energy (E_a) and overall ΔE are 154 kJ/mol and 136 kJ/mol, respectively. **(a)** Sketch the energy profile for this reaction, and label E_a and ΔE. **(b)** What is the activation energy for the reverse reaction?

14.51 Based on their activation energies and energy changes and assuming that all collision factors are the same, which of the following reactions would be fastest and which would be slowest? Explain your answer. **(a)** $E_a = 45$ kJ/mol; $\Delta E = -25$ kJ/mol; **(b)** $E_a = 35$ kJ/mol; $\Delta E = -10$ kJ/mol; **(c)** $E_a = 55$ kJ/mol; $\Delta E = 10$ kJ/mol.

14.52 Which of the reactions in Exercise 14.51 will be fastest in the reverse direction? Which will be slowest? Explain.

14.53 A certain first-order reaction has a rate constant of 2.75×10^{-2} s^{-1} at 20°C. What is the value of k at 60°C if **(a)** $E_a = 75.5$ kJ/mol; **(b)** $E_a = 105$ kJ/mol?

14.54 Understanding the high-temperature behavior of nitrogen oxides is essential for controlling pollution generated in automobile engines. The decomposition of nitric oxide (NO) to N_2 and O_2 is second order with a rate constant of 0.0796 M^{-1} s^{-1} at 737°C and 0.0815 M^{-1} s^{-1} at 947°C. Calculate the activation energy for the reaction.

14.55 The rate of the reaction

$$CH_3COOC_2H_5(aq) + OH^-(aq) \longrightarrow$$
$$CH_3COO^-(aq) + C_2H_5OH(aq)$$

was measured at several temperatures, and the following data were collected:

Temperature (°C)	k(M⁻¹ s⁻¹)
15	0.0521
25	0.101
35	0.184
45	0.332

Using these data, graph ln k versus $1/T$. Using your graph, determine the value of E_a.

14.56 The temperature dependence of the rate constant for the reaction is tabulated as follows:

Temperature (K)	$k(M^{-1}\,s^{-1})$
600	0.028
650	0.22
700	1.3
750	6.0
800	23

Calculate E_a and A.

[14.57] The activation energy of a certain reaction is 65.7 kJ/mol. How many times faster will the reaction occur at 50°C than at 0°C?

[14.58] The following is a quote from an article in the August 18, 1998, issue of *The New York Times* about the breakdown of cellulose and starch: "A drop of 18 degrees Fahrenheit [from 77°F to 59°F] lowers the reaction rate six times; a 36-degree drop [from 77°F to 41°F] produces a fortyfold decrease in the rate." **(a)** Calculate activation energies for the breakdown process based on the two estimates of the effect of temperature on rate. Are the values consistent? **(b)** Assuming the value of E_a calculated from the 36-degree drop and assuming that the rate of breakdown is first order with a half-life at 25°C of 2.7 years, calculate the half-life for breakdown at a temperature of −15°C.

Reaction Mechanisms

14.59 **(a)** What is meant by the term *elementary reaction?* **(b)** What is the difference between a *unimolecular* and a *bimolecular* elementary reaction? **(c)** What is a *reaction mechanism?*

14.60 **(a)** What is meant by the term *molecularity?* **(b)** Why are termolecular elementary reactions so rare? **(c)** What is an *intermediate* in a mechanism?

14.61 What is the molecularity of each of the following elementary reactions? Write the rate law for each.
(a) $Cl_2(g) \longrightarrow 2\,Cl(g)$
(b) $OCl^-(g) + H_2O(g) \longrightarrow HOCl(g) + OH^-(g)$
(c) $NO(g) + Cl_2(g) \longrightarrow NOCl_2(g)$

14.62 What is the molecularity of each of the following elementary reactions? Write the rate law for each.
(a) $2\,NO(g) \longrightarrow N_2O_2(g)$

(b) $H_2\overset{\displaystyle CH_2}{\overset{\diagup\diagdown}{C\!-\!CH_2}}(g) \longrightarrow CH_2\!=\!CH\!-\!CH_3(g)$

(c) $SO_3(g) \longrightarrow SO_2(g) + O(g)$

14.63 **(a)** Based on the following reaction profile, how many intermediates are formed in the reaction A $\longrightarrow$ D? **(b)** How many transition states are there? **(c)** Which step is the fastest? **(d)** Is the reaction A $\longrightarrow$ D exothermic or endothermic?

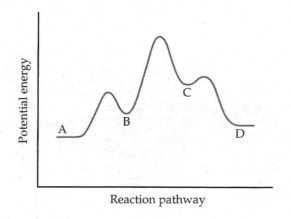

Reaction pathway

14.64 Consider the following energy profile.

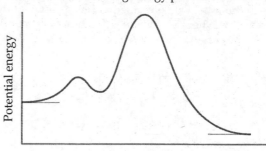

Reaction pathway

(a) How many elementary reactions are in the reaction mechanism? **(b)** How many intermediates are formed in the reaction? **(c)** Which step is rate limiting? **(d)** Is the overall reaction exothermic or endothermic?

14.65 The following mechanism has been proposed for the gas-phase reaction of H_2 with ICl:

$$H_2(g) + ICl(g) \longrightarrow HI(g) + HCl(g)$$
$$HI(g) + ICl(g) \longrightarrow I_2(g) + HCl(g)$$

(a) Write the balanced equation for the overall reaction. **(b)** Identify any intermediates in the mechanism. **(c)** Write rate laws for each elementary reaction in the mechanism. **(d)** If the first step is slow and the second one is fast, what rate law do you expect to be observed for the overall reaction?

14.66 The decomposition of hydrogen peroxide is catalyzed by iodide ion. The catalyzed reaction is thought to proceed by a two-step mechanism:

$$H_2O_2(aq) + I^-(aq) \longrightarrow H_2O(l) + IO^-(aq) \qquad \text{(slow)}$$
$$IO^-(aq) + H_2O_2(aq) \longrightarrow H_2O(l) + O_2(g) + I^-(aq) \qquad \text{(fast)}$$

(a) Write the rate law for each of the elementary reactions of the mechanism. **(b)** Write the chemical equation for the overall process. **(c)** Identify the intermediate, if any, in the mechanism. **(d)** Assuming that the first step of the mechanism is rate determining, predict the rate law for the overall process.

14.67 The reaction $2\,NO(g) + Cl_2(g) \longrightarrow 2\,NOCl(g)$ obeys the rate law, rate $= k[NO]^2[Cl_2]$. The following mechanism has been proposed for this reaction:

$$NO(g) + Cl_2(g) \longrightarrow NOCl_2(g)$$

$$NOCl_2(g) + NO(g) \longrightarrow 2\,NOCl(g)$$

(a) What would the rate law be if the first step were rate determining? (b) Based on the observed rate law, what can we conclude about the relative rates of the two steps?

14.68 You have studied the gas-phase oxidation of HBr by O_2:

$$4\,HBr(g) + O_2(g) \longrightarrow 2\,H_2O(g) + 2\,Br_2(g)$$

You find the reaction to be first order with respect to HBr and first order with respect to O_2. You propose the following mechanism:

$$HBr(g) + O_2(g) \longrightarrow HOOBr(g)$$

$$HOOBr(g) + HBr(g) \longrightarrow 2\,HOBr(g)$$

$$HOBr(g) + HBr(g) \longrightarrow H_2O(g) + Br_2(g)$$

(a) Indicate how the elementary reactions add to give the overall reaction. [*Hint:* You will need to multiply the coefficients of one of the equations by 2.] (b) Based on the rate law, which step is rate determining? (c) What are the intermediates in this mechanism? (d) If you are unable to detect HOBr or HOOBr among the products, does this disprove your mechanism?

Catalysis

14.69 (a) What part of the energy profile of a reaction is affected by a catalyst? (b) What is the difference between a homogeneous and a heterogeneous catalyst?

14.70 (a) Most heterogeneous catalysts of importance are extremely finely divided solid materials. Why is particle size important? (b) What role does adsorption play in the action of a heterogeneous catalyst?

14.71 The oxidation of SO_2 to SO_3 is catalyzed by NO_2. The reaction proceeds as follows:

$$NO_2(g) + SO_2(g) \longrightarrow NO(g) + SO_3(g)$$

$$2\,NO(g) + O_2(g) \longrightarrow 2\,NO_2(g)$$

(a) Show that the two reactions can be summed to give the overall oxidation of SO_2 by O_2 to give SO_3. [*Hint:* The top reaction must be multiplied by a factor so the NO and NO_2 cancel out.] (b) Why do we consider NO_2 a catalyst and not an intermediate in this reaction? (c) Is this an example of homogeneous catalysis or heterogeneous catalysis?

14.72 NO catalyzes the decomposition of N_2O, possibly by the following mechanism:

$$NO(g) + N_2O(g) \longrightarrow N_2(g) + NO_2(g)$$

$$2\,NO_2(g) \longrightarrow 2\,NO(g) + O_2(g)$$

(a) What is the chemical equation for the overall reaction? Show how the two steps can be added to give the overall equation. (b) Why is NO considered a catalyst and not an intermediate? (c) If experiments show that during the decomposition of N_2O, NO_2 does not accumulate in measurable quantities, does this rule out the proposed mechanism? If you think not, suggest what might be going on.

14.73 Many metallic catalysts, particularly the precious-metal ones, are often deposited as very thin films on a substance of high surface area per unit mass, such as alumina (Al_2O_3) or silica (SiO_2). Why is this an effective way of utilizing the catalyst material?

14.74 (a) If you were going to build a system to check the effectiveness of automobile catalytic converters on cars, what substances would you want to look for in the car exhaust? (b) Automobile catalytic converters have to work at high temperatures, as hot exhaust gases stream through them. In what ways could this be an advantage? In what ways a disadvantage? (c) Why is the rate of flow of exhaust gases over a catalytic converter important?

14.75 When D_2 reacts with ethylene (C_2H_4) in the presence of a finely divided catalyst, ethane with two deuteriums, $CH_2D\!-\!CH_2D$, is formed. (Deuterium, D, is an isotope of hydrogen of mass 2.) Very little ethane forms in which two deuteriums are bound to one carbon (for example, $CH_3\!-\!CHD_2$). Use the sequence of steps involved in the reaction to explain why this is so.

14.76 Heterogeneous catalysts that perform hydrogenation reactions, as illustrated in Figure 14.21, are subject to poisoning, which shuts down their catalytic ability. Compounds of sulfur are often poisons. Suggest a mechanism by which such compounds might act as poisons.

14.77 (a) Explain the importance of enzymes in biological systems. (b) What chemical transformations are catalyzed (*i*) by the enzyme catalase, (*ii*) by nitrogenase?

14.78 There are literally thousands of enzymes at work in complex living systems such as human beings. What properties of the enzymes give rise to their ability to distinguish one substrate from another?

[14.79] The activation energy of an uncatalyzed reaction is 95 kJ/mol. The addition of a catalyst lowers the activation energy to 55 kJ/mol. Assuming that the collision factor remains the same, by what factor will the catalyst increase the rate of the reaction at (a) 25°C, (b) 125°C?

[14.80] Suppose that a certain biologically important reaction is quite slow at physiological temperature (37°C) in the absence of a catalyst. Assuming that the collision factor remains the same, by how much must an enzyme lower the activation energy of the reaction in order to achieve a 1×10^5-fold increase in the reaction rate?

Additional Exercises

14.81 Hydrogen sulfide (H_2S) is a common and troublesome pollutant in industrial wastewaters. One way to remove H_2S is to treat the water with chlorine, in which case the following reaction occurs:

$$H_2S(aq) + Cl_2(aq) \longrightarrow S(s) + 2\,H^+(aq) + 2\,Cl^-(aq)$$

The rate of this reaction is first order in each reactant. The rate constant for the disappearance of H_2S at 28°C is $3.5 \times 10^{-2}\,M^{-1}\,s^{-1}$. If at a given time the concentration of H_2S is $2.0 \times 10^{-4}\,M$ and that of Cl_2 is $0.050\,M$, what is the rate of formation of Cl^-?

14.82 The reaction $2\,NO(g) + O_2(g) \longrightarrow 2\,NO_2(g)$ is second order in NO and first order in O_2. When $[NO] = 0.040\,M$ and $[O_2] = 0.035\,M$, the observed rate of disappearance of NO is $9.3 \times 10^{-5}\,M/s$. **(a)** What is the rate of disappearance of O_2 at this moment? **(b)** What is the value of the rate constant? **(c)** What are the units of the rate constant? **(d)** What would happen to the rate if the concentration of NO were increased by a factor of 1.8?

14.83 For the reaction of iodide ion with hypochorite ion, $I^-(aq) + OCl^-(aq) \longrightarrow OI^-(aq) + Cl^-(aq)$, the reaction is found to be first order each in iodide and hypochlorite ions, and inversely proportional to the concentration of hydroxide ion present in the solution. **(a)** Write the rate law for the reaction. **(b)** By what factor will the rate change if the concentration of iodide ion is tripled? **(c)** By what factor will the rate change if the hydroxide ion concentration is doubled?

14.84 Consider the following reaction between mercury(II) chloride and oxalate ion:

$$2\,HgCl_2(aq) + C_2O_4{}^{2-}(aq) \longrightarrow$$
$$2\,Cl^-(aq) + 2\,CO_2(g) + Hg_2Cl_2(s)$$

The initial rate of this reaction was determined for several concentrations of $HgCl_2$ and $C_2O_4{}^{2-}$, and the following rate data were obtained for the rate of disappearance of $C_2O_4{}^{2-}$:

Experiment	[HgCl₂] (M)	[C₂O₄²⁻] (M)	Rate (M/s)
1	0.164	0.15	3.2×10^{-5}
2	0.164	0.45	2.9×10^{-4}
3	0.082	0.45	1.4×10^{-4}
4	0.246	0.15	4.8×10^{-5}

(a) What is the rate law for this reaction? **(b)** What is the value of the rate constant? **(c)** What is the reaction rate when the concentration of $HgCl_2$ is $0.050\,M$ and that of $C_2O_4{}^{2-}$ is $0.10\,M$, if the temperature is the same as that used to obtain the data shown?

14.85 The reaction $2\,NO_2 \longrightarrow 2\,NO + O_2$ has the rate constant $k = 0.63\,M^{-1}\,s^{-1}$. Based on the units for k, is the reaction first or second order in NO_2? If the initial concentration of NO_2 is $0.100\,M$, how would you determine how long it would take for the concentration to decrease to $0.025\,M$?

14.86 **(a)** The decomposition of H_2O_2, $H_2O_2(aq) \longrightarrow H_2O(l) + \frac{1}{2} O_2(g)$, is a first-order reaction. At a particular temperature near room temperature, the rate constant equals $7.0 \times 10^{-4}\,s^{-1}$. Calculate the half-life at this temperature. **(b)** At 415°C, $(CH_2)_2O$ decomposes in the gas phase, $(CH_2)_2O(g) \longrightarrow CH_4(g) + CO(g)$. If the reaction is first order with a half-life of 56.3 min at this temperature, calculate the rate constant in s^{-1}.

14.87 Urea (NH_2CONH_2) is the end product in protein metabolism in animals. The decomposition of urea in $0.1\,M$ HCl occurs according to the reaction

$$NH_2CONH_2(aq) + H^+(aq) + 2\,H_2O(l) \longrightarrow$$
$$2\,NH_4{}^+(aq) + HCO_3{}^-(aq)$$

The reaction is first order in urea and first order overall. When $[NH_2CONH_2] = 0.200\,M$, the rate at 61.05°C is $8.56 \times 10^{-5}\,M/s$. **(a)** What is the value for the rate constant, k? **(b)** What is the concentration of urea in this solution after $4.00 \times 10^3\,s$ if the starting concentration is $0.500\,M$? **(c)** What is the half-life for this reaction at 61.05°C?

[14.88] The rate of a first-order reaction is followed by spectroscopy, monitoring the absorption of a colored reactant. The reaction occurs in a 1.00-cm sample cell, and the only colored species in the reaction has a molar absorptivity constant of $5.60 \times 10^3\,cm^{-1}\,M^{-1}$. **(a)** Calculate the initial concentration of the colored reactant if the absorbance is 0.605 at the beginning of the reaction. **(b)** The absorbance falls to 0.250 within 30.0 min. Calculate the rate constant in units of s^{-1}. **(c)** Calculate the half-life of the reaction. **(d)** How long does it take for the absorbance to fall to 0.100?

14.89 Cyclopentadiene (C_5H_6) reacts with itself to form dicyclopentadiene ($C_{10}H_{12}$). A $0.0400\,M$ solution of C_5H_6 was monitored as a function of time as the reaction $2\,C_5H_6 \longrightarrow C_{10}H_{12}$ proceeded. The following data were collected:

Time (s)	[C₅H₆] (M)
0.0	0.0400
50.0	0.0300
100.0	0.0240
150.0	0.0200
200.0	0.0174

Plot $[C_5H_6]$ versus time, $\ln[C_5H_6]$ versus time, and $1/[C_5H_6]$ versus time. What is the order of the reaction? What is the value of the rate constant?

14.90 **(a)** Two reactions have identical values for E_a. Does this ensure that they will have the same rate constant if run at the same temperature? Explain. **(b)** Two similar reactions have the same rate constant at 25°C, but at 35°C one of the reactions has a higher rate constant than the other. Account for these observations.

14.91 The first-order rate constant for reaction of a particular organic compound with water varies with temperature as follows:

Temperature (K)	Rate Constant (s^{-1})
300	3.2×10^{-11}
320	1.0×10^{-9}
340	3.0×10^{-8}
355	2.4×10^{-7}

From these data, calculate the activation energy in units of kJ/mol.

14.92 The following mechanism has been proposed for the reaction of NO with H_2 to form N_2O and H_2O:

$$NO(g) + NO(g) \longrightarrow N_2O_2(g)$$
$$N_2O_2(g) + H_2(g) \longrightarrow N_2O(g) + H_2O(g)$$

(a) Show that the elementary reactions of the proposed mechanism add to provide a balanced equation for the reaction. (b) Write a rate law for each elementary reaction in the mechanism. (c) Identify any intermediates in the mechanism. (d) The observed rate law is rate = $k[NO]^2[H_2]$. If the proposed mechanism is correct, what can we conclude about the relative speeds of the first and second reactions?

14.93 Using Figure 14.20 as your basis, draw the energy profile for the bromide ion–catalyzed decomposition of hydrogen peroxide. (a) Label the curve with the activation energies for reactions [14.30] and [14.31]. (b) Notice from Figure 14.19(b) that when $Br^-(aq)$ is added initially, Br_2 accumulates to some extent during the reaction. What does this tell us about the relative rates of reactions [14.30] and [14.31]?

[14.94] The following mechanism has been proposed for the gas-phase reaction of chloroform ($CHCl_3$) and chlorine:

Step 1: $Cl_2(g) \underset{k_{-1}}{\overset{k_1}{\rightleftharpoons}} 2\,Cl(g)$ (fast)

Step 2: $Cl(g) + CHCl_3(g) \overset{k_2}{\longrightarrow} HCl(g) + CCl_3(g)$ (slow)

Step 3: $Cl(g) + CCl_3(g) \overset{k_3}{\longrightarrow} CCl_4(g)$ (fast)

(a) What is the overall reaction? (b) What are the intermediates in the mechanism? (c) What is the molecularity of each of the elementary reactions? (d) What is the rate-determining step? (e) What is the rate law predicted by

this mechanism? [*Hint:* The overall reaction order is not an integer.]

[14.95] In a hydrocarbon solution, the gold compound $(CH_3)_3AuPH_3$ decomposes into ethane (C_2H_6) and a different gold compound, $(CH_3)AuPH_3$. The following mechanism has been proposed for the decomposition of $(CH_3)_3AuPH_3$:

Step 1: $(CH_3)_3AuPH_3 \underset{k_{-1}}{\overset{k_1}{\rightleftharpoons}} (CH_3)_3Au + PH_3$ (fast)

Step 2: $(CH_3)_3Au \overset{k_2}{\longrightarrow} C_2H_6 + (CH_3)Au$ (slow)

Step 3: $(CH_3)Au + PH_3 \overset{k_3}{\longrightarrow} (CH_3)AuPH_3$ (fast)

(a) What is the overall reaction? (b) What are the intermediates in the mechanism? (c) What is the molecularity of each of the elementary steps? (d) What is the rate-determining step? (e) What is the rate law predicted by this mechanism? (f) What would be the effect on the reaction rate of adding PH_3 to the solution of $(CH_3)_3AuPH_3$?

14.96 One of the many remarkable enzymes in the human body is carbonic anhydrase, which catalyzes the interconversion of carbonic acid with carbon dioxide and water. If it were not for this enzyme, the body could not rid itself rapidly enough of the CO_2 accumulated by cell metabolism. The enzyme catalyzes the dehydration (release to air) of up to 10^7 CO_2 molecules per second. Which components of this description correspond to the terms *enzyme, substrate,* and *turnover number*?

14.97 The enzyme *invertase* catalyzes the conversion of sucrose, a disaccharide, to invert sugar, a mixture of glucose and fructose. When the concentration of invertase is 4.2×10^{-7} M and the concentration of sucrose is 0.0077 M, invert sugar is formed at the rate of 1.5×10^{-4} M/s. When the sucrose concentration is doubled, the rate of formation of invert sugar is doubled also. (a) Assuming that the enzyme-substrate model is operative, is the fraction of enzyme tied up as a complex large or small? Explain. (b) Addition of inositol, another sugar, decreases the rate of formation of invert sugar. Suggest a mechanism by which this occurs.

Integrative Exercises

14.98 Dinitrogen pentoxide (N_2O_5) decomposes in chloroform as a solvent to yield NO_2 and O_2. The decomposition is first order with a rate constant at 45°C of 1.0×10^{-5} s^{-1}. Calculate the partial pressure of O_2 produced from 1.00 L of 0.600 M N_2O_5 solution at 45°C over a period of 20.0 h if the gas is collected in a 10.0-L container. (Assume that the products do not dissolve in chloroform.)

[14.99] The reaction between ethyl iodide and hydroxide ion in ethanol (C_2H_5OH) solution, $C_2H_5I(alc) + OH^-(alc) \longrightarrow C_2H_5OH(l) + I^-(alc)$, has an activation energy of 86.8 kJ/mol and a frequency factor of 2.10×10^{11} $M^{-1}\,s^{-1}$.

(a) Predict the rate constant for the reaction at 35°C. (b) A solution of KOH in ethanol is made up by dissolving 0.335 g KOH in ethanol to form 250.0 mL of solution. Similarly, 1.453 g of C_2H_5I is dissolved in ethanol to form 250.0 mL of solution. Equal volumes of the two solutions are mixed. Assuming the reaction is first order in each reactant, what is the initial rate at 35°C? (c) Which reagent in the reaction is limiting, assuming the reaction proceeds to completion?

14.100 Zinc metal dissolves in hydrochloric acid according to the reaction

$$Zn(s) + 2\,HCl(aq) \longrightarrow ZnCl_2(aq) + H_2(g)$$

Suppose you are asked to study the kinetics of this reaction by monitoring the rate of production of $H_2(g)$. **(a)** By using a reaction flask, a manometer, and any other common laboratory equipment, design an experimental apparatus that would allow you to monitor the partial pressure of $H_2(g)$ produced as a function of time. **(b)** Explain how you would use the apparatus to determine the rate law of the reaction. **(c)** Explain how you would use the apparatus to determine the reaction order for [H^+] for the reaction. **(d)** How could you use the apparatus to determine the activation energy of the reaction? **(e)** Explain how you would use the apparatus to determine the effects of changing the form of $Zn(s)$ from metal strips to granules.

14.101 The gas-phase reaction of NO with F_2 to form NOF and F has an activation energy of $E_a = 6.3$ kJ/mol and a frequency factor of $A = 6.0 \times 10^8\ M^{-1}\ s^{-1}$. The reaction is believed to be bimolecular:

$$NO(g) + F_2(g) \longrightarrow NOF(g) + F(g)$$

(a) Calculate the rate constant at 100°C. **(b)** Draw the Lewis structures for the NO and the NOF molecules, given that the chemical formula for NOF is misleading because the nitrogen atom is actually the central atom in the molecule. **(c)** Predict the structure for the NOF molecule. **(d)** Draw a possible transition state for the formation of NOF, using dashed lines to indicate the weak bonds that are beginning to form. **(e)** Suggest a reason for the low activation energy for the reaction.

14.102 The mechanism for the oxidation of HBr by O_2 to form $2\ H_2O$ and Br_2 is shown in Exercise 14.68. **(a)** Calculate the overall standard enthalpy change for the reaction process. **(b)** HBr does not react with O_2 at a measurable rate at room temperature under ordinary conditions. What can you infer from this about the magnitude of the activation energy for the rate-determining step? **(c)** Draw a plausible Lewis structure for the intermediate HOOBr. To what familiar compound of hydrogen and oxygen does it appear similar?

14.103 Enzymes, the catalysts of biological systems, are high molecular weight protein materials. The active site of the enzyme is formed by the three-dimensional arrangement of the protein in solution. When heated in solution, proteins undergo denaturation, a process in which the three-dimensional structure of the protein unravels or at least partly does so. The accompanying graph shows the variation with temperature of the activity of a typical enzyme. The activity increases with temperature to a point above the usual operating region for the enzyme, then declines rapidly with further temperature increases. What role does denaturation play in determining the shape of this curve? How does your explanation fit in with the lock-and-key model of enzyme action?

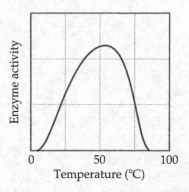

[14.104] Metals often form several cations with different charges. Cerium, for example, forms Ce^{3+} and Ce^{4+} ions, and thallium forms Tl^+ and Tl^{3+} ions. Cerium and thallium ions react as follows:

$$2\ Ce^{4+}(aq) + Tl^{3+}(aq) \longrightarrow 2\ Ce^{3+}(aq) + Tl^{3+}(aq)$$

This reaction is very slow and is thought to occur in a single elementary step. The reaction is catalyzed by the addition of $Mn^{2+}(aq)$, according to the following mechanism:

$$Ce^{4+}(aq) + Mn^{2+}(aq) \longrightarrow Ce^{3+}(aq) + Mn^{3+}(aq)$$
$$Ce^{4+}(aq) + Mn^{3+}(aq) \longrightarrow Ce^{3+}(aq) + Mn^{4+}(aq)$$
$$Mn^{4+}(aq) + Tl^+(aq) \longrightarrow Mn^{2+}(aq) + Tl^{3+}(aq)$$

(a) Write the rate law for the uncatalyzed reaction. **(b)** What is unusual about the uncatalyzed reaction? Why might it be a slow reaction? **(c)** The rate for the catalyzed reaction is first order in [Ce^{4+}] and first order in [Mn^{2+}]. Based on this rate law, which of the steps in the catalyzed mechanism is rate determining? **(d)** Use the available oxidation states of Mn to comment on its special suitability to catalyze this reaction.

[14.105] The rates of many atmospheric reactions are accelerated by the absorption of light by one of the reactants. For example, consider the reaction between methane and chlorine to produce methyl chloride and hydrogen chloride:

Reaction 1: $CH_4(g) + Cl(g) \longrightarrow CH_3Cl(g) + HCl(g)$

This reaction is very slow in the absence of light. However, $Cl_2(g)$ can absorb light to form Cl atoms:

Reaction 2: $Cl_2(g) + h\upsilon \longrightarrow 2\ Cl(g)$

Once the Cl atoms are generated, they can catalyze the reaction of CH_4 and Cl_2, according to the following proposed mechanism:

Reaction 3: $CH_4(g) + Cl(g) \longrightarrow CH_3(g) + HCl(g)$
Reaction 4: $CH_3(g) + Cl_2(g) \longrightarrow CH_3Cl(g) + Cl(g)$

The enthalpy changes and activation energies for these two reactions are tabulated as follows:

Reaction	ΔH°_{rxn} (kJ/mol)	E_a (kJ/mol)
3	+4	17
4	−109	4

(a) By using the bond enthalpy for Cl_2 (Table 8.4), determine the longest wavelength of light that is energetic enough to cause reaction 2 to occur. In which portion of the electromagnetic spectrum is this light found? **(b)** By using the data tabulated here, sketch a quantitative energy profile for the catalyzed reaction represented by reactions 3 and 4. **(c)** By using bond enthalpies, estimate where the reactants, $CH_4(g) + Cl_2(g)$, should be placed on your diagram in part (b). Use this result to estimate the value of E_a for the reaction $CH_4(g) + Cl_2(g) \longrightarrow CH_3(g) + HCl(g) + Cl(g)$. **(d)** The species $Cl(g)$ and $CH_3(g)$ in reactions 3 and 4 are radicals, atoms, or molecules with unpaired electrons. Draw a Lewis structure of CH_3, and verify that it is a radical. **(e)** The sequence of reactions 3 and 4 comprise a radical chain mechanism. Why do you think this is called a "chain reaction"? Propose a reaction that will terminate the chain reaction.

eMEDIA EXERCISES

These exercises make use of the interactive objects available online in OneKey or the Companion Website, and on your Accelerator CD. Access to these resources comes in your MediaPak.

14.106 The **Rates of Reaction** activity (*14.3*) allows you to adjust activation energy, overall energy change, temperature, and starting concentration of a reactant to assess the effect of each variable on initial reaction rate. **(a)** If you want to determine the rate law for the reaction using a series of experiments, which variable(s) *must* you vary, which variable(s) should you *not* vary, and for which variable(s) does it not make any difference? **(b)** Determine the rate law for the reaction. What is the overall order of the reaction? **(c)** Determine the value of the rate constant.

14.107 **(a)** Using data from the **Rates of Reaction** activity (*14.3*), select a temperature (T_1) and an activation energy (E_a) and determine the value of the rate constant (k_1). **(b)** Using the (E_a) and (T_1) from part (a), predict the value of the rate constant (k_2) at a higher temperature, $T_2 = 2\,T_1$. **(c)** Again using E_a from part (a) and the temperature from either part (a) or part (b), predict the value of the rate constant (k_3) at a temperature (T_3) that is *lower* than T_1. Use the simulation to check your answers for parts (a), (b), and (c).

14.108 The **First-Order Process** animation (*14.4*) illustrates the change in concentration over time for a process that is first order overall. **(a)** Determine the rate constant for the process shown. **(b)** Assuming that the first-order process is a chemical reaction, what would normally happen to the value of the half-life if the temperature were increased? **(c)** Many enzyme-catalyzed reactions are first order in the concentration of substrate. However, increasing the temperature does not always increase the rate. Why might this be so?

14.109 Using the numerical value of the rate constant you calculated for the reaction in the previous question and using the same "unit" concentration as in the **First-Order Process** animation (*14.4*), generate a curve for a second-order reaction with Equation 14.16. Reproduce the first-order curve, superimpose the second-order curve onto it, and compare them. What can you say about the relative rates of disappearance of the starting material initially and after a significant period of time has passed?

14.110 In Exercise 14.75, you explained why the combination of ethylene and D_2 in the presence of a catalyst predominantly produces CH_2D-CH_2D. A small amount of product has more than one D bound to a carbon, as in CH_2D-CHD_2. After watching the **Surface Reaction-Hydrogenation** animation (*14.7*), propose a mechanism by which a product with more than one D per carbon atom could arise.

16.1 Acids and Bases:
A Brief Review

16.2 Brønsted–Lowry Acids
and Bases

16.3 The Autoionization of Water

16.4 The pH Scale

16.5 Strong Acids and Bases

16.6 Weak Acids

16.7 Weak Bases

16.8 Relationship Between K_a
and K_b

16.9 Acid-Base Properties
of Salt Solutions

16.10 Acid-Base Behavior
and Chemical Structure

16.11 Lewis Acids and Bases

WHAT'S AHEAD

- We start by reviewing the *Arrhenius* definitions of acid and base. *(Section 16.1)*

- We then learn the more general *Brønsted–Lowry* definitions for acid and base. A Brønsted–Lowry acid is a *proton donor* and a Brønsted–Lowry base is a *proton acceptor*. *(Section 16.2)*

- The *conjugate base* of a Brønsted–Lowry acid is what remains after the acid has donated a proton. Similarly, the *conjugate acid* of a Brønsted–Lowry base is the species that results when the base accepts a proton. Two species that differ by the presence or absence of a proton are known as a *conjugate acid-base pair*. *(Section 16.2)*

- *Autoionization* of water produces small concentrations of H_3O^+ and OH^- ions. The *equilibrium constant* for autoionization, K_w, defines the relationship between H_3O^+ and OH^- concentrations in aqueous solutions. *(Section 16.3)*

- The pH scale ($pH = -\log[H^+]$) is used to describe the acidity or basicity of a solution. *(Section 16.4)*

- *Strong* acids and bases are those that ionize or dissociate completely in aqueous solution, whereas *weak* acids and bases ionize only partially. *(Section 16.5)*

- We learn that the ionization of a weak acid in water is an equilibrium process with an equilibrium constant K_a, which can be used to calculate the pH of a weak acid solution. *(Section 16.6)*

- Likewise, ionization of a weak base in water is an equilibrium process with equilibrium constant K_b, which can be used to calculate the pH of a weak base solution. *(Section 16.7)*

- There is a relationship between the K_a and K_b of any conjugate *acid-base* pair: $K_a \times K_b = K_w$. *(Section 16.8)*

- The ions of a salt can serve as Brønsted–Lowry acids or bases. *(Section 16.9)*

- We continue by exploring the relationship between chemical structure and acid-base behavior. *(Section 16.10)*

- Finally, we learn the *Lewis* definitions of acid and base. A Lewis acid is an *electron acceptor*, and a Lewis base is an *electron donor*. *(Section 16.11)*

Acid-Base Equilibria

WHAT'S THE SOUREST FOOD YOU'VE EVER TASTED? Citrus fruit, such as the lemons shown in the chapter-opening photograph? Sour cherries? Rhubarb? The sour taste of foods is due primarily to the presence of acids. Citric acid ($H_3C_6H_5O_7$), malic acid ($H_2C_4H_4O_5$), oxalic acid ($H_2C_2O_4$), and ascorbic acid, also known as vitamin C ($HC_6H_7O_6$), are present in many fruits as well as in certain vegetables such as rhubarb and tomatoes.

Acids and bases are important in numerous chemical processes that occur around us, from industrial processes to biological ones, from reactions in the laboratory to those in our environment. The time required for a metal object immersed in water to corrode, the ability of an aquatic environment to support fish and plant life, the fate of pollutants washed out of the air by rain, and even the rates of reactions that maintain our lives all critically depend upon the acidity or basicity of solutions. Indeed, an enormous amount of chemistry can be understood in terms of acid-base reactions.

We have encountered acids and bases many times in earlier discussions. For example, a portion of Chapter 4 focused on their reactions. But what makes a substance behave as an acid or as a base? In this chapter we reexamine acids and bases, taking a closer look at how they are identified and characterized. In doing so, we will consider their behavior not only in terms of their structure and bonding but also in terms of the chemical equilibria in which they participate.

VARIETIES OF CITRUS FRUITS (oranges, limes, lemons, and tangerines).
FoodPix/Getty Images, Inc. - FoodPix

16.1 | Acids and Bases: A Brief Review

From the earliest days of experimental chemistry, scientists have recognized acids and bases by their characteristic properties. Acids have a sour taste and cause certain dyes to change color (for example, litmus turns red on contact with acids). Indeed, the word *acid* comes from the Latin word *acidus*, meaning sour or tart. Bases, in contrast, have a bitter taste and feel slippery (soap is a good example). The word *base* comes from an old English meaning of the word, which is "to bring low." (We still use the word *debase* in this sense, meaning to lower the value of something.) When bases are added to acids, they lower the amount of acid. Indeed, when acids and bases are mixed in certain proportions, their characteristic properties disappear altogether. ∞ (Section 4.3)

Historically, chemists have sought to relate the properties of acids and bases to their compositions and molecular structures. By 1830 it was evident that all acids contain hydrogen but not all hydrogen-containing substances are acids. In the 1880s the Swedish chemist Svante Arrhenius (1859–1927) linked acid behavior with the presence of H^+ ions, and base behavior with the presence of OH^- ions in aqueous solution. He defined acids as substances that produce H^+ ions in water, and bases as substances that produce OH^- ions in water. Indeed, the properties of aqueous solutions of acids, such as sour taste, are due to $H^+(aq)$, whereas the properties of aqueous solutions of bases are due to $OH^-(aq)$. Over time the Arrhenius concept of acids and bases came to be stated in the following way: *Acids are substances that, when dissolved in water, increase the concentration of H^+ ions.* Likewise, *bases are substances that, when dissolved in water, increase the concentration of OH^- ions.*

Hydrogen chloride is an Arrhenius acid. Hydrogen chloride gas is highly soluble in water because of its chemical reaction with water, which produces hydrated H^+ and Cl^- ions:

$$HCl(g) \xrightarrow{\;H_2O\;} H^+(aq) + Cl^-(aq) \qquad [16.1]$$

The aqueous solution of HCl is known as hydrochloric acid. Concentrated hydrochloric acid is about 37% HCl by mass and is 12 M in HCl. Sodium hydroxide, on the other hand, is an Arrhenius base. Because NaOH is an ionic compound, it dissociates into Na^+ and OH^- ions when it dissolves in water, thereby releasing OH^- ions into the solution.

 GIVE IT SOME THOUGHT

What two ions are central to the Arrhenius definitions of acids and bases?

16.2 | Brønsted–Lowry Acids and Bases

The Arrhenius concept of acids and bases, while useful, has limitations. For one thing, it is restricted to aqueous solutions. In 1923 the Danish chemist Johannes Brønsted (1879–1947) and the English chemist Thomas Lowry (1874–1936) independently proposed a more general definition of acids and bases. Their concept is based on the fact that acid-base reactions involve the transfer of H^+ ions from one substance to another.

The H^+ Ion in Water

In Equation 16.1 hydrogen chloride is shown ionizing in water to form $H^+(aq)$. *An H^+ ion is simply a proton with no surrounding valence electron.* This small, positively charged particle interacts strongly with the nonbonding electron pairs of water molecules to form hydrated hydrogen ions. For example, the interaction of a proton with one water molecule forms the **hydronium ion**, $H_3O^+(aq)$:

$$H^+ + \overset{..}{:O}\!\!-\!\!H \longrightarrow \left[H\!\!-\!\!\overset{..}{O}\!\!-\!\!H \right]^+ \qquad [16.2]$$

The formation of hydronium ions is one of the complex features of the interaction of the H^+ ion with liquid water. In fact, the H_3O^+ ion can form hydrogen bonds to additional H_2O molecules to generate larger clusters of hydrated hydrogen ions, such as $H_5O_2^+$ and $H_9O_4^+$ (Figure 16.1 ►).

Chemists use $H^+(aq)$ and $H_3O^+(aq)$ interchangeably to represent the same thing—namely the hydrated proton that is responsible for the characteristic properties of aqueous solutions of acids. We often use the $H^+(aq)$ ion for simplicity and convenience, as we did in Equation 16.1. The $H_3O^+(aq)$ ion, however, more closely represents reality.

Proton-Transfer Reactions

When we closely examine the reaction that occurs when HCl dissolves in water, we find that the HCl molecule actually transfers an H^+ ion (a proton) to a water molecule as depicted in Figure 16.2 ▼. Thus, we can represent the reaction as occurring between an HCl molecule and a water molecule to form hydronium and chloride ions:

$$HCl(g) + H_2O(l) \longrightarrow H_3O^+(aq) + Cl^-(aq) \qquad [16.3]$$

The polar H_2O molecule promotes the ionization of acids in water solution by accepting a proton to form H_3O^+.

Brønsted and Lowry proposed defining acids and bases in terms of their ability to transfer protons. According to their definition, *an acid is a substance (molecule or ion) that can donate a proton to another substance. Likewise, a base is a substance that can accept a proton.* Thus, when HCl dissolves in water (Equation 16.3), HCl acts as a **Brønsted–Lowry acid** (it donates a proton to H_2O), and H_2O acts as a **Brønsted–Lowry base** (it accepts a proton from HCl).

Because the emphasis in the Brønsted–Lowry concept is on proton transfer, the concept also applies to reactions that do not occur in aqueous solution. In the reaction between HCl and NH_3, for example, a proton is transferred from the acid HCl to the base NH_3:

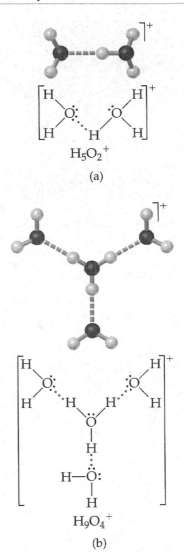

▲ **Figure 16.1 Hydrated hydronium ions.** Lewis structures and molecular models for $H_5O_2^+$ and $H_9O_4^+$. There is good experimental evidence for the existence of both these species.

$$:\!\overset{..}{\underset{..}{Cl}}\!\!-\!\!H + :\overset{H}{\underset{H}{N}}\!\!-\!\!H \longrightarrow :\overset{..}{\underset{..}{Cl}}\!:^- + \left[H\!\!-\!\!\overset{H}{\underset{H}{N}}\!\!-\!\!H \right]^+ \qquad [16.4]$$

▶ **Figure 16.2 A proton-transfer reaction.** When a proton is transferred from HCl to H_2O, HCl acts as the Brønsted–Lowry acid and H_2O acts as the Brønsted–Lowry base.

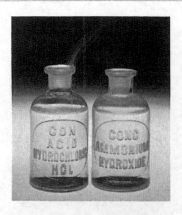

▲ **Figure 16.3 A gas-phase acid-base reaction.** The HCl(*g*) escaping from concentrated hydrochloric acid and the NH$_3$(*g*) escaping from aqueous ammonia (here labeled ammonium hydroxide) combine to form a white fog of NH$_4$Cl(*s*).

This reaction can occur in the gas phase. The hazy film that forms on the windows of general chemistry laboratories and on glassware in the lab is largely solid NH$_4$Cl formed by the gas-phase reaction of HCl and NH$_3$ (Figure 16.3 ◄).

Let's consider another example that compares the relationship between the Arrhenius definitions and the Brønsted–Lowry definitions of acids and bases—an aqueous solution of ammonia, in which the following equilibrium occurs:

$$NH_3(aq) + H_2O(l) \rightleftharpoons NH_4^+(aq) + OH^-(aq) \qquad [16.5]$$

Ammonia is an Arrhenius base because adding it to water leads to an increase in the concentration of OH$^-$(*aq*). It is a Brønsted–Lowry base because it accepts a proton from H$_2$O. The H$_2$O molecule in Equation 16.5 acts as a Brønsted–Lowry acid because it donates a proton to the NH$_3$ molecule.

An acid and a base always work together to transfer a proton. In other words, a substance can function as an acid only if another substance simultaneously behaves as a base. To be a Brønsted–Lowry acid, a molecule or ion must have a hydrogen atom that it can lose as an H$^+$ ion. To be a Brønsted–Lowry base, a molecule or ion must have a nonbonding pair of electrons that it can use to bind the H$^+$ ion.

Some substances can act as an acid in one reaction and as a base in another. For example, H$_2$O is a Brønsted–Lowry base in its reaction with HCl (Equation 16.3) and a Brønsted–Lowry acid in its reaction with NH$_3$ (Equation 16.5). A substance that is capable of acting as either an acid or a base is called **amphiprotic**. An amphiprotic substance acts as a base when combined with something more strongly acidic than itself, and as an acid when combined with something more strongly basic than itself.

💡 **GIVE IT SOME THOUGHT**

In the forward reaction, which substance acts as the Brønsted–Lowry base: HSO$_4^-$(*aq*) + NH$_3$(*aq*) ⇌ SO$_4^{2-}$(*aq*) + NH$_4^+$(*aq*)?

Conjugate Acid-Base Pairs

In any acid-base equilibrium both the forward reaction (to the right) and the reverse reaction (to the left) involve proton transfers. For example, consider the reaction of an acid, which we will denote HX, with water.

$$HX(aq) + H_2O(l) \rightleftharpoons X^-(aq) + H_3O^+(aq) \qquad [16.6]$$

In the forward reaction HX donates a proton to H$_2$O. Therefore, HX is the Brønsted–Lowry acid, and H$_2$O is the Brønsted–Lowry base. In the reverse reaction the H$_3$O$^+$ ion donates a proton to the X$^-$ ion, so H$_3$O$^+$ is the acid and X$^-$ is the base. When the acid HX donates a proton, it leaves behind a substance, X$^-$, which can act as a base. Likewise, when H$_2$O acts as a base, it generates H$_3$O$^+$, which can act as an acid.

An acid and a base such as HX and X$^-$ that differ only in the presence or absence of a proton are called a **conjugate acid-base pair**.* Every acid has a **conjugate base**, formed by removing a proton from the acid. For example, OH$^-$ is the conjugate base of H$_2$O, and X$^-$ is the conjugate base of HX. Similarly, every base has associated with it a **conjugate acid**, formed by adding a proton to the base. Thus, H$_3$O$^+$ is the conjugate acid of H$_2$O, and HX is the conjugate acid of X$^-$.

---

* The word *conjugate* means "joined together as a pair."

In any acid-base (proton-transfer) reaction we can identify two sets of conjugate acid-base pairs. For example, consider the reaction between nitrous acid (HNO_2) and water:

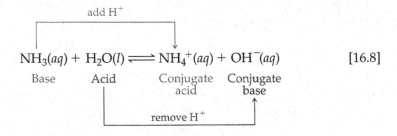

$$HNO_2(aq) + H_2O(l) \rightleftharpoons NO_2^-(aq) + H_3O^+(aq) \qquad [16.7]$$

Acid   Base   Conjugate base   Conjugate acid

Likewise, for the reaction between NH_3 and H_2O (Equation 16.5), we have

ACTIVITY
Conjugate Acids and Bases

$$NH_3(aq) + H_2O(l) \rightleftharpoons NH_4^+(aq) + OH^-(aq) \qquad [16.8]$$

Base   Acid   Conjugate acid   Conjugate base

SAMPLE EXERCISE 16.1 | Identifying Conjugate Acids and Bases

(a) What is the conjugate base of each of the following acids: $HClO_4$, H_2S, PH_4^+, HCO_3^-? (b) What is the conjugate acid of each of the following bases: CN^-, SO_4^{2-}, H_2O, HCO_3^-?

Solution
Analyze: We are asked to give the conjugate base for each of a series of species and to give the conjugate acid for each of another series of species.
Plan: The conjugate base of a substance is simply the parent substance minus one proton, and the conjugate acid of a substance is the parent substance plus one proton.
Solve: (a) $HClO_4$ less one proton (H^+) is ClO_4^-. The other conjugate bases are HS^-, PH_3, and CO_3^{2-}. (b) CN^- plus one proton (H^+) is HCN. The other conjugate acids are HSO_4^-, H_3O^+, and H_2CO_3.
    Notice that the hydrogen carbonate ion (HCO_3^-) is amphiprotic: It can act as either an acid or a base.

PRACTICE EXERCISE

Write the formula for the conjugate acid of each of the following: HSO_3^-, F^-, PO_4^{3-}, CO.
Answers: H_2SO_3, HF, HPO_4^{2-}, HCO^+

SAMPLE EXERCISE 16.2 | Writing Equations for Proton-Transfer Reactions

The hydrogen sulfite ion (HSO_3^-) is amphiprotic. (a) Write an equation for the reaction of HSO_3^- with water, in which the ion acts as an acid. (b) Write an equation for the reaction of HSO_3^- with water, in which the ion acts as a base. In both cases identify the conjugate acid-base pairs.

Solution
Analyze and Plan: We are asked to write two equations representing reactions between HSO_3^- and water, one in which HSO_3^- should donate a proton to water, thereby acting as a Brønsted–Lowry acid, and one in which HSO_3^- should accept a proton from water, thereby acting as a base. We are also asked to identify the conjugate pairs in each equation.

Solve: (a)

$$HSO_3^-(aq) + H_2O(l) \rightleftharpoons SO_3^{2-}(aq) + H_3O^+(aq)$$

The conjugate pairs in this equation are HSO_3^- (acid) and SO_3^{2-} (conjugate base); and H_2O (base) and H_3O^+ (conjugate acid).

(b)

$$HSO_3^-(aq) + H_2O(l) \rightleftharpoons H_2SO_3(aq) + OH^-(aq)$$

The conjugate pairs in this equation are H_2O (acid) and OH^- (conjugate base), and HSO_3^- (base) and H_2SO_3 (conjugate acid).

■ PRACTICE EXERCISE

When lithium oxide (Li_2O) is dissolved in water, the solution turns basic from the reaction of the oxide ion (O^{2-}) with water. Write the reaction that occurs, and identify the conjugate acid-base pairs.
Answer: $O^{2-}(aq) + H_2O(l) \rightleftharpoons OH^-(aq) + OH^-(aq)$. OH^- is the conjugate acid of the base O^{2-}. OH^- is also the conjugate base of the acid H_2O.

Relative Strengths of Acids and Bases

Some acids are better proton donors than others; likewise, some bases are better proton acceptors than others. If we arrange acids in order of their ability to donate a proton, we find that the more easily a substance gives up a proton, the less easily its conjugate base accepts a proton. Similarly, the more easily a base accepts a proton, the less easily its conjugate acid gives up a proton. In other words, *the stronger an acid, the weaker is its conjugate base; the stronger a base, the weaker is its conjugate acid.* Thus, if we know something about the strength of an acid (its ability to donate protons), we also know something about the strength of its conjugate base (its ability to accept protons).

The inverse relationship between the strengths of acids and the strengths of their conjugate bases is illustrated in Figure 16.4 ◄. Here we have grouped acids and bases into three broad categories based on their behavior in water.

1. The *strong acids* completely transfer their protons to water, leaving no undissociated molecules in solution. ⚬⚬⚬ (Section 4.3) Their conjugate bases have a negligible tendency to be protonated (to abstract protons) in aqueous solution.

2. The *weak acids* only partially dissociate in aqueous solution and therefore exist in the solution as a mixture of acid molecules and their constituent ions. The conjugate bases of weak acids show a slight ability to remove protons from water. (*The conjugate bases of weak acids are weak bases.*)

3. The substances with *negligible acidity* are those such as CH_4 that contain hydrogen but do not demonstrate any acidic behavior in water. Their conjugate bases are strong bases, reacting completely with water, abstracting protons to form OH^- ions.

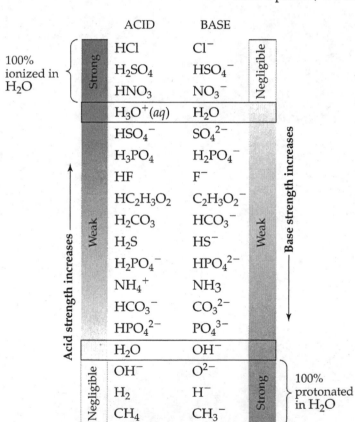

▲ **Figure 16.4 Relative strengths of some conjugate acid-base pairs.** The two members of each pair are listed opposite each other in the two columns. The acids decrease in strength from top to bottom, whereas their conjugate bases increase in strength from top to bottom.

GIVE IT SOME THOUGHT

Using the three categories above, specify the strength of HNO_3 and the strength of its conjugate base, NO_3^-.

We can think of proton-transfer reactions as being governed by the relative abilities of two bases to abstract protons. For example, consider the proton transfer that occurs when an acid HX dissolves in water:

$$HX(aq) + H_2O(l) \rightleftharpoons H_3O^+(aq) + X^-(aq) \qquad [16.9]$$

If H_2O (the base in the forward reaction) is a stronger base than X^- (the conjugate base of HX), then H_2O will abstract the proton from HX to produce H_3O^+ and X^-. As a result, the equilibrium will lie to the right. This describes the behavior of a strong acid in water. For example, when HCl dissolves in water, the solution consists almost entirely of H_3O^+ and Cl^- ions with a negligible concentration of HCl molecules.

$$HCl(g) + H_2O(l) \longrightarrow H_3O^+(aq) + Cl^-(aq) \qquad [16.10]$$

H_2O is a stronger base than Cl^- (Figure 16.4), so H_2O acquires the proton to become the hydronium ion.

When X^- is a stronger base than H_2O, the equilibrium will lie to the left. This situation occurs when HX is a weak acid. For example, an aqueous solution of acetic acid ($HC_2H_3O_2$) consists mainly of $HC_2H_3O_2$ molecules with only a relatively few H_3O^+ and $C_2H_3O_2^-$ ions.

$$HC_2H_3O_2(aq) + H_2O(l) \rightleftharpoons H_3O^+(aq) + C_2H_3O_2^-(aq) \qquad [16.11]$$

$C_2H_3O_2^-$ is a stronger base than H_2O (Figure 16.4) and therefore abstracts the proton from H_3O^+. From these examples, we conclude that *in every acid-base reaction the position of the equilibrium favors transfer of the proton to the stronger base.* That is, the position of the equilibrium favors the reaction of the stronger acid and the stronger base to form the weaker acid and the weaker base. As a result, the equilibrium mixture contains more of the weaker acid and weaker base and less of the stronger acid and stronger base.

■ SAMPLE EXERCISE 16.3 | Predicting the Position of a Proton-Transfer Equilibrium

For the following proton-transfer reaction, use Figure 16.4 to predict whether the equilibrium lies predominantly to the left (that is, $K_c < 1$) or to the right ($K_c > 1$):

$$HSO_4^-(aq) + CO_3^{2-}(aq) \rightleftharpoons SO_4^{2-}(aq) + HCO_3^-(aq)$$

Solution

Analyze: We are asked to predict whether the equilibrium shown lies to the right, favoring products, or to the left, favoring reactants.

Plan: This is a proton-transfer reaction, and the position of the equilibrium will favor the proton going to the stronger of two bases. The two bases in the equation are CO_3^{2-}, the base in the forward reaction as written, and SO_4^{2-}, the conjugate base of HSO_4^-. We can find the relative positions of these two bases in Figure 16.4 to determine which is the stronger base.

Solve: CO_3^{2-} appears lower in the right-hand column in Figure 16.4 and is therefore a stronger base than SO_4^{2-}. CO_3^{2-}, therefore, will get the proton preferentially to become HCO_3^-, while SO_4^{2-} will remain mostly unprotonated. The resulting equilibrium will lie to the right, favoring products (that is, $K_c > 1$).

$$\underset{\text{Acid}}{HSO_4^-(aq)} + \underset{\text{Base}}{CO_3^{2-}(aq)} \rightleftharpoons \underset{\substack{\text{Conjugate} \\ \text{base}}}{SO_4^{2-}(aq)} + \underset{\substack{\text{Conjugate} \\ \text{acid}}}{HCO_3^-(aq)} \qquad K_c > 1$$

Science Fundamentals Second Edition

Comment: Of the two acids in the equation, HSO_4^- and HCO_3^-, the stronger one gives up a proton while the weaker one retains its proton. Thus, the equilibrium favors the direction in which the proton moves from the stronger acid and becomes bonded to the stronger base.

■ PRACTICE EXERCISE

For each of the following reactions, use Figure 16.4 to predict whether the equilibrium lies predominantly to the left or to the right:

(a) $HPO_4^{2-}(aq) + H_2O(l) \rightleftharpoons H_2PO_4^-(aq) + OH^-(aq)$
(b) $NH_4^+(aq) + OH^-(aq) \rightleftharpoons NH_3(aq) + H_2O(l)$

Answers: (a) left, (b) right

16.3 | The Autoionization of Water

One of the most important chemical properties of water is its ability to act as either a Brønsted acid or a Brønsted base, depending on the circumstances. In the presence of an acid, water acts as a proton acceptor; in the presence of a base, water acts as a proton donor. In fact, one water molecule can donate a proton to another water molecule:

$$H-\ddot{O}: + H-\ddot{O}: \rightleftharpoons \left[H-\ddot{O}-H\right]^+ + :\ddot{O}-H^- \qquad [16.12]$$

We call this process the **autoionization** of water. No individual molecule remains ionized for long; the reactions are extremely rapid in both directions. At room temperature only about two out of every 10^9 molecules are ionized at any given instant. Thus, pure water consists almost entirely of H_2O molecules and is an extremely poor conductor of electricity. Nevertheless, the autoionization of water is very important, as we will soon see.

ACTIVITY
K_w

The Ion Product of Water

Because the autoionization of water (Equation 16.12) is an equilibrium process, we can write the following equilibrium-constant expression for it:

$$K_c = [H_3O^+][OH^-] \qquad [16.13]$$

The term $[H_2O]$ is excluded from the equilibrium-constant expression because we exclude the concentrations of pure solids and liquids. ∞∞ (Section 15.4) Because this equilibrium-constant expression refers specifically to the autoionization of water, we use the symbol K_w to denote the equilibrium constant, which we call the **ion-product constant** for water. At 25°C, K_w equals 1.0×10^{-14}. Thus, we have

$$K_w = [H_3O^+][OH^-] = 1.0 \times 10^{-14} \text{ (at 25°C)} \qquad [16.14]$$

Because we use $H^+(aq)$ and $H_3O(aq)^+$ interchangeably to represent the hydrated proton, the autoionization reaction for water can also be written as

$$H_2O(l) \rightleftharpoons H^+(aq) + OH^-(aq) \qquad [16.15]$$

Likewise, the expression for K_w can be written in terms of either H_3O^+ or H^+, and K_w has the same value in either case:

$$K_w = [H_3O^+][OH^-] = [H^+][OH^-] = 1.0 \times 10^{-14} \text{ (at 25°C)} \qquad [16.16]$$

This equilibrium-constant expression and the value of K_w at 25°C are extremely important, and you should commit them to memory.

What makes Equation 16.16 particularly useful is that it is not only applicable to pure water but also to any aqueous solution. Although the equilibrium between $H^+(aq)$ and $OH^-(aq)$ as well as other ionic equilibria are affected somewhat by the presence of additional ions in solution, it is customary to ignore these ionic effects except in work requiring exceptional accuracy. Thus, Equation 16.16 is taken to be valid for any dilute aqueous solution, and it can be used to calculate either $[H^+]$ (if $[OH^-]$ is known) or $[OH^-]$ (if $[H^+]$ is known).

A solution in which $[H^+] = [OH^-]$ is said to be *neutral*. In most solutions H^+ and OH^- concentrations are not equal. As the concentration of one of these ions increases, the concentration of the other must decrease, so that the product of their concentrations equals 1.0×10^{-14}. In acidic solutions $[H^+]$ exceeds $[OH^-]$. In basic solutions $[OH^-]$ exceeds $[H^+]$.

■ SAMPLE EXERCISE 16.4 | Calculating $[H^+]$ for Pure Water

Calculate the values of $[H^+]$ and $[OH^-]$ in a neutral solution at 25°C.

Solution

Analyze: We are asked to determine the concentrations of hydronium and hydroxide ions in a neutral solution at 25°C.
Plan: We will use Equation 16.16 and the fact that, by definition, $[H^+] = [OH^-]$ in a neutral solution.
Solve: We will represent the concentration of $[H^+]$ and $[OH^-]$ in neutral solution with x. This gives

$$[H^+][OH^-] = (x)(x) = 1.0 \times 10^{-14}$$
$$x^2 = 1.0 \times 10^{-14}$$
$$x = 1.0 \times 10^{-7} M = [H^+] = [OH^-]$$

In an acid solution $[H^+]$ is greater than $1.0 \times 10^{-7} M$; in a basic solution $[H^+]$ is less than $1.0 \times 10^{-7} M$.

■ PRACTICE EXERCISE

Indicate whether solutions with each of the following ion concentrations are neutral, acidic, or basic: **(a)** $[H^+] = 4 \times 10^{-9} M$; **(b)** $[OH^-] = 1 \times 10^{-7} M$; **(c)** $[OH^-] = 7 \times 10^{-13} M$.
Answers: **(a)** basic, **(b)** neutral, **(c)** acidic

■ SAMPLE EXERCISE 16.5 | Calculating $[H^+]$ from $[OH^-]$

Calculate the concentration of $H^+(aq)$ in **(a)** a solution in which $[OH^-]$ is 0.010 M, **(b)** a solution in which $[OH^-]$ is $1.8 \times 10^{-9} M$. *Note:* In this problem and all that follow, we assume, unless stated otherwise, that the temperature is 25°C.

Solution

Analyze: We are asked to calculate the hydronium ion concentration in an aqueous solution where the hydroxide concentration is known.
Plan: We can use the equilibrium-constant expression for the autoionization of water and the value of K_w to solve for each unknown concentration.

Solve: **(a)** Using Equation 16.16, we have:

$$[H^+][OH^-] = 1.0 \times 10^{-14}$$

$$[H^+] = \frac{1.0 \times 10^{-14}}{[OH^-]} = \frac{1.0 \times 10^{-14}}{0.010} = 1.0 \times 10^{-12} M$$

This solution is basic because $[OH^-] > [H^+]$

(b) In this instance

$$[H^+] = \frac{1.0 \times 10^{-14}}{[OH^-]} = \frac{1.0 \times 10^{-14}}{1.8 \times 10^{-9}} = 5.6 \times 10^{-6} \, M$$

This solution is acidic because

$$[H^+] > [OH^-]$$

PRACTICE EXERCISE

Calculate the concentration of $OH^-(aq)$ in a solution in which **(a)** $[H^+] = 2 \times 10^{-6} \, M$; **(b)** $[H^+] = [OH^-]$; **(c)** $[H^+] = 100 \times [OH^-]$.
Answers: **(a)** $5 \times 10^{-9} \, M$, **(b)** $1.0 \times 10^{-7} \, M$, **(c)** $1.0 \times 10^{-8} \, M$

16.4 | The pH Scale

The molar concentration of $H^+(aq)$ in an aqueous solution is usually very small. For convenience, we therefore usually express $[H^+]$ in terms of **pH**, which is the negative logarithm in base 10 of $[H^+]$.*

$$pH = -\log[H^+] \qquad\qquad [16.17]$$

If you need to review the use of logs, see Appendix A.

We can use Equation 16.17 to calculate the pH of a neutral solution at 25°C (that is, one in which $[H^+] = 1.0 \times 10^{-7} \, M$):

$$pH = -\log(1.0 \times 10^{-7}) = -(-7.00) = 7.00$$

The pH of a neutral solution is 7.00 at 25°C.

What happens to the pH of a solution as we make the solution acidic? An acidic solution is one in which $[H^+] > 1.0 \times 10^{-7} \, M$. Because of the negative sign in Equation 16.17, *the pH decreases as* $[H^+]$ *increases*. For example, the pH of an acidic solution in which $[H^+] = 1.0 \times 10^{-3} \, M$ is

$$pH = -\log(1.0 \times 10^{-3}) = -(-3.00) = 3.00$$

At 25°C the pH of an acidic solution is less than 7.00.

ACTIVITY
pH Estimation

We can also calculate the pH of a basic solution, one in which $[OH^-] > 1.0 \times 10^{-7} \, M$. Suppose $[OH^-] = 2.0 \times 10^{-3} \, M$. We can use Equation 16.16 to calculate $[H^+]$ for this solution, and Equation 16.17 to calculate the pH:

$$[H^+] = \frac{K_w}{[OH^-]} = \frac{1.0 \times 10^{-14}}{2.0 \times 10^{-3}} = 5.0 \times 10^{-12} \, M$$

$$pH = -\log(5.0 \times 10^{-12}) = 11.30$$

At 25°C the pH of a basic solution is greater than 7.00. The relationships among $[H^+]$, $[OH^-]$, and pH are summarized in Table 16.1 ▼.

TABLE 16.1 Relationships Among $[H^+]$, $[OH^-]$, and pH at 25°C

Solution Type	$[H^+]$ (M)	$[OH^-]$ (M)	pH Value
Acidic	$>1.0 \times 10^{-7}$	$<1.0 \times 10^{-7}$	<7.00
Neutral	$=1.0 \times 10^{-7}$	$=1.0 \times 10^{-7}$	$=7.00$
Basic	$<1.0 \times 10^{-7}$	$>1.0 \times 10^{-7}$	>7.00

---

* Because $[H^+]$ and $[H_3O^+]$ are used interchangeably, you might see pH defined as $-\log[H_3O^+]$.

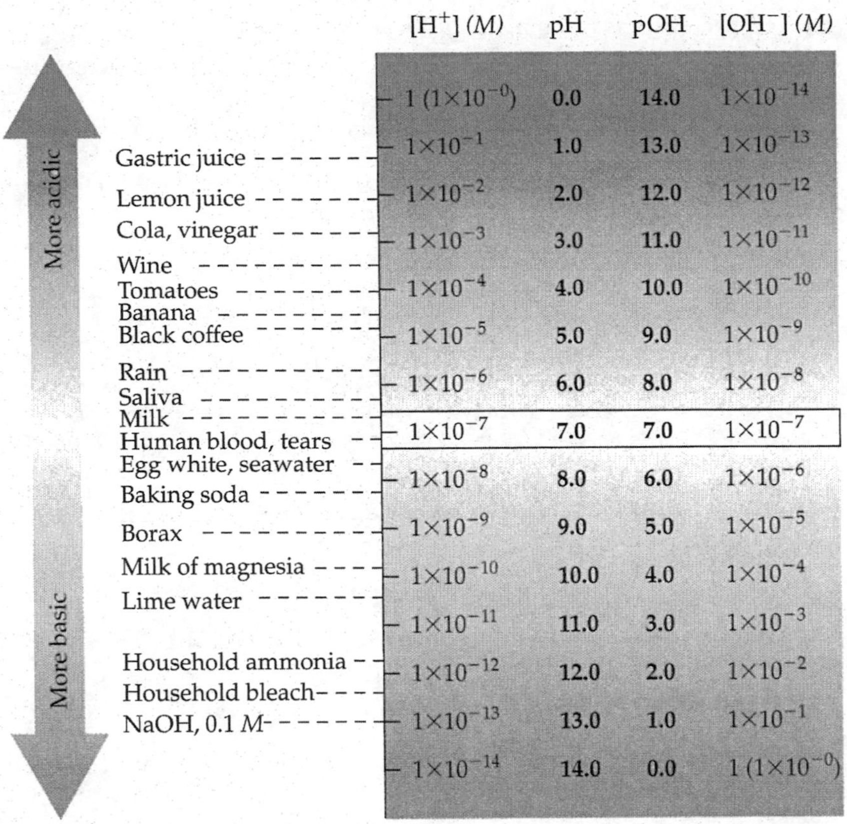

◀ **Figure 16.5   H⁺ concentrations and pH values of some common substances at 25°C.** The pH and pOH of a solution can be estimated using the benchmark concentrations of H^+ and OH^- corresponding to whole-number pH values.

	[H⁺] (M)	pH	pOH	[OH⁻] (M)
	$1\,(1\times10^{-0})$	0.0	14.0	1×10^{-14}
Gastric juice	1×10^{-1}	1.0	13.0	1×10^{-13}
Lemon juice	1×10^{-2}	2.0	12.0	1×10^{-12}
Cola, vinegar	1×10^{-3}	3.0	11.0	1×10^{-11}
Wine				
Tomatoes	1×10^{-4}	4.0	10.0	1×10^{-10}
Banana				
Black coffee	1×10^{-5}	5.0	9.0	1×10^{-9}
Rain	1×10^{-6}	6.0	8.0	1×10^{-8}
Saliva				
Milk				
Human blood, tears	1×10^{-7}	7.0	7.0	1×10^{-7}
Egg white, seawater	1×10^{-8}	8.0	6.0	1×10^{-6}
Baking soda				
Borax	1×10^{-9}	9.0	5.0	1×10^{-5}
Milk of magnesia	1×10^{-10}	10.0	4.0	1×10^{-4}
Lime water				
	1×10^{-11}	11.0	3.0	1×10^{-3}
Household ammonia	1×10^{-12}	12.0	2.0	1×10^{-2}
Household bleach				
NaOH, 0.1 M	1×10^{-13}	13.0	1.0	1×10^{-1}
	1×10^{-14}	14.0	0.0	$1\,(1\times10^{-0})$

More acidic ↑   *More basic* ↓

ACTIVITY
Acids and Bases

The pH values characteristic of several familiar solutions are shown in Figure 16.5 ▲. Notice that a change in [H⁺] by a factor of 10 causes the pH to change by 1. Thus, a solution of pH 6 has 10 times the concentration of $H^+(aq)$ as a solution of pH 7.

 GIVE IT SOME THOUGHT

(a) What is the significance of pH = 7?   **(b)** How does the pH change as OH⁻ is added to the solution?

You might think that when [H⁺] is very small, as it is for some of the examples shown in Figure 16.5, it would be unimportant. Nothing is further from the truth. If [H⁺] is part of a kinetic rate law, then changing its concentration will change the rate. ∞ (Section 14.3) Thus, if the rate law is first order in [H⁺], doubling its concentration will double the rate even if the change is merely from $1 \times 10^{-7}\ M$ to $2 \times 10^{-7}\ M$. In biological systems many reactions involve proton transfers and have rates that depend on [H⁺]. Because the speeds of these reactions are crucial, the pH of biological fluids must be maintained within narrow limits. For example, human blood has a normal pH range of 7.35 to 7.45. Illness and even death can result if the pH varies much from this narrow range.

A convenient way to estimate pH is to use the "benchmark" H⁺ concentrations in Figure 16.5, those for which [H⁺] equals 1×10^{-x}, where x is a whole number from 0 to 14. When [H⁺] is one of these benchmark concentrations, the pH is simply the corresponding pH value, x. When $[H^+] = 1 \times 10^{-4}$, for example, the pH is simply 4. When [H⁺] falls between two benchmark concentrations, the pH will fall between the two corresponding pH values. Consider a solution that is 0.050 M in H⁺. Because 0.050 (that is, 5.0×10^{-2}) is greater than 1.0×10^{-2} and less than 1.0×10^{-1}, we estimate the pH to be between 2.00 and 1.00. Using Equation 16.17 to calculate the pH gives 1.30.

Science Fundamentals Second Edition

■ SAMPLE EXERCISE 16.6 | Calculating pH from [H⁺]

Calculate the pH values for the two solutions described in Sample Exercise 16.5.

Solution

Analyze: We are asked to determine the pH of aqueous solutions for which we have already calculated $[H^+]$.

Plan: We can use the benchmarks in Figure 16.5 to determine the pH for part (a) and to estimate pH for part (b). We can then use Equation 16.17 to calculate pH for part (b).

Solve: (a) In the first instance we found $[H^+]$ to be 1.0×10^{-12} M. Although we can use Equation 16.17 to determine the pH, 1.0×10^{-12} is one of the benchmarks in Figure 16.5, so the pH can be determined without any formal calculation.

$$pH = -\log(1.0 \times 10^{-12}) = -(-12.00) = 12.00$$

The rule for using significant figures with logs is that *the number of decimal places in the log equals the number of significant figures in the original number* (see Appendix A). Because 1.0×10^{-12} has two significant figures, the pH has two decimal places, 12.00.

(b) For the second solution, $[H^+] = 5.6 \times 10^{-6}$ M. Before performing the calculation, it is helpful to estimate the pH. To do so, we note that $[H^+]$ lies between 1×10^{-6} and 1×10^{-5}.

$$1 \times 10^{-6} < 5.6 \times 10^{-6} < 1 \times 10^{-5}$$

Thus, we expect the pH to lie between 6.0 and 5.0. We use Equation 16.17 to calculate the pH.

$$pH = -\log (5.6 \times 10^{-6}) = 5.25$$

Check: After calculating a pH, it is useful to compare it to your prior estimate. In this case the pH, as we predicted, falls between 6 and 5. Had the calculated pH and the estimate not agreed, we should have reconsidered our calculation or estimate or both. Note that although $[H^+]$ lies halfway between the two benchmark concentrations, the calculated pH does not lie halfway between the two corresponding pH values. This is because the pH scale is logarithmic rather than linear.

■ PRACTICE EXERCISE

(a) In a sample of lemon juice $[H^+]$ is 3.8×10^{-4} M. What is the pH? **(b)** A commonly available window-cleaning solution has a $[H^+]$ of 5.3×10^{-9} M. What is the pH?
Answers: **(a)** 3.42, **(b)** 8.28

■ SAMPLE EXERCISE 16.7 | Calculating [H⁺] from pH

A sample of freshly pressed apple juice has a pH of 3.76. Calculate $[H^+]$.

Solution
Analyze: We need to calculate $[H^+]$ from pH.
Plan: We will use Equation 16.17, $pH = -\log[H^+]$, for the calculation.

Solve: From Equation 16.17, we have $pH = -\log[H^+] = 3.76$

Thus, $\log[H^+] = -3.76$

To find $[H^+]$, we need to determine the *antilog* of -3.76. Scientific calculators have an antilog function (sometimes labeled INV log or 10^x) that allows us to perform the calculation:

$$[H^+] = \text{antilog}(-3.76) = 10^{-3.76} = 1.7 \times 10^{-4} M$$

Comment: Consult the user's manual for your calculator to find out how to perform the antilog operation. The number of significant figures in $[H^+]$ is two because the number of decimal places in the pH is two.

Check: Because the pH is between 3.0 and 4.0, we know that $[H^+]$ will be between 1×10^{-3} and 1×10^{-4} M. Our calculated $[H^+]$ falls within this estimated range.

 PRACTICE EXERCISE

A solution formed by dissolving an antacid tablet has a pH of 9.18. Calculate $[H^+]$.
Answer: $[H^+] = 6.6 \times 10^{-10}$ M

Other "p" Scales

The negative log is also a convenient way of expressing the magnitudes of other small quantities. We use the convention that the negative log of a quantity is labeled "p" (quantity). For example, one can express the concentration of OH^- as pOH:

$$pOH = -\log[OH^-] \qquad [16.18]$$

By taking the negative log of both sides of Equation 16.16,

$$-\log[H^+] + (-\log[OH^-]) = -\log K_w \qquad [16.19]$$

we obtain the following useful expression:

$$pH + pOH = 14.00 \text{ (at } 25°C) \qquad [16.20]$$

We will see in Section 16.8 that p scales are also useful when working with equilibrium constants.

🔆 GIVE IT SOME THOUGHT

If the pOH for a solution is 3.00, what is the pH of the solution? Is the solution acidic or basic?

Measuring pH

The pH of a solution can be measured quickly and accurately with a *pH meter* (Figure 16.6 ▶). A complete understanding of how this important device works requires a knowledge of electrochemistry, a subject we take up in Chapter 20. In brief, a pH meter consists of a pair of electrodes connected to a meter capable of measuring small voltages, on the order of millivolts. A voltage, which varies with the pH, is generated when the electrodes are placed in a solution. This voltage is read by the meter, which is calibrated to give pH.

The electrodes used with pH meters come in many shapes and sizes, depending on their intended use. Electrodes have even been developed that are so small that they can be inserted into single living cells in order to monitor the pH of the cell medium. Pocket-size pH meters are also available for use in environmental studies, in monitoring industrial effluents, and in agricultural work.

Although less precise, acid-base indicators can be used to measure pH. An acid-base indicator is a colored substance that itself can exist in either an acid or a base form. The two forms have different colors. Thus, the indicator turns one color in an acid and another color in a base. If you know the pH at which the indicator turns from one form to the other, you can determine whether a solution has a higher or lower pH than this value. Litmus, for example, changes color in the vicinity of pH 7. The color change, however, is not very sharp. Red litmus indicates a pH of about 5 or lower, and blue litmus indicates a pH of about 8 or higher.

Some of the more common indicators are listed in Figure 16.7 ▶. Methyl orange, for example, changes color over the pH interval from 3.1 to 4.4. Below pH 3.1 it is in the acid form, which is red. In the interval between 3.1 and 4.4, it is gradually converted to its basic form, which has a yellow color. By pH 4.4 the conversion is complete, and the solution is yellow. Paper tape that is

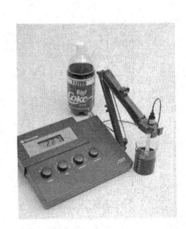

▲ **Figure 16.6 A digital pH meter.** The device is a millivoltmeter, and the electrodes immersed in the solution being tested produce a voltage that depends on the pH of the solution.

Science Fundamentals Second Edition

▶ **Figure 16.7 Some common acid-base indicators.** The pH ranges for the color changes of some common acid-base indicators. Most indicators have a useful range of about 2 pH units.

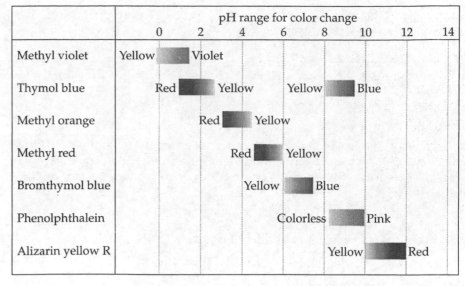

MOVIE
Natural Indicators

impregnated with several indicators and comes complete with a comparator color scale is widely used for approximate determinations of pH.

💡 **GIVE IT SOME THOUGHT**

If phenolphthalein turns pink when added to a solution, what can we conclude about the pH of the solution?

16.5 | Strong Acids and Bases

The chemistry of an aqueous solution often depends critically on the pH of the solution. It is therefore important to examine how the pH of solutions relate to the concentrations of acids and bases. The simplest cases are those involving strong acids and strong bases. Strong acids and bases are *strong electrolytes*, existing in aqueous solution entirely as ions. There are relatively few common strong acids and bases, and we listed these substances in Table 4.2.

Strong Acids

The seven most common strong acids include six monoprotic acids (HCl, HBr, HI, HNO_3, $HClO_3$, and $HClO_4$), and one diprotic acid (H_2SO_4). Nitric acid (HNO_3) exemplifies the behavior of the monoprotic strong acids. For all practical purposes, an aqueous solution of HNO_3 consists entirely of H_3O^+ and NO_3^- ions.

$$HNO_3(aq) + H_2O(l) \longrightarrow H_3O^+(aq) + NO_3^-(aq) \text{ (complete ionization)} \quad [16.21]$$

We have not used equilibrium arrows for Equation 16.21 because the reaction lies entirely to the right, the side with the ions. ∞ (Section 4.1) As noted in Section 16.3, we use $H_3O^+(aq)$ and $H^+(aq)$ interchangeably to represent the hydrated proton in water. Thus, we often simplify the equations for the ionization reactions of acids as follows:

$$HNO_3(aq) \longrightarrow H^+(aq) + NO_3^-(aq)$$

In an aqueous solution of a strong acid, the acid is normally the only significant source of H^+ ions.* As a result, calculating the pH of a solution of a strong

---

* If the concentration of the acid is 10^{-6} M or less, we also need to consider H^+ ions that result from the autoionization of H_2O. Normally, the concentration of H^+ from H_2O is so small that it can be neglected.

monoprotic acid is straightforward because $[H^+]$ equals the original concentration of acid. In a 0.20 M solution of $HNO_3(aq)$, for example, $[H^+]$ = $[NO_3^-]$ = 0.20 M. The situation with the diprotic acid H_2SO_4 is more complex, as we will see in Section 16.6.

SAMPLE EXERCISE 16.8 | Calculating the pH of a Strong Acid

What is the pH of a 0.040 M solution of $HClO_4$?

Solution

Analyze and Plan: We are asked to calculate the pH of a 0.040 M solution of $HClO_4$. Because $HClO_4$ is a strong acid, it is completely ionized, giving $[H^+]$ = $[ClO_4^-]$ = 0.040 M. Because $[H^+]$ lies between benchmarks 1×10^{-2} and 1×10^{-1} in Figure 16.5, we estimate that the pH will be between 2.0 and 1.0.

Solve: The pH of the solution is given by

$$pH = -\log(0.040) = 1.40.$$

Check: Our calculated pH falls within the estimated range.

PRACTICE EXERCISE

An aqueous solution of HNO_3 has a pH of 2.34. What is the concentration of the acid?

Answer: 0.0046 M

Strong Bases

There are relatively few common strong bases. The most common soluble strong bases are the ionic hydroxides of the alkali metals (group 1A) and the heavier alkaline earth metals (group 2A), such as NaOH, KOH, and $Ca(OH)_2$. These compounds completely dissociate into ions in aqueous solution. Thus, a solution labeled 0.30 M NaOH consists of 0.30 M $Na^+(aq)$ and 0.30 M $OH^-(aq)$; there is essentially no undissociated NaOH.

Because these strong bases dissociate entirely into ions in aqueous solution, calculating the pH of their solutions is also straightforward, as shown in Sample Exercise 16.9.

SAMPLE EXERCISE 16.9 | Calculating the pH of a Strong Base

What is the pH of **(a)** a 0.028 M solution of NaOH, **(b)** a 0.0011 M solution of $Ca(OH)_2$?

Solution

Analyze: We're asked to calculate the pH of two solutions, given the concentration of strong base for each.

Plan: We can calculate each pH by two equivalent methods. First, we could use Equation 16.16 to calculate $[H^+]$ and then use Equation 16.17 to calculate the pH. Alternatively, we could use $[OH^-]$ to calculate pOH and then use Equation 16.20 to calculate the pH.

Solve: (a) NaOH dissociates in water to give one OH^- ion per formula unit. Therefore, the OH^- concentration for the solution in (a) equals the stated concentration of NaOH, namely 0.028 M.

Method 1:

$$[H^+] = \frac{1.0 \times 10^{-14}}{0.028} = 3.57 \times 10^{-13}\,M \quad pH = -\log(3.57 \times 10^{-13}) = 12.45$$

Method 2:

$$pOH = -\log(0.028) = 1.55 \qquad pH = 14.00 - pOH = 12.45$$

(b) $Ca(OH)_2$ is a strong base that dissociates in water to give two OH^- ions per formula unit. Thus, the concentration of $OH^-(aq)$ for the solution in part (b) is $2 \times (0.0011\,M) = 0.0022\,M$.

Science Fundamentals Second Edition

Method 1:

$$[H^+] = \frac{1.0 \times 10^{-14}}{0.0022} = 4.55 \times 10^{-12} \, M \quad pH = -\log(4.55 \times 10^{-12}) = 11.34$$

Method 2:

$$pOH = -\log(0.0022) = 2.66 \qquad pH = 14.00 - pOH = 11.34$$

■ PRACTICE EXERCISE

What is the concentration of a solution of **(a)** KOH for which the pH is 11.89;
(b) Ca(OH)$_2$ for which the pH is 11.68?
Answers: **(a)** $7.8 \times 10^{-3} \, M$, **(b)** $2.4 \times 10^{-3} \, M$

Although all the hydroxides of the alkali metals (group 1A) are strong electrolytes, LiOH, RbOH, and CsOH are not commonly encountered in the laboratory. The hydroxides of the heavier alkaline earth metals, Ca(OH)$_2$, Sr(OH)$_2$, and Ba(OH)$_2$, are also strong electrolytes. They have limited solubilities, however, so they are used only when high solubility is not critical.

Strongly basic solutions are also created by certain substances that react with water to form OH$^-$(aq). The most common of these contain the oxide ion. Ionic metal oxides, especially Na$_2$O and CaO, are often used in industry when a strong base is needed. Each mole of O^{2-} reacts with water to form 2 mol of OH$^-$, leaving virtually no O^{2-} remaining in the solution:

$$O^{2-}(aq) + H_2O(l) \longrightarrow 2\,OH^-(aq) \tag{16.22}$$

Thus, a solution formed by dissolving 0.010 mol of Na$_2$O(s) in enough water to form 1.0 L of solution will have [OH$^-$] = 0.020 M and a pH of 12.30.

Ionic hydrides and nitrides also react with H$_2$O to form OH$^-$:

$$H^-(aq) + H_2O(l) \longrightarrow H_2(g) + OH^-(aq) \tag{16.23}$$

$$N^{3-}(aq) + 3\,H_2O(l) \longrightarrow NH_3(aq) + 3\,OH^-(aq) \tag{16.24}$$

Because the anions O^{2-}, H$^-$, and N^{3-} are stronger bases than OH$^-$ (the conjugate base of H$_2$O), they are able to remove a proton from H$_2$O.

GIVE IT SOME THOUGHT

The CH$_3^-$ ion is the conjugate base of CH$_4$, and CH$_4$ shows no evidence of being an acid in water. What happens when CH$_3^-$ is added to water?

16.6 | Weak Acids

ANIMATION
Introduction to Aqueous Acids

Most acidic substances are weak acids and are therefore only partially ionized in aqueous solution. We can use the equilibrium constant for the ionization reaction to express the extent to which a weak acid ionizes. If we represent a general weak acid as HA, we can write the equation for its ionization reaction in either of the following ways, depending on whether the hydrated proton is represented as H$_3$O$^+$(aq) or H$^+$(aq):

$$HA(aq) + H_2O(l) \rightleftharpoons H_3O^+(aq) + A^-(aq) \tag{16.25}$$

or

$$HA(aq) \rightleftharpoons H^+(aq) + A^-(aq) \tag{16.26}$$

Because [H$_2$O] is the solvent, it is omitted from the equilibrium-constant expression, which can be written as either

$$K_c = \frac{[H_3O^+][A^-]}{[HA]} \quad \text{or} \quad K_c = \frac{[H^+][A^-]}{[HA]}$$

TABLE 16.2   Some Weak Acids in Water at 25°C*

Acid	Structural Formula	Conjugate Base	Equilibrium Reaction	K_a
Hydrofluoric (HF)	H—F	F^-	$HF(aq) + H_2O(l) \rightleftharpoons H_3O^+(aq) + F^-(aq)$	6.8×10^{-4}
Nitrous (HNO_2)	H—O—N=O	NO_2^-	$HNO_2(aq) + H_2O(l) \rightleftharpoons H_3O^+(aq) + NO_2^-(aq)$	4.5×10^{-4}
Benzoic ($HC_7H_5O_2$)	H—O—C(=O)—⬡	$C_7H_5O_2^-$	$HC_7H_5O_2(aq) + H_2O(l) \rightleftharpoons H_3O^+(aq) + C_7H_5O_2^-(aq)$	6.3×10^{-5}
Acetic ($HC_2H_3O_2$)	H—O—C(=O)—C(H)(H)—H	$C_2H_3O_2^-$	$HC_2H_3O_2(aq) + H_2O(l) \rightleftharpoons H_3O^+(aq) + C_2H_3O_2^-(aq)$	1.8×10^{-5}
Hypochlorous (HClO)	H—O—Cl	ClO^-	$HClO(aq) + H_2O(l) \rightleftharpoons H_3O^+(aq) + ClO^-(aq)$	3.0×10^{-8}
Hydrocyanic (HCN)	H—C≡N	CN^-	$HCN(aq) + H_2O(l) \rightleftharpoons H_3O^+(aq) + CN^-(aq)$	4.9×10^{-10}
Phenol (HC_6H_5O)	H—O—⬡	$C_6H_5O^-$	$HC_6H_5O(aq) + H_2O(l) \rightleftharpoons H_3O^+(aq) + C_6H_5O^-(aq)$	1.3×10^{-10}

*The proton that ionizes is shown in blue.

As we did for the ion-product constant for the autoionization of water, we change the subscript on this equilibrium constant to indicate the type of equation to which it corresponds.

$$K_a = \frac{[H_3O^+][A^-]}{[HA]} \quad \text{or} \quad K_a = \frac{[H^+][A^-]}{[HA]} \qquad [16.27]$$

ACTIVITY
Equilibrium Constant

The subscript a on K_a denotes that it is an equilibrium constant for the ionization of an acid, so K_a is called the **acid-dissociation constant.**

Table 16.2 ▲ shows the names, structures, and K_a values for several weak acids. A more complete listing is given in Appendix D. Many weak acids are organic compounds composed entirely of carbon, hydrogen, and oxygen. These compounds usually contain some hydrogen atoms bonded to carbon atoms and some bonded to oxygen atoms. In almost all cases the hydrogen atoms bonded to carbon do not ionize in water; instead, the acidic behavior of these compounds is due to the hydrogen atoms attached to oxygen atoms.

The magnitude of K_a indicates the tendency of the acid to ionize in water: *The larger the value of* K_a, *the stronger the acid.* Hydrofluoric acid (HF), for example, is the strongest acid listed in Table 16.2, and phenol (HOC_6H_5) is the weakest. Notice that K_a is typically less than 10^{-3}.

Calculating K_a from pH

In order to calculate either the K_a value for a weak acid or the pH of its solutions, we will use many of the skills for solving equilibrium problems that we developed in Section 15.5. In many cases the small magnitude of K_a allows us to use approximations to simplify the problem. In doing these calculations, it is important to realize that proton-transfer reactions are generally very rapid. As a result, the measured or calculated pH for a weak acid always represents an equilibrium condition.

SAMPLE EXERCISE 16.10 | Calculating K_a and Percent Ionization from Measured pH

A student prepared a 0.10 M solution of formic acid (HCHO$_2$) and measured its pH using a pH meter of the type illustrated in Figure 16.6. The pH at 25°C was found to be 2.38. **(a)** Calculate K_a for formic acid at this temperature. **(b)** What percentage of the acid is ionized in this 0.10 M solution?

Solution

Analyze: We are given the molar concentration of an aqueous solution of weak acid and the pH of the solution at 25°C, and we are asked to determine the value of K_a for the acid and the percentage of the acid that is ionized.

Plan: Although we are dealing specifically with the ionization of a weak acid, this problem is very similar to the equilibrium problems we encountered in Chapter 15. We can solve it using the method first outlined in Sample Exercise 15.8, starting with the chemical reaction and a tabulation of initial and equilibrium concentrations.

Solve: (a) The first step in solving any equilibrium problem is to write the equation for the equilibrium reaction. The ionization equilibrium for formic acid can be written as follows:

$$HCHO_2(aq) \rightleftharpoons H^+(aq) + CHO_2^-(aq)$$

The equilibrium-constant expression is

$$K_a = \frac{[H^+][CHO_2^-]}{[HCHO_2]}$$

From the measured pH, we can calculate $[H^+]$:

$$pH = -\log[H^+] = 2.38$$
$$\log[H^+] = -2.38$$
$$[H^+] = 10^{-2.38} = 4.2 \times 10^{-3}\ M$$

We can do a little accounting to determine the concentrations of the species involved in the equilibrium. We imagine that the solution is initially 0.10 M in HCHO$_2$ molecules. We then consider the ionization of the acid into H$^+$ and CHO$_2^-$. For each HCHO$_2$ molecule that ionizes, one H$^+$ ion and one CHO$_2^-$ ion are produced in solution. Because the pH measurement indicates that $[H^+] = 4.2 \times 10^{-3}\ M$ at equilibrium, we can construct the following table:

	$HCHO_2(aq)$	$\rightleftharpoons$	$H^+(aq)$	+	$CHO_2^-(aq)$
Initial	0.10 M		0		0
Change	$-4.2 \times 10^{-3}\ M$		$+4.2 \times 10^{-3}\ M$		$+4.2 \times 10^{-3}\ M$
Equilibrium	$(0.10 - 4.2 \times 10^{-3})\ M$		$4.2 \times 10^{-3}\ M$		$4.2 \times 10^{-3}\ M$

Notice that we have neglected the very small concentration of H$^+$(aq) that is due to the autoionization of H$_2$O. Notice also that the amount of HCHO$_2$ that ionizes is very small compared with the initial concentration of the acid. To the number of significant figures we are using, the subtraction yields 0.10 M:

$$(0.10 - 4.2 \times 10^{-3})\ M \approx 0.10\ M$$

We can now insert the equilibrium concentrations into the expression for K_a:

$$K_a = \frac{(4.2 \times 10^{-3})(4.2 \times 10^{-3})}{0.10} = 1.8 \times 10^{-4}$$

Check: The magnitude of our answer is reasonable because K_a for a weak acid is usually between 10^{-3} and 10^{-10}.

(b) The percentage of acid that ionizes is given by the concentration of H$^+$ or CHO$_2^-$ at equilibrium, divided by the initial acid concentration, multiplied by 100%.

$$\text{Percent ionization} = \frac{[H^+]_{\text{equilibrium}}}{[HCHO_2]_{\text{initial}}} \times 100\% = \frac{4.2 \times 10^{-3}}{0.10} \times 100\% = 4.2\%$$

Niacin, one of the B vitamins, has the following molecular structure:

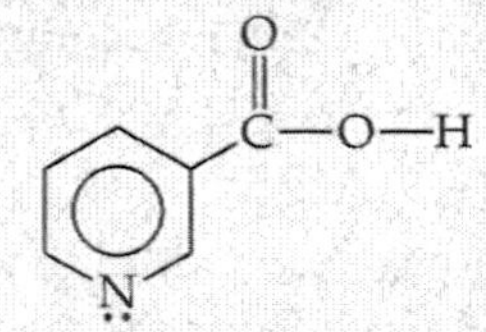

A 0.020 M solution of niacin has a pH of 3.26. **(a)** What percentage of the acid is ionized in this solution? **(b)** What is the acid-dissociation constant, K_a, for niacin?
Answers: **(a)** 2.7%, **(b)** 1.5×10^{-5}

Using K_a to Calculate pH

Knowing the value of K_a and the initial concentration of the weak acid, we can calculate the concentration of $H^+(aq)$ in a solution of a weak acid. Let's calculate the pH of a 0.30 M solution of acetic acid ($HC_2H_3O_2$), the weak acid responsible for the characteristic odor and acidity of vinegar, at 25°C.

Our *first* step is to write the ionization equilibrium for acetic acid:

$$HC_2H_3O_2(aq) \rightleftharpoons H^+(aq) + C_2H_3O_2^-(aq) \qquad [16.28]$$

 Ionization Constants of Weak Acids

According to the structural formula of acetic acid, shown in Table 16.2, the hydrogen that ionizes is the one attached to an oxygen atom. We write this hydrogen separate from the others in the formula to emphasize that only this one hydrogen is readily ionized.

The *second* step is to write the equilibrium-constant expression and the value for the equilibrium constant. From Table 16.2, we have $K_a = 1.8 \times 10^{-5}$. Thus, we can write the following:

$$K_a = \frac{[H^+][C_2H_3O_2^-]}{[HC_2H_3O_2]} = 1.8 \times 10^{-5} \qquad [16.29]$$

As the *third* step, we need to express the concentrations that are involved in the equilibrium reaction. This can be done with a little accounting, as described in Sample Exercise 16.10. Because we want to find the equilibrium value for $[H^+]$, let's call this quantity x. The concentration of acetic acid before any of it ionizes is 0.30 M. The chemical equation tells us that for each molecule of $HC_2H_3O_2$ that ionizes, one $H^+(aq)$ and one $C_2H_2O_2^-(aq)$ are formed. Consequently, if x moles per liter of $H^+(aq)$ form at equilibrium, x moles per liter of $C_2H_3O_2^-(aq)$ must also form, and x moles per liter of $HC_2H_3O_2$ must be ionized. This gives rise to the following table with the equilibrium concentrations shown on the last line:

	$HC_2H_3O_2(aq)$	$\rightleftharpoons$	$H^+(aq)$	+	$C_2H_3O_2^-(aq)$
Initial	0.30 M		0		0
Change	$-x\ M$		$+x\ M$		$+x\ M$
Equilibrium	$(0.30 - x)\ M$		$x\ M$		$x\ M$

As the *fourth* step of the problem, we need to substitute the equilibrium concentrations into the equilibrium-constant expression. The substitutions give the following equation:

$$K_a = \frac{[H^+][C_2H_3O_2^-]}{[HC_2H_3O_2]} = \frac{(x)(x)}{0.30 - x} = 1.8 \times 10^{-5} \qquad [16.30]$$

This expression leads to a quadratic equation in x, which we can solve by using an equation-solving calculator or by using the quadratic formula. We can also simplify the problem, however, by noting that the value of K_a is quite small. As a result, we anticipate that the equilibrium will lie far to the left and that x will be very small compared to the initial concentration of acetic acid. Thus, we will *assume* that x is negligible compared to 0.30, so that $0.30 - x$ is essentially equal to 0.30.

$$0.30 - x \simeq 0.30$$

As we will see, we can (and should!) check the validity of this assumption when we finish the problem. By using this assumption, Equation 16.30 now becomes

$$K_a = \frac{x^2}{0.30} = 1.8 \times 10^{-5}$$

Solving for x, we have

$$x^2 = (0.30)(1.8 \times 10^{-5}) = 5.4 \times 10^{-6}$$

$$x = \sqrt{5.4 \times 10^{-6}} = 2.3 \times 10^{-3}$$

$$[H^+] = x = 2.3 \times 10^{-3}\ M$$

$$pH = -\log(2.3 \times 10^{-3}) = 2.64$$

We should now go back and check the validity of our simplifying assumption that $0.30 - x \simeq 0.30$. The value of x we determined is so small that, for this number of significant figures, the assumption is entirely valid. We are thus satisfied that the assumption was a reasonable one to make. Because x represents the moles per liter of acetic acid that ionize, we see that, in this particular case, less than 1% of the acetic acid molecules ionize:

$$\text{Percent ionization of HC}_2\text{H}_3\text{O}_2 = \frac{0.0023\ M}{0.30\ M} \times 100\% = 0.77\%$$

As a general rule, if the quantity x is more than about 5% of the initial value, it is better to use the quadratic formula. You should always check the validity of any simplifying assumptions after you have finished solving a problem.

 GIVE IT SOME THOUGHT

Why can we generally assume that the equilibrium concentration of a weak acid equals its initial concentration?

Finally, we can compare the pH value of this weak acid to a solution of a strong acid of the same concentration. The pH of the 0.30 M solution of acetic acid is 2.64. By comparison, the pH of a 0.30 M solution of a strong acid such as HCl is $-\log(0.30) = 0.52$. As expected, the pH of a solution of a weak acid is higher than that of a solution of a strong acid of the same molarity.

SAMPLE EXERCISE 16.11 | Using K_a to Calculate pH

Calculate the pH of a 0.20 M solution of HCN. (Refer to Table 16.2 or Appendix D for the value of K_a.)

Solution
Analyze: We are given the molarity of a weak acid and are asked for the pH. From Table 16.2, K_a for HCN is 4.9×10^{-10}.
Plan: We proceed as in the example just worked in the text, writing the chemical equation and constructing a table of initial and equilibrium concentrations in which the equilibrium concentration of H^+ is our unknown.

Solve: Writing both the chemical equation for the ionization reaction that forms $H^+(aq)$ and the equilibrium-constant (K_a) expression for the reaction:

$$HCN(aq) \rightleftharpoons H^+(aq) + CN^-(aq)$$

$$K_a = \frac{[H^+][CN^-]}{[HCN]} = 4.9 \times 10^{-10}$$

HCN(aq)	⇌	H^+(aq)	+	CN^-(aq)
Initial	0.20 M		0	0
Change	$-x$ M		$+x$ M	$+x$ M
Equilibrium	$(0.20 - x)$ M		x M	x M

Next, we tabulate the concentration of the species involved in the equilibrium reaction, letting $x = [H^+]$ at equilibrium:

Substituting the equilibrium concentrations from the table into the equilibrium-constant expression yields

$$K_a = \frac{(x)(x)}{0.20 - x} = 4.9 \times 10^{-10}$$

We next make the simplifying approximation that x, the amount of acid that dissociates, is small compared with the initial concentration of acid; that is,

$$0.20 - x \cong 0.20$$

Thus,

$$\frac{x^2}{0.20} = 4.9 \times 10^{-10}$$

Solving for x, we have

$$x^2 = (0.20)(4.9 \times 10^{-10}) = 0.98 \times 10^{-10}$$

$$x = \sqrt{0.98 \times 10^{-10}} = 9.9 \times 10^{-6} \, M = [H^+]$$

A concentration of $9.9 \times 10^{-6} \, M$ is much smaller than 5% of 0.20, the initial HCN concentration. Our simplifying approximation is therefore appropriate. We now calculate the pH of the solution:

$$pH = -\log[H^+] = -\log(9.9 \times 10^{-6}) = 5.00$$

PRACTICE EXERCISE

The K_a for niacin (Practice Exercise 16.10) is 1.5×10^{-5}. What is the pH of a 0.010 M solution of niacin?
Answer: 3.42

The result obtained in Sample Exercise 16.11 is typical of the behavior of weak acids; the concentration of H^+(aq) is only a small fraction of the concentration of the acid in solution. Those properties of the acid solution that relate directly to the concentration of H^+(aq), such as electrical conductivity and rate of reaction with an active metal, are much less evident for a solution of a weak acid than for a solution of a strong acid. Figure 16.8 ▼ presents an experiment that demonstrates the difference in concentration of H^+(aq) in weak and strong acid solutions of the same concentration. The rate of reaction with the metal is much faster for the solution of a strong acid.

(a)

(b)

◀ **Figure 16.8 Reaction rates for weak and strong acids.** (a) The flask on the left contains 1 M HC$_2$H$_3$O$_2$; the one on the right contains 1 M HCl. Each balloon contains the same amount of magnesium metal. (b) When the Mg metal is dropped into the acid, H$_2$ gas is formed. The rate of H$_2$ formation is higher for the 1 M HCl solution on the right as evidenced by more gas in the balloon.

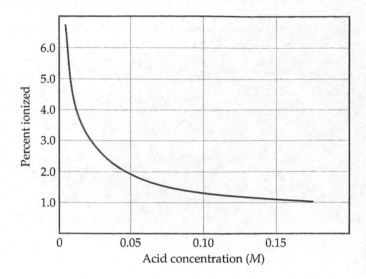

To determine the pH of a solution of a weak acid, you might think that the percent ionization of the acid would be simpler to use than the K_a value. However, the percent ionization at a particular temperature depends not only on the identity of the acid but also on its concentration. As shown in Figure 16.9 ◄, the percent ionization of a weak acid decreases as its concentration increases. This fact is further demonstrated in Sample Exercise 16.12.

◄ **Figure 16.9 The effect of concentration on ionization of a weak acid.** The percent ionization of a weak acid decreases with increasing concentration. The data shown are for acetic acid.

■ SAMPLE EXERCISE 16.12 | Using K_a to Calculate Percent Ionization

Calculate the percentage of HF molecules ionized in **(a)** a 0.10 M HF solution, **(b)** a 0.010 M HF solution.

Solution

Analyze: We are asked to calculate the percent ionization of two HF solutions of different concentration.

Plan: We approach this problem as we would previous equilibrium problems. We begin by writing the chemical equation for the equilibrium and tabulating the known and unknown concentrations of all species. We then substitute the equilibrium concentrations into the equilibrium-constant expression and solve for the unknown concentration, that of H^+.

Solve: (a) The equilibrium reaction and equilibrium concentrations are as follows:

	HF(aq) $\rightleftharpoons$	H^+(aq) +	F^-(aq)
Initial	0.10 M	0	0
Change	$-x\ M$	$+x\ M$	$+x\ M$
Equilibrium	$(0.10 - x)\ M$	$x\ M$	$x\ M$

The equilibrium-constant expression is

$$K_a = \frac{[H^+][F^-]}{[HF]} = \frac{(x)(x)}{0.10 - x} = 6.8 \times 10^{-4}$$

When we try solving this equation using the approximation $0.10 - x = 0.10$ (that is, by neglecting the concentration of acid that ionizes in comparison with the initial concentration), we obtain

$$x = 8.2 \times 10^{-3}\ M$$

Because this value is greater than 5% of 0.10 M, we should work the problem without the approximation, using an equation-solving calculator or the quadratic formula. Rearranging our equation and writing it in standard quadratic form, we have

$$x^2 = (0.10 - x)(6.8 \times 10^{-4})$$
$$= 6.8 \times 10^{-5} - (6.8 \times 10^{-4})x$$
$$x^2 + (6.8 \times 10^{-4})x - 6.8 \times 10^{-5} = 0$$

This equation can be solved using the standard quadratic formula.

$$x = \frac{-b \pm \sqrt{b^2 - 4ac}}{2a}$$

Substituting the appropriate numbers gives	$x = \dfrac{-6.8 \times 10^{-4} \pm \sqrt{(6.8 \times 10^{-4})^2 + 4(6.8 \times 10^{-5})}}{2}$
	$= \dfrac{-6.8 \times 10^{-4} \pm 1.6 \times 10^{-2}}{2}$
Of the two solutions, only the one that gives a positive value for x is chemically reasonable. Thus,	$x = [H^+] = [F^-] = 7.9 \times 10^{-3}\ M$
From our result, we can calculate the percent of molecules ionized:	$\text{Percent ionization of HF} = \dfrac{\text{concentration ionized}}{\text{original concentration}} \times 100\%$
	$= \dfrac{7.9 \times 10^{-3}\ M}{0.10\ M} \times 100\% = 7.9\%$
(b) Proceeding similarly for the 0.010 M solution, we have	$\dfrac{x^2}{0.010 - x} = 6.8 \times 10^{-4}$
Solving the resultant quadratic expression, we obtain	$x = [H^+] = [F^-] = 2.3 \times 10^{-3}\ M$
The percentage of molecules ionized is	$\dfrac{0.0023}{0.010} \times 100\% = 23\%$

Comment: Notice that if we do not use the quadratic formula to solve the problem properly, we calculate 8.2% ionization for (a) and 26% ionization for (b). Notice also that in diluting the solution by a factor of 10, the percentage of molecules ionized increases by a factor of 3. This result is in accord with what we see in Figure 16.9. It is also what we would expect from Le Châtelier's principle. ∞ (Section 15.6) There are more "particles" or reaction components on the right side of the equation than on the left. Dilution causes the reaction to shift in the direction of the larger number of particles because this counters the effect of the decreasing concentration of particles.

▬ PRACTICE EXERCISE

In Practice Exercise 16.10, we found that the percent ionization of niacin ($K_a = 1.5 \times 10^{-5}$) in a 0.020 M solution is 2.7%. Calculate the percentage of niacin molecules ionized in a solution that is **(a)** 0.010 M, **(b)** 1.0 × 10⁻³ M.
Answers: **(a)** 3.8%, **(b)** 12%

Polyprotic Acids

Many acids have more than one ionizable H atom. These acids are known as **polyprotic acids**. For example, each of the H atoms in sulfurous acid (H_2SO_3) can ionize in successive steps:

$$H_2SO_3(aq) \rightleftharpoons H^+(aq) + HSO_3^-(aq) \qquad K_{a1} = 1.7 \times 10^{-2} \qquad [16.31]$$

$$HSO_3^-(aq) \rightleftharpoons H^+(aq) + SO_3^{2-}(aq) \qquad K_{a2} = 6.4 \times 10^{-8} \qquad [16.32]$$

The acid-dissociation constants for these equilibria are labeled K_{a1} and K_{a2}. The numbers on the constants refer to the particular proton of the acid that is ionizing. Thus, K_{a2} always refers to the equilibrium involving removal of the second proton of a polyprotic acid.

In the preceding example K_{a2} is much smaller than K_{a1}. On the basis of electrostatic attractions, we would expect a positively charged proton to be lost more readily from the neutral H_2SO_3 molecule than from the negatively charged HSO_3^- ion. This observation is general: *It is always easier to remove the first proton from a polyprotic acid than to remove the second.* Similarly, for an acid with three ionizable protons, it is easier to remove the second proton than the third. Thus, the K_a values become successively smaller as successive protons are removed.

TABLE 16.3	Acid-Dissociation Constants of Some Common Polyprotic Acids			
Name	Formula	K_{a1}	K_{a2}	K_{a3}
Ascorbic	$H_2C_6H_6O_6$	8.0×10^{-5}	1.6×10^{-12}	
Carbonic	H_2CO_3	4.3×10^{-7}	5.6×10^{-11}	
Citric	$H_3C_6H_5O_7$	7.4×10^{-4}	1.7×10^{-5}	4.0×10^{-7}
Oxalic	$H_2C_2O_4$	5.9×10^{-2}	6.4×10^{-5}	
Phosphoric	H_3PO_4	7.5×10^{-3}	6.2×10^{-8}	4.2×10^{-13}
Sulfurous	H_2SO_3	1.7×10^{-2}	6.4×10^{-8}	
Sulfuric	H_2SO_4	Large	1.2×10^{-2}	
Tartaric	$H_2C_4H_4O_6$	1.0×10^{-3}	4.6×10^{-5}	

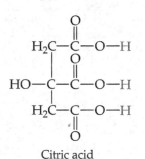

Ascorbic acid
(vitamin C)

Citric acid

GIVE IT SOME THOUGHT

What is meant by the symbol K_{a3} for H_3PO_4?

The acid-dissociation constants for a few common polyprotic acids are listed in Table 16.3 ▲. A more complete list is given in Appendix D. The structures for ascorbic and citric acids are shown in the margin. Notice that the K_a values for successive losses of protons from these acids usually differ by a factor of at least 10^3. Notice also that the value of K_{a1} for sulfuric acid is listed simply as "large." Sulfuric acid is a strong acid with respect to the removal of the first proton. Thus, the reaction for the first ionization step lies completely to the right:

$$H_2SO_4(aq) \longrightarrow H^+(aq) + HSO_4^-(aq) \quad \text{(complete ionization)}$$

HSO_4^-, on the other hand, is a weak acid for which $K_{a2} = 1.2 \times 10^{-2}$.

Because K_{a1} is so much larger than subsequent dissociation constants for these polyprotic acids, almost all of the $H^+(aq)$ in the solution comes from the first ionization reaction. As long as successive K_a values differ by a factor of 10^3 or more, it is possible to obtain a satisfactory estimate of the pH of polyprotic acid solutions by considering only K_{a1}.

SAMPLE EXERCISE 16.13 | Calculating the pH of a Polyprotic Acid Solution

The solubility of CO_2 in pure water at 25°C and 0.1 atm pressure is 0.0037 M. The common practice is to assume that all of the dissolved CO_2 is in the form of carbonic acid (H_2CO_3), which is produced by reaction between the CO_2 and H_2O:

$$CO_2(aq) + H_2O(l) \rightleftharpoons H_2CO_3(aq)$$

What is the pH of a 0.0037 M solution of H_2CO_3?

Solution

Analyze: We are asked to determine the pH of a 0.0037 M solution of a polyprotic acid.

Plan: H_2CO_3 is a diprotic acid; the two acid-dissociation constants, K_{a1} and K_{a2} (Table 16.3), differ by more than a factor of 10^3. Consequently, the pH can be determined by considering only K_{a1}, thereby treating the acid as if it were a monoprotic acid.

Solve: Proceeding as in Sample Exercises 16.11 and 16.12, we can write the equilibrium reaction and equilibrium concentrations as follows:

	$H_2CO_3(aq)$	$\rightleftharpoons$	$H^+(aq)$	$+$	$HCO_3^-(aq)$
Initial	0.0037 M		0		0
Change	$-x$ M		$+x$ M		$+x$ M
Equilibrium	$(0.0037 - x)$ M		x M		x M

The equilibrium-constant expression is as follows:

$$K_{a1} = \frac{[H^+][HCO_3]}{[H_2CO_3]} = \frac{(x)(x)}{0.0037 - x} = 4.3 \times 10^{-7}$$

Solving this equation using an equation-solving calculator, we get

$$x = 4.0 \times 10^{-5} \ M$$

Alternatively, because K_{a1} is small, we can make the simplifying approximation that x is small, so that

$$0.0037 - x \simeq 0.0037$$

Thus,

$$\frac{(x)(x)}{0.0037} = 4.3 \times 10^{-7}$$

Solving for x, we have

$$x^2 = (0.0037)(4.3 \times 10^{-7}) = 1.6 \times 10^{-9}$$

$$x = [H^+] = [HCO_3^-] = \sqrt{1.6 \times 10^{-9}} = 4.0 \times 10^{-5}\ M$$

The small value of x indicates that our simplifying assumption was justified. The pH is therefore

$$pH = -\log[H^+] = -\log(4.0 \times 10^{-5}) = 4.40$$

Comment: If we were asked to solve for $[CO_3^{2-}]$, we would need to use K_{a2}. Let's illustrate that calculation. Using the values of $[HCO_3^-]$ and $[H^+]$ calculated above, and setting $[CO_3^{2-}] = y$, we have the following initial and equilibrium concentration values:

	$HCO_3^-(aq)$ $\rightleftharpoons$	$H^+(aq)$ +	$CO_3^{2-}(aq)$
Initial	$4.0 \times 10^{-5}\ M$	$4.0 \times 10^{-5}\ M$	0
Change	$-y\ M$	$+y\ M$	$+y\ M$
Equilibrium	$(4.0 \times 10^{-5} - y)\ M$	$(4.0 \times 10^{-5} + y)\ M$	$y\ M$

Assuming that y is small compared to 4.0×10^{-5}, we have

$$K_{a2} = \frac{[H^+][CO_3^{2-}]}{[HCO_3^-]} = \frac{(4.0 \times 10^{-5})(y)}{4.0 \times 10^{-5}} = 5.6 \times 10^{-11}$$

$$y = 5.6 \times 10^{-11}\ M = [CO_3^{2-}]$$

The value calculated for y is indeed very small compared to 4.0×10^{-5}, showing that our assumption was justified. It also shows that the ionization of HCO_3^- is negligible compared to that of H_2CO_3, as far as production of H^+ is concerned. However, it is the *only* source of CO_3^{2-}, which has a very low concentration in the solution. Our calculations thus tell us that in a solution of carbon dioxide in water, most of the CO_2 is in the form of CO_2 or H_2CO_3, a small fraction ionizes to form H^+ and HCO_3^-, and an even smaller fraction ionizes to give CO_3^{2-}. Notice also that $[CO_3^{2-}]$ is numerically equal to K_{a2}.

■ PRACTICE EXERCISE

(a) Calculate the pH of a 0.020 M solution of oxalic acid ($H_2C_2O_4$). (See Table 16.3 for K_{a1} and K_{a2}.) **(b)** Calculate the concentration of oxalate ion, $[C_2O_4^{2-}]$, in this solution.
Answers: **(a)** pH = 1.80, **(b)** $[C_2O_4^{2-}] = 6.4 \times 10^{-5}\ M$

16.7 | Weak Bases

Many substances behave as weak bases in water. Weak bases react with water, abstracting protons from H_2O, thereby forming the conjugate acid of the base and OH^- ions.

ANIMATION
Introduction to Aqueous Bases

$$B(aq) + H_2O \rightleftharpoons HB^+ + OH^-(aq) \qquad [16.33]$$

The most commonly encountered weak base is ammonia.

$$NH_3(aq) + H_2O(l) \rightleftharpoons NH_4^+(aq) + OH^-(aq) \qquad [16.34]$$

The equilibrium-constant expression for this reaction can be written as

$$K_b = \frac{[NH_4^+][OH^-]}{[NH_3]} \qquad [16.35]$$

Water is the solvent, so it is omitted from the equilibrium-constant expression.

As with K_w and K_a, the subscript "b" denotes that this equilibrium constant refers to a particular type of reaction, namely the ionization of a weak base in water. The constant K_b is called the **base-dissociation constant**. *The constant* K_b

TABLE 16.4   Some Weak Bases and Their Aqueous Solution Equilibria

Base	Lewis Structure	Conjugate Acid	Equilibrium Reaction	K_b
Ammonia (NH_3)	H—N̈—H (with H below)	NH_4^+	$NH_3 + H_2O \rightleftharpoons NH_4^+ + OH^-$	1.8×10^{-5}
Pyridine (C_5H_5N)	(ring)N:	$C_5H_5NH^+$	$C_5H_5N + H_2O \rightleftharpoons C_5H_5NH^+ + OH^-$	1.7×10^{-9}
Hydroxylamine (H_2NOH)	H—N̈—ÖH (with H below)	H_3NOH^+	$H_2NOH + H_2O \rightleftharpoons H_3NOH^+ + OH^-$	1.1×10^{-8}
Methylamine (NH_2CH_3)	H—N̈—CH_3 (with H below)	$NH_3CH_3^+$	$NH_2CH_3 + H_2O \rightleftharpoons NH_3CH_3^+ + OH^-$	4.4×10^{-4}
Hydrosulfide ion (HS^-)	$[H—\ddot{S}:]^-$	H_2S	$HS^- + H_2O \rightleftharpoons H_2S + OH^-$	1.8×10^{-7}
Carbonate ion (CO_3^{2-})	$[\ddot{O}—C(=\ddot{O})—\ddot{O}]^{2-}$	HCO_3^-	$CO_3^{2-} + H_2O \rightleftharpoons HCO_3^- + OH^-$	1.8×10^{-4}
Hypochlorite ion (ClO^-)	$[:\ddot{Cl}—\ddot{O}:]^-$	$HClO$	$ClO^- + H_2O \rightleftharpoons HClO + OH^-$	3.3×10^{-7}

always refers to the equilibrium in which a base reacts with H_2O to form the corresponding conjugate acid and OH^-. Table 16.4 ▲ lists the names, formulas, Lewis structures, equilibrium reactions, and values of K_b for several weak bases in water. Appendix D includes a more extensive list. These bases contain one or more lone pairs of electrons because a lone pair is necessary to form the bond with H^+. Notice that in the neutral molecules in Table 16.4, the lone pairs are on nitrogen atoms. The other bases listed are anions derived from weak acids.

■ SAMPLE EXERCISE 16.14 | Using K_b to Calculate [OH^-]

Calculate the concentration of OH^- in a 0.15 M solution of NH_3.

Solution

Analyze: We are given the concentration of a weak base and are asked to determine the concentration of OH^-.

Plan: We will use essentially the same procedure here as used in solving problems involving the ionization of weak acids; that is, we write the chemical equation and tabulate initial and equilibrium concentrations.

Solve: We first write the ionization reaction and the corresponding equilibrium-constant (K_b) expression:

$$NH_3(aq) + H_2O(l) \rightleftharpoons NH_4^+(aq) + OH^-(aq)$$

$$K_b = \frac{[NH_4^+][OH^-]}{[NH_3]} = 1.8 \times 10^{-5}$$

We then tabulate the equilibrium concentrations involved in the equilibrium:

	$NH_3(aq)$	+ $H_2O(l)$	$\rightleftharpoons$ $NH_4^+(aq)$	+ $OH^-(aq)$
Initial	0.15 M	—	0	0
Change	$-x$ M	—	$+x$ M	$+x$ M
Equilibrium	$(0.15 - x)$ M	—	x M	x M

(We ignore the concentration of H_2O because it is not involved in the equilibrium-constant expression.) Inserting these quantities into the equilibrium-constant expression gives the following:

$$K_b = \frac{[NH_4^+][OH^-]}{[NH_3]} = \frac{(x)(x)}{0.15 - x} = 1.8 \times 10^{-5}$$

Because K_b is small, we can neglect the small amount of NH_3 that reacts with water, as compared to the total NH_3 concentration; that is, we can neglect x relative to 0.15 M. Then we have

$$\frac{x^2}{0.15} = 1.8 \times 10^{-5}$$

$$x^2 = (0.15)(1.8 \times 10^{-5}) = 2.7 \times 10^{-6}$$

$$x = [NH_4^+] = [OH^-] = \sqrt{2.7 \times 10^{-6}} = 1.6 \times 10^{-3} \, M$$

Check: The value obtained for x is only about 1% of the NH_3 concentration, 0.15 M. Therefore, neglecting x relative to 0.15 was justified.

▬ **PRACTICE EXERCISE**

Which of the following compounds should produce the highest pH as a 0.05 M solution: pyridine, methylamine, or nitrous acid?
Answer: methylamine (because it has the largest K_b value)

Types of Weak Bases

How can we recognize from a chemical formula whether a molecule or ion is able to behave as a weak base? Weak bases fall into two general categories. The first category contains neutral substances that have an atom with a nonbonding pair of electrons that can serve as a proton acceptor. Most of these bases, including all of the uncharged bases listed in Table 16.4, contain a nitrogen atom. These substances include ammonia and a related class of compounds called **amines**. In organic amines, one or more of the N—H bonds in NH_3 is replaced with a bond between N and C. Thus, the replacement of one N—H bond in NH_3 with a N—CH_3 bond gives methylamine, NH_2CH_3 (usually written CH_3NH_2). Like NH_3, amines can abstract a proton from a water molecule by forming an additional N—H bond, as shown here for methylamine:

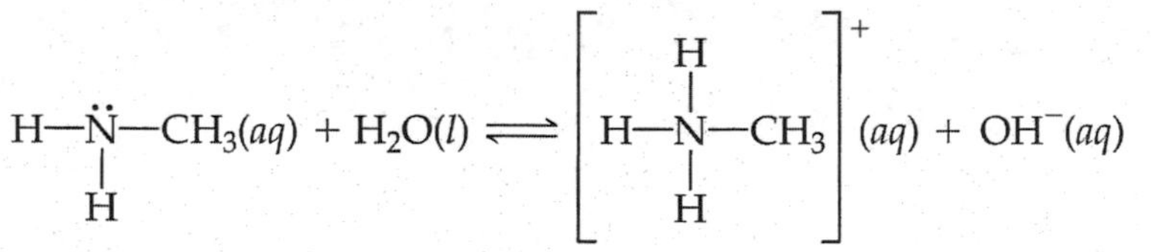

$$H\!-\!\overset{..}{N}\!-\!CH_3(aq) + H_2O(l) \rightleftharpoons \left[H\!-\!\overset{\overset{\displaystyle H}{|}}{\underset{\underset{\displaystyle H}{|}}{N}}\!-\!CH_3 \right]^+ (aq) + OH^-(aq) \qquad [16.36]$$

The chemical formula for the conjugate acid of methylamine is usually written $CH_3NH_3^+$.

The second general category of weak bases consists of the anions of weak acids. In an aqueous solution of sodium hypochlorite (NaClO), for example, NaClO dissociates to give Na^+ and ClO^- ions. The Na^+ ion is always a spectator ion in acid-base reactions. ⚬⚬⚬ (Section 4.3) The ClO^- ion, however, is the conjugate base of a weak acid, hypochlorous acid. Consequently, the ClO^- ion acts as a weak base in water:

$$ClO^-(aq) + H_2O(l) \rightleftharpoons HClO(aq) + OH^-(aq) \qquad K_b = 3.3 \times 10^{-7} \qquad [16.37]$$

■ **SAMPLE EXERCISE 16.15 | Using pH to Determine the Concentration of a Salt**

A solution made by adding solid sodium hypochlorite (NaClO) to enough water to make 2.00 L of solution has a pH of 10.50. Using the information in Equation 16.37, calculate the number of moles of NaClO that were added to the water.

Solution

Analyze: We are given the pH of a 2.00-L solution of NaClO and must calculate the number of moles of NaClO needed to raise the pH to 10.50. NaClO is an ionic compound consisting of Na^+ and ClO^- ions. As such, it is a strong electrolyte that completely dissociates in solution into Na^+, which is a spectator ion, and ClO^- ion, which is a weak base with $K_b = 3.33 \times 10^{-7}$ (Equation 16.37).

Plan: From the pH, we can determine the equilibrium concentration of OH^-. We can then construct a table of initial and equilibrium concentrations in which the initial concentration of ClO^- is our unknown. We can calculate $[ClO^-]$ using the equilibrium-constant expression, K_b.

Solve: We can calculate $[OH^-]$ by using either Equation 16.16 or Equation 16.19; we will use the latter method here:

$$pOH = 14.00 - pH = 14.00 - 10.50 = 3.50$$
$$[OH^-] = 10^{-3.50} = 3.16 \times 10^{-4}\ M$$

This concentration is high enough that we can assume that Equation 16.37 is the only source of OH^-; that is, we can neglect any OH^- produced by the autoionization of H_2O. We now assume a value of x for the initial concentration of ClO^- and solve the equilibrium problem in the usual way.

	$ClO^-(aq)$	$+\ H_2O(l) \rightleftharpoons$	$HClO(aq)$	$+$	$OH^-(aq)$
Initial	$x\ M$	—	0		0
Change	$-3.16 \times 10^{-4}\ M$	—	$+3.16 \times 10^{-4}\ M$		$+3.16 \times 10^{-4}\ M$
Final	$(x - 3.16 \times 10^{-4})\ M$	—	$3.16 \times 10^{-4}\ M$		$3.16 \times 10^{-4}\ M$

We now use the expression for the base-dissociation constant to solve for x:

$$K_b = \frac{[HClO][OH^-]}{[ClO^-]} = \frac{(3.16 \times 10^{-4})^2}{x - 3.16 \times 10^{-4}} = 3.3 \times 10^{-7}$$

Thus

$$x = \frac{(3.16 \times 10^{-4})^2}{3.3 \times 10^{-7}} + (3.16 \times 10^{-4}) = 0.30\ M$$

We say that the solution is 0.30 M in NaClO, even though some of the ClO^- ions have reacted with water. Because the solution is 0.30 M in NaClO and the total volume of solution is 2.00 L, 0.60 mol of NaClO is the amount of the salt that was added to the water.

■ **PRACTICE EXERCISE**

A solution of NH_3 in water has a pH of 11.17. What is the molarity of the solution?
Answer: 0.12 M

16.8 | Relationship Between K_a and K_b

We've seen in a qualitative way that the stronger acids have the weaker conjugate bases. To see if we can find a corresponding *quantitative* relationship, let's consider the NH_4^+ and NH_3 conjugate acid-base pair. Each of these species reacts with water:

$$NH_4^+(aq) \rightleftharpoons NH_3(aq) + H^+(aq) \qquad [16.38]$$

$$NH_3(aq) + H_2O(l) \rightleftharpoons NH_4^+(aq) + OH^-(aq) \qquad [16.39]$$

Each of these equilibria is expressed by a characteristic dissociation constant:

$$K_a = \frac{[NH_3][H^+]}{[NH_4^+]}$$

$$K_b = \frac{[NH_4^+][OH^-]}{[NH_3]}$$

When Equations 16.38 and 16.39 are added together, the NH_4^+ and NH_3 species cancel and we are left with just the autoionization of water.

$$NH_4^+(aq) \rightleftharpoons NH_3(aq) + H^+(aq)$$

$$NH_3(aq) + H_2O(l) \rightleftharpoons NH_4^+(aq) + OH^-(aq)$$

$$H_2O(l) \rightleftharpoons H^+(aq) + OH^-(aq)$$

Recall that when two equations are added to give a third, the equilibrium constant associated with the third equation equals the product of the equilibrium constants for the two equations added together. ∞ (Section 15.2)

Applying this rule to our present example, when we multiply K_a and K_b, we obtain the following:

$$K_a \times K_b = \left(\frac{[\cancel{NH_3}][H^+]}{[\cancel{NH_4^+}]}\right)\left(\frac{[\cancel{NH_4^+}][OH^-]}{[\cancel{NH_3}]}\right)$$

$$= [H^+][OH^-] = K_w$$

Thus, the result of multiplying K_a times K_b is just the ion-product constant for water, K_w (Equation 16.16). This is what we would expect, moreover, because adding Equations 16.38 and 16.39 gave us the autoionization equilibrium for water, for which the equilibrium constant is K_w.

This relationship is so important that it should receive special attention: The product of the acid-dissociation constant for an acid and the base-dissociation constant for its conjugate base is the ion-product constant for water.

$$K_a \times K_b = K_w \qquad\qquad [16.40]$$

As the strength of an acid increases (larger K_a), the strength of its conjugate base must decrease (smaller K_b) so that the product $K_a \times K_b$ equals 1.0×10^{-14} at 25°C. The K_a and K_b data in Table 16.5 ▼ demonstrate this relationship.

By using Equation 16.40, we can calculate K_b for any weak base if we know K_a for its conjugate acid. Similarly, we can calculate K_a for a weak acid if we know K_b for its conjugate base. As a practical consequence, ionization constants are often listed for only one member of a conjugate acid-base pair. For example, Appendix D does not contain K_b values for the anions of weak acids because these can be readily calculated from the tabulated K_a values for their conjugate acids.

If you look up the values for acid- or base-dissociation constants in a chemistry handbook, you may find them expressed as pK_a or pK_b (that is, as $-\log K_a$ or $-\log K_b$). (Section 16.4) Equation 16.40 can be written in terms of pK_a and pK_b by taking the negative log of both sides:

$$pK_a + pK_b = pK_w = 14.00 \quad \text{at } 25°C \qquad\qquad [16.41]$$

TABLE 16.5 Some Conjugate Acid-Base Pairs			
Acid	K_a	**Base**	K_b
HNO_3	(Strong acid)	NO_3^-	(Negligible basicity)
HF	6.8×10^{-4}	F^-	1.5×10^{-11}
$HC_2H_3O_2$	1.8×10^{-5}	$C_2H_3O_2^-$	5.6×10^{-10}
H_2CO_3	4.3×10^{-7}	HCO_3^-	2.3×10^{-8}
NH_4^+	5.6×10^{-10}	NH_3	1.8×10^{-5}
HCO_3^-	5.6×10^{-11}	CO_3^{2-}	1.8×10^{-4}
OH^-	(Negligible acidity)	O^{2-}	(Strong base)

CHEMISTRY AT WORK | Amines and Amine Hydrochlorides

Many amines with low molecular weights have unpleasant "fishy" odors. Amines and NH_3 are produced by the anaerobic (absence of O_2) decomposition of dead animal or plant matter. Two such amines with very disagreeable odors are $H_2N(CH_2)_4NH_2$, known as *putrescine*, and $H_2N(CH_2)_5NH_2$, known as *cadaverine*.

Many drugs, including quinine, codeine, caffeine, and amphetamine (Benzedrine®), are amines. Like other amines, these substances are weak bases; the amine nitrogen is readily protonated upon treatment with an acid. The resulting products are called *acid salts*. If we use A as the abbreviation for an amine, the acid salt formed by reaction with hydrochloric acid can be written as AH^+Cl^-. It is also sometimes written as $A \cdot HCl$ and referred to as a hydrochloride. Amphetamine hydrochloride, for example, is the acid salt formed by treating amphetamine with HCl:

$$\langle \bigcirc \rangle - CH_2 - \underset{\underset{CH_3}{|}}{CH} - \ddot{N}H_2(aq) + HCl(aq) \longrightarrow$$

Amphetamine

$$\langle \bigcirc \rangle - CH_2 - \underset{\underset{CH_3}{|}}{CH} - NH_3^+Cl^-(aq)$$

Amphetamine hydrochloride

Such acid salts are much less volatile, more stable, and generally more water-soluble than the corresponding neutral amines. Many drugs that are amines are sold and administered as acid salts. Some examples of over-the-counter medications that contain amine hydrochlorides as active ingredients are shown in Figure 16.10 ▼.
Related Exercises: 16.77, 16.78, 16.114, and 16.123

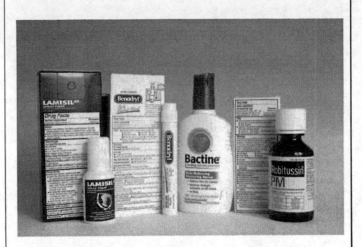

▲ **Figure 16.10** Some over-the-counter medications in which an amine hydrochloride is a major active ingredient.

■ **SAMPLE EXERCISE 16.16** | Calculating K_a or K_b for a Conjugate Acid-Base Pair
Calculate **(a)** the base-dissociation constant, K_b, for the fluoride ion (F^-); **(b)** the acid-dissociation constant, K_a, for the ammonium ion (NH_4^+).

Solution
Analyze: We are asked to determine dissociation constants for F^-, the conjugate base of HF, and NH_4^+, the conjugate acid of NH_3.
Plan: Although neither F^- nor NH_4^+ appears in the tables, we can find the tabulated values for ionization constants for HF and NH_3, and use the relationship between K_a and K_b to calculate the ionization constants for each of the conjugates.
Solve: (a) K_a for the weak acid, HF, is given in Table 16.2 and Appendix D as $K_a = 6.8 \times 10^{-4}$. We can use Equation 16.40 to calculate K_b for the conjugate base, F^-:

$$K_b = \frac{K_w}{K_a} = \frac{1.0 \times 10^{-14}}{6.8 \times 10^{-4}} = 1.5 \times 10^{-11}$$

(b) K_b for NH_3 is listed in Table 16.4 and in Appendix D as $K_b = 1.8 \times 10^{-5}$. Using Equation 16.40, we can calculate K_a for the conjugate acid, NH_4^+:

$$K_a = \frac{K_w}{K_b} = \frac{1.0 \times 10^{-14}}{1.8 \times 10^{-5}} = 5.6 \times 10^{-10}$$

(a) Which of the following anions has the largest base-dissociation constant: NO_2^-, PO_4^{3-}, or N_3^-? **(b)** The base quinoline has the following structure:

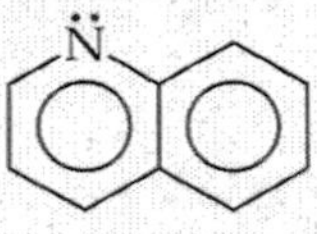

Its conjugate acid is listed in handbooks as having a pK_a of 4.90. What is the base-dissociation constant for quinoline?
Answers: **(a)** PO_4^{3-} ($K_b = 2.4 \times 10^{-2}$), **(b)** 7.9×10^{-10}

16.9 | Acid-Base Properties of Salt Solutions

Even before you began this chapter, you were undoubtedly aware of many substances that are acidic, such as HNO_3, HCl, and H_2SO_4, and others that are basic, such as $NaOH$ and NH_3. However, our recent discussions have indicated that ions can also exhibit acidic or basic properties. For example, we calculated K_a for NH_4^+ and K_b for F^- in Sample Exercise 16.16. Such behavior implies that salt solutions can be acidic or basic. Before proceeding with further discussions of acids and bases, let's examine the way dissolved salts can affect pH.

We can assume that when salts dissolve in water, they are completely dissociated; nearly all salts are strong electrolytes. Consequently, the acid-base properties of salt solutions are due to the behavior of their constituent cations and anions. Many ions are able to react with water to generate $H^+(aq)$ or $OH^-(aq)$. This type of reaction is often called **hydrolysis**. The pH of an aqueous salt solution can be predicted qualitatively by considering the ions of which the salt is composed.

An Anion's Ability to React with Water

In general, an anion, X^-, in solution can be considered the conjugate base of an acid. For example, Cl^- is the conjugate base of HCl and $C_2H_3O_2^-$ is the conjugate base of $HC_2H_3O_2$. Whether an anion reacts with water to produce hydroxide depends upon the strength of the acid to which it is conjugate. To identify the acid and assess its strength, we can simply add a proton to the anion's formula:

$$X^- \text{ plus a proton } (H^+) \text{ gives } HX$$

If the acid determined in this way is one of the strong acids listed at the beginning of Section 16.5, then the anion in question will have a negligible tendency to abstract protons from water (Section 16.2). Consequently, the anion X^- will not affect the pH of the solution. The presence of Cl^- in an aqueous solution, for example, does not result in the production of any OH^- and does not affect the pH. Thus, Cl^- is always a spectator in acid-base chemistry.

Conversely, if HX is *not* one of the seven strong acids, then it is a weak acid. In this case the conjugate base X^- is a weak base. This anion will therefore react to a small extent with water to produce the weak acid and hydroxide ions:

$$X^-(aq) + H_2O(l) \rightleftharpoons HX(aq) + OH^-(aq) \qquad [16.42]$$

The OH^- ion generated in this way increases the pH of the solution, making it basic. Acetate ion ($C_2H_3O_2^-$), for example, being the conjugate base of a weak acid, reacts with water to produce acetic acid and hydroxide ions, thereby increasing the pH of the solution.*

$$C_2H_3O_2^-(aq) + H_2O(l) \rightleftharpoons HC_2H_3O_2(aq) + OH^-(aq) \qquad [16.43]$$

 GIVE IT SOME THOUGHT

What effect will each of the following ions have on the pH of a solution: NO_3^- and CO_3^{2-}?

Anions that still have ionizable protons, such as HSO_3^-, are amphiprotic. ∞ (Section 16.2) They can act as either acids or bases. Their behavior toward water will be determined by the relative magnitudes of K_a and K_b for the ion, as shown in Sample Exercise 16.17. If $K_a > K_b$, the ion will cause the solution to be acidic. If $K_b > K_a$, the solution will be basic.

A Cation's Ability to React with Water

Polyatomic cations whose formulas contain one or more protons can be considered the conjugate acids of weak bases. NH_4^+, for example, is the conjugate acid of the weak base NH_3. Thus, NH_4^+ is a weak acid and will donate a proton to water, producing hydronium ions and thereby lowering the pH:

$$NH_4^+(aq) + H_2O(l) \rightleftharpoons NH_3(aq) + H_3O^+(aq) \qquad [16.44]$$

Most metal ions can also react with water to decrease the pH of an aqueous solution. The mechanism by which metal ions produce acidic solutions is described in Section 16.11. However, ions of alkali metals and of the heavier alkaline earth metals do not react with water and therefore do not affect pH. Note that these exceptions are the cations found in the strong bases. ∞ (Section 16.5)

 GIVE IT SOME THOUGHT

Which of the following cations has no effect on the pH of a solution: K^+, Fe^{2+}, or Al^{3+}?

Combined Effect of Cation and Anion in Solution

If an aqueous salt solution contains an anion that does not react with water and a cation that does not react with water, we expect the pH to be neutral. If the solution contains an anion that reacts with water to produce hydroxide and a cation that does not react with water, we expect the pH to be basic. If the solution contains a cation that reacts with water to produce hydronium and an anion that does not react with water, we expect the pH to be acidic. Finally, a solution may contain an anion and a cation *both* capable of reacting with water. In this case both hydroxide and hydronium will be produced. Whether the solution is basic, neutral, or acidic will depend upon the relative abilities of the ions to react with water.

To summarize:

1. An anion that is the conjugate base of a strong acid, for example, Br^-, will not affect the pH of a solution.

2. An anion that is the conjugate base of a weak acid, for example, CN^-, will cause an increase in pH.

---

* These rules apply to what are called normal salts. These salts are those that contain no ionizable protons on the anion. The pH of an acid salt (such as $NaHCO_3$ or NaH_2PO_4) is affected not only by the hydrolysis of the anion but also by its acid dissociation, as shown in Sample Exercise 16.17.

(a)   (b)   (c)

◄ **Figure 16.11 Salt solutions can be neutral, acidic, or basic.** These three solutions contain the acid-base indicator bromthymol blue. (a) The NaCl solution is neutral (pH = 7.0); (b) the NH_4Cl solution is acidic (pH = 3.5); (c) the NaClO solution is basic (pH = 9.5).

3. A cation that is the conjugate acid of a weak base, for example, $CH_3NH_3^+$, will cause a decrease in pH.

4. The cations of group 1A and heavier members of group 2A (Ca^{2+}, Sr^{2+}, and Ba^{2+}) will not affect pH. These are the cations of the strong Arrhenius bases.

5. Other metal ions will cause a decrease in pH.

6. When a solution contains both the conjugate base of a weak acid and the conjugate acid of a weak base, the ion with the larger equilibrium constant, K_a or K_b, will have the greater influence on the pH.

Figure 16.11 ▲ demonstrates the influence of several salts on pH.

▬▬ SAMPLE EXERCISE 16.17 | Predicting the Relative Acidity of Salt Solutions

 Acid-Base Classification of Salts

List the following solutions in order of increasing pH: (i) 0.1 M $Ba(C_2H_3O_2)_2$, (ii) 0.1 M NH_4Cl, (iii) 0.1 M NH_3CH_3Br, (iv) 0.1 M KNO_3.

Solution
Analyze: We are asked to arrange a series of salt solutions in order of increasing pH (that is, from the most acidic to the most basic).
Plan: We can determine whether the pH of a solution is acidic, basic, or neutral by identifying the ions in solution and by assessing how each ion will affect the pH.
Solve: Solution (i) contains barium ions and acetate ions. Ba^{2+} is an ion of one of the heavy alkaline earth metals and will therefore not affect the pH (summary point 4). The anion, $C_2H_3O_2^-$, is the conjugate base of the weak acid $HC_2H_3O_2$ and will hydrolyze to produce OH^- ions, thereby making the solution basic (summary point 2). Solutions (ii) and (iii) both contain cations that are conjugate acids of weak bases and anions that are conjugate bases of strong acids. Both solutions will therefore be acidic. Solution (i) contains NH_4^+, which is the conjugate acid of NH_3 ($K_b = 1.8 \times 10^{-5}$). Solution (iii) contains $NH_3CH_3^+$, which is the conjugate acid of NH_2CH_3 ($K_b = 4.4 \times 10^{-4}$). Because NH_3 has the smaller K_b and is the weaker of the two bases, NH_4^+ will be the stronger of the two conjugate acids. Solution (ii) will therefore be the more acidic of the two. Solution (iv) contains the K^+ ion, which is the cation of the strong base KOH, and the NO_3^- ion, which is the conjugate base of the strong acid HNO_3. Neither of the ions in solution (iv) will react with water to any appreciable extent, making the solution neutral. Thus, the order of pH is 0.1 M NH_4Cl < 0.1 M NH_3CH_3Br < 0.1 M KNO_3 < 0.1 M $Ba(C_2H_3O_2)_2$.

▬▬ PRACTICE EXERCISE
In each of the following, indicate which salt will form the more acidic (or less basic) 0.010 M solution: **(a)** $NaNO_3$, $Fe(NO_3)_3$; **(b)** KBr, KBrO; **(c)** CH_3NH_3Cl, $BaCl_2$, **(d)** NH_4NO_2, NH_4NO_3.
Answers: **(a)** $Fe(NO_3)_3$, **(b)** KBr, **(c)** CH_3NH_3Cl, **(d)** NH_4NO_3

◼ **SAMPLE EXERCISE 16.18** | Predicting Whether the Solution of an Amphiprotic
Anion is Acidic or Basic

Predict whether the salt Na_2HPO_4 will form an acidic solution or a basic solution on
dissolving in water.

Solution
Analyze: We are asked to predict whether a solution of Na_2HPO_4 will be acidic or
basic. This substance is an ionic compound composed of Na^+ and HPO_4^{2-} ions.
Plan: We need to evaluate each ion, predicting whether each is acidic or basic. Because Na^+ is the cation of a strong base, $NaOH$, we know that Na^+ has no influence
on pH. It is merely a spectator ion in acid-base chemistry. Thus, our analysis of
whether the solution is acidic or basic must focus on the behavior of the HPO_4^{2-} ion.
We need to consider the fact that HPO_4^{2-} can act as either an acid or a base.

$$HPO_4^{2-}(aq) \rightleftharpoons H^+(aq) + PO_4^{3-}(aq) \qquad \text{[16.45]}$$

$$HPO_4^{2-}(aq) + H_2O \rightleftharpoons H_2PO_4^-(aq) + OH^-(aq) \qquad \text{[16.46]}$$

The reaction with the larger equilibrium constant will determine whether the solution is acidic or basic.
Solve: The value of K_a for Equation 16.45, as shown in Table 16.3, is 4.2×10^{-13}. We
must calculate the value of K_b for Equation 16.46 from the value of K_a for its conjugate
acid, $H_2PO_4^-$. We make use of the relationship shown in Equation 16.40.

$$K_a \times K_b = K_w$$

We want to know K_b for the base HPO_4^{2-}, knowing the value of K_a for the conjugate
acid $H_2PO_4^-$:

$$K_b(HPO_4^{2-}) \times K_a(H_2PO_4^-) = K_w = 1.0 \times 10^{-14}$$

Because K_a for $H_2PO_4^-$ is 6.2×10^{-8} (Table 16.3), we calculate K_b for HPO_4^{2-} to
be 1.6×10^{-7}. This is more than 10^5 times larger than K_a for HPO_4^{2-}; thus, the reaction shown in Equation 16.46 predominates over that in Equation 16.45, and the solution will be basic.

◼ **PRACTICE EXERCISE**
Predict whether the dipotassium salt of citric acid ($K_2HC_6H_5O_7$) will form an acidic
or basic solution in water (see Table 16.3 for data).
Answer: acidic

16.10 | Acid-Base Behavior and Chemical Structure

When a substance is dissolved in water, it may behave as an acid, behave as a
base, or exhibit no acid-base properties. How does the chemical structure of a
substance determine which of these behaviors is exhibited by the substance?
For example, why do some substances that contain OH groups behave as bases,
releasing OH^- ions into solution, whereas others behave as acids, ionizing to
release H^+ ions? Why are some acids stronger than others? In this section we
will discuss briefly the effects of chemical structure on acid-base behavior.

Factors that Affect Acid Strength

A molecule containing H will transfer a proton only if the H—X bond is polarized in the following way:

$$\overset{\longrightarrow}{H—X}$$

In ionic hydrides, such as NaH, the reverse is true; the H atom possesses a negative charge and behaves as a proton acceptor (Equation 16.23). Essentially
nonpolar H—X bonds, such as the H—C bond in CH_4, produce neither acidic
nor basic aqueous solutions.

A second factor that helps determine whether a molecule containing an H—X bond will donate a proton is the strength of the bond. Very strong bonds are less easily dissociated than weaker ones. This factor is important, for example, in the case of the hydrogen halides. The H—F bond is the most polar H—X bond. You therefore might expect that HF would be a very strong acid if the first factor was all that mattered. However, the energy required to dissociate HF into H and F atoms is much higher than it is for the other hydrogen halides, as shown in Table 8.4. As a result, HF is a weak acid, whereas all the other hydrogen halides are strong acids in water.

A third factor that affects the ease with which a hydrogen atom ionizes from HX is the stability of the conjugate base, X^-. In general, the greater the stability of the conjugate base, the stronger is the acid. The strength of an acid is often a combination of all three factors: the polarity of the H—X bond, the strength of the H—X bond, and the stability of the conjugate base, X^-.

Binary Acids

In general, the H—X bond strength is the most important factor determining acid strength among the binary acids (those containing hydrogen and just one other element) in which X is in the same *group* in the periodic table. The strength of an H—X bond tends to decrease as the element X increases in size. As a result, the bond strength decreases and the acidity increases down a group. Thus, HCl is a stronger acid than HF, and H_2S is a stronger acid than H_2O.

Bond strengths change less moving across a row in the periodic table than they do down a group. As a result, bond polarity is the major factor determining acidity for binary acids in the same *row*. Thus, acidity increases as the electronegativity of the element X increases, as it generally does moving from left to right in a row. For example, the acidity of the second-row elements varies in the following order: $CH_4 < NH_3 \ll H_2O < HF$. Because the C—H bond is essentially nonpolar, CH_4 shows no tendency to form H^+ and CH_3^- ions. Although the N—H bond is polar, NH_3 has a nonbonding pair of electrons on the nitrogen atom that dominates its chemistry, so NH_3 acts as a base rather than as an acid. The periodic trends in the acid strengths of binary compounds of hydrogen and the nonmetals of periods 2 and 3 are summarized in Figure 16.12 ▼.

 GIVE IT SOME THOUGHT

What is the major factor determining the increase in acidity of binary acids going down a column of the periodic table? What is the major factor going across a period?

GROUP				
	4A	5A	6A	7A
Period 2	CH₄ No acid or base properties	NH₃ Weak base	H₂O ---	HF Weak acid
Period 3	SiH₄ No acid or base properties	PH₃ Weak base	H₂S Weak acid	HCl Strong acid

Increasing acid strength →
← Increasing base strength

◀ **Figure 16.12 Trends in acid-base properties of binary hydrides.** The acidity of the binary compounds of hydrogen and nonmetals increases moving left to right across a period and moving top to bottom down a group.

Oxyacids

Many common acids, such as sulfuric acid, contain one or more O—H bonds:

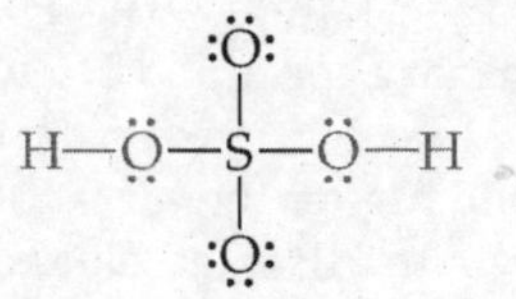

$$H-\ddot{\underset{..}{O}}-\underset{\underset{:\ddot{O}:}{|}}{\overset{\overset{:\ddot{O}:}{|}}{S}}-\ddot{\underset{..}{O}}-H$$

Acids in which OH groups and possibly additional oxygen atoms are bound to a central atom are called **oxyacids**. The OH group is also present in bases. What factors determine whether an OH group will behave as a base or as an acid?

Let's consider an OH group bound to some atom Y, which might in turn have other groups attached to it:

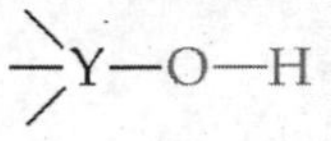

$$-\overset{|}{\underset{/}{Y}}-O-H$$

At one extreme, Y might be a metal, such as Na, K, or Mg. Because of their low electronegativities, the pair of electrons shared between Y and O is completely transferred to oxygen, and an ionic compound containing OH⁻ is formed. Such compounds are therefore sources of OH⁻ ions and behave as bases.

When Y is a nonmetal, the bond to O is covalent and the substance does not readily lose OH⁻. Instead, these compounds are either acidic or neutral. As a general rule, as the electronegativity of Y increases, so will the acidity of the substance. This happens for two reasons: First, as electron density is drawn toward Y, the O—H bond becomes weaker and more polar, thereby favoring loss of H⁺ (Figure 16.13 ◄). Second, because the conjugate base is usually an anion, its stability generally increases as the electronegativity of Y increases.

Many oxyacids contain additional oxygen atoms bonded to the central atom Y. The additional electronegative oxygen atoms pull electron density from the O—H bond, further increasing its polarity. Increasing the number of oxygen atoms also helps stabilize the conjugate base by increasing its ability to "spread out" its negative charge. Thus, the strength of an acid will increase as additional electronegative atoms bond to the central atom Y.

We can summarize these ideas as two simple rules that relate the acid strength of oxyacids to the electronegativity of Y and to the number of groups attached to Y.

1. For oxyacids that have the same number of OH groups and the same number of O atoms, acid strength increases with increasing electronegativity of the central atom Y. For example, the strength of the hypohalous acids, which have the structure H—O—Y, increases as the electronegativity of Y increases (Table 16.6 ◄).

2. For oxyacids that have the same central atom Y, acid strength increases as the number of oxygen atoms attached to Y increases. For example, the strength of the oxyacids of chlorine steadily increases from hypochlorous acid ($HClO$) to perchloric acid ($HClO_4$):

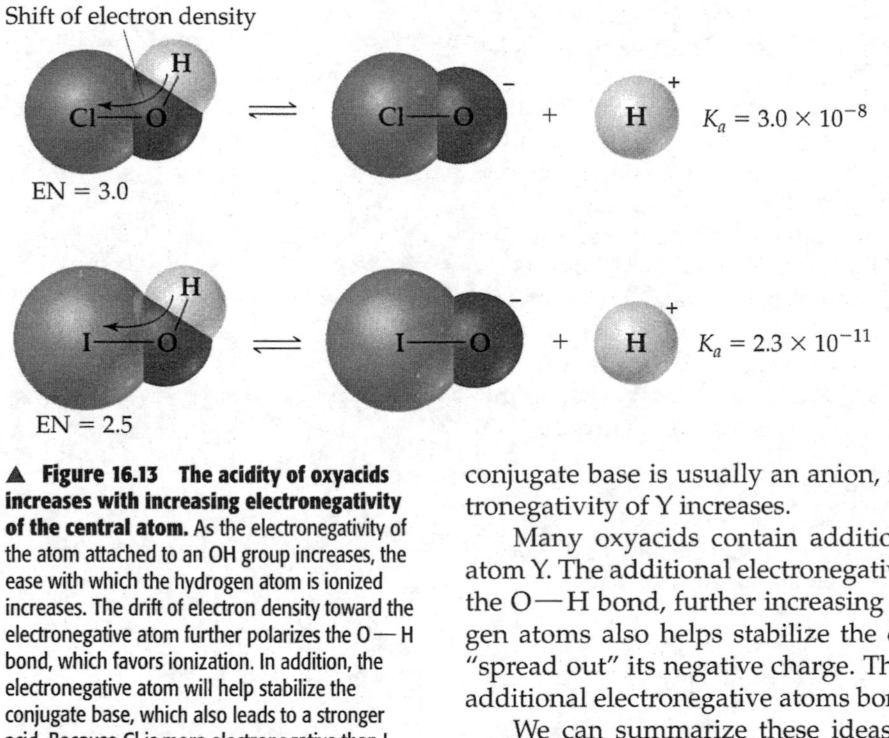

▲ **Figure 16.13 The acidity of oxyacids increases with increasing electronegativity of the central atom.** As the electronegativity of the atom attached to an OH group increases, the ease with which the hydrogen atom is ionized increases. The drift of electron density toward the electronegative atom further polarizes the O—H bond, which favors ionization. In addition, the electronegative atom will help stabilize the conjugate base, which also leads to a stronger acid. Because Cl is more electronegative than I, HClO is a stronger acid than HIO.

TABLE 16.6 Electronegativity Values (EN) of Y and Acid-Dissociation Constants

Acid	EN of Y	K_a
HClO	3.0	3.0×10^{-8}
HBrO	2.8	2.5×10^{-9}
HIO	2.5	2.3×10^{-11}

(In Figure 16.13: $K_a = 3.0 \times 10^{-8}$, EN = 3.0; $K_a = 2.3 \times 10^{-11}$, EN = 2.5; "Shift of electron density")

Hypochlorous	Chlorous	Chloric	Perchloric

$$H-\ddot{\underset{..}{O}}-\ddot{\underset{..}{Cl}}: \qquad H-\ddot{\underset{..}{O}}-\ddot{\underset{..}{Cl}}-\ddot{\underset{..}{O}}: \qquad H-\ddot{\underset{..}{O}}-\underset{\overset{\overset{\displaystyle :\ddot{O}:}{|}}{\quad}}{Cl}-\ddot{\underset{..}{O}}: \qquad H-\ddot{\underset{..}{O}}-\underset{\underset{\displaystyle :\ddot{\underset{..}{O}}:}{\overset{\displaystyle :\ddot{O}:}{|}}}{\overset{|}{Cl}}-\ddot{\underset{..}{O}}:$$

$K_a = 3.0 \times 10^{-8}$	$K_a = 1.1 \times 10^{-2}$	Strong acid	Strong acid

→ Increasing acid strength

Because the oxidation number of the central atom increases as the number of attached O atoms increases, this correlation can be stated in an equivalent way: In a series of oxyacids, the acidity increases as the oxidation number of the central atom increases.

SAMPLE EXERCISE 16.19 | Predicting Relative Acidities from Composition and Structure

Arrange the compounds in each of the following series in order of increasing acid strength: **(a)** AsH_3, HI, NaH, H_2O; **(b)** H_2SeO_3, H_2SeO_4, H_2O.

Solution

Analyze: We are asked to arrange two sets of compounds in order from weakest acid to strongest acid.

Plan: For the binary acids in part (a), we will consider the electronegativities of As, I, Na, and O, respectively. For the oxyacids in part (b), we will consider the number of oxygen atoms bonded to the central atom and the similarities between the Se-containing compounds and some more familiar acids.

Solve: (a) The elements from the left side of the periodic table form the most basic binary hydrogen compounds because the hydrogen in these compounds carries a negative charge. Thus NaH should be the most basic compound on the list. Because arsenic is less electronegative than oxygen, we might expect that AsH_3 would be a weak base toward water. That is also what we would predict by an extension of the trends shown in Figure 16.13. Further, we expect that the binary hydrogen compounds of the halogens, as the most electronegative element in each period, will be acidic relative to water. In fact, HI is one of the strong acids in water. Thus the order of increasing acidity is $NaH < AsH_3 < H_2O < HI$.

(b) The acidity of oxyacids increases as the number of oxygen atoms bonded to the central atom increases. Thus, H_2SeO_4 will be a stronger acid than H_2SeO_3; in fact, the Se atom in H_2SeO_4 is in its maximum positive oxidation state, and so we expect it to be a comparatively strong acid, much like H_2SO_4. H_2SeO_3 is an oxyacid of a nonmetal that is similar to H_2SO_3. As such, we expect that H_2SeO_3 is able to donate a proton to H_2O, indicating that H_2SeO_3 is a stronger acid than H_2O. Thus, the order of increasing acidity is $H_2O < H_2SeO_3 < H_2SeO_4$.

PRACTICE EXERCISE

In each of the following pairs choose the compound that leads to the more acidic (or less basic) solution: **(a)** HBr, HF; **(b)** PH_3, H_2S; **(c)** HNO_2, HNO_3; **(d)** H_2SO_3, H_2SeO_3.
Answers: **(a)** HBr, **(b)** H_2S, **(c)** HNO_3, **(d)** H_2SO_3

Carboxylic Acids

Another large group of acids is illustrated by acetic acid ($HC_2H_3O_2$):

$$H-\underset{\underset{\displaystyle H}{|}}{\overset{\overset{\displaystyle H}{|}}{C}}-\overset{\overset{\displaystyle :O:}{\|}}{C}-\ddot{\underset{..}{O}}-H$$

The portion of the structure shown in blue is called the *carboxyl group*, which is often written as COOH. Thus, the chemical formula of acetic acid is often

:O:
‖
H—C—Ö—H

Formic acid

:O:
‖
C—Ö—H

Benzoic acid

written as CH_3COOH, where only the hydrogen atom in the carboxyl group can be ionized. Acids that contain a carboxyl group are called **carboxylic acids**, and they form the largest category of organic acids. Formic acid and benzoic acid, whose structures are drawn in the margin, are further examples of this large and important category of acids.

Acetic acid (CH_3COOH) is a weak acid ($K_a = 1.8 \times 10^{-5}$). Methanol (CH_3OH), on the other hand, is not an acid in water. Two factors contribute to the acidic behavior of carboxylic acids. First, the additional oxygen atom attached to the carboxyl group carbon draws electron density from the O—H bond, increasing its polarity and helping to stabilize the conjugate base. Second, the conjugate base of a carboxylic acid (a *carboxylate anion*) can exhibit resonance (Section 8.6), which contributes further to the stability of the anion by spreading the negative charge over several atoms:

$$
\begin{array}{ccc}
H \quad :O: & & H \quad :\ddot{O}:^- \\
| \quad\quad \| & & | \quad\quad | \\
H—C—C—\ddot{O}:^- & \longleftrightarrow & H—C—C=\ddot{O} \\
| & \text{resonance} & | \\
H & & H
\end{array}
$$

The acid strength of carboxylic acids also increases as the number of electronegative atoms in the acid increases. For example, trifluoroacetic acid (CF_3COOH) has $K_a = 5.0 \times 10^{-1}$; the replacement of three hydrogen atoms of acetic acid with more electronegative fluorine atoms leads to a large increase in acid strength.

GIVE IT SOME THOUGHT

What group of atoms is present in all carboxylic acids?

16.11 | Lewis Acids and Bases

For a substance to be a proton acceptor (a Brønsted–Lowry base), it must have an unshared pair of electrons for binding the proton. NH_3, for example, acts as a proton acceptor. Using Lewis structures, we can write the reaction between H^+ and NH_3 as follows:

$$
H^+ + \begin{array}{c} H \\ | \\ :N—H \\ | \\ H \end{array} \longrightarrow \left[\begin{array}{c} H \\ | \\ H—N—H \\ | \\ H \end{array} \right]^+
$$

G. N. Lewis was the first to notice this aspect of acid-base reactions. He proposed a definition of acid and base that emphasizes the shared electron pair: A **Lewis acid** is an electron-pair acceptor, and a **Lewis base** is an electron-pair donor.

Every base that we have discussed thus far—whether it be OH^-, H_2O, an amine, or an anion—is an electron-pair donor. Everything that is a base in the Brønsted–Lowry sense (a proton acceptor) is also a base in the Lewis sense (an electron-pair donor). In the Lewis theory, however, a base can donate its electron pair to something other than H^+. The Lewis definition therefore greatly increases the number of species that can be considered acids; H^+ is a Lewis acid, but not the only one. For example, consider the reaction between NH_3 and BF_3. This reaction occurs because BF_3 has a vacant orbital in its valence shell. ∞∞ (Section 8.7) It therefore acts as an electron-pair acceptor (a Lewis acid) toward NH_3, which donates the electron pair. The curved arrow shows the donation of a pair of electrons from N to B to form a covalent bond:

 **ANIMATION**
Lewis Acid-Base Theory

$$H—\overset{\displaystyle H}{\underset{\displaystyle H}{N}}: + \overset{\displaystyle F}{\underset{\displaystyle F}{B}}—F \longrightarrow H—\overset{\displaystyle H}{\underset{\displaystyle H}{N}}—\overset{\displaystyle F}{\underset{\displaystyle F}{B}}—F$$

Lewis base   Lewis acid

CHEMISTRY AND LIFE | The Amphiprotic Behavior of Amino Acids

Amino acids are the building blocks of proteins. The general structure of amino acids is shown here, where different amino acids have different R groups attached to the central carbon atom:

$$H—\overset{\displaystyle H}{\underset{\displaystyle H}{N}}—\overset{\displaystyle R}{\underset{\displaystyle }{C}}—\overset{\displaystyle :O:}{\underset{\displaystyle }{C}}—\ddot{O}—H$$

Amine group (basic)   Carboxyl group (acidic)

For example, in *glycine*, which is the simplest amino acid, R is a hydrogen atom, whereas in *alanine*, R is a CH_3 group.

$$H_2N—\overset{\displaystyle H}{\underset{\displaystyle H}{C}}—COOH \qquad H_2N—\overset{\displaystyle CH_3}{\underset{\displaystyle H}{C}}—COOH$$

Glycine   Alanine

Amino acids contain a carboxyl group and can therefore serve as acids. They also contain an NH_2 group, characteristic of amines (Section 16.7), and thus they can also act as bases. Amino acids, therefore, are amphiprotic. For glycine, we might expect that the acid and the base reactions with water would be as follows:

Acid: $H_2N—CH_2—COOH(aq) + H_2O(l) \rightleftharpoons$
$$H_2N—CH_2—COO^-(aq) + H_3O^+(aq) \qquad [16.47]$$

Base: $H_2N—CH_2—COOH(aq) + H_2O(l) \rightleftharpoons$
$$^+H_3N—CH_2—COOH(aq) + OH^-(aq) \qquad [16.48]$$

The pH of a solution of glycine in water is about 6.0, indicating that it is a slightly stronger acid than a base.

The acid-base chemistry of amino acids is somewhat more complicated than shown in Equations 16.47 and 16.48, however. Because the COOH can act as an acid and the NH_2 group can act as a base, amino acids undergo a "self-contained" Brønsted–Lowry acid-base reaction in which the proton of the carboxyl group is transferred to the basic nitrogen atom:

$$H—\overset{\displaystyle H}{\underset{\displaystyle \underset{\uparrow}{H}}{N}}—\overset{\displaystyle H}{\underset{\displaystyle }{C}}—\overset{\displaystyle O}{\underset{\displaystyle }{C}}—OH \rightleftharpoons H—\overset{\displaystyle H}{\underset{\displaystyle H}{\overset{+}{N}}}—\overset{\displaystyle H}{\underset{\displaystyle H}{C}}—\overset{\displaystyle O}{\underset{\displaystyle }{C}}—O^-$$

proton transfer   [16.49]

Neutral molecule   Zwitterion

Although the form of the amino acid on the right side of Equation 16.49 is electrically neutral overall, it has a positively charged end and a negatively charged end. A molecule of this type is called a *zwitterion* (German for "hybrid ion").

Do amino acids exhibit any properties indicating that they behave as zwitterions? If so, they should behave similar to ionic substances. ∞ (Section 8.2) Crystalline amino acids (Figure 16.14 ▼) have relatively high melting points, usually above 200°C, which is characteristic of ionic solids. Amino acids are far more soluble in water than in nonpolar solvents. In addition, the dipole moments of amino acids are large, consistent with a large separation of charge in the molecule. Thus, the ability of amino acids to act simultaneously as acids and bases has important effects on their properties.
Related Exercise: 16.115

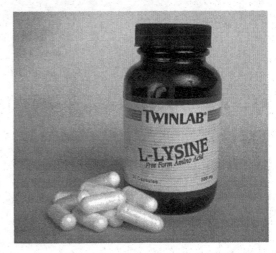

▲ **Figure 16.14 Lysine.** One of the amino acids found in proteins, lysine is available as a dietary supplement. The L on the label refers to a specific arrangement of atoms that is found in naturally occurring amino acids. Molecules with the L arrangement are mirror images of molecules with the D arrangement, much like our left hand is a mirror image of our right hand.

GIVE IT SOME THOUGHT

What feature must any molecule or ion have to act as a Lewis base?

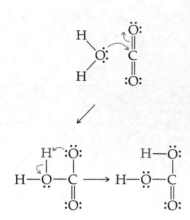

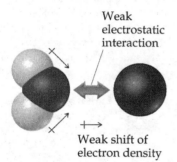

Our emphasis throughout this chapter has been on water as the solvent and on the proton as the source of acidic properties. In such cases we find the Brønsted–Lowry definition of acids and bases to be the most useful. In fact, when we speak of a substance as being acidic or basic, we are usually thinking of aqueous solutions and using these terms in the Arrhenius or Brønsted–Lowry sense. The advantage of the Lewis theory is that it allows us to treat a wider variety of reactions, including those that do not involve proton transfer, as acid-base reactions. To avoid confusion, a substance like BF_3 is rarely called an acid unless it is clear from the context that we are using the term in the sense of the Lewis definition. Instead, substances that function as electron-pair acceptors are referred to explicitly as "Lewis acids."

Lewis acids include molecules that, like BF_3, have an incomplete octet of electrons. In addition, many simple cations can function as Lewis acids. For example, Fe^{3+} interacts strongly with cyanide ions to form the ferricyanide ion, $Fe(CN)_6^{3-}$.

$$Fe^{3+} + 6[:C \equiv N:]^- \longrightarrow [Fe(C \equiv N:)_6]^{3-}$$

The Fe^{3+} ion has vacant orbitals that accept the electron pairs donated by the ions; we will learn more in Chapter 24 about just which orbitals are used by the Fe^{3+} ion. The metal ion is highly charged, too, which contributes to the interaction with CN^- ions.

Some compounds with multiple bonds can behave as Lewis acids. For example, the reaction of carbon dioxide with water to form carbonic acid (H_2CO_3) can be pictured as an attack by a water molecule on CO_2, in which the water acts as an electron-pair donor and the CO_2 as an electron-pair acceptor, as shown in the margin. The electron pair of one of the carbon–oxygen double bonds is moved onto the oxygen, leaving a vacant orbital on the carbon that can act as an electron-pair acceptor. We have shown the shift of these electrons with arrows. After forming the initial acid-base product, a proton moves from one oxygen to another, thereby forming carbonic acid. A similar kind of Lewis acid-base reaction takes place when any oxide of a nonmetal dissolves in water to form an acidic solution.

Hydrolysis of Metal Ions

As we have already seen, most metal ions behave as acids in aqueous solution. ∞ (Section 16.9) For example, an aqueous solution of $Cr(NO_3)_3$ is quite acidic. An aqueous solution of $ZnCl_2$ is also acidic, though to a lesser extent. The Lewis concept helps explain the interactions between metal ions and water molecules that give rise to this acidic behavior.

Because metal ions are positively charged, they attract the unshared electron pairs of water molecules. It is primarily this interaction, referred to as *hydration*, that causes salts to dissolve in water. ∞ (Section 13.1) The process of hydration can be thought of as a Lewis acid-base interaction in which the metal ion acts as a Lewis acid and the water molecules as Lewis bases. When a water molecule interacts with the positively charged metal ion, electron density is drawn from the oxygen, as illustrated in Figure 16.15 ◀. This flow of electron density causes the $O-H$ bond to become more polarized; as a result, water molecules bound to the metal ion are more acidic than those in the bulk solvent.

The hydrated Fe^{3+} ion, $Fe(H_2O)_6^{3+}$, which we usually represent simply as $Fe^{3+}(aq)$, acts as a source of protons:

$$Fe(H_2O)_6^{3+}(aq) \rightleftharpoons Fe(H_2O)_5(OH)^{2+}(aq) + H^+(aq) \qquad [16.50]$$

The acid-dissociation constant for this hydrolysis reaction has the value $K_a = 2 \times 10^{-3}$, so $Fe^{3+}(aq)$ is a fairly strong acid. Acid-dissociation constants for

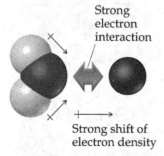

Weak
electrostatic
interaction

⊢⟶
Weak shift of
electron density

Strong
electron
interaction

⊢⟶
Strong shift of
electron density

▲ **Figure 16.15 The acidity of a hydrated cation depends on cation charge and size.** The interaction between a water molecule and a cation is much stronger when the cation is a smaller ion of higher charge. The pull of electron density toward the cation weakens the polar $O-H$ bond of the water molecule and allows the transfer of a H^+ ion to a nearby water molecule. As a result, hydrated cations tend to be acidic, with their acidities increasing with increasing charge and decreasing size.

Salt:	NaNO₃	Ca(NO₃)₂	Zn(NO₃)₂	Al(NO₃)₃
Indicator:	Bromthymol blue	Bromthymol blue	Methyl red	Methyl orange
Estimated pH:	7.0	6.9	5.5	3.5

▲ **Figure 16.16   Effect of cations on the pH of a solution.** The pH values of 1.0 M solutions of a series of nitrate salts are estimated using acid-base indicators.

hydrolysis reactions generally increase with increasing charge and decreasing radius of the ion (Figure 16.15). Thus, the Cu^{2+} ion, which has a smaller charge and a larger radius than Fe^{3+}, forms less acidic solutions than Fe^{3+}: The K_a for $Cu^{2+}(aq)$ is 1×10^{-8}. The acid hydrolysis of a number of salts of metal ions is demonstrated in Figure 16.16 ▲. Note that the Na^+ ion, which is large and has only a 1+ charge (and which we have previously identified as the cation of a strong base), exhibits no acid hydrolysis and yields a neutral solution.

GIVE IT SOME THOUGHT

Which of the following cations will be most acidic and why: Ca^{2+}, Fe^{2+}, Fe^{3+}?

SAMPLE INTEGRATIVE EXERCISE | Putting Concepts Together

Phosphorous acid (H_3PO_3) has the following Lewis structure.

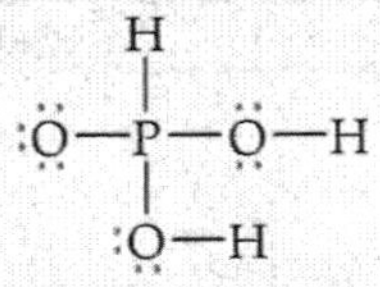

$$\overset{\displaystyle H}{\underset{\displaystyle \overset{|}{:\!\ddot{O}\!-\!H}}{\overset{|}{:\ddot{O}\!-\!P\!-\!\ddot{O}\!-\!H}}}$$

(a) Explain why H_3PO_3 is diprotic and not triprotic. **(b)** A 25.0-mL sample of a solution of H_3PO_3 is titrated with 0.102 M NaOH. It requires 23.3 mL of NaOH to neutralize both acidic protons. What is the molarity of the H_3PO_3 solution? **(c)** This solution has a pH of 1.59. Calculate the percent ionization and K_{a1} for H_3PO_3, assuming that $K_{a1} \gg K_{a2}$. **(d)** How does the osmotic pressure of a 0.050 M solution of HCl compare with that of a 0.050 M solution of H_3PO_3? Explain.

Solution The problem asks us to explain why there are only two ionizable protons in the H_3PO_3 molecule. Further, we are asked to calculate the molarity of a solution of H_3PO_3, given titration-experiment data. We then need to calculate the percent ionization of the H_3PO_3 solution in part (b). Finally, we are asked to compare the osmotic pressure of a 0.050 M solution of H_3PO_3 with that of an HCl solution of the same concentration.

We will use what we have learned about molecular structure and its impact on acidic behavior to answer part (a). We will then use stoichiometry and the relationship between pH and $[H^+]$ to answer parts (b) and (c). Finally, we will consider acid strength in order to compare the colligative properties of the two solutions in part (d).

(a) Acids have polar H—X bonds. From Figure 8.6 we see that the electronegativity of H is 2.1 and that of P is also 2.1. Because the two elements have the same electronegativity, the H—P bond is nonpolar. ∞ (Section 8.4) Thus, this H cannot be acidic. The other two H atoms, however, are bonded to O, which has an electronegativity of 3.5. The H—O bonds are therefore polar, with H having a partial positive charge. These two H atoms are consequently acidic.

(b) The chemical equation for the neutralization reaction is

$$H_3PO_3(aq) + 2\,NaOH(aq) \longrightarrow Na_2HPO_3(aq) + H_2O(l)$$

From the definition of molarity, $M = \text{mol/L}$, we see that moles $= M \times L$. ∞ (Section 4.5) Thus, the number of moles of NaOH added to the solution is $(0.0233\ L)(0.102\ \text{mol/L}) = 2.377 \times 10^{-3}$ mol NaOH. The balanced equation indicates that 2 mol of NaOH is consumed for each mole of H_3PO_3. Thus, the number of moles of H_3PO_3 in the sample is

$$(2.377 \times 10^{-3}\ \text{mol NaOH})\left(\frac{1\ \text{mol}\ H_3PO_3}{2\ \text{mol NaOH}}\right) = 1.189 \times 10^{-3}\ \text{mol}\ H_3PO_3$$

The concentration of the H_3PO_3 solution, therefore, equals $(1.189 \times 10^{-3}\ \text{mol})/(0.0250\ L) = 0.0475\ M$.

(c) From the pH of the solution, 1.59, we can calculate $[H^+]$ at equilibrium.

$$[H^+] = \text{antilog}(-1.59) = 10^{-1.59} = 0.026\ M\ \text{(two significant figures)}$$

Because $K_{a1} \gg K_{a2}$, the vast majority of the ions in solution are from the first ionization step of the acid.

$$H_3PO_3(aq) \rightleftharpoons H^+(aq) + H_2PO_3^-(aq)$$

Because one $H_2PO_3^-$ ion forms for each H^+ ion formed, the equilibrium concentrations of H^+ and $H_2PO_3^-$ are equal: $[H^+] = [H_2PO_3^-] = 0.026\ M$. The equilibrium concentration of H_3PO_3 equals the initial concentration minus the amount that ionizes to form H^+ and $H_2PO_3^-$: $[H_3PO_3] = 0.0475\ M - 0.026\ M = 0.022\ M$ (two significant figures). These results can be tabulated as follows:

	$H_2PO_3^-(aq)$ $\rightleftharpoons$	$H^+(aq)$ +	$H_3PO_3(aq)$
Initial	0.0475 M	0	0
Change	−0.026 M	+0.026 M	+0.026 M
Equilibrium	0.022 M	0.026 M	0.026 M

The percent ionization is

$$\text{Percent ionization} = \frac{[H^+]_{\text{equilibrium}}}{[H_3PO_3]_{\text{initial}}} \times 100\% = \frac{0.026\ M}{0.0475\ M} \times 100\% = 55\%$$

The first acid-dissociation constant is

$$K_{a1} = \frac{[H^+][H_2PO_3^-]}{[H_3PO_3]} = \frac{(0.026)(0.026)}{0.022} = 0.030$$

(d) Osmotic pressure is a colligative property and depends on the total concentration of particles in solution. ∞ (Section 13.5) Because HCl is a strong acid, a 0.050 M solution will contain 0.050 M $H^+(aq)$ and 0.050 M $Cl^-(aq)$, or a total of 0.100 mol/L of particles. Because H_3PO_3 is a weak acid, it ionizes to a lesser extent than HCl, and, hence, there are fewer particles in the H_3PO_3 solution. As a result, the H_3PO_3 solution will have the lower osmotic pressure.

SUMMARY AND KEY TERMS

Section 16.1   Acids and bases were first recognized by the properties of their aqueous solutions. For example, acids turn litmus red, whereas bases turn litmus blue. Arrhenius recognized that the properties of acidic solutions are due to $H^+(aq)$ ions and those of basic solutions are due to $OH^-(aq)$ ions.

Section 16.2   The Brønsted–Lowry concept of acids and bases is more general than the Arrhenius concept and emphasizes the transfer of a proton (H^+) from an acid to a base. The H^+ ion, which is merely a proton with no surrounding valence electrons, is strongly bound to water. For this reason, the **hydronium ion**, $H_3O^+(aq)$, is often used to represent the predominant form of H^+ in water instead of the simpler $H^+(aq)$.

A **Brønsted–Lowry acid** is a substance that donates a proton to another substance; a **Brønsted–Lowry base** is a substance that accepts a proton from another substance. Water is an **amphiprotic** substance, one that can function as either a Brønsted–Lowry acid or base, depending on the substance with which it reacts.

The **conjugate base** of a Brønsted–Lowry acid is the species that remains when a proton is removed from the acid. The **conjugate acid** of a Brønsted–Lowry base is the species formed by adding a proton to the base. Together, an acid and its conjugate base (or a base and its conjugate acid) are called a **conjugate acid-base pair**.

The acid-base strengths of conjugate acid-base pairs are related: The stronger an acid, the weaker its conjugate base; the weaker an acid, the stronger its conjugate base. In every acid-base reaction, the position of the equilibrium favors the transfer of the proton from the stronger acid to the stronger base.

Section 16.3   Water ionizes to a slight degree, forming $H^+(aq)$ and $OH^-(aq)$. The extent of this **autoionization** is expressed by the **ion-product constant** for water:

$$K_w = [H^+][OH^-] = 1.0 \times 10^{-14} \ (25°C)$$

This relationship describes both pure water and aqueous solutions. The K_w expression indicates that the product of $[H^+]$ and $[OH^-]$ is a constant. Thus, as $[H^+]$ increases, $[OH^-]$ decreases. Acidic solutions are those that contain more $H^+(aq)$ than $OH^-(aq)$; basic solutions contain more $OH^-(aq)$ than $H^+(aq)$.

Section 16.4   The concentration of $H^+(aq)$ can be expressed in terms of **pH**: $pH = -\log[H^+]$. At 25°C the pH of a neutral solution is 7.00, whereas the pH of an acidic solution is below 7.00, and the pH of a basic solution is above 7.00. The pX notation is also used to represent the negative log of other small quantities, as in pOH and pK_w. The pH of a solution can be measured using a pH meter, or it can be estimated using acid-base indicators.

Section 16.5   Strong acids are strong electrolytes, ionizing completely in aqueous solution. The common strong acids are HCl, HBr, HI, HNO_3, $HClO_3$, $HClO_4$, and

H_2SO_4. The conjugate bases of strong acids have negligible basicity.

Common strong bases are the ionic hydroxides of alkali metals and the heavy alkaline earth metals. The cations of strong bases have negligible acidity.

Section 16.6   Weak acids are weak electrolytes; only part of the molecules exist in solution in ionized form. The extent of ionization is expressed by the **acid-dissociation constant**, K_a, which is the equilibrium constant for the reaction $HA(aq) \rightleftharpoons H^+(aq) + A^-(aq)$, which can also be written $HA(aq) + H_2O(l) \rightleftharpoons H_3O^+(aq) + A^-(aq)$. The larger the value of K_a, the stronger the acid. The concentration of a weak acid and its K_a value can be used to calculate the pH of a solution.

Polyprotic acids, such as H_2SO_3, have more than one ionizable proton. These acids have acid-dissociation constants that decrease in magnitude in the order $K_{a1} > K_{a2} > K_{a3}$. Because nearly all the $H^+(aq)$ in a polyprotic acid solution comes from the first dissociation step, the pH can usually be estimated satisfactorily by considering only K_{a1}.

Sections 16.7 and 16.8   Weak bases include NH_3, **amines**, and the anions of weak acids. The extent to which a weak base reacts with water to generate the corresponding conjugate acid and OH^- is measured by the **base-dissociation constant**, K_b. This is the equilibrium constant for the reaction $B(aq) + H_2O(l) \rightleftharpoons HB^+(aq) + OH^-(aq)$, where B is the base.

The relationship between the strength of an acid and the strength of its conjugate base is expressed quantitatively by the equation $K_a \times K_b = K_w$, where K_a and K_b are dissociation constants for conjugate acid-base pairs.

Section 16.9   The acid-base properties of salts can be ascribed to the behavior of their respective cations and anions. The reaction of ions with water, with a resultant change in pH, is called **hydrolysis**. The cations of the alkali metals and the alkaline earth metals and the anions of strong acids do not undergo hydrolysis. They are always spectator ions in acid-base chemistry.

Section 16.10   The tendency of a substance to show acidic or basic characteristics in water can be correlated with its chemical structure. Acid character requires the presence of a highly polar H—X bond. Acidity is also favored when the H—X bond is weak and when the X^- ion is very stable.

For **oxyacids** with the same number of OH groups and the same number of O atoms, acid strength increases with increasing electronegativity of the central atom. For oxyacids with the same central atom, acid strength increases as the number of oxygen atoms attached to the central atom increases. The structures of **carboxylic acids**, which are organic acids containing the COOH group, also helps us to understand their acidity.

Section 16.11 The Lewis concept of acids and bases emphasizes the shared electron pair rather than the proton. A **Lewis acid** is an electron-pair acceptor, and a **Lewis base** is an electron-pair donor. The Lewis concept is more general than the Brønsted–Lowry concept because it can apply to cases in which the acid is some substance other than H^+. The Lewis concept helps to explain why many hydrated metal cations form acidic aqueous solutions. The acidity of these cations generally increases as their charge increases and as the size of the metal ion decreases.

VISUALIZING CONCEPTS

16.1 (a) Identify the Brønsted–Lowry acid and the Brønsted–Lowry base in the following reaction:

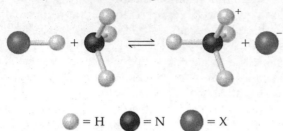

⬤ = H   ⬤ = N   ⬤ = X

(b) Identify the Lewis acid and the Lewis base in the reaction. [Sections 16.2 and 16.11]

16.2 The following diagrams represent aqueous solutions of two monoprotic acids, HA (A = X or Y). The water molecules have been omitted for clarity. (a) Which is the stronger acid, HX or HY? (b) Which is the stronger base, X^- or Y^-? (c) If you mix equal concentrations of HX and NaY, will the equilibrium

$$HX(aq) + Y^-(aq) \rightleftharpoons HY(aq) + X^-(aq)$$

lie mostly to the right ($K_c > 1$) or to the left ($K_c < 1$)? [Section 16.2]

⬤⬤ = HA   ⬤⊕ = H_3O^+ ⬤⊖ = A^-

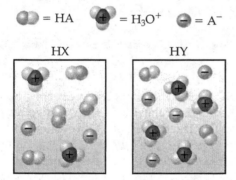

HX   HY

16.3 The following diagrams represent aqueous solutions of three acids, HX, HY, and HZ. The water molecules have been omitted for clarity, and the hydrated proton is represented as a simple sphere rather than as a hydronium ion. (a) Which of the acids is a strong acid? Explain. (b) Which acid would have the smallest acid-dissociation constant, K_a? (c) Which solution would have the highest pH? [Sections 16.5 and 16.6]

HX   HY   HZ

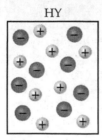

16.4 (a) Which of these three lines represents the effect of concentration on the percent ionization of a weak acid? (b) Explain in qualitative terms why the curve you choose has the shape it does. [Section 16.6]

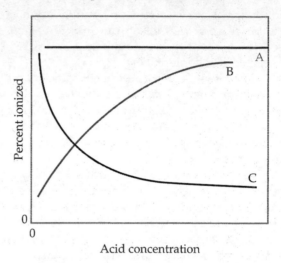

16.5 Refer to the diagrams accompanying Exercise 16.3. (a) Rank the anions, X^-, Y^-, and Z^-, in order of increasing basicity. (b) Which of the ions would have the largest base-dissociation constant, K_b? [Sections 16.2 and 16.8]

16.6 (a) Draw the Lewis structure for the following molecule and explain why it is able to act as a base. (b) To what class of organic compounds does this substance belong? [Section 16.7]

16.7 The following diagram represents an aqueous solution formed by dissolving a sodium salt of a weak acid in water. The diagram shows only the Na^+ ions, the X^- ions, and the HX molecules. What ion is missing from the diagram? If the drawing is completed by drawing all the ions, how many of the missing ions should be shown? [Section 16.9]

16.8 (a) What kinds of acids are represented by the following molecular models? (b) Indicate how the acidity of each molecule is affected by increasing the electronegativity of the atom X, and explain the origin of the effect. [Section 16.10]

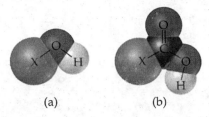

(a)   (b)

16.9 In this model of acetylsalicylic acid (aspirin), identify the carboxyl group in the molecule. [Section 16.10]

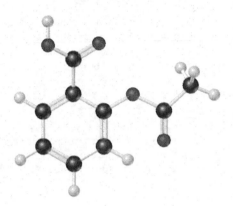

16.10 (a) The following diagram represents the reaction of PCl_4^+ with Cl^-. Draw the Lewis structures for the reactants and products, and identify the Lewis acid and the Lewis base in the reaction.

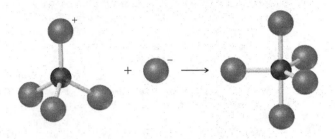

(b) The following reaction represents the acidity of a hydrated cation. How does the equilibrium constant for the reaction change as the charge of the cation increases? [Section 16.11]

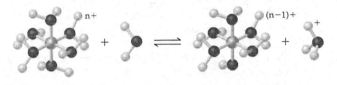

EXERCISES

Arrhenius and Brønsted–Lowry Acids and Bases

16.11 Although HCl and H_2SO_4 have very different properties as pure substances, their aqueous solutions possess many common properties. List some general properties of these solutions, and explain their common behavior in terms of the species present.

16.12 Although pure NaOH and CaO have very different properties, their aqueous solutions possess many common properties. List some general properties of these solutions, and explain their common behavior in terms of the species present.

16.13 (a) What is the difference between the Arrhenius and the Brønsted–Lowry definitions of an acid? (b) $NH_3(g)$ and $HCl(g)$ react to form the ionic solid $NH_4Cl(s)$ (Figure 16.3). Which substance is the Brønsted–Lowry acid in this reaction? Which is the Brønsted–Lowry base?

16.14 (a) What is the difference between the Arrhenius and the Brønsted–Lowry definitions of a base? (b) When ammonia is dissolved in water, it behaves both as an Arrhenius base and as a Brønsted–Lowry base. Explain.

16.15 Give the conjugate base of the following Brønsted–Lowry acids: (a) HIO_3, (b) NH_4^+, (c) $H_2PO_4^-$, (d) $HC_7H_5O_2$.

16.16 Give the conjugate acid of the following Brønsted–Lowry bases: (a) CN^-, (b) O^{2-}, (c) HPO_4^{2-}, (d) $C_2H_5NH_2$.

16.17 Designate the Brønsted–Lowry acid and the Brønsted–Lowry base on the left side of each of the following equations, and also designate the conjugate acid and conjugate base on the right side:
(a) $NH_4^+(aq) + CN^-(aq) \rightleftharpoons HCN(aq) + NH_3(aq)$
(b) $(CH_3)_3N(aq) + H_2O(l) \rightleftharpoons$
$(CH_3)_3NH^+(aq) + OH^-(aq)$
(c) $HCHO_2(aq) + PO_4^{3-}(aq) \rightleftharpoons$
$CHO_2^-(aq) + HPO_4^{2-}(aq)$

16.18 Designate the Brønsted–Lowry acid and the Brønsted–Lowry base on the left side of each equation, and also designate the conjugate acid and conjugate base on the right side.
(a) $HBrO(aq) + H_2O(l) \rightleftharpoons H_3O^+(aq) + BrO^-(aq)$
(b) $HSO_4^-(aq) + HCO_3^-(aq) \rightleftharpoons$
$SO_4^{2-}(aq) + H_2CO_3(aq)$
(c) $HSO_3^-(aq) + H_3O^+(aq) \rightleftharpoons H_2SO_3(aq) + H_2O(l)$

16.19 (a) The hydrogen oxalate ion ($HC_2O_4^-$) is amphiprotic. Write a balanced chemical equation showing how it acts as an acid toward water and another equation showing how it acts as a base toward water. (b) What is the conjugate acid of $HC_2O_4^-$? What is its conjugate base?

16.20 (a) Write an equation for the reaction in which $H_2C_6O_5H_7^-(aq)$ acts as a base in $H_2O(l)$. (b) Write an equation for the reaction in which $H_7C_6O_5H_7^-(aq)$ acts as an acid in $H_2O(l)$. (c) What is the conjugate acid of $H_2C_6O_5H_7^-$? What is its conjugate base?

16.21 Label each of the following as being a strong acid, a weak acid, or a species with negligible acidity. In each case write the formula of its conjugate base, and indicate whether the conjugate base is a strong base, a weak base, or a species with negligible basicity: **(a)** HNO_2, **(b)** H_2SO_4, **(c)** HPO_4^{2-}, **(d)** CH_4, **(e)** $CH_3NH_3^+$ (an ion related to NH_4^+).

16.22 Label each of the following as being a strong base, a weak base, or a species with negligible basicity. In each case write the formula of its conjugate acid, and indicate whether the conjugate acid is a strong acid, a weak acid, or a species with negligible acidity: **(a)** $C_2H_3O_2^-$, **(b)** HCO_3^-, **(c)** O^{2-}, **(d)** Cl^-, **(e)** NH_3.

16.23 **(a)** Which of the following is the stronger Brønsted–Lowry acid, HBrO or HBr? **(b)** Which is the stronger Brønsted–Lowry base, F^- or Cl^-? Briefly explain your choices.

16.24 **(a)** Which of the following is the stronger Brønsted–Lowry acid, HNO_3 or HNO_2? **(b)** Which is the stronger

Brønsted–Lowry base, NH_3 or H_2O? Briefly explain your choices.

16.25 Predict the products of the following acid-base reactions, and also predict whether the equilibrium lies to the left or to the right of the equation:
(a) $O^{2-}(aq) + H_2O(l) \rightleftharpoons$
(b) $HC_2H_3O_2(aq) + HS^-(aq) \rightleftharpoons$
(c) $NO_3^-(aq) + H_2O(l) \rightleftharpoons$

16.26 Predict the products of the following acid-base reactions, and also predict whether the equilibrium lies to the left or to the right of the equation:
(a) $NH_4^+(aq) + OH^-(aq) \rightleftharpoons$
(b) $C_2H_3O_2^-(aq) + H_3O^+(aq) \rightleftharpoons$
(c) $HCO_3^-(aq) + F^-(aq) \rightleftharpoons$

Autoionization of Water

16.27 **(a)** What is meant by the term *autoionization*? **(b)** Explain why pure water is a poor conductor of electricity. **(c)** You are told that an aqueous solution is acidic. What does this statement mean?

16.28 **(a)** Write a chemical equation that illustrates the autoionization of water. **(b)** Write the expression for the ion-product constant for water, K_w. Why is $[H_2O]$ absent from this expression? **(c)** A solution is described as basic. What is meant by this statement?

16.29 Calculate $[H^+]$ for each of the following solutions, and indicate whether the solution is acidic, basic, or neutral: **(a)** $[OH^-] = 0.00045\ M$; **(b)** $[OH^-] = 8.8 \times 10^{-9}\ M$; **(c)** a solution in which $[OH^-]$ is 100 times greater than $[H^+]$.

16.30 Calculate $[OH^-]$ for each of the following solutions, and indicate whether the solution is acidic, basic, or neutral: **(a)** $[H^+] = 0.0075\ M$; **(b)** $[H^+] = 6.5 \times 10^{-10}\ M$; **(c)** a solution in which $[H^+]$ is 10 times greater than $[OH^-]$.

16.31 At the freezing point of water (0°C), $K_w = 1.2 \times 10^{-15}$. Calculate $[H^+]$ and $[OH^-]$ for a neutral solution at this temperature.

16.32 Deuterium oxide (D_2O, where D is deuterium, the hydrogen-2 isotope) has an ion-product constant, K_w, of 8.9×10^{-16} at 20°C. Calculate $[D^+]$ and $[OD^-]$ for pure (neutral) D_2O at this temperature.

The pH Scale

16.33 By what factor does $[H^+]$ change for a pH change of **(a)** 2.00 units, **(b)** 0.50 units?

16.34 Consider two solutions, solution A and solution B. $[H^+]$ in solution A is 500 times greater than that in solution B. What is the difference in the pH values of the two solutions?

16.35 **(a)** If NaOH is added to water, how does $[H^+]$ change? How does pH change? **(b)** Use the pH benchmarks in Figure 16.5 to estimate the pH of a solution with $[H^+] = 0.0006\ M$. Is the solution acidic or basic? **(c)** If the pH of the solution is 5.2, first estimate and then calculate the molar concentrations of $H^+(aq)$ and $OH^-(aq)$ in the solution.

16.36 **(a)** If HNO_3 is added to water, how does $[OH^-]$ change? How does pH change? **(b)** Use the pH benchmarks in Figure 16.5 to estimate the pH of a solution with $[OH^-] = 0.014\ M$. Is the solution acidic or basic? **(c)** If pH = 6.6, first estimate and then calculate the molar concentrations of $H^+(aq)$ and $OH^-(aq)$ in the solution.

16.37 Complete the following table by calculating the missing entries and indicating whether the solution is acidic or basic.

$[H^+]$	$[OH^-]$	pH	pOH	Acidic or basic?
$7.5 \times 10^{-3}\ M$				
	$3.6 \times 10^{-10}\ M$			
		8.25		
			5.70	

16.38 Complete the following table by calculating the missing entries. In each case indicate whether the solution is acidic or basic.

pH	pOH	$[H^+]$	$[OH^-]$	Acidic or basic?
4.75				
	11.89			
		$6.5 \times 10^{-3}\ M$		
			$8.6 \times 10^{-7}\ M$	

16.39 The average pH of normal arterial blood is 7.40. At normal body temperature (37°C), $K_w = 2.4 \times 10^{-14}$. Calculate $[H^+]$, $[OH^-]$, and pOH for blood at this temperature.

16.40 Carbon dioxide in the atmosphere dissolves in raindrops to produce carbonic acid (H_2CO_3), causing the pH of clean, unpolluted rain to range from about 5.2 to 5.6. What are the ranges of $[H^+]$ and $[OH^-]$ in the raindrops?

Strong Acids and Bases

16.41 **(a)** What is a strong acid? **(b)** A solution is labeled 0.500 M HCl. What is [H^+] for the solution? **(c)** Which of the following are strong acids: HF, HCl, HBr, HI?

16.42 **(a)** What is a strong base? **(b)** A solution is labeled 0.045 M Sr(OH)$_2$. What is [OH^-] for the solution? **(c)** Is the following statement true or false? Because Mg(OH)$_2$ is not very soluble, it cannot be a strong base. Explain.

16.43 Calculate the pH of each of the following strong acid solutions: **(a)** 8.5×10^{-3} M HBr, **(b)** 1.52 g of HNO$_3$ in 575 mL of solution, **(c)** 5.00 mL of 0.250 M HClO$_4$ diluted to 50.0 mL, **(d)** a solution formed by mixing 10.0 mL of 0.100 M HBr with 20.0 mL of 0.200 M HCl.

16.44 Calculate the pH of each of the following strong acid solutions: **(a)** 0.00835 M HNO$_3$, **(b)** 0.525 g of HClO$_4$ in 2.00 L of solution, **(c)** 5.00 mL of 1.00 M HCl diluted to 0.500 L, **(d)** a mixture formed by adding 50.0 mL of 0.020 M HCl to 150 mL of 0.010 M HI.

16.45 Calculate [OH^-] and pH for **(a)** 1.5×10^{-3} M Sr(OH)$_2$, **(b)** 2.250 g of LiOH in 250.0 mL of solution, **(c)** 1.00 mL

of 0.175 M NaOH diluted to 2.00 L, **(d)** a solution formed by adding 5.00 mL of 0.105 M KOH to 15.0 mL of 9.5×10^{-2} M Ca(OH)$_2$.

16.46 Calculate [OH^-] and pH for each of the following strong base solutions: **(a)** 0.012 M KOH, **(b)** 1.565 g of KOH in 500.0 mL of solution, **(c)** 10.0 mL of 0.0105 M Ca(OH)$_2$ diluted to 500.0 mL, **(d)** a solution formed by mixing 10.0 mL of 0.015 M Ba(OH)$_2$ with 40.0 mL of 7.5×10^{-3} M NaOH.

16.47 Calculate the concentration of an aqueous solution of NaOH that has a pH of 11.50.

16.48 Calculate the concentration of an aqueous solution of Ca(OH)$_2$ that has a pH of 12.05.

[16.49] Calculate the pH of a solution made by adding 15.00 g of sodium hydride (NaH) to enough water to make 2.500 L of solution.

[16.50] Calculate the pH of a solution made by adding 2.50 g of lithium oxide (Li$_2$O) to enough water to make 1.500 L of solution.

Weak Acids

16.51 Write the chemical equation and the K_a expression for the ionization of each of the following acids in aqueous solution. First show the reaction with $H^+(aq)$ as a product and then with the hydronium ion: **(a)** HBrO$_2$, **(b)** HC$_3$H$_5$O$_2$.

16.52 Write the chemical equation and the K_a expression for the acid dissociation of each of the following acids in aqueous solution. First show the reaction with $H^+(aq)$ as a product and then with the hydronium ion: **(a)** HC$_6$H$_5$O, **(b)** HCO$_3^-$.

16.53 Lactic acid (HC$_3$H$_5$O$_3$) has one acidic hydrogen. A 0.10 M solution of lactic acid has a pH of 2.44. Calculate K_a.

16.54 Phenylacetic acid (HC$_8$H$_7$O$_2$) is one of the substances that accumulates in the blood of people with phenylketonuria, an inherited disorder that can cause mental retardation or even death. A 0.085 M solution of HC$_8$H$_7$O$_2$ is found to have a pH of 2.68. Calculate the K_a value for this acid.

16.55 A 0.100 M solution of chloroacetic acid (ClCH$_2$COOH) is 11.0% ionized. Using this information, calculate [ClCH$_2$COO$^-$], [H^+], [ClCH$_2$COOH], and K_a for chloroacetic acid.

16.56 A 0.100 M solution of bromoacetic acid (BrCH$_2$COOH) is 13.2% ionized. Calculate [H^+], [BrCH$_2$COO$^-$], and [BrCH$_2$COOH].

16.57 A particular sample of vinegar has a pH of 2.90. Assuming that acetic acid is the only acid that vinegar contains ($K_a = 1.8 \times 10^{-5}$), calculate the concentration of acetic acid in the vinegar.

16.58 How many moles of HF ($K_a = 6.8 \times 10^{-4}$) must be present in 0.200 L to form a solution with a pH of 3.25?

16.59 The acid-dissociation constant for benzoic acid (HC$_7$H$_5$O$_2$) is 6.3×10^{-5}. Calculate the equilibrium concentrations of H$_3$O$^+$, C$_7$H$_5$O$_2^-$, and HC$_7$H$_5$O$_2$ in the solution if the initial concentration of HC$_7$H$_5$O$_2$ is 0.050 M.

16.60 The acid-dissociation constant for hypochlorous acid (HClO) is 3.0×10^{-8}. Calculate the concentrations of H$_3$O$^+$, ClO$^-$, and HClO at equilibrium if the initial concentration of HClO is 0.0075 M.

16.61 Calculate the pH of each of the following solutions (K_a and K_b values are given in Appendix D): **(a)** 0.095 M

propionic acid (HC$_3$H$_5$O$_2$), **(b)** 0.100 M hydrogen chromate ion (HCrO$_4^-$), **(c)** 0.120 M pyridine (C$_5$H$_5$N).

16.62 Determine the pH of each of the following solutions (K_a and K_b values are given in Appendix D): **(a)** 0.125 M hypochlorous acid, **(b)** 0.0085 M phenol, **(c)** 0.095 M hydroxylamine.

16.63 Saccharin, a sugar substitute, is a weak acid with $pK_a = 2.32$ at 25°C. It ionizes in aqueous solution as follows:

$$HNC_7H_4SO_3(aq) \rightleftharpoons H^+(aq) + NC_7H_4SO_3^-(aq)$$

What is the pH of a 0.10 M solution of this substance?

16.64 The active ingredient in aspirin is acetylsalicylic acid (HC$_9$H$_7$O$_4$), a monoprotic acid with $K_a = 3.3 \times 10^{-4}$ at 25°C. What is the pH of a solution obtained by dissolving two extra-strength aspirin tablets, containing 500 mg of acetylsalicylic acid each, in 250 mL of water?

16.65 Calculate the percent ionization of hydrazoic acid (HN$_3$) in solutions of each of the following concentrations (K_a is given in Appendix D): **(a)** 0.400 M, **(b)** 0.100 M, **(c)** 0.0400 M.

16.66 Calculate the percent ionization of propionic acid (HC$_3$H$_5$O$_2$) in solutions of each of the following concentrations (K_a is given in Appendix D): **(a)** 0.250 M, **(b)** 0.0800 M, **(c)** 0.0200 M.

[16.67] Show that for a weak acid, the percent ionization should vary as the inverse square root of the acid concentration.

[16.68] For solutions of a weak acid, a graph of pH versus the log of the initial acid concentration should be a straight line. What is the magnitude of the slope of that line?

[16.69] Citric acid, which is present in citrus fruits, is a triprotic acid (Table 16.3). Calculate the pH and the citrate ion (C$_6$H$_5$O$_7^{3-}$) concentration for a 0.050 M solution of citric acid. Explain any approximations or assumptions that you make in your calculations.

[16.70] Tartaric acid is found in many fruits, including grapes. It is partially responsible for the dry texture of certain wines. Calculate the pH and the tartarate ion (C$_4$H$_4$O$_6^{2-}$) concentration for a 0.250 M solution of tartaric acid, for which the acid-dissociation constants are listed in Table 16.3. Explain any approximations or assumptions that you make in your calculation.

Weak Bases

16.71 What is the essential structural feature of all Brønsted–Lowry bases?

16.72 What are two kinds of molecules or ions that commonly function as weak bases?

16.73 Write the chemical equation and the K_b expression for the ionization of each of the following bases in aqueous solution: **(a)** dimethylamine, $(CH_3)_2NH$; **(b)** carbonate ion, CO_3^{2-}; **(c)** formate ion, CHO_2^-.

16.74 Write the chemical equation and the K_b expression for the reaction of each of the following bases with water: **(a)** propylamine, $C_3H_7NH_2$; **(b)** monohydrogen phosphate ion, HPO_4^{2-}; **(c)** benzoate ion, $C_6H_5CO_2^-$.

16.75 Calculate the molar concentration of OH^- ions in a 0.075 M solution of ethylamine $(C_2H_5NH_2)$ $(K_b = 6.4 \times 10^{-4})$. Calculate the pH of this solution.

16.76 Calculate the molar concentration of OH^- ions in a 1.15 M solution of hypobromite ion (BrO^-; $K_b = 4.0 \times 10^{-6}$). What is the pH of this solution?

16.77 Ephedrine, a central nervous system stimulant, is used in nasal sprays as a decongestant. This compound is a weak organic base:

$$C_{10}H_{15}ON(aq) + H_2O(l) \rightleftharpoons C_{10}H_{15}ONH^+(aq) + OH^-(aq)$$

A 0.035 M solution of ephedrine has a pH of 11.33. **(a)** What are the equilibrium concentrations of $C_{10}H_{15}ON$, $C_{10}H_{15}ONH^+$, and OH^-? **(b)** Calculate K_b for ephedrine.

16.78 Codeine $(C_{18}H_{21}NO_3)$ is a weak organic base. A 5.0×10^{-3} M solution of codeine has a pH of 9.95. Calculate the value of K_b for this substance. What is the pK_b for this base?

The K_a–K_b Relationship; Acid-Base Properties of Salts

16.79 Although the acid-dissociation constant for phenol (C_6H_5OH) is listed in Appendix D, the base-dissociation constant for the phenolate ion $(C_6H_5O^-)$ is not. **(a)** Explain why it is not necessary to list both K_a for phenol and K_b for the phenolate ion. **(b)** Calculate K_b for the phenolate ion. **(c)** Is the phenolate ion a weaker or stronger base than ammonia?

16.80 We can calculate K_b for the carbonate ion if we know the K_a values of carbonic acid (H_2CO_3). **(a)** Is K_{a1} or K_{a2} of carbonic acid used to calculate K_b for the carbonate ion? Explain. **(b)** Calculate K_b for the carbonate ion. **(c)** Is the carbonate ion a weaker or stronger base than ammonia?

16.81 **(a)** Given that K_a for acetic acid is 1.8×10^{-5} and that for hypochlorous acid is 3.0×10^{-8}, which is the stronger acid? **(b)** Which is the stronger base, the acetate ion or the hypochlorite ion? **(c)** Calculate K_b values for $C_2H_3O_2^-$ and ClO^-.

16.82 **(a)** Given that K_b for ammonia is 1.8×10^{-5} and that for hydroxylamine is 1.1×10^{-8}, which is the stronger base? **(b)** Which is the stronger acid, the ammonium ion or the hydroxylammonium ion? **(c)** Calculate K_a values for NH_4^+ and H_3NOH^+.

16.83 Using data from Appendix D, calculate $[OH^-]$ and pH for each of the following solutions: **(a)** 0.10 M NaCN, **(b)** 0.080 M Na_2CO_3, **(c)** a mixture that is 0.10 M in $NaNO_2$ and 0.20 M in $Ca(NO_2)_2$.

16.84 Using data from Appendix D, calculate $[OH^-]$ and pH for each of the following solutions: **(a)** 0.085 M NaF, **(b)** 0.055 M Na_2S, **(c)** a mixture that is 0.045 M in $NaC_2H_3O_2$ and 0.055 M in $Ba(C_2H_3O_2)_2$.

16.85 Predict whether aqueous solutions of the following compounds are acidic, basic, or neutral: **(a)** NH_4Br, **(b)** $FeCl_3$, **(c)** Na_2CO_3, **(d)** $KClO_4$, **(e)** $NaHC_2O_4$.

16.86 Predict whether aqueous solutions of the following substances are acidic, basic, or neutral: **(a)** $CrBr_3$, **(b)** LiI, **(c)** K_3PO_4, **(d)** $[CH_3NH_3]Cl$, **(e)** $KHSO_4$.

16.87 An unknown salt is either NaF, NaCl, or NaOCl. When 0.050 mol of the salt is dissolved in water to form 0.500 L of solution, the pH of the solution is 8.08. What is the identity of the salt?

16.88 An unknown salt is either KBr, NH_4Cl, KCN, or K_2CO_3. If a 0.100 M solution of the salt is neutral, what is the identity of the salt?

16.89 Sorbic acid $(HC_6H_7O_2)$ is a weak monoprotic acid with $K_a = 1.7 \times 10^{-5}$. Its salt (potassium sorbate) is added to cheese to inhibit the formation of mold. What is the pH of a solution containing 11.25 g of potassium sorbate in 1.75 L of solution?

16.90 Trisodium phosphate (Na_3PO_4) is available in hardware stores as TSP and is used as a cleaning agent. The label on a box of TSP warns that the substance is very basic (caustic or alkaline). What is the pH of a solution containing 45.0 g of TSP in a liter of solution?

Acid-Base Character and Chemical Structure

16.91 How does the acid strength of an oxyacid depend on **(a)** the electronegativity of the central atom; **(b)** the number of nonprotonated oxygen atoms in the molecule?

16.92 **(a)** How does the strength of an acid vary with the polarity and strength of the $H-X$ bond? **(b)** How does the acidity of the binary acid of an element vary as a function of the electronegativity of the element? How does this relate to the position of the element in the periodic table?

16.93 Explain the following observations: **(a)** HNO_3 is a stronger acid than HNO_2; **(b)** H_2S is a stronger acid than H_2O; **(c)** H_2SO_4 is a stronger acid than HSO_4^-;

(d) H_2SO_4 is a stronger acid than H_2SeO_4; **(e)** CCl_3COOH is a stronger acid than CH_3COOH.

16.94 Explain the following observations: **(a)** HCl is a stronger acid than H_2S; **(b)** H_3PO_4 is a stronger acid than H_3AsO_4; **(c)** $HBrO_3$ is a stronger acid than $HBrO_2$; **(d)** $H_2C_2O_4$ is a stronger acid than $HC_2O_4^-$; **(e)** benzoic acid (C_6H_5COOH) is a stronger acid than phenol (C_6H_5OH).

16.95 Based on their compositions and structures and on conjugate acid-base relationships, select the stronger base in each of the following pairs: **(a)** BrO^- or ClO^-, **(b)** BrO^- or BrO_2^-, **(c)** HPO_4^{2-} or $H_2PO_4^-$.

16.96 Based on their compositions and structures and on conjugate acid-base relationships, select the stronger base in each of the following pairs: (a) NO_3^- or NO_2^-, (b) PO_4^{3-} or AsO_4^{3-}, (c) HCO_3^- or CO_3^{2-}.

16.97 Indicate whether each of the following statements is true or false. For each statement that is false, correct the statement so that it is true. (a) In general, the acidity of binary acids increases from left to right in a given row of the periodic table. (b) In a series of acids that have the same central atom, acid strength increases with the number of hydrogen atoms bonded to the central atom. (c) Hydrotelluric acid (H_2Te) is a stronger acid than H_2S because Te is more electronegative than S.

16.98 Indicate whether each of the following statements is true or false. For each statement that is false, correct the statement so that it is true. (a) Acid strength in a series of H—X molecules increases with increasing size of X. (b) For acids of the same general structure but differing electronegativities of the central atoms, acid strength decreases with increasing electronegativity of the central atom. (c) The strongest acid known is HF because fluorine is the most electronegative element.

Lewis Acids and Bases

16.99 If a substance is an Arrhenius base, is it necessarily a Brønsted–Lowry base? Is it necessarily a Lewis base? Explain.

16.100 If a substance is a Lewis acid, is it necessarily a Brønsted–Lowry acid? Is it necessarily an Arrhenius acid? Explain.

16.101 Identify the Lewis acid and Lewis base among the reactants in each of the following reactions:
(a) $Fe(ClO_4)_3(s) + 6 H_2O(l) \rightleftharpoons$
$$Fe(H_2O)_6^{3+}(aq) + 3 ClO_4^-(aq)$$
(b) $CN^-(aq) + H_2O(l) \rightleftharpoons HCN(aq) + OH^-(aq)$
(c) $(CH_3)_3N(g) + BF_3(g) \rightleftharpoons (CH_3)_3NBF_3(s)$

(d) $HIO(lq) + NH_2^-(lq) \rightleftharpoons NH_3(lq) + IO^-(lq)$
(lq denotes liquid ammonia as solvent)

16.102 Identify the Lewis acid and Lewis base in each of the following reactions:
(a) $HNO_2(aq) + OH^-(aq) \rightleftharpoons NO_2^-(aq) + H_2O(l)$
(b) $FeBr_3(s) + Br^-(aq) \rightleftharpoons FeBr_4^-(aq)$
(c) $Zn^{2+}(aq) + 4 NH_3(aq) \rightleftharpoons Zn(NH_3)_4^{2+}(aq)$
(d) $SO_2(g) + H_2O(l) \rightleftharpoons H_2SO_3(aq)$

16.103 Predict which member of each pair produces the more acidic aqueous solution: (a) K^+ or Cu^{2+}, (b) Fe^{2+} or Fe^{3+}, (c) Al^{3+} or Ga^{3+}. Explain.

16.104 Which member of each pair produces the more acidic aqueous solution: (a) $ZnBr_2$ or $CdCl_2$, (b) $CuCl$ or $Cu(NO_3)_2$, (c) $Ca(NO_3)_2$ or $NiBr_2$? Explain.

Additional Exercises

16.105 In your own words, define or explain (a) K_w, (b) K_a, (c) pOH.

16.106 Indicate whether each of the following statements is correct or incorrect. For those that are incorrect, explain why they are wrong.
(a) Every Brønsted–Lowry acid is also a Lewis acid.
(b) Every Lewis acid is also a Brønsted–Lowry acid.
(c) Conjugate acids of weak bases produce more acidic solutions than conjugate acids of strong bases.
(d) K^+ ion is acidic in water because it causes hydrating water molecules to become more acidic.
(e) The percent ionization of a weak acid in water increases as the concentration of acid decreases.

16.107 Hemoglobin plays a part in a series of equilibria involving protonation-deprotonation and oxygenation-deoxygenation. The overall reaction is approximately as follows:

$$HbH^+(aq) + O_2(aq) \rightleftharpoons HbO_2(aq) + H^+(aq)$$

where Hb stands for hemoglobin, and HbO_2 for oxyhemoglobin. (a) The concentration of O_2 is higher in the lungs and lower in the tissues. What effect does high $[O_2]$ have on the position of this equilibrium? (b) The normal pH of blood is 7.4. Is the blood acidic, basic, or neutral? (c) If the blood pH is lowered by the presence of large amounts of acidic metabolism products, a condition known as acidosis results. What effect does lowering blood pH have on the ability of hemoglobin to transport O_2?

[16.108] What is the pH of a solution that is 2.5×10^{-9} M in NaOH? Does your answer make sense?

16.109 Which of the following solutions has the higher pH? (a) a 0.1 M solution of a strong acid or a 0.1 M solution of a weak acid, (b) a 0.1 M solution of an acid with $K_a = 2 \times 10^{-3}$ or one with $K_a = 8 \times 10^{-6}$, (c) a 0.1 M solution of a base with $pK_b = 4.5$ or one with $pK_b = 6.5$.

16.110 Caproic acid ($HC_6H_{11}O_2$) is found in small amounts in coconut and palm oils and is used in making artificial flavors. A saturated solution of the acid contains 11 g/L and has a pH of 2.94. Calculate K_a for the acid.

[16.111] A hypothetical acid H_2X is both a strong acid and a diprotic acid. (a) Calculate the pH of a 0.050 M solution of H_2X, assuming that only one proton ionizes per acid molecule. (b) Calculate the pH of the solution from part (a), now assuming that both protons of each acid molecule completely ionize. (c) In an experiment it is observed that the pH of a 0.050 M solution of H_2X is 1.27. Comment on the relative acid strengths of H_2X and HX^-. (d) Would a solution of the salt NaHX be acidic, basic, or neutral? Explain.

16.112 Arrange the following 0.10 M solutions in order of increasing acidity (decreasing pH): (i) NH_4NO_3, (ii) $NaNO_3$, (iii) $NH_4C_2H_3O_2$, (iv) NaF, (v) $NaC_2H_3O_2$.

[16.113] What are the concentrations of H^+, $H_2PO_4^-$, HPO_4^{2-}, and PO_4^{3-} in a 0.0250 M solution of H_3PO_4?

[16.114] Many moderately large organic molecules containing basic nitrogen atoms are not very soluble in water as neutral molecules, but they are frequently much more soluble as their acid salts. Assuming that pH in the stomach is 2.5, indicate whether each of the following compounds would be present in the stomach as the neutral base or in the protonated form: nicotine, $K_b = 7 \times 10^{-7}$; caffeine, $K_b = 4 \times 10^{-14}$; strychnine, $K_b = 1 \times 10^{-6}$; quinine, $K_b = 1.1 \times 10^{-6}$.

[16.115] The amino acid glycine (H_2N—CH_2—COOH) can participate in the following equilibria in water:

$$H_2N\text{—}CH_2\text{—}COOH + H_2O \rightleftharpoons$$
$$H_2N\text{—}CH_2\text{—}COO^- + H_3O^+ \quad K_a = 4.3 \times 10^{-3}$$

$$H_2N\text{—}CH_2\text{—}COOH + H_2O \rightleftharpoons$$
$$^+H_3N\text{—}CH_2\text{—}COOH + OH^- \quad K_b = 6.0 \times 10^{-5}$$

(a) Use the values of K_a and K_b to estimate the equilibrium constant for the intramolecular proton transfer to form a zwitterion:

$$H_2N\text{—}CH_2\text{—}COOH \rightleftharpoons {}^+H_3N\text{—}CH_2\text{—}COO^-$$

What assumptions did you need to make? **(b)** What is the pH of a 0.050 M aqueous solution of glycine? **(c)** What would be the predominant form of glycine in a solution with pH 13? With pH 1?

Integrative Exercises

16.117 Calculate the number of $H^+(aq)$ ions in 1.0 mL of pure water at 25°C.

16.118 How many milliliters of concentrated hydrochloric acid solution (36.0% HCl by mass, density = 1.18 g/mL) are required to produce 10.0 L of a solution that has a pH of 2.05?

16.119 The volume of an adult's stomach ranges from about 50 mL when empty to 1 L when full. If its volume is 400 mL and its contents have a pH of 2, how many moles of H^+ does it contain? Assuming that all the H^+ comes from HCl, how many grams of sodium hydrogen carbonate will totally neutralize the stomach acid?

16.120 Atmospheric CO_2 levels have risen by nearly 20% over the past 40 years from 315 ppm to 375 ppm. **(a)** Given that the average pH of clean, unpolluted rain today is 5.4, determine the pH of unpolluted rain 40 years ago. Assume that carbonic acid (H_2CO_3) formed by the reaction of CO_2 and water is the only factor influencing pH.

$$CO_2(g) + H_2O(l) \rightleftharpoons H_2CO_3(aq)$$

(b) What volume of CO_2 at 25°C and 1.0 atm is dissolved in a 20.0-L bucket of today's rainwater?

[16.121] In many reactions the addition of $AlCl_3$ produces the same effect as the addition of H^+. **(a)** Draw a Lewis structure for $AlCl_3$ in which no atoms carry formal charges, and determine its structure using the VSEPR method. **(b)** What characteristic is notable about the structure in part (a) that helps us understand the acidic character of $AlCl_3$? **(c)** Predict the result of the reaction between $AlCl_3$ and NH_3 in a solvent that does not participate as a reactant. **(d)** Which acid-base theory is most suitable for discussing the similarities between $AlCl_3$ and H^+?

[16.122] What is the boiling point of a 0.10 M solution of $NaHSO_4$ if the solution has a density of 1.002 g/mL?

[16.123] Cocaine is a weak organic base whose molecular formula is $C_{17}H_{21}NO_4$. An aqueous solution of cocaine was found to have a pH of 8.53 and an osmotic pressure of 52.7 torr at 15°C. Calculate K_b for cocaine.

[16.124] The iodate ion is reduced by sulfite according to the following reaction:

$$IO_3^-(aq) + 3\,SO_3^{2-}(aq) \longrightarrow I^-(aq) + 3\,SO_4^{2-}(aq)$$

[16.116] The structural formula for acetic acid is shown in Table 16.2. Replacing hydrogen atoms on the carbon with chlorine atoms causes an increase in acidity, as follows:

Acid	Formula	K_a (25°C)
Acetic	CH_3COOH	1.8×10^{-5}
Chloroacetic	$CH_2ClCOOH$	1.4×10^{-3}
Dichloroacetic	$CHCl_2COOH$	3.3×10^{-2}
Trichloroacetic	CCl_3COOH	2×10^{-1}

Using Lewis structures as the basis of your discussion, explain the observed trend in acidities in the series. Calculate the pH of a 0.010 M solution of each acid.

The rate of this reaction is found to be first order in IO_3^-, first order in SO_3^{2-}, and first order in H^+. **(a)** Write the rate law for the reaction. **(b)** By what factor will the rate of the reaction change if the pH is lowered from 5.00 to 3.50? Does the reaction proceed faster or slower at the lower pH? **(c)** By using the concepts discussed in Section 14.6, explain how the reaction can be pH-dependent even though H^+ does not appear in the overall reaction.

[16.125] **(a)** Using dissociation constants from Appendix D, determine the value for the equilibrium constant for each of the following reactions. (Remember that when reactions are added, the corresponding equilibrium constants are multiplied.)
(i) $HCO_3^-(aq) + OH^-(aq) \rightleftharpoons CO_3^{2-}(aq) + H_2O(l)$
(ii) $NH_4^+(aq) + CO_3^{2-}(aq) \rightleftharpoons$
$$NH_3(aq) + HCO_3^-(aq)$$
(b) We usually use single arrows for reactions when the forward reaction is appreciable (K much greater than 1) or when products escape from the system, so that equilibrium is never established. If we follow this convention, which of these equilibria might be written with a single arrow?

[16.126] Lactic acid, $CH_3CH(OH)COOH$, received its name because it is present in sour milk as a product of bacterial action. It is also responsible for the soreness in muscles after vigorous exercise. **(a)** The pK_a of lactic acid is 3.85. Compare this with the value for propionic acid (CH_3CH_2COOH, $pK_a = 4.89$), and explain the difference. **(b)** Calculate the lactate ion concentration in a 0.050 M solution of lactic acid. **(c)** When a solution of sodium lactate, ($CH_3CH(OH)COO)Na$, is mixed with an aqueous copper(II) solution, it is possible to obtain a solid salt of copper(II) lactate as a blue-green hydrate, $(CH_3CH(OH)COO)_2$ Cu·xH_2O. Elemental analysis of the solid tells us that the solid is 22.9% Cu and 26.0% C by mass. What is the value for x in the formula for the hydrate? **(d)** The acid-dissociation constant for the $Cu^{2+}(aq)$ ion is 1.0×10^{-8}. Based on this value and the acid-dissociation constant of lactic acid, predict whether a solution of copper(II) lactate will be acidic, basic, or neutral. Explain your answer.

eMEDIA EXERCISES

These exercises make use of the interactive objects available online in OneKey or the Companion Website, and on your Accelerator CD. Access to these resources comes in your MediaPak.

16.127 You can measure the pH in the **Acids and Bases** activity (*16.4*) for aqueous solutions of 13 different compounds. **(a)** List the compounds available in the simulation, and identify each as a strong acid, a weak acid, a strong base, or a weak base. **(b)** For each compound, measure and record the pH of a 0.05 *M* solution.

16.128 **(a)** Using data from the **Acids and Bases** activity (*16.4*), calculate the K_a of HNO_2. **(b)** Determine the percent ionization of HNO_2 at 2.0 *M*, 0.20 *M*, 0.020 *M*, and 0.0020 *M* concentrations. **(c)** Explain the trend in percent ionization using Le Châtelier's principle.

16.129 The **Introduction to Aqueous Acids** animation (*16.6*) illustrates the ionization in water of two different strong acids and one weak acid. **(a)** Given that all three ionize to produce hydrogen ion in water, what is it about the behavior of the weak acid that makes it different from the strong acids? **(b)** What is the consequence of this difference in terms of pH?

16.130 The **Introduction to Aqueous Bases** animation (*16.7*) illustrates the ionization of a weak base. **(a)** Write the equation that corresponds to the ionization of ammonia in water. **(b)** In the animation the ammonia molecule ionizes, producing aqueous hydroxide. What is it about the behavior of ammonia in water that makes ammonia a *weak* base?

16.131 The K_b of ammonia is 1.8×10^{-5}. **(a)** Calculate the concentration of aqueous ammonia that would have a pH of 8.5. Use the **Acids and Bases** activity (*16.4*) to check your answer. **(b)** What is the percent ionization of ammonia at this concentration?

16.132 Use the **Equilibrium Constant** activity (*16.6*) to experiment with the ionization of a weak acid. Choose the $HA \rightleftharpoons H^+ + A^-$ reaction and enter the K_a of acetic acid (1.8×10^{-5}). **(a)** Enter a starting HA concentration of 0.1 *M* and determine the equilibrium concentration of H^+. **(b)** By what percentage did the concentration of HA change? **(c)** By what percentage did the concentration of H^+ change? **(d)** Calculate pH and pOH of the 0.1 *M* solution of acetic acid.

eLABORATORY EXERCISES

These exercises allow students to apply the concepts and skills for this chapter in the simulated laboratory of Virtual ChemLab. Worksheets for each of these exercises are found in the Virtual ChemLab Workbook in your MediaPak.

16.133 *(VCL 16-1) Ionization Constants of Weak Acids*
An acid-base indicator is usually a weak acid with a characteristic color in the protonated and deprotonated forms. In this assignment you will monitor the color of an acetic acid solution containing *bromocresol green* as an indicator as the pH is changed, and estimate the ionization constant, K_a, for the indicator.

16.134 *(VCL 16-2) Acid-Base Classification of Salts*
In this assignment you will be asked to classify aqueous solutions of salts as to whether they are acidic, basic, or neutral. This is most easily done by first identifying how both the cation and anion affect the pH of the solution and then combine the effects. After predicting the acid-base properties of these salts, you will then test your predictions in the laboratory.

16.135 *(VCL 16-3) Ranking Salt Solutions by pH*
In this assignment you will be asked to rank a set of aqueous solutions of acids, bases, and salts in order of increasing pH of the solutions. After ranking these solutions, you will then test your predictions in the laboratory.

17.1 The Common-Ion Effect

17.2 Buffered Solutions

17.3 Acid-Base Titrations

17.4 Solubility Equilibria

17.5 Factors that Affect Solubility

17.6 Precipitation and Separation of Ions

17.7 Qualitative Analysis for Metallic Elements

WHAT'S AHEAD

- We begin by considering a specific example of Le Châtelier's principle known as the *common-ion effect*. *(Section 17.1)*

- We then consider the composition of *buffered solutions*, or *buffers*, and learn how they resist pH change upon the addition of small amounts of strong acid or strong base. *(Section 17.2)*

- We continue by examining acid-base titration in detail, and we explore how to determine pH at any point in an acid-base titration. *(Section 17.3)*

- Next, we learn how to use equilibrium constants known as *solubility-product constants* to determine to what extent a sparingly soluble salt will dissolve in water, and we investigate some of the factors that affect solubility. *(Sections 17.4 and 17.5)*

- Continuing the discussion of solubility equilibria, we learn how to precipitate ions selectively. *(Section 17.6)*

- The chapter concludes with an explanation of how the principles of solubility and complexation equilibria can be used to identify ions qualitatively in solution. *(Section 17.7)*

Additional Aspects
of Aqueous Equilibria

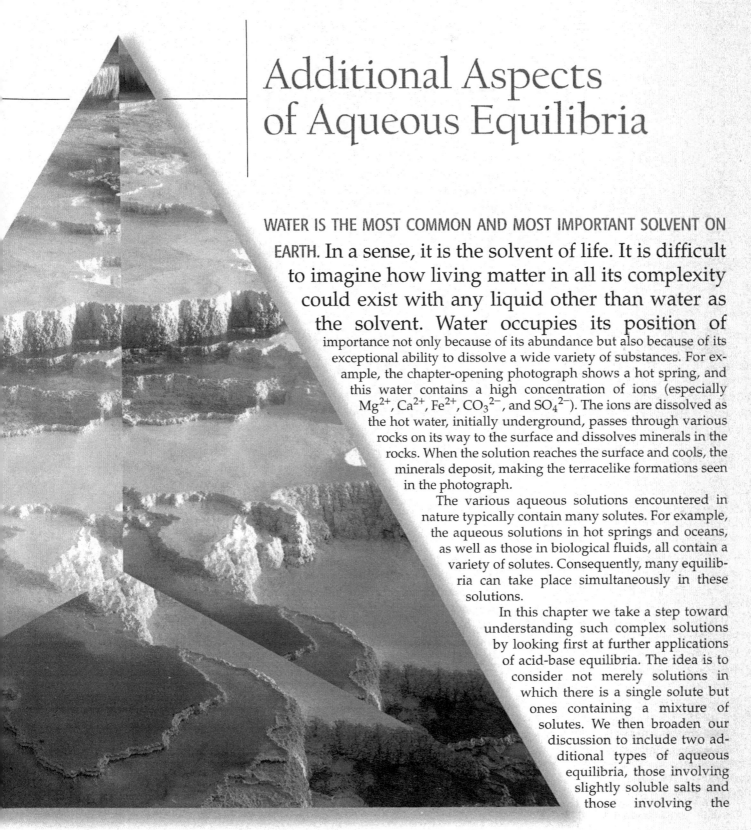

WATER IS THE MOST COMMON AND MOST IMPORTANT SOLVENT ON EARTH. In a sense, it is the solvent of life. It is difficult to imagine how living matter in all its complexity could exist with any liquid other than water as the solvent. Water occupies its position of importance not only because of its abundance but also because of its exceptional ability to dissolve a wide variety of substances. For example, the chapter-opening photograph shows a hot spring, and this water contains a high concentration of ions (especially Mg^{2+}, Ca^{2+}, Fe^{2+}, CO_3^{2-}, and SO_4^{2-}). The ions are dissolved as the hot water, initially underground, passes through various rocks on its way to the surface and dissolves minerals in the rocks. When the solution reaches the surface and cools, the minerals deposit, making the terracelike formations seen in the photograph.

The various aqueous solutions encountered in nature typically contain many solutes. For example, the aqueous solutions in hot springs and oceans, as well as those in biological fluids, all contain a variety of solutes. Consequently, many equilibria can take place simultaneously in these solutions.

In this chapter we take a step toward understanding such complex solutions by looking first at further applications of acid-base equilibria. The idea is to consider not merely solutions in which there is a single solute but ones containing a mixture of solutes. We then broaden our discussion to include two additional types of aqueous equilibria, those involving slightly soluble salts and those involving the

MAMMOTH HOT SPRING in Yellowstone National Park.

721

formation of metal complexes in solution. For the most part, the discussions and calculations in this chapter are an extension of those in Chapters 15 and 16.

17.1 | The Common-Ion Effect

In Chapter 16 we examined the equilibrium concentrations of ions in solutions containing a weak acid or a weak base. We now consider solutions that contain not only a weak acid, such as acetic acid ($HC_2H_3O_2$), but also a soluble salt of that acid, such as $NaC_2H_3O_2$. What happens when $NaC_2H_3O_2$ is added to a solution of $HC_2H_3O_2$? Because $C_2H_3O_2^-$ is a weak base, the pH of the solution increases; that is, [H^+] decreases. ∞ (Section 16.9) It is instructive, however, to view this effect from the perspective of Le Châtelier's principle. ∞ (Section 15.6)

Sodium acetate, $NaC_2H_3O_2$, is a soluble ionic compound and is therefore a strong electrolyte. ∞ (Section 4.1) Consequently, it dissociates completely in aqueous solution to form Na^+ and $C_2H_3O_2^-$ ions:

$$NaC_2H_3O_2(aq) \longrightarrow Na^+(aq) + C_2H_3O_2^-(aq)$$

In contrast, $HC_2H_3O_2$ is a weak electrolyte that ionizes as follows:

$$HC_2H_3O_2(aq) \rightleftharpoons H^+(aq) + C_2H_3O_2^-(aq) \qquad [17.1]$$

The addition of $C_2H_3O_2^-$, from $NaC_2H_3O_2$, causes this equilibrium to shift to the left, thereby decreasing the equilibrium concentration of $H^+(aq)$.

$$HC_2H_3O_2(aq) \rightleftharpoons H^+(aq) + C_2H_3O_2^-(aq)$$

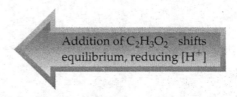

Addition of $C_2H_3O_2^-$ shifts equilibrium, reducing [H^+]

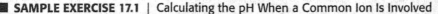

The dissociation of the weak acid $HC_2H_3O_2$ decreases when we add the strong electrolyte $NaC_2H_3O_2$, which has an ion in common with it. We can generalize this observation, which we call the **common-ion effect**: *The extent of ionization of a weak electrolyte is decreased by adding to the solution a strong electrolyte that has an ion in common with the weak electrolyte.* Sample Exercises 17.1 and 17.2 illustrate how equilibrium concentrations may be calculated when a solution contains a mixture of a weak electrolyte and a strong electrolyte that have a common ion. The procedures are similar to those encountered for weak acids and weak bases in Chapter 16.

ANIMATION
Common-Ion Effect

SAMPLE EXERCISE 17.1 | Calculating the pH When a Common Ion Is Involved

What is the pH of a solution made by adding 0.30 mol of acetic acid ($HC_2H_3O_2$) and 0.30 mol of sodium acetate ($NaC_2H_3O_2$) to enough water to make 1.0 L of solution?

Solution
Analyze: We are asked to determine the pH of a solution of a weak electrolyte ($HC_2H_3O_2$) and a strong electrolyte ($NaC_2H_3O_2$) that share a common ion, $C_2H_3O_2^-$.

Plan: In any problem in which we must determine the pH of a solution containing a mixture of solutes, it is helpful to proceed by a series of logical steps:

1. Identify the major species in solution, and consider their acidity or basicity.
2. Identify the important equilibrium that is the source of H^+ and therefore determines pH.
3. Tabulate the concentrations of ions involved in the equilibrium.
4. Use the equilibrium-constant expression to calculate [H^+] and then pH.

Solve: First, because $HC_2H_3O_2$ is a weak electrolyte and $NaC_2H_3O_2$ is a strong electrolyte, the major species in the solution are $HC_2H_3O_2$ (a weak acid), Na^+ (which is neither acidic nor basic and is therefore a spectator in the acid-base chemistry), and $C_2H_3O_2^-$ (which is the conjugate base of $HC_2H_3O_2$).

Second, $[H^+]$ and, therefore, the pH are controlled by the dissociation equilibrium of $HC_2H_3O_2$:

$$HC_2H_3O_2(aq) \rightleftharpoons H^+(aq) + C_2H_3O_2^-(aq)$$

(We have written the equilibrium using $H^+(aq)$ rather than $H_3O^+(aq)$, but both representations of the hydrated hydrogen ion are equally valid.)

Third, we tabulate the initial and equilibrium concentrations much as we did in solving other equilibrium problems in Chapters 15 and 16:

	$HC_2H_3O_2(aq)$	$\rightleftharpoons$ $H^+(aq)$	$+ C_2H_3O_2^-(aq)$
Initial	0.30 M	0	0.30 M
Change	$-x$ M	$+x$ M	$+x$ M
Equilibrium	$(0.30 - x)$ M	x M	$(0.30 + x)$ M

The equilibrium concentration of $C_2H_3O_2^-$ (the common ion) is the initial concentration that is due to $NaC_2H_3O_2$ (0.30 M) plus the change in concentration (x) that is due to the ionization of $HC_2H_3O_2$.

Now we can use the equilibrium-constant expression:

$$K_a = 1.8 \times 10^{-5} = \frac{[H^+][C_2H_3O_2^-]}{[HC_2H_3O_2]}$$

(The dissociation constant for $HC_2H_3O_2$ at 25°C is from Appendix D; addition of $NaC_2H_3O_2$ does not change the value of this constant.)

Substituting the equilibrium-constant concentrations from our table into the equilibrium expression gives

$$K_a = 1.8 \times 10^{-5} = \frac{x(0.30 + x)}{0.30 - x}$$

Because K_a is small, we assume that x is small compared to the original concentrations of $HC_2H_3O_2$ and $C_2H_3O_2^-$ (0.30 M each). Thus, we can ignore the very small x relative to 0.30 M, giving

$$K_a = 1.8 \times 10^{-5} = \frac{x(0.30)}{0.30}$$
$$x = 1.8 \times 10^{-5} M = [H^+]$$

The resulting value of x is indeed small relative to 0.30, justifying the approximation made in simplifying the problem.

Finally, we calculate the pH from the equilibrium concentration of $H^+(aq)$:

$$pH = -\log(1.8 \times 10^{-5}) = 4.74$$

Comment: In Section 16.6 we calculated that a 0.30 M solution of $HC_2H_3O_2$ has a pH of 2.64, corresponding to $[H^+] = 2.3 \times 10^{-3}$ M. Thus, the addition of $NaC_2H_3O_2$ has substantially decreased $[H^+]$, as we would expect from Le Châtelier's principle.

■ PRACTICE EXERCISE
Calculate the pH of a solution containing 0.085 M nitrous acid (HNO_2; $K_a = 4.5 \times 10^{-4}$) and 0.10 M potassium nitrite (KNO_2).
Answer: 3.42

■ SAMPLE EXERCISE 17.2 | Calculating Ion Concentrations When a Common Ion is Involved
Calculate the fluoride ion concentration and pH of a solution that is 0.20 M in HF and 0.10 M in HCl.

Solution
Analyze: We are asked to determine the concentration of F^- and the pH in a solution containing the weak acid HF and the strong acid HCl. In this case the common ion is H^+.
Plan: We can again use the four steps outlined in Sample Exercise 17.1.

Solve: Because HF is a weak acid and HCl is a strong acid, the major species in solution are HF, H⁺, and Cl⁻. The Cl⁻, which is the conjugate base of a strong acid, is merely a spectator ion in any acid-base chemistry. The problem asks for [F⁻], which is formed by ionization of HF. Thus, the important equilibrium is

$$HF(aq) \rightleftharpoons H^+(aq) + F^-(aq)$$

The common ion in this problem is the hydrogen or hydronium ion. Now we can tabulate the initial and equilibrium concentrations of each species involved in this equilibrium:

	$HF(aq)$	$\rightleftharpoons$	$H^+(aq)$	+	$F^-(aq)$
Initial	0.20 M		0.10 M		0
Change	$-x$ M		$+x$ M		$+x$ M
Equilibrium	$(0.20 - x)$ M		$(0.10 + x)$ M		x M

The equilibrium constant for the ionization of HF, from Appendix D, is 6.8×10^{-4}. Substituting the equilibrium-constant concentrations into the equilibrium expression gives

$$K_a = 6.8 \times 10^{-4} = \frac{[H^+][F^-]}{[HF]} = \frac{(0.10 + x)(x)}{0.20 - x}$$

If we assume that x is small relative to 0.10 or 0.20 M, this expression simplifies to

$$\frac{(0.10)(x)}{0.20} = 6.8 \times 10^{-4}$$

$$x = \frac{0.20}{0.10}(6.8 \times 10^{-4}) = 1.4 \times 10^{-3} M = [F^-]$$

This F⁻ concentration is substantially smaller than it would be in a 0.20 M solution of HF with no added HCl. The common ion, H⁺, suppresses the ionization of HF. The concentration of H⁺(aq) is

$$[H^+] = (0.10 + x) M \approx 0.10 M$$

Thus,

$$pH = 1.00$$

Comment: Notice that for all practical purposes, [H⁺] is due entirely to the HCl; the HF makes a negligible contribution by comparison.

PRACTICE EXERCISE

Calculate the formate ion concentration and pH of a solution that is 0.050 M in formic acid (HCHO₂; $K_a = 1.8 \times 10^{-4}$) and 0.10 M in HNO₃.
Answer: [CHO₂⁻] = 9.0×10^{-5}; pH = 1.00

Sample Exercises 17.1 and 17.2 both involve weak acids. The ionization of a weak base is also decreased by the addition of a common ion. For example, the addition of NH₄⁺ (as from the strong electrolyte NH₄Cl) causes the base-dissociation equilibrium of NH₃ to shift to the left, decreasing the equilibrium concentration of OH⁻ and lowering the pH:

$$NH_3(aq) + H_2O(l) \rightleftharpoons NH_4^+(aq) + OH^-(aq) \qquad [17.2]$$

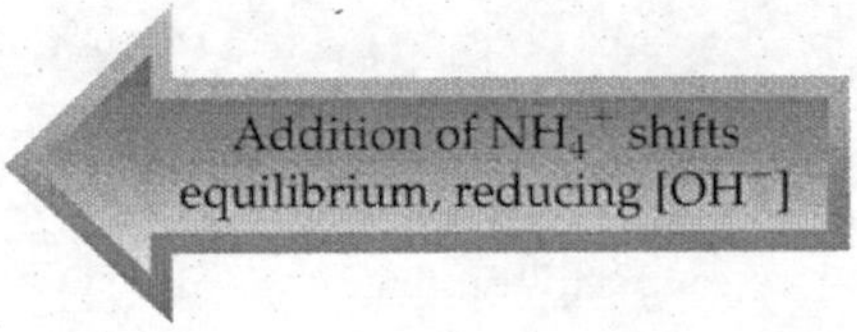

Addition of NH₄⁺ shifts equilibrium, reducing [OH⁻]

GIVE IT SOME THOUGHT

A mixture of 0.10 mol of NH_4Cl and 0.12 mol of NH_3 is added to enough water to make 1.0 L of solution. (a) What are the initial concentrations of the major species in the solution? (b) Which of the ions in this solution is a spectator ion in any acid-base chemistry occurring in the solution? (c) What equilibrium reaction determines $[OH^-]$ and therefore the pH of the solution?

17.2 | Buffered Solutions

Solutions such as those discussed in Section 17.1, which contain a weak conjugate acid-base pair, can resist drastic changes in pH upon the addition of small amounts of strong acid or strong base. These solutions are called **buffered solutions** (or merely **buffers**). Human blood, for example, is a complex aqueous mixture with a pH buffered at about 7.4 (see the "Chemistry and Life" box near the end of this section). Much of the chemical behavior of seawater is determined by its pH, buffered at about 8.1 to 8.3 near the surface. Buffered solutions find many important applications in the laboratory and in medicine (Figure 17.1 ▶).

Composition and Action of Buffered Solutions

A buffer resists changes in pH because it contains both an acidic species to neutralize OH^- ions and a basic species to neutralize H^+ ions. The acidic and basic species that make up the buffer, however, must not consume each other through a neutralization reaction. These requirements are fulfilled by a weak acid-base conjugate pair such as $HC_2H_3O_2$–$C_2H_3O_2^-$ or NH_4^+–NH_3. Thus, buffers are often prepared by mixing a weak acid or a weak base with a salt of that acid or base. The $HC_2H_3O_2$–$C_2H_3O_2^-$ buffer can be prepared, for example, by adding $NaC_2H_3O_2$ to a solution of $HC_2H_3O_2$; the NH_4^+–NH_3 buffer can be prepared by adding NH_4Cl to a solution of NH_3. By choosing appropriate components and adjusting their relative concentrations, we can buffer a solution at virtually any pH.

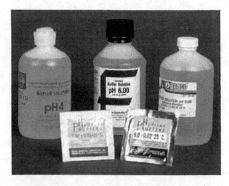
▲ **Figure 17.1   Buffer solutions.** Prepackaged buffer solutions and ingredients for making up buffer solutions of predetermined pH can be purchased.

GIVE IT SOME THOUGHT

Which of the following conjugate acid-base pairs will not function as a buffer: $HCHO_2$ and CHO_2^-; HCO_3^- and CO_3^{2-}; HNO_3 and NO_3^-? Explain.

To understand better how a buffer works, let's consider a buffer composed of a weak acid (HX) and one of its salts (MX, where M^+ could be Na^+, K^+, or another cation). The acid-dissociation equilibrium in this buffered solution involves both the acid and its conjugate base:

$$HX(aq) \rightleftharpoons H^+(aq) + X^-(aq) \qquad [17.3]$$

The corresponding acid-dissociation-constant expression is

$$K_a = \frac{[H^+][X^-]}{[HX]} \qquad [17.4]$$

Solving this expression for $[H^+]$, we have

$$[H^+] = K_a \frac{[HX]}{[X^-]} \qquad [17.5]$$

We see from this expression that $[H^+]$, and thus the pH, is determined by two factors: the value of K_a for the weak-acid component of the buffer and the ratio of the concentrations of the conjugate acid-base pair, $[HX]/[X^-]$.

▶ **Figure 17.2 Buffer action.** When a small portion of OH⁻ is added to a buffer consisting of a mixture of the weak acid HF and its conjugate base (left), the OH⁻ reacts with the HF, decreasing [HF] and increasing [F⁻] in the buffer. Conversely, when a small portion of H⁺ is added to the buffer (right), the H⁺ reacts with the F⁻, decreasing [F⁻] and increasing [HF] in the buffer. Because pH depends on the ratio of F⁻ to HF, the resulting pH change is small.

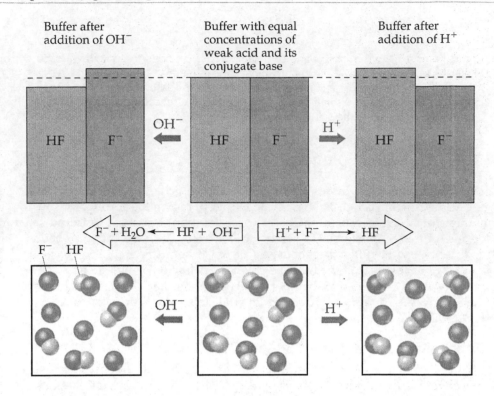

If OH⁻ ions are added to the buffered solution, they react with the acid component of the buffer to produce water and the base component (X^-):

$$OH^-(aq) + HX(aq) \longrightarrow H_2O(l) + X^-(aq) \qquad [17.6]$$

This reaction causes [HX] to decrease and [X⁻] to increase. As long as the amounts of HX and X⁻ in the buffer are large compared to the amount of OH⁻ added, however, the ratio [HX]/[X⁻] doesn't change much, and thus the change in pH is small. A specific example of such a buffer, the HF/F⁻ buffer, is shown in Figure 17.2 ▲.

If H⁺ ions are added, they react with the base component of the buffer:

$$H^+(aq) + X^-(aq) \longrightarrow HX(aq) \qquad [17.7]$$

This reaction can also be represented using H_3O^+:

$$H_3O^+(aq) + X^-(aq) \longrightarrow HX(aq) + H_2O(l)$$

Using either equation, the reaction causes [X⁻] to decrease and [HX] to increase. As long as the change in the ratio [HX]/[X⁻] is small, the change in pH will be small.

Figure 17.2 shows a buffer consisting of equal concentrations of hydrofluoric acid and fluoride ion (center). The addition of OH⁻ (left) reduces [HF] and increases [F⁻]. The addition of H⁺ (right) reduces [F⁻] and increases [HF].

 GIVE IT SOME THOUGHT

(a) What happens when NaOH is added to a buffer composed of $HC_2H_3O_2$ and $C_2H_3O_2^-$? (b) What happens when HCl is added to this buffer?

Calculating the pH of a Buffer

Because conjugate acid-base pairs share a common ion, we can use the same procedures to calculate the pH of a buffer that we used to treat the common-ion effect (see Sample Exercise 17.1). However, an alternate approach is sometimes taken that is based on an equation derived from Equation 17.5. Taking the negative log of both sides of Equation 17.5, we have

$$-\log[H^+] = -\log\left(K_a \frac{[HX]}{[X^-]}\right) = -\log K_a - \log\frac{[HX]}{[X^-]}$$

Because $-\log[H^+] = pH$ and $-\log K_a = pK_a$, we have

$$pH = pK_a - \log\frac{[HX]}{[X^-]} = pK_a + \log\frac{[X^-]}{[HX]} \qquad [17.8]$$

In general,

$$pH = pK_a + \log\frac{[base]}{[acid]} \qquad [17.9]$$

where [acid] and [base] refer to the equilibrium concentrations of the conjugate acid-base pair. Note that when [base] = [acid], pH = pK_a.

Equation 17.9 is known as the **Henderson–Hasselbalch equation**. Biologists, biochemists, and others who work frequently with buffers often use this equation to calculate the pH of buffers. In doing equilibrium calculations, we have seen that we can normally neglect the amounts of the acid and base of the buffer that ionize. Therefore, we can usually use the starting concentrations of the acid and base components of the buffer directly in Equation 17.9.

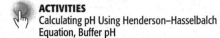

ACTIVITIES
Calculating pH Using Henderson–Hasselbalch Equation, Buffer pH

SAMPLE EXERCISE 17.3 | Calculating the pH of a Buffer

What is the pH of a buffer that is 0.12 M in lactic acid ($HC_3H_5O_3$) and 0.10 M in sodium lactate? For lactic acid, $K_a = 1.4 \times 10^{-4}$.

Solution

Analyze: We are asked to calculate the pH of a buffer containing lactic acid ($HC_3H_5O_3$) and its conjugate base, the lactate ion ($C_3H_5O_3^-$).

Plan: We will first determine the pH using the method described in Section 17.1. The major species in solution are $HC_3H_5O_3$, Na^+, and $C_3H_5O_3^-$. The Na^+ ion is a spectator ion. The $HC_3H_5O_3$–$C_3H_5O_3^-$ conjugate acid-base pair determines [H^+] and thus pH; [H^+] can be determined using the acid-dissociation equilibrium of lactic acid.

Solve: The initial and equilibrium concentrations of the species involved in this equilibrium are

	$HC_3H_5O_3(aq)$	$\rightleftharpoons$ $H^+(aq)$	+ $C_3H_5O_3^-(aq)$
Initial	0.12 M	0	0.10 M
Change	$-x$ M	$+x$ M	$+x$ M
Equilibrium	$(0.12 - x)$ M	x M	$(0.10 + x)$ M

The equilibrium concentrations are governed by the equilibrium expression:

$$K_a = 1.4 \times 10^{-4} = \frac{[H^+][C_3H_5O_3]}{[HC_3H_5O_3]} = \frac{x(0.10 + x)}{(0.12 - x)}$$

Because K_a is small and a common ion is present, we expect x to be small relative to either 0.12 or 0.10 M. Thus, our equation can be simplified to give

$$K_a = 1.4 \times 10^{-4} = \frac{x(0.10)}{0.12}$$

Solving for x gives a value that justifies our approximation:

$$[H^+] = x = \left(\frac{0.12}{0.10}\right)(1.4 \times 10^{-4}) = 1.7 \times 10^{-4}\ M$$

$$pH = -\log(1.7 \times 10^{-4}) = 3.77$$

Alternatively, we could have used the Henderson–Hasselbalch equation to calculate pH directly:

$$pH = pK_a + \log\left(\frac{[base]}{[acid]}\right) = 3.85 + \log\left(\frac{0.10}{0.12}\right)$$

$$= 3.85 + (-0.08) = 3.77$$

PRACTICE EXERCISE

Calculate the pH of a buffer composed of 0.12 M benzoic acid and 0.20 M sodium benzoate. (Refer to Appendix D.)
Answer: 4.42

■ SAMPLE EXERCISE 17.4 | Preparing a Buffer

How many moles of NH_4Cl must be added to 2.0 L of 0.10 M NH_3 to form a buffer whose pH is 9.00? (Assume that the addition of NH_4Cl does not change the volume of the solution.)

Solution

Analyze: Here we are asked to determine the amount of NH_4^+ ion required to prepare a buffer of a specific pH.

Plan: The major species in the solution will be NH_4^+, Cl^-, and NH_3. Of these, the Cl^- ion is a spectator (it is the conjugate base of a strong acid). Thus, the NH_4^+–NH_3 conjugate acid-base pair will determine the pH of the buffer solution. The equilibrium relationship between NH_4^+ and NH_3 is given by the base-dissociation constant for NH_3:

$$NH_3(aq) + H_2O(l) \rightleftharpoons NH_4^+(aq) \qquad K_b = \frac{[NH_4^+][OH^-]}{[NH_3]} = 1.8 \times 10^{-5}$$

The key to this exercise is to use this K_b expression to calculate $[NH_4^+]$.

Solve: We obtain $[OH^-]$ from the given pH:

$$pOH = 14.00 - pH = 14.00 - 9.00 = 5.00$$

and so

$$[OH^-] = 1.0 \times 10^{-5} M$$

Because K_b is small and the common ion NH_4^+ is present, the equilibrium concentration of NH_3 will essentially equal its initial concentration:

$$[NH_3] = 0.10 M$$

We now use the expression for K_b to calculate $[NH_4^+]$:

$$[NH_4^+] = K_b \frac{[NH_3]}{[OH^-]} = (1.8 \times 10^{-5})\frac{(0.10\ M)}{(1.0 \times 10^{-5}\ M)} = 0.18\ M$$

Thus, in order for the solution to have pH = 9.00, $[NH_4^+]$ must equal 0.18 M. The number of moles of NH_4Cl needed to produce this concentration is given by the product of the volume of the solution and its molarity:

$$(2.0\ L)(0.18\ mol\ NH_4Cl/L) = 0.36\ mol\ NH_4Cl$$

Comment: Because NH_4^+ and NH_3 are a conjugate acid-base pair, we could use the Henderson–Hasselbalch equation (Equation 17.9) to solve this problem. To do so requires first using Equation 16.41 to calculate pK_a for NH_4^+ from the value of pK_b for NH_3. We suggest you try this approach to convince yourself that you can use the Henderson–Hasselbalch equation for buffers for which you are given K_b for the conjugate base rather than K_a for the conjugate acid.

■ PRACTICE EXERCISE

Calculate the concentration of sodium benzoate that must be present in a 0.20 M solution of benzoic acid ($HC_7H_5O_2$) to produce a pH of 4.00.

Answer: 0.13 M

Buffer Capacity and pH Range

Two important characteristics of a buffer are its capacity and its effective pH range. **Buffer capacity** is the amount of acid or base the buffer can neutralize before the pH begins to change to an appreciable degree. The buffer capacity depends on the amount of acid and base from which the buffer is made. The pH of the buffer depends on the K_a for the acid and on the relative concentrations of the acid and base that comprise the buffer. According to Equation 17.5, for example, $[H^+]$ for a 1-L solution that is 1 M in $HC_2H_3O_2$ and 1 M in $NaC_2H_3O_2$ will be the same as for a 1-L solution that is 0.1 M in $HC_2H_3O_2$ and 0.1 M in $NaC_2H_3O_2$. The first solution has a greater buffering capacity, however, because it contains more $HC_2H_3O_2$ and $C_2H_3O_2^-$. The greater the amounts of the conjugate acid-base pair, the more resistant the ratio of their concentrations, and hence the pH, is to change.

The **pH range** of any buffer is the pH range over which the buffer acts effectively. Buffers most effectively resist a change in pH in *either* direction when the concentrations of weak acid and conjugate base are about the same. From Equation 17.9 we see that when the concentrations of weak acid and conjugate base are equal, $pH = pK_a$. This relationship gives the optimal pH of any buffer. Thus, we usually try to select a buffer whose acid form has a pK_a close to the desired pH. In practice, we find that if the concentration of one component of the buffer is more than 10 times the concentration of the other component, the buffering action is poor. Because $\log 10 = 1$, buffers usually have a usable range within ± 1 pH unit of pK_a.

GIVE IT SOME THOUGHT

What is the optimal pH buffered by a solution containing $HC_2H_3O_2$ and $NaC_2H_3O_2$? (K_a for $HC_2H_3O_2$ is 1.8×10^{-5}.)

Addition of Strong Acids or Bases to Buffers

Let's now consider in a more quantitative way the response of a buffered solution to the addition of a strong acid or base. In solving these problems, it is important to understand that reactions between strong acids and weak bases proceed essentially to completion, as do those between strong bases and weak acids. Thus, as long as we do not exceed the buffering capacity of the buffer, we can assume that the strong acid or strong base is completely consumed by reaction with the buffer.

Consider a buffer that contains a weak acid HX and its conjugate base X^-. When a strong acid is added to this buffer, the added H^+ is consumed by X^- to produce HX; thus, [HX] increases and $[X^-]$ decreases. When a strong base is added to the buffer, the added OH^- is consumed by HX to produce X^-; in this case [HX] decreases and $[X^-]$ increases. These situations were summarized in Figure 17.2.

To calculate how the pH of the buffer responds to the addition of a strong acid or a strong base, we follow the strategy outlined in Figure 17.3 ▼:

1. Consider the acid-base neutralization reaction, and determine its effect on [HX] and $[X^-]$. This stage of the procedure is a *stoichiometry calculation*.

2. Use K_a and the new concentrations of [HX] and $[X^-]$ from step 1 to calculate $[H^+]$. This second stage of the procedure is a standard *equilibrium calculation* and is most easily done using the Henderson–Hasselbalch equation.

The complete procedure is illustrated in Sample Exercise 17.5.

ACTIVITY
Buffer pH Calculation

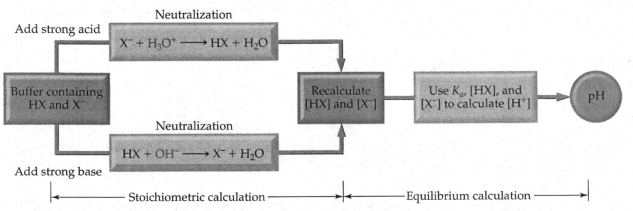

▲ **Figure 17.3 Calculation of the pH of a buffer after the addition of acid or base.** First consider how the neutralization reaction between the added strong acid or strong base and the buffer affects the composition of the buffer (stoichiometry calculation). Then calculate the pH of the remaining buffer (equilibrium calculation). As long as the amount of added acid or base does not exceed the buffer capacity, the Henderson–Hasselbalch equation, Equation 17.9, can be used for the equilibrium calculation.

■ SAMPLE EXERCISE 17.5 | Calculating pH Changes in Buffers

A buffer is made by adding 0.300 mol $HC_2H_3O_2$ and 0.300 mol $NaC_2H_3O_2$ to enough water to make 1.00 L of solution. The pH of the buffer is 4.74 (Sample Exercise 17.1). **(a)** Calculate the pH of this solution after 0.020 mol of NaOH is added. **(b)** For comparison, calculate the pH that would result if 0.020 mol of NaOH was added to 1.00 L of pure water (neglect any volume changes).

Solution

Analyze: We are asked to determine the pH of a buffer after addition of a small amount of strong base, and to compare the pH change to the pH that would result if we were to add the same amount of strong base to pure water.

Plan: **(a)** Solving this problem involves the two steps outlined in Figure 17.3. Thus, we must first do a stoichiometry calculation to determine how the added OH^- reacts with the buffer and affects its composition. Then we can use the resultant composition of the buffer and either the Henderson–Hasselbalch equation or the equilibrium-constant expression for the buffer to determine the pH.

Solve: *Stoichiometry Calculation:* We assume that the OH^- provided by NaOH is completely consumed by $HC_2H_3O_2$, the weak acid component of the buffer. We can set up a table to see how this reaction changes the composition of the buffer changes. A more compact convention for this type of calculation, however, is to write the number of moles of each species prior to reaction above the equation and the number of moles of each species after reaction below the equation. Prior to the reaction in which the added hydroxide is consumed by acetic acid, there are 0.300 mol each of acetic acid and acetate ion, and 0.020 mol of hydroxide ion.

Before rxn: 0.300 mol   0.020 mol   0.300 mol

$$HC_2H_3O_2(aq) + OH^-(aq) \longrightarrow H_2O(l) + C_2H_3O_2^-(aq)$$

Because the amount of OH^- added is smaller than the amount of $HC_2H_3O_2$, all the added OH^- will be consumed. An equal amount of $HC_2H_3O_2$ will be consumed, and the same amount of $C_2H_3O_2^-$ will be produced. We write these new, post-reaction amounts below the equation.

Before rxn: 0.300 mol   0.020 mol   0.300 mol

$$HC_2H_3O_2(aq) + OH^-(aq) \longrightarrow H_2O(l) + C_2H_3O_2^-(aq)$$

After rxn: 0.280 mol   0 mol   0.320 mol

Equilibrium Calculation: We now turn our attention to the equilibrium that will determine the pH of the buffer, namely the ionization of acetic acid.

$$HC_2H_3O_2(aq) \rightleftharpoons H^+(aq) + C_2H_3O_2^-(aq)$$

Using the quantities of $HC_2H_3O_2$ and $C_2H_3O_2^-$ remaining in the buffer, we can determine the pH using the Henderson–Hasselbalch equation.

$$pH = 4.74 + \log \frac{0.320 \text{ mol}/1.00 \text{ L}}{0.280 \text{ mol}/1.00 \text{ L}} = 4.80$$

Comment: Notice that we could have used mole amounts in place of concentrations in the Henderson–Hasselbalch equation and gotten the same result. The volumes of the acid and base are equal and cancel.

If 0.020 mol of H^+ was added to the buffer, we would proceed in a similar way to calculate the resulting pH of the buffer. In this case the pH decreases by 0.06 units, giving pH = 4.68, as shown in the figure in the margin.

(b) To determine the pH of a solution made by adding 0.020 mol of NaOH to 1.00 L of pure water, we can first determine pOH using Equation 16.18 and subtracting from 14.

$$pH = 14 - (-\log 0.020) = 12.30$$

Note that although the small amount of NaOH is enough to change the pH of water significantly, the pH of the buffer changes very little.

■ PRACTICE EXERCISE

Determine **(a)** the pH of the original buffer described in Sample Exercise 17.5 after the addition of 0.020 mol HCl, and **(b)** the pH of the solution that would result from the addition of 0.020 mol HCl to 1.00 L of pure water.
Answers: **(a)** 4.68, **(b)** 1.70

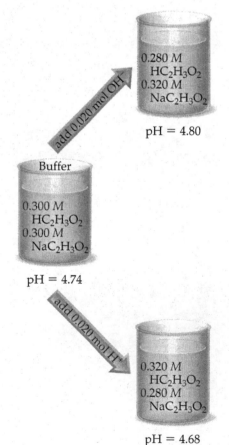

0.280 M
$HC_2H_3O_2$
0.320 M
$NaC_2H_3O_2$

pH = 4.80

add 0.020 mol OH^-

Buffer

0.300 M
$HC_2H_3O_2$
0.300 M
$NaC_2H_3O_2$

pH = 4.74

add 0.020 mol H^+

0.320 M
$HC_2H_3O_2$
0.280 M
$NaC_2H_3O_2$

pH = 4.68

CHEMISTRY AND LIFE | Blood as a Buffered Solution

Many of the chemical reactions that occur in living systems are extremely sensitive to pH. Many of the enzymes that catalyze important biochemical reactions, for example, are effective only within a narrow pH range. For this reason the human body maintains a remarkably intricate system of buffers, both within tissue cells and in the fluids that transport cells. Blood, the fluid that transports oxygen to all parts of the body (Figure 17.4 ▼), is one of the most prominent examples of the importance of buffers in living beings.

Human blood is slightly basic with a normal pH of 7.35 to 7.45. Any deviation from this normal pH range can have extremely disruptive effects on the stability of cell membranes, the structures of proteins, and the activities of enzymes. Death may result if the blood pH falls below 6.8 or rises above 7.8. When the pH falls below 7.35, the condition is called *acidosis*; when it rises above 7.45, the condition is called *alkalosis*. Acidosis is the more common tendency because ordinary metabolism generates several acids within the body.

The major buffer system that is used to control the pH of blood is the *carbonic acid–bicarbonate buffer system*. Carbonic acid (H_2CO_3) and bicarbonate ion (HCO_3^-) are a conjugate acid-base pair. In addition, carbonic acid can decompose into carbon dioxide gas and water. The important equilibria in this buffer system are

$$H^+(aq) + HCO_3^-(aq) \rightleftharpoons H_2CO_3(aq) \rightleftharpoons H_2O(l) + CO_2(g)$$
$$[17.10]$$

Several aspects of these equilibria are notable. First, although carbonic acid is a diprotic acid, the carbonate ion (CO_3^{2-}) is unimportant in this system. Second, one of the components of this equilibrium, CO_2, is a gas, which provides a mechanism for the body to adjust the equilibria. Removal of CO_2 via exhalation shifts the equilibria to the right, consuming H^+ ions. Third, the buffer system in blood operates at a pH of 7.4, which is fairly far removed from the pK_{a1} value of H_2CO_3 (6.1 at physiological temperatures). In order for the buffer to have a pH of 7.4, the ratio [base]/[acid] must have a value of about 20. In normal blood plasma the concentrations of HCO_3^- and H_2CO_3 are about 0.024 M and 0.0012 M, respectively. As a consequence, the buffer has a high capacity to neutralize additional acid, but only a low capacity to neutralize additional base.

The principal organs that regulate the pH of the carbonic acid–bicarbonate buffer system are the lungs and kidneys. Some of the receptors in the brain are sensitive to the concentrations of H^+ and CO_2 in bodily fluids. When the concentration of CO_2 rises, the equilibria in Equation 17.10 shift to the left, which leads to the formation of more H^+. The receptors trigger a reflex to breathe faster and deeper, increasing the rate of elimination of CO_2 from the lungs and shifting the equilibria back to the right. The kidneys absorb or release H^+ and HCO_3^-; much of the excess acid leaves the body in urine, which normally has a pH of 5.0 to 7.0.

The regulation of the pH of blood plasma relates directly to the effective transport of O_2 to bodily tissues. Oxygen is carried by the protein hemoglobin, which is found in red blood cells. Hemoglobin (Hb) reversibly binds both H^+ and O_2. These two substances compete for the Hb, which can be represented approximately by the following equilibrium:

$$HbH^+ + O_2 \rightleftharpoons HbO_2 + H^+ \qquad [17.11]$$

Oxygen enters the blood through the lungs, where it passes into the red blood cells and binds to Hb. When the blood reaches tissue in which the concentration of O_2 is low, the equilibrium in Equation 17.11 shifts to the left and O_2 is released. An increase in H^+ ion concentration (decrease in blood pH) also shifts this equilibrium to the left, as does increasing temperature.

During periods of strenuous exertion, three factors work together to ensure the delivery of O_2 to active tissues: (1) As O_2 is consumed, the equilibrium in Equation 17.11 shifts to the left according to Le Châtelier's principle. (2) Exertion raises the temperature of the body, also shifting the equilibrium to the left. (3) Large amounts of CO_2 are produced by metabolism, which shifts the equilibrium in Equation 17.10 to the left, thus decreasing the pH. Other acids, such as lactic acid, are also produced during strenuous exertion as tissues become starved for oxygen. The decrease in pH shifts the hemoglobin equilibrium to the left, delivering more O_2. In addition, the decrease in pH stimulates an increase in the rate of breathing, which furnishes more O_2 and eliminates CO_2. Without this elaborate arrangement, the O_2 in tissues would be rapidly depleted, making further activity impossible.

Related Exercises: 17.17 and 17.86

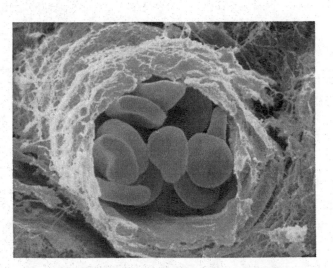

▲ **Figure 17.4   Red blood cells.** A scanning electromicrograph of a group of red blood cells traveling through a small branch of an artery. Blood is a buffered solution whose pH is maintained between 7.35 and 7.45.

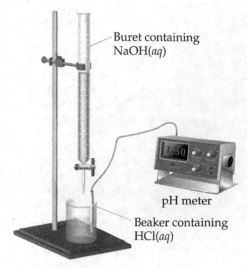

Buret containing
NaOH(*aq*)

pH meter

Beaker containing
HCl(*aq*)

▲ **Figure 17.5 Measuring pH during a titration.** A typical setup for using a pH meter to measure data for a titration curve. In this case a standard solution of NaOH (the titrant) is added by buret to a solution of HCl. The HCl solution is stirred during the titration to ensure uniform composition.

ANIMATION
Acid-Base Titration

ACTIVITY
Acid-Base Titration

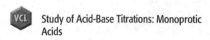

Study of Acid-Base Titrations: Monoprotic Acids

17.3 | Acid-Base Titrations

In Section 4.6 we briefly described *titrations*. In an acid-base titration, a solution containing a known concentration of base is slowly added to an acid (or the acid is added to the base). Acid-base indicators can be used to signal the *equivalence point* of a titration (the point at which stoichiometrically equivalent quantities of acid and base have been brought together). Alternatively, a pH meter can be used to monitor the progress of the reaction producing a **pH titration curve**, a graph of the pH as a function of the volume of the added titrant. The shape of the titration curve makes it possible to determine the equivalence point in the titration. The titration curve can also be used to select suitable indicators and to determine the K_a of the weak acid or the K_b of the weak base being titrated.

A typical apparatus for measuring pH during a titration is illustrated in Figure 17.5 ◄. The titrant is added to the solution from a buret, and the pH is continually monitored using a pH meter. To understand why titration curves have certain characteristic shapes, we will examine the curves for three kinds of titrations: (1) strong acid–strong base, (2) weak acid–strong base, and (3) polyprotic acid–strong base. We will also briefly consider how these curves relate to those involving weak bases.

GIVE IT SOME THOUGHT

For the setup shown in Figure 17.5, will pH increase or decrease as titrant is added?

Strong Acid–Strong Base Titrations

The titration curve produced when a strong base is added to a strong acid has the general shape shown in Figure 17.6 ▶. This curve depicts the pH change that occurs as 0.100 *M* NaOH is added to 50.0 mL of 0.100 *M* HCl. The pH can be calculated at various stages of the titration. To help understand these calculations, we can divide the curve into four regions:

1. *The initial pH:* The pH of the solution before the addition of any base is determined by the initial concentration of the strong acid. For a solution of 0.100 *M* HCl, [H⁺] = 0.100 *M*, and hence pH = −log(0.100) = 1.000. Thus, the initial pH is low.

2. *Between the initial pH and the equivalence point:* As NaOH is added, the pH increases slowly at first and then rapidly in the vicinity of the equivalence point. The pH of the solution before the equivalence point is determined by the concentration of acid that has not yet been neutralized. This calculation is illustrated in Sample Exercise 17.6(a).

3. *The equivalence point:* At the equivalence point an equal number of moles of the NaOH and HCl have reacted, leaving only a solution of their salt, NaCl. The pH of the solution is 7.00 because the cation of a strong base (in this case Na⁺) and the anion of a strong acid (in this case Cl⁻) do not hydrolyze and therefore have no appreciable effect on pH. ∞ (Section 16.9)

4. *After the equivalence point:* The pH of the solution after the equivalence point is determined by the concentration of the excess NaOH in the solution. This calculation is illustrated in Sample Exercise 17.6(b).

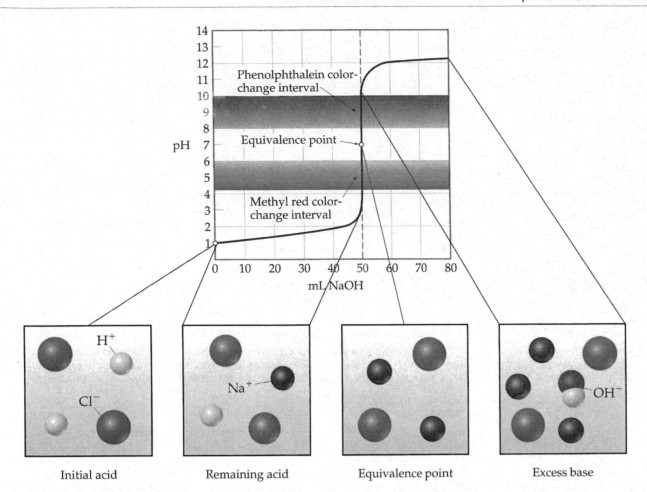

▲ **Figure 17.6 Adding a strong base to a strong acid.** The pH curve for titration of 50.0 mL of a 0.100 *M* solution of a strong acid with a 0.100 *M* solution of a strong base. In this case the acid is HCl and the base is NaOH. The pH starts out at a low value characteristic of the acid and then increases as base is added, rising rapidly at the equivalence point. Both phenolphthalein and methyl red change color at the equivalence point. (For clarity, water molecules have been omitted from the molecular art.)

■ **SAMPLE EXERCISE 17.6** | Calculating pH for a Strong Acid–Strong Base Titration

Calculate the pH when the following quantities of 0.100 *M* NaOH solution have been added to 50.0 mL of 0.100 *M* HCl solution: **(a)** 49.0 mL, **(b)** 51.0 mL.

Solution

Analyze: We are asked to calculate the pH at two points in the titration of a strong acid with a strong base. The first point is just prior to the equivalence point, so we expect the pH to be determined by the small amount of strong acid that has not yet been neutralized. The second point is just after the equivalence point, so we expect this pH to be determined by the small amount of excess strong base.

Plan: (a) As the NaOH solution is added to the HCl solution, $H^+(aq)$ reacts with $OH^-(aq)$ to form H_2O. Both Na^+ and Cl^- are spectator ions, having negligible effect on the pH. In order to determine the pH of the solution, we must first determine how many moles of H^+ were originally present and how many moles of OH^- were added. We can then calculate how many moles of each ion remain after the neutralization reaction. In order to calculate $[H^+]$, and hence pH, we must also remember that the volume of the solution increases as we add titrant, thus diluting the concentration of all solutes present.

Solve: The number of moles of H^+ in the original HCl solution is given by the product of the volume of the solution (50.0 mL = 0.0500 L) and its molarity (0.100 *M*):

$$(0.0500 \text{ L soln})\left(\frac{0.100 \text{ mol } H^+}{1 \text{ L soln}}\right) = 5.00 \times 10^{-3} \text{ mol } H^+$$

Likewise, the number of moles of OH^- in 49.0 mL of 0.100 M NaOH is

$$(0.0490 \text{ L soln})\left(\frac{0.100 \text{ mol } OH^-}{1 \text{ L soln}}\right) = 4.90 \times 10^{-3} \text{ mol } OH^-$$

Because we have not yet reached the equivalence point, there are more moles of H^+ present than OH^-. Each mole of OH^- will react with one mole of H^+. Using the convention introduced in Sample Exercise 17.5,

Before rxn:	5.00×10^{-3} mol		4.90×10^{-3} mol	
	$H^+(aq)$	+	$OH^-(aq)$	$\longrightarrow H_2O(l)$
After rxn:	0.10×10^{-3} mol		0.00 mol	

During the course of the titration, the volume of the reaction mixture increases as the NaOH solution is added to the HCl solution. Thus, at this point in the titration, the solution has a volume of 50.0 mL + 49.0 mL = 99.0 mL. (We assume that the total volume is the sum of the volumes of the acid and base solutions.) Thus, the concentration of $H^+(aq)$ is

$$[H^+] = \frac{\text{moles } H^+(aq)}{\text{liters soln}} = \frac{0.10 \times 10^{-3} \text{ mol}}{0.09900 \text{ L}} = 1.0 \times 10^{-3} \text{ M}$$

The corresponding pH equals

$$-\log(1.0 \times 10^{-3}) = 3.00$$

Plan: (b) We proceed in the same way as we did in part (a), except we are now past the equivalence point and have more OH^- in the solution than H^+. As before, the initial number of moles of each reactant is determined from their volumes and concentrations. The reactant present in smaller stoichiometric amount (the limiting reactant) is consumed completely, leaving an excess this time of hydroxide ion.

Solve:

Before rxn:	5.00×10^{-3} mol		5.10×10^{-3} mol	
	$H^+(aq)$	+	$OH^-(aq)$	$\longrightarrow H_2O(l)$
After rxn:	0.0 mol		0.10×10^{-3} mol	

In this case the total volume of the solution is

50.0 mL + 51.0 mL = 101.0 mL = 0.1010 L

Hence, the concentration of $OH^-(aq)$ in the solution is

$$[OH^-] = \frac{\text{moles } OH^-(aq)}{\text{liters soln}} = \frac{0.10 \times 10^{-3} \text{ mol}}{0.1010 \text{ L}} = 1.0 \times 10^{-3} \text{ M}$$

Thus, the pOH of the solution equals

$$pOH = -\log(1.0 \times 10^{-3}) = 3.00$$

and the pH equals

$$pH = 14.00 - pOH = 14.00 - 3.00 = 11.00$$

PRACTICE EXERCISE

Calculate the pH when the following quantities of 0.100 M HNO_3 have been added to 25.0 mL of 0.100 M KOH solution: **(a)** 24.9 mL, **(b)** 25.1 mL.
Answers: **(a)** 10.30, **(b)** 3.70

Optimally, an indicator would change color at the equivalence point in a titration. In practice, however, that is unnecessary. The pH changes very rapidly near the equivalence point, and in this region merely a drop of titrant can change the pH by several units. Thus, an indicator beginning and ending its color change anywhere on this rapid-rise portion of the titration curve will give a sufficiently accurate measure of the volume of titrant needed to reach the equivalence point. The point in a titration where the indicator changes color is called the *end point* to distinguish it from the actual equivalence point that it closely approximates.

In Figure 17.6 we see that the pH changes very rapidly from about 4 to about 10 near the equivalence point. Consequently, an indicator for this strong

(a)   (b)

acid–strong base titration can change color anywhere in this range. Most strong acid–strong base titrations are carried out using phenolphthalein as an indicator (Figure 4.19) because it dramatically changes color in this range. From Figure 16.7, we see that phenolphthalein changes color from pH 8.3 to 10.0. Several other indicators would also be satisfactory, including methyl red, which changes color from pH 4.2 to 6.0 (Figure 17.7 ▲).

Titration of a solution of a strong base with a solution of a strong acid would yield an analogous curve of pH versus added acid. In this case, however, the pH would be high at the outset of the titration and low at its completion, as shown in Figure 17.8 ▶.

Weak Acid–Strong Base Titrations

The curve for the titration of a weak acid by a strong base is very similar in shape to that for the titration of a strong acid by a strong base. Consider, for example, the titration curve for the titration of 50.0 mL of 0.100 M acetic acid ($HC_2H_3O_2$) with 0.100 M NaOH shown in Figure 17.9 ▶. We can calculate the pH at points along this curve, using principles we have discussed earlier. As in the case of the titration of a strong acid by a strong base, we can divide the curve into four regions:

1. *The initial pH:* This pH is just the pH of the 0.100 M $HC_2H_3O_2$. We performed calculations of this kind in Section 16.6. The calculated pH of 0.100 M $HC_2H_3O_2$ is 2.89.

2. *Between the initial pH and the equivalence point:* To determine pH in this range, we must consider the neutralization of the acid.

$$HC_2H_3O_2(aq) + OH^-(aq) \longrightarrow C_2H_3O_2^-(aq) + H_2O(l) \qquad [17.12]$$

Prior to reaching the equivalence point, part of the $HC_2H_3O_2$ is neutralized to form $C_2H_3O_2^-$. Thus, the solution contains a mixture of $HC_2H_3O_2$ and $C_2H_3O_2^-$.

The approach we take in calculating the pH in this region of the titration curve involves two main steps. First, we consider the neutralization reaction between $HC_2H_3O_2$ and OH^- to determine the concentrations of $HC_2H_3O_2$ and $C_2H_3O_2^-$ in the solution. Next, we calculate the pH of this buffer pair

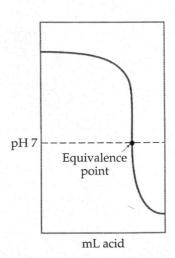

pH 7 - - - - - - - - - - - - ●- - -
Equivalence
point

mL acid

▲ **Figure 17.8 Adding a strong acid to a strong base.** The shape of a pH curve for titration of a strong base with a strong acid. The pH starts out at a high value characteristic of the base and then decreases as acid is added, dropping rapidly at the equivalence point.

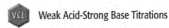 Weak Acid-Strong Base Titrations

Science Fundamentals Second Edition

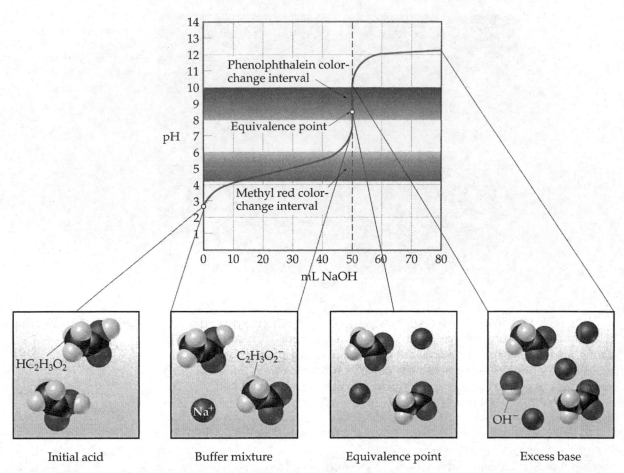

Initial acid   Buffer mixture   Equivalence point   Excess base

▲ **Figure 17.9   Adding a strong base to a weak acid.** The curve shows the variation in pH as 0.100 M NaOH solution is added to 50.0 mL of 0.100 M acetic acid solution. Phenolphthalein changes color at the equivalence point, but methyl red does not. (For clarity, water molecules have been omitted from the molecular art.)

ACTIVITY
Titration Calculation

▼ **Figure 17.10   Procedure for calculating the pH when a weak acid is partially neutralized by a strong base.** First consider the effect of the neutralization reaction (stoichiometry calculation). Then determine the pH of the resultant buffer mixture (equilibrium calculation). An analogous procedure can be used for the addition of strong acid to a weak base.

using procedures developed in Sections 17.1 and 17.2. The general procedure is diagrammed in Figure 17.10 ▼ and illustrated in Sample Exercise 17.7.

3. *The equivalence point:* The equivalence point is reached after adding 50.0 mL of 0.100 M NaOH to the 50.0 mL of 0.100 M $HC_2H_3O_2$. At this point the 5.00×10^{-3} mol of NaOH completely reacts with the 5.00×10^{-3} mol of $HC_2H_3O_2$ to form 5.00×10^{-3} mol of their salt, $NaC_2H_3O_2$. The Na^+ ion of this salt has no significant effect on the pH. The $C_2H_3O_2^-$ ion, however, is a weak base, and the pH at the equivalence point is therefore greater than 7. Indeed, the pH at the equivalence point is always above 7 in a weak acid–strong base titration because the anion of the salt formed is a weak base.

4. *After the equivalence point:* In this region of the titration curve, $[OH^-]$ from the reaction of $C_2H_3O_2^-$ with water is negligible compared to $[OH^-]$ from the excess NaOH. Thus, the pH is determined by the concentration of OH^- from the excess NaOH. The method for calculating pH in this region is therefore like that for the strong acid–strong base titration illustrated in

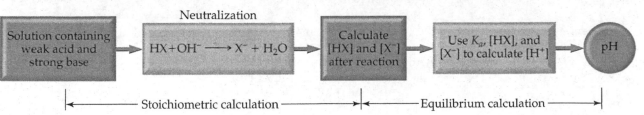

Neutralization

| Solution containing weak acid and strong base | $HX + OH^- \longrightarrow X^- + H_2O$ | Calculate $[HX]$ and $[X^-]$ after reaction | Use K_a, $[HX]$, and $[X^-]$ to calculate $[H^+]$ | pH |

|←———— Stoichiometric calculation ————→|←———— Equilibrium calculation ————→|

Sample Exercise 17.6(b). Thus, the addition of 51.0 mL of 0.100 M NaOH to 50.0 mL of either 0.100 M HCl or 0.100 M HC$_2$H$_3$O$_2$ yields the same pH, 11.00. Notice in Figures 17.6 and 17.9 that the titration curves for the titrations of both the strong acid and the weak acid are the same after the equivalence point.

■ SAMPLE EXERCISE 17.7 | Calculating pH for a Weak Acid–Strong Base Titration

Calculate the pH of the solution formed when 45.0 mL of 0.100 M NaOH is added to 50.0 mL of 0.100 M HC$_2$H$_3$O$_2$ ($K_a = 1.8 \times 10^{-5}$).

Solution

Analyze: We are asked to calculate the pH prior to the equivalence point of the titration of a weak acid with a strong base.

Plan: We first must determine the number of moles of weak acid and strong base that have been combined. This will tell us how much of the weak acid's conjugate base has been produced, and we can solve for pH using the equilibrium-constant expression.

Solve: *Stoichiometry Calculation:* The product of the volume and concentration of each solution gives the number of moles of each reactant present before the neutralization:

$$(0.0500 \text{ L soln})\left(\frac{0.100 \text{ mol HC}_2\text{H}_3\text{O}_2}{1 \text{ L soln}}\right) = 5.00 \times 10^{-3} \text{ mol HC}_2\text{H}_3\text{O}_2$$

$$(0.0450 \text{ L soln})\left(\frac{0.100 \text{ mol NaOH}}{1 \text{ L soln}}\right) = 4.50 \times 10^{-3} \text{ mol NaOH}$$

The 4.50×10^{-3} mol of NaOH consumes 4.50×10^{-3} mol of HC$_2$H$_3$O$_2$:

Before rxn:	5.00×10^{-3} mol	4.50×10^{-3} mol	0.0 mol
	HC$_2$H$_3$O$_2$(aq) +	OH$^-$(aq) $\longrightarrow$	C$_2$H$_3$O$_2$$^-$($aq$) + H$_2$O($l$)
After rxn:	0.50×10^{-3} mol	0.0 mol	4.50×10^{-3} mol

The total volume of the solution is

$$45.0 \text{ mL} + 50.0 \text{ mL} = 95.0 \text{ mL} = 0.0950 \text{ L}$$

The resulting molarities of HC$_2$H$_3$O$_2$ and C$_2$H$_3$O$_2$$^-$ after the reaction are therefore

$$[\text{HC}_2\text{H}_3\text{O}_2] = \frac{0.50 \times 10^{-3} \text{ mol}}{0.0950 \text{ L}} = 0.0053 \ M$$

$$[\text{C}_2\text{H}_3\text{O}_2^-] = \frac{4.50 \times 10^{-3} \text{ mol}}{0.0950 \text{ L}} = 0.0474 \ M$$

Equilibrium Calculation: The equilibrium between HC$_2$H$_3$O$_2$ and C$_2$H$_3$O$_2$$^-$ must obey the equilibrium-constant expression for HC$_2$H$_3$O$_2$:

$$K_a = \frac{[\text{H}^+][\text{C}_2\text{H}_3\text{O}_2^-]}{[\text{HC}_2\text{H}_3\text{O}_2]} = 1.8 \times 10^{-5}$$

Solving for [H$^+$] gives

$$[\text{H}^+] = K_a \times \frac{[\text{HC}_2\text{H}_3\text{O}_2]}{[\text{C}_2\text{H}_3\text{O}_2^-]} = (1.8 \times 10^{-5}) \times \left(\frac{0.0053}{0.0474}\right) = 2.0 \times 10^{-6} \ M$$

$$\text{pH} = -\log(2.0 \times 10^{-6}) = 5.70$$

Comment: We could have solved for pH equally well using the Henderson–Hasselbalch equation.

■ PRACTICE EXERCISE

(a) Calculate the pH in the solution formed by adding 10.0 mL of 0.050 M NaOH to 40.0 mL of 0.0250 M benzoic acid (HC$_7$H$_5$O$_2$, $K_a = 6.3 \times 10^{-5}$). **(b)** Calculate the pH in the solution formed by adding 10.0 mL of 0.100 M HCl to 20.0 mL of 0.100 M NH$_3$.

Answers: **(a)** 4.20, **(b)** 9.26

■ SAMPLE EXERCISE 17.8 | Calculating the pH at the Equivalence Point

Calculate the pH at the equivalence point in the titration of 50.0 mL of 0.100 M HC$_2$H$_3$O$_2$ with 0.100 M NaOH.

Solution

Analyze: We are asked to determine the pH at the equivalence point of the titration of a weak acid with a strong base. Because the neutralization of a weak acid produces its anion, which is a weak base, we expect the pH at the equivalence point to be greater than 7.

Plan: We should first determine how many moles of acetic acid there are initially. This will tell us how many moles of acetate ion there will be at the equivalence point. We then must determine the volume of the solution at the equivalence point and the resultant concentration of acetate ion. Because the acetate ion is a weak base, we can calculate the pH using K_b and the concentration of acetate as we did for other weak bases in Section 16.7.

Solve: The number of moles of acetic acid in the initial solution is obtained from the volume and molarity of the solution:

$$\text{Moles} = M \times L = (0.100 \text{ mol/L})(0.0500 \text{ L}) = 5.00 \times 10^{-3} \text{ mol } HC_2H_3O_2$$

Hence 5.00×10^{-3} mol of $C_2H_3O_2^-$ is formed. It will take 50.0 mL of NaOH to reach the equivalence point (Figure 17.9). The volume of this salt solution at the equivalence point is the sum of the volumes of the acid and base, 50.0 mL + 50.0 mL = 100.0 mL = 0.1000 L. Thus, the concentration of $C_2H_3O_2^-$ is

$$[C_2H_3O_2^-] = \frac{5.00 \times 10^{-3} \text{ mol}}{0.1000 \text{ L}} = 0.0500 \, M$$

The $C_2H_3O_2^-$ ion is a weak base.

$$C_2H_3O_2^-(aq) + H_2O(l) \rightleftharpoons HC_2H_3O_2(aq) + OH^-(aq)$$

The K_b for $C_2H_3O_2^-$ can be calculated from the K_a value of its conjugate acid, $K_b = K_w/K_a = (1.0 \times 10^{-14})/(1.8 \times 10^{-5}) = 5.6 \times 10^{-10}$. Using the K_b expression, we have

$$K_b = \frac{[HC_2H_3O_2^-][OH^-]}{[C_2H_3O_2^-]} = \frac{(x)(x)}{0.0500 - x} = 5.6 \times 10^{-10}$$

Making the approximation that $0.0500 - x \simeq 0.0500$, and then solving for x, we have $x = [OH^-] = 5.3 \times 10^{-6} \, M$, which gives pOH = 5.28 and pH = 8.72.

Check: The pH is above 7, as expected for the salt of a weak acid and strong base.

■ PRACTICE EXERCISE

Calculate the pH at the equivalence point when **(a)** 40.0 mL of 0.025 M benzoic acid ($HC_7H_5O_2$, $K_a = 6.3 \times 10^{-5}$) is titrated with 0.050 M NaOH; **(b)** 40.0 mL of 0.100 M NH_3 is titrated with 0.100 M HCl.
Answers: **(a)** 8.21, **(b)** 5.28

The pH titration curves for weak acid–strong base titrations differ from those for strong acid–strong base titrations in three noteworthy ways:

1. The solution of the weak acid has a higher initial pH than a solution of a strong acid of the same concentration.

2. The pH change at the rapid-rise portion of the curve near the equivalence point is smaller for the weak acid than it is for the strong acid.

3. The pH at the equivalence point is above 7.00 for the weak acid–strong base titration.

To illustrate these differences further, consider the family of titration curves shown in Figure 17.11 ◀. As expected, the initial pH of the weak acid solutions is always higher than that of the strong acid solution of the same concentration. Notice also that the pH change near the equivalence point becomes less marked as the acid becomes weaker (that is, as K_a becomes smaller). Finally, the pH at the equivalence point steadily increases as K_a decreases. It is virtually impossible to determine the equivalence point when pK_a is 10 or higher because the pH change is too small and gradual.

Because the pH change near the equivalence point becomes smaller as K_a decreases, the choice of indicator for a weak acid–strong base titration is more critical than it is for a strong acid–strong base titration. When 0.100 M $HC_2H_3O_2$ ($K_a = 1.8 \times 10^{-5}$) is titrated with 0.100 M NaOH, for example, as shown in Figure 17.9, the pH increases rapidly only over the pH range of about 7 to 10. Phenolphthalein is therefore an ideal indicator because it changes color from pH 8.3 to 10.0, close to the pH at the equivalence point. Methyl red is a poor choice, however, because its color change occurs from 4.2 to 6.0, which begins well before the equivalence point is reached.

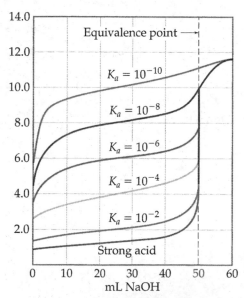

▲ Figure 17.11   Effect of K_a on titration curves. This set of curves shows the influence of acid strength (K_a) on the shape of the curve for titration with NaOH. Each curve represents titration of 50.0 mL of 0.10 M acid with 0.10 M NaOH. The weaker the acid, the higher the initial pH and the smaller the pH change at the equivalence point.

Titration of a weak base (such as 0.100 M NH$_3$) with a strong acid solution (such as 0.100 M HCl) leads to the titration curve shown in Figure 17.12 ▶. In this particular example the equivalence point occurs at pH 5.28. Thus, methyl red would be an ideal indicator, but phenolphthalein would be a poor choice.

 GIVE IT SOME THOUGHT

Why is the choice of indicator more crucial for a weak acid–strong base titration than for a strong acid–strong base titration?

Titrations of Polyprotic Acids

When weak acids contain more than one ionizable H atom, as in phosphorous acid (H$_3$PO$_3$), reaction with OH$^-$ occurs in a series of steps. Neutralization of H$_3$PO$_3$ proceeds in two stages. ∞ (Chapter 16 Sample Integrative Exercise)

$$H_3PO_3(aq) + OH^-(aq) \longrightarrow H_2PO_3^-(aq) + H_2O(l) \qquad [17.13]$$

$$H_2PO_3^-(aq) + OH^-(aq) \longrightarrow HPO_3^{2-}(aq) + H_2O(l) \qquad [17.14]$$

When the neutralization steps of a polyprotic acid or polybasic base are sufficiently separated, the substance exhibits a titration curve with multiple equivalence points. Figure 17.13 ▼ shows the two distinct equivalence points in the titration curve for the H$_3$PO$_3$–H$_2$PO$_3^-$–HPO$_3^{2-}$ system.

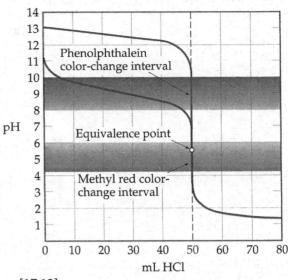

▲ **Figure 17.12 Adding a strong acid to a base.** The blue curve shows pH versus volume of added HCl in the titration of 50.0 mL of 0.10 M ammonia (weak base) with 0.10 M HCl. The red curve shows pH versus added acid for the titration of 0.10 M NaOH (strong base). Both phenolphthalein and methyl red change color at the equivalence point in the titration of the strong base. Phenolphthalein changes color before the equivalence point in the titration of the weak base.

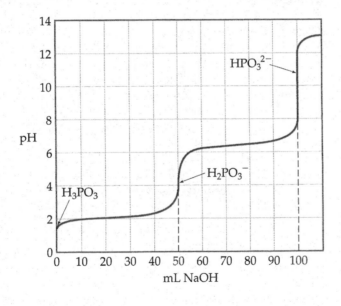

 Study of Acid-Base Titrations: Polyprotic Acids

◀ **Figure 17.13 Diprotic acid.** Titration curve for the reaction of 50.0 mL of 0.10 M H$_3$PO$_3$ with 0.10 M NaOH.

17.4 | Solubility Equilibria

The equilibria that we have considered thus far in this chapter have involved acids and bases. Furthermore, they have been homogeneous; that is, all the species have been in the same phase. Through the rest of this chapter we will consider the equilibria involved in the dissolution or precipitation of ionic compounds. These reactions are heterogeneous.

The dissolving and precipitating of compounds are phenomena that occur both within us and around us. Tooth enamel dissolves in acidic solutions, for example, causing tooth decay. The precipitation of certain salts in our kidneys produces kidney stones. The waters of the earth contain salts dissolved as water passes over and through the ground. Precipitation of $CaCO_3$ from groundwater is responsible for the formation of stalactites and stalagmites within limestone caves (Figure 4.1).

In our earlier discussion of precipitation reactions, we considered some general rules for predicting the solubility of common salts in water. ∞ (Section 4.2) These rules give us a qualitative sense of whether a compound will have a low or high solubility in water. By considering solubility equilibria, in contrast, we can make quantitative predictions about the amount of a given compound that will dissolve. We can also use these equilibria to analyze the factors that affect solubility.

The Solubility-Product Constant, K_{sp}

Recall that a *saturated solution* is one in which the solution is in contact with undissolved solute. ∞ (Section 13.2) Consider, for example, a saturated aqueous solution of $BaSO_4$ that is in contact with solid $BaSO_4$. Because the solid is an ionic compound, it is a strong electrolyte and yields $Ba^{2+}(aq)$ and $SO_4^{2-}(aq)$ ions upon dissolving. The following equilibrium is readily established between the undissolved solid and hydrated ions in solution:

$$BaSO_4(s) \rightleftharpoons Ba^{2+}(aq) + SO_4^{2-}(aq) \qquad [17.15]$$

ACTIVITY
Solubility Product Constant

As with any other equilibrium, the extent to which this dissolution reaction occurs is expressed by the magnitude of its equilibrium constant. Because this equilibrium equation describes the dissolution of a solid, the equilibrium constant indicates how soluble the solid is in water and is referred to as the **solubility-product constant** (or simply the **solubility product**). It is denoted K_{sp}, where *sp* stands for solubility product. The equilibrium-constant expression for this process is written according to the same rules as those that apply to any equilibrium-constant expression. That is, the concentration terms of the products are multiplied together, and each is raised to the power of its stoichiometric coefficient in the balanced chemical equation. These are divided by the concentration terms of the reactants multiplied together, and each raised to the power of its stoichiometric coefficient. Solids, liquids, and solvents do not appear in the equilibrium-constant expressions for heterogeneous equilibria, however. ∞ (Section 15.3)

The solubility product equals the product of the concentration of the ions involved in the equilibrium, each raised to the power of its coefficient in the equilibrium equation.

Thus, the solubility-product expression for the equilibrium expressed in Equation 17.15 is

$$K_{sp} = [Ba^{2+}][SO_4^{2-}] \qquad [17.16]$$

Even though $[BaSO_4]$ is excluded from the equilibrium-constant expression, some undissolved $BaSO_4(s)$ must be present in order for the system to be at equilibrium.

In general, the solubility-product constant (K_{sp}) is the equilibrium constant for the equilibrium that exists between a solid ionic solute and its ions in a saturated aqueous solution. The values of K_{sp} at 25°C for many ionic solids are tabulated in Appendix D. The value of K_{sp} for $BaSO_4$ is 1.1×10^{-10}, a very small number, indicating that only a very small amount of the solid will dissolve in water.

■ SAMPLE EXERCISE 17.9 | Writing Solubility-Product (K_{sp}) Expressions

Write the expression for the solubility-product constant for CaF_2, and look up the corresponding K_{sp} value in Appendix D.

Solution
Analyze and Plan: We are asked to write an equilibrium-constant expression for the process by which CaF_2 dissolves in water. We apply the same rules for writing any

equilibrium-constant expression, making sure to exclude the solid reactant from the expression. We assume that the compound dissociates completely into its component ions.

$$CaF_2(s) \rightleftharpoons Ca^{2+}(aq) + 2\,F^-(aq)$$

Solve: Following the italicized rule stated previously, the expression for K_{sp} is

$$K_{sp} = [Ca^{2+}][F^-]^2$$

In Appendix D we see that this K_{sp} has a value of 3.9×10^{-11}.

■ PRACTICE EXERCISE

Give the solubility-product-constant expressions and the values of the solubility-product constants (from Appendix D) for the following compounds: **(a)** barium carbonate, **(b)** silver sulfate.
Answers: **(a)** $K_{sp} = [Ba^{2+}][CO_3^{2-}] = 5.0 \times 10^{-9}$; **(b)** $K_{sp} = [Ag^+]^2[SO_4^{2-}] = 1.5 \times 10^{-5}$

Solubility and K_{sp}

It is important to distinguish carefully between solubility and the solubility-product constant. The solubility of a substance is the quantity that dissolves to form a saturated solution. ∞ (Section 13.2) Solubility is often expressed as grams of solute per liter of solution (g/L). The molar solubility is the number of moles of the solute that dissolve in forming a liter of saturated solution of the solute (mol/L). The solubility-product constant (K_{sp}) is the equilibrium constant for the equilibrium between an ionic solid and its saturated solution and is a unitless number. Thus, the magnitude of K_{sp} is a measure of how much of the solid dissolves to form a saturated solution.

  GIVE IT SOME THOUGHT

Without doing a calculation, predict which of the following compounds will have the greatest molar solubility in water: AgCl ($K_{sp} = 1.8 \times 10^{-10}$), AgBr ($K_{sp} = 5.0 \times 10^{-13}$), or AgI ($K_{sp} = 8.3 \times 10^{-17}$).

The solubility of a substance can change considerably as the concentrations of other solutes change. The solubility of $Mg(OH)_2$, for example, depends highly on pH. The solubility is also affected by the concentrations of other ions in solution, especially Mg^{2+}. In contrast, the solubility-product constant, K_{sp}, has only one value for a given solute at any specific temperature.*

In principle, it is possible to use the K_{sp} value of a salt to calculate solubility under a variety of conditions. In practice, great care must be taken in doing so for the reasons indicated in "A Closer Look" on the limitations of solubility products in Section 17.5. Agreement between measured solubility and that calculated from K_{sp} is usually best for salts whose ions have low charges (1+ and 1−) and do not hydrolyze. Figure 17.14 ▶ summarizes the relationships among various expressions of solubility and K_{sp}.

▲ **Figure 17.14 Relationships between solubility and K_{sp}.** The solubility of any compound in grams per liter can be converted to molar solubility. The molar solubility can be used to determine the concentrations of ions in solution. The concentration of ions can be used to calculate K_{sp}. The steps can be reversed, and solubility calculated from K_{sp}.

---

* This is strictly true only for very dilute solutions. The values of equilibrium constants are somewhat altered when the total concentration of ionic substances in water is increased. However, we will ignore these effects, which are taken into consideration only for work that requires exceptional accuracy.

SAMPLE EXERCISE 17.10 | Calculating K_{sp} from Solubility

Solid silver chromate is added to pure water at 25°C. Some of the solid remains undissolved at the bottom of the flask. The mixture is stirred for several days to ensure that equilibrium is achieved between the undissolved $Ag_2CrO_4(s)$ and the solution. Analysis of the equilibrated solution shows that its silver ion concentration is 1.3×10^{-4} M. Assuming that Ag_2CrO_4 dissociates completely in water and that there are no other important equilibria involving the Ag^+ or CrO_4^{2-} ions in the solution, calculate K_{sp} for this compound.

Solution

Analyze: We are given the equilibrium concentration of Ag^+ in a saturated solution of Ag_2CrO_4. From this, we are asked to determine the value of the solubility-product constant for the dissolution of Ag_2CrO_4.

Plan: The equilibrium equation and the expression for K_{sp} are

$$Ag_2CrO_4(s) \rightleftharpoons 2\,Ag^+(aq) + CrO_4^{2-}(aq) \qquad K_{sp} = [Ag^+]^2[CrO_4^{2-}]$$

To calculate K_{sp}, we need the equilibrium concentrations of Ag^+ and CrO_4^{2-}. We know that at equilibrium $[Ag^+] = 1.3 \times 10^{-4}$ M. All the Ag^+ and CrO_4^{2-} ions in the solution come from the Ag_2CrO_4 that dissolves. Thus, we can use $[Ag^+]$ to calculate $[CrO_4^{2-}]$.

Solve: From the chemical formula of silver chromate, we know that there must be 2 Ag^+ ions in solution for each CrO_4^{2-} ion in solution. Consequently, the concentration of CrO_4^{2-} is half the concentration of Ag^+.

$$[CrO_4^{2-}] = \left(\frac{1.3 \times 10^{-4}\ \text{mol } Ag^+}{L}\right)\left(\frac{1\ \text{mol } CrO_4^{2-}}{2\ \text{mol } Ag^+}\right) = 6.5 \times 10^{-5}\ M$$

We can now calculate the value of K_{sp}.

$$K_{sp} = [Ag^+]^2[CrO_4^{2-}] = (1.3 \times 10^{-4})^2(6.5 \times 10^{-5}) = 1.1 \times 10^{-12}$$

Check: We obtain a small value, as expected for a slightly soluble salt. Furthermore, the calculated value agrees well with the one given in Appendix D, 1.2×10^{-12}.

PRACTICE EXERCISE

A saturated solution of $Mg(OH)_2$ in contact with undissolved solid is prepared at 25°C. The pH of the solution is found to be 10.17. Assuming that $Mg(OH)_2$ dissociates completely in water and that there are no other simultaneous equilibria involving the Mg^{2+} or OH^- ions in the solution, calculate K_{sp} for this compound.
Answer: 1.6×10^{-12}

SAMPLE EXERCISE 17.11 | Calculating Solubility from K_{sp}

The K_{sp} for CaF_2 is 3.9×10^{-11} at 25°C. Assuming that CaF_2 dissociates completely upon dissolving and that there are no other important equilibria affecting its solubility, calculate the solubility of CaF_2 in grams per liter.

Solution

Analyze: We are given K_{sp} for CaF_2 and are asked to determine solubility. Recall that the *solubility* of a substance is the quantity that can dissolve in solvent, whereas the *solubility-product constant*, K_{sp}, is an equilibrium constant.

Plan: We can approach this problem by using our standard techniques for solving equilibrium problems. We write the chemical equation for the dissolution process and set up a table of the initial and equilibrium concentrations. We then use the equilibrium-constant expression. In this case we know K_{sp}, and so we solve for the concentrations of the ions in solution.

Solve: Assume initially that none of the salt has dissolved, and then allow x moles/liter of CaF_2 to dissociate completely when equilibrium is achieved.

	$CaF_2(s)$	$\rightleftharpoons$	Ca^{2+}	+	$2\,F^-(aq)$
Initial	—		0		0
Change	—		$+x\ M$		$+2x\ M$
Equilibrium	—		$x\ M$		$2x\ M$

The stoichiometry of the equilibrium dictates that $2x$ moles/liter of F^- are produced for each x moles/liter of CaF_2 that dissolve. We now use the expression for K_{sp} and substitute the equilibrium concentrations to solve for the value of x:

$$K_{sp} = [Ca^{2+}][F^-]^2 = (x)(2x)^2 = 4x^3 = 3.9 \times 10^{-11}$$

$$x = \sqrt[3]{\frac{3.9 \times 10^{-11}}{4}} = 2.1 \times 10^{-4}\ M$$

(Remember that $\sqrt[3]{y} = y^{1/3}$; to calculate the cube root of a number, you can use the y^x function on your calculator, with $x = \frac{1}{3}$.) Thus, the molar solubility of CaF_2 is 2.1×10^{-4} mol/L. The mass of CaF_2 that dissolves in water to form a liter of solution is

$$\left(\frac{2.1 \times 10^{-4} \text{ mol } CaF_2}{1 \text{ L soln}}\right)\left(\frac{78.1 \text{ g } CaF_2}{1 \text{ mol } CaF_2}\right) = 1.6 \times 10^{-2} \text{ g } CaF_2/\text{L soln}$$

Check: We expect a small number for the solubility of a slightly soluble salt. If we reverse the calculation, we should be able to recalculate K_{sp}: $K_{sp} = (2.1 \times 10^{-4})(4.2 \times 10^{-4})^2 = 3.7 \times 10^{-11}$, close to the starting value for K_{sp}, 3.9×10^{-11}.

Comment: Because F^- is the anion of a weak acid, you might expect that the hydrolysis of the ion would affect the solubility of CaF_2. The basicity of F^- is so small ($K_b = 1.5 \times 10^{-11}$), however, that the hydrolysis occurs to only a slight extent and does not significantly influence the solubility. The reported solubility is 0.017 g/L at 25°C, in good agreement with our calculation.

PRACTICE EXERCISE

The K_{sp} for LaF_3 is 2×10^{-19}. What is the solubility of LaF_3 in water in moles per liter?
Answer: 9.28×10^{-6} mol/L

 A CLOSER LOOK | Limitations of Solubility Products

The concentrations of ions calculated from K_{sp} sometimes deviate appreciably from those found experimentally. In part, these deviations are due to electrostatic interactions between ions in solution, which can lead to ion pairs. (See "A Closer Look" on colligative properties of electrolyte solutions in Section 13.5.) These interactions increase in magnitude both as the concentrations of the ions increase and as their charges increase. The solubility calculated from K_{sp} tends to be low unless it is corrected to account for these interactions between ions. Chemists have developed procedures for correcting for these "ionic-strength" or "ionic-activity" effects, and these procedures are examined in more advanced chemistry courses. As an example of the effect of these interionic interactions, consider $CaCO_3$ (calcite), whose solubility product, $K_{sp} = 4.5 \times 10^{-9}$, gives a calculated solubility of 6.7×10^{-5} mol/L. Making corrections for the interionic interactions in the solution yields a higher solubility, 7.3×10^{-5} mol/L. The reported solubility, however, is twice as high (1.4×10^{-4} mol/L), so there must be one or more additional factors involved.

Another common source of error in calculating ion concentrations from K_{sp} is ignoring other equilibria that occur simultaneously in the solution. It is also possible, for example, that acid-base equilibria take place simultaneously with solubility equilibria. In particular, both basic anions and cations with high charge-to-size ratios undergo hydrolysis reactions that can measurably increase the solubilities of their salts. For example, $CaCO_3$ contains the basic carbonate ion ($K_b = 1.8 \times 10^{-4}$), which hydrolyzes in water: $CO_3^{2-}(aq) + H_2O(l) \rightleftharpoons HCO_3^-(aq) + OH^-(aq)$. If we consider both the effect of the interionic interactions in the solution and the effect of the simultaneous solubility and hydrolysis equilibria, we calculate a solubility of 1.4×10^{-4} mol/L, in agreement with the measured value.

Finally, we generally assume that ionic compounds dissociate completely into their component ions when they dissolve. This assumption is not always valid. When MgF_2 dissolves, for example, it yields not only Mg^{2+} and F^- ions but also MgF^+ ions in solution. Thus, we see that calculating solubility using K_{sp} can be more complicated than it first appears and it requires considerable knowledge of the equilibria occurring in solution.

17.5 | Factors that Affect Solubility

The solubility of a substance is affected not only by temperature but also by the presence of other solutes. The presence of an acid, for example, can have a major influence on the solubility of a substance. In Section 17.4 we considered the dissolving of ionic compounds in pure water. In this section we examine three factors that affect the solubility of ionic compounds: the presence of common ions, the pH of the solution, and the presence of complexing agents. We will also examine the phenomenon of *amphoterism*, which is related to the effects of both pH and complexing agents.

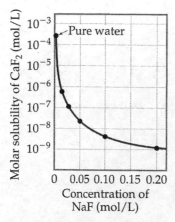

▲ Figure 17.15 Common-ion effect.
The way in which NaF concentration affects the solubility of CaF$_2$ demonstrates the common-ion effect. Notice that the CaF$_2$ solubility is on a logarithmic scale.

Common-Ion Effect

The presence of either Ca^{2+}(aq) or F$^-$(aq) in a solution reduces the solubility of CaF$_2$, shifting the solubility equilibrium of CaF$_2$ to the left.

$$CaF_2(s) \rightleftharpoons Ca^{2+}(aq) + 2\,F^-(aq)$$

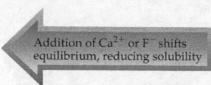

Addition of Ca^{2+} or F$^-$ shifts equilibrium, reducing solubility

This reduction in solubility is another application of the common-ion effect. ∞ (Section 17.1) In general, *the solubility of a slightly soluble salt is decreased by the presence of a second solute that furnishes a common ion.* Figure 17.15 ◄ shows how the solubility of CaF$_2$ decreases as NaF is added to the solution. Sample Exercise 17.12 shows how the K_{sp} can be used to calculate the solubility of a slightly soluble salt in the presence of a common ion.

■■ SAMPLE EXERCISE 17.12 | Calculating the Effect of a Common Ion on Solubility

Calculate the molar solubility of CaF$_2$ at 25°C in a solution that is **(a)** 0.010 M in Ca(NO$_3$)$_2$, **(b)** 0.010 M in NaF.

Solution

Analyze: We are asked to determine the solubility of CaF$_2$ in the presence of two strong electrolytes, each of which contains an ion common to CaF$_2$. In (a) the common ion is Ca^{2+} and NO$_3$$^-$ is a spectator ion. In (b) the common ion is F$^-$ and Na$^+$ is a spectator ion.

Plan: Because the slightly soluble compound is CaF$_2$, we need to use the K_{sp} for this compound, which is available in Appendix D:

$$K_{sp} = [Ca^{2+}][F^-]^2 = 3.9 \times 10^{-11}$$

The value of K_{sp} is unchanged by the presence of additional solutes. Because of the common-ion effect, however, the solubility of the salt will decrease in the presence of common ions. We can again use our standard equilibrium techniques of starting with the equation for CaF$_2$ dissolution, setting up a table of initial and equilibrium concentrations, and using the K_{sp} expression to determine the concentration of the ion that comes only from CaF$_2$.

Solve: (a) In this instance the initial concentration of Ca^{2+} is 0.010 M because of the dissolved Ca(NO$_3$)$_2$:

	CaF$_2$(s)	$\rightleftharpoons$	Ca^{2+}(aq)	+	2 F$^-$(aq)
Initial	—		0.010 M		0
Change	$-x\,M$		$+x\,M$		$+2x\,M$
Equilibrium	—		$(0.010 + x)\,M$		$2x\,M$

Substituting into the solubility-product expression gives

$$K_{sp} = 3.9 \times 10^{-11} = [Ca^{2+}][F^-]^2 = (0.010 + x)(2x)^2$$

This would be a messy problem to solve exactly, but fortunately it is possible to simplify matters greatly. Even without the common-ion effect, the solubility of CaF$_2$ is very small. Assume that the 0.010 M concentration of Ca^{2+} from Ca(NO$_3$)$_2$ is very much greater than the small additional concentration resulting from the solubility of CaF$_2$; that is, x is small compared to 0.010 M, and 0.010 + x ≃ 0.010. We then have

$$3.9 \times 10^{-11} = (0.010)(2x)^2$$

$$x^2 = \frac{3.9 \times 10^{-11}}{4(0.010)} = 9.8 \times 10^{-10}$$

$$x = \sqrt{9.8 \times 10^{-10}} = 3.1 \times 10^{-5}\,M$$

The very small value for x validates the simplifying assumption we have made. Our calculation indicates that 3.1×10^{-5} mol of solid CaF$_2$ dissolves per liter of the 0.010 M Ca(NO$_3$)$_2$ solution.

(b) In this case the common ion is F^-, and at equilibrium we have

$$[Ca^{2+}] = x \quad \text{and} \quad [F^-] = 0.010 + 2x$$

Assuming that $2x$ is small compared to 0.010 M (that is, $0.010 + 2x \simeq 0.010$), we have

$$3.9 \times 10^{-11} = x(0.010)^2$$

$$x = \frac{3.9 \times 10^{-11}}{(0.010)^2} = 3.9 \times 10^{-7} \, M$$

Thus, 3.9×10^{-7} mol of solid CaF_2 should dissolve per liter of 0.010 M NaF solution.

Comment: The molar solubility of CaF_2 in pure water is $2.1 \times 10^{-4} \, M$ (Sample Exercise 17.11). By comparison, our calculations above show that the solubility of CaF_2 in the presence of 0.010 M Ca^{2+} is $3.1 \times 10^{-5} \, M$, and in the presence of 0.010 M F^- ion it is $3.9 \times 10^{-7} \, M$. Thus, the addition of either Ca^{2+} or F^- to a solution of CaF_2 decreases the solubility. However, the effect of F^- on the solubility is more pronounced than that of Ca^{2+} because $[F^-]$ appears to the second power in the K_{sp} expression for CaF_2, whereas Ca^{2+} appears to the first power.

PRACTICE EXERCISE

The value for K_{sp} for manganese(II) hydroxide, $Mn(OH)_2$, is 1.6×10^{-13}. Calculate the molar solubility of $Mn(OH)_2$ in a solution that contains 0.020 M NaOH.
Answer: $4.0 \times 10^{-10} \, M$

Solubility and pH

The solubility of any substance whose anion is basic will be affected to some extent by the pH of the solution. Consider $Mg(OH)_2$, for example, for which the solubility equilibrium is

$$Mg(OH)_2(s) \rightleftharpoons Mg^{2+}(aq) + 2\,OH^-(aq) \quad K_{sp} = 1.8 \times 10^{-11} \quad [17.17]$$

A saturated solution of $Mg(OH)_2$ has a calculated pH of 10.52 and contains $[Mg^{2+}] = 1.7 \times 10^{-4} \, M$. Now suppose that solid $Mg(OH)_2$ is equilibrated with a solution buffered at a more acidic pH of 9.0. The pOH, therefore, is 5.0, so $[OH^-] = 1.0 \times 10^{-5}$. Inserting this value for $[OH^-]$ into the solubility-product expression, we have

$$K_{sp} = [Mg^{2+}][OH^-]^2 = 1.8 \times 10^{-11}$$

$$[Mg^{2+}](1.0 \times 10^{-5})^2 = 1.8 \times 10^{-11}$$

$$[Mg^{2+}] = \frac{1.8 \times 10^{-11}}{(1.0 \times 10^{-5})^2} = 0.18 \, M$$

Thus, $Mg(OH)_2$ dissolves in the solution until $[Mg^{2+}] = 0.18 \, M$. It is apparent that $Mg(OH)_2$ is quite soluble in this solution. If the concentration of OH^- was reduced even further by making the solution more acidic, the Mg^{2+} concentration would have to increase to maintain the equilibrium condition. Thus, a sample of $Mg(OH)_2$ will dissolve completely if sufficient acid is added (Figure 17.16 ▶).

The solubility of almost any ionic compound is affected if the solution is made sufficiently acidic or basic. The effects are very noticeable, however, only when one or both ions involved are at least moderately acidic or basic. The metal hydroxides, such as $Mg(OH)_2$, are examples of compounds containing a strongly basic ion, the hydroxide ion.

As we have seen, the solubility of $Mg(OH)_2$ greatly increases as the acidity of the solution increases. The solubility of CaF_2 increases as the solution becomes more acidic, too, because the F^- ion is a weak base; it is the conjugate base of the weak acid HF. As a result, the solubility equilibrium of CaF_2 is shifted to the right as the concentration of F^- ions is reduced by protonation to form HF.

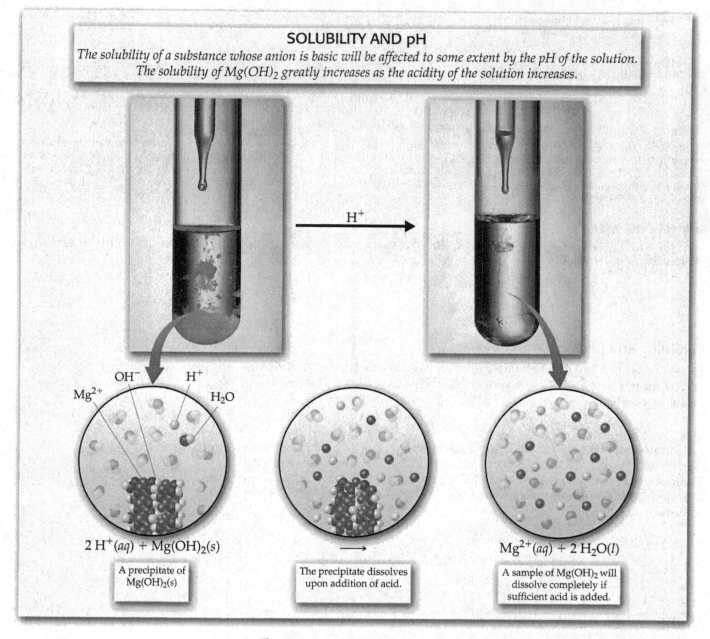

SOLUBILITY AND pH

The solubility of a substance whose anion is basic will be affected to some extent by the pH of the solution. The solubility of Mg(OH)$_2$ greatly increases as the acidity of the solution increases.

H$^+$

OH$^-$ H$^+$

Mg^{2+} H$_2$O

$2\,H^+(aq) + Mg(OH)_2(s)$

$\longrightarrow$

$Mg^{2+}(aq) + 2\,H_2O(l)$

A precipitate of Mg(OH)$_2$(s)

The precipitate dissolves upon addition of acid.

A sample of Mg(OH)$_2$ will dissolve completely if sufficient acid is added.

▲ **Figure 17.16 Dissolution of a precipitate in acid. (A white precipitate of Mg(OH)$_2$(s) in contact with its saturated solution is in the test tube on the left. The dropper poised above the solution surface contains hydrochloric acid. (The anions accompanying the acid have been omitted to simplify the art.))**

ANIMATION
Dissolution of Mg(OH)$_2$ by Acid

Thus, the solution process can be understood in terms of two consecutive reactions.

$$CaF_2(s) \rightleftharpoons Ca^{2+}(aq) + 2\,F^-(aq) \qquad [17.18]$$

$$F^-(aq) + H^+(aq) \rightleftharpoons HF(aq) \qquad [17.19]$$

The equation for the overall process is

$$CaF_2(s) + 2\,H^+(aq) \rightleftharpoons Ca^{2+}(aq) + 2\,HF(aq) \qquad [17.20]$$

CHEMISTRY AND LIFE | Sinkholes

A principal cause of sinkholes is the dissolution of limestone, which is calcium carbonate, by groundwater. Although $CaCO_3$ has a relatively small solubility-product constant, it is quite soluble in the presence of acid.

$$CaCO_3(s) \rightleftharpoons Ca^{2+}(aq) + CO_3^{2-}(aq) \qquad K_{sp} = 4.5 \times 10^{-9}$$

Rainwater is naturally acidic, with a pH range of 5 to 6, and can become more acidic when it comes into contact with decaying plant matter. Because carbonate ion is the conjugate base of the weak acid, hydrogen carbonate ion (HCO_3^-), it readily combines with hydrogen ion.

$$CO_3^{2-}(aq) + H^+(aq) \longrightarrow HCO_3^-(aq)$$

The consumption of carbonate ion shifts the dissolution equilibrium to the right, thus increasing the solubility of $CaCO_3$. This can have profound consequences in areas where the terrain consists of porous calcium carbonate bedrock covered by a relatively thin layer of clay and/or topsoil. As acidic water percolates through and gradually dissolves the limestone, it creates underground voids. A sinkhole results when the overlying ground can no longer be supported by the remaining bedrock and collapses into the underground cavity [Figure 17.17(a) ▼]. Sinkholes are one of a variety of geologic features known as *karst* landforms. Other karst landforms, also caused by the dissolution of bedrock by groundwater, include caves and underground streams. The sudden formation of large sinkholes can pose a serious threat to life and property [Figure 17.17(b)]. The existence of deep sinkholes also increases the risk of contamination of the aquifer.

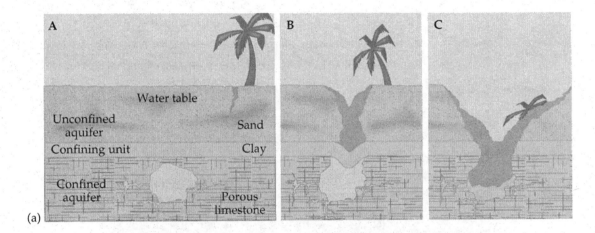

▲ **Figure 17.17 Sinkhole formation.** (a) The sequence A ⟶ B ⟶ C shows how a sinkhole forms. An underground void develops as limestone, $CaCO_3(s)$, dissolves. Collapse of the overlying ground into an underground cavity causes sinkhole formation. (b) The large sinkhole shown here has destroyed several buildings and part of a highway.

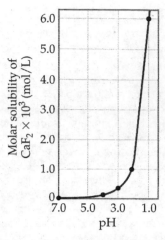

▲ Figure 17.18 The effect of pH on the solubility of CaF₂. The solubility increases as the solution becomes more acidic (lower pH). Notice that the vertical scale has been multiplied by 10^3.

Figure 17.18 ◄ shows how the solubility of CaF_2 changes with pH.

Other salts that contain basic anions, such as CO_3^{2-}, PO_4^{3-}, CN^-, or S^{2-}, behave similarly. These examples illustrate a general rule: *The solubility of slightly soluble salts containing basic anions increases as [H^+] increases (as pH is lowered).* The more basic the anion, the more the solubility is influenced by pH. Salts with anions of negligible basicity (the anions of strong acids) are unaffected by pH changes.

> ### SAMPLE EXERCISE 17.13 | Predicting the Effect of Acid on Solubility
>
> Which of the following substances will be more soluble in acidic solution than in basic solution: **(a)** $Ni(OH)_2(s)$, **(b)** $CaCO_3(s)$, **(c)** $BaF_2(s)$, **(d)** $AgCl(s)$?
>
> **Solution**
> **Analyze:** The problem lists four sparingly soluble salts, and we are asked to determine which will be more soluble at low pH than at high pH.
> **Plan:** Ionic compounds that dissociate to produce a basic anion will be more soluble in acid solution.
> **Solve: (a)** $Ni(OH)_2(s)$ will be more soluble in acidic solution because of the basicity of OH^-; the H^+ ion reacts with the OH^- ion, forming water.
>
> $$Ni(OH)_2(s) \rightleftharpoons Ni^{2+}(aq) + 2\,OH^-(aq)$$
> $$\underline{2\,OH^-(aq) + 2\,H^+(aq) \rightleftharpoons 2\,H_2O(l)}$$
> Overall: $Ni(OH)_2(s) + 2\,H^+(aq) \rightleftharpoons Ni^{2+}(aq) + 2\,H_2O(l)$
>
> **(b)** Similarly, $CaCO_3(s)$ dissolves in acid solutions because CO_3^{2-} is a basic anion.
>
> $$CaCO_3(s) \rightleftharpoons Ca^{2+}(aq) + CO_3^{2-}(aq)$$
> $$CO_3^{2-}(aq) + 2\,H^+(aq) \rightleftharpoons H_2CO_3(aq)$$
> $$\underline{H_2CO_3(aq) \longrightarrow CO_2(g) + H_2O(l)}$$
> Overall: $CaCO_3(s) + 2\,H^+(aq) \longrightarrow Ca^{2+}(aq) + CO_2(g) + H_2O(l)$
>
> The reaction between CO_3^{2-} and H^+ occurs in a stepwise fashion, first forming HCO_3^-. H_2CO_3 forms in appreciable amounts only when the concentration of H^+ is sufficiently high.
> **(c)** The solubility of BaF_2 is also enhanced by lowering the pH, because F^- is a basic anion.
>
> $$BaF_2(s) \rightleftharpoons Ba^{2+}(aq) + 2\,F^-(aq)$$
> $$\underline{2\,F^-(aq) + 2\,H^+(aq) \rightleftharpoons 2\,HF(aq)}$$
> Overall: $BaF_2(s) + 2\,H^+(aq) \longrightarrow Ba^{2+}(aq) + 2\,HF(aq)$
>
> **(d)** The solubility of AgCl is unaffected by changes in pH because Cl^- is the anion of a strong acid and therefore has negligible basicity.
>
> ### PRACTICE EXERCISE
> Write the net ionic equation for the reaction of the following copper(II) compounds with acid: **(a)** CuS, **(b)** $Cu(N_3)_2$.
> **Answers: (a)** $CuS(s) + H^+(aq) \rightleftharpoons Cu^{2+}(aq) + HS^-(aq)$
> **(b)** $Cu(N_3)_2(s) + 2\,H^+(aq) \rightleftharpoons Cu^{2+}(aq) + 2\,HN_3(aq)$

Formation of Complex Ions

A characteristic property of metal ions is their ability to act as Lewis acids, or electron-pair acceptors, toward water molecules, which act as Lewis bases, or electron-pair donors. ∞∞ (Section 16.11) Lewis bases other than water can also interact with metal ions, particularly with transition-metal ions. Such interactions can dramatically affect the solubility of a metal salt. AgCl, for example, which has $K_{sp} = 1.8 \times 10^{-10}$, will dissolve in the presence of aqueous ammonia because Ag^+ interacts with the Lewis base NH_3, as shown in

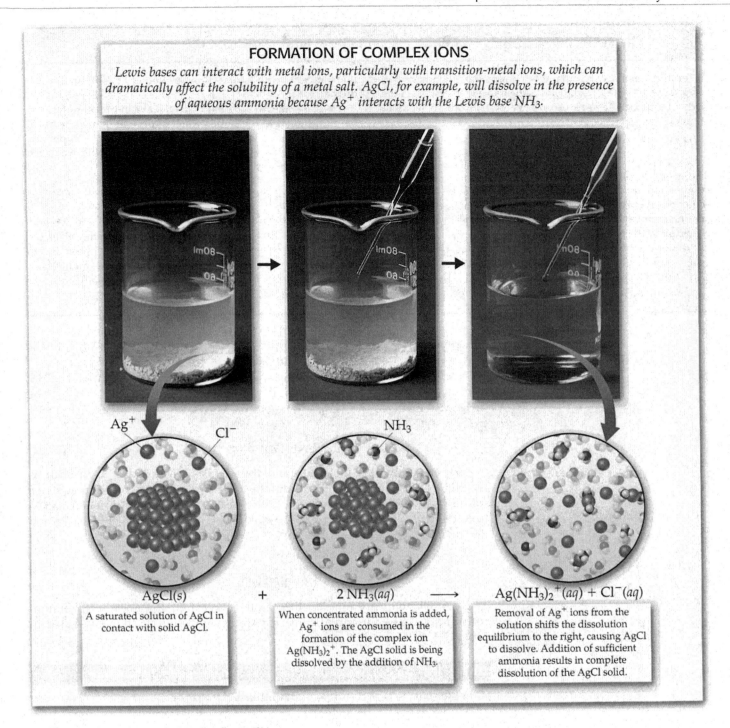

FORMATION OF COMPLEX IONS

Lewis bases can interact with metal ions, particularly with transition-metal ions, which can dramatically affect the solubility of a metal salt. AgCl, for example, will dissolve in the presence of aqueous ammonia because Ag^+ interacts with the Lewis base NH_3.

Ag^+ Cl^- NH_3 $Ag(NH_3)_2^+(aq) + Cl^-(aq)$

$$AgCl(s) \quad + \quad 2\,NH_3(aq) \quad \longrightarrow \quad Ag(NH_3)_2^+(aq) + Cl^-(aq)$$

| A saturated solution of AgCl in contact with solid AgCl. | When concentrated ammonia is added, Ag^+ ions are consumed in the formation of the complex ion $Ag(NH_3)_2^+$. The AgCl solid is being dissolved by the addition of NH_3. | Removal of Ag^+ ions from the solution shifts the dissolution equilibrium to the right, causing AgCl to dissolve. Addition of sufficient ammonia results in complete dissolution of the AgCl solid. |

▲ **Figure 17.19   Using NH₃(aq) to dissolve AgCl(s).**

Figure 17.19 ▲. This process can be viewed as the sum of two reactions, the dissolution of AgCl and the Lewis acid-base interaction between Ag^+ and NH_3.

$$AgCl(s) \rightleftharpoons Ag^+(aq) + Cl^-(aq) \qquad [17.21]$$

$$Ag^+(aq) + 2\,NH_3(aq) \rightleftharpoons Ag(NH_3)_2^+(aq) \qquad [17.22]$$

Overall: $AgCl(s) + 2\,NH_3(aq) \rightleftharpoons Ag(NH_3)_2^+(aq) + Cl^-(aq) \qquad [17.23]$

CHEMISTRY AND LIFE | Tooth Decay and Fluoridation

Tooth enamel consists mainly of a mineral called hydroxy-apatite, $Ca_{10}(PO_4)_6(OH)_2$. It is the hardest substance in the body. Tooth cavities are caused when acids dissolve tooth enamel.

$$Ca_{10}(PO_4)_6(OH)_2(s) + 8\,H^+(aq) \longrightarrow$$
$$10\,Ca^{2+}(aq) + 6\,HPO_4^{2-}(aq) + 2\,H_2O(l)$$

The resultant Ca^{2+} and HPO_4^{2-} ions diffuse out of the tooth enamel and are washed away by saliva. The acids that attack the hydroxyapatite are formed by the action of specific bacteria on sugars and other carbohydrates present in the plaque adhering to the teeth.

Fluoride ion, present in drinking water, toothpaste, and other sources, can react with hydroxyapatite to form fluoroapatite, $Ca_{10}(PO_4)_6F_2$. This mineral, in which F^- has replaced OH^-, is much more resistant to attack by acids because the flu-oride ion is a much weaker Brønsted–Lowry base than the hydroxide ion.

Because the fluoride ion is so effective in preventing cavities, it is added to the public water supply in many places to give a concentration of 1 mg/L (1 ppm). The compound added may be NaF or Na_2SiF_6. Na_2SiF_6 reacts with water to release fluoride ions by the following reaction:

$$SiF_6^{2-}(aq) + 2\,H_2O(l) \longrightarrow 6\,F^-(aq) + 4\,H^+(aq) + SiO_2(s)$$

About 80% of all toothpastes now sold in the United States contain fluoride compounds, usually at the level of 0.1% fluoride by mass. The most common compounds in toothpastes are sodium fluoride (NaF), sodium monofluorophosphate (Na_2PO_3F), and stannous fluoride (SnF_2). *Related Exercise: 17.103*

The presence of NH_3 drives the top reaction, the dissolution of AgCl, to the right as $Ag^+(aq)$ is consumed to form $Ag(NH_3)_2^+$.

For a Lewis base such as NH_3 to increase the solubility of a metal salt, it must be able to interact more strongly with the metal ion than water does. The NH_3 must displace solvating H_2O molecules (Sections 13.1 and 16.11) in order to form $Ag(NH_3)_2^+$:

$$Ag^+(aq) + 2\,NH_3(aq) \rightleftharpoons Ag(NH_3)_2^+(aq) \qquad [17.24]$$

An assembly of a metal ion and the Lewis bases bonded to it, such as $Ag(NH_3)_2^+$, is called a **complex ion**. The stability of a complex ion in aqueous solution can be judged by the size of the equilibrium constant for its formation from the hydrated metal ion. For example, the equilibrium constant for formation of $Ag(NH_3)_2^+$ (Equation 17.24) is 1.7×10^7:

$$K_f = \frac{[Ag(NH_3)_2^+]}{[Ag^+][NH_3]^2} = 1.7 \times 10^7 \qquad [17.25]$$

The equilibrium constant for this kind of reaction is called a **formation constant**, K_f. The formation constants for several complex ions are listed in Table 17.1 ▼.

TABLE 17.1	Formation Constants for Some Metal Complex Ions in Water at 25°C	
Complex Ion	K_f	**Equilibrium Equation**
$Ag(NH_3)_2^+$	1.7×10^7	$Ag^+(aq) + 2\,NH_3(aq) \rightleftharpoons Ag(NH_3)_2^+(aq)$
$Ag(CN)_2^-$	1×10^{21}	$Ag^+(aq) + 2\,CN^-(aq) \rightleftharpoons Ag(CN)_2^-(aq)$
$Ag(S_2O_3)_2^{3-}$	2.9×10^{13}	$Ag^+(aq) + 2\,S_2O_3^{2-}(aq) \rightleftharpoons Ag(S_2O_3)_2^{3-}(aq)$
$CdBr_4^{2-}$	5×10^3	$Cd^{2+}(aq) + 4\,Br^-(aq) \rightleftharpoons CdBr_4^{2-}(aq)$
$Cr(OH)_4^-$	8×10^{29}	$Cr^{3+}(aq) + 4\,OH^-(aq) \rightleftharpoons Cr(OH)_4^-(aq)$
$Co(SCN)_4^{2-}$	1×10^3	$Co^{2+}(aq) + 4\,SCN^-(aq) \rightleftharpoons Co(SCN)_4^{2-}(aq)$
$Cu(NH_3)_4^{2+}$	5×10^{12}	$Cu^{2+}(aq) + 4\,NH_3(aq) \rightleftharpoons Cu(NH_3)_4^{2+}(aq)$
$Cu(CN)_4^{2-}$	1×10^{25}	$Cu^{2+}(aq) + 4\,CN^-(aq) \rightleftharpoons Cu(CN)_4^{2-}(aq)$
$Ni(NH_3)_6^{2+}$	1.2×10^9	$Ni^{2+}(aq) + 6\,NH_3(aq) \rightleftharpoons Ni(NH_3)_6^{2+}(aq)$
$Fe(CN)_6^{4-}$	1×10^{35}	$Fe^{2+}(aq) + 6\,CN^-(aq) \rightleftharpoons Fe(CN)_6^{4-}(aq)$
$Fe(CN)_6^{3-}$	1×10^{42}	$Fe^{3+}(aq) + 6\,CN^-(aq) \rightleftharpoons Fe(CN)_6^{3-}(aq)$

■ **SAMPLE EXERCISE 17.14** | Evaluating an Equilibrium Involving a Complex Ion

Calculate the concentration of Ag^+ present in solution at equilibrium when concentrated ammonia is added to a 0.010 M solution of $AgNO_3$ to give an equilibrium concentration of $[NH_3]$ = 0.20 M. Neglect the small volume change that occurs when NH_3 is added.

Solution

Analyze: When $NH_3(aq)$ is added to $Ag^+(aq)$, a reaction occurs forming $Ag(NH_3)_2^+$ as shown in Equation 17.22. We are asked to determine what concentration of $Ag^+(aq)$ will remain uncombined when the NH_3 concentration is brought to 0.20 M in a solution originally 0.010 M in $AgNO_3$.

Plan: We first assume that the $AgNO_3$ is completely dissociated giving 0.10 M Ag^+. Because K_f for the formation of $Ag(NH_3)_2^+$ is quite large, we assume that essentially all the Ag^+ is then converted to $Ag(NH_3)_2^+$ and approach the problem as though we are concerned with the *dissociation* of $Ag(NH_3)_2^+$ rather than its *formation*. In order to facilitate this approach, we will need to reverse the equation to represent the formation of Ag^+ and NH_3 from $Ag(NH_3)_2^+$ and also make the corresponding change to the equilibrium constant.

$$Ag(NH_3)_2^+(aq) \rightleftharpoons Ag^+(aq) + 2\,NH_3(aq)$$

$$\frac{1}{K_f} = \frac{1}{1.7 \times 10^7} = 5.9 \times 10^{-8}$$

Solve: If $[Ag^+]$ is 0.010 M initially, then $[Ag(NH_3)_2^+]$ will be 0.010 M following addition of the NH_3. We now construct a table to solve this equilibrium problem. Note that the NH_3 concentration given in the problem is an *equilibrium* concentration rather than an initial concentration.

	$Ag(NH_3)_2^+(aq)$ $\rightleftharpoons$	$Ag^+(aq)$ +	$2\,NH_3(aq)$
Initial	0.010 M	0 M	
Change	$-x\ M$	$+x\ M$	
Equilibrium	$0.010 - x\ M$	$x\ M$	0.20 M

Because the concentration of Ag^+ is very small, we can ignore x in comparison with 0.010. Thus, $0.010 - x \approx 0.010\ M$. Substituting these values into the equilibrium-constant expression for the dissociation of $Ag(NH_3)_2^+$, we obtain

$$\frac{[Ag^+][NH_3]^2}{[Ag(NH_3)_2^+]} = \frac{(x)(0.20)^2}{0.010} = 5.9 \times 10^{-8}$$

Solving for x, we obtain $x = 1.5 \times 10^{-8}\ M = [Ag^+]$. Thus, formation of the $Ag(NH_3)_2^+$ complex drastically reduces the concentration of free Ag^+ ion in solution.

■ **PRACTICE EXERCISE**

Calculate $[Cr^{3+}]$ in equilibrium with $Cr(OH)_4^-$ when 0.010 mol of $Cr(NO_3)_3$ is dissolved in a liter of solution buffered at pH 10.0.
Answer: $1 \times 10^{-16}\ M$

The general rule is that the solubility of metal salts increases in the presence of suitable Lewis bases, such as NH_3, CN^-, or OH^-, if the metal forms a complex with the base. The ability of metal ions to form complexes is an extremely important aspect of their chemistry. In Chapter 24 we will take a much closer look at complex ions. In that chapter and others we will see applications of complex ions to areas such as biochemistry, metallurgy, and photography.

Amphoterism

Some metal oxides and hydroxides that are relatively insoluble in neutral water dissolve in strongly acidic and strongly basic solutions. These substances are soluble in strong acids and bases because they themselves are capable of

behaving as either an acid or base; they are **amphoteric oxides and bases**. Amphoteric oxides and hydroxides include those of Al^{3+}, Cr^{3+}, Zn^{2+}, and Sn^{2+}. Notice that the term *amphoteric* is applied to the behavior of insoluble oxides and hydroxides that can be made to dissolve in either acidic or basic solutions. The similar term *amphiprotic*, which we encountered in Section 16.2, relates more generally to any molecule or ion that can either gain or lose a proton.

These species dissolve in acidic solutions because they contain basic anions. What makes amphoteric oxides and hydroxides special, though, is that they also dissolve in strongly basic solutions (Figure 17.20 ▼). This behavior

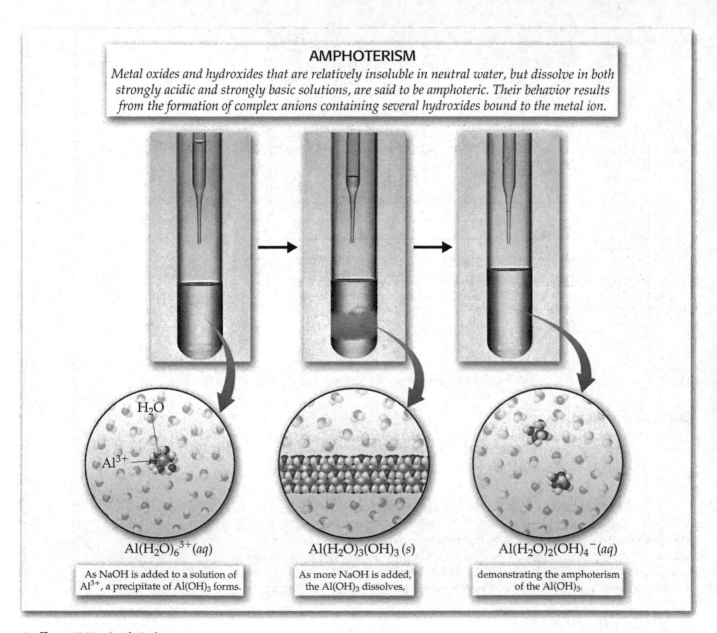

AMPHOTERISM

Metal oxides and hydroxides that are relatively insoluble in neutral water, but dissolve in both strongly acidic and strongly basic solutions, are said to be amphoteric. Their behavior results from the formation of complex anions containing several hydroxides bound to the metal ion.

H_2O

Al^{3+}

$Al(H_2O)_6^{3+}(aq)$

$Al(H_2O)_3(OH)_3 (s)$

$Al(H_2O)_2(OH)_4^-(aq)$

As NaOH is added to a solution of Al^{3+}, a precipitate of $Al(OH)_3$ forms.

As more NaOH is added, the $Al(OH)_3$ dissolves,

demonstrating the amphoterism of the $Al(OH)_3$.

▲ **Figure 17.20   Amphoterism.**

results from the formation of complex anions containing several (typically four) hydroxides bound to the metal ion.

$$Al(OH)_3(s) + OH^-(aq) \rightleftharpoons Al(OH)_4^-(aq) \qquad [17.26]$$

Amphoterism is often explained by the behavior of the water molecules that surround the metal ion and that are bonded to it by Lewis acid-base interactions. ∞ (Section. 16.11) For example, $Al^{3+}(aq)$ is more accurately represented as $Al(H_2O)_6^{3+}(aq)$ because six water molecules are bonded to the Al^{3+} in aqueous solution. Recall from Section 16.11 that this hydrated ion is a weak acid. As a strong base is added, $Al(H_2O)_6^{3+}$ loses protons in a stepwise fashion, eventually forming neutral and water-insoluble $Al(H_2O)_3(OH)_3$. This substance then dissolves upon removal of an additional proton to form the anion $Al(H_2O)_2(OH)_4^-$. The reactions that occur are as follows:

$$Al(H_2O)_6^{3+}(aq) + OH^-(aq) \rightleftharpoons Al(H_2O)_5(OH)^{2+}(aq) + H_2O(l)$$

$$Al(H_2O)_5(OH)^{2+}(aq) + OH^-(aq) \rightleftharpoons Al(H_2O)_4(OH)_2^+(aq) + H_2O(l)$$

$$Al(H_2O)_4(OH)_2^+(aq) + OH^-(aq) \rightleftharpoons Al(H_2O)_3(OH)_3(s) + H_2O(l)$$

$$Al(H_2O)_3(OH)_3(s) + OH^-(aq) \rightleftharpoons Al(H_2O)_2(OH)_4^-(aq) + H_2O(l)$$

Removing additional protons is possible, but each successive reaction occurs less readily than the one before. As the charge on the ion becomes more negative, it becomes increasingly difficult to remove a positively charged proton. Addition of an acid reverses these reactions. The proton adds in a stepwise fashion to convert the OH^- groups to H_2O, eventually re-forming $Al(H_2O)_6^{3+}$. The common practice is to simplify the equations for these reactions by excluding the bound H_2O molecules. Thus, we usually write Al^{3+} instead of $Al(H_2O)_6^{3+}$, $Al(OH)_3$ instead of $Al(H_2O)_3(OH)_3$, $Al(OH)_4^-$ instead of $Al(H_2O)_2(OH)_4^-$, and so forth.

The extent to which an insoluble metal hydroxide reacts with either acid or base varies with the particular metal ion involved. Many metal hydroxides—such as $Ca(OH)_2$, $Fe(OH)_2$, and $Fe(OH)_3$—are capable of dissolving in acidic solution but do not react with excess base. These hydroxides are not amphoteric.

The purification of aluminum ore in the manufacture of aluminum metal provides an interesting application of the property of amphoterism. As we have seen, $Al(OH)_3$ is amphoteric, whereas $Fe(OH)_3$ is not. Aluminum occurs in large quantities as the ore *bauxite*, which is essentially Al_2O_3 with additional water molecules. The ore is contaminated with Fe_2O_3 as an impurity. When bauxite is added to a strongly basic solution, the Al_2O_3 dissolves because the aluminum forms complex ions, such as $Al(OH)_4^-$. The Fe_2O_3 impurity, however, is not amphoteric and remains as a solid. The solution is filtered, getting rid of the iron impurity. Aluminum hydroxide is then precipitated by addition of acid. The purified hydroxide receives further treatment and eventually yields aluminum metal. ∞ (Section 23.3)

 GIVE IT SOME THOUGHT

What kind of behavior characterizes an amphoteric oxide or an amphoteric hydroxide?

17.6 | Precipitation and Separation of Ions

Equilibrium can be achieved starting with the substances on either side of a chemical equation. The equilibrium among $BaSO_4(s)$, $Ba^{2+}(aq)$, and $SO_4^{2-}(aq)$ (Equation 17.15) can be achieved starting with solid $BaSO_4$. It can also be reached starting with solutions of salts containing Ba^{2+} and SO_4^{2-}, say $BaCl_2$ and Na_2SO_4. When these two solutions are mixed, $BaSO_4$ will precipitate if the product of the initial ion concentrations, $Q = [Ba^{2+}][SO_4^{2-}]$, is greater than K_{sp}.

The use of the reaction quotient, Q, to determine the direction in which a reaction must proceed to reach equilibrium was discussed earlier. ∞ (Section 15.5) The possible relationships between Q and K_{sp} are summarized as follows:

If $Q > K_{sp}$, precipitation occurs until $Q = K_{sp}$.

If $Q = K_{sp}$, equilibrium exists (saturated solution).

If $Q < K_{sp}$, solid dissolves until $Q = K_{sp}$.

▉▉ SAMPLE EXERCISE 17.15 | Predicting Whether a Precipitate Will Form

Will a precipitate form when 0.10 L of 8.0×10^{-3} M $Pb(NO_3)_2$ is added to 0.40 L of 5.0×10^{-3} M Na_2SO_4?

Solution
Analyze: The problem asks us to determine whether a precipitate will form when two salt solutions are combined.
Plan: We should determine the concentrations of all ions immediately upon mixing of the solutions and compare the value of the reaction quotient, Q, to the solubility-product constant, K_{sp}, for any potentially insoluble product. The possible metathesis products are $PbSO_4$ and $NaNO_3$. Sodium salts are quite soluble; $PbSO_4$ has a K_{sp} of 6.3×10^{-7} (Appendix D), however, and will precipitate if the Pb^{2+} and SO_4^{2-} ion concentrations are high enough for Q to exceed K_{sp} for the salt.

Solve: When the two solutions are mixed, the total volume becomes 0.10 L + 0.40 L = 0.50 L. The number of moles of Pb^{2+} in 0.10 L of 3.0×10^{-3} M $Pb(NO_3)_2$ is

$$(0.10 \text{ L})\left(8.0 \times 10^{-3}\frac{\text{mol}}{\text{L}}\right) = 8.0 \times 10^{-4} \text{ mol}$$

The concentration of Pb^{2+} in the 0.50-L mixture is therefore

$$[Pb^{2+}] = \frac{8.0 \times 10^{-4} \text{ mol}}{0.50 \text{ L}} = 1.6 \times 10^{-3} \text{ M}$$

The number of moles of SO_4^{2-} in 0.40 L of 5.0×10^{-3} M Na_2SO_4 is

$$(0.40 \text{ L})\left(5.0 \times 10^{-3}\frac{\text{mol}}{\text{L}}\right) = 2.0 \times 10^{-3} \text{ mol}$$

Therefore, $[SO_4^{2-}]$ in the 0.50-L mixture is

$$[SO_4^{2-}] = \frac{2.0 \times 10^{-3} \text{ mol}}{0.50 \text{ L}} = 4.0 \times 10^{-3} \text{ M}$$

We then have

$$Q = [Pb^{2+}][SO_4^{2-}] = (1.6 \times 10^{-3})(4.0 \times 10^{-3}) = 6.4 \times 10^{-6}$$

Because $Q > K_{sp}$, $PbSO_4$ will precipitate.

▉▉ PRACTICE EXERCISE

Will a precipitate form when 0.050 L of 2.0×10^{-2} M NaF is mixed with 0.010 L of 1.0×10^{-2} M $Ca(NO_3)_2$?
Answer: Yes, CaF_2 precipitates because $Q = 4.6 \times 10^{-8}$ is larger than $K_{sp} = 3.9 \times 10^{-11}$

Selective Precipitation of Ions

Ions can be separated from each other based on the solubilities of their salts. Consider a solution containing both Ag^+ and Cu^{2+}. If HCl is added to the solution, AgCl ($K_{sp} = 1.8 \times 10^{-10}$) precipitates, while Cu^{2+} remains in solution because $CuCl_2$ is soluble. Separation of ions in an aqueous solution by using a reagent that forms a precipitate with one or a few of the ions is called *selective precipitation*.

ACTIVITY
Selective Precipitation of Ions

SAMPLE EXERCISE 17.16 | Calculating Ion Concentrations for Precipitation

A solution contains 1.0×10^{-2} M Ag^+ and 2.0×10^{-2} M Pb^{2+}. When Cl^- is added to the solution, both AgCl ($K_{sp} = 1.8 \times 10^{-10}$) and $PbCl_2$ ($K_{sp} = 1.7 \times 10^{-5}$) precipitate from the solution. What concentration of Cl^- is necessary to begin the precipitation of each salt? Which salt precipitates first?

Solution

Analyze: We are asked to determine the concentration of Cl^- necessary to begin the precipitation from a solution containing Ag^+ and Pb^{2+} ions, and to predict which metal chloride will begin to precipitate first.

Plan: We are given K_{sp} values for the two possible precipitates. Using these and the metal ion concentrations, we can calculate what concentration of Cl^- ion would be necessary to begin precipitation of each. The salt requiring the lower Cl^- ion concentration will precipitate first.

Solve: For AgCl we have

$$K_{sp} = [Ag^+][Cl^-] = 1.8 \times 10^{-10}$$

Because $[Ag^+] = 1.0 \times 10^{-2}$ M, the greatest concentration of Cl^- that can be present without causing precipitation of AgCl can be calculated from the K_{sp} expression:

$$K_{sp} = [1.0 \times 10^{-2}][Cl^-] = 1.8 \times 10^{-10}$$

$$[Cl^-] = \frac{1.8 \times 10^{-10}}{1.0 \times 10^{-2}} = 1.8 \times 10^{-8} \text{ M}$$

Any Cl^- in excess of this very small concentration will cause AgCl to precipitate from solution. Proceeding similarly for $PbCl_2$, we have

$$K_{sp} = [Pb^{2+}][Cl^-]^2 = 1.7 \times 10^{-5}$$

$$[2.0 \times 10^{-2}][Cl^-]^2 = 1.7 \times 10^{-5}$$

$$[Cl^-]^2 = \frac{1.7 \times 10^{-5}}{2.0 \times 10^{-2}} = 8.5 \times 10^{-4}$$

$$[Cl^-] = \sqrt{8.5 \times 10^{-4}} = 2.9 \times 10^{-2} \text{ M}$$

Thus, a concentration of Cl^- in excess of 2.9×10^{-2} M will cause $PbCl_2$ to precipitate.

Comparing the concentrations of Cl^- required to precipitate each salt, we see that as Cl^- is added to the solution, AgCl will precipitate first because it requires a much smaller concentration of Cl^-. Thus, Ag^+ can be separated from Pb^{2+} by slowly adding Cl^- so $[Cl^-]$ is between 1.8×10^{-8} M and 2.9×10^{-2} M.

PRACTICE EXERCISE

A solution consists of 0.050 M Mg^{2+} and 0.020 M Cu^{2+}. Which ion will precipitate first as OH^- is added to the solution? What concentration of OH^- is necessary to begin the precipitation of each cation? [$K_{sp} = 1.8 \times 10^{-11}$ for $Mg(OH)_2$, and $K_{sp} = 2.2 \times 10^{-20}$ for $Cu(OH)_2$.]

Answer: $Cu(OH)_2$ precipitates first. $Cu(OH)_2$ begins to precipitate when $[OH^-]$ exceeds 1.0×10^{-9} M; $Mg(OH)_2$ begins to precipitate when $[OH^-]$ exceeds 1.9×10^{-5} M.

Sulfide ion is often used to separate metal ions because the solubilities of sulfide salts span a wide range and depend greatly on the pH of the solution. Cu^{2+} and Zn^{2+}, for example, can be separated by bubbling H_2S gas through an acidified solution. Because CuS ($K_{sp} = 6 \times 10^{-37}$) is less soluble than ZnS ($K_{sp} = 2 \times 10^{-25}$), CuS precipitates from an acidified solution (pH = 1) while ZnS does not (Figure 17.21 ▶):

$$Cu^{2+}(aq) + H_2S(aq) \rightleftharpoons CuS(s) + 2 H^+(aq) \qquad [17.27]$$

The CuS can be separated from the Zn^{2+} solution by filtration. The CuS can then be dissolved by using a high concentration of H^+, shifting the equilibrium shown in Equation 17.27 to the left.

GIVE IT SOME THOUGHT

What experimental conditions will leave the smallest concentration of Cu^{2+} ions in solution according to Equation 17.27?

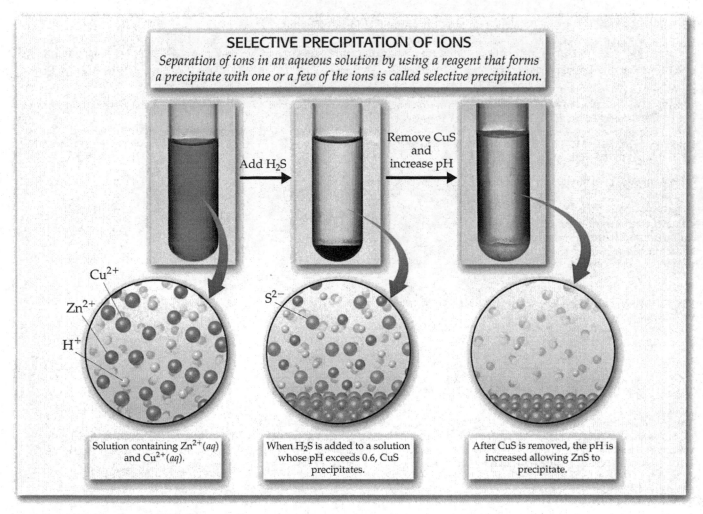

SELECTIVE PRECIPITATION OF IONS

Separation of ions in an aqueous solution by using a reagent that forms a precipitate with one or a few of the ions is called selective precipitation.

Add H₂S

Remove CuS and increase pH

Cu²⁺
Zn²⁺
H⁺
S²⁻

Solution containing Zn²⁺(aq) and Cu²⁺(aq).

When H₂S is added to a solution whose pH exceeds 0.6, CuS precipitates.

After CuS is removed, the pH is increased allowing ZnS to precipitate.

▲ **Figure 17.21   Selective precipitation.**

17.7 | Qualitative Analysis for Metallic Elements

In this chapter we have seen several examples of equilibria involving metal ions in aqueous solution. In this final section we look briefly at how solubility equilibria and complex-ion formation can be used to detect the presence of particular metal ions in solution. Before the development of modern analytical instrumentation, it was necessary to analyze mixtures of metals in a sample by so-called wet chemical methods. For example, a metallic sample that might contain several metallic elements was dissolved in a concentrated acid solution. This solution was then tested in a systematic way for the presence of various metal ions.

Qualitative analysis determines only the presence or absence of a particular metal ion, whereas **quantitative analysis** determines how much of a given substance is present. Wet methods of qualitative analysis have become less important as a means of analysis. They are frequently used in general chemistry laboratory programs, however, to illustrate equilibria, to teach the properties of common metal ions in solution, and to develop laboratory skills. Typically, such analyses proceed in three stages: (1) The ions are separated into broad groups

Identification of Cations in Solution

on the basis of solubility properties. (2) The individual ions within each group are then separated by selectively dissolving members in the group. (3) The ions are then identified by means of specific tests.

A scheme in general use divides the common cations into five groups, as shown in Figure 17.22 ▶. The order of addition of reagents is important. The most selective separations—those that involve the smallest number of ions—are carried out first. The reactions that are used must proceed so far toward completion that any concentration of cations remaining in the solution is too small to interfere with subsequent tests. Let's take a closer look at each of these five groups of cations, briefly examining the logic used in this qualitative analysis scheme.

1. *Insoluble chlorides:* Of the common metal ions, only Ag^+, Hg_2^{2+}, and Pb^{2+} form insoluble chlorides. When dilute HCl is added to a mixture of cations, therefore, only $AgCl$, Hg_2Cl_2, and $PbCl_2$ will precipitate, leaving the other cations in solution. The absence of a precipitate indicates that the starting solution contains no Ag^+, Hg_2^{2+}, or Pb^{2+}.

2. *Acid-insoluble sulfides:* After any insoluble chlorides have been removed, the remaining solution, now acidic, is treated with H_2S. Only the most insoluble metal sulfides—CuS, Bi_2S_3, CdS, PbS, HgS, As_2S_3, Sb_2S_3, and SnS_2—can precipitate. (Note the very small values of K_{sp} for some of these sulfides in Appendix D.) Those metal ions whose sulfides are somewhat more soluble— for example, ZnS or NiS—remain in solution.

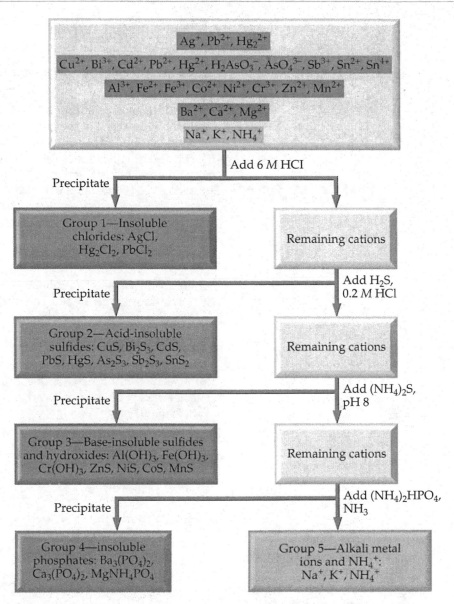

▲ **Figure 17.22 Qualitative analysis.** A flowchart showing the separation of cations into groups as a part of a common scheme for identifying cations.

ACTIVITY
Qualitative Analysis

3. *Base-insoluble sulfides and hydroxides:* After the solution is filtered to remove any acid-insoluble sulfides, the remaining solution is made slightly basic, and $(NH_4)_2S$ is added. In basic solutions the concentration of S^{2-} is higher than in acidic solutions. Thus, the ion products for many of the more soluble sulfides are made to exceed their K_{sp} values and precipitation occurs. The metal ions precipitated at this stage are Al^{3+}, Cr^{3+}, Fe^{3+}, Zn^{2+}, Ni^{2+}, Co^{2+}, and Mn^{2+}. (Actually, the Al^{3+}, Fe^{3+}, and Cr^{3+} ions do not form insoluble sulfides; instead they are precipitated as insoluble hydroxides at the same time.)

4. *Insoluble phosphates:* At this point the solution contains only metal ions from periodic table groups 1A and 2A. Adding $(NH_4)_2HPO_4$ to a basic solution precipitates the group 2A elements Mg^{2+}, Ca^{2+}, Sr^{2+}, and Ba^{2+} because these metals form insoluble phosphates.

5. *The alkali metal ions and NH_4^+:* The ions that remain after removing the insoluble phosphates form a small group. We can test for each ion individually. A flame test can be used to determine the presence of K^+, for example, because the flame turns a characteristic violet color if K^+ is present.

GIVE IT SOME THOUGHT

If a precipitate forms upon addition of HCl to an aqueous solution, what conclusions can you draw about the contents of the solution?

Additional separation and testing is necessary to determine which ions are present within each of the groups. Consider, for example, the ions of the insoluble chloride group. The precipitate containing the metal chlorides is boiled in water. The $PbCl_2$ is relatively soluble in hot water, whereas $AgCl$ and Hg_2Cl_2 are not. The hot solution is filtered, and a solution of Na_2CrO_4 is added to the filtrate. If Pb^{2+} is present, a yellow precipitate of $PbCrO_4$ forms. The test for Ag^+ consists of treating the metal chloride precipitate with dilute ammonia. Only Ag^+ forms an ammonia complex. If $AgCl$ is present in the precipitate, it will dissolve in the ammonia solution.

$$AgCl(s) + 2\,NH_3(aq) \rightleftharpoons Ag(NH_3)_2^+(aq) + Cl^-(aq) \qquad [17.28]$$

After treatment with ammonia, the solution is filtered and the filtrate made acidic by adding nitric acid. The nitric acid removes ammonia from solution by forming NH_4^+, thus releasing Ag^+, which re-forms the $AgCl$ precipitate.

$$Ag(NH_3)_2^+(aq) + Cl^-(aq) + 2\,H^+(aq) \rightleftharpoons AgCl(s) + 2\,NH_4^+(aq) \quad [17.29]$$

The analyses for individual ions in the acid-insoluble and base-insoluble sulfides are a bit more complex, but the same general principles are involved. The detailed procedures for carrying out such analyses are given in many laboratory manuals.

SAMPLE INTEGRATIVE EXERCISE | Putting Concepts Together

A sample of 1.25 L of HCl gas at 21°C and 0.950 atm is bubbled through 0.500 L of 0.150 M NH_3 solution. Assuming that all the HCl dissolves and that the volume of the solution remains 0.500 L, calculate the pH of the resulting solution.

Solution The number of moles of HCl gas is calculated from the ideal-gas law.

$$n = \frac{PV}{RT} = \frac{(0.950\text{ atm})(1.25\text{ L})}{(0.0821\text{ L-atm/mol-K})(294\text{ K})} = 0.0492\text{ mol HCl}$$

The number of moles of NH_3 in the solution is given by the product of the volume of the solution and its concentration.

$$\text{Moles }NH_3 = (0.500\text{ L})(0.150\text{ mol }NH_3/\text{L}) = 0.0750\text{ mol }NH_3$$

The acid HCl and base NH_3 react, transferring a proton from HCl to NH_3, producing NH_4^+ and Cl^- ions.

$$HCl(g) + NH_3(aq) \longrightarrow NH_4^+(aq) + Cl^-(aq)$$

To determine the pH of the solution, we first calculate the amount of each reactant and each product present at the completion of the reaction.

	HCl(g)	+	NH₃(aq)	⟶	NH₄⁺(aq)	+	Cl⁻(aq)
Before rxn:	0.0492 mol		0.0750 mol		0 mol		0 mol
After rxn:	0 mol		0.0258 mol		0.0492 mol		0.0492 mol

Thus, the reaction produces a solution containing a mixture of NH_3, NH_4^+, and Cl^-. The NH_3 is a weak base ($K_b = 1.8 \times 10^{-5}$), NH_4^+ is its conjugate acid, and Cl^- is neither acidic nor basic. Consequently, the pH depends on $[NH_3]$ and $[NH_4^+]$.

$$[NH_3] = \frac{0.0258\text{ mol }NH_3}{0.500\text{ L soln}} = 0.0516\ M$$

$$[NH_4^+] = \frac{0.0492\text{ mol }NH_4^+}{0.500\text{ L soln}} = 0.0984\ M$$

We can calculate the pH using either K_b for NH_3 or K_a for NH_4^+. Using the K_b expression, we have

$$NH_3(aq) \quad + \quad H_2O(l) \rightleftharpoons NH_4^+(aq) \quad + \quad OH^-(aq)$$

Initial	0.05156 M	—	0.0984 M	0
Change	−x M	—	+x M	+x M
Equilibrium	(0.0516 − x) M	—	(0.0984 + x) M	x M

$$K_b = \frac{[NH_4^+][OH^-]}{[NH_3]} = \frac{(0.0984 + x)(x)}{(0.0516 - x)} \simeq \frac{(0.0984)x}{0.0516} = 1.8 \times 10^{-5}$$

$$x = [OH^-] = \frac{(0.0516)(1.8 \times 10^{-5})}{0.0984} = 9.4 \times 10^{-6} \, M$$

Hence, pOH $= -\log(9.4 \times 10^{-6}) = 5.03$ and pH $= 14.00 - pOH = 14.00 - 5.03 = 8.97$.

SUMMARY AND KEY TERMS

Section 17.1 In this chapter we've considered several types of important equilibria that occur in aqueous solution. Our primary emphasis has been on acid-base equilibria in solutions containing two or more solutes and on solubility equilibria. The dissociation of a weak acid or weak base is repressed by the presence of a strong electrolyte that provides an ion common to the equilibrium. This phenomenon is called the **common-ion effect**.

Section 17.2 A particularly important type of acid-base mixture is that of a weak conjugate acid-base pair. Such mixtures function as **buffered solutions (buffers)**. Addition of small amounts of a strong acid or a strong base to a buffered solution causes only small changes in pH because the buffer reacts with the added acid or base. (Strong acid–strong base, strong acid–weak base, and weak acid–strong base reactions proceed essentially to completion.) Buffered solutions are usually prepared from a weak acid and a salt of that acid or from a weak base and a salt of that base. Two important characteristics of a buffered solution are its **buffer capacity** and its pH. The pH can be calculated using K_a or K_b. The relationship between pH, pK_a, and the concentrations of an acid and its conjugate base can be expressed by the **Henderson–Hasselbalch equation**: $pH = pK_a + \log \frac{[base]}{[acid]}$.

Section 17.3 The plot of the pH of an acid (or base) as a function of the volume of added base (or acid) is called a **pH titration curve**. Titration curves aid in selecting a proper pH indicator for an acid-base titration. The titration curve of a strong acid–strong base titration exhibits a large change in pH in the immediate vicinity of the equivalence point; at the equivalence point for this titration, pH = 7. For strong acid–weak base or weak acid–strong base titrations, the pH change in the vicinity of the equivalence point is not as large. Furthermore, the pH at the equivalence point is not 7 in either of these cases. Rather, it is the pH of the salt solution that results from the neutralization reaction. It is possible to calculate the pH at any point of the titration curve by first considering the stoichiometry of the reaction between the acid and base and then examining equilibria involving remaining solute species.

Section 17.4 The equilibrium between a solid compound and its ions in solution provides an example of heterogeneous equilibrium. The **solubility-product constant** (or simply the **solubility product**), K_{sp}, is an equilibrium constant that expresses quantitatively the extent to which the compound dissolves. The K_{sp} can be used to calculate the solubility of an ionic compound, and the solubility can be used to calculate K_{sp}.

Section 17.5 Several experimental factors, including temperature, affect the solubilities of ionic compounds in water. The solubility of a slightly soluble ionic compound is decreased by the presence of a second solute that furnishes a common ion (the common-ion effect). The solubility of compounds containing basic anions increases as the solution is made more acidic (as pH decreases). Salts with anions of negligible basicity (the anions of strong acids) are unaffected by pH changes.

The solubility of metal salts is also affected by the presence of certain Lewis bases that react with metal ions to form stable **complex ions**. Complex-ion formation in aqueous solution involves the displacement by Lewis bases (such as NH_3 and CN^-) of water molecules attached to the metal ion. The extent to which such complex formation occurs is expressed quantitatively by the **formation constant** for the complex ion. **Amphoteric oxides and hydroxides** are those that are only slightly soluble in water but dissolve on addition of either acid or base. Acid-base reactions involving the

OH⁻ or H₂O groups bound to the metal ions give rise to the amphoterism.

Section 17.6 Comparison of the ion product, Q, with the value of K_{sp} can be used to judge whether a precipitate will form when solutions are mixed or whether a slightly soluble salt will dissolve under various conditions. Precipitates form when $Q > K_{sp}$. Ions can be separated from each other based on the solubilities of their salts.

Section 17.7 Metallic elements vary a great deal in the solubilities of their salts, in their acid-base behavior,

and in their tendencies to form complex ions. These differences can be used to separate and detect the presence of metal ions in mixtures. **Qualitative analysis** determines the presence or absence of species in a sample, whereas **quantitative analysis** determines how much of each species is present. The qualitative analysis of metal ions in solution can be carried out by separating the ions into groups on the basis of precipitation reactions and then analyzing each group for individual metal ions.

VISUALIZING CONCEPTS

17.1 The following boxes represent aqueous solutions containing a weak acid, HX, and its conjugate base, X⁻. Water molecules and cations are not shown. Which solution has the highest pH? Explain. [Section 17.1]

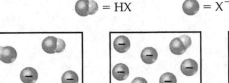

17.2 The beaker on the right contains 0.1 M acetic acid solution with methyl orange as an indicator. The beaker on the left contains a mixture of 0.1 M acetic acid and 0.1 M sodium acetate with methyl orange. **(a)** Using Figure 16.7, estimate the pH of each solution, and explain the difference. **(b)** Which solution is better able to maintain its pH when small amounts of NaOH are added? Explain. [Sections 17.1 and 17.2]

17.3 The drawing on the left represents a buffer composed of equal concentrations of a weak acid, HX, and its conju-

gate base, X⁻. The heights of the columns are proportional to the concentrations of the components of the buffer. **(a)** Which of the three drawings (1), (2), (3) represents the buffer after the addition of a strong acid? **(b)** Which of the three represents the buffer after the addition of a strong base? **(c)** Which of the three represents a situation that cannot arise from the addition of either an acid or a base? [Section 17.2]

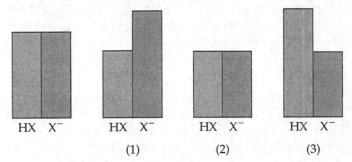

HX X⁻   HX X⁻   HX X⁻   HX X⁻
(1)   (2)   (3)

17.4 The following drawings represent solutions at various stages of the titration of a weak acid, HA, with NaOH. (The Na⁺ ions and water molecules have been omitted for clarity.) To which of the following regions of the titration curve does each drawing correspond: **(a)** before addition of NaOH, **(b)** after addition of NaOH but before equivalence point, **(c)** at equivalence point, **(d)** after equivalence point? [Section 17.3]

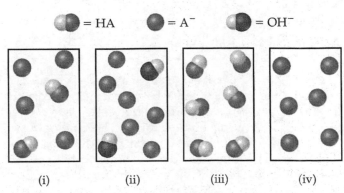

= HA   = A⁻   = OH⁻

(i)   (ii)   (iii)   (iv)

17.5 Match the following descriptions of titration curves with the diagrams: **(a)** strong acid added to strong base,

(b) strong acid added to weak base, (c) strong acid added to strong base, (d) strong base added to polyprotic acid. [Section 17.3]

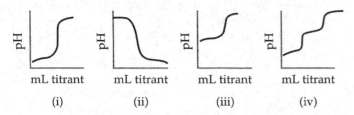

(i)   (ii)   (iii)   (iv)

17.6 The following drawings represent saturated solutions of three ionic compounds of silver—AgX, AgY, and AgZ. (Na$^+$ cations, which might also be present for charge balance, are not shown.) Which compound has the smallest K_{sp}? [Section 17.4]

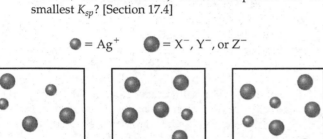

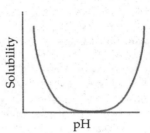

17.7 The following graphs represent the behavior of BaCO$_3$ under different circumstances. In each case the vertical axis indicates the solubility of the BaCO$_3$ and the horizontal axis represents the concentration of some other reagent. **(a)** Which graph represents what happens to the solubility of BaCO$_3$ as HNO$_3$ is added? **(b)** Which graph represents what happens to the BaCO$_3$ solubility as Na$_2$CO$_3$ is added? **(c)** Which represents what happens to the BaCO$_3$ solubility as NaNO$_3$ is added? [Section 17.5]

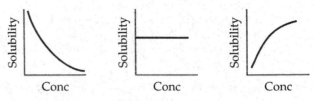

17.8 What is the name given to the kind of behavior demonstrated by a metal hydroxide in this graph? [Section 17.5]

EXERCISES

Common-Ion Effect

17.9 **(a)** What is the common-ion effect? **(b)** Give an example of a salt that can decrease the ionization of HNO$_2$ in solution.

17.10 **(a)** Consider the equilibrium B(aq) + H$_2$O(l) $\rightleftharpoons$ HB$^+$(aq) + OH$^-$(aq). Using Le Châtelier's principle, explain the effect of the presence of a salt of HB$^+$ on the ionization of B. **(b)** Give an example of a salt that can decrease the ionization of NH$_3$ in solution.

17.11 Does the pH increase, decrease, or remain the same when each of the following is added: **(a)** NaNO$_2$ to a solution of HNO$_2$; **(b)** (CH$_3$NH$_3$)Cl to a solution of CH$_3$NH$_2$; **(c)** sodium formate to a solution of formic acid; **(d)** potassium bromide to a solution of hydrobromic acid; **(e)** HCl to a solution of NaC$_2$H$_3$O$_2$?

17.12 Indicate whether the pH increases, decreases, or remains the same when each of the following is added: **(a)** Ca(C$_7$H$_5$O$_2$)$_2$ to a solution of HC$_7$H$_5$O$_2$; **(b)** pyridinium nitrate, (C$_5$H$_5$NH)(NO$_3$), to a solution of pyridine, C$_5$H$_5$N; **(c)** ammonia to a solution of hydrochloric acid; **(d)** sodium hydrogen carbonate to a solution of carbonic acid; **(e)** NaClO$_4$ to a solution of NaOH.

17.13 Use information from Appendix D to calculate the pH of **(a)** a solution that is 0.060 M in potassium propionate (KC$_3$H$_5$O$_2$) and 0.085 M in propionic acid (HC$_3$H$_5$O$_2$); **(b)** a solution that is 0.075 M in trimethylamine, (CH$_3$)$_3$N, and 0.10 M in trimethylammonium chloride, (CH$_3$)$_3$NHCl; **(c)** a solution that is made by mixing 50.0 mL of 0.15 M acetic acid and 50.0 mL of 0.20 M sodium acetate.

17.14 Use information from Appendix D to calculate the pH of **(a)** a solution that is 0.160 M in sodium formate (NaCHO$_2$) and 0.260 M in formic acid (HCHO$_2$); **(b)** a solution that is 0.210 M in pyridine (C$_5$H$_5$N) and 0.350 M in pyridinium chloride (C$_5$H$_5$NHCl); **(c)** a solution that is made by combining 125 mL of 0.050 M hydrofluoric acid with 50.0 mL of 0.10 M sodium fluoride.

17.15 **(a)** Calculate the percent ionization of 0.0075 M butanoic acid ($K_a = 1.5 \times 10^{-5}$). **(b)** Calculate the percent ionization of 0.0075 M butanoic acid in a solution containing 0.085 M sodium butanoate.

17.16 **(a)** Calculate the percent ionization of 0.085 M lactic acid ($K_a = 1.4 \times 10^{-4}$). **(b)** Calculate the percent ionization of 0.085 M lactic acid in a solution containing 0.050 M sodium lactate.

Science Fundamentals Second Edition

Buffers

17.17 Explain why a mixture of $HC_2H_3O_2$ and $NaC_2H_3O_2$ can act as a buffer while a mixture of HCl and NaCl cannot.

17.18 Explain why a mixture formed by mixing 100 mL of $0.100\ M\ HC_2H_3O_2$ and 50 mL of $0.100\ M$ NaOH will act as a buffer.

17.19 (a) Calculate the pH of a buffer that is $0.12\ M$ in lactic acid and $0.11\ M$ in sodium lactate. (b) Calculate the pH of a buffer formed by mixing 85 mL of $0.13\ M$ lactic acid with 95 mL of $0.15\ M$ sodium lactate.

17.20 (a) Calculate the pH of a buffer that is $0.120\ M$ in $NaHCO_3$ and $0.105\ M$ in Na_2CO_3. (b) Calculate the pH of a solution formed by mixing 65 mL of $0.20\ M$ $NaHCO_3$ with 75 mL of $0.15\ M\ Na_2CO_3$.

17.21 A buffer is prepared by adding 20.0 g of acetic acid $(HC_2H_3O_2)$ and 20.0 g of sodium acetate $(NaC_2H_3O_2)$ to enough water to form 2.00 L of solution. (a) Determine the pH of the buffer. (b) Write the complete ionic equation for the reaction that occurs when a few drops of hydrochloric acid are added to the buffer. (c) Write the complete ionic equation for the reaction that occurs when a few drops of sodium hydroxide solution are added to the buffer.

17.22 A buffer is prepared by adding 5.0 g of ammonia (NH_3) and 20.0 g of ammonium chloride (NH_4Cl) to enough water to form 2.50 L of solution. (a) What is the pH of this buffer? (b) Write the complete ionic equation for the reaction that occurs when a few drops of nitric acid are added to the buffer. (c) Write the complete ionic equation for the reaction that occurs when a few drops of potassium hydroxide solution are added to the buffer.

17.23 How many moles of sodium hypobromite (NaBrO) should be added to 1.00 L of $0.050\ M$ hypobromous acid (HBrO) to form a buffer solution of pH 9.15? Assume that no volume change occurs when the NaBrO is added.

17.24 How many grams of sodium lactate $(NaC_3H_5O_3)$ should be added to 1.00 L of $0.150\ M$ lactic acid $(HC_3H_5O_3)$ to form a buffer solution with pH 4.00? Assume that no volume change occurs when the $NaC_3H_5O_3$ is added.

17.25 A buffer solution contains 0.10 mol of acetic acid and 0.13 mol of sodium acetate in 1.00 L. (a) What is the pH of this buffer? (b) What is the pH of the buffer after the addition of 0.02 mol of KOH? (c) What is the pH of the buffer after the addition of 0.02 mol of HNO_3?

17.26 A buffer solution contains 0.12 mol of propionic acid $(HC_3H_5O_2)$ and 0.10 mol of sodium propionate $(NaC_3H_5O_2)$ in 1.50 L. (a) What is the pH of this buffer? (b) What is the pH of the buffer after the addition of 0.01 mol of NaOH? (c) What is the pH of the buffer after the addition of 0.01 mol of HI?

17.27 (a) What is the ratio of HCO_3^- to H_2CO_3 in blood of pH 7.4? (b) What is the ratio of HCO_3^- to H_2CO_3 in an exhausted marathon runner whose blood pH is 7.1?

17.28 A buffer, consisting of $H_2PO_4^-$ and HPO_4^{2-}, helps control the pH of physiological fluids. Many carbonated soft drinks also use this buffer system. What is the pH of a soft drink in which the major buffer ingredients are 6.5 g of NaH_2PO_4 and 8.0 g of Na_2HPO_4 per 355 mL of solution?

17.29 You have to prepare a pH 3.50 buffer, and you have the following $0.10\ M$ solutions available: $HCHO_2$, $HC_2H_3O_2$, H_3PO_4, $NaCHO_2$, $NaC_2H_3O_2$, and NaH_2PO_4. Which solutions would you use? How many milliliters of each solution would you use to make approximately a liter of the buffer?

17.30 You have to prepare a pH 4.80 buffer, and you have the following $0.10\ M$ solutions available: formic acid, sodium formate, propionic acid, sodium propionate, phosphoric acid, and sodium dihydrogen phosphate. Which solutions would you use? How many milliliters of each solution would you use to make approximately a liter of the buffer?

Acid-Base Titrations

17.31 The accompanying graph shows the titration curves for two monoprotic acids. (a) Which curve is that of a strong acid? (b) What is the approximate pH at the equivalence point of each titration? (c) How do the original concentrations of the two acids compare if 40.0 mL of each is titrated to the equivalence point with the same volume of $0.100\ M$ base?

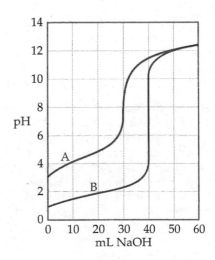

17.32 How does titration of a strong, monoprotic acid with a strong base differ from titration of a weak, monoprotic acid with a strong base with respect to the following: **(a)** quantity of base required to reach the equivalence point, **(b)** pH at the beginning of the titration, **(c)** pH at the equivalence point, **(d)** pH after addition of a slight excess of base, **(e)** choice of indicator for determining the equivalence point?

17.33 Predict whether the equivalence point of each of the following titrations is below, above, or at pH 7: **(a)** $NaHCO_3$ titrated with NaOH, **(b)** NH_3 titrated with HCl, **(c)** KOH titrated with HBr.

17.34 Predict whether the equivalence point of each of the following titrations is below, above, or at pH 7: **(a)** formic acid titrated with NaOH, **(b)** calcium hydroxide titrated with perchloric acid, **(c)** pyridine titrated with nitric acid.

17.35 Two monoprotic acids, both 0.100 M in concentration, are titrated with 0.100 M NaOH. The pH at the equivalence point for HX is 8.8, and that for HY is 7.9. **(a)** Which is the weaker acid? **(b)** Which indicators in Figure 16.7 could be used to titrate each of these acids?

17.36 Assume that 30.0 mL of a 0.10 M solution of a weak base B that accepts one proton is titrated with a 0.10 M solution of the monoprotic strong acid HX. **(a)** How many moles of HX have been added at the equivalence point? **(b)** What is the predominant form of B at the equivalence point? **(c)** What factor determines the pH at the equivalence point? **(d)** Which indicator, phenolphthalein or methyl red, is likely to be the better choice for this titration?

17.37 How many milliliters of 0.0850 M NaOH are required to titrate each of the following solutions to the equivalence point: **(a)** 40.0 mL of 0.0900 M HNO_3, **(b)** 35.0 mL of 0.0850 M $HC_2H_3O_2$, **(c)** 50.0 mL of a solution that contains 1.85 g of HCl per liter?

17.38 How many milliliters of 0.105 M HCl are needed to titrate each of the following solutions to the equivalence point: **(a)** 55.0 mL of 0.0950 M NaOH, **(b)** 22.5 mL of 0.118 M NH_3, **(c)** 125.0 mL of a solution that contains 1.35 g of NaOH per liter?

17.39 A 20.0-mL sample of 0.200 M HBr solution is titrated with 0.200 M NaOH solution. Calculate the pH of the solution after the following volumes of base have been added: **(a)** 15.0 mL, **(b)** 19.9 mL, **(c)** 20.0 mL, **(d)** 20.1 mL, **(e)** 35.0 mL.

17.40 A 30.0-mL sample of 0.150 M KOH is titrated with 0.125 M $HClO_4$ solution. Calculate the pH after the following volumes of acid have been added: **(a)** 30.0 mL, **(b)** 35.0 mL, **(c)** 36.0 mL, **(d)** 37.0 mL, **(e)** 40.0 mL.

17.41 A 35.0-mL sample of 0.150 M acetic acid ($HC_2H_3O_2$) is titrated with 0.150 M NaOH solution. Calculate the pH after the following volumes of base have been added: **(a)** 0 mL, **(b)** 17.5 mL, **(c)** 34.5 mL, **(d)** 35.0 mL, **(e)** 35.5 mL, **(f)** 50.0 mL.

17.42 Consider the titration of 30.0 mL of 0.030 M NH_3 with 0.025 M HCl. Calculate the pH after the following volumes of titrant have been added: **(a)** 0 mL, **(b)** 10.0 mL, **(c)** 20.0 mL, **(d)** 35.0 mL, **(e)** 36.0 mL, **(f)** 37.0 mL.

17.43 Calculate the pH at the equivalence point for titrating 0.200 M solutions of each of the following bases with 0.200 M HBr: **(a)** sodium hydroxide (NaOH), **(b)** hydroxylamine (NH_2OH), **(c)** aniline ($C_6H_5NH_2$).

17.44 Calculate the pH at the equivalence point in titrating 0.100 M solutions of each of the following with 0.080 M NaOH: **(a)** hydrobromic acid (HBr), **(b)** lactic acid ($HC_3H_5O_3$), **(c)** sodium hydrogen chromate ($NaHCrO_4$).

Solubility Equilibria and Factors Affecting Solubility

17.45 **(a)** Why is the concentration of undissolved solid not explicitly included in the expression for the solubility-product constant? **(b)** Write the expression for the solubility-product constant for each of the following strong electrolytes: AgI, $SrSO_4$, $Fe(OH)_2$, and Hg_2Br_2.

17.46 **(a)** Explain the difference between solubility and solubility-product constant. **(b)** Write the expression for the solubility-product constant for each of the following ionic compounds: $MnCO_3$, $Hg(OH)_2$, and $Cu_3(PO_4)_2$.

17.47 **(a)** If the molar solubility of CaF_2 at 35°C is 1.24×10^{-3} mol/L, what is K_{sp} at this temperature? **(b)** It is found that 1.1×10^{-2} g of SrF_2 dissolves per 100 mL of aqueous solution at 25°C. Calculate the solubility product for SrF_2. **(c)** The K_{sp} of $Ba(IO_3)_2$ at 25°C is 6.0×10^{-10}. What is the molar solubility of $Ba(IO_3)_2$?

17.48 **(a)** The molar solubility of $PbBr_2$ at 25°C is 1.0×10^{-2} mol/L. Calculate K_{sp}. **(b)** If 0.0490 g of $AgIO_3$ dissolves per liter of solution, calculate the solubility-product constant. **(c)** Using the appropriate K_{sp} value from Appendix D, calculate the solubility of $Cu(OH)_2$ in grams per liter of solution.

17.49 A 1.00-L solution saturated at 25°C with calcium oxalate (CaC_2O_4) contains 0.0061 g of CaC_2O_4. Calculate the solubility-product constant for this salt at 25°C.

17.50 A 1.00-L solution saturated at 25°C with lead(II) iodide contains 0.54 g of PbI_2. Calculate the solubility-product constant for this salt at 25°C.

17.51 Using Appendix D, calculate the molar solubility of AgBr in **(a)** pure water, **(b)** 3.0×10^{-2} M $AgNO_3$ solution, **(c)** 0.10 M NaBr solution.

17.52 Calculate the solubility of LaF_3 in grams per liter in **(a)** pure water, **(b)** 0.010 M KF solution, **(c)** 0.050 M $LaCl_3$ solution.

17.53 Calculate the solubility of $Mn(OH)_2$ in grams per liter when buffered at pH **(a)** 7.0, **(b)** 9.5, **(c)** 11.8.

17.54 Calculate the molar solubility of $Fe(OH)_2$ when buffered at pH **(a)** 7.0, **(b)** 10.0, **(c)** 12.0.

17.55 Which of the following salts will be substantially more soluble in acidic solution than in pure water: **(a)** $ZnCO_3$, **(b)** ZnS, **(c)** BiI_3, **(d)** AgCN, **(e)** $Ba_3(PO_4)_2$?

17.56 For each of the following slightly soluble salts, write the net ionic equation, if any, for reaction with acid: **(a)** MnS, **(b)** PbF_2, **(c)** $AuCl_3$, **(d)** $Hg_2C_2O_4$, **(e)** CuBr.

17.57 From the value of K_f listed in Table 17.1, calculate the concentration of Cu^{2+} in 1.0 L of a solution that contains a total of 1×10^{-3} mol of copper(II) ion and that is 0.10 M in NH_3.

17.58 To what final concentration of NH_3 must a solution be adjusted to just dissolve 0.020 mol of NiC_2O_4 ($K_{sp} = 4 \times 10^{-10}$) in 1.0 L of solution? [*Hint:* You can neglect the hydrolysis of $C_2O_4^{2-}$ because the solution will be quite basic.]

17.59 By using the values of K_{sp} for AgI and K_f for $Ag(CN)_2^-$, calculate the equilibrium constant for the reaction

$$AgI(s) + 2\,CN^-(aq) \rightleftharpoons Ag(CN)_2^-(aq) + I^-(aq)$$

17.60 Using the value of K_{sp} for Ag_2S, K_{a1} and K_{a2} for H_2S, and $K_f = 1.1 \times 10^5$ for $AgCl_2^-$, calculate the equilibrium constant for the following reaction:

$$Ag_2S(s) + 4\,Cl^-(aq) + 2\,H^+(aq) \rightleftharpoons$$
$$2\,AgCl_2^-(aq) + H_2S(aq)$$

Precipitation; Qualitative Analysis

17.61 **(a)** Will $Ca(OH)_2$ precipitate from solution if the pH of a 0.050 M solution of $CaCl_2$ is adjusted to 8.0? **(b)** Will Ag_2SO_4 precipitate when 100 mL of 0.050 M $AgNO_3$ is mixed with 10 mL of 5.0×10^{-2} M Na_2SO_4 solution?

17.62 **(a)** Will $Co(OH)_2$ precipitate from solution if the pH of a 0.020 M solution of $Co(NO_3)_2$ is adjusted to 8.5? **(b)** Will $AgIO_3$ precipitate when 100 mL of 0.010 M $AgNO_3$ is mixed with 10 mL of 0.015 M $NaIO_3$? (K_{sp} of $AgIO_3$ is 3.1×10^{-8}.)

17.63 Calculate the minimum pH needed to precipitate $Mn(OH)_2$ so completely that the concentration of Mn^{2+} is less than 1 μg per liter [1 part per billion (ppb)].

17.64 Suppose that a 10-mL sample of a solution is to be tested for Cl^- ion by addition of 1 drop (0.2 mL) of 0.10 M $AgNO_3$. What is the minimum number of grams of Cl^- that must be present in order for $AgCl(s)$ to form?

17.65 A solution contains 2.0×10^{-4} M Ag^+ and 1.5×10^{-3} M Pb^{2+}. If NaI is added, will AgI ($K_{sp} = 8.3 \times 10^{-17}$) or PbI_2 ($K_{sp} = 7.9 \times 10^{-9}$) precipitate first? Specify the concentration of I^- needed to begin precipitation.

17.66 A solution of Na_2SO_4 is added dropwise to a solution that is 0.010 M in Ba^{2+} and 0.010 M in Sr^{2+}. **(a)** What concentration of SO_4^{2-} is necessary to begin precipitation? (Neglect volume changes. $BaSO_4$: $K_{sp} = 1.1 \times 10^{-10}$; $SrSO_4$: $K_{sp} = 3.2 \times 10^{-7}$.) **(b)** Which cation precipitates first? **(c)** What is the concentration of SO_4^{2-} when the second cation begins to precipitate?

17.67 A solution containing an unknown number of metal ions is treated with dilute HCl; no precipitate forms. The pH is adjusted to about 1, and H_2S is bubbled through. Again, no precipitate forms. The pH of the solution is then adjusted to about 8. Again, H_2S is bubbled through. This time a precipitate forms. The filtrate from this solution is treated with $(NH_4)_2HPO_4$. No precipitate forms. Which metal ions discussed in Section 17.7

are possibly present? Which are definitely absent within the limits of these tests?

17.68 An unknown solid is entirely soluble in water. On addition of dilute HCl, a precipitate forms. After the precipitate is filtered off, the pH is adjusted to about 1 and H_2S is bubbled in; a precipitate again forms. After filtering off this precipitate, the pH is adjusted to 8 and H_2S is again added; no precipitate forms. No precipitate forms upon addition of $(NH_4)_2HPO_4$. The remaining solution shows a yellow color in a flame test. Based on these observations, which of the following compounds might be present, which are definitely present, and which are definitely absent: CdS, $Pb(NO_3)_2$, HgO, $ZnSO_4$, $Cd(NO_3)_2$, and Na_2SO_4?

17.69 In the course of various qualitative analysis procedures, the following mixtures are encountered: **(a)** Zn^{2+} and Cd^{2+}, **(b)** $Cr(OH)_3$ and $Fe(OH)_3$, **(c)** Mg^{2+} and K^+, **(d)** Ag^+ and Mn^{2+}. Suggest how each mixture might be separated.

17.70 Suggest how the cations in each of the following solution mixtures can be separated: **(a)** Na^+ and Cd^{2+}, **(b)** Cu^{2+} and Mg^{2+}, **(c)** Pb^{2+} and Al^{3+}, **(d)** Ag^+ and Hg^{2+}.

17.71 **(a)** Precipitation of the group 4 cations (Figure 17.22) requires a basic medium. Why is this so? **(b)** What is the most significant difference between the sulfides precipitated in group 2 and those precipitated in group 3? **(c)** Suggest a procedure that would serve to redissolve the group 3 cations following their precipitation.

17.72 A student who is in a great hurry to finish his laboratory work decides that his qualitative analysis unknown contains a metal ion from the insoluble phosphate group, group 4 (Figure 17.22). He therefore tests his sample directly with $(NH_4)_2HPO_4$, skipping earlier tests for the metal ions in groups 1, 2, and 3. He observes a precipitate and concludes that a metal ion from group 4 is indeed present. Why is this possibly an erroneous conclusion?

Additional Exercises

17.73 Furoic acid ($HC_5H_3O_3$) has a K_a value of 6.76×10^{-4} at 25°C. Calculate the pH at 25°C of **(a)** a solution formed by adding 35.0 g of furoic acid and 30.0 g of sodium furoate ($NaC_5H_3O_3$) to enough water to form 0.250 L of solution; **(b)** a solution formed by mixing 30.0 mL of 0.250 M $HC_5H_3O_3$ and 20.0 mL of 0.22 M $NaC_5H_3O_3$

and diluting the total volume to 125 mL; **(c)** a solution prepared by adding 50.0 mL of 1.65 M NaOH solution to 0.500 L of 0.0850 M $HC_5H_3O_3$.

17.74 The acid-base indicator bromcresol green is a weak acid. The yellow acid and blue base forms of the indicator are present in equal concentrations in a solution when the pH is 4.68. What is the pK_a for bromcresol green?

17.75 Equal quantities of 0.010 M solutions of an acid HA and a base B are mixed. The pH of the resulting solution is 9.2. **(a)** Write the equilibrium equation and equilibrium-constant expression for the reaction between HA and B. **(b)** If K_a for HA is 8.0×10^{-5}, what is the value of the equilibrium constant for the reaction between HA and B? **(c)** What is the value of K_b for B?

17.76 Two buffers are prepared by adding an equal number of moles of formic acid ($HCHO_2$) and sodium formate ($NaCHO_2$) to enough water to make 1.00 L of solution. Buffer A is prepared using 1.00 mol each of formic acid and sodium formate. Buffer B is prepared by using 0.010 mol of each. **(a)** Calculate the pH of each buffer, and explain why they are equal. **(b)** Which buffer will have the greater buffer capacity? Explain. **(c)** Calculate the change in pH for each buffer upon the addition of 1.0 mL of 1.00 M HCl. **(d)** Calculate the change in pH for each buffer upon the addition of 10 mL of 1.00 M HCl. **(e)** Discuss your answers for parts (c) and (d) in light of your response to part (b).

17.77 A biochemist needs 750 mL of an acetic acid–sodium acetate buffer with pH 4.50. Solid sodium acetate ($NaC_2H_3O_2$) and glacial acetic acid ($HC_2H_3O_2$) are available. Glacial acetic acid is 99% $HC_2H_3O_2$ by mass and has a density of 1.05 g/mL. If the buffer is to be 0.20 M in $HC_2H_3O_2$, how many grams of $NaC_2H_3O_2$ and how many milliliters of glacial acetic acid must be used?

17.78 A sample of 0.2140 g of an unknown monoprotic acid was dissolved in 25.0 mL of water and titrated with 0.0950 M NaOH. The acid required 27.4 mL of base to reach the equivalence point. **(a)** What is the molar mass of the acid? **(b)** After 15.0 mL of base had been added in the titration, the pH was found to be 6.50. What is the K_a for the unknown acid?

17.79 Show that the pH at the halfway point of a titration of a weak acid with a strong base (where the volume of added base is half of that needed to reach the equivalence point) is equal to pK_a for the acid.

17.80 Potassium hydrogen phthalate, often abbreviated KHP, can be obtained in high purity and is used to determine the concentrations of solutions of strong bases. Strong bases react with the hydrogen phthalate ion as follows:

$$HP^-(aq) + OH^-(aq) \longrightarrow H_2O(l) + P^{2-}(aq)$$

The molar mass of KHP is 204.2 g/mol and K_a for the HP^- ion is 3.1×10^{-6}. **(a)** If a titration experiment begins with 0.4885 g of KHP and has a final volume of about 100 mL, which indicator from Figure 16.7 would be most appropriate? **(b)** If the titration required 38.55 mL of NaOH solution to reach the end point, what is the concentration of the NaOH solution?

17.81 If 40.00 mL of 0.100 M Na_2CO_3 is titrated with 0.100 M HCl, calculate **(a)** the pH at the start of the titration; **(b)** the volume of HCl required to reach the first equivalence point and the predominant species present at this point; **(c)** the volume of HCl required to reach the second equivalence point and the predominant species present at this point; **(d)** the pH at the second equivalence point.

17.82 A hypothetical weak acid, HA, was combined with NaOH in the following proportions: 0.20 mol of HA, 0.080 mol of NaOH. The mixture was diluted to a total volume of 1.0 L, and the pH measured. **(a)** If pH = 4.80, what is the pK_a of the acid? **(b)** How many additional moles of NaOH should be added to the solution to increase the pH to 5.00?

[17.83] What is the pH of a solution made by mixing 0.30 mol NaOH, 0.25 mol Na_2HPO_4, and 0.20 mol H_3PO_4 with water and diluting to 1.00 L?

[17.84] Suppose you want to do a physiological experiment that calls for a pH 6.5 buffer. You find that the organism with which you are working is not sensitive to the weak acid H_2X ($K_{a1} = 2 \times 10^{-2}$; $K_{a2} = 5.0 \times 10^{-7}$), or its sodium salts. You have available a 1.0 M solution of this acid and a 1.0 M solution of NaOH. How much of the NaOH solution should be added to 1.0 L of the acid to give a buffer at pH 6.50? (Ignore any volume change.)

[17.85] How many microliters of 1.000 M NaOH solution must be added to 25.00 mL of a 0.1000 M solution of lactic acid ($HC_3H_5O_3$) to produce a buffer with pH = 3.75?

17.86 A person suffering from anxiety begins breathing rapidly and as a result suffers alkalosis, an increase in blood pH. **(a)** Using Equation 17.10, explain how rapid breathing can cause the pH of blood to increase. **(b)** One cure for this problem is breathing in a paper bag. Why does this procedure lower blood pH?

17.87 For each pair of compounds, use K_{sp} values to determine which has the greater molar solubility: **(a)** CdS or CuS, **(b)** $PbCO_3$ or $BaCrO_4$, **(c)** $Ni(OH)_2$ or $NiCO_3$, **(d)** AgI or Ag_2SO_4.

17.88 A saturated solution of $Mg(OH)_2$ in water has a pH of 10.38. Estimate the K_{sp} for this compound.

17.89 Excess $Ca(OH)_2$ is shaken with water to produce a saturated solution. The solution is filtered, and a 50.00-mL sample titrated with HCl requires 11.23 mL of 0.0983 M HCl to reach the end point. Calculate K_{sp} for $Ca(OH)_2$. Compare your result with that in Appendix D. Do you think the solution was kept at 25°C?

17.90 The solubility-product constant for barium permanganate, $Ba(MnO_4)_2$, is 2.5×10^{-10}. Suppose that solid $Ba(MnO_4)_2$ is in equilibrium with a solution of $KMnO_4$. What concentration of $KMnO_4$ is required to establish a concentration of 2.0×10^{-8} M for the Ba^{2+} ion in solution?

17.91 Calculate the ratio of $[Ca^{2+}]$ to $[Fe^{2+}]$ in a lake in which the water is in equilibrium with deposits of both $CaCO_3$ and $FeCO_3$, assuming that the water is slightly basic and that the hydrolysis of the carbonate ion can therefore be ignored.

[17.92] The solubility products of $PbSO_4$ and $SrSO_4$ are 6.3×10^{-7} and 3.2×10^{-7}, respectively. What are the values of $[SO_4^{2-}]$, $[Pb^{2+}]$, and $[Sr^{2+}]$ in a solution at equilibrium with both substances?

[17.93] What pH buffer solution is needed to give a Mg^{2+} concentration of 3.0×10^{-2} M in equilibrium with solid magnesium oxalate?

[17.94] The value of K_{sp} for $Mg_3(AsO_4)_2$ is 2.1×10^{-20}. The AsO_4^{3-} ion is derived from the weak acid H_3AsO_4 ($pK_{a1} = 2.22$; $pK_{a2} = 6.98$; $pK_{a3} = 11.50$). When asked to calculate the molar solubility of $Mg_3(AsO_4)_2$ in water, a student used the K_{sp} expression and assumed that $[Mg^{2+}] = 1.5[AsO_4^{3-}]$. Why was this a mistake?

[17.95] The solubility product for $Zn(OH)_2$ is 3.0×10^{-16}. The formation constant for the hydroxo complex, $Zn(OH)_4^{2-}$, is 4.6×10^{17}. What concentration of OH^- is required to dissolve 0.015 mol of $Zn(OH)_2$ in a liter of solution?

Integrative Exercises

17.96 (a) Write the net ionic equation for the reaction that occurs when a solution of hydrochloric acid (HCl) is mixed with a solution of sodium formate ($NaCHO_2$). **(b)** Calculate the equilibrium constant for this reaction. **(c)** Calculate the equilibrium concentrations of Na^+, Cl^-, H^+, CHO_2^-, and $HCHO_2$ when 50.0 mL of 0.15 M HCl is mixed with 50.0 mL of 0.15 M $NaCHO_2$.

17.97 (a) A 0.1044-g sample of an unknown monoprotic acid requires 22.10 mL of 0.0500 M NaOH to reach the end point. What is the molecular weight of the unknown? **(b)** As the acid is titrated, the pH of the solution after the addition of 11.05 mL of the base is 4.89. What is the K_a for the acid? **(c)** Using Appendix D, suggest the identity of the acid. Do both the molecular weight and K_a value agree with your choice?

17.98 A sample of 7.5 L of NH_3 gas at 22°C and 735 torr is bubbled into a 0.50-L solution of 0.40 M HCl. Assuming that all the NH_3 dissolves and that the volume of the solution remains 0.50 L, calculate the pH of the resulting solution.

17.99 Aspirin has the structural formula

At body temperature (37°C), K_a for aspirin equals 3×10^{-5}. If two aspirin tablets, each having a mass of 325 mg, are dissolved in a full stomach whose volume is 1 L and whose pH is 2, what percent of the aspirin is in the form of neutral molecules?

17.100 What is the pH at 25°C of water saturated with CO_2 at a partial pressure of 1.10 atm? The Henry's law constant for CO_2 at 25°C is 3.1×10^{-2} mol/L-atm. The CO_2 is an acidic oxide, reacting with H_2O to form H_2CO_3.

17.101 The osmotic pressure of a saturated solution of strontium sulfate at 25°C is 21 torr. What is the solubility product of this salt at 25°C?

17.102 A concentration of 10–100 parts per billion (by mass) of Ag^+ is an effective disinfectant in swimming pools. However, if the concentration exceeds this range, the Ag^+ can cause adverse health effects. One way to maintain an appropriate concentration of Ag^+ is to add a slightly soluble salt to the pool. Using K_{sp} values from Appendix D, calculate the equilibrium concentration of Ag^+ in parts per billion that would exist in equilibrium with **(a)** AgCl, **(b)** AgBr, **(c)** AgI.

[17.103] Fluoridation of drinking water is employed in many places to aid in the prevention of dental caries. Typically the F^- ion concentration is adjusted to about 1 ppb. Some water supplies are also "hard"; that is, they contain certain cations such as Ca^{2+} that interfere with the action of soap. Consider a case where the concentration of Ca^{2+} is 8 ppb. Could a precipitate of CaF_2 form under these conditions? (Make any necessary approximations.)

⦿ e MEDIA EXERCISES

These exercises make use of the interactive objects available online in OneKey or the Companion Website, and on your Accelerator CD. Access to these resources comes in your MediaPak.

17.104 The **Common-Ion Effect** animation (17.1) shows the solubility of an iodide salt being reduced by the addition of sodium iodide. **(a)** How would you expect the solubility of the salt to be affected by the addition of a strong acid? **(b)** How would you expect it to be affected by the addition of a strong base? Explain your reasoning for both answers.

17.105 (a) Using data from the **Calculating pH Using Henderson–Hasselbalch Equation** activity (17.2), determine the pK_a of benzoic acid ($C_6H_5CO_2H$). **(b)** Using the pK_a that you determined in part (a), calculate the pH of a 0.0015 M aqueous solution of benzoic acid. **(c)** Will the pH of the solution in part (b) change if it is diluted with water to twice its original volume? Explain.

(d) Will the pH of a buffer change when it is diluted with water to twice its original volume? If not, explain why not.

17.106 In Exercise 17.21 you calculated the pH of a buffer prepared by adding 20.0 g each of acetic acid and sodium acetate to enough water to make a 2.00-L solution. **(a)** Use the **Calculating pH Using Henderson–Hasselbalch Equation** activity (17.2) to prepare this buffer and verify your answer to Exercise 17.21. **(b)** Describe what is meant by the term *buffer capacity*. **(c)** Of which could you add more to the above buffer without causing a drastic change in pH, strong acid or strong base?

17.107 The **Dissolution of Mg(OH)$_2$ by Acid** animation (17.5) shows how the relatively insoluble solid $Mg(OH)_2$ can be made more soluble in water by the addition of acid. **(a)** Write the net ionic equation for the process by which magnesium hydroxide dissolves in neutral water. **(b)** Write the net ionic equation for the combination of two hydronium ions with two hydroxide ions. **(c)** Show that the net ionic equations in parts (a) and (b) add to give the overall net ionic equation shown in the anima-

tion. **(d)** Calculate the equilibrium constant for the process represented by the overall net ionic equation (i.e., dissolution of magnesium hydroxide in aqueous acid). **(e)** Determine the solubility of magnesium hydroxide in 0.010 M HCl.

⬡ eLABORATORY EXERCISES

These exercises allow students to apply the concepts and skills for this chapter in the simulated laboratory of Virtual ChemLab. Worksheets for each of these exercises are found in the Virtual ChemLab Workbook in your MediaPak.

17.108 *(VCL 17-1) Study of Acid-Base Titrations: Monoprotic Acids*

Titrations provide a method of quantitatively measuring the concentration of an unknown solution. In an acid-base titration this is done by delivering a titrant of known concentration into an analyte of known volume. (The concentration of an unknown titrant can also be determined by titration with an analyte of known concentration and volume.) Titration curves (graphs of volume versus pH) have characteristic shapes. By comparison, the graph can be used to determine the strength or weakness of an acid or base. The equivalence point of the titration, or the point where the analyte has been completely consumed by the titrant, is identified by the point where the pH changes rapidly over a small volume of titrant delivered. In this assignment you will observe this titration curve by titrating the strong acid HCl with the strong base NaOH.

17.109 *(VCL 17-2) Weak Acid–Strong Base Titrations*

In this assignment you will observe a titration curve associated with a weak acid and strong base by titrating the acid CH_3COOH (acetic acid) with the base NaOH. You will also predict the pH at the equivalence point, validate your prediction experimentally, and calculate the equilibrium constant for the neutralization reaction.

17.110 *(VCL 17-3) Strong Acid–Weak Base Titrations*

In this assignment you will observe a titration curve associated with a strong acid and weak base by titrating the weak base $NaHCO_3$ (baking soda) with the strong acid HCl. You will also predict the pH at the equivalence point, validate your prediction experimentally, and calculate the equilibrium constant for the neutralization reaction.

17.111 *(VCL 17-4) Weak Acid–Weak Base Titrations*

In this assignment you will observe a titration curve associated with a weak acid and weak base by titrating the acid CH_3COOH (acetic acid) with the weak base NH_3. You will also predict the pH at the equivalence point, validate your prediction experimentally, and calculate the equilibrium constant for the neutralization reaction.

17.112 *(VCL 17-5) Study of Acid-Base Titrations: Polyprotic Acids*

Titrations provide a method of quantitatively measuring the concentration of an unknown solution. The equivalence point of the titration, or the point where the analyte has been completely consumed by the titrant, is identified by the point where the pH changes

rapidly over a small volume of titrant delivered. For polyprotic acids, there will be multiple equivalence points. In this assignment you will observe a polyprotic acid titration curve by titrating the acid H_2SO_3 with the strong base NaOH.

17.113 *(VCL 17-6) Acid-Base Standardization*

In this assignment you will determine the molarity of an unknown solution of NaOH by titrating against a primary standard, potassium hydrogen phthalate (KHP).

17.114 *(VCL 17-7) Analysis of Baking Soda*

In this assignment you will determine the mass percent of an unknown sample of baking soda ($NaHCO_3$) by titrating with an NaOH solution of known concentration.

17.115 *(VCL 17-8) Identification of Cations in Solution: Flame Tests*

The process of determining the composition of a sample by conducting chemical tests is called qualitative analysis. By using the appropriate tests and applying logic, the identities of the ions present in an unknown solution can be determined. A qualitative analysis scheme is typically made up of a systematic set of chemical reactions where a certain subset of the ions present in the solution are selectively precipitated and removed. The colors of the precipitates and solutions provide the means to identify the ions present. Flame tests are also used to identify certain ions that are difficult to identify chemically. In this assignment you will learn how flame tests are used to identify the cations Na^+ and K^+. As you complete this analysis, remember that careful observation and logical reasoning are the keys to a successful qualitative analysis.

17.116 *(VCL 17-9) Identification of Cations in Solution: Ag^+, Hg_2^{2+}, Pb^{2+}*

In this assignment you will learn the basics of a qualitative analysis scheme by performing an analysis on a mixture of Ag^+, Hg_2^{2+}, and Pb^{2+}.

17.117 *(VCL 17-10) Identification of Cations in Solution: Co^{2+}, Cr^{2+}, Cu^{2+}*

In this assignment you will learn the basics of a qualitative analysis scheme by performing an analysis on a mixture of Co^{2+}, Cr^{3+}, and Cu^{2+}.

17.118 *(VCL 17-11) Identification of Cations in Solution: Ba^{2+}, Sr^{2+}, Ca^{2+}, Mg^{2+}*

In this assignment you will need to develop your own qualitative analysis scheme to separate and identify the group II cations Ba^{2+}, Sr^{2+}, Ca^{2+}, and Mg^{2+}.

17.119 *(VCL 17-12) Identification of Cations in Solution: Co^{2+}, Cu^{2+}, Ni^{2+}*

In this assignment you will need to develop your own qualitative analysis scheme to separate and identify the transition-metal cations Co^{2+}, Cu^{2+}, and Ni^{2+}.

Science Fundamentals Second Edition

Chapter 23

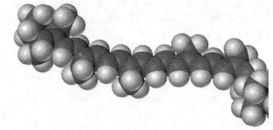

Organic Chemistry

From the very beginning of chemical studies in the mid-1700s, people noticed that substances from plants and animals were more difficult to purify and work with than those from minerals. To express this difference, the term *organic chemistry* was used to mean the study of compounds from living organisms, while *inorganic chemistry* was used for the study of compounds from nonliving sources. Today we know that there are no fundamental differences between organic

▲ Flamingos owe their color to organic chemicals in their diet. Without these compounds, the feathers eventually turn white.

CONTENTS

23.1 The Nature of Organic Molecules

23.2 Alkanes and Their Isomers

23.3 Drawing Organic Structures

23.4 The Shapes of Organic Molecules

23.5 Naming Alkanes

23.6 Cycloalkanes

23.7 Reactions of Alkanes

23.8 Families of Organic Molecules: Functional Groups

23.9 Alkenes and Alkynes

23.10 Reactions of Alkenes and Alkynes

23.11 Aromatic Compounds and Their Reactions

23.12 Alcohols, Ethers, and Amines

23.13 Aldehydes and Ketones

23.14 Carboxylic Acids, Esters, and Amides

23.15 Synthetic Polymers

■ Interlude—*Natural or Synthetic?*

985

and inorganic compounds—the same principles apply to both. The only common characteristic of compounds from living sources is that all contain the element *carbon*. Thus, **organic chemistry** is now defined as the study of carbon compounds.

Why is carbon special, and why do chemists still treat organic chemistry as a separate branch of science? The answers to these questions involve the ability of carbon atoms to bond together, forming long chains and rings. Of all the elements, only carbon is able to form such an immense array of compounds, from methane, with one carbon atom, to deoxyribonucleic acid (DNA), with tens of billions of carbon atoms. More than 19 million organic compounds have been made, and thousands of new ones are made each week in chemical laboratories throughout the world.

23.1 | The Nature of Organic Molecules

Let's review what we've seen in earlier chapters about organic molecules:

- Carbon is *tetravalent* (Section 7.5); it has four outer-shell electrons ($1s^2\,2s^2\,2p^2$) and forms four bonds. In methane, for instance, carbon is bonded to four hydrogen atoms:

$$H-\underset{\underset{\textstyle H}{\textstyle |}}{\overset{\overset{\textstyle H}{\textstyle |}}{C}}-H \qquad \text{Methane, } CH_4$$

- Organic molecules have *covalent bonds* (Section 7.1). In ethane, for instance, all bonds result from the sharing of two electrons, either between C and C or between C and H:

$$H\!:\!\overset{\overset{\textstyle H}{..}}{\underset{\underset{\textstyle H}{..}}{C}}\!:\!\overset{\overset{\textstyle H}{..}}{\underset{\underset{\textstyle H}{..}}{C}}\!:\!H \;=\; H-\underset{\underset{\textstyle H}{\textstyle |}}{\overset{\overset{\textstyle H}{\textstyle |}}{C}}-\underset{\underset{\textstyle H}{\textstyle |}}{\overset{\overset{\textstyle H}{\textstyle |}}{C}}-H \qquad \text{Ethane, } C_2H_6 \text{ or } CH_3CH_3$$

- Organic molecules have *polar covalent bonds* when carbon bonds to an element on the right or left side of the periodic table (Section 7.4). In chloromethane, the electronegative chlorine atom attracts electrons more strongly than carbon does, polarizing the C–Cl bond so that carbon has a partial positive charge, $\delta+$. In methyllithium, the lithium attracts electrons less strongly than carbon does, polarizing the carbon–lithium bond so that carbon has a partial negative charge, $\delta-$. In electrostatic potential maps, the chloromethane carbon thus appears blue (electron-poor), while the methyllithium carbon appears red (electron-rich).

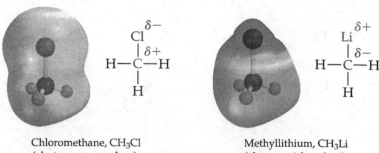

Chloromethane, CH_3Cl
(electron-poor carbon)

Methyllithium, CH_3Li
(electron-rich carbon)

- Carbon can form *multiple covalent bonds* by sharing more than two electrons with a neighboring atom (Section 7.5). In ethylene, the two carbon atoms share four electrons in a double bond. In acetylene, the two carbons share six electrons in a triple bond:

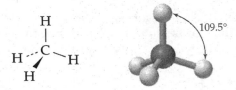

H:C:::C:H = H—C≡C—H   Acetylene, C_2H_2

- Organic molecules have specific three-dimensional shapes, which can be predicted by the VSEPR model (Section 7.9). When carbon is bonded to four atoms, as in methane, the bonds are oriented toward the four corners of a tetrahedron with carbon in the center and with H–C–H angles near 109.5°:

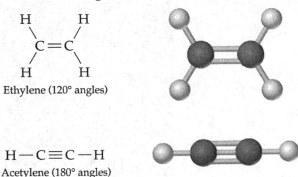

When carbon bonds to three atoms, as in ethylene, the bonds are at angles of approximately 120° to one another. When carbon bonds to two atoms, as in acetylene, the bonds are at angles of 180°.

Ethylene (120° angles)

Acetylene (180° angles)

- Carbon uses *hybrid atomic orbitals* for bonding (Sections 7.11 and 7.12). A carbon that bonds to four atoms uses sp^3 orbitals, formed by the combination of an atomic s orbital with three atomic p orbitals. These sp^3 orbitals point toward the corners of a tetrahedron, accounting for the observed geometry of carbon.

  Doubly bonded carbons are sp^2-hybridized. Carbon has three sp^2 hybrid orbitals, which lie in a plane and point toward the corners of an equilateral triangle, and one unhybridized p orbital, which is oriented at a 90° angle to the plane of the sp^2 hybrids. When two sp^2-hybridized carbon atoms approach each other with sp^2 orbitals aligned head-on for sigma bonding, the unhybridized p orbitals on each carbon overlap to form a pi bond, resulting in a net carbon–carbon double bond.

  Triply bonded carbons are sp-hybridized. Carbon has two sp hybrid orbitals, which are 180° away from each other, and two unhybridized p orbitals, which are oriented 90° from the sp hybrids and 90° from each other. When two sp-hybridized carbon atoms approach each other with sp orbitals aligned head-on for sigma bonding, the p orbitals on each carbon overlap to form two pi bonds, resulting in a net carbon–carbon triple bond.

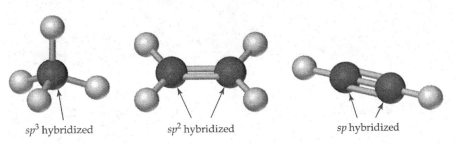

sp^3 hybridized sp^2 hybridized sp hybridized

Science Fundamentals Second Edition

Covalent bonding gives organic compounds properties that are quite different from those of ionic compounds. Intermolecular forces between individual organic molecules are relatively weak, and organic compounds therefore have lower melting and boiling points than do ionic compounds. In fact, many simple organic compounds are liquid at room temperature. In addition, most organic compounds are insoluble in water and don't conduct electricity. Only a few small polar organic molecules such as glucose, acetic acid, and ethyl alcohol dissolve in water.

23.2 | Alkanes and Their Isomers

Why are there so many organic compounds? The answer is that a relatively small number of atoms can bond together in a great many ways. Take molecules that contain only carbon and hydrogen (**hydrocarbons**) and have only single bonds. Such compounds belong to the family of organic molecules called **saturated hydrocarbons**, or **alkanes**.

The paraffin wax coating ▶ that makes these apples so shiny is a mixture of alkanes.

If you imagine ways that one carbon and four hydrogens can combine, only methane, CH_4, is possible. If you imagine ways that two carbons and six hydrogens can combine, only ethane, C_2H_6, is possible; and if you imagine the combination of three carbons with eight hydrogens, only propane, C_3H_8, is possible.

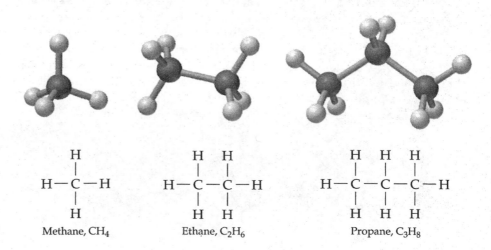

Methane, CH_4 Ethane, C_2H_6 Propane, C_3H_8

When larger numbers of carbons and hydrogens combine, though, *more than one structure can result*. There are two ways in which molecules with the formula C_4H_{10} can be formed: Either the four carbons can be in a row, or they can be in a branched arrangement. Similarly, there are three ways in which molecules with the formula C_5H_{12} can result, and even more ways for larger alkanes. Compounds with all their carbons connected in a row are called **straight-chain alkanes**, and those with a branching connection of carbons are called **branched-chain alkanes**.

C_4H_{10}

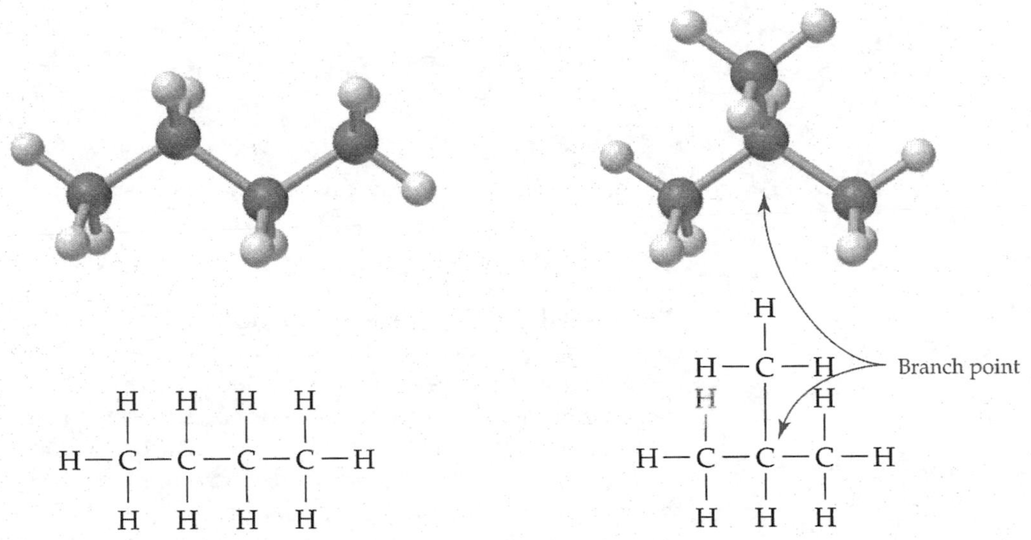

Butane (straight chain)

2-Methylpropane (branched chain)

Branch point

C_5H_{12}

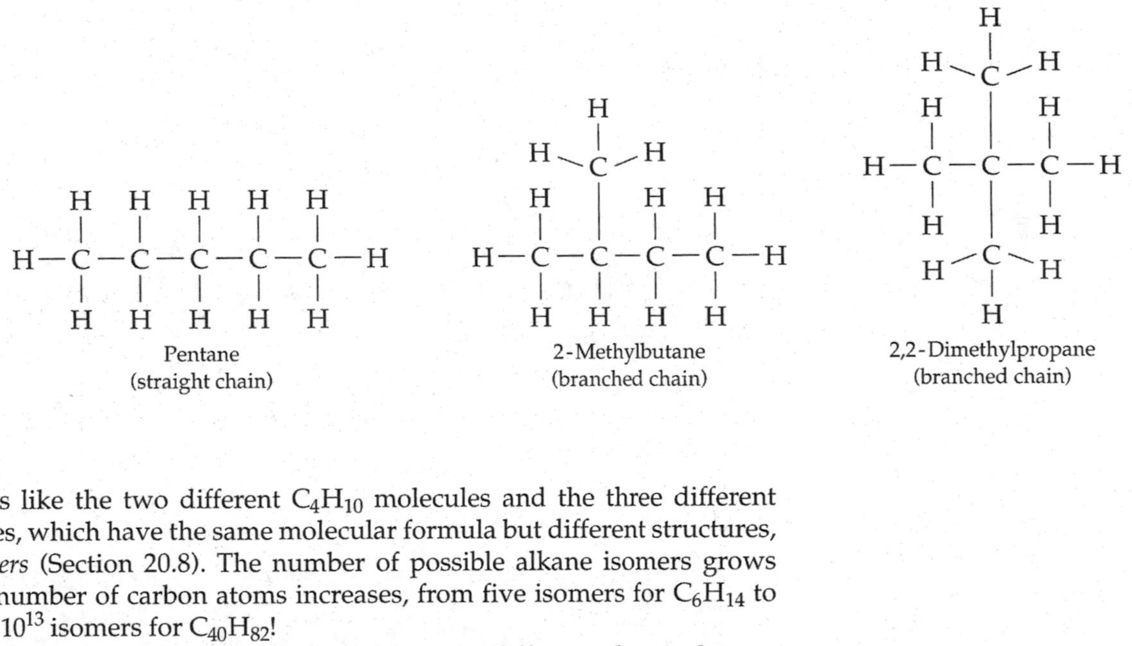

Pentane
(straight chain)

2-Methylbutane
(branched chain)

2,2-Dimethylpropane
(branched chain)

Compounds like the two different C_4H_{10} molecules and the three different C_5H_{12} molecules, which have the same molecular formula but different structures, are called *isomers* (Section 20.8). The number of possible alkane isomers grows rapidly as the number of carbon atoms increases, from five isomers for C_6H_{14} to more than 6×10^{13} isomers for $C_{40}H_{82}$!

It's important to realize that different isomers are different chemical compounds. They have different structures, different chemical properties, and different physical properties, such as melting point and boiling point. For example, ethyl alcohol (ethanol, or grain alcohol) and dimethyl ether both have the formula C_2H_6O, yet ethyl alcohol is a liquid with a boiling point of 78.5°C, whereas dimethyl ether is a gas with a boiling point of −23°C.

Boiling Points activity

Science Fundamentals Second Edition

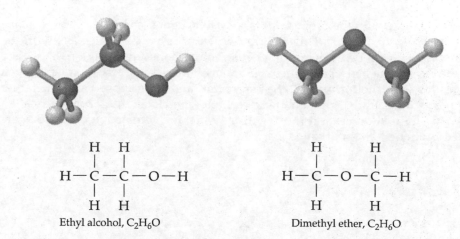

Ethyl alcohol, C_2H_6O Dimethyl ether, C_2H_6O

▶ **PROBLEM 23.1**   Draw the straight-chain isomer with the formula C_7H_{16}.

▶ **PROBLEM 23.2**   Draw the five alkane isomers with the formula C_6H_{14}.

23.3 | Drawing Organic Structures

It's both awkward and time-consuming to draw all the bonds and all the atoms in an organic molecule, even for a relatively small one like C_4H_{10}. Thus, a shorthand way of drawing **condensed structures** is often used. In condensed structures, carbon–hydrogen and most carbon–carbon single bonds aren't shown; rather, they're "understood." If a carbon atom has three hydrogens bonded to it, we write CH_3; if the carbon has two hydrogens bonded to it, we write CH_2; and so on. For example, the four-carbon, straight-chain alkane (called *butane*) and its branched-chain isomer (called *2-methylpropane*, or *isobutane*) can be written in the following way:

Butane Condensed
Structure activity

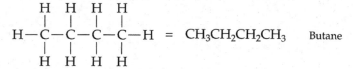

Note that the horizontal bonds between carbons aren't shown—the CH_3 and CH_2 units are simply placed next to each other—but the vertical bond in 2-methylpropane is shown for clarity.

WORKED KEY CONCEPT EXAMPLE 23.1

Give the formula of the following compound, and convert the model into a condensed structure:

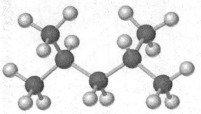

Strategy and Solution

The compound has 7 carbons and 16 hydrogens: C_7H_{16}. Its condensed structure is

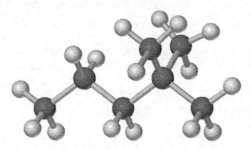

$$
\begin{array}{cc}
CH_3 & CH_3 \\
| & | \\
\end{array}
$$
$$CH_3CHCH_2CHCH_3$$

▶ **PROBLEM 23.3** Draw the three isomers of C_5H_{12} as condensed structures.

KEY CONCEPT PROBLEM 23.4 Give the formula of the following molecular model, and convert the model into a condensed structure.

23.4 | The Shapes of Organic Molecules

The condensed structure of an organic molecule implies nothing about three-dimensional shape; it only indicates the connections among atoms. Thus, a molecule can be arbitrarily drawn in many different ways. The branched-chain alkane called 2-methylbutane, for instance, might be represented by any of the following structures. All have four carbons connected in a row, with a –CH_3 branch on the second carbon from the end.

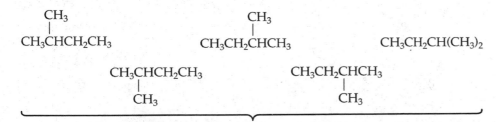

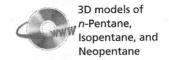

3D models of *n*-Pentane, Isopentane, and Neopentane

Some representations of 2-methylbutane

In fact, 2-methylbutane has no one single shape because *rotation* occurs around carbon–carbon single bonds. The two parts of a molecule joined by a carbon–carbon single bond are free to spin around the bond, giving rise to an infinite number of possible three-dimensional structures. Thus, a large sample of 2-methylbutane contains a great many molecules that are constantly changing their shape. At any given instant, though, most of the molecules have an extended, zigzag shape, which is slightly more stable than other possibilities. The same is true for other alkanes.

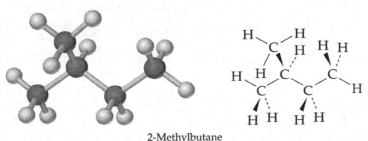

2-Methylbutane

Science Fundamentals Second Edition

WORKED EXAMPLE 23.2

The following condensed structures have the same formula, C_8H_{18}. Which of them represent the same molecule?

(a)
$$\begin{array}{cc} CH_3 & CH_3 \\ | & | \\ CH_3CHCH_2CHCH_2CH_3 \end{array}$$

(b)
$$\begin{array}{cc} CH_3 & CH_3 \\ | & | \\ CH_3CH_2CHCH_2CHCH_3 \end{array}$$

(c)
$$\begin{array}{cc} CH_3 & CH_3 \\ | & | \\ CH_3CHCH_2CH_2CHCH_3 \end{array}$$

STRATEGY

Pay attention to the order of connection between atoms. Don't get confused by the apparent differences caused by writing a structure right-to-left versus left-to-right.

SOLUTION

Structure (a) has a straight chain of six carbons with $-CH_3$ branches on the second and fourth carbons from the end. Structure (b) also has a straight chain of six carbons with $-CH_3$ branches on the second and fourth carbons from the end and is therefore identical to (a). The only difference between (a) and (b) is that one is written "forward" and one is written "backward." Structure (c) has a straight chain of six carbons with $-CH_3$ branches on the second and *fifth* carbons from the end, so it is an isomer of (a) and (b).

▶ **PROBLEM 23.5** Which of the following structures are identical?

(a)
$$\begin{array}{cc} CH_3 & CH_3 \\ | & | \\ CH_3CH_2CCH_2CHCH_3 \\ | \\ CH_3 \end{array}$$

(b)
$$\begin{array}{cc} CH_3 & CH_3 \\ | & | \\ CH_3CHCH_2CH_2CHCH_2CH_3 \end{array}$$

(c)
$$\begin{array}{c} CH_2CH_3 \\ | \\ CH_3CCH_2CHCH_3 \\ | \quad | \\ CH_3 \ CH_3 \end{array}$$

◀ **KEY CONCEPT PROBLEM 23.6** Are the following two structures identical?

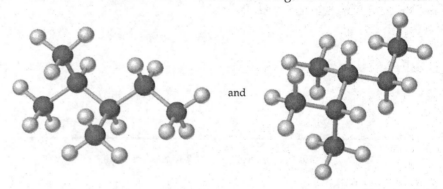

and

23.5 | Naming Alkanes

In earlier times, when relatively few pure organic chemicals were known, new compounds were named at the whim of their discoverer. Thus, urea is a crystalline substance first isolated from urine, and the barbiturates are a group of tranquilizing agents named by their discoverer in honor of his friend Barbara. As more and more compounds became known, however, the need for a systematic method of naming organic compounds became apparent.

The system of naming now used was devised by the International Union of Pure and Applied Chemistry, abbreviated IUPAC. In the IUPAC system, a chemical name has three parts: prefix, parent, and suffix. The parent name tells how many carbon atoms are present in the longest continuous chain; the suffix identifies what family the molecule belongs to; and the prefix (if needed) specifies the location of various substituent groups attached to the parent chain:

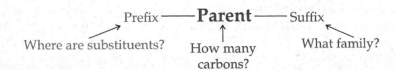

Straight-chain alkanes are named by counting the number of carbon atoms in the chain and adding the suffix -*ane*. With the exception of the first four compounds—methane, ethane, propane, and butane—whose names have historical origins, the alkanes are named from Greek numbers according to the number of carbons present. Thus, *pent*ane is the five-carbon alkane, *hex*ane is the six-carbon alkane, and so on, as shown in Table 23.1.

TABLE 23.1	Names of Straight-Chain Alkanes				
Number of Carbons	Structure	Name	Number of Carbons	Structure	Name
1	CH_4	Methane	6	$CH_3CH_2CH_2CH_2CH_2CH_3$	Hexane
2	CH_3CH_3	Ethane	7	$CH_3CH_2CH_2CH_2CH_2CH_2CH_3$	Heptane
3	$CH_3CH_2CH_3$	Propane	8	$CH_3CH_2CH_2CH_2CH_2CH_2CH_2CH_3$	Octane
4	$CH_3CH_2CH_2CH_3$	Butane	9	$CH_3CH_2CH_2CH_2CH_2CH_2CH_2CH_2CH_3$	Nonane
5	$CH_3CH_2CH_2CH_2CH_3$	Pentane	10	$CH_3CH_2CH_2CH_2CH_2CH_2CH_2CH_2CH_2CH_3$	Decane

Branched-chain alkanes are named by following four steps:

Step 1. Name the main chain. Find the longest continuous chain of carbons in the molecule, and use the name of that chain as the parent name. The longest chain may not always be obvious from the manner of writing; you may have to "turn corners" to find it:

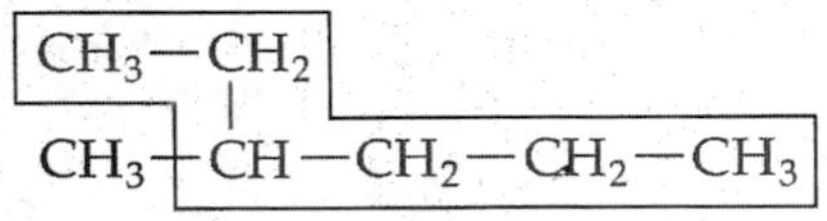

$$CH_3-CH_2$$
$$CH_3-CH-CH_2-CH_2-CH_3$$

Named as hexane, not as a pentane, because the longest chain has six carbons.

If you prefer, you can redraw the structure so that the longest chain is on one line:

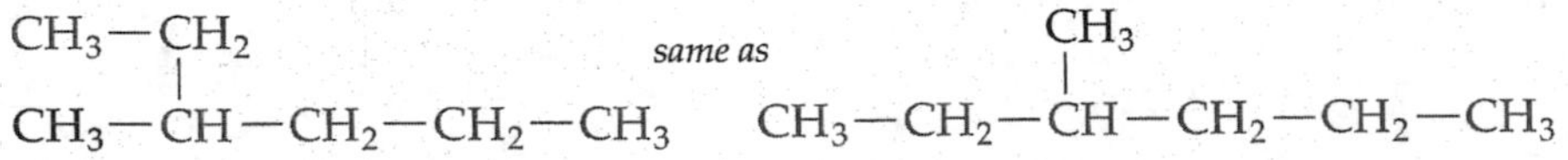

$$CH_3-CH_2$$
$$CH_3-CH-CH_2-CH_2-CH_3$$ *same as* $$CH_3-CH_2-CH-CH_2-CH_2-CH_3$$
$$CH_3$$

Step 2. Number the carbon atoms in the main chain. Beginning at the end nearer the first branch point, number each carbon atom in the parent chain:

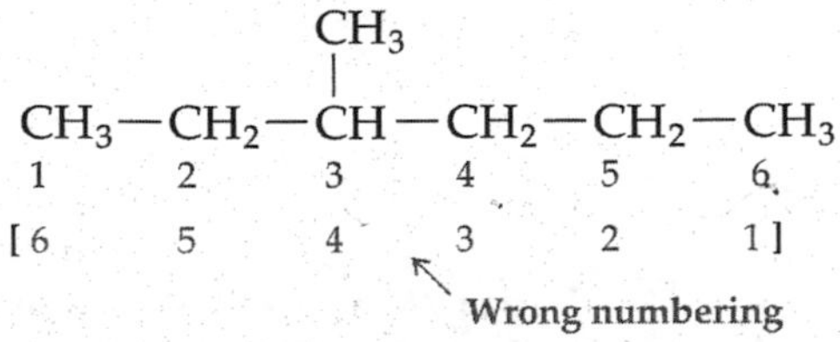

$$CH_3$$
$$CH_3-CH_2-CH-CH_2-CH_2-CH_3$$
$$123456$$
$$[654321]$$
Wrong numbering

The first (and only) branch occurs at the third carbon, C3, if we start numbering from the left, but would occur at C4 if we started from the right by mistake.

Step 3. Identify and number the branching substituent. Assign a number to each branching substituent group on the parent chain according to its point of attachment.

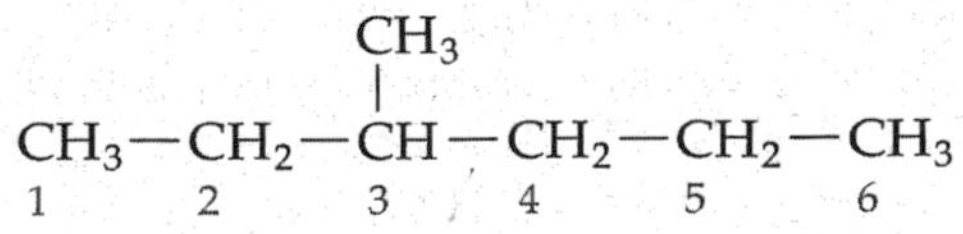

$$CH_3$$
$$CH_3-CH_2-CH-CH_2-CH_2-CH_3$$
$$123456$$

The main chain is a hexane. There is a –CH_3 substituent group connected to C3 of the chain.

Science Fundamentals Second Edition

If there are two substituent groups on the same carbon, assign the same number to both. There must always be as many numbers in the name as there are substituents.

$$CH_3-CH_2-\underset{\underset{\underset{CH_3}{|}}{\overset{\overset{CH_2-CH_3}{|}}{C}}}{}-CH_2-CH_2-CH_3$$

$$\underset{1}{}\quad\underset{2}{}\quad\underset{3}{}\quad\underset{4}{}\quad\underset{5}{}\quad\underset{6}{}$$

The main chain is hexane. There are two substituents, a $-CH_3$ and a $-CH_2CH_3$, both connected to C3 of the chain.

The $-CH_3$ and $-CH_2CH_3$ substituents that branch off the main chain in this compound are called **alkyl groups**. You can think of an alkyl group as the part of an alkane that remains when a hydrogen is removed. For example, removal of a hydrogen from methane, CH_4, gives the *methyl group*, $-CH_3$, and removal of a hydrogen from ethane, CH_3CH_3, gives the *ethyl group*, $-CH_2CH_3$. Alkyl groups are named by replacing the *-ane* ending of the parent alkane with an *-yl* ending.

Methane	A methyl group	Ethane	An ethyl group

Step 4. Write the name as a single word. Use hyphens to separate the different prefixes, and use commas to separate numbers when there are more than one. If two or more different substituent groups are present, list them in alphabetical order. If two or more identical substituents are present, use one of the prefixes *di-*, *tri-*, *tetra-*, and so forth, but don't use these numerical prefixes for alphabetizing purposes. That is, a prefix like "dimethyl" is listed alphabetically under "m" rather than under "d". Look at the following examples to see how names are written:

3-Methylhexane—a six-carbon main chain with a 3-methyl substituent

3-Ethyl-3-methylhexane—a six-carbon main chain with 3-ethyl and 3-methyl substituents

3,3-Dimethylhexane—a six-carbon main chain with two 3-methyl substituents

More About Alkyl Groups

It doesn't matter which hydrogen is removed from CH_4 to form a methyl group or which hydrogen is removed from CH_3CH_3 to form an ethyl group because all the hydrogen atoms in each molecule are equivalent. The eight hydrogens in $CH_3CH_2CH_3$, however, are not all equivalent. Propane has two "kinds" of hydrogens—six on the end carbons and two on the middle carbon. Depending on which kind of hydrogen is removed, two different propyl groups result. Removing one of the six hydrogens attached to an end carbon yields a straight-chain group called *propyl*, and removing one of the two hydrogens attached to the middle carbon yields a branched-chain group called *isopropyl*.

Similarly, there are four different kinds of butyl groups. Two (butyl and *sec*-butyl) are derived from straight-chain butane, and two (isobutyl and *tert*-butyl) are derived from branched-chain isobutane. The prefixes *sec*- (for *secondary*) and *tert*- (for *tertiary*) refer to the number of other carbon atoms attached to the branching carbon. There are two other carbons attached to the branch point in a *sec*-butyl group and three other carbons attached to the branch point in a *tert*-butyl group.

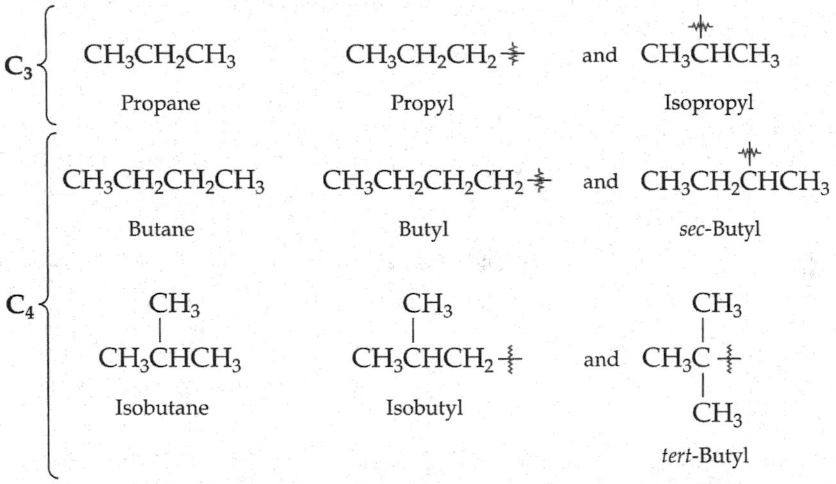

C_3 {
$CH_3CH_2CH_3$ — Propane

$CH_3CH_2CH_2$— Propyl

and CH_3CHCH_3 — Isopropyl
}

C_4 {
$CH_3CH_2CH_2CH_3$ — Butane

$CH_3CH_2CH_2CH_2$— Butyl

and $CH_3CH_2CHCH_3$ — *sec*-Butyl

$\underset{CH_3CHCH_3}{\overset{CH_3}{|}}$ — Isobutane

$\underset{CH_3CHCH_2}{\overset{CH_3}{|}}$— Isobutyl

and $\underset{\underset{CH_3}{|}}{\overset{CH_3}{|}}CH_3C$— — *tert*-Butyl
}

Keep in mind that alkyl groups themselves are not stable compounds and that the "removal" of a hydrogen from an alkane is just a useful way of looking at things, not a chemical reaction. Alkyl groups are simply parts of molecules that help us to name compounds.

WORKED EXAMPLE 23.3

What is the IUPAC name of the following alkane?

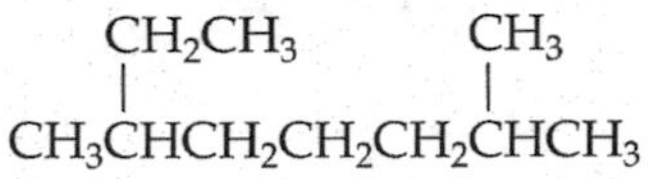

$$\underset{CH_3CHCH_2CH_2CH_2CHCH_3}{\overset{CH_2CH_3 \qquad\quad CH_3}{|\qquad\qquad\quad |}}$$

STRATEGY

Follow the steps outlined in the text: First, identify and number the longest continuous chain. Then identify the substituents and write the name.

SOLUTION

The molecule has a chain of eight carbons (octane) with two methyl substituents. Numbering from the end nearer the first methyl substituent indicates that the methyls are at C2 and C6, giving the name 2,6-dimethyloctane. The numbers are separated by a comma and are set off from the rest of the name by a hyphen.

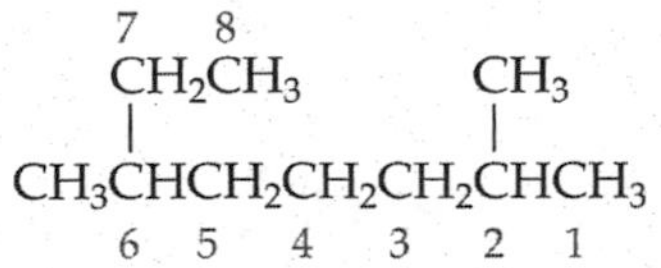

$$\overset{7\quad 8}{\underset{6\ \ 5\ \ \ 4\ \ \ 3\ \ \ 2\ \ \ 1}{\underset{CH_3CHCH_2CH_2CH_2CHCH_3}{\overset{CH_2CH_3 \qquad\quad CH_3}{|\qquad\qquad\quad |}}}}\qquad \text{2,6-Dimethyloctane}$$

WORKED EXAMPLE 23.4

Draw the structure of 3-isopropyl-2-methylhexane.

STRATEGY AND SOLUTION

First, look at the parent name (hexane) and draw its carbon structure:

C—C—C—C—C—C   Hexane

Next, find the substituents (3-isopropyl and 2-methyl) and place them on the proper carbons:

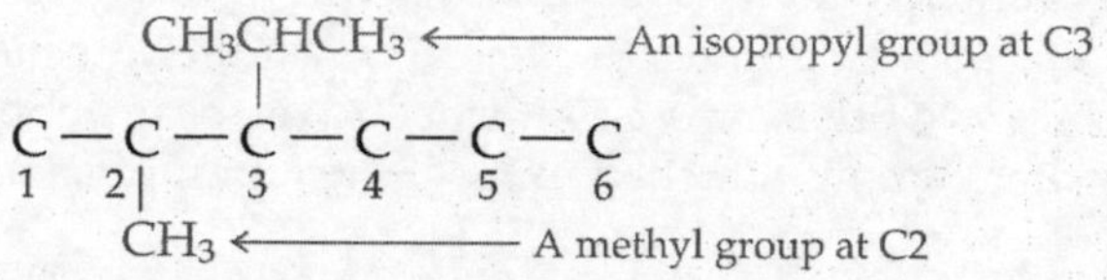

CH₃CHCH₃ ←——— An isopropyl group at C3
|
C — C — C — C — C — C
1   2| 3   4   5   6
CH₃ ←——— A methyl group at C2

Finally, add hydrogens to complete the structure:

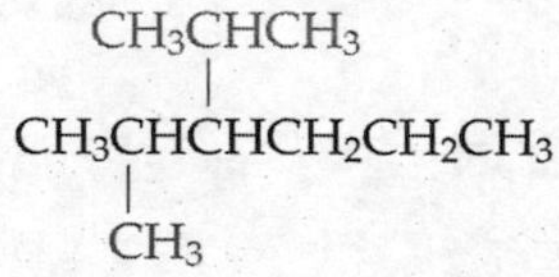

CH₃CHCH₃
|
CH₃CHCHCH₂CH₂CH₃   3-Isopropyl-2-methylhexane
|
CH₃

▶ **PROBLEM 23.7**   What are the IUPAC names of the following alkanes?

(a) The three isomers of C₅H₁₂

(b)   CH₃
                 |
     CH₃CH₂CHCHCH₃
              |
              CH₂CH₃

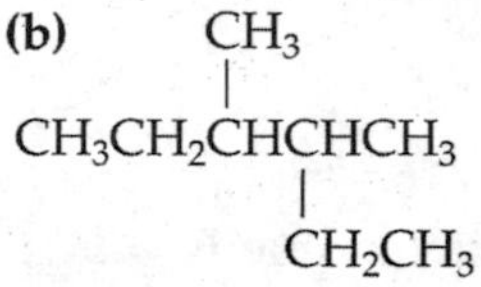

(c) CH₃   CH₃
     | |
     CH₃CHCH₂CHCH₃

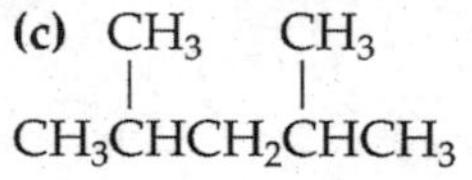

(d) CH₃   CH₂CH₃
     | |
     CH₃CCH₂CH₂CHCH₃
     |
     CH₃

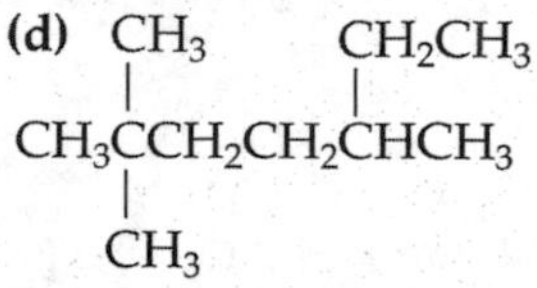

▶ **PROBLEM 23.8**   Draw condensed structures corresponding to the following IUPAC names:

(a) 3,4-Dimethylnonane
(b) 3-Ethyl-4,4-dimethylheptane
(c) 2,2-Dimethyl-4-propyloctane
(d) 2,2,4-Trimethylpentane

●**KEY CONCEPT PROBLEM 23.9**   What is the IUPAC name of the following alkane?

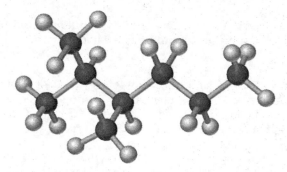

23.6 | Cycloalkanes

The compounds we've been dealing with thus far have all been open-chain, or *acyclic*, alkanes. **Cycloalkanes**, which contain rings of carbon atoms, are also well known and are widespread throughout nature. Compounds of all ring sizes from 3 through 30 carbons and beyond have been prepared. The four simplest cycloalkanes having three carbons (cyclopropane), four carbons (cyclobutane), five carbons (cyclopentane), and six carbons (cyclohexane) are shown at the top of the next page.

Science Fundamentals Second Edition

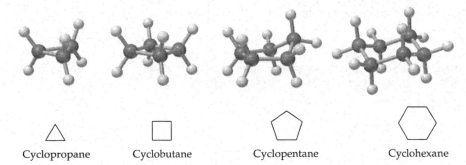

Cyclopropane   Cyclobutane   Cyclopentane   Cyclohexane

3D models of
Cyclopropane,
Cyclobutane,
Cyclopentane,
and Cyclohexane

Even condensed structures are awkward for cyclic molecules, and a stream-lined way of drawing structures is often used in which cycloalkanes are represented by polygons. A triangle represents cyclopropane, a square represents cyclobutane, and so on. Carbon and hydrogen atoms aren't shown explicitly in these structures. A carbon atom is simply understood to be at every junction of lines, and the proper number of hydrogen atoms needed to give each carbon four bonds is supplied mentally. Methylcyclohexane, for instance, looks like this:

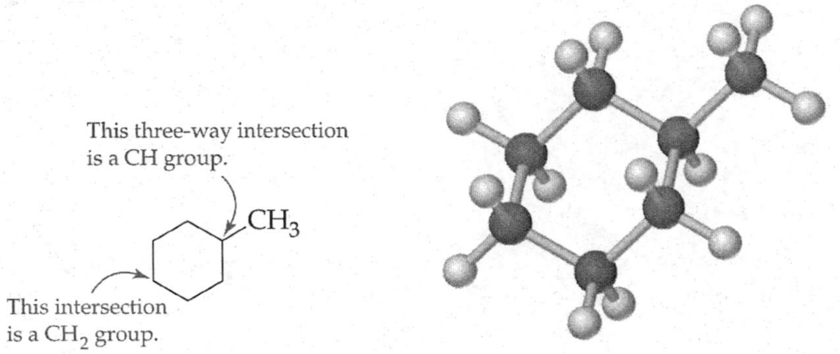

This three-way intersection
is a CH group.

This intersection
is a CH_2 group.

Methylcyclohexane

As you might expect, the C–C bonds in cyclopropane and cyclobutane are considerably distorted from the ideal 109.5° value. Cyclopropane, for example, has the shape of an equilateral triangle, with C–C–C angles of 60°. As a result, the bonds in three- and four-membered rings are weaker than normal, and the molecules are more reactive than other alkanes. Cyclopentane, cyclohexane, and larger cycloalkanes, however, pucker into shapes that allow bond angles to be near their normal tetrahedral value, as shown in the computer-generated models at the beginning of this section.

Substituted cycloalkanes are named using the cycloalkane as the parent name and identifying the positions on the ring where substituents are attached. Start numbering at the group that has alphabetical priority, and proceed in the direction that gives the second substituent the lower possible number. For example,

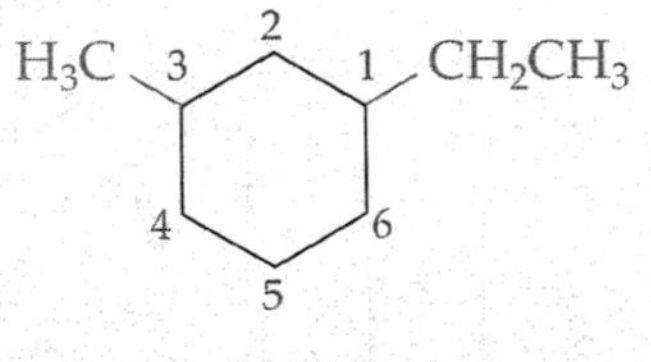

H_3C 3   2   1 CH_2CH_3
4   6
5

1-Ethyl-3-methylcyclohexane

Not 1-methyl-3-ethylcyclohexane
or 1-ethyl-5-methylcyclohexane
or 1-methyl-5-ethylcyclohexane

WORKED EXAMPLE 23.5

What is the IUPAC name of the following cycloalkane?

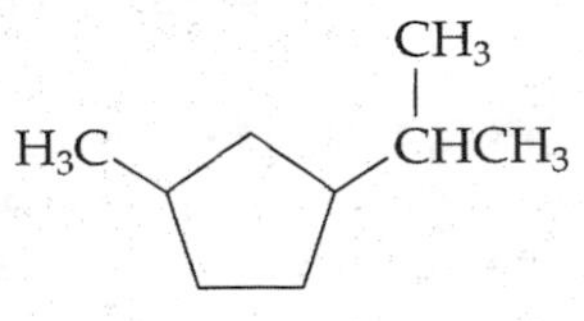

CH_3
|
H_3C $CHCH_3$

STRATEGY

First, identify the parent cycloalkane (cyclopentane) and the two substituents (a methyl group and an isopropyl group). Then, number the ring beginning at the group having alphabetical priority (isopropyl rather than methyl), and proceed in a direction that gives the second group the lower possible number.

SOLUTION

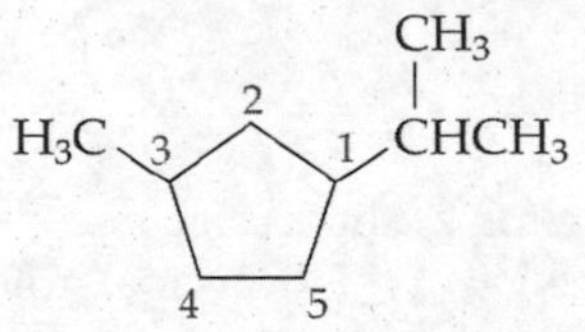

1-Isopropyl-3-methylcyclopentane

▶ **PROBLEM 23.10**   Give IUPAC names for the following cycloalkanes:

(a)   **(b)** 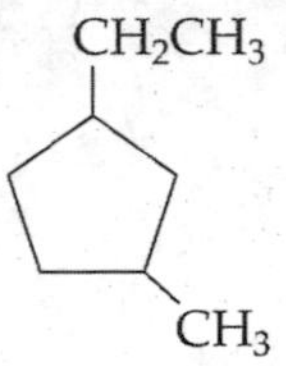   **(c)**

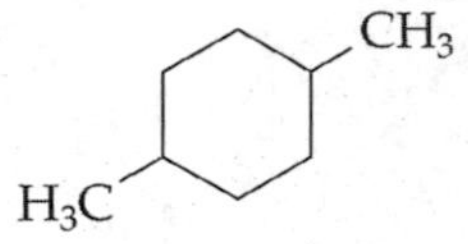

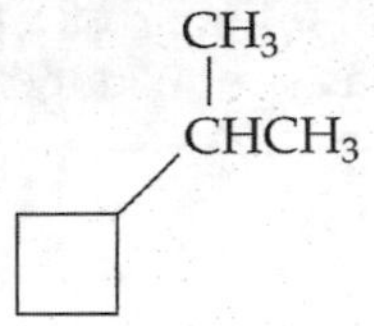

▶ **PROBLEM 23.11**   Draw structures corresponding to the following IUPAC names. Use polygons for the rings.

(a) 1,1-Dimethylcyclobutane   (b) 1-*tert*-Butyl-2-methylcyclopentane
(c) 1,3,5-Trimethylcycloheptane

23.7 | Reactions of Alkanes

Alkanes have relatively low chemical reactivity and are inert to acids, bases, and most other common laboratory reagents. They do, however, react with oxygen and with halogens under appropriate conditions. The chemical reaction of alkanes with oxygen occurs during combustion in an engine or furnace when the alkane is burned as fuel. Carbon dioxide and water are formed as products, and a large amount of heat is released. For example, methane, the main component of natural gas, reacts with oxygen to release 890 kJ per mole of methane burned:

$$CH_4(g) + 2\,O_2(g) \longrightarrow CO_2(g) + 2\,H_2O(l) \qquad \Delta H° = -890\ kJ$$

Propane (the LP gas used in campers and rural homes), gasoline (a mixture of C_5–C_{11} alkanes), kerosene (a mixture of C_{11}–C_{14} alkanes), and other alkanes burn similarly.

Methane gas is burned off ▶ from these oil wells.

The reaction of alkanes with Cl_2 or Br_2 occurs when a mixture of the two reactants is irradiated with ultraviolet light, denoted by *hv*. Depending on the relative amounts of the two reactants and on the time allowed for the reaction, a sequential substitution of the alkane hydrogen atoms by halogen occurs, leading to a mixture of halogenated products. Methane, for example, reacts with chlorine to yield a mixture of chloromethane (CH_3Cl), dichloromethane (methylene chloride; CH_2Cl_2), trichloromethane (chloroform; $CHCl_3$), and tetrachloromethane (carbon tetrachloride; CCl_4):

$$CH_4 + Cl_2 \xrightarrow{h\nu} CH_3Cl + HCl$$
$$\xrightarrow{Cl_2} CH_2Cl_2 + HCl$$
$$\xrightarrow{Cl_2} CHCl_3 + HCl$$
$$\xrightarrow{Cl_2} CCl_4 + HCl$$

Halogenation of Methane activity

▶ **PROBLEM 23.12**   Draw all the monochloro substitution products ($C_5H_{11}Cl$) you would expect to obtain from chlorination of 2-methylbutane.

23.8 | Families of Organic Molecules: Functional Groups

Chemists have learned through experience that organic compounds can be classified into families according to their structural features and that the chemical behavior of family members is often predictable. The structural features that make it possible to class compounds together are called *functional groups*. A **functional group** is an atom or group of atoms within a molecule that has a characteristic chemical behavior. A given functional group undergoes the same kinds of reactions in every molecule it's a part of. Look at the carbon–carbon double-bond functional group, for example. Ethylene (C_2H_4), the simplest compound with a double bond, undergoes reactions that are remarkably similar to those of menthene ($C_{10}H_{16}$), a much larger and more complex molecule. Both, for example, react with Br_2 to give products in which a Br atom has added to each of the double-bond carbons (Figure 23.1).

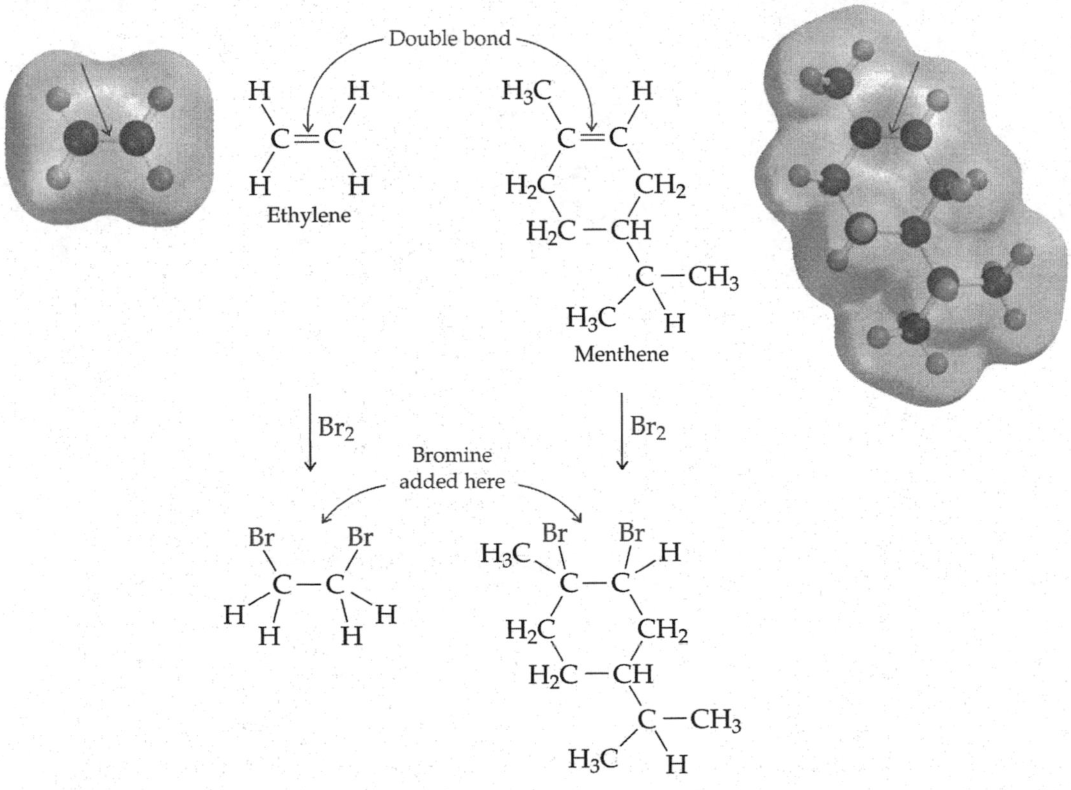

▼ **FIGURE 23.1**   The reactions of ethylene and menthene with bromine. In both molecules, electrostatic potential maps show similar polarity patterns for the carbon–carbon double bond functional group. Bromine therefore reacts with both in the same way, regardless of the size and complexity of the remainder of the molecule.

The example shown in Figure 23.1 is typical: *The chemistry of an organic molecule, regardless of its size and complexity, is largely determined by the functional groups it contains.* Table 23.2 lists some of the most common functional groups and gives

TABLE 23.1	Some Important Families of Organic Molecules			
Family Name	**Functional Group Structure**	**Simple Example**	**Name**	**Name Ending**
Alkane	(contains only C—H and C—C single bonds)	CH_3CH_3	Ethane	-ane
Alkene	$\diagdown$C=C$\diagup$	$H_2C{=}CH_2$	Ethene (Ethylene)	-ene
Alkyne	—C≡C—	H—C≡C—H	Ethyne (Acetylene)	-yne
Arene (aromatic)	(benzene ring structure)	(benzene structure)	Benzene	None
Alcohol	—C—O—H	CH_3OH	Methanol	-ol
Ether	—C—O—C—	CH_3OCH_3	Dimethyl ether	ether
Amine	—C—N—	CH_3NH_2	Methylamine	-amine
Aldehyde	—C—C—H (with C=O)	CH_3CH (with O)	Ethanal (Acetaldehyde)	-al
Ketone	—C—C—C— (with C=O)	CH_3CCH_3 (with O)	Propanone (Acetone)	-one
Carboxylic acid	—C—C—O—H (with C=O)	CH_3COH (with O)	Ethanoic acid (Acetic acid)	-oic acid
Ester	—C—C—O—C— (with C=O)	CH_3COCH_3 (with O)	Methyl ethanoate (Methyl acetate)	-oate
Amide	—C—C—N— (with C=O)	CH_3CNH_2 (with O)	Ethanamide (Acetamide)	-amide

*The bonds whose connections aren't specified are assumed to be attached to carbon or hydrogen atoms in the rest of the molecule.

examples of their occurrence. Some functional groups, such as alkenes, alkynes, and aromatic rings, have only carbon–carbon double or triple bonds; others contain single bonds to oxygen, nitrogen, or halogen atoms; and still others have carbon–oxygen double bonds.

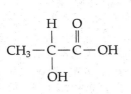

3D models of Ethane, Ethene, Ethyne, Benzene, Ethanol, Dimethyl Ether, Ethylamine, Ethanal, Diethyl Ketone, Ethanoic Acid, Ethyl Acetate, and Acetamide

▶ **PROBLEM 23.13** Locate and identify the functional groups in the following molecules:

(a) Lactic acid, from sour milk

$$CH_3 - \underset{\underset{OH}{|}}{\overset{\overset{H}{|}}{C}} - \overset{\overset{O}{\|}}{C} - OH$$

(b) Styrene, used to make polystyrene

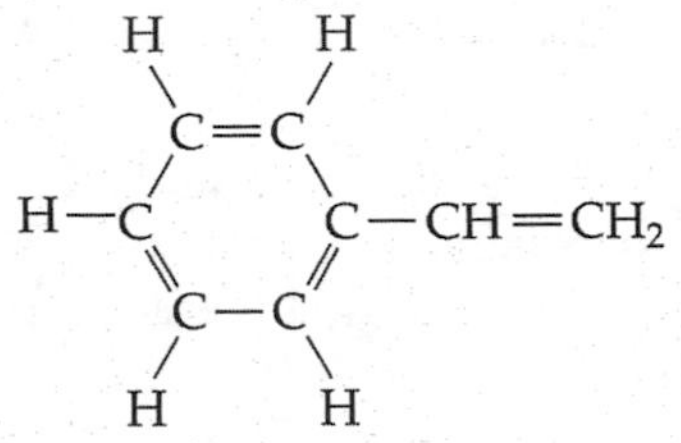

$$H-C \underset{\underset{H}{C}-C}{\overset{\overset{H}{C}=C\overset{H}{\diagup}}{}} C-CH=CH_2$$

▶ **PROBLEM 23.14** Propose structures for molecules that fit the following descriptions:

(a) C_2H_4O, containing an aldehyde functional group
(b) $C_3H_6O_2$, containing a carboxylic acid functional group

23.9 | Alkenes and Alkynes

In contrast to alkanes, which have only single bonds, alkenes and alkynes have *multiple* bonds: **Alkenes** are hydrocarbons that contain a carbon–carbon double bond, and **alkynes** are hydrocarbons that contain a carbon–carbon triple bond. Both groups of compounds are **unsaturated**, meaning that they have fewer hydrogens per carbon than the related alkanes. Ethylene ($H_2C=CH_2$), for example, has the formula C_2H_4, whereas ethane (CH_3CH_3) has the formula C_2H_6.

Alkenes are named by counting the longest chain of carbons that contains the double bond and adding the suffix *-ene*. Thus, ethylene, the simplest alkene, is followed by propene, butene, pentene, hexene, and so on. Note that ethylene should properly be called *ethene*, but the name ethylene has been used for so long that it is universally accepted. Similarly, the name *propylene* is often used for propene.

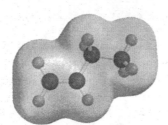
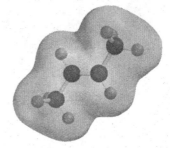

$H_2C=CH_2$	$H_2C=CHCH_3$	$H_2C=CHCH_2CH_3$	$CH_3CH=CHCH_3$
Ethylene (ethene)	Propylene (propene)	1-Butene	2-Butene

Isomers are possible for butene and higher alkenes, depending on the position of the double bond in the chain, which must be specified by a numerical prefix. Numbering starts from the chain end nearer the double bond, and only the first of the double-bond carbons is cited. If a substituent is present on the chain, its identity is noted and its position of attachment is given. If the double bond is equidistant from both ends of the chain, numbering starts from the end nearer the substituent.

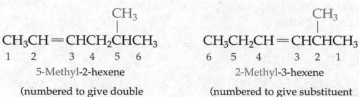

5-Methyl-2-hexene
(numbered to give double bond the lower number)

2-Methyl-3-hexene
(numbered to give substituent the lower number when the double bond is equidistant from both ends)

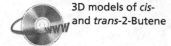

3D models of *cis*- and *trans*-2-Butene

In addition to the alkene isomers that exist because of double-bond *position*, alkene isomers can also exist because of double-bond *geometry*. For instance, there are two geometrical, or **cis–trans isomers**, of 2-butene, which differ in their geometry about the double bond. The cis isomer has its two –CH₃ groups on the same side of the double bond, and the trans isomer has its two –CH₃ groups on opposite sides. Like other kinds of isomers we've discussed, the individual cis and trans isomers of an alkene are different substances with different physical properties and different (although often similar) chemical behavior. *cis*-2-Butene boils at 4°C, for example, but *trans*-2-butene boils at 0.9°C.

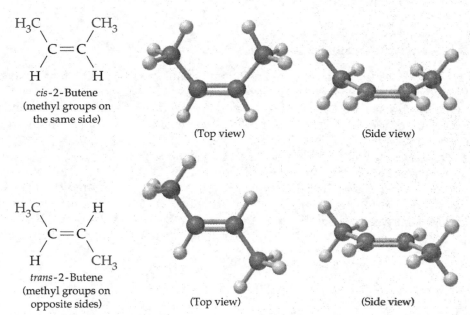

cis-2-Butene
(methyl groups on the same side)

(Top view)

(Side view)

trans-2-Butene
(methyl groups on opposite sides)

(Top view)

(Side view)

Cis-Trans Isomerism activity

Cis–trans isomerism in alkenes arises because the electronic structure of the carbon–carbon double bond makes bond rotation energetically unfavorable at normal temperatures. Were it to occur, rotation would break the pi part of the double bond by disrupting the sideways overlap of two parallel *p* orbitals (Figure 23.2). In fact, an energy input of 240 kJ/mol is needed to cause bond rotation.

FIGURE 23.2 Rotation ▶ around a carbon–carbon double bond requires a large amount of energy because *p* orbital overlap is destroyed. Cis–trans alkene isomers are stable and do not interchange as a result of this barrier to rotation.

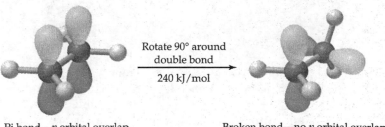

Pi bond—*p* orbital overlap

Rotate 90° around double bond

240 kJ/mol

Broken bond—no *p* orbital overlap

Science Fundamentals Second Edition

Alkynes are similar in many respects to alkenes and are named using the suffix *-yne*. The simplest alkyne, HC≡CH, is often called by its alternative name *acetylene* rather than by its systematic name *ethyne*.

Ethyne 3D model

		1 2 3 4	4 3 2 1
HC≡CH	CH₃C≡CH	CH₃C≡CCH₃	CH₃CH₂C≡CH
Ethyne (Acetylene)	Propyne	2-Butyne	1-Butyne

As with alkenes, isomers are possible for butyne and higher alkynes, depending on the position of the triple bond in the chain. Unlike the alkenes, however, no cis–trans isomers are possible for alkynes because of their linear geometry.

WORKED EXAMPLE 23.6

Draw the structure of *cis*-3-heptene.

STRATEGY

The name 3-heptene indicates that the molecule has seven carbons (*hept-*) and has a double bond between carbons 3 and 4. The prefix *cis-* indicates that the two alkyl groups attached to the double-bond carbons lie on the same side of the double bond.

SOLUTION

$$\underset{CH_3CH_2}{\overset{1\quad 2}{}} \quad \underset{CH_2CH_2CH_3}{\overset{5\quad 6\quad 7}{}}$$
$$\underset{H}{\overset{}{}} \ \ 3C{=}C4 \ \ \underset{H}{\overset{}{}} \qquad \textit{cis}\text{-3-Heptene}$$

▶ **PROBLEM 23.15**   Give IUPAC names for the following alkenes and alkynes:

(a)
$$\underset{CH_3CHCH{=}CH_2}{\overset{CH_3}{\overset{|}{}}}$$

(b) $$\underset{CH_3C{=}CHCH_2CH_3}{\overset{CH_3CH_2CH_2}{\overset{|}{}}}$$

(c)
$$\underset{HC{\equiv}CCHCH_2CH_2CH_3}{\overset{CH_2CH_3}{\overset{|}{}}}$$

▶ **PROBLEM 23.16**   Draw structures corresponding to the following IUPAC names:

(a) 2,2-Dimethyl-3-hexene   (b) 4-Isopropyl-2-heptyne
(c) *trans*-3-Heptene

23.10 | Reactions of Alkenes and Alkynes

The most important transformations of alkenes and alkynes are **addition reactions**. That is, a reagent we might write in a general way as X–Y adds to the multiple bond of the unsaturated reactant to yield a saturated product. Alkenes and alkynes react similarly, but we'll look only at alkenes because they're more common.

$$\underset{/}{\overset{\backslash}{}}C{=}C\underset{\backslash}{\overset{/}{}} + \ X{-}Y \ \rightarrow \ \underset{|}{\overset{X}{\overset{|}{-}}}\underset{|}{\overset{Y}{\overset{|}{-}}}C{-}C{-} \qquad \textbf{An addition reaction}$$

Addition of Hydrogen   Alkenes react with hydrogen gas in the presence of a platinum or palladium catalyst to yield the corresponding alkane product. For example,

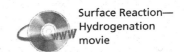
Surface Reaction—
Hydrogenation
movie

$$CH_3CH_2CH{=}CH_2 + H_2 \xrightarrow[\text{catalyst}]{Pd} CH_3CH_2CH_2CH_3$$
$$\qquad\text{1-Butene} \qquad\qquad\qquad\qquad \text{Butane}$$

Science Fundamentals Second Edition

This addition of hydrogen to an alkene, often called **hydrogenation**, is used commercially to convert unsaturated vegetable oils to the saturated fats used in margarine and cooking fats.

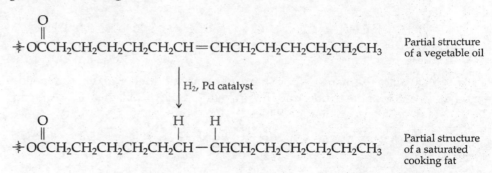

Addition of Cl₂ and Br₂ Alkenes react with the halogens Cl_2 and Br_2 to give dihaloalkane addition products, a process called **halogenation**. For example,

$$H_2C=CH_2 + Cl_2 \longrightarrow H-\underset{\underset{H}{|}}{\overset{\overset{Cl}{|}}{C}}-\underset{\underset{H}{|}}{\overset{\overset{Cl}{|}}{C}}-H$$

Ethene
(Ethylene)

1,2-Dichloroethane

Approximately 10 million tons of 1,2-dichloroethane are manufactured each year in the United States by the reaction of ethylene with chlorine. The process is the first step in making PVC [poly(vinyl chloride)] plastics.

Addition of Water Alkenes don't react with pure water, but in the presence of a strong acid catalyst such as sulfuric acid, a **hydration** reaction takes place to yield an *alcohol*. An –H from water adds to one carbon, and an –OH adds to the other. For example, nearly 300 million gallons of ethyl alcohol (ethanol) are produced each year in the United States by the acid-catalyzed addition of water to ethylene:

$$H_2C=CH_2 + H_2O \xrightarrow[\text{catalyst}]{H_2SO_4} H-\underset{\underset{H}{|}}{\overset{\overset{H}{|}}{C}}-\underset{\underset{H}{|}}{\overset{\overset{OH}{|}}{C}}-H$$

Ethene
(Ethylene)

Ethanol
(an alcohol)

▶ **PROBLEM 23.17** Show the products of the reaction of 2-butene with the following:

(a) H_2, Pd catalyst   (b) Br_2 (c) H_2O, H_2SO_4 catalyst

▶ **PROBLEM 23.18** The reaction of 2-pentene with H_2O in the presence of H_2SO_4 yields a mixture of two alcohol products. Draw their structures.

 KEY CONCEPT PROBLEM 23.19 Draw the structure of the alcohol you would expect to obtain by acid-catalyzed reaction of the following cyclic alkene with H_2O:

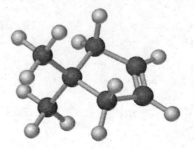

Science Fundamentals Second Edition

23.11 | Aromatic Compounds and Their Reactions

In the early days of organic chemistry, the word *aromatic* was used to describe certain fragrant substances from fruits, trees, and other natural sources. Chemists soon realized, however, that substances grouped as aromatic behaved in a chemically different manner from most other organic compounds. Today, the term **aromatic** refers to the class of compounds that can be represented as having a six-membered ring with three double bonds. Benzene is the simplest aromatic compound, but aspirin, the steroid sex hormone estradiol, and many other important compounds also contain aromatic rings.

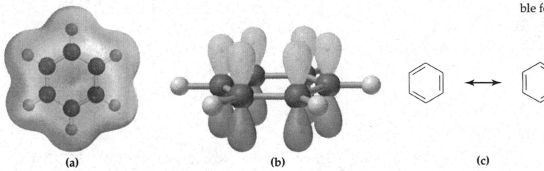

Benzene   Aspirin   Estradiol

Benzene is a flat, symmetrical molecule that is often represented as a six-membered ring with three double bonds. The problem with this representation, however, is that it gives the wrong impression about benzene's chemical reactivity. Because benzene appears to have three double bonds, we might expect it to react with H_2, Br_2, and H_2O to give the same kinds of addition products that alkenes do. In fact, though, benzene and other aromatic compounds are much less reactive than alkenes and don't normally undergo addition reactions.

Benzene's relative lack of reactivity is a consequence of its electronic structure. As shown by the orbital picture in Figure 23.3b, each of the six carbons in benzene is sp^2-hybridized and has a p orbital perpendicular to the ring. When these p orbitals overlap to form pi bonds, there are two possibilities, shown in Figure 23.3c.

▲ Benzaldehyde, a close structural relative of benzene, is an aromatic compound responsible for the odor of cherries.

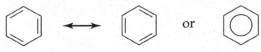

(a)   (b)   (c)

Neither of the two equivalent structures in Figure 23.3c is correct by itself. Rather, each represents one resonance form of the true benzene structure, which is a resonance hybrid of the two. (For a review of resonance, you might want to reread Section 7.7). Benzene is stable because its six pi electrons are spread equally around the entire ring. The six electrons aren't confined to specific double bonds in the normal way, so benzene doesn't react to give addition products in the normal way. Such an idea is hard to show using lines for covalent bonds, so chemists sometimes represent the six electrons as a circle inside the six-membered ring. In this book, though, we'll indicate aromatic rings by showing just one of the individual resonance structures because it's easier to keep track of electrons that way.

▲ **FIGURE 23.3** Some representations of benzene: **(a)** an electrostatic potential map; **(b)** an orbital picture; and **(c)** two equivalent resonance structures, which differ only in the positions of the double bonds.

Benzene 3D model

or

Science Fundamentals Second Edition

Substituted aromatic compounds are named using the suffix *-benzene*. Thus, C_6H_5Br is bromobenzene, $C_6H_5CH_3$ is methylbenzene (also called *toluene*), $C_6H_5NO_2$ is nitrobenzene, and so on. Disubstituted aromatic compounds are named using one of the prefixes *ortho-*, *meta-*, or *para-*. An *ortho-* or *o*-disubstituted benzene has its two substituents in a 1,2 relationship on the ring; a *meta-* or *m*-disubstituted benzene has its two substituents in a 1,3 relationship; and a *para-* or *p*-disubstituted benzene has its substituents in a 1,4 relationship. When the benzene ring itself is a substituent, the name *phenyl* (pronounced **fen**-nil) is used.

ortho-Dimethylbenzene   *meta*-Dibromobenzene   *para*-Dinitrobenzene   A phenyl group

Unlike alkenes, which undergo addition reactions, aromatic compounds usually undergo **substitution reactions**. That is, a group Y *substitutes* for one of the hydrogen atoms on the aromatic ring without changing the ring itself. It doesn't matter which of the six ring hydrogens in benzene is replaced, because all six are equivalent.

$$\text{C}_6\text{H}_5\text{H} + X-Y \longrightarrow \text{C}_6\text{H}_5\text{Y} + H-X \qquad \textbf{A substitution reaction}$$

Nitration Substitution of a nitro group ($-NO_2$) for a ring hydrogen occurs when benzene reacts with nitric acid in the presence of sulfuric acid as catalyst. Nitration of aromatic rings is a key step in the synthesis of explosives such as TNT (trinitrotoluene) and many important pharmaceutical agents. Nitrobenzene itself is a starting material for preparing many of the brightly colored dyes used in clothing.

Benzene $+ HNO_3 \xrightarrow{H_2SO_4}$ Nitrobenzene $+ H_2O$ Trinitrotoluene (TNT)

Halogenation Substitution of a bromine or chlorine for a ring hydrogen occurs when benzene reacts with Br_2 or Cl_2 in the presence of $FeBr_3$ or $FeCl_3$ as catalyst. The chlorination of an aromatic ring is a step used in the synthesis of numerous pharmaceutical agents, such as the tranquilizer Valium.

Benzene $+ Cl_2 \xrightarrow{FeCl_3}$ Chlorobenzene $+ HCl$ Diazepam (Valium)

▲ The dyes used to add the bright colors to clothing are made by a process that begins with an aromatic nitration reaction.

Sulfonation Substitution of a sulfonic acid group (–SO₃H) for a ring hydrogen occurs when benzene reacts with concentrated sulfuric acid and sulfur trioxide. Aromatic-ring sulfonation is a key step in the synthesis of such compounds as aspirin and the sulfa-drug family of antibiotics.

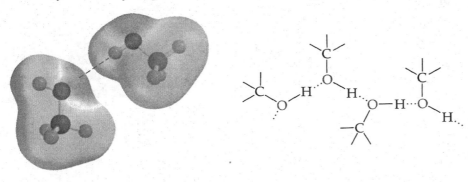

Benzene   + SO₃   —H₂SO₄→   Benzenesulfonic acid   Sulfanilamide (a sulfa antibiotic)

▶ **PROBLEM 23.20**   Draw structures corresponding to the following names:

(a) *o*-Dibromobenzene   (b) *p*-Chloronitrobenzene   (c) *m*-Diethylbenzene

▶ **PROBLEM 23.21**   Write the products from reaction of the following reagents with *p*-dimethylbenzene (also called *p*-xylene):

(a) Br₂, FeBr₃   (b) HNO₃, H₂SO₄   (c) SO₃, H₂SO₄

▶ **PROBLEM 23.22**   Reaction of Br₂/FeBr₃ with toluene (methylbenzene) can lead to a mixture of *three* substitution products. Show the structure of each.

23.12 | Alcohols, Ethers, and Amines

Alcohols

Alcohols can be viewed either as derivatives of water, in which one of the hydrogens is replaced by an organic substituent, or as derivatives of alkanes, in which one of the hydrogens is replaced by a hydroxyl group (–OH).

Water

A hydrocarbon

An alcohol   for example: CH₃CH₂OH

Ethanol

Like water, alcohols form hydrogen bonds (Section 10.2), which affect many of their chemical and physical properties. Alcohols are generally higher-boiling than alkanes of similar size, and simple alcohols are often soluble in water because of their ability to form hydrogen bonds to the solvent (Figure 23.4).

◀ **FIGURE 23.4**   Alcohols, like water, form intermolecular hydrogen bonds. As a result, alcohols are relatively high boiling and are often soluble in water.

Alcohols are named by identifying the point of attachment of the –OH group to the hydrocarbon chain and using the suffix *-ol* to replace the terminal *-e* in the alkane name. Numbering of the chain begins at the end nearer the –OH group. For example,

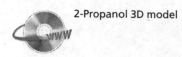

2-Propanol 3D model

$$\underset{\substack{3 \quad 2 \quad 1 \\ \text{1-Propanol}}}{CH_3CH_2CH_2OH} \qquad \underset{\substack{1 \quad 2 \quad 3 \\ \text{2-Propanol}}}{CH_3\overset{\overset{\displaystyle OH}{|}}{C}HCH_3} \qquad \underset{\substack{1 \quad 2| \quad 3 \\ CH_3 \\ \text{2-Methyl-2-propanol}}}{CH_3\overset{\overset{\displaystyle OH}{|}}{C}CH_3} \qquad \underset{\text{Cyclohexanol}}{}$$

Alcohols are among the most important and commonly encountered of all organic chemicals. Methanol (CH_3OH), the simplest member of the family, was once known as *wood alcohol* because it was prepared by heating wood in the absence of air. Approximately 1.6 billion gallons of methanol are manufactured each year in the United States by catalytic reduction of carbon monoxide with hydrogen gas:

$$CO + 2\,H_2 \xrightarrow[\text{ZnO/Cr}_2\text{O}_3 \text{ catalyst}]{400°C} CH_3OH$$

Although toxic to humans, causing blindness in low doses (15 mL) and death in larger amounts (100–200 mL), methanol is an important industrial starting material for preparing formaldehyde (CH_2O), acetic acid (CH_3CO_2H), and other chemicals.

Ethanol (CH_3CH_2OH) is one of the oldest known pure organic chemicals. Its production by fermentation of grains and sugars and its subsequent purification by distillation go back at least as far as the twelfth century A.D. Sometimes called *grain alcohol*, ethanol is the "alcohol" present in all wines (10–13%), beers (3–5%), and distilled liquors (35–90%). Fermentation is carried out by adding yeast to an aqueous sugar solution and allowing enzymes in the yeast to break down carbohydrates into ethanol and CO_2:

$$\underset{\text{Glucose}}{C_6H_{12}O_6} \xrightarrow{\text{Yeast}} 2\,CO_2 + 2\,\underset{\text{Ethanol}}{CH_3CH_2OH}$$

Only about 5% of the ethanol produced industrially comes from fermentation. Most is obtained by acid-catalyzed addition of water to ethylene (Section 23.10).

2-Propanol [(CH_3)$_2$CHOH], commonly called isopropyl alcohol or *rubbing alcohol*, is used primarily as a solvent. It is prepared industrially by addition of water to propene:

$$\underset{\substack{\text{Propene} \\ \text{(Propylene)}}}{CH_3CH{=}CH_2} + H_2O \xrightarrow[\text{catalyst}]{\text{Acid}} \underset{\text{2-Propanol}}{CH_3\overset{\overset{\displaystyle OH}{|}}{C}HCH_3}$$

Still other important alcohols include 1,2-ethanediol (ethylene glycol), 1,2,3-propanetriol (glycerol), and the aromatic compound phenol. Ethylene glycol is the principal constituent of automobile antifreeze, glycerol is used as a moisturizing agent in many foods and cosmetics, and phenol is used for preparing nylon, epoxy adhesives, and heat-setting resins.

$HOCH_2CH_2OH$

1,2-Ethanediol
(Ethylene glycol)

$$\underset{\text{1,2,3-Propanetriol}}{\underset{\text{(Glycerol)}}{HOCH_2CHCH_2OH}}$$
OH

Phenol

Ethers

Ethers can be viewed as derivatives of water in which both hydrogens are replaced by organic substituents. They are fairly inert chemically and so are often used as reaction solvents. Diethyl ether, the most common member of the ether family, was used for many years as a surgical anesthetic agent but has now been replaced by safer nonflammable alternatives.

Diethyl Ether 3D
model

$CH_3CH_2OCH_2CH_3$
Diethyl ether

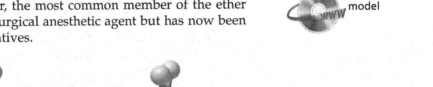

Amines

Amines are organic derivatives of ammonia in the same way that alcohols and ethers are organic derivatives of water. That is, one or more of the ammonia hydrogens is replaced in amines by an organic substituent. As the following examples indicate, the suffix -*amine* is used in naming these compounds:

Ammonia   Methylamine   Dimethylamine   Trimethylamine   Benzeneamine
(Aniline)

Like ammonia, amines are bases because they can use the lone pair of electrons on nitrogen to accept H^+ from an acid and give ammonium salts (Section 15.12). Because they're ionic, ammonium salts are much more soluble in water than are neutral amines. Thus, a water-insoluble amine such as

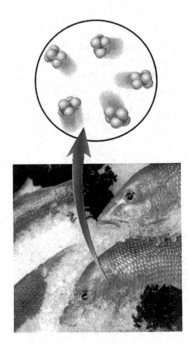

▲ The characteristic aroma of ripe fish is due to methyl-amine, CH_3NH_2.

Science Fundamentals Second Edition

triethylamine dissolves readily in water when converted to its ammonium salt by reaction with HCl.

$$CH_3CH_2-\overset{\cdot\cdot}{\underset{\underset{CH_2CH_3}{|}}{N}}-CH_2CH_3 + HCl(aq) \longrightarrow CH_3CH_2-\overset{\overset{H}{|}}{\underset{\underset{CH_2CH_3}{|}}{N^+}}-CH_2CH_3 \quad Cl^-(aq)$$

Triethylamine
(water-insoluble)

Triethylammonium chloride
(water-soluble)

This increase in water solubility on conversion of an amine to its protonated salt has enormous practical consequences in drug delivery. Many important amine-containing drugs, such as morphine (a painkiller) and tetracycline (an antibiotic), are insoluble in aqueous body fluids and are thus difficult to deliver to the appropriate site within the body. Converting these drugs to their ammonium salts, however, increases their solubility to the point where delivery through the bloodstream becomes possible.

▶ **PROBLEM 23.23**   Write the structures of the ammonium salts produced by reaction of the following amines with HCl:

(a)
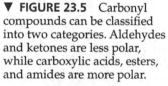
NHCH$_3$

(b)

$$CH_3CH_2CH_2NH_2$$

23.13 | Aldehydes and Ketones

Look back at the functional groups listed in Table 23.2 and you'll see that many of them have a carbon–oxygen double bond (C=O), called a **carbonyl group** (pronounced car-bo-**neel**). Carbonyl-containing compounds are everywhere. Carbohydrates, fats, proteins, and nucleic acids all contain carbonyl groups; most pharmaceutical agents contain carbonyl groups; and many of the synthetic polymers used for clothing and other applications contain carbonyl groups.

As shown by the electrostatic potential maps in Figure 23.5, the C=O bond in carbonyl compounds is polar because the electronegative oxygen atom attracts electrons from the carbon atom. Nevertheless, some carbonyl compounds are more polar than others because of what else is bonded to the carbonyl carbon atom.

It's useful to classify carbonyl compounds into two categories, based on the nature of the groups bonded to the C=O and on the chemical consequences that

▼ **FIGURE 23.5**   Carbonyl compounds can be classified into two categories. Aldehydes and ketones are less polar, while carboxylic acids, esters, and amides are more polar.

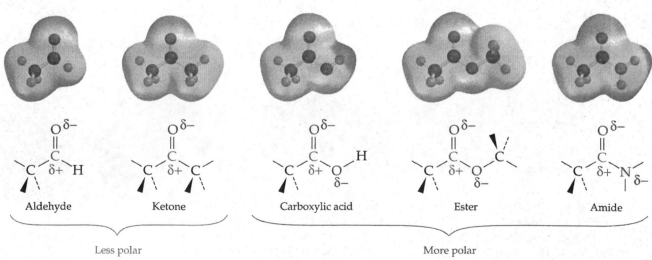

result. In one category are *aldehydes* and *ketones*. In the other are *carboxylic acids, esters,* and *amides*. In aldehydes and ketones, the carbonyl carbon is bonded to atoms (H and C) that are not strongly electronegative and thus contribute no additional polarity to the molecule. In carboxylic acids, esters, and amides, however, the carbonyl carbon *is* bonded to an atom (O or N) that is strongly electronegative, giving these compounds even greater polarity and greater chemical reactivity (Figure 23.5).

Aldehydes, which have a hydrogen atom bonded to the carbonyl group, and **ketones**, which have two carbon atoms bonded to the carbonyl group, are used throughout chemistry and biology. For example, an aqueous solution of formaldehyde (properly named *methanal*) is used under the name *formalin* as a biological sterilant and preservative. Formaldehyde is also used in the chemical industry as a starting material for the manufacture of the plastics Bakelite and melamine, as a component of the adhesives used to bind plywood, and as a part of the foam insulation used in houses. Note that formaldehyde differs from other aldehydes in having two hydrogens attached to the carbonyl group rather than one. Acetone (properly named *propanone*) is perhaps the most widely used of all organic solvents. You might have seen cans of acetone sold in paint stores for general-purpose cleanup work. When naming these groups of compounds, use the suffix *-al* for aldehydes and use the suffix *-one* for ketones.

3D models of Ethanal and Dimethyl Ketone

$$\underset{\text{Formaldehyde}\atop\text{(Methanal)}}{\overset{\overset{\displaystyle O}{\|}}{HCH}} \qquad \underset{\text{Acetaldehyde}\atop\text{(Ethanal)}}{\overset{\overset{\displaystyle O}{\|}}{CH_3CH}} \qquad \underset{\text{Acetone}\atop\text{(Propanone)}}{\overset{\overset{\displaystyle O}{\|}}{CH_3CCH_3}} \qquad \underset{\text{2-Butanone}}{\overset{\overset{\displaystyle O}{\|}}{\underset{1\ \ \ 2\,3\ \ \ 4}{CH_3CCH_2CH_3}}} \qquad \underset{\text{Cyclohexanone}}{}$$

Aldehyde and ketone functional groups are also present in many biologically important compounds. Glucose and most other sugars contain aldehyde groups, for instance. Testosterone and many other steroid hormones contain ketone groups.

Aldehyde —

$$\underset{\underset{HO\ \ OH\ \ \ OH}{|\quad\ |\quad\ \ |}}{HOCH_2CHCHCHCHCH}\overset{OH\quad O}{\overset{|\qquad\|}{}}$$

Glucose—a pentahydroxyhexanal

Ketone —

Testosterone—a steroid hormone

The industrial preparation of simple aldehydes and ketones usually involves an oxidation reaction of the related alcohol. Thus, formaldehyde is prepared by oxidation of methanol, and acetone is prepared by oxidation of 2-propanol.

$$\underset{\text{Methanol}}{\overset{\overset{\displaystyle OH}{|}}{H-\underset{\underset{H}{|}}{C}-H}} \quad \xrightarrow{\text{Air, 300°C}} \quad \underset{\text{Formaldehyde}}{\overset{\overset{\displaystyle O}{\|}}{\underset{H\qquad H}{C}}}$$

$$\underset{\text{2-Propanol}}{\overset{\overset{\displaystyle OH}{|}}{\underset{\underset{H}{|}}{CH_3CCH_3}}} \quad \xrightarrow{\text{Air, 300°C}} \quad \underset{\text{Acetone}}{\overset{\overset{\displaystyle O}{\|}}{CH_3CCH_3}}$$

Science Fundamentals Second Edition

23.14 | Carboxylic Acids, Esters, and Amides

Carboxylic acids, esters, and amides have their carbonyl groups bonded to an atom (O or N) that strongly attracts electrons. All three families undergo carbonyl-group substitution reactions, in which a group we can represent as −Y substitutes for the −OH, −OC, or −N group of the carbonyl reactant.

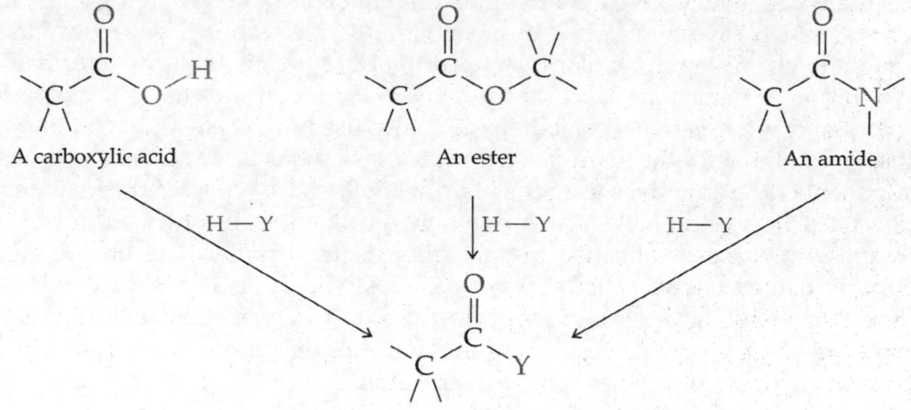

A carboxylic acid   An ester   An amide

A carbonyl-group substitution reaction

Carboxylic Acids

Acetic Acid 3D model

Carboxylic acids, which contain the $-\overset{O}{\overset{\|}{C}}-OH$ functional group, occur widely throughout the plant and animal kingdoms. Acetic acid (ethanoic acid), for example, is the principal organic constituent of vinegar, and butanoic acid is responsible for the odor of rancid butter. In addition, long-chain carboxylic acids such as stearic acid are components of all animal fats and vegetable oils. Although many carboxylic acids have common names—*acetic* acid instead of *ethanoic* acid, for instance—systematic names are derived by replacing the final *-e* of the corresponding alkane with *-oic acid*.

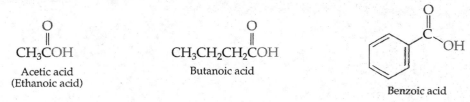

CH₃COH
Acetic acid
(Ethanoic acid)

CH₃CH₂CH₂COH
Butanoic acid

Benzoic acid

CH₃CH₂CH₂CH₂CH₂CH₂CH₂CH₂CH₂CH₂CH₂CH₂CH₂CH₂CH₂CH₂COH
Stearic acid
(Octadecanoic acid)

As their name implies, carboxylic acids are *acidic*—they dissociate slightly in aqueous solution to give H_3O^+ and a **carboxylate anion**. Carboxylic acids are much weaker than inorganic acids like HCl or H_2SO_4, however. The K_a of acetic acid, for example, is 1.78×10^{-5} ($pK_a = 4.75$), meaning that only about 1% of acetic acid molecules dissociate in a 1.0 M aqueous solution. Note in the following electrostatic potential map of acetic acid that the acidic −OH hydrogen is positively polarized (blue).

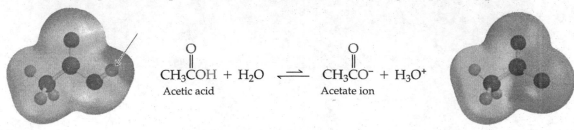

$$CH_3COH + H_2O \rightleftharpoons CH_3CO^- + H_3O^+$$
Acetic acid   Acetate ion

One of the most important chemical transformations of carboxylic acids is their acid-catalyzed reaction with an alcohol to yield an ester. Acetic acid, for example, reacts with ethanol in the presence of H_2SO_4 to yield ethyl acetate, a widely used solvent. The reaction is a typical carbonyl-group substitution, with $-OCH_2CH_3$ from the alcohol replacing $-OH$ from the acid.

$$CH_3-\overset{\overset{\textstyle O}{\|}}{C}\boxed{-OH + H-}OCH_2CH_3 \xrightarrow[\text{catalyst}]{H^+} CH_3-\overset{\overset{\textstyle O}{\|}}{C}-OCH_2CH_3 + H_2O$$

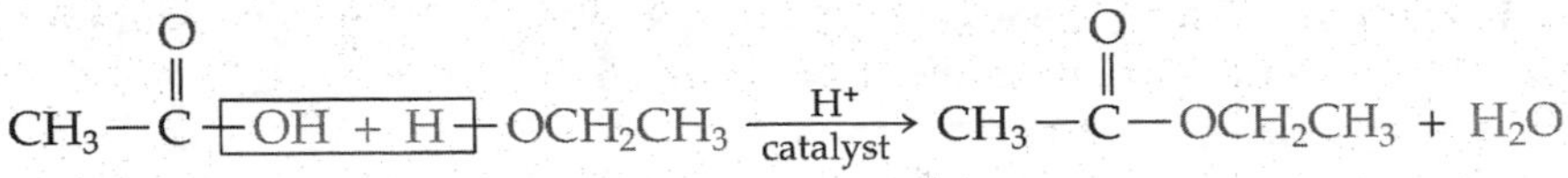

Acetic acid   Ethanol   Ethyl acetate

Ethyl Acetate 3D model

Esters

Esters, which contain the $-\overset{\overset{\textstyle O}{\|}}{C}-O-C$ functional group, have many uses in medicine, industry, and living systems. In medicine, a number of important pharmaceutical agents, including aspirin and the local anesthetic benzocaine, are esters. In industry, polyesters such as Dacron and Mylar are used to make synthetic fibers and films. In nature, many simple esters are responsible for the fragrant odors of fruits and flowers. For example, pentyl acetate is found in bananas, and octyl acetate is found in oranges.

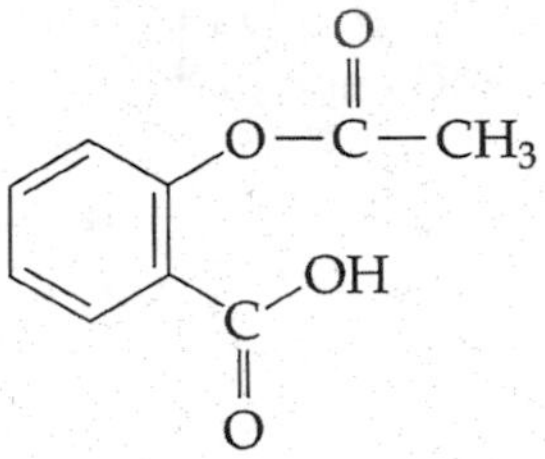

Aspirin

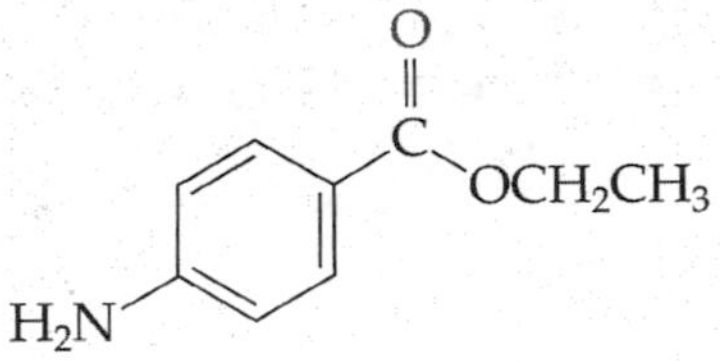

Benzocaine

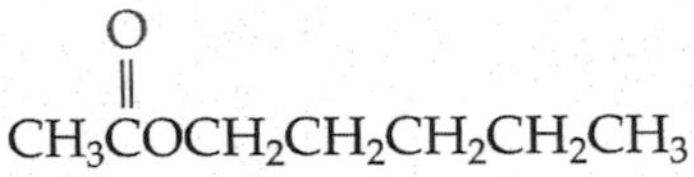

$$CH_3COCH_2CH_2CH_2CH_2CH_3$$

Pentyl acetate

▲ The odor of these bananas is due to pentyl acetate, a simple ester.

The most important reaction of esters is their conversion by a carbonyl-group substitution reaction into carboxylic acids. Both in the laboratory and in the body, esters undergo a reaction with water—a *hydrolysis*—that splits the ester molecule into a carboxylic acid and an alcohol. The net effect is a substitution of –OC by –OH. Although the reaction is slow in pure water, it is catalyzed by both acid and base. Base-catalyzed ester hydrolysis is often called *saponification*, from the Latin word *sapo* meaning "soap." Soap, in fact, is a mixture of sodium salts of long-chain carboxylic acids and is produced by hydrolysis with aqueous NaOH of the naturally occurring esters in animal fat.

$$CH_3-\overset{\overset{\textstyle O}{\|}}{C}\boxed{-OCH_2CH_3 + H}-O-H \xrightarrow[\text{catalyst}]{H^+ \text{ or } OH^-} CH_3-\overset{\overset{\textstyle O}{\|}}{C}-OH + H-OCH_2CH_3$$

Ethyl acetate   Acetic acid   Ethanol

Since esters are derived from carboxylic acids and alcohols, they are named by first identifying the alcohol-related part and then the acid-related part, using the *-ate* ending. Ethyl acetate, for example, is the ester derived from ethanol and acetic acid.

Amides

Amides are compounds with the $-\overset{\overset{\textstyle O}{\|}}{C}-N$ functional group. Without amides, there would be no life. As we'll see in the next chapter, the amide bond between nitrogen and a carbonyl-group carbon is the fundamental link used by organisms for forming proteins. In addition, some synthetic polymers such as nylon contain amide groups, and important pharmaceutical agents such as acetaminophen, the aspirin substitute found in Tylenol and Excedrin, are amides.

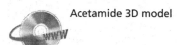 Acetamide 3D model

$$\overset{\overset{\textstyle O}{\|}}{\overset{|}{+}CCH_2CH_2CH_2CH_2C}-\overset{\overset{\textstyle H}{|}}{N}CH_2CH_2CH_2CH_2CH_2CH_2\overset{\overset{\textstyle H}{|}}{N}+$$

Repeating unit of nylon 66

Acetaminophen

Unlike amines, which also contain nitrogen (Section 23.12), amides are neutral rather than basic. Amides do not act as proton acceptors and do not form ammonium salts when treated with acid. The neighboring carbonyl group causes the unshared pair of electrons on nitrogen to be held tightly, thus preventing the electrons from bonding to H^+.

Although better methods are normally used, amides can be prepared by the reaction of a carboxylic acid with ammonia or an amine, just as esters are prepared by the reaction of a carboxylic acid with an alcohol. In both cases, water is a by-product, and the –OH part of the carboxylic acid is replaced. Amides are named by first citing the *N*-alkyl group on the amine part (*N* because the group is attached to nitrogen) and then identifying the carboxylic acid part using the *-amide* ending.

$$CH_3\overset{\overset{\textstyle O}{\|}}{C}\boxed{-OH + H}-\underset{\underset{\textstyle H}{|}}{N}CH_3 \xrightarrow{\text{Heat}} CH_3\overset{\overset{\textstyle O}{\|}}{C}-\underset{\underset{\textstyle H}{|}}{N}CH_3 + H_2O$$

Acetic acid   Methylamine   *N*-Methylacetamide
                                        (an amide)

Amides undergo an acid- or base-catalyzed hydrolysis reaction with water in the same way that esters do. Just as an ester yields a carboxylic acid and an alcohol, an amide yields a carboxylic acid and an amine (or ammonia). The net effect is a substitution of –N by –OH. This hydrolysis of amides is the key process that occurs in the stomach during digestion of proteins.

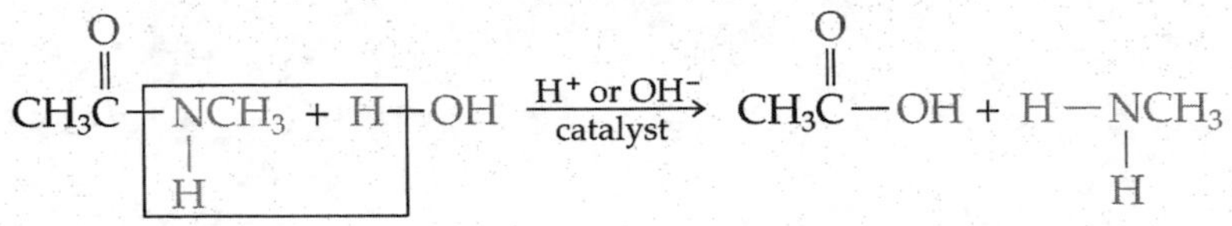

N-Methylacetamide   Acetic acid   Methylamine

WORKED EXAMPLE 23.7

Give the systematic names of the following compounds:

(a)

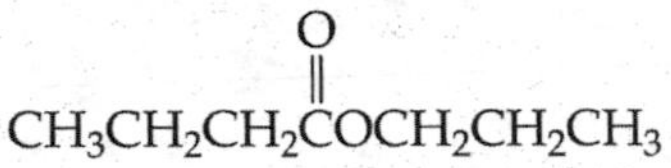

$$CH_3CH_2CH_2COCH_2CH_2CH_3$$

(b)

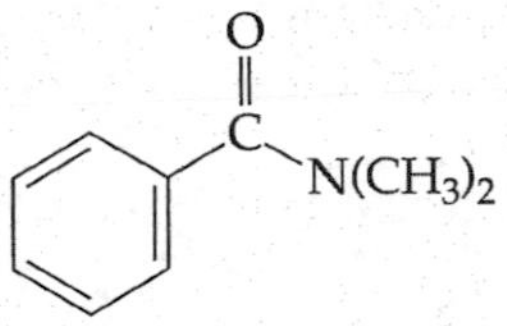

STRATEGY

First identify the alcohol-derived or amine-derived part, and then assign the name.

SOLUTION

(a) This ester is derived from propyl alcohol and butanoic acid. It's name is propyl butanoate.

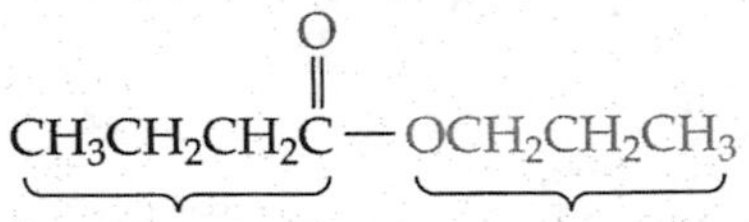

CH_3CH_2CH_2C—OCH_2CH_2CH_3   Propyl butanoate

Butanoic acid   Propanol

(b) This amide is derived from dimethylamine and benzoic acid. It's name is N,N-dimethylbenzamide.

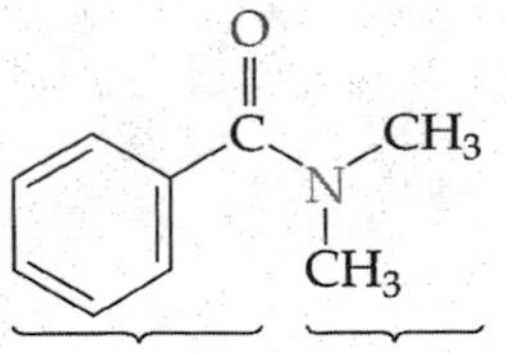

N,N-Dimethylbenzamide

Benzoic   Dimethylamine
acid

WORKED EXAMPLE 23.8

Write the products of the following reactions:

(a)

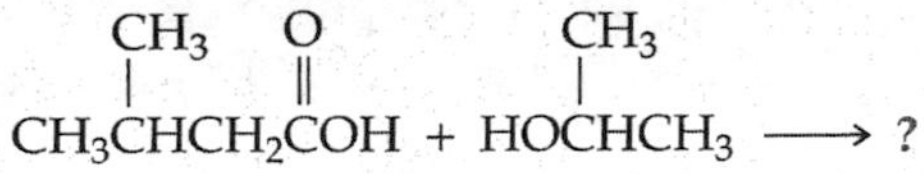

(b)

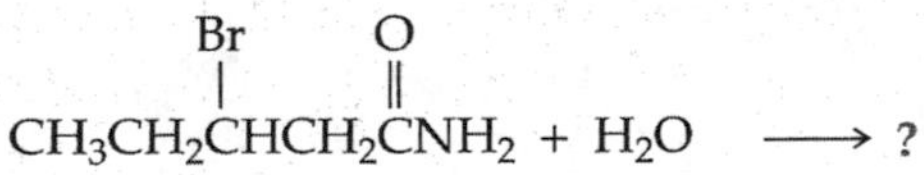

STRATEGY

The reaction of a carboxylic acid with an alcohol yields an ester plus water, and the reaction of an amide with water yields a carboxylic acid and an amine (or ammonia). Write the reagents to show how H_2O is removed, and then connect the remaining fragments to complete the substitution reaction.

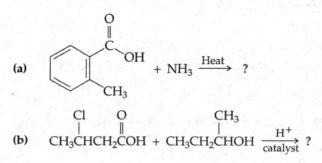

▶ **PROBLEM 23.24** Draw structures corresponding to the following names:

(a) 4-Methylpentanoic acid   (b) Isopropyl benzoate
(c) N-Ethylpropanamide

▶ **PROBLEM 23.25** Write the products of the following reactions:

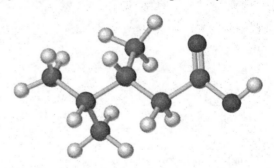

☛**KEY CONCEPT PROBLEM 23.26** Draw the structure of the ester you would obtain by acid-catalyzed reaction of the following carboxylic acid with 2-propanol:

23.15 | Synthetic Polymers

Polymers are large molecules formed by the repetitive bonding together of many smaller molecules, called **monomers**. As we'll see in the next chapter, biological polymers occur throughout nature. Cellulose and starch are polymers built from small sugar monomers, proteins are polymers built from amino acid monomers, and nucleic acids are polymers built from nucleotide monomers. The basic idea is the same, but synthetic polymers are much less complex than biopolymers because the starting monomer units are usually smaller and simpler.

Science Fundamentals Second Edition

TABLE 23.3	Some Alkene Polymers and Their Uses		
Monomer Name	**Structure**	**Polymer Name**	**Uses**
Ethylene	$H_2C{=}CH_2$	Polyethylene	Packaging, bottles
Propylene	$H_2C{=}CH{-}CH_3$	Polypropylene	Bottles, rope, pails medical tubing
Vinyl chloride	$H_2C{=}CH{-}Cl$	Poly(vinyl chloride)	Insulation, plastic pipe
Styrene	$H_2C{=}CH{-}\bigcirc$	Polystyrene	Foams and molded plastics
Acrylonitrile	$H_2C{=}CH{-}C{\equiv}N$	Orlon, Acrilan	Fibers, outdoor carpeting

Many simple alkenes called **vinyl monomers** undergo polymer-forming (*polymerization*) reactions: Ethylene yields polyethylene, propylene (propene) yields polypropylene, styrene yields polystyrene, and so forth. The polymer molecules that result may have anywhere from a few hundred to many thousand monomer units incorporated into a long chain. Some commercially important polymers are listed in Table 23.3.

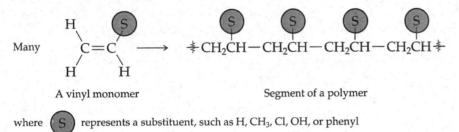

A vinyl monomer   Segment of a polymer

where (S) represents a substituent, such as H, CH_3, Cl, OH, or phenyl

The fundamental process in alkene polymerization is a double-bond addition reaction similar to those discussed in Section 23.10. A species called an *initiator*, In•, first adds to the double bond of an alkene, yielding a reactive intermediate that in turn adds to a second alkene molecule to produce another reactive intermediate, and so on.

▲ These striking examples of suburban yard art are made of polypropylene, an alkene polymer.

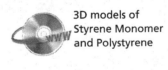

3D models of Styrene Monomer and Polystyrene

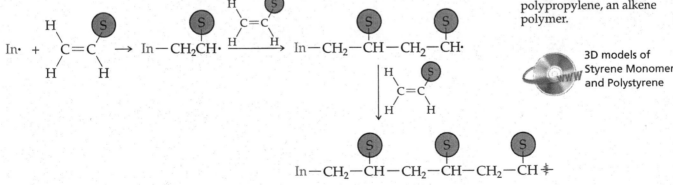

A second kind of polymerization process occurs when molecules with two functional groups react. We've seen, for example, that a carboxylic acid reacts with an amine to yield an amide (Section 23.14). If a molecule with two carboxylic acid groups reacts with a molecule having two amino groups, an initial reaction joins the two molecules together, and further reactions then link more and more

Science Fundamentals Second Edition

molecules together until a giant polyamide chain results. Nylon 66, one of the most important such polymers, is prepared by heating adipic acid (hexanedioic acid) with 1,6-hexanediamine at 280°C.

$$H_2NCH_2CH_2CH_2CH_2CH_2CH_2NH_2 + HO\overset{O}{\overset{\|}{C}}CH_2CH_2CH_2CH_2\overset{O}{\overset{\|}{C}}OH$$

1,6-Hexanediamine   Hexanedioic acid
                          (Adipic acid)

280°C

$$\left[NHCH_2CH_2CH_2CH_2CH_2CH_2NH-\overset{O}{\overset{\|}{C}}CH_2CH_2CH_2CH_2\overset{O}{\overset{\|}{C}} \right]_n + n\ H_2O$$

A segment of nylon 66   Amide bond

Nylons have many uses, both in engineering applications and in fibers. High impact strength and resistance to abrasion make nylon an excellent material for bearings and gears. High tensile strength makes it suitable as fibers for a range of applications from clothing to mountaineering ropes to carpets.

Just as diacids and diamines react to give *polyamides*, diacids and dialcohols react to give *polyesters*. The most industrially important polyester, made from reaction of terephthalic acid (1,4-benzenedicarboxylic acid) with ethylene glycol (1,2-ethanediol), is used under the trade name Dacron to make clothing fiber and under the name Mylar to make plastic film and recording tape.

▲ Climbing ropes are made of Perlon, one of the many varieties of nylon.

Terephthalic acid

+

$HOCH_2CH_2OH$

Ethylene glycol
(1,2-Ethanediol)

A polyester (Dacron, Mylar)

▶ **PROBLEM 23.27** Identify the monomer units used to make the following polymers:

(a)
$$\left[\overset{CO_2CH_3}{\underset{|}{CH}}-CH_2-\overset{CO_2CH_3}{\underset{|}{CH}}-CH_2 \right]$$

(b)
$$\left[OCH_2CH_2CH_2O-\overset{O}{\overset{\|}{C}}CH_2CH_2\overset{O}{\overset{\|}{C}}-O \right]$$

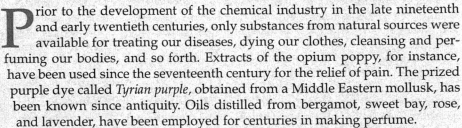

Interlude   Natural or Synthetic?

▲ Whether from the laboratory or from food, the vitamin C is the same.

Prior to the development of the chemical industry in the late nineteenth and early twentieth centuries, only substances from natural sources were available for treating our diseases, dying our clothes, cleansing and perfuming our bodies, and so forth. Extracts of the opium poppy, for instance, have been used since the seventeenth century for the relief of pain. The prized purple dye called *Tyrian purple*, obtained from a Middle Eastern mollusk, has been known since antiquity. Oils distilled from bergamot, sweet bay, rose, and lavender, have been employed for centuries in making perfume.

Many of these so-called *natural products* were first used without any knowledge of their chemical composition. As organic chemistry developed, though, chemists learned how to work out the structures of the compounds in natural products. The disease-curing properties of limes and other citrus fruits, for example, were known for centuries but the chemical structure of vitamin C, the active ingredient, was not determined until 1933. Today there is a revival of interest in folk remedies, and a large effort is being made to identify medicinally important chemical compounds found in plants.

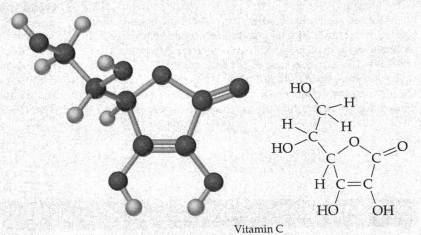

Vitamin C
(ascorbic acid)

Once a structure is known, organic chemists try to *synthesize* the compound in the laboratory. If the starting materials are inexpensive and the synthesis process is simple enough, it may become more economical to manufacture a compound than to isolate it from a plant or bacterium. In the case of vitamin C, a complete synthesis was achieved in 1933, and it is now much cheaper to synthesize it from glucose than to extract it from citrus or other natural sources. Worldwide, more than 80 million pounds are synthesized each year.

But is the "synthetic" vitamin C as good as the "natural" one? Some people still demand vitamins only from natural sources, assuming that natural is somehow better. Although eating an orange is probably better than taking a tablet, the difference lies in the many other substances present in the orange. The vitamin C itself is exactly the same, just as the NaCl produced by reacting sodium and chlorine in the laboratory is exactly the same as the NaCl found in the ocean. Natural and synthetic compounds are identical in all ways; neither is better than the other.

▶ **PROBLEM 23.28**   Identify the functional groups present in vitamin C.

1019

Science Fundamentals Second Edition

757

Summary

Organic chemistry is the study of carbon compounds. The more than 19 million known organic compounds can be organized into families according to the functional groups they contain. A **functional group** is an atom or group of atoms within a molecule that has characteristic chemical behavior and undergoes the same kinds of reactions in every molecule it's a part of.

The simplest compounds are the **saturated hydrocarbons**, or **alkanes**, which contain only carbon and hydrogen and have only single bonds. **Straight-chain alkanes** have all their carbons connected in a row, **branched-chain alkanes** have a branched connection of atoms in their chain, and **cyclo-alkanes** have a ring of carbon atoms. Isomerism is possible in alkanes having four or more carbons. Straight-chain alkanes are named in the IUPAC system by adding the family ending *-ane* to the Greek number that tells how many carbon atoms are present. Branched-chain alkanes are named by identifying the longest continuous chain of carbon atoms and then telling what **alkyl groups** are present as branches off the main chain. Alkanes are chemically rather inert, although they undergo combustion with oxygen and undergo a **substitution reaction** with chlorine.

Alkenes are hydrocarbons that contain a carbon–carbon double bond, and **alkynes** are hydrocarbons that contain a carbon–carbon triple bond. **Cis–trans isomers** are possible for substituted alkenes because of the lack of rotation about the carbon–carbon double bond. The cis isomer has two substituents on the same side of the double bond, and the trans isomer has two substituents on opposite sides. The most important transformations of alkenes and alkynes are **addition reactions**, in which a substance adds to the multiple bond to yield a saturated product.

Aromatic compounds are often represented as having a six-membered ring with three double bonds. These compounds usually undergo **substitution reactions**, in which a group substitutes for one of the hydrogen atoms on the aromatic ring. **Alcohols** and **ethers** can be thought of as derivatives of water in which one or both of the hydrogens are replaced by an organic substituent. Similarly, **amines** are derivatives of ammonia in which one or more of the ammonia hydrogens are replaced by an organic substituent. Amines are bases and can be protonated by acids to yield ammonium salts.

Compounds that contain a **carbonyl group**, C=O, can be classified into two categories: In **aldehydes** and **ketones**, the carbonyl-group carbon is bonded to atoms (H and C) that don't attract electrons strongly. In **carboxylic acids**, **esters**, and **amides**, the carbonyl-group carbon is bonded to an atom (O or N) that *does* attract electrons strongly. As a result, these three families of compounds undergo **carbonyl-group substitution reactions**, in which a group –Y substitutes for the –OH, –OC, or –N group of the carbonyl reactant.

Polymers are large molecules formed when many smaller **monomers** bond together. Alkene polymers such as polyethylene result from the polymerization of simple alkenes. Nylons and polyesters result from the sequential reaction of two difunctional molecules.

Key Words

addition reaction *1003*	branched-chain alkane *989*	ether *1009*	saturated hydrocarbon *988*
alcohol *1007*	carbonyl group *1010*	functional group *999*	straight-chain alkane *989*
aldehyde *1011*	carboxylate anion *1012*	halogenation *1004*	substitution reaction *1006*
alkane *988*	carboxylic acid *1012*	hydration *1004*	
alkene *1001*	cis–trans isomers *1002*	hydrocarbon *988*	unsaturated *1001*
alkyl group *994*	condensed structure *990*	hydrogenation *1004*	vinyl monomer *1017*
alkyne *1001*		ketone *1011*	
amide *1014*	cycloalkane *996*	monomer *1016*	
amine *1009*	ester *1013*	organic chemistry *986*	
aromatic *1005*		polymer *1016*	

Key Concept Summary

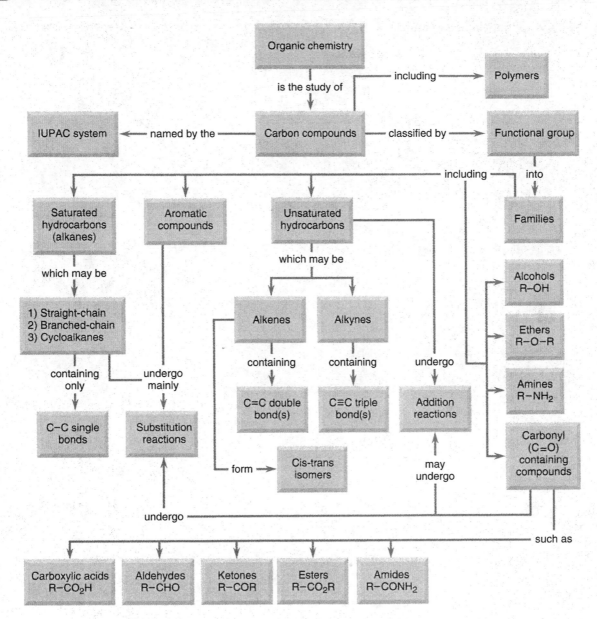

Understanding Key Concepts

Problems 23.1–23.28 appear within the chapter.

23.29 Convert the following model into a condensed structure, and draw the structures of two isomeric compounds.

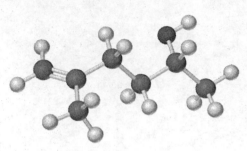

23.30 Convert each of the following models into a condensed formula:

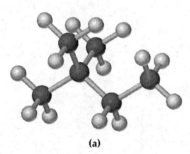

(a)

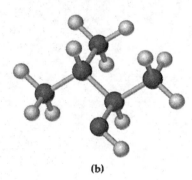

(b)

23.31 Convert each of the following models into a chemical structure:

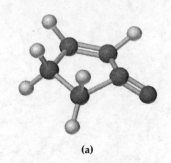

(a)

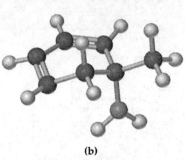

(b)

23.32 Identify the functional groups in each of the following compounds:

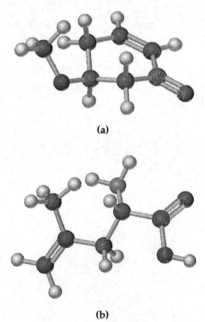

(a)

(b)

23.33 Give systematic names for the following compounds:

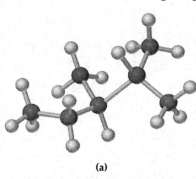

(a)

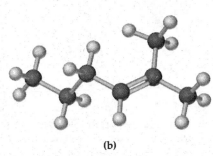

(b)

23.34 The following structure represents a segment of an alkene polymer. Identify the monomer from which the polymer was made.

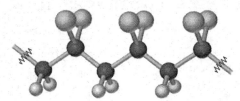

23.35 Identify the carboxylic acid and alcohol from which the following ester was made:

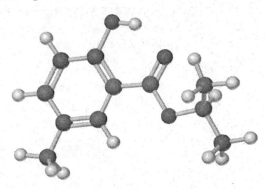

23.36 Draw two isomers of the following compound:

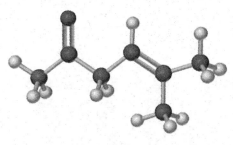

23.37 Draw three resonance forms for naphthalene, showing the positions of the double bonds.

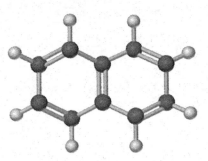

Additional Problems

Functional Groups and Isomers

23.38 What are functional groups, and why are they important?

23.39 Describe the structure of the functional group in each of the following families:

(a) Alkene

(b) Alcohol

(c) Ester

(d) Amine

23.40 Propose structures for molecules that meet the following descriptions:

(a) A ketone with the formula $C_5H_{10}O$

(b) An ester with the formula $C_6H_{12}O_2$

(c) A compound with formula $C_2H_5NO_2$ that is both an amine and a carboxylic acid

23.41 Write structures for each of the following molecular formulas. You may have to use rings and/or multiple bonds in some instances.

(a) C_2H_7N

(b) C_4H_8

(c) C_2H_4O

(d) CH_2O_2

Science Fundamentals Second Edition

23.42 There are three isomers with the formula C_3H_8O. Draw their structures.

23.43 Write as many isomers as you can that fit the following descriptions:

    (a) Alcohols with formula $C_4H_{10}O$

    (b) Amines with formula C_3H_9N

    (c) Ketones with formula $C_5H_{10}O$

    (d) Aldehydes with formula $C_5H_{10}O$

23.44 Identify the functional groups in the following molecules:

    (a)

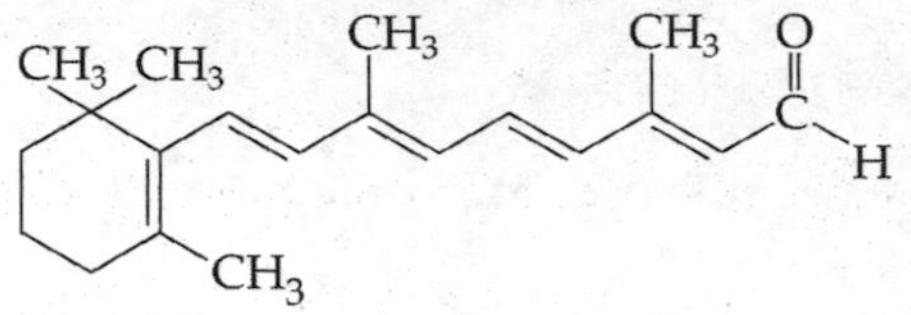

Retinal (Vitamin A)

    (b)

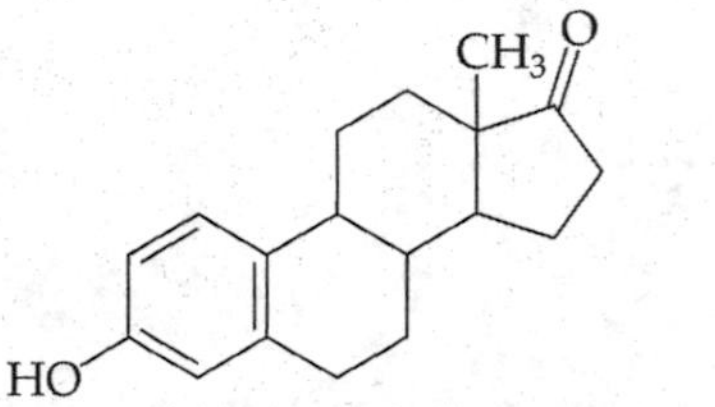

Estrone, a female sex hormone

23.45 Identify the functional groups in cocaine.

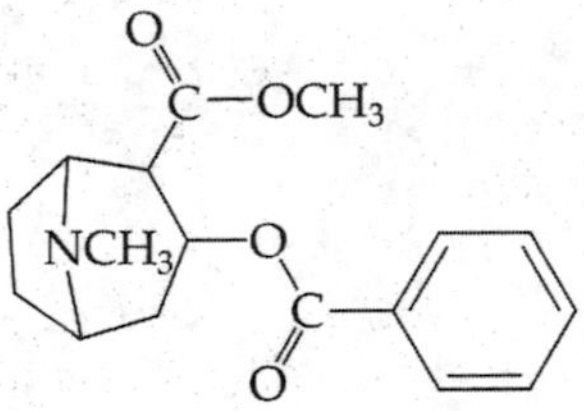

Cocaine

Alkanes

23.46 What is the difference between a straight-chain alkane and a branched-chain alkane?

23.47 What is the difference between an alkane and an alkyl group?

23.48 What kind of hybrid orbitals does carbon use in forming alkanes?

23.49 Why are alkanes said to be saturated?

23.50 If someone reported the preparation of a compound with the formula C_3H_9, most chemists would be skeptical. Why?

23.51 What is wrong with each of the following structures?

    (a) $CH_3{=}CHCH_2CH_2OH$

    (b) $CH_3CH_2CH{=}\overset{\overset{\textstyle O}{\|}}{C}CH_3$

    (c) $CH_3CH_2C{\equiv}CH_2CH_3$

23.52 What are the IUPAC names of the following alkanes?

    (a) $CH_3CH_2CH_2CH_2\overset{\overset{\textstyle CH_2CH_3}{|}}{\underset{\underset{\textstyle CH_3}{|}}{C}}HCHCH_2CH_3$

    (b) $CH_3CH_2CH_2\overset{\overset{\textstyle CH_3CHCH_3}{|}}{C}HCH_2\underset{\underset{\textstyle CH_3}{|}}{C}HCH_3$

    (c) $CH_3\overset{\overset{\textstyle CH_3}{|}}{\underset{\underset{\textstyle CH_3}{|}}{C}}CH_2CH_2CH_2\overset{\overset{\textstyle CH_3}{|}}{C}HCH_3$

    (d) $CH_3CH_2CH_2\overset{\overset{\textstyle CH_2CH_2CH_2CH_3}{|}}{\underset{\underset{\textstyle CH_2CH_3}{|}}{C}}CH_3$

23.53 The following compound, known commonly as isooctane, is used as a reference substance for determining the octane rating of gasoline. What is the IUPAC name of isooctane?

    $CH_3\overset{\overset{\textstyle CH_3}{|}}{\underset{\underset{\textstyle CH_3}{|}}{C}}CH_2\overset{\overset{\textstyle CH_3}{|}}{C}HCH_3$ Isooctane

23.54 Write condensed structures for each of the following compounds:

    (a) 3-Ethylhexane

    (b) 2,2,3-Trimethylpentane

    (c) 3-Ethyl-3,4-dimethylheptane

    (d) 5-Isopropyl-2-methyloctane

23.55 Draw structures corresponding to the following IUPAC names:

    (a) Cyclooctane

    (b) 1,1-Dimethylcyclopentane

    (c) 1,2,3,4-Tetramethylcyclobutane

    (d) 4-Ethyl-1,1-dimethylcyclohexane

23.56 Give IUPAC names for each of the following cycloalkanes:

    (a)

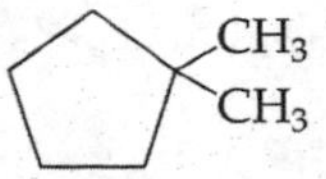

    (b)

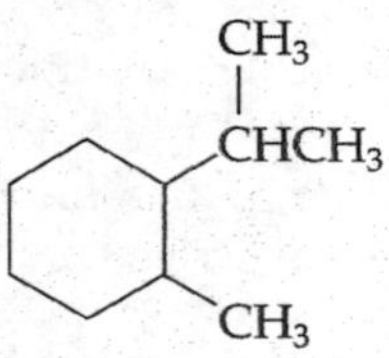

    (c)

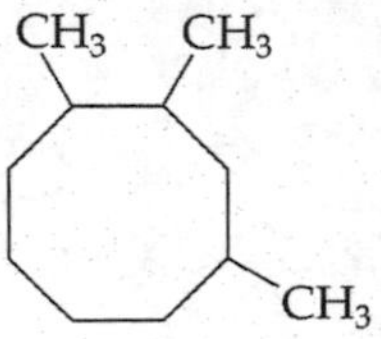

23.57 The following names are incorrect. What is wrong with each, and what are the correct names?

(a)
$$CH_3CCH_2CH_2CH_3$$
with CH_3 above and CH_2CH_3 below the second carbon
4-Ethyl-4-methylpentane

(b)
$$CH_3CHCH_2CHCH_2CH_3$$
with CH_2CH_3 above the second carbon and CH_3 below the fourth carbon
5-Ethyl-3-methylhexane

(c) 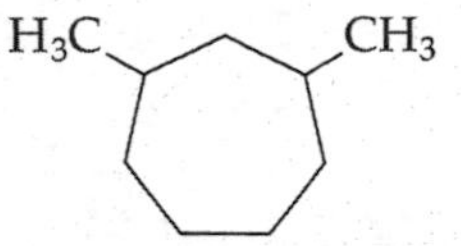 H_3C — (cycloheptane ring) — CH_3

1,4-Dimethylcyclooctane

23.58 Give IUPAC names for each of the five isomers with the formula C_6H_{14}.

23.59 Draw structures and give IUPAC names for the nine isomers of C_7H_{16}.

23.60 Write the formulas of all monochlorinated substitution products that might result from a substitution reaction of the following substances with Cl_2:

(a) Hexane

(b) 3-Methylpentane

(c) Methylcyclohexane

23.61 Which of the following reactions is likely to have a higher yield? Explain.

(a) $$CH_3CCH_3 + Cl_2 \xrightarrow{h\nu} CH_3CCH_2Cl$$
with CH_3 above and CH_3 below each central carbon

(b) $$CH_3CHCH_2CH_3 + Cl_2 \xrightarrow{h\nu} CH_3CHCH_2CH_2Cl$$
with CH_3 above the second carbon on each side

Alkenes, Alkynes, and Aromatic Compounds

23.62 What kind of hybrid orbitals does carbon use in forming the following?

(a) Double bonds

(b) Triple bonds

(c) Aromatic rings

23.63 Why are alkenes, alkynes, and aromatic compounds said to be unsaturated?

23.64 Not all compounds that smell nice are called "aromatic," and not all compounds called "aromatic" smell nice. Explain.

23.65 What is meant by the term *addition reaction*?

23.66 Write structural formulas for compounds that meet the following descriptions:

(a) An alkene with five carbons

(b) An alkyne with four carbons

(c) A substituted aromatic compound with eight carbons

23.67 How many dienes (compounds with two double bonds) are there with the formula C_5H_8? Draw structures of as many as you can.

23.68 Give IUPAC names for the following compounds:

(a) $$CH_3CHCH=CHCH_3$$
with CH_3 above the second carbon

(b) $$CH_3CH_2CHCH_3$$
with $CH=CH_2$ above the third carbon

(c) 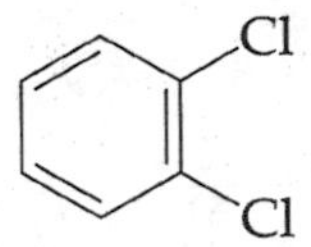 ortho-dichlorobenzene (ring with two Cl)

(d) $$CH_3CH=CCH_3$$
with CH_3 above the third carbon

(e) $$CH_3CH_2C\equiv CCH_2CH_2CHCH_3$$
with CH_3 above the seventh carbon

23.69 Draw structures corresponding to the following IUPAC names:

(a) *cis*-2-Hexene

(b) 2-Methyl-3-hexene

(c) 2-Methyl-1,3-butadiene

23.70 Ignoring cis–trans isomers, there are five alkenes with the formula C_5H_{10}. Draw structures for as many as you can, and give their IUPAC names. Which can exist as cis–trans isomers?

23.71 There are three alkynes with the formula C_5H_8. Draw and name them.

23.72 Which of the following compounds are capable of cis–trans isomerism?

(a) 1-Hexene

(b) 2-Hexene

(c) 3-Hexene

23.73 Which of the following compounds are capable of cis–trans isomerism?

(a) $$CH_3CHCH=CHCH_3$$
with CH_3 above the second carbon

(b) $$CH_3CH_2CHCH_3$$
with $CH=CH_2$ above the third carbon

(c) $$CH_3CH=CHCHCH_2CH_3$$
with Cl above the fourth carbon

23.74 Draw structures of the following compounds, indicating the cis or trans geometry of the double bond if necessary:

(a) *cis*-3-Heptene

(b) *cis*-4-Methyl-2-pentene

(c) *trans*-2,5-Dimethyl-3-hexene

Science Fundamentals Second Edition

23.75 The following names are incorrect by IUPAC rules. Draw the structures represented and give the correct names.

   (a) 2-Methyl-4-hexene

   (b) 5,5-Dimethyl-3-hexyne

   (c) 2-Butyl-1-propene

   (d) 1,5-Diethylbenzene

23.76 Why is cis–trans isomerism possible for alkenes but not for alkanes or alkynes?

23.77 Why do you suppose small-ring cycloalkenes such as cyclohexene don't exist as cis–trans isomers?

23.78 Write equations for the reaction of 2,3-dimethyl-2-butene with each of the following reagents:

   (a) H_2 and Pd catalyst

   (b) Br_2

   (c) H_2O and H_2SO_4 catalyst

23.79 Write equations for the reaction of 2-methyl-2-butene with the reagents given in Problem 23.78.

23.80 Write equations for the reaction of *p*-dichlorobenzene with the following reagents:

   (a) Br_2 and $FeBr_3$ catalyst

   (b) HNO_3 and H_2SO_4 catalyst

   (c) H_2SO_4 and SO_3

   (d) Cl_2 and $FeCl_3$ catalyst

23.81 Benzene and other aromatic compounds don't normally react with hydrogen in the presence of a palladium catalyst. If very high pressures (200 atm) and high temperatures are used, however, benzene will add three molecules of H_2 to give an addition product. What is a likely structure for the product?

Alcohols, Amines, and Carbonyl Compounds

23.82 Draw structures corresponding to the following names:

   (a) 2,4-Dimethyl-2-pentanol

   (b) 2,2-Dimethylcyclohexanol

   (c) 5,5-Diethyl-1-heptanol

   (d) 3-Ethyl-3-hexanol

23.83 Draw structures corresponding to the following names:

   (a) Propylamine

   (b) Diethylamine

   (c) *N*-Methylpropylamine

23.84 Assume that you have samples of quinine (an amine) and menthol (an alcohol). What simple chemical test could you do to distinguish between them?

23.85 Assume that you're given samples of pentanoic acid and methyl butanoate, both of which have the formula $C_5H_{10}O_2$. Describe how you can tell them apart.

23.86 What is the structural difference between an aldehyde and a ketone?

23.87 How do aldehydes and ketones differ from carboxylic acids, esters, and amides?

23.88 How are industrially important ketones and aldehydes usually prepared?

23.89 What general kind of reaction do carboxylic acids, esters, and amides undergo?

23.90 Identify the kinds of carbonyl groups in the following molecules (aldehyde, amide, ester, or ketone):

   (a)

   (b) $CH_3CH_2CH_2CHO$

   (c) $CH_3CHCH_2COCH_3$ with CH_3 substituent

   (d)

   (e) $CH_3CHCH_2COOCH_3$ with CH_3 substituent

23.91 Draw and name compounds that meet the following descriptions:

   (a) Three different amides with the formula $C_5H_{11}NO$

   (b) Three different esters with the formula $C_6H_{12}O_2$

23.92 Write the equation for the dissociation of benzoic acid in water. If the K_a of benzoic acid is 6.5×10^{-5}, what is its percent dissociation in a 1.0 M solution?

23.93 Assume that you have a sample of acetic acid ($pK_a = 4.75$) dissolved in water.

   (a) Draw the structure of the major species present in the water solution.

   (b) Now assume that aqueous HCl is added to the acetic acid solution until pH 2 is reached. Draw the structure of the major species present.

   (c) Finally, assume that aqueous NaOH is added to the acetic acid solution until pH 12 is reached. Draw the structure of the major species present.

23.94 Give the IUPAC names of the following compounds:

   (a) $CH_3CHCH_2CH_2COCH_3$ with CH_3 substituent and O

   (b) $CH_3CCH_2CH_2COH$ with CH_3 substituents and O

   (c) $CH_3CH_2CH_2CHCNH_2$ with CH_3 substituent and O

23.95 Give the IUPAC names of the following compounds:

   (a) $CH_3CHCH_2CH_2CNCH_3$ with CH_2CH_3 and CH_3 substituents and O

   (b) $CH_3CHCOCHCH_3$ with CH_3 and CH_3 substituents and O

   (c)

23.96 Draw structures corresponding to the following IUPAC names:

(a) Methyl pentanoate

(b) Isopropyl 2-methylbutanoate

(c) Cyclohexyl acetate

23.97 Draw structures corresponding to the following IUPAC names:

(a) 3-Methylpentanamide

(b) *N*-Phenylacetamide

(c) *N*-Ethyl-*N*-methylbenzamide

23.98 Write equations showing how you could prepare each of the esters in Problem 23.96 from the appropriate alcohols and carboxylic acids.

23.99 Write equations showing how you could prepare each of the amides in Problem 23.97 from the appropriate amines and carboxylic acids.

23.100 Novocaine, a local anesthetic, has the following structure. Identify the functional groups present in novocaine, and show the structures of the alcohol and carboxylic acid you would use to prepare it.

$$H_2N - \text{(benzene ring)} - \overset{\overset{O}{\|}}{C} - OCH_2CH_2\overset{\overset{CH_2CH_3}{|}}{N}CH_2CH_3$$

Novocaine

23.101 Ordinary soap is a mixture of the sodium or potassium salts of long-chain carboxylic acids that arise from saponification of animal fat. Draw the structures of soap molecules produced in the following reaction:

$$\begin{array}{l} CH_2O\overset{\overset{O}{\|}}{C}(CH_2)_{14}CH_3 \\ | \quad\;\; \overset{O}{\|} \\ CHO\overset{}{C}(CH_2)_7CH{=}CH(CH_2)_7CH_3 + 3\,KOH \longrightarrow \\ | \quad\;\; \overset{O}{\|} \\ CH_2O\overset{}{C}(CH_2)_{16}CH_3 \end{array}$$

A fat

Polymers

23.102 What is the difference between a monomer and a polymer?

23.103 What is the difference between a polymer like polyethylene and a polymer like nylon?

23.104 Show the structure of poly(vinyl chloride) by drawing several repeating units. Vinyl chloride is $H_2C{=}CHCl$.

23.105 Show the structures of the polymers you would obtain from the following monomers:

(a) $F_2C{=}CF_2$ gives Teflon

(b) $H_2C{=}CHCO_2CH_3$ gives Lucite

23.106 Show the monomer units you would use to prepare the following alkene polymers:

(a) $\dashv CH_2\overset{\overset{CN}{|}}{C}HCH_2\overset{\overset{CN}{|}}{C}HCH_2\overset{\overset{CN}{|}}{C}H \vdash$

(b) $\dashv CH_2\overset{\overset{CH_3}{|}}{C}HCH_2\overset{\overset{CH_3}{|}}{C}HCH_2\overset{\overset{CH_3}{|}}{C}H \vdash$

(c) $\dashv CH_2\overset{\overset{Cl}{|}}{\underset{\underset{Cl}{|}}{C}}CH_2\overset{\overset{Cl}{|}}{\underset{\underset{Cl}{|}}{C}}CH_2\overset{\overset{Cl}{|}}{\underset{\underset{Cl}{|}}{C}} \vdash$

23.107 What monomer unit is used to prepare poly(methyl cyanoacrylate), also known as "superglue"?

$$\dashv CH_2 - \overset{\overset{CO_2CH_3}{|}}{\underset{\underset{CN}{|}}{C}} - CH_2 - \overset{\overset{CO_2CH_3}{|}}{\underset{\underset{CN}{|}}{C}} - CH_2 - \overset{\overset{CO_2CH_3}{|}}{\underset{\underset{CN}{|}}{C}} \vdash$$

Poly(methyl cyanoacrylate)

23.108 Kevlar, a nylon polymer prepared by the reaction of 1,4-benzenedicarboxylic acid (terephthalic acid) with *p*-diaminobenzene, is so strong that it's used to make bulletproof vests. Draw the structure of a segment of Kevlar.

23.109 Draw the structure of a segment of the polyester that results from the reaction of ethylene glycol (HOCH$_2$CH$_2$OH) with butanedioic acid (HO$_2$CCH$_2$CH$_2$CO$_2$H).

General Problems

23.110 Draw structural formulas for the following compounds:

(a) 2-Methylheptane

(b) 4-Ethyl-2-methylhexane

(c) 4-Ethyl-3,4-dimethyloctane

(d) 2,4,4-Trimethylheptane

(e) 1,1-Dimethylcyclopentane

(f) 4-Isopropyl-3-methylheptane

23.111 Give IUPAC names for the following alkanes:

(a)
$$CH_3CH_2CH_2\underset{\underset{CH_3}{|}}{CH}\underset{\underset{CH_3}{|}}{CH}CH_3$$

(b)
$$CH_3CH_2CH_2\underset{\underset{CH_2CH_2CH_2CH_3}{|}}{CH}\underset{\underset{CH_3}{|}}{CH}CH_3$$

(c)
$$CH_3\underset{\underset{CH_3}{|}}{CH}CH_2\underset{\underset{CH_2CH_3}{|}}{\overset{\overset{CH_2CH_3}{|}}{C}}CH_3$$

(d)
$$CH_3CH_2\underset{\underset{CH_2CH_3}{|}}{\overset{\overset{CH_2CH_3}{|}}{C}}CH_2CH_3$$

23.112 Assume that you have two unlabeled bottles, one with cyclohexane and one with cyclohexene. How could you tell them apart by doing chemical reactions?

23.113 Assume you have two unlabeled bottles, one with cyclohexene and one with benzene. How could you tell them apart by doing chemical reactions?

23.114 Write the products of the following reactions:

(a)
$$CH_3CH_2CH=CH\underset{\underset{CH_3}{|}}{CH}CH_3 \xrightarrow[\text{Pd catalyst}]{H_2}$$

(b)
$$Br-\langle\bigcirc\rangle-Br \xrightarrow[H_2SO_4]{HNO_3}$$

(c)
$$\xrightarrow[H_2SO_4]{H_2O}$$

23.115 Show the structure of the nylon polymer that results from heating 6-aminohexanoic acid.

$$H_2NCH_2CH_2CH_2CH_2CH_2\overset{\overset{O}{\|}}{C}OH \xrightarrow{Heat}$$
6-Aminohexanoic acid

Multi-Concept Problems

23.116 Fumaric acid is an organic substance widely used as a food additive. Its elemental composition is 41.4% C, 3.5% H, and 55.1% O. A solution made by dissolving 0.1500 g of fumaric acid in water and diluting to a volume of 100.0 mL gave rise to an osmotic pressure of 240.3 mm Hg at 298 K. On titration of a sample weighing 0.573 g, 94.1 mL of 0.105 M NaOH was required to reach an equivalence point. Fumaric acid reacts with 1 mol of HCl to give an addition product and with 1 mol of H_2 to give a reduction product.

(a) What is the empirical formula of fumaric acid?

(b) What is the molecular mass of fumaric acid?

(c) Draw three possible structures for fumaric acid.

(d) If fumaric acid contains a trans double bond, which of your structures is correct?

23.117 When 0.0552 g of an unknown liquid containing only C, H, and O was subjected to combustion analysis, 0.1213 g of CO_2 and 0.0661 g of H_2O were formed.

(a) Calculate a formula for the unknown, and write a balanced equation for the combustion reaction.

(b) Is the formula you calculated an empirical formula or a molecular formula? Explain.

(c) Draw three possible structures for the compound, and identify the functional groups in each.

(d) Reaction of the compound with CrO_3 yields acetone. Which of the three structures you drew in part (c) is most likely to be correct?

(e) Combustion of 5.000 g of the compound releases 166.9 kJ of heat. Look up $\Delta H_f°$ values for $CO_2(g)$ and $H_2O(l)$ in Appendix B, and calculate $\Delta H_f°$ for the compound.

23.118 Reaction of methyl propanoate ($CH_3CH_2CO_2CH_3$) with ammonia gives methanol plus a second product with the formula C_3H_7NO.

(a) Propose a structure, and give a name for the second product.

(b) Draw two resonance structures for the product.

(c) Predict the geometry around the three carbon atoms and the nitrogen atom in the product according to VSEPR theory.

(d) Experimentally, the nitrogen atom in the product is found to be trigonal planar, with bond angles near 120°. How does this result compare with your prediction? Sketch a *p*-orbital picture of the product, and account for the experimental geometry.

 eMedia Problems

23.119 Use the **Boiling Points** activity (*eChapter 23.2*) to get the boiling points of the first six straight-chain alkanes (methane, ethane, propane, butane, pentane, and hexane) and the corresponding alcohols derived by replacing one of the CH_3 hydrogens at the end of each chain with an OH group.

(a) For a given number of carbons, which has the higher boiling point, the alkane or the alcohol? Explain this observation in terms of intermolecular forces.

(b) Does the difference in boiling point for an alkane and its corresponding alcohol increase or decrease with increasing number of carbons?

(c) Using your answer from part **(b)**, describe how the relative importance of hydrogen bonding and London dispersion forces changes with increasing length of a carbon chain. Which type of interaction contributes more significantly to the overall intermolecular forces for small molecules, and which for large molecules?

23.120 Determine the boiling points of at least five different alcohols and their corresponding amines using the **Boiling Points** activity (*eChapter 23.2*).

(a) Based on the boiling points, which functional group, OH or NH_2, appears to exhibit more significant hydrogen bonding?

(b) Draw electron-dot structures of alcohol and amine functional groups. Use the electron-dot structures to explain the observation that one group exhibits more significant hydrogen bonding than the other.

23.121 From the **3D Models** of *n*-pentane, isopentane, and neopentane (*eChapter 23.4*) draw expanded and condensed structures for each molecule. Name these molecules using proper IIUPAC nomenclature.

23.122 Draw structural formulas from all of the **3D Models** of the examples of the families of organic molecules in *eChapter 23.8*. Circle the functional group in each of the molecules. Which families do you expect to exhibit hydrogen bonding?

23.123 Look at the **Styrene Monomer 3D Model** (*eChapter 23.15*) and draw the structural formula for styrene. Name the functional group on the monomer. Draw the structural formula for a segment of the polymer containing 3 styrene monomers.

23.124 Watch the **Synthesis of Nylon 610** movie (*eChapter 23.15*) and complete the following equation for the polymerization process by drawing structural formulas for the reactants and for a segment of the polymer product. Include the formula for the other product.

$$ClCO(CH_2)_8COCl + NH_2(CH)_6NH_2$$

Chapter 24

Biochemistry

The ultimate goal of chemistry is to understand the world around us on a molecular level, and a knowledge of **biochemistry**—the chemistry of living organisms—is a crucial part of that goal. In this chapter, we'll look at the main classes of biomolecules: proteins, carbohydrates, lipids, and nucleic acids. First, though, we'll take a brief look at biochemical energetics to see where biochemical energy comes from and how it is used by organisms.

CONTENTS

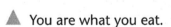
▲ You are what you eat.

24.1 Biochemical Energy
24.2 Amino Acids and Peptides
24.3 Amino Acids and Molecular Handedness
24.4 Proteins
24.5 Levels of Protein Structure
24.6 Enzymes
24.7 Carbohydrates
24.8 Handedness of Carbohydrates
24.9 Cyclic Structures of Monosaccharides

24.10 Some Common Disaccharides and Polysaccharides
24.11 Lipids
24.12 Nucleic Acids
24.13 Base Pairing in DNA: The Watson–Crick Model
24.14 Nucleic Acids and Heredity
■ *Interlude*—DNA Fingerprinting

1031

Science Fundamentals Second Edition

24.1 | Biochemical Energy

All living things do mechanical work. Microorganisms engulf food, plants bend toward the sun, animals move about. Organisms also do the chemical work of synthesizing biomolecules needed for energy storage, growth, and repair. Even individual cells do work when they move molecules and ions across cell membranes.

In animals, it is the energy extracted from food and released in the exquisitely interconnected reactions of *metabolism* that allows work to be done. All animals are powered by the cellular oxidation of biomolecules containing mainly carbon, hydrogen, and oxygen. The end products of this biological oxidation are carbon dioxide, water, and energy, just as they are when an organic fuel such as methane is burned with oxygen in a furnace.

$$C, H, O \text{ (food molecules)} + O_2 \longrightarrow CO_2 + H_2O + \text{Energy}$$

The energy used by the vast majority of living organisms comes ultimately from the sun. Photosynthesis in plants converts sunlight to potential energy stored mainly in the chemical bonds of carbohydrates. Plant-eating animals use some of this energy for living and store the rest of it, mainly in the chemical bonds of fats. Other animals, including humans, then eat plants and smaller animals and make use of the chemical energy these organisms have stored.

The energy used by almost ▶ all living organisms ultimately comes from the sun. Plants use solar energy for the photosynthesis of glucose from CO_2, and animals then eat the plants.

The sum of the many organic reactions that take place in cells is called **metabolism**. These reactions usually occur in long sequences, which may be either linear or cyclic. In a linear sequence, the product of one reaction serves as the starting material for the next. In a cyclic sequence, a series of reactions regenerates the first reactant and produces other products along the way.

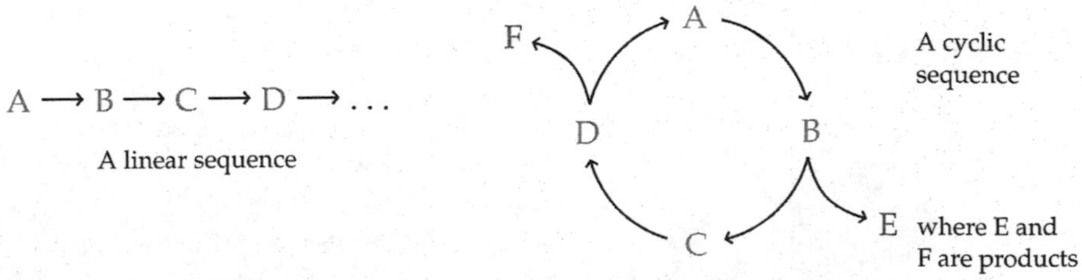

$$A \longrightarrow B \longrightarrow C \longrightarrow D \longrightarrow \ldots$$

A linear sequence

A cyclic sequence

where E and F are products

Those reaction sequences that break molecules apart are known collectively as **catabolism**, while those that put building blocks back together to assemble larger molecules are known as **anabolism**. Catabolic reactions generally release energy that is used to power living organisms, whereas anabolic reactions generally absorb energy. The overall picture of catabolism and energy production can be roughly divided into the four stages shown in Figure 24.1.

Science Fundamentals Second Edition

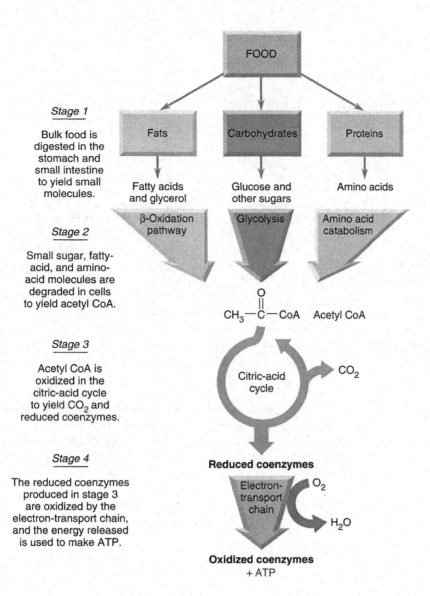

◄ **FIGURE 24.1** An overview of catabolic pathways in the four stages of food degradation and the production of biochemical energy.

Stage 1

Bulk food is digested in the stomach and small intestine to yield small molecules.

Stage 2

Small sugar, fatty-acid, and amino-acid molecules are degraded in cells to yield acetyl CoA.

Stage 3

Acetyl CoA is oxidized in the citric-acid cycle to yield CO_2 and reduced coenzymes.

Stage 4

The reduced coenzymes produced in stage 3 are oxidized by the electron-transport chain, and the energy released is used to make ATP.

The first stage of catabolism, *digestion*, takes place in the stomach and small intestine when bulk food is broken down into small molecules such as simple sugars, long-chain carboxylic acids (called *fatty acids*), and amino acids. In stage 2, these small molecules are further degraded in cells to yield two-carbon acetyl groups $CH_3C{=}O$ attached to a large carrier molecule called *coenzyme A*. The resultant compound, *acetyl coenzyme A* (*acetyl CoA*), is an intermediate in the breakdown of all the main classes of food molecules.

Acetyl groups are oxidized in the third stage of catabolism, the *citric acid cycle*, to yield carbon dioxide and water. This stage releases a great deal of energy that is used in stage 4, the *electron-transport chain*, to make molecules of **adenosine triphosphate (ATP)**. ATP, the final product of food catabolism, plays a pivotal role in the production of biological energy. As the crucial molecule for driving many metabolic reactions, ATP has been called the "energy currency of the living cell." Catabolic reactions "pay off" in ATP by synthesizing it from *adenosine diphosphate* (ADP) plus hydrogen phosphate ion, HPO_4^{2-}. Anabolic reactions "spend" ATP by transferring a phosphate group to other molecules, thereby regenerating ADP. The entire process of energy production revolves around the $ATP \rightleftharpoons ADP$ interconversion.

ATP 3D model

Science Fundamentals Second Edition

Diphosphate group

Adenosine diphosphate (ADP)

Triphosphate group

Adenosine triphosphate (ATP)

$+ H_2O$

Because the primary metabolic function of ATP is to drive reactions, biochemists often refer to it as a "high-energy molecule" or an "energy storehouse." These terms don't mean that ATP is somehow different from other compounds; they mean only that ATP releases a large amount of energy when its P–O–P (*phosphoric anhydride*) bonds are broken and a phosphate group is transferred.

What does the body do with ATP? Recall from Sections 8.14 and 17.7 that a chemical reaction is favorable, or spontaneous, if the free-energy change (ΔG) for the process is negative. Conversely, a reaction is unfavorable if the free-energy change is positive. The change in free energy depends on two factors: the release or absorption of heat (ΔH) and the increase or decrease in entropy (ΔS). The larger the amount of heat released and the greater the increase in entropy, the more favorable the reaction.

$$\Delta G = \Delta H - T\Delta S$$

Reactions in living organisms are no different from reactions in laboratory flasks. Both follow the same laws, and both have the same kinds of energy requirements. For any biochemical reaction to occur spontaneously, ΔG must be negative. For example, oxidation of 1 mol of glucose, the principal source of energy for animals, has $\Delta G° = -2870$ kJ.

$$HOCH_2CHCHCHCHCH + 6\,O_2 \longrightarrow 6\,CO_2 + 6\,H_2O \qquad \Delta G° = -2870 \text{ kJ}$$

Glucose ($C_6H_{12}O_6$)

Reactions in which the free-energy change is positive can also occur, but such reactions can't be spontaneous. An example is the conversion of glucose to glucose-6-phosphate, an important step in the breakdown of dietary carbohydrates.

$$HOCH_2CHCHCHCHCH \xrightarrow[-H_2O]{HPO_4^{2-}} {}^-OPOCH_2CHCHCHCHCH \qquad \Delta G° = +13.8 \text{ kJ}$$

Glucose   Glucose-6-phosphate

What usually happens when an energetically unfavorable reaction occurs is that it is "coupled" to an energetically favorable reaction so that the *overall* free-energy change for the combined reactions is favorable. For example, the reaction of glucose with hydrogen phosphate ion (HPO_4^{2-}) to yield glucose-6-phosphate plus water does not take place spontaneously because it is energetically unfavorable by 13.8 kJ. When ATP is involved, however, the reaction of ATP with water to yield ADP plus hydrogen phosphate ion is energetically *favorable* by about 30.5 kJ. Thus, if the two reactions are coupled, the overall process for the synthesis of glucose-6-phosphate is favorable by about 16.7 kJ. That is, the free-energy change for the reaction of ATP with water is so favorable that it can "drive" the unfavorable reaction of glucose with hydrogen phosphate ion.

$$\text{Glucose} + HPO_4{}^{2-} \longrightarrow \text{Glucose-6-phosphate} + H_2O \qquad \Delta G° = +13.8 \text{ kJ}$$
$$ATP + H_2O \longrightarrow ADP + HPO_4{}^{2-} + H^+ \qquad \Delta G° = -30.5 \text{ kJ}$$

Net: $\text{Glucose} + ATP \longrightarrow \text{Glucose-6-phosphate} + ADP + H^+ \qquad \Delta G° = -16.7 \text{ kJ}$

It's this ability to drive otherwise unfavorable reactions that makes ATP so useful. In fact, most of the thousands of reactions going on in your body every minute are somehow coupled to ATP. It's no exaggeration to say that the transfer of a phosphate group from ATP is the single most important chemical reaction in making life possible.

▶ **PROBLEM 24.1** One of the steps in fat metabolism is the reaction of glycerol [$HOCH_2$–$CH(OH)$–CH_2OH] with ATP to yield glycerol-1-phosphate. Draw the structure of glycerol-1-phosphate.

24.2 | Amino Acids and Peptides

Taken from the Greek *proteios*, meaning "primary," the name *protein* aptly describes a group of biological molecules that are of primary importance to all living organisms. Approximately 50% of the body's dry weight is protein, and almost all the reactions that occur in the body are catalyzed by proteins. In fact, a human body contains over *100,000* different kinds of proteins.

Proteins have many different biological functions. Some, such as the keratin in skin, hair, and fingernails, serve a structural purpose. Others, such as the insulin that controls glucose metabolism, act as *hormones*—chemical messengers that coordinate the activities of different cells in an organism. And still other proteins, such as DNA polymerase, are *enzymes*, the biological catalysts that carry out body chemistry. All **proteins** are biological polymers made up of many amino acid molecules linked together to form a long chain. As their name implies, *amino acids* contain two functional groups, a basic amino group ($-NH_2$) and an acidic $-CO_2H$ group. Alanine is one of the simplest examples.

▲ Bird feathers are made largely of the protein *keratin*.

$$\underset{\underset{NH_2}{|}}{CH_3CHCOH} \overset{O}{\overset{\|}{}}$$

Alanine—an amino acid

Two or more amino acids can link together by forming amide bonds (Section 23.14), usually called **peptide bonds**. A *dipeptide* results when two amino acids link together by formation of a peptide bond between the $-NH_2$ group of one and the $-CO_2H$ group of the other. Similarly, a *tripeptide* results when three amino acids link together with two peptide bonds, and so on. Short chains of up to 100 amino acids are usually called **polypeptides**, while the term *protein* is reserved for longer chains.

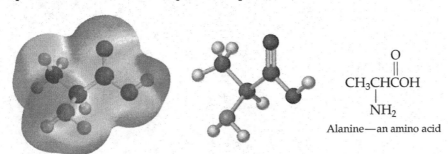

α Amino acids—The groups symbolized by R and R' represent different amino acid side chains.

A peptide bond

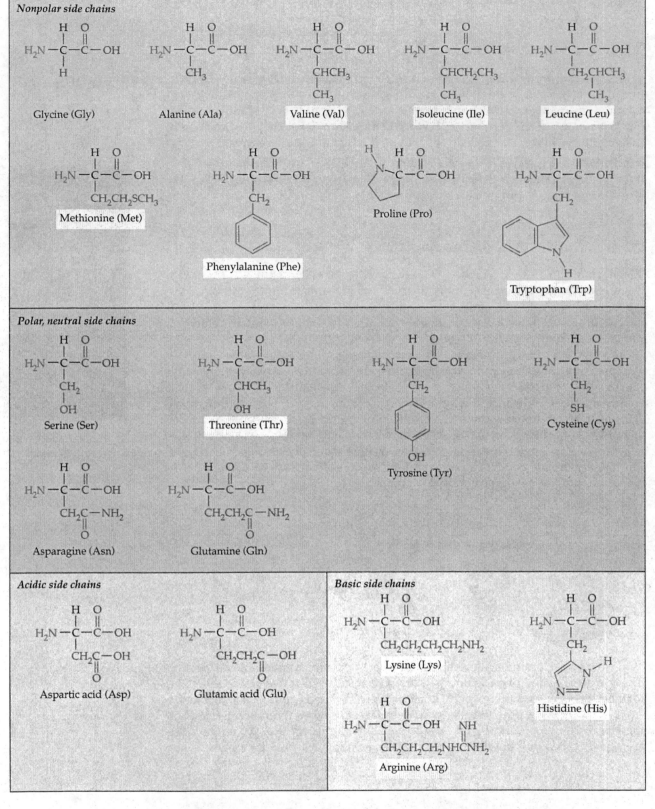

▲ **FIGURE 24.2** Structures of the 20 α-amino acids found in proteins. Fifteen of the 20 have neutral side chains, two have acidic side chains, and three have basic side chains. The names of the 10 essential amino acids are highlighted.

Twenty different amino acids are commonly found in proteins, as shown in Figure 24.2. Each amino acid is referred to by a three-letter shorthand code, such as Ala (alanine), Gly (glycine), Pro (proline), and so on. All 20 are called **alpha-(α-) amino acids** because the amino group in each is connected to the carbon atom *alpha to* (next to) the carboxylic acid group. Nineteen of the 20 have an $-NH_2$ amino group, and one (proline) has an $-NH-$ amino group as part of a ring.

The 20 amino acids differ only in the nature of the group attached to the α carbon. Usually called the *side chain*, this group can be symbolized in a general way by the letter R. (In a broader context, the symbol R is used throughout organic chemistry to refer to an organic fragment of unspecified structure.) Our bodies can synthesize only 10 of the 20 amino acids. The remaining 10, highlighted in Figure 24.2, are called *essential amino acids* because they must be obtained from the diet.

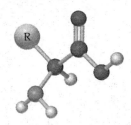

α carbon

$$R-\underset{\underset{NH_2}{|}}{CH}-\overset{\overset{O}{\|}}{C}OH$$

Side chain

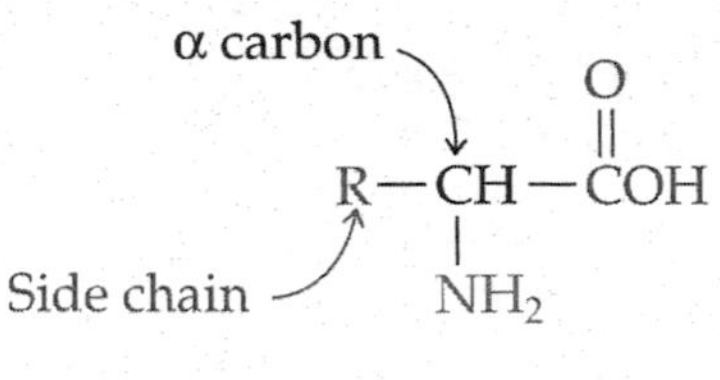

Generalized structure of an α-amino acid

The 20 common amino acids are classified as *neutral*, *basic*, or *acidic*, depending on the structure of their side chains. Fifteen of the 20 have neutral side chains. Two (aspartic acid and glutamic acid) have an additional carboxylic acid group in their side chains and are classified as acidic amino acids. Three (lysine, arginine, and histidine) have an additional amine function in their side chains and are classified as basic amino acids. The 15 neutral amino acids can be further divided into those with nonpolar side chains and those with polar functional groups such as amide or hydroxyl groups. Nonpolar side chains are often described as *hydrophobic* (water fearing) because they are not attracted to water, while polar side chains are described as *hydrophilic* (water loving) because they *are* attracted to water.

▲ Corn is particularly low in lysine, one of the essential amino acids.

WORKED EXAMPLE 24.1

Identify the following amino acid, and tell from the electrostatic potential map whether its side chain is acidic, basic, neutral nonpolar, or neutral polar.

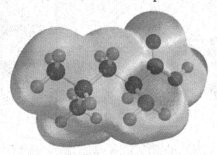

STRATEGY

Identify the amino acid by looking at Figure 24.2, and predict its polarity by looking for electron-rich (red) or electron-poor (blue) regions in the side chain.

SOLUTION

The amino acid is leucine. It is nonpolar because it contains a hydrocarbon side chain that has neither electron-rich nor electron-poor groups.

▶ **PROBLEM 24.2** Which common amino acids contain an aromatic (benzene-like) ring? Which contain sulfur? Which are alcohols? Which have alkyl-group side chains?

▶ **PROBLEM 24.3** Draw alanine using wedges and dashes to show the tetrahedral geometry of its α carbon.

KEY CONCEPT PROBLEM 24.4 Identify the following amino acid, and tell from the electrostatic potential map whether its side chain is acidic, basic, neutral nonpolar, or neutral polar.

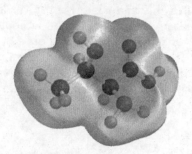

24.3 | Amino Acids and Molecular Handedness

Chirality movie

3D models of L-Alanine and D-Alanine

We saw in Section 20.9 that certain molecules lack a plane of symmetry and are therefore *chiral*. When held up to a mirror, a chiral molecule is not identical to its reflected image. Instead, the molecule and its mirror image have a right-hand/left-hand relationship. Compare alanine and propane, for example (Figure 24.3). An alanine molecule is chiral; it has no symmetry plane and can exist in two forms—a "right-handed" form called D-alanine (from *dextro*, Latin for "right") and a "left-handed" form called L-alanine (from *levo*, Latin for "left"). Propane, however, is achiral. It has a symmetry plane cutting through the three carbons and thus exists in only a single form.

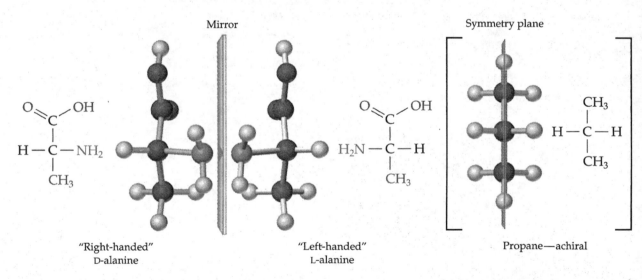

"Right-handed" D-alanine

"Left-handed" L-alanine

Propane—achiral

▲ **FIGURE 24.3** Alanine (2-aminopropanoic acid) has no symmetry plane; the two "halves" of the molecule are not mirror images. Thus, alanine can exist in two forms— a "right-handed" form and a "left-handed" form. Propane, however, has a symmetry plane and is achiral.

Why are some organic molecules chiral while others are not? The answer has to do with the three-dimensional nature of organic molecules. We've seen that carbon forms four bonds that are oriented toward the four corners of a regular tetrahedron. Whenever a carbon atom is bonded to four *different* atoms or groups of atoms, chirality results. If a carbon is bonded to two or more of the same groups, however, no chirality is possible. In alanine, for example, carbon 2 is bonded to four different groups: a $-CO_2H$ group, an $-H$ atom, an $-NH_2$ group, and a $-CH_3$ group. Thus, alanine is chiral. In propane, however, each of the carbons is bonded to at least two groups—the $-H$ atoms—that are identical. Thus, propane is achiral.

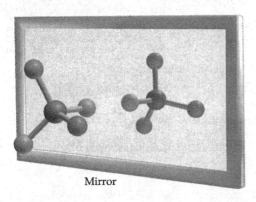

C2	*Groups attached to C2*		C2	*Groups attached to C2*

Alanine—chiral

1. —CO₂H
2. —H
3. —NH₂
4. —CH₃ } Different

Propane—achiral

1. —CH₃
2. —CH₃ } Identical
3. —H
4. —H } Identical

As mentioned in Section 20.9, the two mirror-image forms of a chiral molecule are called *enantiomers*, or *optical isomers*. The mirror-image relationship of the enantiomers of a molecule with four different groups on a chiral carbon atom is shown in Figure 24.4.

◀ **FIGURE 24.4** A molecule with a carbon atom that is bonded to four different groups is chiral and is not identical to its mirror image. It thus exists in two enantiomeric forms.

Mirror

Of the 20 common amino acids, 19 are chiral because they have four different groups bonded to their α carbons, –H, –NH₂, –CO₂H, and –R (the side chain). Only glycine, $H_2NCH_2CO_2H$, is achiral. Even though the naturally occurring chiral α-amino acids can exist as pairs of enantiomers, only L-amino acids are found in proteins. When drawn with the –CO₂H group at the top and the side-chain R group at the bottom, an L-amino acid has its –NH₂ group coming out of the plane of the paper on the left side of the structure:

An L-amino acid

WORKED EXAMPLE 24.2

Lactic acid can be isolated from sour milk. Is lactic acid chiral?

$$CH_3 - CH - COH \quad \text{Lactic acid}$$
$$\quad\quad 3 \quad\; 2 \quad\; 1$$

with OH on C2 and O double-bonded to C1.

STRATEGY

To find out if lactic acid is chiral, list the groups attached to each carbon, and see if any carbon is attached to four *different* groups.

SOLUTION

Groups on carbon 1	Groups on carbon 2	Groups on carbon 3
1. –OH	1. –CO_2H	1. –$CH(OH)CO_2H$
2. =O	2. –OH	2. –H
3. –$CH(OH)CH_3$	3. –H	3. –H
	4. –CH_3	4. –H

Of the three carbons, carbon 2 has four different groups, so lactic acid is chiral.

▶ **PROBLEM 24.5**   Which of the following objects are chiral?

  (a) A glove   **(b)** A baseball   **(c)** A screw   **(d)** A nail

▶ **PROBLEM 24.6**   2-Aminopropane is an achiral molecule, but 2-aminobutane is chiral. Explain.

▶ **PROBLEM 24.7**   Which of the following molecules are chiral?

  (a) 3-Chloropentane   **(b)** 2-Chloropentane   **(c)** $CH_3CHCH_2CHCH_2CH_3$ with two CH_3 groups on the 2nd and 4th carbons

◀ **KEY CONCEPT PROBLEM 24.9**   Two of the following three molecules are identical, and one is the enantiomer of the other two. Which one is the enantiomer?

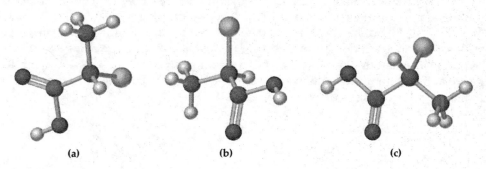

(a)   (b)   (c)

24.4 | Proteins

Proteins and Amino Acids movie

Proteins are amino acid polymers in which the individual amino acids, often called *residues*, are linked together by peptide (amide) bonds. The repeating chain of amide linkages to which the side chains are attached is called the *backbone*.

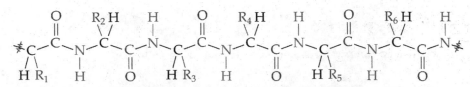

A segment of a protein backbone. The side-chain R groups
of the individual amino acids are substituents on the backbone.

Since amino acids can be assembled in any order, depending on which –CO_2H group joins with which –NH_2 group, the number of possible isomeric peptides increases rapidly as the number of amino acid residues increases. There are six ways in which three different amino acids can be joined, more than 40,000 ways in which the eight amino acids present in the blood pressure–regulating hormone angiotensin II can be joined (Figure 24.5), and a staggering number of ways in which the *1800* amino acids in myosin, the major component of muscle filaments, can be arranged.

▼ **FIGURE 24.5** The structure of angiotensin II, an octapeptide in blood plasma that regulates blood pressure.

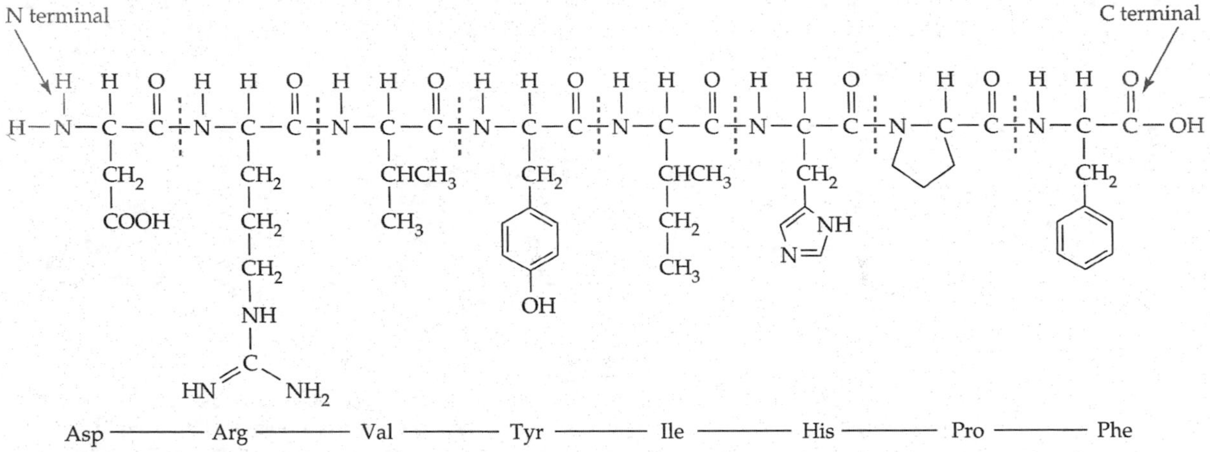

N terminal

C terminal

Asp —— Arg —— Val —— Tyr —— Ile —— His —— Pro —— Phe

No matter how long the chain, all noncyclic proteins have an **N-terminal amino acid** with a free $-NH_2$ group on one end and a **C-terminal amino acid** with a free $-CO_2H$ group on the other end. By convention, a protein is written with the N-terminal residue on the left and the C-terminal residue on the right, and its name is indicated with the three-letter abbreviations listed in Figure 24.2. Thus, angiotensin II (Figure 24.5) is abbreviated Asp-Arg-Val-Tyr-Ile-His-Pro-Phe.

Proteins are classified according to their three-dimensional shape as either *fibrous* or *globular*. Fibrous proteins, such as collagen and the keratins, consist of polypeptide chains arranged side by side in long filaments. Because these proteins are tough and insoluble in water, they are used in nature for structural materials like skin, tendons, hair, ligaments, and muscle. Globular proteins, by contrast, are usually coiled into compact, nearly spherical shapes, as seen in the computer-generated picture of the digestive enzyme pepsin in Figure 24.6. Most of the 2000 or so known enzymes present inside cells are globular proteins.

Another way to classify proteins is according to biological function. As indicated in Table 24.1, proteins have a remarkable diversity of roles.

▲ **FIGURE 24.6** A computer-generated view of the enzyme pepsin, a typical globular protein.

TABLE 24.1	Some Biological Functions of Proteins	
Type	**Function**	**Example**
Enzymes	Catalyze biological processes	Pepsin
Hormones	Regulate body processes	Insulin
Storage proteins	Store nutrients	Ferritin
Transport proteins	Transport oxygen and other substances through the body	Hemoglobin
Structural proteins	Form an organism's structure	Collagen
Protective proteins	Help fight infection	Antibodies
Contractile proteins	Form muscles	Actin, myosin
Toxic proteins	Serve as a defense for the plant or animal	Snake venoms

WORKED EXAMPLE 24.3

Draw the structure of the dipeptide Ala-Ser.

STRATEGY

First, look up the names and structures of the two amino acids, Ala (alanine) and Ser (serine). Since alanine is N-terminal and serine is C-terminal, Ala-Ser must have an amide bond between the alanine $-CO_2H$ and the serine $-NH_2$.

SOLUTION

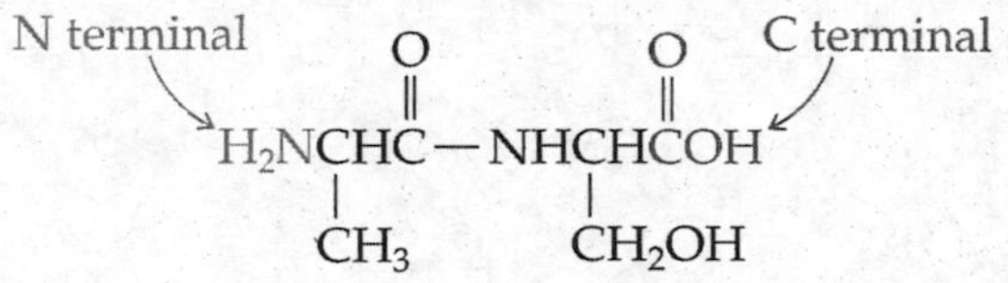

$$N\ terminal \overset{O}{\underset{\underset{CH_3}{|}}{H_2NCHC}} - \overset{O}{\underset{\underset{CH_2OH}{|}}{NHCHCOH}}\ C\ terminal$$

Alanine   Serine

Ala-Ser

▶ **PROBLEM 24.10** Use the three-letter shorthand notations to name the two isomeric dipeptides that can be made from valine and cysteine. Draw both structures.

▶ **PROBLEM 24.11** Name the six tripeptides that contain valine, tyrosine, and glycine.

24.5 | Levels of Protein Structure

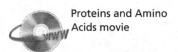
Proteins and Amino Acids movie

With molecular masses of up to one-half *million* amu, many proteins are so large that the word *structure* takes on a broader meaning with these immense molecules than it does with simple organic molecules. In fact, chemists usually speak about four levels of structure when describing proteins. The **primary structure** of a protein specifies the sequence in which the various amino acids are linked together. **Secondary structure** refers to how segments of the protein chain are oriented into a regular pattern. **Tertiary structure** refers to how the entire protein chain is coiled and folded into a specific three-dimensional shape, and **quaternary structure** refers to how several protein chains can aggregate to form a larger unit.

Primary Structure

Primary structure is the most fundamental of the four structural levels because it is the protein's amino acid sequence that determines its overall shape and function. So crucial is primary structure to function that the change of only one amino acid out of several hundred can drastically alter biological properties. The disease sickle-cell anemia, for example, is caused by a genetic defect in blood hemoglobin whereby valine is substituted for glutamic acid at only one position in a chain of 146 amino acids.

Secondary Protein Structure

When looking at the primary structure of a protein like angiotensin II in Figure 24.5, you might get the idea that the molecule is long and threadlike. In fact, though, most proteins fold in such a way that segments of the protein chain orient into regular patterns, called *secondary structures*. There are two common kinds of patterns: the *alpha-helix* and the *beta-pleated sheet*.

Keratin, a fibrous protein found in wool, hair, fingernails, and feathers, wraps into a helical coil, much like the cord on a telephone (Figure 24.7). Called an **alpha- (α-) helix**, this secondary structure is stabilized by the formation of hydrogen bonds (Section 10.2) between the N–H group of one amino acid and the C=O group of another amino acid four residues away. Each turn of the helix contains 3.6 amino acid residues, with a distance between turns of 0.54 nm.

Science Fundamentals Second Edition

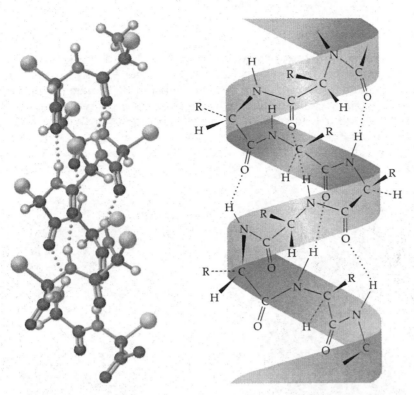

▲ Sheep's wool is made largely of keratin, a fibrous protein with an α-helical secondary structure.

Fibroin, the fibrous protein found in silk, has a secondary structure called a **beta- (β-) pleated sheet**, in which a polypeptide chain doubles back on itself after a hairpin bend. The two sections of the chain on either side of the bend line up in a parallel arrangement held together by hydrogen bonds (Figure 24.8). Although not as common as the α-helix, small pleated-sheet regions are often found in proteins.

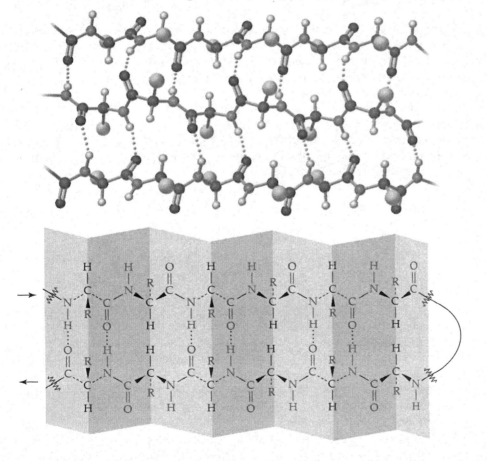

▲ Silk is made of fibroin, a fibrous protein with a pleated-sheet secondary structure.

◀ **FIGURE 24.8** The β-pleated-sheet secondary structure of silk fibroin. The amino acid side chains, shown in green, are above and below the rough plane of the sheet. (Dotted lines indicate hydrogen bonds between chains.)

▲ The muscles of sea mammals contain myoglobin, a globular protein that stores oxygen.

Hemoglobin 3D model

Tertiary Protein Structure

Secondary protein structures result primarily from hydrogen bonding between amide linkages along the protein backbone, but higher levels of structure result primarily from interactions of side-chain R groups in the protein. Myoglobin, for example, is a globular protein found in the skeletal muscles of sea mammals, where it stores oxygen needed to sustain the animals during long dives. With a single chain of 153 amino acid residues, myoglobin consists of eight straight segments, each of which adopts an α-helical secondary structure. These helical sections then fold up further to form a compact, nearly spherical, tertiary structure (Figure 24.9).

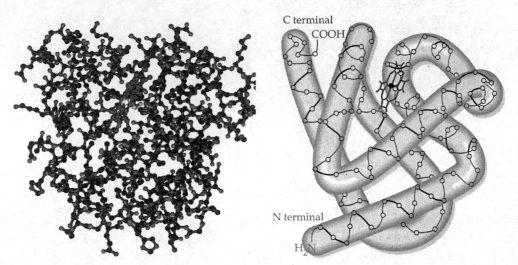

▲ **FIGURE 24.9** Secondary and tertiary structure of myoglobin, a globular protein found in the muscles of sea mammals. Myoglobin has eight helical sections.

The most important force stabilizing a protein's tertiary structure results from the hydrophobic interactions of hydrocarbon side chains on amino acids. Those amino acids with neutral, nonpolar side chains have a strong tendency to congregate on the hydrocarbonlike interior of a protein molecule, away from the aqueous medium. Those amino acids with polar side chains, by contrast, are usually found on the exterior of the protein where they can be solvated by water. Also important for stabilizing a protein's tertiary structure are *disulfide bridges* (covalent S–S bonds formed between nearby cysteine residues), *salt bridges* (ionic attractions between positively and negatively charged sites on the protein), and hydrogen bonds between nearby amino acids.

$$O=C \qquad\qquad C=O \qquad O=C \qquad\qquad C=O$$
$$|\qquad\qquad\qquad |\qquad\qquad |\qquad\qquad\qquad |$$
$$CHCH_2SH + HSCH_2CH \xrightarrow{[O]} CHCH_2S-SCH_2CH$$
$$|\qquad\qquad\qquad |\qquad\qquad |\qquad\qquad\qquad |$$
$$NH \qquad\qquad\qquad NH \qquad\qquad NH \qquad\qquad\qquad NH$$

Two cysteine residues   A disulfide bridge

24.6 | Enzymes

Enzymes are large proteins that act as catalysts for biological reactions. A *catalyst*, as we saw in Section 12.12, is an agent that speeds up the rate of a chemical reaction without itself undergoing change. For example, sulfuric acid catalyzes the reaction of a carboxylic acid with an alcohol to yield an ester (Section 23.14).

Science Fundamentals Second Edition

Enzymes, too, catalyze reactions that might otherwise occur very slowly, but they differ from catalysts like sulfuric acid in two important respects. First, enzymes are much larger, more complicated molecules than simple inorganic catalysts. Second, enzymes are far more specific in their action. Sulfuric acid catalyzes the reaction of nearly *every* carboxylic acid with nearly *every* alcohol, but enzymes often catalyze only a *single* reaction of a single compound, called the enzyme's **substrate**. For example, the enzyme *amylase* found in human digestive systems is able to catalyze the breakdown of starch to yield glucose but has no effect on cellulose, even though starch and cellulose are structurally similar. Thus, humans can digest potatoes (starch) but not grass (cellulose).

$$\text{Starch} + H_2O \xrightarrow{\text{Amylase}} \text{Many glucose molecules}$$

$$\text{Cellulose} + H_2O \xrightarrow{\text{Amylase}} \text{No reaction}$$

The catalytic activity of an enzyme is measured by its *turnover number*, which is defined as the number of substrate molecules acted on by one molecule of enzyme per second. As indicated in Table 24.2, enzymes vary greatly in their turnover number. Most enzymes have values in the 1–20,000 range, but carbonic anhydrase, which catalyzes the reaction of CO_2 with water to yield bicarbonate ion, acts on *600,000* substrate molecules per second.

In addition to their protein part, many enzymes contain small, nonprotein parts called **cofactors**. In such enzymes, the protein part is called an *apoenzyme*, and the entire assembly of apoenzyme plus cofactor is called a *holoenzyme*. Only holoenzymes are active as catalysts; neither apoenzyme nor cofactor alone can catalyze a reaction.

Holoenzyme = Apoenzyme + Cofactor

An enzyme cofactor can be either an inorganic ion (usually a metal cation) or a small organic molecule called a **coenzyme**. In fact, the requirement of many enzymes for metal-ion cofactors is the main reason behind our dietary need for trace minerals. Iron, zinc, copper, manganese, molybdenum, cobalt, nickel, and selenium are all essential trace elements that function as enzyme cofactors. A large number of different organic molecules also serve as coenzymes. Often, although not always, the coenzyme is a *vitamin*. Thiamine (vitamin B_1), for example, is a coenzyme required in the metabolism of carbohydrates.

TABLE 24.2	Turnover Numbers of Some Enzymes	
Enzyme	**Turnover Number (s^{-1})**
Carbonic anhydrase	600,000
Acetylcholinesterase	25,000
β-Amylase	18,000
Penicillinase	2,000
DNA polymerase I	15

Thiamine (vitamin B_1); an enzyme cofactor

How Enzymes Work: The Lock-and-Key Model

According to the **lock-and-key model**, an enzyme is pictured as a large, irregularly shaped molecule with a cleft, or crevice, in its middle. Inside the crevice is an **active site**, a small region with the shape and chemical composition necessary to bind the substrate and catalyze the appropriate reaction. In other words, the active site acts like a lock into which only a specific key can fit (Figure 24.10). An enzyme's active site is lined by various acidic, basic, and neutral amino acid side chains, all properly positioned for maximum interaction with the substrate.

Enzyme-catalyzed reactions begin when the substrate migrates into the active site to form an enzyme–substrate complex. No covalent bonds are formed; the enzyme and substrate are held together by hydrogen bonds and by

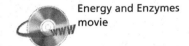

Energy and Enzymes movie

FIGURE 24.10 According ▶ to the lock-and-key model, an enzyme is a large, three-dimensional molecule containing a crevice with an active site. Only a substrate whose shape and structure are complementary to those of the active site can fit into the enzyme. The active site of the enzyme hexose kinase is visible as the cleft on the left in this computer-generated structure, as is the fit of the substrate (yellow) in the active site.

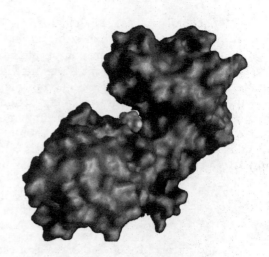

weak intermolecular attractions between functional groups. With enzyme and substrate thus held together in a precisely defined arrangement, the appropriately positioned functional groups in the active site carry out a chemical reaction on the substrate molecule, and enzyme plus product then separate:

$$E \ + \ S \longrightarrow E\text{-}S \longrightarrow E \ + \ P$$

| Enzyme | Substrate | Complex | Enzyme | Product |

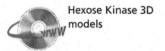

Hexose Kinase 3D models

As an example of enzyme action, look in Figure 24.11 at the enzyme hexose kinase, which catalyzes the reaction of adenosine triphosphate (ATP) with glucose to yield glucose-6-phosphate and adenosine diphosphate (ADP). The enzyme first binds a molecule of ATP cofactor at a position near the active site, and glucose then bonds to the active site with its C6 hydroxyl group held rigidly in position next to the ATP molecule. Reaction ensues, and the two products are released from the enzyme.

FIGURE 24.11 The hexose ▶ kinase–catalyzed reaction of glucose with ATP. Glucose enters the cleft of the enzyme and binds to the active site, where it reacts with a molecule of ATP cofactor held nearby.

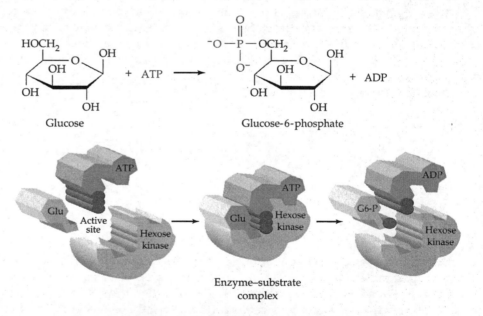

Glucose + ATP ⟶ Glucose-6-phosphate + ADP

Enzyme–substrate complex

Compare the enzyme-catalyzed reaction shown in Figure 24.11 with the same reaction in the absence of enzyme. Without enzyme present, the two reactants would spend most of their time surrounded by solvent molecules, far away from each other and only occasionally bumping together. With an enzyme present, however, the two reactants are forced into close contact. Enzymes act as catalysts because of their ability to bring reactants together, hold them at the exact distance and with the exact orientation necessary for reaction, and provide acidic or basic sites as required.

Science Fundamentals Second Edition

24.7 | Carbohydrates

Carbohydrates occur in every living organism. The starch in food and the cellulose in grass are nearly pure carbohydrate. Modified carbohydrates form part of the coating around all living cells, and other carbohydrates are found in the DNA that carries genetic information from one generation to the next.

The word *carbohydrate* was used originally to describe glucose, which has the formula $C_6H_{12}O_6$ and was once thought to be a "hydrate of carbon," $C_6(H_2O)_6$. Although this view was soon abandoned, the word persisted and is now used to refer to a large class of polyhydroxylated aldehydes and ketones. Glucose, for example, is a six-carbon aldehyde with five hydroxyl groups.

Glucose 3D model

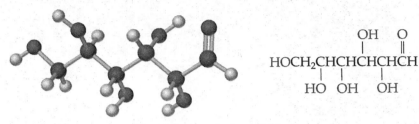

Glucose—a pentahydroxy aldehyde

Carbohydrates are classified as either *simple* or *complex*. Simple sugars, or **monosaccharides**, are carbohydrates such as glucose and fructose that can't be broken down into smaller molecules by hydrolysis with aqueous acid. Complex carbohydrates, or **polysaccharides**, are compounds such as cellulose and starch that are made of many simple sugars linked together. On hydrolysis, polysaccharides are cleaved to yield many molecules of simple sugars.

Monosaccharides are further classified as either aldoses or ketoses. An *aldose* contains an aldehyde carbonyl group; a *ketose* contains a ketone carbonyl group (Section 23.13). The *-ose* suffix indicates a sugar, and the number of carbon atoms in the sugar is specified by using one of the prefixes *tri-*, *tetr-*, *pent-*, or *hex-*. Thus, glucose is an aldohexose (a six-carbon aldehyde sugar), fructose is a ketohexose (a six-carbon ketone sugar), and ribose is an aldopentose (a five-carbon aldehyde sugar). Most commonly occurring sugars are either aldopentoses or aldohexoses.

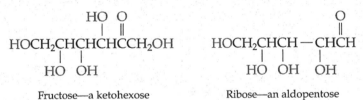

Fructose—a ketohexose   Ribose—an aldopentose

▶ **PROBLEM 24.12** Classify each of the following monosaccharides:

(a) $HOCH_2CHCHCHCH$ (b) $HOCH_2CCH_2OH$ (c) $HOCH_2CHCHCH$

24.8 | Handedness of Carbohydrates

We saw in Section 24.3 that compounds are chiral if they have a carbon atom bonded to four different atoms or groups of atoms. Such compounds lack a plane of symmetry and can exist as a pair of enantiomers in either a "right-handed" D form or a "left-handed" L form. For instance, the simple triose glyceraldehyde is chiral because it has four different groups bonded to C2: –CHO, –H, –OH, and –CH₂OH. Of the two enantiomers, only D-glyceraldehyde occurs naturally.

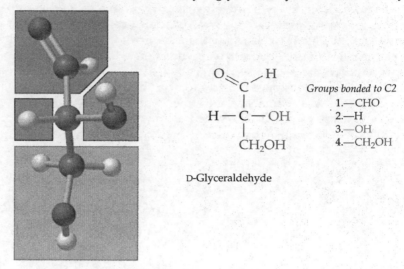

Groups bonded to C2
1.—CHO
2.—H
3.—OH
4.—CH₂OH

D-Glyceraldehyde

Chirality of
D-Glyceraldehyde
activity

Glyceraldehyde has only one chiral carbon atom and can exist as two enantiomers, but other sugars have two, three, four, or even more chiral carbons. In general, a compound with n chiral carbon atoms has a maximum of 2^n possible isomeric forms. Glucose, for example, has four chiral carbon atoms, so a total of $2^4 = 16$ isomers are possible, differing in the spatial arrangements of the substituents around the chiral carbon atoms.

Four different groups are
attached to these atoms

$$HO-\overset{\overset{\displaystyle H}{|}}{\underset{\underset{\displaystyle H}{|}}{C}}-\overset{\overset{\displaystyle H}{|}}{\underset{\underset{\displaystyle OH}{|}}{C}}-\overset{\overset{\displaystyle H}{|}}{\underset{\underset{\displaystyle OH}{|}}{C}}-\overset{\overset{\displaystyle OH}{|}}{\underset{\underset{\displaystyle H}{|}}{C}}-\overset{\overset{\displaystyle H}{|}}{\underset{\underset{\displaystyle OH}{|}}{C}}-C\overset{O}{\underset{H}{}}$$

Glucose

▶ **PROBLEM 24.13** Draw tetrahedral representations of the two glyceraldehyde enantiomers using wedged, dashed, and normal lines to show three-dimensionality.

▶ **PROBLEM 24.14** Ribose has three chiral carbon atoms. What is the maximum number of isomers?

⬥ **KEY CONCEPT PROBLEM 24.15** Classify the following monosaccharide, and identify each chiral carbon in its structure.

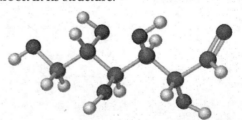

24.9 | Cyclic Structures of Monosaccharides

Glucose and other monosaccharides are often shown for convenience as having open-chain structures. They actually exist, however, primarily as cyclic molecules in which an –OH group near the bottom of the chain adds to the carbonyl group near the top of the chain to form a ring. In glucose itself, ring formation occurs between the –OH group on C5 and the C=O group at C1 (Figure 24.12).

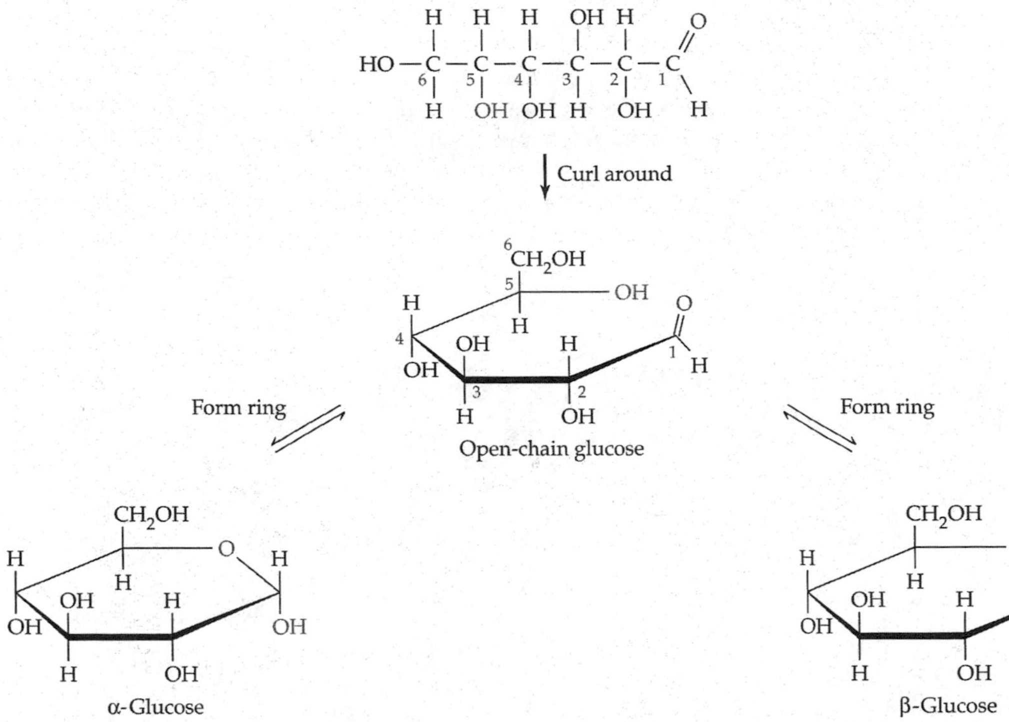

$$HO-\underset{\underset{H}{|}}{\overset{\overset{H}{|}}{C}}-\underset{\underset{OH}{|}}{\overset{\overset{H}{|}}{C}}-\underset{\underset{OH}{|}}{\overset{\overset{H}{|}}{C}}-\underset{\underset{H}{|}}{\overset{\overset{OH}{|}}{C}}-\underset{\underset{OH}{|}}{\overset{\overset{H}{|}}{C}}-\overset{\overset{O}{\|}}{C}\diagdown H$$

$6 \quad 5 \quad 4 \quad 3 \quad 2 \quad 1$

↓ Curl around

⁶CH₂OH
Open-chain glucose

◀ **FIGURE 24.12** The cyclic α and β forms of D-glucose that result from ring formation between the —OH group at C5 and the C=O group at C1. The α form has the —OH group at C1 on the bottom side of the ring; the β form has the —OH group on the top.

Form ring ⟸   ⟹ Form ring

CH₂OH

α-Glucose

CH₂OH

β-Glucose

3D models of
α-D-Glucose and
β-D-Glucose

Note that two cyclic forms of glucose can result from ring formation, depending on whether the newly formed —OH group at C1 is on the bottom or top side of the ring. The ordinary crystalline glucose you might take from a bottle is entirely the cyclic α form, in which the C1 —OH group is on the bottom side of the ring. At equilibrium in water solution, however, all three forms are present in the proportion 0.02% open-chain form, 36% α form, and 64% β form.

24.10 | Some Common Disaccharides and Polysaccharides

Lactose

Lactose, or *milk sugar*, is the major carbohydrate present in mammalian milk. Human milk, for example, is about 7% lactose. Structurally, lactose is a disaccharide whose hydrolysis with aqueous acid yields one molecule of glucose and one molecule of another monosaccharide called galactose. The two sugars are bonded together by what is called a *1,4 link*—a bridging oxygen atom between C1 of β-galactose and C4 of β-glucose.

Lactose 3D model

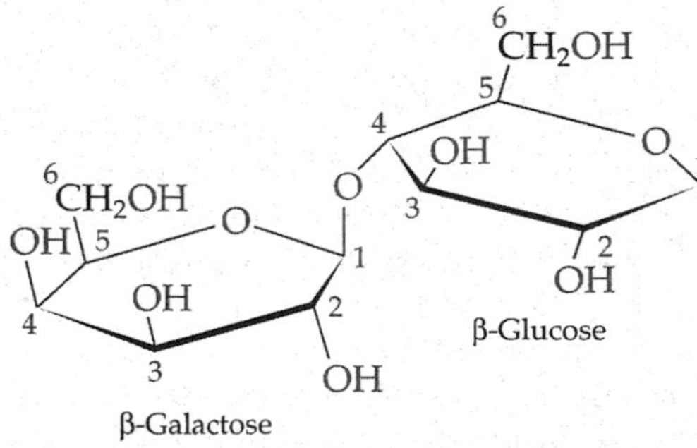

⁶CH₂OH
β-Glucose

⁶CH₂OH
β-Galactose

Lactose

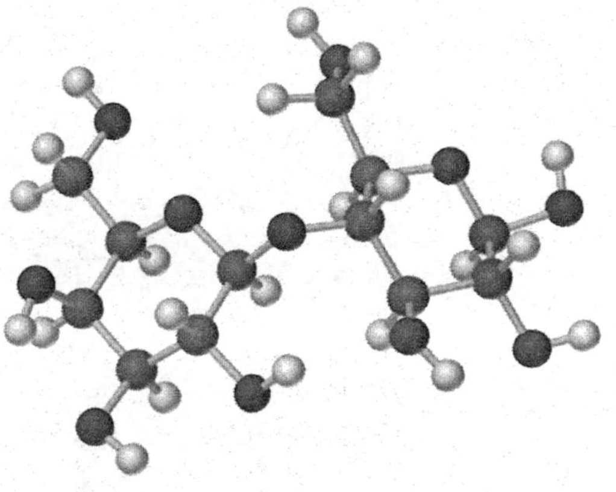

Sucrose

Sucrose, or plain table sugar, is probably the most common pure organic chemical in the world. Although sucrose is found in many plants, sugar beets (20% by mass) and sugar cane (15% by mass) are the most common sources. Hydrolysis of sucrose yields one molecule of glucose and one molecule of fructose. The 1:1 mixture of glucose and fructose that results, often called *invert sugar*, is commonly used as a food additive.

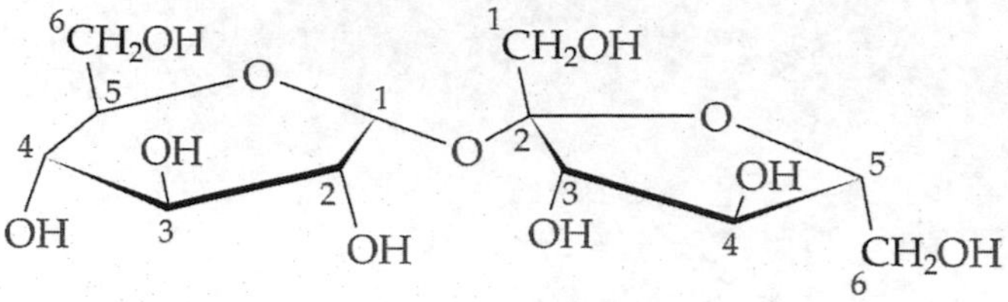

α-Glucose

β-Fructose

Sucrose

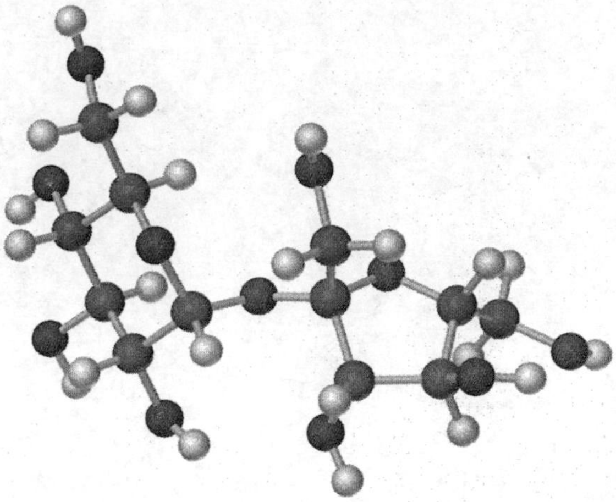

Cellulose and Starch

Cellulose 3D model

Cellulose, the fibrous substance that forms the structural material in grasses, leaves, and stems, consists of several thousand β-glucose molecules joined together by 1,4 links to form an immense polysaccharide.

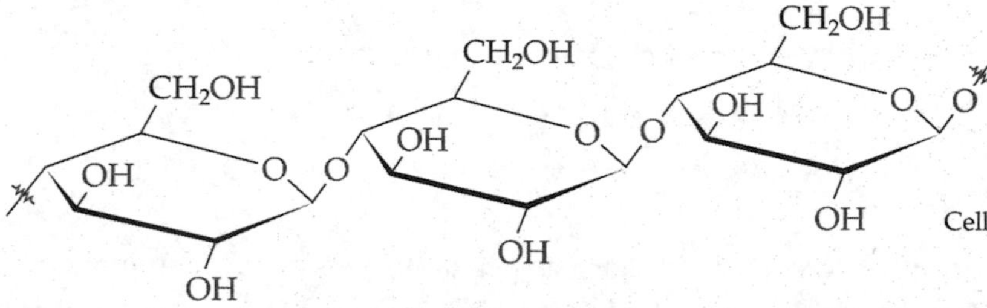

β-Glucose units

Cellulose

Starch, like cellulose, is also a polymer of glucose. Unlike cellulose, though, starch is edible. Indeed, the starch in such vegetables as beans, rice, and potatoes is an essential part of the human diet. Structurally, starch differs from cellulose in that it contains α- rather than β-glucose units. Starch is also more structurally complex than cellulose and is of two types: *amylose* and *amylopectin*. Amylose, which accounts for about 20% of starch, consists of several hundred to 1000 α-glucose units joined together in a long chain by 1,4 links (Figure 24.13a). Amylopectin, which accounts for about 80% of starch, is much larger than amylose (up to 100,000 glucose units per molecule) and has branches approximately every 25 units along its chain. A glucose molecule at a branch point uses two of its hydroxyl groups (those at C4 and C6) to form links to two other sugars (Figure 24.13b).

Starch molecules are digested in the stomach by enzymes called *α-glycosidases*, which break down the polysaccharide chain and release individual glucose molecules. As is usually the case with enzyme-catalyzed reactions, α-glycosidases are

Science Fundamentals Second Edition

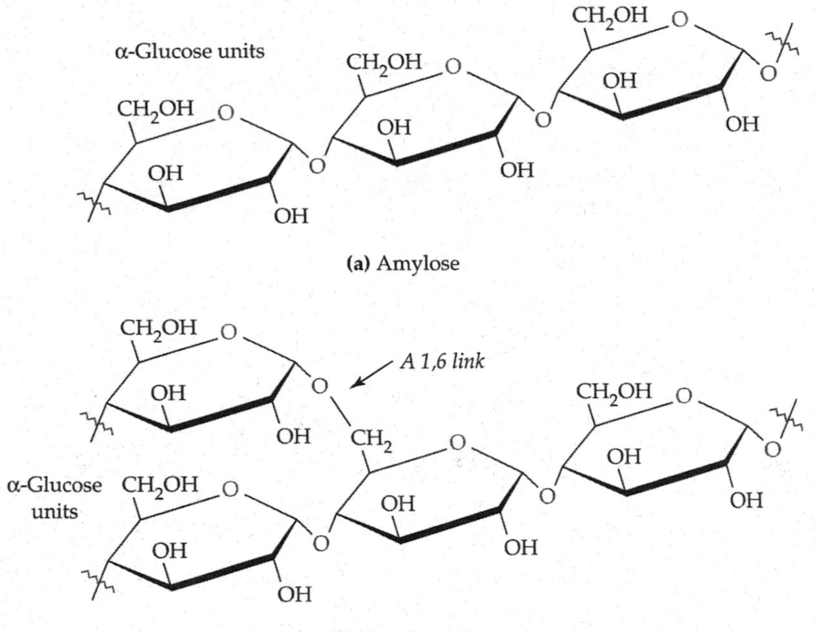

α-Glucose units

CH₂OH

OH

OH

CH₂OH

OH

OH

CH₂OH

OH

OH

(a) Amylose

CH₂OH

OH

OH

A 1,6 link

CH₂

α-Glucose units

CH₂OH

OH

OH

OH

CH₂OH

OH

OH

(b) Amylopectin

◄ **FIGURE 24.13** Glucose polymers in starch. **(a)** Amylose consists of linear chains of α-glucose units linked by 1,4 bonds. **(b)** Amylopectin has branch points about every 25 sugars in the chain. A glucose unit at a branch point uses two of its hydroxyls (at C4 and C6) to form 1,4 and 1,6 links to two other sugars.

highly specific in their action. They hydrolyze only the links between α units while leaving the links between β units untouched. Thus, starch is easily digested but cellulose is not.

Glycogen

Glycogen, sometimes called *animal starch*, serves the same food storage role in animals that starch serves in plants. After we eat starch and the body breaks it down into simple glucose units, some of the glucose is used immediately as fuel and some is stored in the body as glycogen for later use. Structurally, glycogen is similar to amylopectin in being a long polymer of α-glucose units with branch points in its chain. Glycogen has many more branches than amylopectin, however, and is much larger—up to 1 million glucose units per glycogen molecule.

24.11 | Lipids

Lipids are less well known to most people than are proteins or carbohydrates, yet they are just as essential to life. Lipids have many important biological roles, serving as sources of fuel storage, as protective coatings around many plants and insects, and as major components of the membranes that surround every living cell.

Chemically, a **lipid** is a naturally occurring organic molecule that dissolves in a nonpolar organic solvent when a sample of plant or animal tissue is crushed or ground. Because they're defined by solubility—a physical property—rather than by chemical structure, it's not surprising that there are a great many different kinds of lipids (Figure 24.14). Note that all the lipids in Figure 24.14 contain large hydrocarbon portions, which accounts for their solubility behavior.

Fats and Oils

Animal fats and vegetable oils are the most plentiful lipids in nature. Although they appear physically different—animal fats like butter and lard are usually solid, whereas vegetable oils like corn and peanut oil are liquid—their structures

▲ Glycogen provides the stored energy that lets these marathoners finish the race.

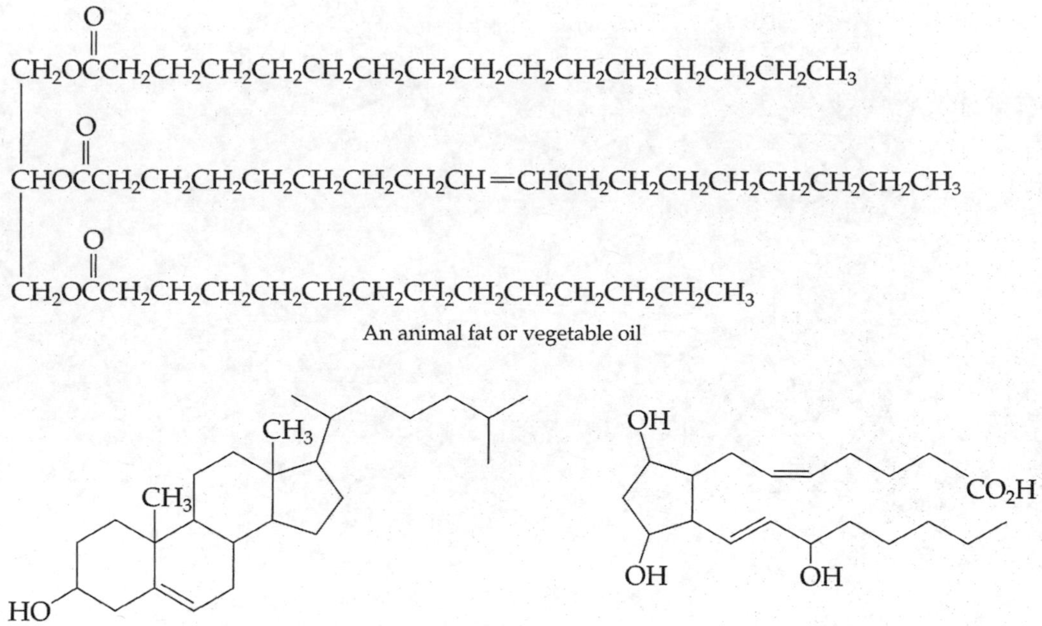

$$CH_2OCCH_2CH_2CH_2CH_2CH_2CH_2CH_2CH_2CH_2CH_2CH_2CH_2CH_2CH_2CH_3$$

(over O, double bond)

$$CHOCCH_2CH_2CH_2CH_2CH_2CH_2CH_2CH=CHCH_2CH_2CH_2CH_2CH_2CH_2CH_2CH_3$$

(over O, double bond)

$$CH_2OCCH_2CH_2CH_2CH_2CH_2CH_2CH_2CH_2CH_2CH_2CH_2CH_2CH_3$$

An animal fat or vegetable oil

Cholesterol—a steroid

PGF$_{2\alpha}$—a prostaglandin

▲ **FIGURE 24.14** Structures of some representative lipids isolated from plant and animal tissue by extraction with nonpolar organic solvents. All have large hydrocarbon portions.

are similar. All fats and oils are **triacylglycerols**, or *triglycerides*, esters of glycerol (1,2,3-propanetriol) with three long-chain carboxylic acids called **fatty acids**. The fatty acids are usually unbranched and have an even number of carbon atoms in the range 12–22.

As shown by the triacylglycerol structure in Figure 24.14, the three fatty acids of a given molecule need not be the same. Furthermore, the fat or oil from a given source is a complex mixture of many different triacylglycerols. Table 24.3 shows the structures of some commonly occurring fatty acids, and Table 24.4 lists the composition of several fats and oils. Note that vegetable oils are largely unsaturated but animal fats contain a high percentage of saturated fatty acids.

TABLE 24.3	Structures of Some Common Fatty Acids			

Name	No. of Carbons	No. of Double Bonds	Structure	Melting Point (°C)
Saturated				
Myristic	14	0	$CH_3(CH_2)_{12}CO_2H$	54
Palmitic	16	0	$CH_3(CH_2)_{14}CO_2H$	63
Stearic	18	0	$CH_3(CH_2)_{16}CO_2H$	69
Unsaturated				
Oleic	18	1	$CH_3(CH_2)_7CH=CH(CH_2)_7CO_2H$	13
Linoleic	18	2	$CH_3(CH_2)_4CH=CHCH_2CH=CH(CH_2)_7CO_2H$	−5
Linolenic	18	3	$CH_3CH_2CH=CHCH_2CH=CHCH_2CH=CH(CH_2)_7CO_2H$	−11

TABLE 24.4	Approximate Composition of Some Common Fats and Oils				
	Saturated Fatty Acids (%)			Unsaturated Fatty Acids (%)	
Source	C_{14} Myristic	C_{16} Palmitic	C_{18} Stearic	C_{18} Oleic	C_{18} Linoleic
Animal Fat					
Butter	10	25	10	25	5
Human fat	3	25	8	46	10
Whale blubber	8	12	3	35	10
Vegetable Oil					
Corn	1	10	4	35	45
Olive	1	5	5	80	7
Peanut	—	7	5	60	20

Palmitic Acid 3D model

About 40 different fatty acids occur naturally. Palmitic acid (C_{16}) and stearic acid (C_{18}) are the most abundant saturated acids; oleic and linoleic acids (both C_{18}) are the most abundant unsaturated ones. Oleic acid is *monounsaturated* because it has only one double bond, but linoleic and linolenic acids are *polyunsaturated fatty acids* (called *PUFAs*) because they have more than one carbon–carbon double bond. Although the reasons are not yet clear, it appears that a diet rich in saturated fats leads to a higher level of blood cholesterol and consequent higher risk of heart attack than a diet rich in unsaturated fats.

The data in Table 24.3 show that unsaturated fatty acids generally have lower melting points than their saturated counterparts, a trend that's also true for triacylglycerols. Since vegetable oils have a higher proportion of unsaturated fatty acids than do animal fats, they have lower melting points and appear as liquids rather than solids. This behavior arises because the carbon–carbon double bonds in unsaturated vegetable oils introduce bends and kinks into the hydrocarbon chains, making it difficult for the chains to nestle closely together in crystals.

The carbon–carbon double bonds in vegetable oils can be hydrogenated to yield saturated fats in the same way that any alkene can react with hydrogen to yield an alkane (Section 23.10). By carefully controlling the extent of hydrogenation, the final product can have any desired consistency. Margarine, for example, is prepared so that only about two-thirds of the double bonds present in the starting vegetable oil are hydrogenated.

$$\underset{\text{Partial structure of a vegetable oil}}{\overset{\displaystyle O \atop \displaystyle \|}{\text{┊OCCH}_2\text{CH}_2\text{CH}_2\text{CH}_2\text{CH}_2\text{CH}_2\text{CH}_2\text{CH}=\text{CHCH}_2\text{CH}=\text{CHCH}_2\text{CH}=\text{CHCH}_2\text{CH}_3}}$$

$\Big\downarrow$ H$_2$, Pd catalyst

$$\underset{\text{Saturated product}}{\overset{\displaystyle O \atop \displaystyle \|}{\text{┊OCCH}_2\text{CH}_2\text{CH}_2\text{CH}_2\text{CH}_2\text{CH}_2\text{CH}_2\text{CH}_2\text{CH}_2\text{CH}_2\text{CH}_2\text{CH}_2\text{CH}_2\text{CH}_2\text{CH}_2\text{CH}_2\text{CH}_3}}$$

▶ **PROBLEM 24.16** Show the structure of glyceryl trioleate, a fat molecule whose components are glycerol and three oleic acid units.

Steroids

A **steroid** is a lipid whose structure is based on the tetracyclic (four-ring) system shown in the following examples. Three of the rings are six-membered, while the fourth is five-membered. Steroids have many diverse roles throughout both the plant and animal kingdoms. Some steroids, such as digitoxigenin, isolated from the purple foxglove *Digitalis purpurea*, are used in medicine as heart stimulants. Others, such as hydrocortisone, are hormones, and still others have a variety of different physiological functions.

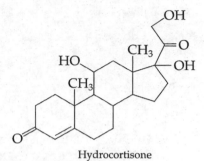

Digitoxigenin   Hydrocortisone

The purple foxglove, a ▶ common backyard plant, contains the steroidal heart stimulant digitoxigenin.

Cholesterol 3D model

Cholesterol, an unsaturated alcohol whose structure is shown in Figure 24.14, is the most abundant animal steroid. It has been estimated that a 60 kg (130 lb) person has a total of about 175 g of cholesterol distributed throughout the body. Much of this cholesterol is bonded through ester links to fatty acids, but some is found as the free alcohol. Gallstones, for example, are nearly pure cholesterol.

Cholesterol serves two important functions in the body. First, it is a minor component of cell membranes, where it helps to keep the membranes fluid. Second, it serves as the body's starting material for the synthesis of all other steroids, including the sex hormones. Although news reports sometimes make cholesterol sound dangerous, there would be no life without it. The human body obtains its cholesterol both by synthesis in the liver and by ingestion of food. Even on a strict no-cholesterol diet, an adult is able to synthesize approximately 800 mg per day.

24.12 | Nucleic Acids

How does a seed "know" what kind of plant to become? How does a fertilized ovum know how to grow into a human being? How does a cell know what part of the body it's in so that it can carry out the right reactions? The answers to such questions involve the biological molecules called **nucleic acids. Deoxyribonucleic acid (DNA)** and **ribonucleic acid (RNA)** are the chemical carriers of an organism's genetic information. Coded in an organism's DNA is all the information that determines the nature of the organism and all the directions that are needed for producing the thousands of different proteins required by the organism.

Just as proteins are polymers made of amino acid units, nucleic acids are polymers made up of **nucleotide** units linked together to form a long chain. Each nucleotide is composed of a **nucleoside** plus phosphoric acid, H_3PO_4, and each nucleoside is composed of an aldopentose sugar plus an amine base.

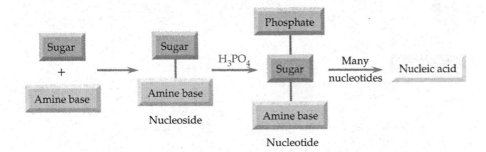

Nucleic Acids activity

The sugar component in RNA is ribose, and the sugar in DNA is 2-deoxyribose (2-deoxy means that oxygen is missing from C2 of ribose).

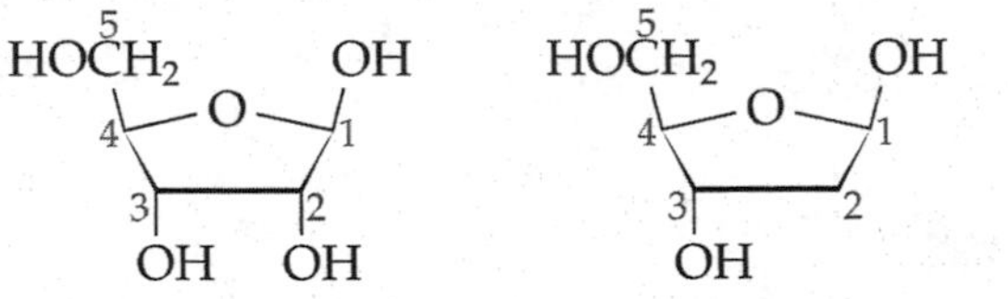

Ribose   2-Deoxyribose

Four different cyclic amine bases occur in DNA: adenine, guanine, cytosine, and thymine. Adenine, guanine, and cytosine also occur in RNA, but thymine is replaced in RNA by a related base called uracil.

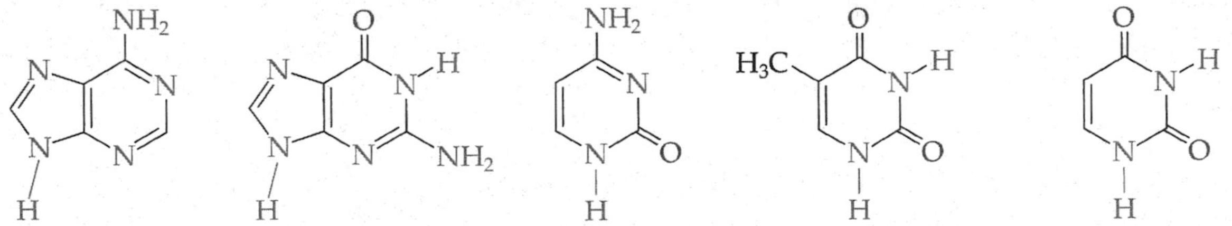

Adenine (A)	Guanine (G)	Cytosine (C)	Thymine (T)	Uracil (U)
DNA	DNA	DNA	DNA	RNA
RNA	RNA	RNA		

In both DNA and RNA, the cyclic amine base is bonded to C1' of the sugar, and the phosphoric acid is bonded to the C5' sugar position. Thus, nucleosides and nucleotides have the general structures shown in Figure 24.15. (In discussions of RNA and DNA, numbers with a prime superscript refer to positions on the sugar component of a nucleotide; numbers without a prime refer to positions on the cyclic amine base.)

3D models of Adenine, Guanine, Cytosine, Thymine, and Uracil

Science Fundamentals Second Edition

FIGURE 24.15 General ▶ structures of **(a)** a nucleoside and **(b)** a nucleotide. When Y = H, the sugar is deoxy-ribose; when Y = OH, the sugar is ribose.

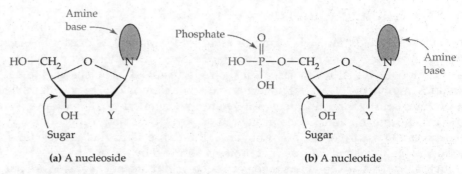

(a) A nucleoside   **(b)** A nucleotide

Nucleotides join together in nucleic acids by forming a phosphate ester bond between the phosphate group at the 5′ end of one nucleotide and the hydroxyl group on the sugar component at the 3′ end of another nucleotide (Figure 24.16).

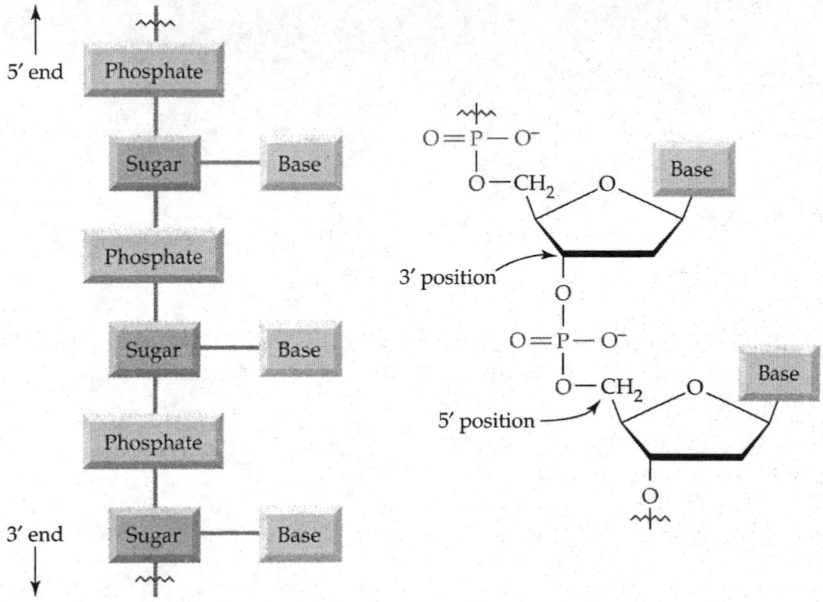

FIGURE 24.16 General- ▶ ized structure of a nucleic acid.

5′ end · Phosphate

Sugar — Base

Phosphate

Sugar — Base

Phosphate

3′ end · Sugar — Base

O=P—O⁻
  |
  O—CH₂ — Base
3′ position

  O
  |
O=P—O⁻
  |
  O—CH₂ — Base
5′ position

Just as the structure of a protein depends on its sequence of individual amino acids, the structure of a nucleic acid depends on its sequence of individual nucleotides. To carry the analogy further, just as a protein has a polyamide back-bone with different side chains attached to it, a nucleic acid has an alternating sugar–phosphate backbone with different amine base side chains attached.

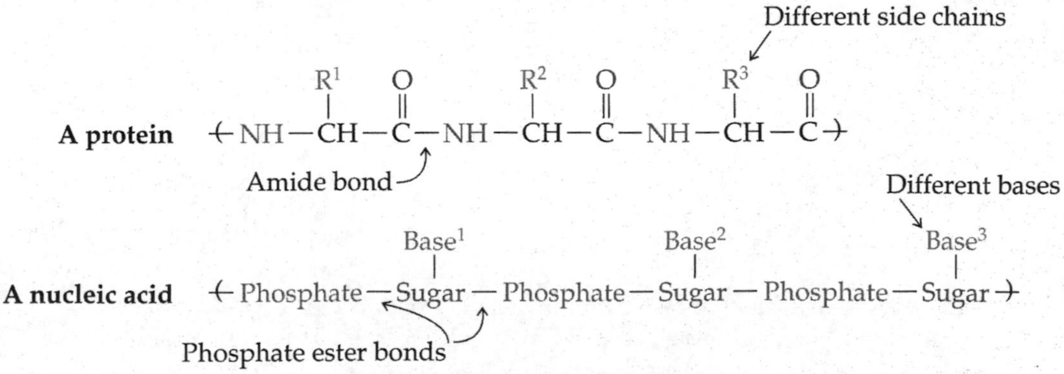

Different side chains

A protein $\left(\text{NH}-\underset{\underset{R^1}{|}}{\text{CH}}-\underset{\overset{\|}{O}}{\text{C}}-\text{NH}-\underset{\underset{R^2}{|}}{\text{CH}}-\underset{\overset{\|}{O}}{\text{C}}-\text{NH}-\underset{\underset{R^3}{|}}{\text{CH}}-\underset{\overset{\|}{O}}{\text{C}}\right)$

Amide bond

Different bases

A nucleic acid $\left(\text{Phosphate}-\underset{\underset{\text{Base}^1}{|}}{\text{Sugar}}-\text{Phosphate}-\underset{\underset{\text{Base}^2}{|}}{\text{Sugar}}-\text{Phosphate}-\underset{\underset{\text{Base}^3}{|}}{\text{Sugar}}\right)$

Phosphate ester bonds

The sequence of nucleotides is described by starting at the 5′ phosphate end and identifying the bases in order. Abbreviations are used for each nucleotide: A for adenosine, G for guanosine, C for cytidine, T for thymidine, and U for uracil. Thus, a typical DNA sequence might be written as -T-A-G-G-C-T-.

WORKED EXAMPLE 24.4

Draw the full structure of the DNA dinucleotide C-T.

SOLUTION

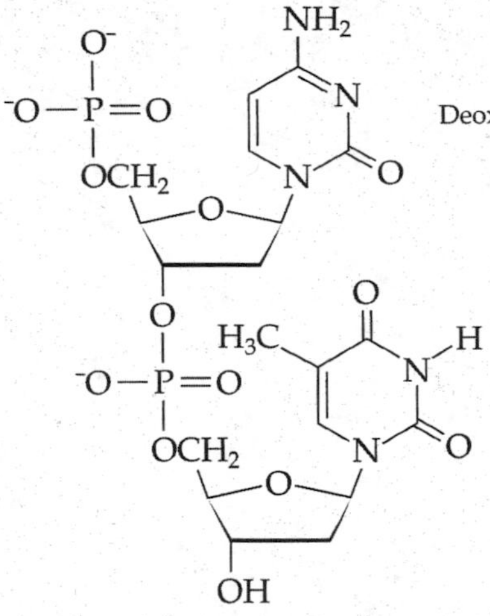

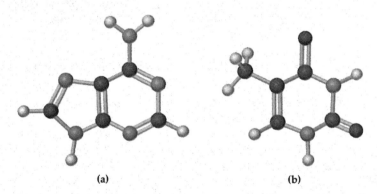

Deoxycytidine (C)

Deoxythymidine (T)

▶ **PROBLEM 24.17**   Draw the full structure of the DNA dinucleotide A-G.

▶ **PROBLEM 24.18**   Draw the full structure of the RNA dinucleotide U-A.

KEY CONCEPT PROBLEM 24.19   Identify the following bases, and tell whether each is found in DNA, RNA, or both.

(a)   (b)

24.13 | Base Pairing in DNA: The Watson–Crick Model

Molecules of DNA isolated from different tissues of the same species have the same proportions of nucleotides, but molecules from different species can have quite different proportions. For example, human DNA contains about 30% each of A and T and about 20% each of G and C, but the bacterium *Clostridium perfringens* contains about 37% each of A and T and only 13% each of G and C. Note that in both cases, the bases occur in pairs. Adenine and thymine are usually present in equal amounts, as are guanine and cytosine. Why should this be?

According to the **Watson–Crick model**, DNA consists of two polynucleotide strands coiled around each other in a *double helix*. The sugar–phosphate backbone is on the outside of the helix, and the amine bases are on the inside, so that a base on one strand points directly in toward a base on the second strand. The two strands run in opposite directions and are held together by hydrogen bonds between pairs of bases. Adenine and thymine form two strong hydrogen bonds to each other, but not to G or C; G and C form three strong hydrogen bonds to each other, but not to A or T (Figure 24.17).

3D models of the A-T Base Pair, the G-C Base Pair, and DNA

Science Fundamentals Second Edition

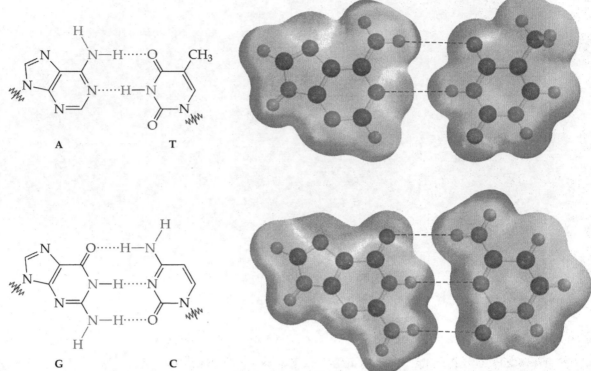

▲ **FIGURE 24.17** Hydrogen bonding between base pairs in the DNA double helix. Electrostatic potential maps show that the faces of the bases are relatively neutral (green), while the edges have positive (blue) and negative (red) regions. Pairing A with T and G with C brings together oppositely charged regions.

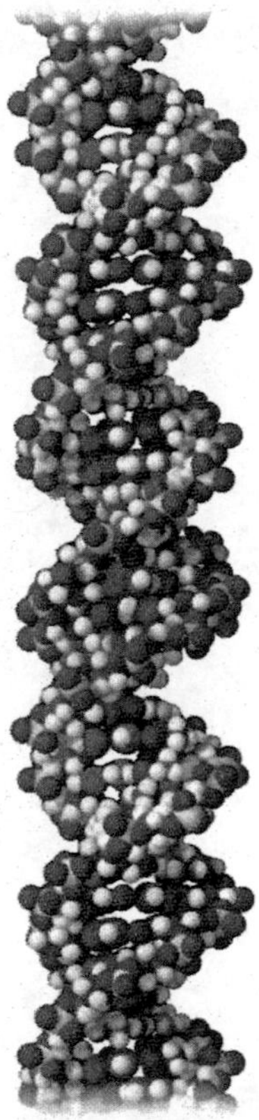

The two strands of the DNA double helix aren't identical; rather, they're complementary. Whenever a G base occurs in one strand, a C base occurs opposite it in the other strand. When an A base occurs in one strand, a T base occurs in the other strand. This complementary pairing of bases explains why A and T are always found in equal amounts, as are G and C. Figure 24.18 illustrates this base pairing, showing how the two complementary strands coil into the double helix. X-ray measurements show that the DNA double helix is 2.0 nm wide, that there are exactly 10 base pairs in each full turn, and that each turn is 3.4 nm high.

▲ **FIGURE 24.18** The coil of the sugar–phosphate backbone is visible on the outside of the DNA double helix in this computer-generated structure, while the hydrogen-bonded pairs of amine bases lie flat on the inside.

WORKED EXAMPLE 24.5

What sequence of bases on one strand of DNA is complementary to the sequence G-C-A-T-T-A-T on another strand?

STRATEGY

Since A and G form complementary pairs with T and C, respectively, go through the given sequence replacing A with T, G with C, T with A, and C with G

SOLUTION

| Original: | G-C-A-T-T-A-T |
| Complement: | C-G-T-A-A-T-A |

▶ **PROBLEM 24.20** What sequence of bases on one strand of DNA is complementary to the following sequence on another strand?

G-G-C-C-C-G-T-A-A-T

24.14 | Nucleic Acids and Heredity

Most DNA of higher organisms, both plant and animal, is found in the nucleus of cells in the form of threadlike strands that are coated with proteins and wound into complex assemblies called **chromosomes**. Each chromosome is made up of several thousand **genes**, where a gene is a segment of a DNA chain that contains the instructions necessary to make a specific protein. By decoding the right genes at the right time, an organism uses genetic information to synthesize the thousands of proteins needed for living. Thus, the function of DNA is to act as a storage medium for an organism's genetic information. The function of RNA is to read, decode, and use the information received from DNA to make proteins.

Three main processes take place in the transfer and use of genetic information: **Replication** is the means by which identical copies of DNA are made, forming additional molecules and preserving genetic information for passing on to offspring. **Transcription** is the means by which information in the DNA is transferred to and decoded by RNA. **Translation** is the means by which RNA uses the information to build proteins.

Replication ⟲ DNA $\xrightarrow{\text{Transcription}}$ RNA $\xrightarrow{\text{Translation}}$ Proteins

Replication

DNA replication is an enzyme-catalyzed process that begins with a partial unwinding of the double helix. As the DNA strands separate and bases are exposed, new nucleotides line up on each strand in a complementary manner, A to T and C to G, and two new strands begin to grow. Each new strand is complementary to its old template strand, and two new, identical DNA double helixes are produced (Figure 24.19).

▼ **FIGURE 24.19**   DNA replication. A portion of the DNA double helix unwinds, and complementary nucleotides line up for linking to yield two new DNA molecules. Each of the new DNA molecules contains one of the original strands and one new strand.

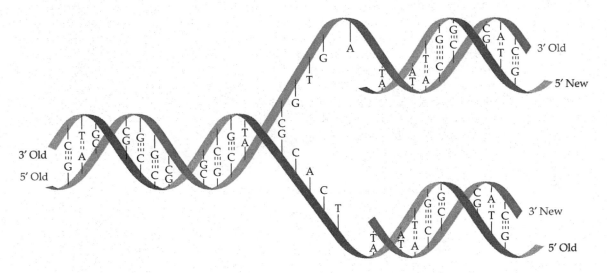

The magnitude of the replication process is extraordinary. The nucleus of a human cell contains 46 chromosomes (23 pairs), each of which consists of one large DNA molecule. Each chromosome, in turn, is made up of several thousand genes, and the sum of all genes in a human cell (the *genome*) is approximately 3 billion base pairs. This immense base sequence is faithfully copied during replication, with an error occurring only about once each 10 billion–100 billion bases.

DNA Replication movie

Transcription

The genetic instructions contained in DNA are transcribed into RNA when a small portion of the DNA double helix unwinds and one of the two DNA strands acts as a template for complementary *ribonucleotides* to line up, a process similar to that of DNA replication (Figure 24.20). The only difference is that uracil (U) rather than thymine lines up opposite adenine. Once completed, the RNA molecule separates from the DNA template, and the DNA rewinds to its stable double-helix conformation.

FIGURE 24.20 Transcription of DNA to synthesize RNA. A small portion of the DNA double helix unwinds, and one of the two DNA strands acts as a template on which ribonucleotides line up. The RNA produced is complementary to the DNA strand from which it is transcribed.

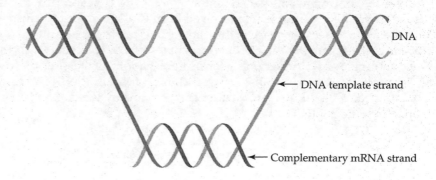

DNA

DNA template strand

Complementary mRNA strand

Translation

Protein biosynthesis is directed by a special kind of RNA called *messenger RNA*, or *mRNA*, and takes place on knobby protuberances within a cell called *ribosomes*. The specific ribonucleotide sequence in mRNA acts like a long coded sentence to specify the order in which different amino acid residues are to be joined. Each of the estimated 100,000 proteins in the human body is synthesized from a different mRNA that has been transcribed from a specific gene segment on DNA.

Each "word" along the mRNA chain consists of a series of three ribonucleotides that is specific for a given amino acid. For example, the series cytosine-uracil-guanine (C-U-G) on mRNA is a three-letter word directing that the amino acid leucine be incorporated into the growing protein. The words are read by another kind of RNA called *transfer RNA*, or *tRNA*. Each of the 60 or so different tRNAs contains a complementary base sequence that allows it to recognize a three-letter word on mRNA and act as a carrier to bring a specific amino acid into place for transfer to the growing peptide chain (Figure 24.21). When synthesis of the protein is completed, a "stop" word signals the end, and the protein is released from the ribosome.

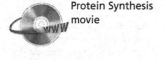

Protein Synthesis movie

FIGURE 24.21 Protein biosynthesis. Messenger RNA is read by tRNA that contains complementary three-base sequences. Transfer RNA then assembles the proper amino acids (AA$_1$, AA$_2$, and so on) into position for incorporation into the peptide.

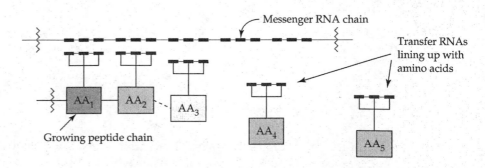

Messenger RNA chain

Transfer RNAs lining up with amino acids

AA$_1$ AA$_2$ AA$_3$ AA$_4$ AA$_5$

Growing peptide chain

WORKED EXAMPLE 24.6

What RNA base sequence is complementary to the following DNA base sequence?

G-C-C-T-A-A-G-T-G

STRATEGY

Go through the DNA sequence replacing A with U, G with C, T with A, and C with G.

SOLUTION

Original DNA:	G-C-C-T-A-A-G-T-G
Complementary RNA:	C-G-G-A-U-U-C-A-C

▶ **PROBLEM 24.21**   Show how uracil can form strong hydrogen bonds to adenine.

▶ **PROBLEM 24.22**   What RNA sequence is complementary to the following DNA sequence?

C-G-T-G-A-T-T-A-C-A

▶ **PROBLEM 24.23**   From what DNA sequence was the following RNA sequence transcribed?

U-G-C-A-U-C-G-A-G-U

DNA Fingerprinting

Being a criminal is a lot harder now than it was in the good old days, and part of the reason is the development of *DNA fingerprinting*. DNA fingerprinting arose from the discovery in 1984 that human genes contain short, repeating sequences of noncoding DNA, called *short tandem repeat* (STR) loci. The base sequences in these STR loci are slightly different for every individual (except identical twins), so a pattern unique to each person can be obtained by determining the sequences.

Perhaps the most common and well-publicized use of DNA fingerprinting is that carried out by crime laboratories to link suspects to biological evidence—blood, hair follicles, skin, semen, or even items of clothing—found at a crime scene. Thousands of court cases have now been decided based on DNA evidence.

Forensic laboratories in the United States have agreed on 13 core STR loci that are most accurate for identification of an individual. Based on these 13 loci, a Combined DNA Index System (CODIS) has been established to serve as a registry of convicted offenders. If the profile of sequences from a known individual and the profile from DNA obtained at a crime scene match, the probability is approximately 82 billion to 1 that the DNA is from the same individual. In paternity cases, where the DNA of father and offspring are related but not fully identical, the identity of the father can be established with a probability of 100,000 to 1.

▲ Historians have wondered for many years whether Thomas Jefferson fathered a child by Sally Hemings. DNA fingerprinting evidence obtained in 1998 is not conclusive but suggests that he well may have.

Even after several generations have passed, paternity can still be implied by DNA analysis of the Y chromosome of direct male-line descendants. The most well-known such case is that of Thomas Jefferson, who is thought to have fathered a child by his slave Sally Hemings. Although Jefferson himself has no male-line descendants, DNA analysis of the male-line descendants of Jefferson's paternal uncle showed the same Y chromosome as a male-line descendant of Eston Hemings, youngest son of Sally Hemings.

Among its many other applications, DNA fingerprinting is widely used for the diagnosis of genetic disorders. Cystic fibrosis, hemophilia, Huntington's disease, Tay–Sachs disease, and sickle-cell anemia are among the many diseases that can be detected, enabling early treatment of an affected child. In addition, the U.S. Department of Defense now requires blood and saliva samples from all military personnel. The samples are stored, and DNA is extracted should the need for identification of a casualty arise.

▶ **PROBLEM 24.24** What characteristic of human DNA makes fingerprinting possible?

1062

Summary

Fats, carbohydrates, and proteins are **metabolized** in the body to yield acetyl CoA, which is further degraded in the citric acid cycle to yield two molecules of CO_2 plus a large amount of energy. The energy output of the various steps in the citric acid cycle is coupled to the electron-transport chain, a series of enzyme-catalyzed reactions whose ultimate purpose is to synthesize **adenosine triphosphate (ATP)**.

Proteins are large biomolecules consisting of **α-amino acids** linked together by amide, or peptide, bonds. Twenty amino acids are commonly found in proteins, and all except glycine have a handedness. In general, any carbon atom bonded to four different groups has a handedness and is said to be chiral. Proteins can be classified either by shape or biological function. Fibrous proteins are tough, threadlike, and water insoluble; globular proteins are compact, water soluble, and mobile within cells. Some proteins are enzymes, some are hormones, and some are structural or transport agents.

A protein's **primary structure** is its amino acid sequence. Its **secondary structure** is the orientation of segments of the protein chain into a regular pattern, such as an **α-helix** or a **β-pleated sheet**. Its **tertiary structure** is the three-dimensional shape into which the entire protein molecule is coiled.

Enzymes are large proteins that function as biological catalysts and whose specificity is due to a **lock-and-key** fit between enzyme and **substrate**. Enzymes contain a crevice, inside which is an **active site**, a small three-dimensional region of the enzyme with the specific shape necessary to bind the proper substrate.

Carbohydrates are polyhydroxy aldehydes and ketones. Simple carbohydrates such as glucose can't be hydrolyzed to smaller molecules; complex carbohydrates such as starch and cellulose contain many simple sugars linked together. **Monosaccharides** such as glucose exist as a mixture of an open-chain form and two cyclic forms called the α form and the β form. Disaccharides such as sucrose contain two simple sugars joined by a linking oxygen atom.

Lipids are the naturally occurring organic molecules that dissolve in a nonpolar solvent. There are a great many different kinds of lipids. Animal fats and vegetable oils are **triacylglycerols**—esters of glycerol with three long-chain **fatty acids**. The fatty acids are unbranched, have an even number of carbon atoms, and may be either saturated or unsaturated.

Deoxyribonucleic acid (DNA) and **ribonucleic acid (RNA)** are the chemical carriers of an organism's genetic information. Nucleic acids are made up of many individual building blocks, called **nucleotides**, linked together to form a long chain. Each nucleotide consists of a cyclic amine base linked to C1 of a sugar, with the sugar in turn linked to phosphoric acid. The sugar component in RNA is ribose; the sugar in DNA is 2-deoxyribose. The bases in DNA are adenine (A), guanine (G), cytosine (C), and thymine (T); the bases in RNA are adenine, guanine, cytosine, and uracil (U). Molecules of DNA consist of two complementary polynucleotide strands held together by hydrogen bonds between bases on the two strands and coiled into a double helix. Adenine and thymine form hydrogen bonds only to each other, as do cytosine and guanine.

Three processes take place in the transfer of genetic information: **Replication** is the process by which identical copies of DNA are made and genetic information is preserved. **Transcription** is the process by which messenger RNA is produced. **Translation** is the process by which mRNA directs protein synthesis.

Key Words

active site *1045*
adenosine triphosphate (ATP) *1033*
alpha- (α-) amino acid *1037*
alpha- (α-) helix *1042*
anabolism *1032*
beta- (β-) pleated sheet *1043*
biochemistry *1031*
C-terminal amino acid *1041*
carbohydrate *1047*

catabolism *1032*
chromosome *1059*
coenzyme *1045*
cofactor *1045*
deoxyribonucleic acid (DNA) *1055*
enzyme *1044*
fatty acid *1052*
gene *1059*
lipid *1051*
lock-and-key model *1045*
metabolism *1032*

monosaccharide *1047*
N-terminal amino acid *1041*
nucleic acid *1055*
nucleoside *1055*
nucleotide *1055*
peptide bond *1035*
polypeptide *1035*
polysaccharide *1047*
primary structure *1042*
protein *1035*
quaternary structure *1042*

replication *1059*
ribonucleic acid (RNA) *1055*
secondary structure *1042*
steroid *1054*
substrate *1045*
tertiary structure *1042*
transcription *1059*
translation *1059*
triacylglycerol *1052*
Watson–Crick model *1057*

Key Concept Summary

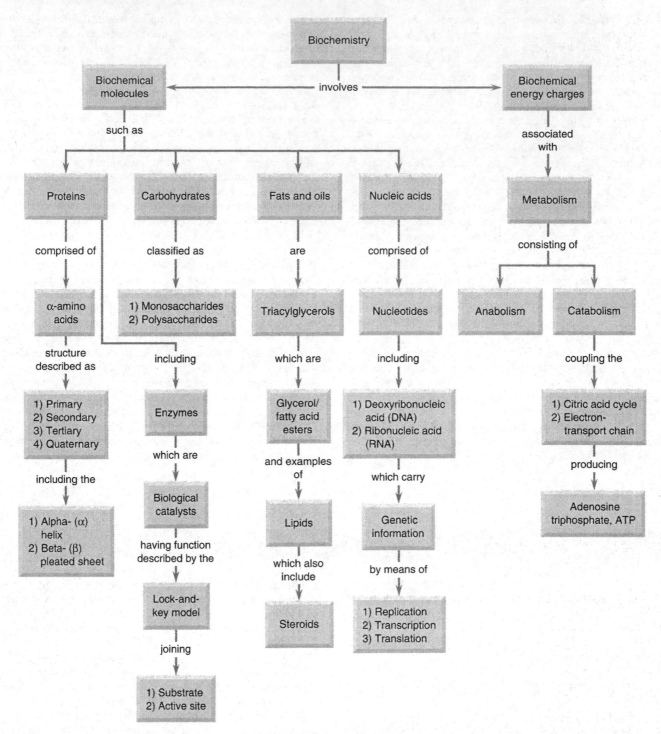

Problems 24.1–24.24 appear within the chapter.

24.25 Identify the following amino acids, and tell whether each is acidic, basic, or neutral.

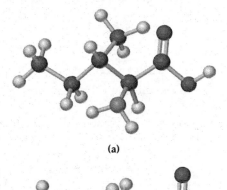

(a)

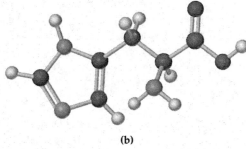

(b)

24.26 Identify the following amino acids:

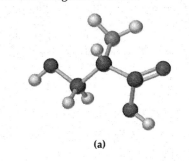

(a)

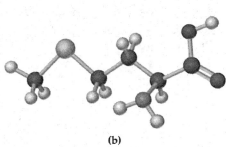

(b)

24.27 Does the following model represent a D-amino acid or an L-amino acid? Identify it.

24.28 Is the following model of glucose in the α form or the β form?

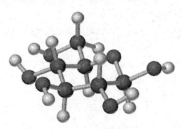

24.29 The following model represents D-ribose in its open-chain form. Is ribose an aldose or a ketose? How many chiral carbon atoms does ribose have?

24.30 Identify the following dipeptide:

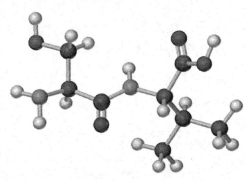

24.31 Identify the following amine bases found in nucleic acids:

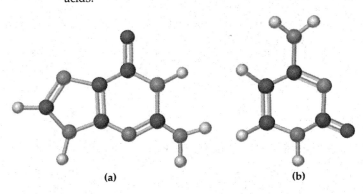

(a)   **(b)**

Science Fundamentals Second Edition

Additional Problems

Amino Acids, Peptides, and Proteins

24.32 What does the prefix "α" mean when referring to α-amino acids?

24.33 Why are the naturally occurring amino acids called L-amino acids?

24.34 What amino acids do the following abbreviations stand for?

(a) Ser   (b) Thr   (c) Pro

(d) Phe   (e) Cys

24.35 Name and draw the structures of amino acids that fit the following descriptions:

(a) Contains an isopropyl group

(b) Contains an alcohol group

(c) Contains a thiol (–SH) group

(d) Contains an aromatic ring

24.36 Much of the chemistry of amino acids is the familiar chemistry of carboxylic acid and amine functional groups. What products would you expect to obtain from the following reactions of glycine?

(a) $H_2NCH_2\overset{\displaystyle O}{\overset{\displaystyle \|}{C}}OH + CH_3OH \xrightarrow[\text{catalyst}]{H_2SO_4}$

(b) $H_2NCH_2\overset{\displaystyle O}{\overset{\displaystyle \|}{C}}OH + HCl \longrightarrow$

24.37 *Aspartame*, marketed under the trade name Nutra-Sweet for use as a nonnutritive sweetener, is the methyl ester of a simple dipeptide. Identify the two amino acids present in aspartame, and show all the products of digestion, assuming that both amide and ester bonds are hydrolyzed in the stomach.

Aspartame

24.38 Identify the amino acids present in the following hexapeptide:

24.39 Look at the structure of angiotensin II in Figure 24.5, and identify both the N-terminal and C-terminal amino acids.

24.40 What is meant by the following terms as they apply to proteins?

(a) Primary structure

(b) Secondary structure

(c) Tertiary structure

24.41 What is the difference between fibrous and globular proteins?

24.42 What kinds of intramolecular interactions are important in stabilizing a protein's tertiary structure?

24.43 What kind of bonding stabilizes helical and β-pleated-sheet secondary protein structures?

24.44 Why is cysteine such an important amino acid for defining the tertiary structure of proteins?

24.45 Which of the following amino acids are most likely to be found on the outside of a globular protein, and which on the inside? Explain.

(a) Valine   (b) Leucine

(c) Aspartic acid   (d) Asparagine

24.46 Use the three-letter abbreviations to name all tripeptides containing methionine, isoleucine, and lysine.

24.47 How many tetrapeptides containing alanine, serine, leucine, and glutamic acid do you think there are? Use the three-letter abbreviations to name three.

24.48 Write structural formulas for the two dipeptides containing phenylalanine and glutamic acid.

24.49 Write the structural formula of Asp-Met-Pro-Gly.

Molecular Handedness

24.50 Which of the following objects are chiral?

(a) A shoe   (b) A bed

(c) A lightbulb   (d) A flowerpot

24.51 Give two examples of chiral objects and two examples of achiral objects.

24.52 Which of the following compounds are chiral?

(a) 2,4-Dimethylheptane

(b) 5-Ethyl-3,3-dimethylheptane

24.53 Draw chiral molecules that meet the following descriptions:

(a) A chloroalkane, $C_5H_{11}Cl$

(b) An alcohol, $C_6H_{14}O$

(c) An alkene, C_6H_{12}

(d) An alkane, C_8H_{18}

24.54 There are eight alcohols with the formula $C_5H_{12}O$. Draw them, and tell which are chiral.

24.55 Propose structures for compounds that meet the following descriptions:

(a) A chiral alcohol with four carbons

(b) A chiral aldehyde

(c) A compound with two chiral centers

Carbohydrates

24.56 What is the structural difference between an aldose and a ketose?

24.57 Classify each of the following carbohydrates by indicating the nature of its carbonyl group and the number of carbon atoms present. For example, glucose is an aldohexose.

(a)
$$\begin{array}{c} OH \quad O \\ | \quad \quad || \\ HOCH_2CHCHCHCH \\ | \quad | \\ OH \quad OH \end{array}$$

(b)
$$\begin{array}{c} OH \quad \quad O \\ | \quad \quad \quad || \\ HOCH_2CHCHCHCHCH \\ | \quad | \quad | \\ OH \quad HO \quad OH \end{array}$$

(c)
$$\begin{array}{c} OH \quad \quad O \\ | \quad \quad \quad || \\ HOCH_2CHCHCHCCH_2OH \\ | \quad | \\ HO \quad OH \end{array}$$

24.58 Starch and cellulose are both polymers of glucose. What is the main structural difference between them, and what different roles do they serve in nature?

24.59 Starch and glycogen are both α-linked polymers of glucose. What is the structural difference between them, and what different roles do they serve in nature?

24.60 Write the open-chain structure of a ketotetrose.

24.61 Write the open-chain structure of a four-carbon deoxy sugar.

24.62 D-Mannose, an aldohexose found in orange peels, has the following structure in open-chain form. Coil mannose around, and draw it in cyclic α and β forms.

$$\begin{array}{c} HO \quad OH \quad O \\ | \quad \quad | \quad \quad || \\ HOCH_2CHCHCHCH-CH \\ \quad | \quad | \\ \quad HO \quad OH \end{array}$$ D-Mannose

24.63 Draw D-galactose in its cyclic α and β forms.

$$\begin{array}{c} HO \quad OH \quad \quad O \\ | \quad \quad | \quad \quad \quad || \\ HOCH_2CHCHCHCH-CH \\ \quad | \quad \quad \quad | \\ \quad HO \quad \quad \quad OH \end{array}$$ D-Galactose

24.64 Show two D-mannose molecules (Problem 24.62) attached by an α-1,4 link.

24.65 Show two D-galactose molecules (Problem 24.63) attached by a β-1,4 link.

Lipids

24.66 What is a fatty acid?

24.67 What does it mean to say that fats and oils are triacylglycerols?

24.68 Draw the structure of glycerol myristate, a fat made from glycerol and three myristic acid molecules (see Table 24.3).

24.69 Spermaceti, a fragrant substance isolated from sperm whales, was a common ingredient in cosmetics until its use was banned in 1976 to protect the whales from extinction. Chemically, spermaceti is cetyl palmitate, the ester of palmitic acid (see Table 24.3) with cetyl alcohol (the straight-chain C_{16} alcohol). Show the structure of spermaceti.

24.70 There are two isomeric fat molecules whose components are glycerol, one palmitic acid, and two stearic acids (see Table 24.3). Draw the structures of both, and explain how they differ.

24.71 One of the two molecules you drew in Problem 24.70 is chiral. Which molecule is chiral, and why?

24.72 Draw the structures of all products you would obtain by reaction of the following lipid with aqueous KOH. What are the names of the products?

$$\begin{array}{c} \quad \quad \quad O \\ \quad \quad \quad || \\ CH_2-O-C(CH_2)_{16}CH_3 \\ | \\ \quad \quad \quad O \\ \quad \quad \quad || \\ CH-O-C(CH_2)_7CH=CH(CH_2)_7CH_3 \\ | \\ \quad \quad \quad O \\ \quad \quad \quad || \\ CH_2-O-C(CH_2)_7CH=CHCH_2CH=CHCH_2CH=CHCH_2CH_3 \end{array}$$

Science Fundamentals Second Edition

24.73 Draw the structure of the product you would obtain on hydrogenation of the lipid in Problem 24.72. What is its name? Would the product have a higher or lower melting point than the original lipid? Why?

24.74 What products would you obtain by treating oleic acid with the following reagents?

(a) Br_2

(b) H_2, Pd catalyst

(c) CH_3OH, HCl catalyst

24.75 Look up the structure of linoleic acid in Table 24.3, and draw all potential products of its reaction with 2 mol of HCl.

Nucleic Acids

24.76 What is a nucleotide, and what three kinds of components does it contain?

24.77 What are the names of the sugars in DNA and RNA, and how do they differ?

24.78 Where in the cell is most DNA found?

24.79 What is meant by the following terms as they apply to nucleic acids?

(a) Base pairing   (b) Replication

(c) Translation   (d) Transcription

24.80 What is the difference between a gene and a chromosome?

24.81 What genetic information does a single gene contain?

24.82 Show by drawing structures how the phosphate and sugar components of a nucleic acid are joined.

24.83 Show by drawing structures how the sugar and amine base components of a nucleic acid are joined.

24.84 Draw the complete structure of deoxycytidine 5′-phosphate, one of the four deoxyribonucleotides.

24.85 Draw the complete structure of guanosine 5′-phosphate, one of the four ribonucleotides.

24.86 If the sequence T-A-C-C-G-A appeared on one strand of DNA, what sequence would appear opposite it on the other strand?

24.87 What sequence would appear on the mRNA molecule transcribed from the DNA in Problem 24.86?

24.88 Human insulin is composed of two polypeptide chains. One chain contains 21 amino acids, and the other contains 30 amino acids. How many nucleotides are present in the DNA to code for each chain?

24.89 The DNA from sea urchins contains about 32% A and about 18% G. What percentages of T and C would you expect in sea urchin DNA? Explain.

General Problems

24.90 One of the constituents of the carnauba wax used in floor and furniture polish is an ester of a C_{32} straight-chain alcohol with a C_{20} straight-chain carboxylic acid. Draw the structure of this ester.

24.91 Cytochrome c is an important enzyme found in the cells of all aerobic organisms. Elemental analysis of cytochrome c shows that it contains 0.43% iron. What is the minimum molecular mass of this enzyme?

24.92 The catabolism of glucose to yield carbon dioxide and water has $\Delta G° = -2870$ kJ/mol. What is the value of $\Delta G°$ for the photosynthesis of glucose from carbon dioxide and water in green plants?

24.93 The *endorphins* are a group of naturally occurring neuroproteins that act in a manner similar to morphine to control pain. Research has shown that the biologically active part of the endorphin molecule is a simple pentapeptide called an *enkephalin*, with the structure Tyr-Gly-Gly-Phe-Met. Draw the complete structure of this enkephalin.

24.94 Write full structures for the following peptides, and indicate the positions of the amide bonds:

(a) Val-Phe-Cys

(b) Glu-Pro-Ile-Leu

24.95 The α-helical segments of myoglobin and other proteins stop when a proline residue is encountered in the chain. Why is proline never encountered in a protein α-helix?

24.96 Jojoba wax, used in candles and cosmetics, is partially composed of the ester of stearic acid and a straight-chain C_{22} alcohol. Draw the structure of this ester.

24.97 Write representative structures for the following:

(a) A fat

(b) A vegetable oil

(c) A steroid

24.98 What DNA sequence is complementary to the following sequence?

A-G-T-T-C-A-T-C-G

24.99 Protonation of the side chain in arginine occurs on the double-bonded nitrogen atom. Draw three resonance structures of the protonated product.

Science Fundamentals Second Edition

Multi-Concept Problems

24.100 The relative degree of unsaturation in a fat or oil is expressed as an *iodine number*. Olive oil, for instance, is highly unsaturated and has an iodine number of 172, while butter is much less unsaturated and has an iodine number of 37. Defined as the number of grams of I_2 absorbed per 100 grams of fat, the iodine number is based on the fact that the carbon–carbon double bonds in fats and oils undergo an addition reaction with I_2. The larger the number of double bonds, the larger the amount of I_2 that reacts.

To determine an iodine number, a known amount of fat is treated with a known amount of I_2. When the reaction is complete (about 1 h), the amount of excess I_2 remaining is determined by titration with $Na_2S_2O_3$ according to the equation

$$2\,Na_2S_2O_3(aq) + I_2(aq) \longrightarrow Na_2S_4O_6(aq) + 2\,NaI(aq)$$

Knowing both the amount of I_2 originally added and the amount remaining after reaction, the iodine number can be calculated.

Assume that 0.500 g of human milk fat is allowed to react with 25.0 mL of 0.200 M I_2 solution and that 81.99 mL of 0.100 M $Na_2S_2O_3$ is required for complete reaction with the excess I_2.

(a) What amount (in grams) of I_2 was added initially?

(b) How many grams of I_2 reacted with the milk fat, and how many grams were in excess?

(c) What is the iodine number of human milk fat?

(d) Assuming a molecular mass of 800 amu, how many double bonds does an average molecule of milk fat contain?

24.101 The protonated form of a neutral amino acid such as alanine is a diprotic acid, H_2A^+, with two acid dissociation constants, one for the $-NH_3^+$ group and one for the $-CO_2H$ group.

$pK_a = 9.69$ $pK_a = 2.34$

Alanine
(protonated)

(a) Which group is more acidic, the $-NH_3^+$ or the $-CO_2H$?

(b) What percentage of each form—protonated (H_2A^+), neutral (HA), and deprotonated (A^-)—is present in aqueous solution at pH = 4.00?

(c) What percentage of each form—protonated (H_2A^+), neutral (HA), and deprotonated (A^-)—is present in aqueous solution at pH = 8.50?

(d) At what pH is the neutral form present in maximum amount?

Science Fundamentals Second Edition

eMedia Problems

24.102 Watch the **Chirality** movie (*eChapter 24.3*), and answer the following questions:

(a) What conditions are required for a carbon in a molecule to be chiral?

(b) How many chiral carbons are there in the structure in Problem 24.7(c)?

24.103 Choose 2 of the amino acids from the **3D Models** in *eChapter 24.2*, and draw structural formulas. Draw the structural formula for the dipeptide formed by a condensation reaction between the two. What would be the other product?

24.104 View the **3D Models** of L-alanine and D-alanine in *eChapter 24.3*. Draw structural formulas for each molecule showing the chiral nature of the isomers. Identify the functional groups on the central carbon.

24.105 Watch the **Energy and Enzymes** movie (*eChapter 24.6*) and answer the following questions:

(a) What is meant by the term *inhibition*?

(b) Name two different ways that enzyme inhibition can occur.

24.106 Choose one of the **3D Models** of amine bases in *eChapter 24.12*, and draw the structural formula. Use the structure you have drawn along with the sugar ribose to write out the first three reaction steps represented in the **Nucleic Acid** activity to demonstrate the formation a nucleotide.

Notes

Notes

Notes

Notes